Biological Science

Brief Contents

A Student-Centered Approach to the Study of Biology

Since its trailblazing First Edition, *Biological Science* has delivered numerous biology teaching innovations that emphasize higher-order thinking skills and conceptual understanding rather than an encyclopedic grasp of what is known about biology. With each edition, this approach has grown and improved to better help students make the shift from being novice learners to expert learners. Central to this shift is a student-centered approach that provides deep support for the learning of core content and the development of key skills that help students learn and practice biology.

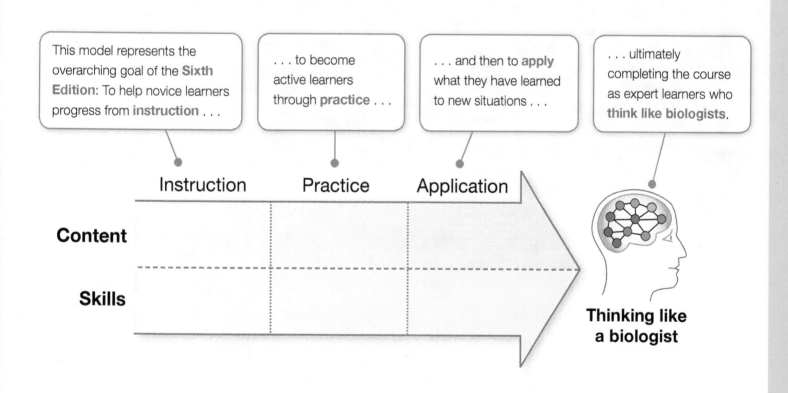

This model represents the overarching goal of the **Sixth Edition**: To help novice learners progress from **instruction** . . .

. . . to become active learners through **practice** . . .

. . . and then to **apply** what they have learned to new situations . . .

. . . ultimately completing the course as expert learners who **think like biologists**.

Instruction   Practice   Application

Content

Skills

Thinking like a biologist

On the pages that follow, we will show how the text and MasteringBiology resources work together to achieve this goal.

Develop a Conceptual Understanding of Biology

Unique Chapter-opening Roadmaps set the table for learning by visually grouping and organizing information to help students anticipate key ideas as well as recognize meaningful relationships and connections that are explored in the chapter that follows.

1

Biology and the Tree of Life

This vervet monkey baby is exploring its new world and learning how to find food and stay alive. It represents one of the key characteristics of life introduced in this chapter—replication.

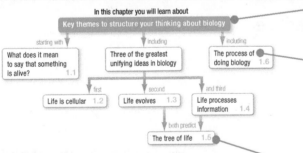

In this chapter you will learn about

Key themes to structure your thinking about biology

starting with
- What does it mean to say that something is alive? 1.1

including
- Three of the greatest unifying ideas in biology

including
- The process of doing biology 1.6

first
- Life is cellular 1.2

second
- Life evolves 1.3

and third
- Life processes information 1.4

both predict
- The tree of life 1.5

n essence, biological science is the study of life. It searches for ideas and observations that unify our understanding of the diversity of life—from bacteria living in hot springs to humans and majestic sequoia trees.

The goals of this chapter are to introduce the nature of life and explore how biologists go about studying it. The chapter also introduces themes that will resonate throughout this book:

- Analyzing how organisms work at the molecular level.
- Understanding organisms in terms of their evolutionary history.
- Helping you learn to think like a biologist.

Let's begin with what may be the most fundamental question of all: What is life?

BIG PICTURE

This chapter is part of the Big Picture. See how on pages 16–17.

Each **Roadmap** begins with a statement of why the chapter topic is important.

Key topics from each chapter are previewed, and related ideas are connected through **linking words**.

Chapter section numbers help students find key ideas easily in the chapter.

Big Picture Concept Maps are referenced on the opening page of related chapters, pointing students to summary pages that help them synthesize challenging topics.

Big Picture Concept Maps integrate visuals and words to help students synthesize information about challenging topics in biology that span multiple chapters and units.

Instruction   Practice   Application

Content   **New Diversity Big Picture**

Skills

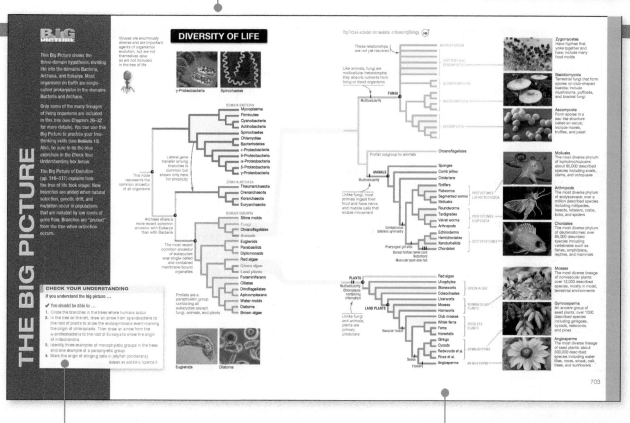

"You should be able to…" activities encourage students to analyze important patterns within each Big Picture concept map.

Big Picture topics include:

- Doing Biology, pp. 16–17
- The Chemistry of Life, pp. 140–141
- Energy for Life, pp. 232–233
- Genetic Information, pp. 396–397
- Evolution, pp. 516–517
- **NEW!** Diversity of Life, pp. 702–703
- Plant and Animal Form and Function, pp. 816–817
- Ecology, pp. 1162–1163

MasteringBiology®

Big Picture concept map tutorials are challenging, higher-level activities that require students to build their own concept map and to answer questions about the content. They are automatically graded to make it easy for professors to assign. New to the **Sixth Edition** are tutorials on diversity.

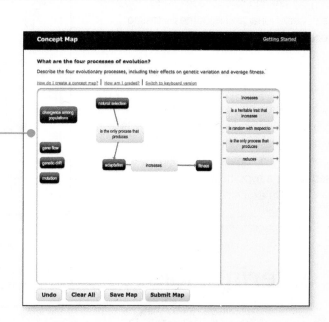

Engage in Scientific Inquiry and Active Problem-Solving

A wide variety of practice questions and exercises are designed to encourage readers to pause and test their understanding as they proceed through each chapter. All questions and exercises are highlighted in blue throughout the text.

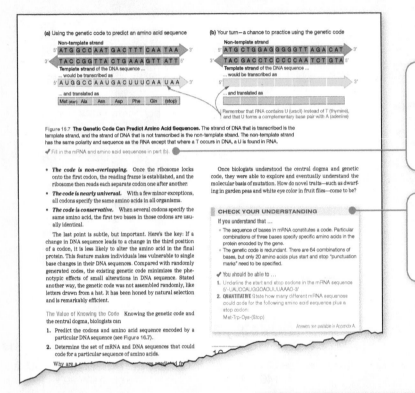

Figure and table caption questions and exercises ask students to critically examine information in figures and tables.

Check Your Understanding activities ask students to work with important concepts in the chapter.

Research boxes teach students how we know what we know about biology by using current and classic research to model the observational and hypothesis-testing process of scientific discovery.

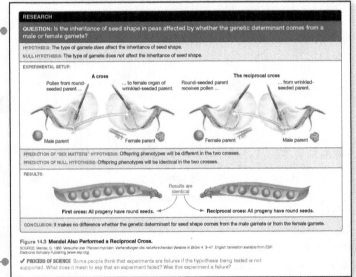

Each Research box concludes with a **question or exercise** that asks students to think critically about experimental design by predicting outcomes, analyzing the setup used to test a hypothesis, or interpreting data found in experimental results

MasteringBiology® **"Solve It" Tutorials** engage learners in a multi-step investigation of a "mystery" or open question in which students must analyze real data.

Steps to Building Understanding

Each chapter ends with three groups of questions that build in difficulty

✔ TEST YOUR KNOWLEDGE

Begin by testing your basic knowledge of new information.

✔ TEST YOUR UNDERSTANDING

Once you're confident with the basics, demonstrate your deeper understanding of the material.

✔ TEST YOUR PROBLEM-SOLVING SKILLS

Work towards mastery of the content by answering questions that challenge you at the highest level of competency.

NEW! "Put It All Together" case studies appear at the end of every chapter and provide a brief summary of contemporary biology research in action. Each case study connects what students learn in class with current, real-world biology research questions. At least one question requires students to **analyze real data** or apply **quantitative skills**.

MasteringBiology®

NEW! Case study questions from the end of chapter are assignable in MasteringBiology.

NEW! Classroom activity questions about the case study are available for clickers to help instructors easily incorporate the case studies into their classroom teaching.

✔ PUT IT ALL TOGETHER: Case Study

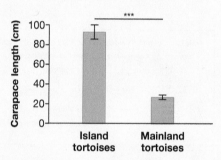

How does gigantism affect the physiology of animals?

Many species of animals on islands are larger than related species on the mainland. Scientists hypothesize that this phenomenon, called island gigantism, evolved in response to the scarcity of competitors and predators on islands. Reduced competition and predation allows species to exploit more resources and frees them from the need to hide in small refuges.

11. **QUANTITATIVE** The graph shown here compares the average carapace (shell) length of mainland and island tortoises. Summarize the results (*** means $P < 0.001$, see BioSkills 3), then use the data to predict whether the surface area/volume ratio is higher in mainland or island tortoises.

Source: Jaffe, A. L., G. J. Slater, and M. E. Alfaro. 2011. *Biology Letters* 7: 558–561.

12. Which tortoises, mainland or island, need to eat more food per gram of their body mass?

13. Which of the following might be a trade-off of gigantism experienced by giant island tortoises?
    a. They cool very rapidly during cold weather.
    b. It would be difficult to sustain their high mass-specific metabolic rates on a diet of plants alone.
    c. It could be more difficult to avoid thermally unfavorable conditions.
    d. They could hide from nonnative predators more easily.

14. **CAUTION** True or false: The body temperatures of island tortoises always closely match the temperatures in their environments.

15. Suppose that a small mainland tortoise and a large island tortoise are placed in the same pen at a zoo. Which tortoise will be more poikilothermic, the small or large tortoise? Why?

16. **CAUTION** On a trip to the Galápagos Islands, you overhear a group of tourists refer to tortoises as "cold blooded." Explain why this word is not accurate to describe a giant tortoise.

Develop Skills for Success in Biology and Beyond...

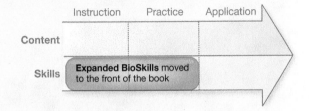

NEW! Unique BioSkills reference section is now placed earlier in the text to draw attention to key skills students need to succeed in biology. Previously located in an appendix at the end of the text, this easy-to-find reference material now follows Chapter 1 to better support the development of skills throughout the course. Each BioSkill includes practice exercises.

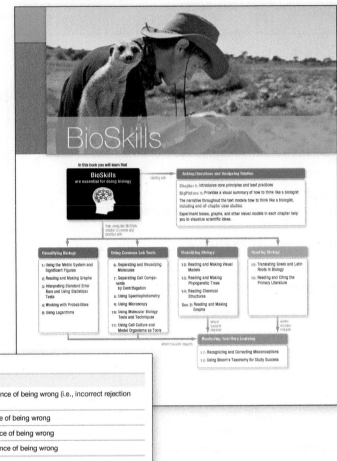

Table B3.1 Asterisk Rating System for *P* Values and Statistical Significance

P Value	Asterisk Rating	Statistical Significance Level	Meaning
$P > 0.05$	None	Not significant	Greater than a 1 in 20 chance of being wrong (i.e., incorrect rejection of the null hypothesis)
$P < 0.05$	*	Statistically significant	Less than a 1 in 20 chance of being wrong
$P < 0.01$	**	Statistically significant	Less than a 1 in 100 chance of being wrong
$P < 0.001$	***	Statistically significant	Less than a 1 in 1000 chance of being wrong

EXPANDED! BioSkill on Interpreting Standard Error Bars and Using Statistical Tests includes a new discussion of commonly used tests, such as chi square, t-test, and analysis of variance (ANOVA). A new section discusses interpreting *P* values and statistical significance.

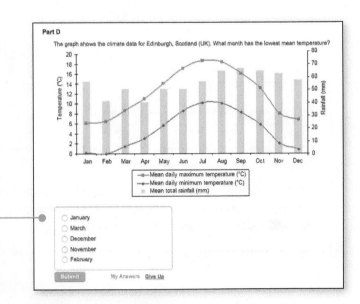

MasteringBiology®

BioSkills review questions are available in the Study Area for self-paced learning and practice. Additional BioSkills questions in the item library are assignable for homework.

Model-based reasoning boxes, videos, and aligned questions added throughout book and in MasteringBiology

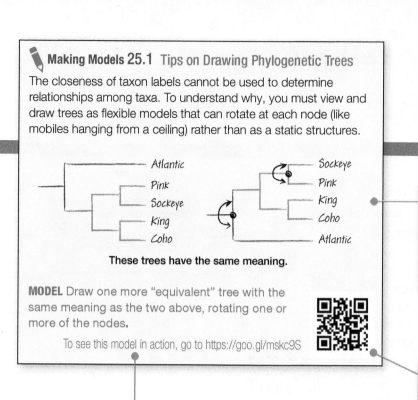

✏️ **Making Models 25.1** Tips on Drawing Phylogenetic Trees

The closeness of taxon labels cannot be used to determine relationships among taxa. To understand why, you must view and draw trees as flexible models that can rotate at each node (like mobiles hanging from a ceiling) rather than as a static structures.

These trees have the same meaning.

MODEL Draw one more "equivalent" tree with the same meaning as the two above, rotating one or more of the nodes.

To see this model in action, go to https://goo.gl/mskc9S

NEW! Unique Making Models boxes appear at strategic points throughout chapters as a guide for developing a deeper understanding of biology concepts by interpreting and creating visual models.

Readers can access the videos via **QR codes**, through the eText, or in the Study Area of MasteringBiology.

NEW! Interactive whiteboard videos accompany each Making Models box to reinforce learning and to demonstrate how to build visual models.

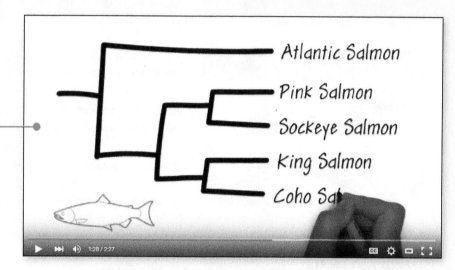

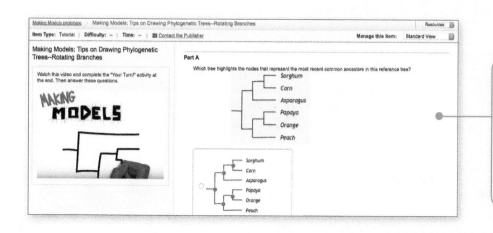

MasteringBiology®

NEW! Making Models activities are assignable for homework and include the whiteboard videos plus application questions that help in developing the skills of interpreting visual models.

For Instructors: Easily Align Assessment with Your Course Goals

Informed by current science education research and curriculum reform strategies, the Sixth Edition instructor resources provide a broad range of easy-to-use assessment options.

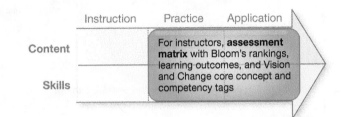

NEW! Chapter Assessment Grids help instructors quickly identify suitable assessment questions in the text according to learning outcomes, Bloom's taxonomy ranking, core concepts and core competencies discussed in the *Vision and Change in Undergraduate Biology Education* report, and, when applicable, common student misconceptions.

BLOOMS TAXONOMY RANKING	"Blue Thread" questions, including end-of-chapter problems, are ranked according to **Bloom's taxonomy** and are assignable in MasteringBiology.
LEARNING OUTCOMES	Each question is tagged to a publisher-provided **Learning Outcome**. Instructors may also track their own Learning Outcomes using MasteringBiology.
MISCONCEPTIONS	**NEW!** When applicable, **common student misconceptions** are addressed and identified with targeted questions.
VISION & CHANGE CORE CONCEPTS	**NEW!** Each question that covers a **Core Concept** from the *Vision and Change in Undergraduate Biology Education* report is noted in the chapter assessment grid and in MasteringBiology.
VISION & CHANGE CORE COMPETENCIES	**NEW! Core Competencies** from the *Vision and Change in Undergraduate Biology Education* report are indicated in the chapter assessment grid and in MasteringBiology.

MasteringBiology®

EXPANDED! Questions, activities, and tutorials are tagged by Bloom's ranking, Learning Outcome, and Vision and Change Core Concepts and Core Competencies.

Source			
Book/Source	**Chapter**	**Display By**	**Learning Outcomes**
Freeman, Biological Science, 6e	39 Plant Nutrition	Learning Outcomes	All

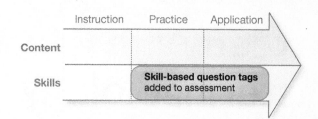

	Instruction	Practice	Application
Content			
Skills		**Skill-based question tags** added to assessment	

An extensive selection of mid- and high-level assessment questions are provided throughout each chapter to help students learn, practice, and prepare for tests.

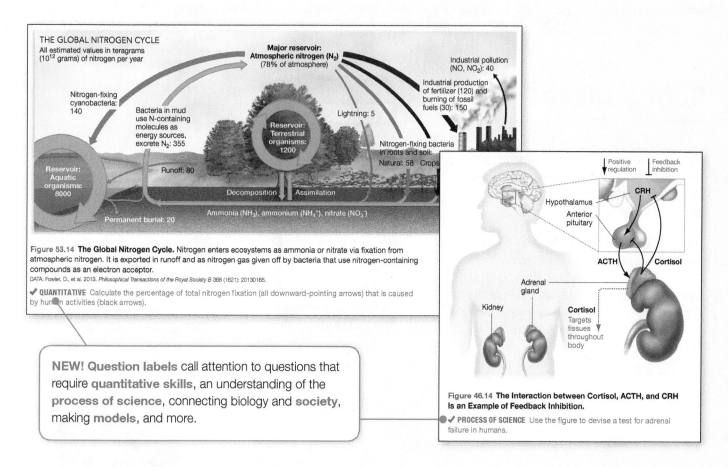

THE GLOBAL NITROGEN CYCLE
All estimated values in teragrams (10^{12} grams) of nitrogen per year

Major reservoir:
Atmospheric nitrogen (N_2)
(78% of atmosphere)

Industrial pollution (NO, NO_2): 40

Industrial production of fertilizer (120) and burning of fossil fuels (30): 150

Nitrogen-fixing cyanobacteria: 140

Bacteria in mud use N-containing molecules as energy sources, excrete N_2: 355

Lightning: 5

Reservoir: Terrestrial organisms: 1200

Nitrogen-fixing bacteria in roots and soil:
Natural: 58 Crops

Reservoir: Aquatic organisms: 8000

Runoff: 80

Decomposition Assimilation

Ammonia (NH_3), ammonium (NH_4^+), nitrate (NO_3^-)

Permanent burial: 20

Figure 53.14 **The Global Nitrogen Cycle.** Nitrogen enters ecosystems as ammonia or nitrate via fixation from atmospheric nitrogen. It is exported in runoff and as nitrogen gas given off by bacteria that use nitrogen-containing compounds as an electron acceptor.
DATA: Fowler, D., et al. 2013. *Philosophical Transactions of the Royal Society B* 368 (1621): 20130165.

✔ **QUANTITATIVE** Calculate the percentage of total nitrogen fixation (all downward-pointing arrows) that is caused by human activities (black arrows).

Positive regulation | Feedback inhibition

CRH

Hypothalamus
Anterior pituitary

ACTH | Cortisol

Adrenal gland

Kidney

Cortisol
Targets tissues throughout body

Figure 46.14 **The Interaction between Cortisol, ACTH, and CRH Is an Example of Feedback Inhibition.**

✔ **PROCESS OF SCIENCE** Use the figure to devise a test for adrenal failure in humans.

NEW! Question labels call attention to questions that require **quantitative skills**, an understanding of the **process of science**, connecting biology and **society**, making **models**, and more.

NEW! Caution questions address topics for which students often hold common misconceptions. Answers to Caution questions include information that addresses the misconception.

5. **CAUTION** According to data presented in this chapter, which one of the following statements is correct?
   a. When individuals change in response to challenges from the environment, their altered traits are passed on to offspring.
   b. Species are created independently of each other and do not change over time.
   c. Populations—not individuals—change when natural selection occurs.
   d. The traits of populations become more perfect over time.

Succeed with MasteringBiology®

MasteringBiology is a powerful online learning and assessment system proven to improve results by engaging students before, during, and after class with a deep library of helpful activities. Mastering brings learning full circle by continuously adapting to each student and making learning more personal than ever—before, during, and after class.

Before Class

NEW! Dynamic Study Modules provide students with multiple sets of questions with extensive feedback so that they can test, learn, and retest until they achieve mastery of the textbook material.

NEW! More mobile-friendly Pre-class reading quizzes help students pinpoint concepts that they understand and concepts with which they need more help. By identifying topics that are most difficult for them, students are better prepared to ask questions and more likely to listen actively.

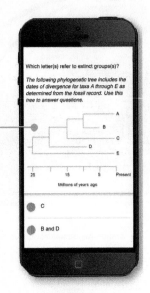

During Class

NEW! Learning Catalytics™ allows students to use their smartphone, tablet, or laptop to respond individually or in groups to questions in class. Visit learningcatalytics.com to learn more.

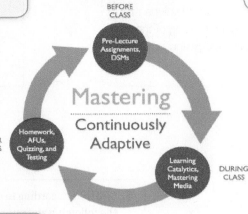

Mastering
Continuously
Adaptive

BEFORE CLASS — Pre-Lecture Assignments, DSMs

AFTER CLASS — Homework, AFUs, Quizzing, and Testing

DURING CLASS — Learning Catalytics, Mastering Media

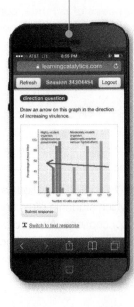

After Class

NEW! Optional Adaptive Follow-up Assignments are based on each student's performance on the original MasteringBiology assignment and provide additional questions and activities tailored to each student's needs.

Hundreds of self-paced tutorials and coaching activities provide students with individualized coaching with specific hints and feedback on the toughest topics in the course.

NEW! Pearson eText 2.0 integrates the text with videos and animations, in a format that adapts to the device being used. Features include student and instructor note-taking, highlighting, bookmarking, search, and hotlinked glossary.

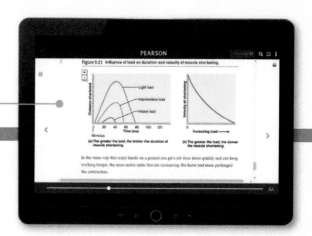

MasteringBiology offers a wide variety of tutorials that can be assigned as homework. Examples include:

BioFlix® Tutorials use 3-D, movie-quality animations and coaching exercises to help students master tough topics outside of class. Animations can also be shown in class.

NEW! HHMI Short Films, documentary-quality movies from the Howard Hughes Medical Institute, engage students in topics from the discovery of the double helix to evolution, with assignable questions.

NEW! Galapagos Evolution Videos, filmed by Peter and Rosemary Grant, bring to life the dynamic evolutionary processes that impact Darwin's finches on Daphne Major Island.

INSTRUCTOR AND STUDENT RESOURCES

For Instructors

Instructor's Resource DVD Set
© 2017 | 0134255011 / 9780134255019
Everything you need for lectures is in one place, including video segments that demonstrate how to incorporate active-learning techniques into your own classroom, PowerPoint® Lecture Outlines, and over 300 additional animations.

Instructor's Guide (Download only)
Includes learning objectives, lecture outlines, vocabulary, active learning lecture activities, and clicker questions.

TestGen Test Bank (Download Only)
All of the exam questions in the Test Bank have been peer reviewed, providing questions that set the standard for quality and accuracy. Questions have been improved by evaluating user data from MasteringBiology. Test questions are ranked according to Bloom's taxonomy.

For Students

Study Guide by Warren Burggren et. al.
© 2017 | 0134254155 / 9780134254159
The Study Guide presents a breakdown of key biological concepts, difficult topics, and quizzes to help students prepare for exams.

Practicing Biology: A Student Workbook
© 2017 | 0134261941 / 9780134261942
This workbook provides a variety of hands-on activities such as mapping and modeling to suit different learning styles and help students discover which topics they need more help on. Students learn biology by doing biology.

BIOLOGICAL SCIENCE

Vervet monkey,
Chlorocebus pygerythrus

Scott Freeman • Kim Quillin • Lizabeth Allison • Michael Black
Greg Podgorski • Emily Taylor • Jeff Carmichael

Biological Science

Third Custom Edition for University of North Dakota
Biology 150

Taken from:
Biological Science, Sixth Edition
by Scott Freeman, Kim Quillin, Lizabeth Allison, Michael Black, Greg Podgorski,
Emily Taylor, and Jeff Carmichael

 ISBN 10: 1-323-44207-3
ISBN 13: 978-1-323-44207-4

Detailed Contents

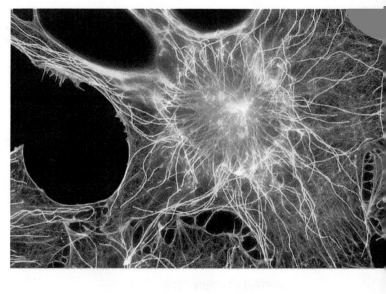

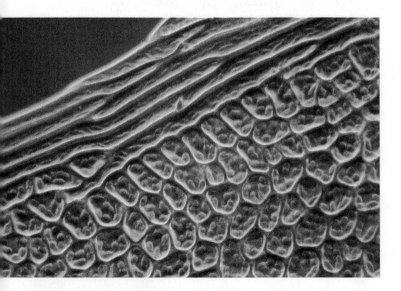

About the Authors

A Letter from Scott:

I started working on *Biological Science* in 1997 with a simple goal: To help change the way biology is taught. After just shy of 20,000 hours of work on four editions of this text, that goal still gets me out of bed in the morning. But instead of focusing my energies on textbook writing, I've decided to devote myself full-time to research on student learning and developing new courses for undergraduate and graduate students at the University of Washington.

I have passed the torch to an all-star cast of leading scientists and educators who have enthusiastically taught from, and contributed to, previous editions of *Biological Science*. The new team brings their passion, talent, and creativity to the book, with expertise that spans the breadth of the life sciences. Just as important, they work beautifully together because they think alike. They are driven by a shared concern for student learning, a commitment to the craft of writing, and a background in evidence-based teaching.

These pages provide a brief introduction to Liz Allison, Michael Black, Greg Podgorski, Kim Quillin, Jeff Carmichael, and Emily Taylor. As a group, they've built on the book's existing strengths and infused this edition with fresh energy, perspective, and ideas. I'm full of admiration for what they have accomplished, and excited about the impact this edition will have on biology students from all over the world.

—*Scott Freeman*

Scott Freeman received a Ph.D. in Zoology from the University of Washington and was subsequently awarded an Alfred P. Sloan Postdoctoral Fellowship in Molecular Evolution at Princeton University. He has done research in evolutionary biology on topics ranging from nest parasitism to the molecular systematics of the blackbird family and is coauthor, with Jon Herron, of the standard-setting undergraduate text *Evolutionary Analysis*. Scott is the recipient of a Distinguished Teaching Award from the University of Washington and is currently a Principal Lecturer in the UW Department of Biology, where he teaches introductory biology for majors, a writing-intensive course for majors called The Tree of Life, and a graduate seminar in college science teaching. Scott's current research focuses on how active learning affects student learning and academic performance.

Lizabeth A. Allison is Chancellor Professor of Biology at the College of William & Mary. She received her Ph.D. in Zoology from the University of Washington, specializing in molecular and cellular biology. Before coming to William & Mary, she spent eight years as a faculty member at the University of Canterbury in New Zealand. Liz teaches introductory biology for majors and upper-division molecular biology courses. She has mentored graduate students and more than 100 undergraduate research students, many of them coauthoring papers with her on intracellular trafficking of the thyroid hormone receptor in normal and cancer cells. The recipient of numerous awards, including a State Council for Higher Education in Virginia (SCHEV) Outstanding Faculty Award in 2009, Liz received one of the three inaugural Arts & Sciences Faculty Awards for Teaching Excellence in 2011, and a Plumeri Award for Faculty Excellence in 2012. In addition to her work on this text, she is author of *Fundamental Molecular Biology*, now in its second edition, with a third edition underway. *Lead Author; Chapter 1 and BioSkills* laalli@wm.edu

Michael Black received his Ph.D. in Microbiology & Immunology from Stanford University School of Medicine as a Howard Hughes Predoctoral Fellow. After graduation, he studied cell biology as a Burroughs Wellcome Postdoctoral Fellow at the MRC Laboratory of Molecular Biology in Cambridge, England. His current research focuses on the use of molecules to identify and track the transmission of microbes in the environment. Michael is a professor of Cell & Molecular Biology at California Polytechnic State University in San Luis Obispo, where he teaches introductory and advanced classes for majors in cell biology and microbiology. In addition to his teaching and research activities, Michael serves as the director of the Undergraduate Biotechnology Lab, where he works alongside undergraduate technicians to integrate research projects and inquiry-based activities into undergraduate classes. *Chapters 2–12, 33, and 48* mblack@calpoly.edu

Greg Podgorski received his Ph.D. in Molecular and Cellular Biology from Penn State University and has been a postdoctoral fellow at the Max Plank Institute for Biochemistry and Columbia University. His research interests are in biology education, developmental genetics, and computational biology. Greg's most recent work has been in mathematical modeling of how patterns of different cell types emerge during development and how tumors recruit new blood vessels in cancer. Greg has been teaching at Utah State University for more than 20 years in courses that include introductory biology for majors and for nonmajors, genetics, cell biology, developmental biology, and microbiology, and he has offered courses in nonmajors biology in Beijing and Hong Kong. He's won teaching awards at Utah State University and has been recognized by the National Academies as a Teaching Fellow and a Teaching Mentor.
Chapters 13–21
greg.podgorski@usu.edu

Jeff Carmichael received his B.S. in Biology from Slippery Rock University in Pennsylvania and his Ph.D. in Plant Biology from the University of Georgia. As an undergraduate student, he spent some time studying enzyme kinetics through a fellowship at Oak Ridge National Laboratory in Tennessee. His graduate work focused on sexual reproduction in an intriguing group of seed plants. He has been teaching and coordinating Introductory Biology at the University of North Dakota (UND) for more than 20 years. He also serves in the Office of Instructional Development where he helps other faculty members incorporate evidence-based best teaching practices in their courses. He has received excellence in teaching awards at UND and as a graduate student in Georgia. His revision of Unit 6 and part of Unit 5 of the Sixth Edition is his first foray into textbook writing.
Chapters 26–29 and 34–38
Jeffrey.Carmichael@und.edu

Kim Quillin received her B.A. in Biology at Oberlin College *summa cum laude* and her Ph.D. in Integrative Biology from the University of California, Berkeley as a National Science Foundation Graduate Fellow. Kim has worked in the trenches with Scott Freeman on every edition of *Biological Science*, starting with the ground-up development of the illustrations in the first edition in 1999 and expanding her role in each edition, always with the focus of helping students to think like biologists. Kim currently teaches introductory biology at Salisbury University, a member of the University System of Maryland, where she is actively involved in the ongoing student-centered reform of the concepts-and-methods course for biology majors. Her current research focuses on the scholarship of teaching and learning with an emphasis on visual model-based reasoning as a science process skill.
Chapters 22–25, 30–32, 49–54
kxquillin@salisbury.edu

Emily Taylor earned a B.A. in English at the University of California, Berkeley followed by a Ph.D. in Biological Sciences from Arizona State University, where she conducted research in the field of environmental physiology as a National Science Foundation Graduate Research Fellow. She is currently an associate professor of Biological Sciences at the California Polytechnic State University in San Luis Obispo. Her student-centered research program focuses on the endocrine and reproductive physiology of free-ranging reptiles, especially rattlesnakes. She teaches numerous undergraduate and graduate courses, including introductory biology, anatomy and physiology, endocrinology, and herpetology, and received the California Faculty Association's Distinguished Educator Award in 2010 and Cal Poly's Distinguished Teaching Award in 2012.
Chapters 39–47
etaylor@calpoly.edu

Preface to Instructors

From the very first edition, *Biological Science's* unique emphasis on the process of scientific discovery and guiding students to think like biologists has placed this book at the forefront of change in the way we teach biology. The Sixth Edition embraces this legacy and continues to exemplify the principles outlined in the recent *Vision and Change in Undergraduate Biology Education* report. As in previous editions, the cutting-edge biology in the Sixth Edition is pitched at the right level for introductory students, and is as accurate and as exciting as ever for instructors and students alike. New findings from education research continue to inform and inspire the coauthor team's thinking about *Biological Science*—we know more today than ever before about how students learn. These findings demand that we constantly look for new ways to increase student engagement in the learning process. Innovative features new to this edition offer students even more opportunities to actively apply concepts in new situations; evaluate experimental design, hypotheses, and data; synthesize results; and make and interpret models. For instructors, additional resources are provided to help align course activities and learning goals with their assessment strategies.

Core Values

In the Sixth Edition, the coauthor team has strived to extend the vision and maintain the core values of *Biological Science*—to provide a book and online resources for instructors who embrace the challenge of boosting students to higher levels of learning, and to provide a book that helps students each step of the way in learning to think like scientists, regardless of their starting point in the process. Dedicated instructors have high expectations of their students. The Sixth Edition provides tools to help students build their cognitive mastery in both biology content and transferrable skills—to learn at the level called for by the National Academy of Sciences, the Howard Hughes Medical Institute, the American Association of Medical Academies, and the National Science Foundation. Reports such as *Biology 2010, Scientific Foundations for Future Physicians,* and *Vision and Change* all place a premium on fundamental concepts and skills as well as connecting core ideas across all levels of biology.

What's New in This Edition

The Sixth Edition contains many new or expanded features, all of them designed to provide students with initial instruction in content and skills, followed by opportunities for lots of practice in applying knowledge and skills to new contexts. The ultimate goal is for students to learn to construct their own knowledge and think like biologists.

- **Relocated and Expanded BioSkills Section** Instructors recognize that biology students need to develop foundational science skills in addition to content knowledge. Since the Third Edition, *Biological Science* has provided a unique, robust set of materials and activities in an appendix to guide students who need extra help with the skills emphasized in the book. In the Sixth Edition, the BioSkills materials have been placed between Chapters 1 and 2 to emphasize their importance as a resource for success in doing biology, and to make it easier for students to access them throughout the course. The BioSkills are grouped within five broad categories depicted in a new opening road map: Quantifying Biology, Using Common Lab Tools, Visualizing Biology, Reading Biology, and Monitoring Your Own Learning. Four new BioSkills have been added: Using Spectrophotometry, Using Molecular Biology Tools and Techniques, Reading and Making Visual Models, and Recognizing and Correcting Misconceptions. Existing BioSkills have been updated to support new features in the Sixth Edition. For example, the explanation of statistical tests has been expanded, and *P* values are introduced to provide students with essential quantitative skills for interpreting data in the end-of-chapter case studies. BioSkills include practice questions, are cross-referenced throughout the text, and can be assigned online in MasteringBiology®.

- **Making Models Boxes** Reports like *Vision and Change* cite the importance of developing model-based reasoning skills. To help attain this goal, Making Models boxes have been added throughout the book to explicitly teach students how to use visual models to learn and do biology. Each Making Models box has three components: instruction in interpreting or creating a specific type of model, an example of that type of model, and an application question so that students can immediately practice their skills. In addition to the guidance in the text, online video versions are accessible via QR code so students can watch and interact with a dynamic presentation of modeling. Lastly, the video version is also included in an assignable MasteringBiology activity that tests students with higher-level questions.

- **Put It All Together Case Studies** The end-of-chapter question sets for every chapter now include a case study. Case studies briefly introduce contemporary biology research in action, followed by questions that ask students to apply the chapter's content and skills to the research topic. Instructor resources include clicker questions to give instructors the opportunity to use the case studies as discussion prompts in the classroom. A constant hallmark of this text is its emphasis on experimental evidence—on teaching how we know what we know. The case studies expand this emphasis, requiring students to evaluate real data and to see how ongoing scientific research is related to core biological ideas.

- **Big Picture on Biological Diversity** Introduced in the Fourth Edition, Big Picture concept maps integrate words and visuals to help students synthesize information about challenging topics that span multiple chapters and units. In response to requests from instructors and students, a new Big Picture has been added on the Diversity of Life, illustrating the relationships among the major taxonomic groups in the tree of life.

- **Integrated Chapters** Three newly consolidated chapters reorganize and integrate information to better serve instructors and students. Chapter 20 (The Molecular Revolution: Biotechnology and Beyond) merges the most essential information on genome analysis that was previously discussed in separate chapters, while moving details of fundamental techniques to the BioSkills. Core material on the general principles of development, particularly those related to genetics and evolution, now forms the closing chapter of a streamlined unit on Gene Structure and Expression (Chapter 21). Content on plant and animal development has been moved from the former developmental biology unit to the respective reproduction and development chapters of the How Plants Work (Chapter 38) and How Animals Work (Chapter 47) units.

- **Skill-Based Question Tags** *Biological Science* has long emphasized skill development, and reports like *Vision and Change* also encourage this focus for introductory majors. To help students and instructors identify opportunities to practice key skills, questions are tagged to indicate the following: *Process of Science* questions explore the application of the scientific process; *Model* questions ask students to interpret or construct visual models; *Society* questions explore the relationship between science and society; *Quantitative* questions help students perform quantitative analysis and mathematical reasoning; and *Caution* questions address topics for which students often hold common misconceptions. Answers to *Caution* questions include information that addresses the misconception.

- **Detailed Assessment Matrix** At the beginning of the revision process, we thoroughly evaluated the assessment program and focused on revising it throughout the creation of the Sixth Edition. To aid our analysis, we looked at the question data collected in MasteringBiology, and we created an assessment matrix for each chapter that identifies how each question is related to learning outcomes, Bloom's level, common misconceptions, and *Vision and Change* core concepts and competencies. We hope the tool will assist instructors in selecting the most appropriate assessment items to align with the goals of their course.

- **Expanded Use of Summary Tables** The art program is further enhanced in this edition by additional illustrated summary tables that deliver content in a streamlined way and facilitate comparison and analysis by students. For example, the diversity boxes from the Fifth Edition's The Diversification of Life unit have been redesigned as photographic summary tables. These tables make subject areas more accessible to visual learners and reinforce a chapter's key concepts.

Hallmark Features of the Text

We are excited to introduce new features to the Sixth Edition. At the same time, we are committed to strengthening the hallmark features that make this book unique.

- **Road Maps** Starting with the Fifth Edition, each chapter opens with a concept map that visually groups and organizes information to help students anticipate key ideas as well as recognize meaningful relationships and connections among ideas. While the Road Maps help students look forward as they engage with a chapter, **Big Picture** concept maps integrate words and visuals to help students synthesize information about challenging topics that span multiple chapters or units. Together, these two features help students navigate chapter content and see the forest for the trees.

- **Opportunities for Practice** "Blue Thread" questions, integrated throughout the text, are designed to help students identify what they do and do not understand. The idea is that if students really understand a piece of information or a concept, they should be able to do something with it. As in the Fifth Edition, all questions in the text are assigned a Bloom's taxonomy level to help both students and instructors understand whether a question requires higher-order or lower-order cognitive skills.

  - **In-text "You Should Be Able To" questions** focus on topics and concepts that professors and students have identified as most key or difficult in each chapter.

  - **Caption questions and exercises** challenge students to examine the information in a figure or table critically—not just absorb it.

  - **Check Your Understanding boxes** present two to three tasks that students should be able to complete in order to demonstrate a mastery of summarized key ideas.

  - **End-of-chapter questions** are organized in three levels of increasing difficulty so students can build from lower- to higher-order cognitive levels of assessment.

- **Focus on Real Data** Students now have expanded opportunities to develop skills at working with real data from the primary literature. Sources of the data presented in Research Boxes, graphs, and end-of-chapter Case Studies are cited to model good practice for students and to provide a resource for students and instructors who wish to evaluate the original data more deeply.

Integration of Media

The textbook continues to be supported by MasteringBiology, the most powerful online homework, tutorial, and assessment system available. Tutorials follow the Socratic method, coaching students to the correct answer by offering feedback specific to a student's errors or misconceptions as well as supplying hints that students can access if they get stuck. Instructors can associate content with publisher-provided learning outcomes or create their own. Content highlights include the following:

- **Making Models Activities** Whiteboard videos—accessible online via QR code or the Study Area in MasteringBiology, bring the Making Models feature from the book to life to help students develop their visual modeling skills. The videos are also included in assignable activities that allow students to practice modeling and to apply their understanding to new situations.

- **Case Study Questions** Put It All Together Case Study questions are assignable in MasteringBiology. Additional clicker questions are also provided in instructor resources to facilitate classroom activities.

- **Solve It Tutorials** These activities allow students to act like scientists in simulated investigations. Each tutorial presents an interesting, real-world question that students will answer by analyzing and interpreting data.

- **Experimental Inquiry Tutorials** The call to teach students about the process of science has never been louder. To support such teaching, there are 10 interactive tutorials on classic scientific experiments—ranging from Meselson–Stahl on DNA replication to the Grants' work on Galápagos finches and Connell's work on competition. Students who use these tutorials should be better prepared to think critically about experimental design and evaluate the wider implications of the data—preparing them to do the work of real scientists in the future.

- **BioFlix® Animations and Tutorials** BioFlix are movie-quality, 3-D animations that focus on the most difficult core topics and are accompanied by in-depth, online tutorials that provide hints and feedback to guide student learning. Eighteen BioFlix animations and tutorials tackle topics such as meiosis, mitosis, DNA replication, photosynthesis, homeostasis, and the carbon cycle.

- **HHMI Short Films Activities** Documentary-quality movies from HHMI are available in MasteringBiology with assignable questions to make sure students understand key ideas.

- **Galápagos Evolution Video Activities** These incredible videos, filmed on the Galápagos Islands by Peter and Rosemary Grant, bring to life the dynamic evolutionary processes that have an impact on Darwin's finches on Daphne Major Island. Six videos explore important concepts and data from the Grants' field research, and assignable activities keep students focused on the important take-away points.

- **End-of-Chapter Questions** A broad range of end-of-chapter questions are available to assign in MasteringBiology.

- **Blue Thread Questions** Over 500 questions based on the Blue Thread questions in the textbook are assignable in MasteringBiology.

- **Big Picture Concept Map Tutorials** A new, more engaging concept mapping tool is the basis for highly interactive, challenging concept map activities based on the Big Picture figures in the textbook. Students build their own concept maps, which are auto-graded, and then answer questions to make sure they understand key ideas and make important connections.

- **BioSkills Activities** Activities based on the BioSkills content in the textbook are assignable in MasteringBiology, including activities to support the new BioSkills.

- **Reading Quiz Questions** Every chapter includes reading quiz questions that can be assigned to ensure students read the textbook and understand the basics. These quizzes are perfect as a pre-lecture assignment to get students into the content before class, allowing instructors to use class time more effectively.

Serving a Community of Teachers

All of us on the coauthor team are motivated by a deep commitment to students and to supporting the efforts of dedicated teachers. Our passion in life is doing and teaching biology. At various points along our diverse paths, we have been inspired by our own teachers when we were students, and now are inspired by our colleagues as we strive to become even better teacher-scholars. In the tradition of all previous editions of *Biological Science*, we have tried to infuse this textbook with the spirit and practice of evidence-based teaching. We welcome your comments, suggestions, and questions.

Many thanks for all you do for your students.

Content Highlights of the Sixth Edition

As discussed in the preface, a major focus of this revision is to introduce unique, innovative features designed to provide students with initial instruction in content and skills, as well as lots of practice in applying knowledge and skills to new contexts—with the ultimate goal of helping students learn to construct their own knowledge and think like biologists. As in each edition, to ensure that the content reflects the current state of science and is accurate, the author team has scrutinized every chapter to add new, relevant content, update descriptions when appropriate, and adjust the approach to certain topics to enhance student comprehension. New content emphasizes overarching themes—including how advances in understanding gene expression and genome structure inform all of biology, from development to evolution to physiology to ecology, and the profound impact of global climate change on life on Earth. In this section, some of the key content improvements to the textbook are highlighted.

Chapter 1 Biology and the Tree of Life New section titles emphasize the theme of five characteristics of life, within a framework of three unifying theories: the cell theory, the theory of evolution, and new coverage of the chromosome theory of inheritance. A brief introduction to the central dogma of molecular biology is added to provide students with a framework for understanding the connections between genes and phenotype early on in the book.

Chapter 2 Water and Carbon: The Chemical Basis of Life A more thorough explanation of chemical energy is included, covering the role of electronegativity, bond strength, and position of shared electrons with respect to the atomic nuclei. An expanded discussion addresses how molecular shape influences polarity and how changes in entropy are responsible for hydrophobic interactions between nonpolar molecules in a polar solvent.

Chapter 3 Protein Structure and Function The presentation of how electron sharing gives peptide bonds characteristics similar to double bonds is improved. Updated art more clearly illustrates how protein folding forms a substrate-specific active site in an enzyme. The introduction of prions is revised to describe how changes in protein structure may lead to cell death.

Chapter 4 Nucleic Acids and the RNA World The description of ATP hydrolysis is revised to avoid the common misconception that breaking phosphate bonds releases energy. The art and text are updated to present the geometry of nitrogenous bases relative to the sugar–phosphate backbone in double-stranded DNA. The role of hydrophobic interactions in shaping and stabilizing the DNA double helix is explained.

Chapter 5 An Introduction to Carbohydrates The impact of carbohydrate structure is emphasized by comparing the cleavage of maltose and lactose and exploring the basis of lactose intolerance that occurs in adults. The glycolipids and glycoproteins that serve as the ABO blood group antigens are introduced.

Chapter 6 Lipids, Membranes, and the First Cells Illustrations of fats and phospholipids are revised to emphasize similarity in structure. The description of osmosis is updated to include the effect of pressure on water transport and the concentration of solutes across a membrane at equilibrium.

Chapter 7 Inside the Cell Updated content highlights the differences in cell structure in eukaryotes, bacteria, and archaea. A revised description of receptor-mediated endocytosis, phagocytosis, and autophagy includes a new figure that illustrates how these pathways are involved in recycling components via lysosomes.

Chapter 8 Energy and Enzymes: An Introduction to Metabolism The introduction to potential and kinetic energy is expanded. The description of chemical energy is revised to focus on chemical bonds, support changes in Chapter 2, and address a common misconception that individual electrons carry energy. Illustrations of chemical bonds are updated to more accurately represent the correlation between bond length and chemical energy. The role of energetic coupling in converting endergonic reactions into exergonic reactions is clarified.

Chapter 9 Cellular Respiration and Fermentation Figures and text are updated to track the number of intermediates and products in each of the metabolic pathways. Redox potential is introduced as a measure of the ability of molecules to be reduced in redox reactions. The description of the fermentation pathways is expanded.

Chapter 10 Photosynthesis Greater emphasis is placed on the events responsible for converting the kinetic energy in light to potential energy stored in chemical bonds. Content is revised to address the misconceptions that the products of photosynthesis are used only to manufacture carbohydrates and that chloroplasts supply the ATP necessary for all other cellular functions. Figures and text are updated to more easily track the inputs and outputs in the photosynthetic reactions.

Chapter 11 Cell–Cell Interactions New content is added to the discussion of lipid-soluble signaling molecules and how second messengers in a signal transduction pathway can lead to many diverse cellular responses. A new quantitative question that addresses signal amplification is added. The discussion of the yeast pheromone response is expanded to draw connections between cell signaling and remodeling of the cell wall.

Chapter 12 The Cell Cycle Figures are updated to clearly distinguish differences between replicated and unreplicated chromosomes. New questions are added that address the application of a pulse–chase assay and common misconceptions associated with chromosome number during mitosis. New content is added covering the role of microtubules in chromosome movement and cell-cycle checkpoints.

Chapter 13 Meiosis Increased attention is paid to topics students are known to struggle with, such as the distinction between sister chromatids and homologous chromosomes, and the number of chromosomes and DNA molecules present in each daughter cell at the end of meiosis I compared with the end of meiosis II. The How Do Mistakes Occur? section is streamlined to focus on general themes of how aneuploidy arises during meiosis.

Chapter 14 Mendel and the Gene There is a sharper focus on challenging concepts, including the relationship between genotype and phenotype, the ability to consider phenotypes at levels that range from the molecular to the organismal, the meaning of dominance relationships, the significance of genetic mapping, and the importance of the chromosome theory of inheritance.

Chapter 15 DNA and the Gene: Synthesis and Repair Coverage is expanded on the Okazaki experiment and on the Nobel Prize–winning experiments of Greider and colleagues on telomeres and telomerase, so that students can more easily understand these investigations and their significance.

Chapter 16 How Genes Work Greater emphasis is placed on illustrating how the central dogma links genotype to phenotype. A stronger point is made that mutations can occur anywhere in the genome, not just in protein-coding sequences.

Chapter 17 Transcription, RNA Processing, and Translation New content helps students better understand polarity relationships among DNA, mRNA, and polypeptides. Three existing figures and one table are modified to improve clarity.

Chapter 18 Control of Gene Expression in Bacteria The discussion of the mechanism for glucose-mediated control of the *lac* operon is revised to highlight the continuing debate over the way catabolite repression works. The chapter is streamlined to allow students to focus on the fundamentals of how gene regulatory molecules control gene expression.

Chapter 19 Control of Gene Expression in Eukaryotes The material on control of translation is updated and reorganized, including a new example of global regulation of translation by mTor. Discussion of RNA interference is expanded, including a significantly modified figure showing how microRNAs are processed and how they function, and new discussion of how RNA interference can control chromatin condensation. The discussion of transcription initiation and the accompanying figure are updated.

Chapter 20 The Molecular Revolution: Biotechnology and Beyond Material previously spread across two chapters is merged to provide a more focused overview of major aims and techniques of genomics and related fields, including recent innovations such as CRISPR-Cas9 genome editing. Specific details of fundamental techniques are relocated to the BioSkills section for students and instructors who desire this level of coverage.

Chapter 21 Genes, Development, and Evolution Essential concepts previously spread across several chapters are brought together in this chapter, and it now links the Gene Structure and Expression unit to the Evolutionary Patterns and Processes unit by using molecular and cellular aspects of developmental biology as a bridge. New material on determination, induced pluripotent stem cells (iPS cells), and de-differentiation in cancer cells is included.

Chapter 22 Evolution by Natural Selection The historical introduction is simplified and illustrated in a new figure that compares different conceptual models of life's diversity. The homology section is updated to include developmental processes, and the three levels of homology are highlighted in a new summary table. More practice is provided in applying Darwin's postulates and reading phylogenetic trees. There is increased focus on overcoming common evolutionary misconceptions throughout the chapter. More plant examples are included. Focus on the ecological context of evolution is also increased.

Chapter 23 Evolutionary Processes The introduction to the Hardy–Weinberg principle is simplified and updated with some new examples. Increased attention is given to students' struggle to distinguish gene flow and genetic drift, and there are new follow-up questions. The summary table on evolutionary processes now includes icons to help students distinguish evolutionary processes, effect on genetic variation, and effect on fitness.

Chapter 24 Speciation New examples emphasize the origin of biodiversity, variation in rate of speciation, and biogeography, and illustrate the role of sexual selection and genetic mechanisms in speciation. Icons are now included in three summary tables to help students visualize mechanisms of reproductive isolation, species concepts, and outcomes of secondary contact between populations.

Chapter 25 Phylogenies and the History of Life The terms "microevolution" and "macroevolution" are now defined in the introduction. The phylogenetics section is updated to include more diverse examples. There is increased emphasis on avoiding common misconceptions in interpreting and drawing trees. The fossil review is reorganized into a photographic summary table. Dates in the history of life time line are updated. New evidence regarding causes of the end-Cretaceous extinction is introduced.

Chapter 26 Bacteria and Archaea New content is included on the role of endospores in the prokaryote life cycle, and recent studies on the human microbiome are highlighted. The section on themes in diversification is expanded to include mechanisms of gene transfer (e.g., transformation, transduction, and conjugation). Recent ideas that call into question the traditional three-domain tree of life hypothesis are presented.

Chapter 27 Protists Discussion of the role of endosymbiosis in the origin of mitochondria and chloroplasts is streamlined to focus on key concepts. The coverage of euglenids now includes a description of the flexible pellicle of this group, to underscore the point that most protist lineages are characterized by distinct microscopic features. Coverage of slime molds is expanded to include more on the structure and movement of plasmodial slime molds. Greater attention is paid to guiding students step-by-step through complex protist life cycles.

Chapter 28 Green Algae and Land Plants The updated discussion of the origin of plants now recognizes the conjugating algae (Zygnematophyceae) as one of the closest living relatives to land plants. Alternation of generations—the fundamental life cycle of all land plants—is now emphasized and presented with greater clarity.

Chapter 29 Fungi Content is updated to emphasize the important role of asexual spores (conidia) in the reproductive cycle of fungi. The unique relationship between a fungus and ants resulting in "zombie ants" is highlighted to illustrate the diversity of fungal lifestyles.

Chapter 30 An Introduction to Animals The chapter is updated to include insights gleaned from new genetic and developmental data, emphasizing that evolution is not a straightforward march from simple to complex.

Chapter 31 Protostome Animals The revised introduction is organized as a walk-through of a phylogeny to provide context from the previous chapter. Characteristics traditionally used to distinguish protostome development are deemphasized in light of recent research showing many exceptions. A new figure shows the phylogeny of arthropods, including insects within the Crustacea.

Chapter 32 Deuterostome Animals The echinoderm section has an increased emphasis on ecology and process of science, including Paine's keystone predator study. The invertebrate chordate section is expanded to include ascidians, thalaceans, and larvaceans. The key innovations section is revised and streamlined as a walk-through of the chordate phylogeny. The human evolution section is updated, including reference to new hominin species and an image of a Neanderthal woman.

Chapter 33 Viruses A new section on the role of viruses in shaping the evolution of organisms is introduced. A discussion of the SARS-CoV and MERS-CoV outbreaks is included to illustrate the international network of researchers that works to identify and control emerging viral infections. New content on how viruses impact society is included, along with new material covering recent discoveries on how the Ebola virus infects cells.

Chapter 34 Plant Form and Function The chapter is reorganized to discuss the structure and function of cells and tissues before placing them in the context of primary and secondary growth. Practice is provided on calculating and comparing the relationship between surface area and volume in different types of plant structures. Content on secondary growth is expanded to emphasize how trees make the transition from primary to secondary growth.

Chapter 35 Water and Sugar Transport in Plants The discussion of water potential and water movement is streamlined to bring key concepts into sharper focus. Recent work on the role of the SWEET genes in sugar transport is introduced.

Chapter 36 Plant Nutrition Discussion of parasitic plants is broadened and now includes dodder and ghost plants as examples.

Chapter 37 Plant Sensory Systems, Signals, and Responses The discussion of phototropins is streamlined to focus on key concepts. The role of phytochrome in circadian rhythms and etiolation is introduced. A summary table on key plant growth regulators is now illustrated with photographs to show the impact of hormones on plant growth and development.

Chapter 38 Plant Reproduction and Development The chapter is reorganized to merge essential information previously spread across several chapters and bring flowering plant reproduction and development together in a single, integrated story. Discussions of flower structure, pollination, fertilization, the formation of seeds and fruits, and embryogenesis are updated and streamlined. Coverage of vegetative development emphasizes the roles of apical meristems and genes involved in embryogenesis and leaf formation.

Chapter 39 Animal Form and Function The discussion of mammalian thermoregulation is moved into the section on homeostasis. In the introduction to animal tissue types, more explicit structure–function examples are given for each tissue type. The section on regulatory homeostasis is updated, and the idea that regulation and conformation are two ends of a spectrum is introduced. The expressions "warm-blooded" and "cold-blooded" are addressed to explain why these terms are problematic to use in biology. The section on countercurrent multipliers is simplified.

Chapter 40 Water and Electrolyte Balance in Animals The material on reabsorption in insect Malpighian tubules is streamlined. There is a discussion of how the vasa recta absorbs water and ions without disrupting the interstitial fluid gradient. A brief statement about how aldosterone functions in pH regulation of body fluids is added.

Chapter 41 Animal Nutrition The section on diabetes is expanded, and the importance of low cell glucose in addition to high blood glucose in untreated diabetes is stressed. A new figure addresses the relationship between obesity and type 2 diabetes.

Chapter 42 Gas Exchange and Circulation Oxygen–hemoglobin dissociation figures are redrawn more accurately, and new content helps students understand the meaning of a sigmoidal curve. The open circulatory system common to most invertebrates is illustrated with a new figure showing circulation in a spider.

Chapter 43 Animal Nervous Systems A new figure shows the relationships among sensory neurons, motor neurons, and interneurons. Review of material from earlier chapters on how ions are transported across membranes is streamlined. The discussion of the magnitude of action potentials and how action potentials propagate down an axon is clarified. Revisions emphasize that new action potentials are continuously generated along the entire length of an axon, addressing the misconception that a single action potential travels from one end to the other. Updated information is included on the hippocampus, the enteric nervous system, and the technique of optogenetics, a major breakthrough in neuroscience.

Chapter 44 Animal Sensory Systems The section on taste is updated to reflect new knowledge about the structure and function of gustation, and the likely existence of more than just five taste sensations. The role of mechanoreception in taste—by providing information about texture—is introduced. New content highlights one of the chapter's key ideas: Animals do not rely on senses independently and instead integrate information from multiple sensory modalities.

Chapter 45 Animal Movement A new figure shows examples of hydrostatic skeletons, endoskeletons, and exoskeletons. A brief section is added addressing the misconception that muscles grow by adding new cells during weight-lifting/training (in fact, the cells simply grow). A new section discusses the role of bone in calcium storage and the process of bone remodeling. Osteoblasts and osteoclasts are introduced, and osteoporosis is discussed briefly.

Chapter 46 Chemical Signals in Animals Content is rearranged to flow more logically: first introducing cell signaling, next discussing how hormones stimulate cells, then giving examples of what hormones can do, and finally describing how hormones are regulated overall. Discussion of the discovery of hormones is updated for historical accuracy and includes a new research box on Berthold's classic experiment on roosters, which shows that a chemical blood-borne messenger (later characterized as testosterone) can affect behavior and anatomy. Control of blood-glucose levels by insulin and glucagon is now used to illustrate how hormones maintain homeostasis.

Chapter 47 Animal Reproduction and Development Material previously spread across several chapters is merged to bring reproduction and development together to tell a single, integrated story. Coverage of fertilization is now integrated with egg development; coverage of cleavage, gastrulation, and organogenesis is combined into a new, descriptive section on embryonic development. New content covers formation of the central nervous system from the neural tube. The chapter now focuses more on the physiology of reproduction in mammals, but retains a comparative approach by including examples ranging from insects to marsupials.

Chapter 48 The Immune System in Animals Content is updated on the activation of B cells and allergens that are involved in mast-cell activation in allergic reactions. Coverage of the link between high levels of hygiene and the rising occurrence of allergies and autoimmune diseases in Westernized countries is expanded.

Chapter 49 An Introduction to Ecology The introduction is revised to clarify the relationship between traditional ecology and the study of human impacts. The niche concept is introduced as a tool to relate organisms to environmental conditions. The theory of plate tectonics and a figure showing continental drift are added to the section on biogeography. The Coriolis effect, prevailing winds, ocean gyres, and El Niño are added to the climate

section. Information from the Fifth Edition's biome boxes is integrated into the text and included in new photographic summary tables on terrestrial and aquatic biomes.

Chapter 50 Behavioral Ecology The introduction includes increased emphasis on fitness trade-offs and variation among organisms in a population (population thinking). Section case studies are updated, including a new opportunity for students to practice with optimal foraging in bees, a new data graphic on sexual selection in *Anolis* lizards, and a new photo of monkeys engaged in reciprocal grooming. A new section addresses the misconception that individuals act for the good of the species.

Chapter 51 Population Ecology The mark–recapture Quantitative Methods box is expanded. The figure and discussion of the life-history continuum are expanded. The exponential growth section is revised for a clearer walk-through of the equations and more direct assistance with common misconceptions. A new photographic summary table of density-dependent factors is added. Human population content is updated. Applications to conservation are expanded.

Chapter 52 Community Ecology More plant examples are included. The case studies on species interactions are updated and clarified. The community structure section now begins with a discussion of how pairwise interactions combine to form webs of interactions, introducing the food web as an example. A discussion of bottom-up and top-down influences on community structure is now included.

Chapter 53 Ecosystems and Global Ecology Updates and clarifications are made throughout the chapter, particularly in the section on climate change, including updated data graphics. Nutrient-cycle figures are modified to distinguish natural and human-caused processes. A section on phosphorus cycling is added. The concept of tipping points is added, and the interaction of multiple variables is emphasized.

Chapter 54 Biodiversity and Conservation Biology Updates and clarifications are made throughout the chapter. A new figure contrasts resistance and resilience. A new data graphic emphasizes the resource intensity of beef. Overall, more emphasis is placed on the positive effects of conservation action, including a new full-page photographic summary table of conservation strategies.

Acknowledgments

Reviewers

The peer review system is the key to quality and clarity in science publishing. In addition to providing a filter, the investment that respected individuals make in vetting the material—catching errors or inconsistencies and making suggestions to improve the presentation—gives authors, editors, and readers confidence that the text meets rigorous professional standards.

Peer review plays the same role in textbook publishing. The time and care that this book's reviewers have invested is a tribute to their professional integrity, their scholarship, and their concern for the quality of teaching. Virtually every page in this edition has been revised and improved based on insights from the following individuals.

Claudio Aguilar, *Purdue University*
Marc Albrecht, *University of Nebraska*
Walid Al-Ghoul, *Chicago State University*
Göran Arnqvist, *Uppsala University, Sweden*
Andrea Aspbury, *Texas State University, San Marcos*
Christofer Bang, *Arizona State University*
Miriam Barlow, *University of California, Merced*
Mark Barsoum, *Davidson College*
Vernon Bauer, *Frances Marion University*
Erin Becker, *University of California, Davis*
Vagner Benedito, *West Virginia University*
Jonathon Bennett, *Towson University*
Aimee Bernard, *University of Colorado, Denver*
Ashok Bidwai, *West Virginia University*
Wendy Binder, *Loyola Marymount University*
Jaime Blair, *Franklin and Marshall College*
Michelle Boone, *Miami University, Ohio*
Mirjana Brockett, *Georgia Institute of Technology*
David Buchwalter, *North Carolina State University*
Romi Burks, *Southwestern University*
Patrick Cafferty, *Emory University*
Susan Capasso, *St. Vincent's College*
Dale Casamatta, *University of North Florida*
David Chambers, *Concord University*
Rebekah Chapman, *Georgia State University*
Sixue Chen, *University of Florida*
Kendra Cheruvelil, *Michigan State University*
Soochin Cho, *Creighton University*
Clark Coffman, *Iowa State University*
Rachel Cohen, *Minnesota State University, Mankato*
William Cohen, *University of Kentucky*
Ron Cooper, *University of California, Los Angeles*
David Coughlin, *Widener University*
Karen Curto, *University of Pittsburgh*
James Daly, *State University of New York at Purchase*
Suni Dharmasiri, *Texas State University, San Marcos*
Scott Dobrin, *University of Maine at Presque Isle*

Kevin Dixon, *Florida State University*
Peter Ducey, *SUNY Cortland*
David Featherstone, *University of Illinois at Chicago*
Jeffrey Firestone, *University of Maryland*
Sarah Firestone, *University of Maryland*
Kirsten Fisher, *California State University, Los Angeles*
Mark Flood, *Fairmont State University*
Cerrone Foster, *East Tennessee State University*
Caitlin Gabor, *Texas State University, San Marcos*
Theresa Geiman, *Loyola University Maryland*
Brian Gibbens, *University of Minnesota*
Matt Gilg, *University of North Florida*
Eva Gonzales, *Saint Louis University*
Tamar Goulet, *University of Mississippi*
Eric Green, *Salt Lake Community College*
Teshell K. Greene, *Virginia State University*
Kelly Grussendorf, *Minnesota State University, Mankato*
Nancy Guild, *University of Colorado, Boulder*
Kristin Hardy, *California Polytechnic State University, San Luis Obispo*
David Hanson, *University of New Mexico*
Christopher Haynes, *Shelton State Community College*
Donata Henry, *Tulane University*
Mar-Elise Hill, *Northern Arizona University*
Jennifer Holloway, *Faulkner State Community College*
Bernadette Holthuis, *University of Florida*
Kelly Howe, *University of New Mexico*
Deborah Hutchinson, *Seattle University*
Dianne Jennings, *Virginia Commonwealth University*
Luis Jimenez, *Bergen Community College*
Hua Jin, *University of Illinois at Chicago*
Heather Joesting, *Armstrong State University*
Greg Jones, *Santa Fe College*
Seth Jones, *University of Kentucky*
Pavan Kadandale, *University of California, Irvine*
Lou Kim, *Florida International University*
Samantha King, *University of North Carolina at Chapel Hill*
Arshad Khan, *University of Texas at El Paso*
Anton Komar, *Cleveland State University*
Margaret Kovach, *University of Tennessee at Chattanooga*
Patrick Krug, *California State University, Los Angeles*
Kim Lackey, *University of Alabama*
Michael LaMontagne, *Missouri State University*
Kirkwood Land, *University of the Pacific*
Jeanne Lawless, *Binghamton University*
Daewoo Lee, *Ohio University*
Brenda Leicht, *University of Iowa*
Craig Lending, *The College at Brockport*
Vicky Lentz, *SUNY Oneonta*
Tatyana Lobova, *Old Dominion University*
Cindy Malone, *California State University, Northridge*
Kathy Rath Marr, *Lakeland College*
Jennifer Metzler, *Ball State University*

Justin Meyer, *University of California, San Diego*
James Mickle, *North Carolina State University*
Allison Miller, *Saint Louis University*
Brooks Miner, *Ithaca College*
Chad Montgomery, *Truman State University*
Tsafrir Mor, *Arizona State University*
Deborah Muldavin, *Central New Mexico Community College*
Ross Nehm, *Stony Brook University*
Jennifer Osterhage, *University of Kentucky*
Robert Osuna, *SUNY Albany*
Karla Passalacqua, *Emory University*
Debra Pires, *University of California, Los Angeles*
Erin Questad, *California State Polytechnic University, Pomona*
Stacey Raimondi, *Elmhurst College*
Elizabeth Randolph, *Front Range Community College*
Marceau Ratard, *Delgado Community College*
Mark Reedy, *Creighton University*
Melissa Murray Reedy, *University of Illinois at Urbana-Champaign*
Larry G. Riley, *California State University, Fresno*
Laurel Roberts, *University of Pittsburgh*
Deborah Roess, *Colorado State University*
Anthony Rossi, *University of North Florida*
Tobili Sam-Yellowe, *Cleveland State University*
Thomas Sasek, *University of Louisiana at Monroe*
Leena Sawant, *Houston Community College*
Jennifer Scoggins, *Florida State University, Panama City*
Joan Sharp, *Simon Fraser University*
Gidi Shemer, *University of North Carolina at Chapel Hill*
Leah Sheridan, *Ohio University*
Girish C Shukla, *Cleveland State University*
Amanda Simons, *Framingham State University*
Chrissy Simmons, *Southern Illinois University, Edwardsville*
Denise Slayback-Barry, *Indiana University–Purdue University, Indianapolis*
Paul Small, *Eureka College*
Nancy Solomon, *Miami University, Ohio*
Chrissy Spencer, *Georgia Institute of Technology*
Joshua Springer, *Purdue University*
Robert Sterner, *University of Minnesota, Duluth*
Shannon Stevenson, *University of Minnesota, Duluth*
Tara Stoulig, *Southeastern Louisiana University*
Adam Summers, *University of Washington*
Billie Swalla, *University of Washington*
Zuzana Swigonova, *University of Pittsburgh*
Heather Thieringer, *Princeton University*
Mark Thogerson, *Grand Valley State University*
Alexandru Tomescu, *Humboldt State University*
Mike Twiner, *University of Michigan-Dearborn*
Melvin Tyree, *University of Alberta, Canada*
Catherine Ueckert, *Northern Arizona University*
John VandenBrooks, *Arizona State University*
Bina Vanmali, *Arizona State University*
Sebastián Vélez, *Worcester State University*
Audra Warren, *Faulkner State Community College*
Doris Watt, *Saint Mary's College*
Shuo Wei, *West Virginia University*
Dennis Welker, *Utah State University*
Kira Wennstrom, *Shoreline Community College*

Mark Westneat, *University of Chicago*
Allison Wiedemeier, *University of Louisiana at Monroe*
Robert Wise, *University of Wisconsin—Oshkosh*
Virginia White, *Riverside City College*
Jenn Yost, *California Polytechnic State University, San Luis Obispo*
Robert Yost, *Indiana University — Purdue University Indianapolis*
Ted Young, *University of Washington*
Brittany Ziegler, *Minnesota State University, Mankato*

Contributors

We are grateful for the hard work and creativity of the contributors who worked on an impressive array of print and online support materials.

Ana Araya-Anchetta, *Northern Arizona University*
Andrea Aspbury, *Texas State University, San Marcos*
Brian Bagatto, *University of Akron*
Jay Brewster, *Pepperdine University*
Warren Burggren, *University of North Texas*
Patrick Cafferty, *Emory University*
Tim Christensen, *East Carolina University*
David Coughlin, *Widener University*
Karen Curto, *University of Pittsburgh*
Candice Damiani, *University of Pittsburgh*
Clarissa Dirks, *The Evergreen State College*
Lisa Elfring, *University of Arizona*
Caitlin Gabor, *Texas State University, San Marcos*
Kathy Gillen, *Kenyon College*
Nancy Ann Guild, *University of Colorado, Boulder*
Jutta Heller, *University of Washington—Tacoma*
Laurel Hester, *Keuka College*
Mar-Elise Hill, *Northern Arizona University*
Mark Holbrook, *University of Iowa*
Kristine Kaiser, *Pomona College*
Jacob L. Kerby, *University of South Dakota*
Aric Krogstad, *Arizona State University*
Craig Lending, *SUNY Brockport*
Cindy Malone, *California State University, Northridge*
Jim Manser, *Harvey Mudd College*
Brad Mehrtens, *University of Illinois at Urbana—Champaign*
Jennifer Osterhage, *University of Kentucky*
Melissa Murray Reedy, *University of Illinois at Urbana—Champaign*
Ann Riedl, *Front Range Community College*
Anthony Rossi, *University of North Florida*
Christina T. Russin, *Northwestern University*
Joan Sharp, *Simon Fraser University*
Cara Shillington, *Eastern Michigan University*
Nancy Solomon, *Miami University*
Anna Soper, *University of Massachusetts Amherst*
Chrissy Spencer, *Georgia Institute of Technology*
Zuzana Swigonova, *University of Pittsburgh*
Catherine Ueckert, *Northern Arizona University*
Bina Vanmali, *Arizona State University*

We also offer a special thanks to Stephen Thomas of *Michigan State University* who brought the Making Models videos to life.

Book Team

Anyone who has been involved in a major production knows that many people work behind the scenes to make it all happen. The coauthor team is indebted to the many talented individuals who have made this book possible.

Astute comments by development editors Stephanie Keep, Moira Lerner Nelson, Jennifer Angel, Mary Catherine Hager, and Matt Lee vastly improved both the scientific accuracy and the clarity of writing on the revised manuscript.

The final version of the text was copyedited with mastery by Chris Thillen and expertly proofread by Pete Shanks. Art was rendered by Imagineering Media Services, while Eric Schrader and Kristen Piljay researched hundreds of new photographs for the Sixth Edition. The book's clean, innovative design was developed by Marilyn Perry and Tani Hasegawa. Text and art were skillfully set in the design by Integra.

Creating MasteringBiology® tutorials and activities requires a large team. Media content development was overseen by Tania Mlawer and Sarah Jensen. Libby Reiser and Ziki Dekel served as media producers, developing and coordinating new and revised media content. We also benefitted from the media guidance of Lee Ann Doctor, Laura Tommasi, Charles Hall, and Sarah Young-Dualan. Project Managers Eddie Lee and Chelsea Logan oversaw creation of the Instructor Resource DVD.

Pearson's talented sales reps, who listen to professors, advise the editorial staff, and get the book into students' hands, are supported by the boundless energy of Executive Marketing Manager Lauren Harp and Vice President of Marketing Christy Lesko. Marketing materials were produced by Jane Campbell.

The vision and resources required to run this entire enterprise are the responsibility of Editor-in-Chief Beth Wilbur, who provided wise, inspirational, and focused leadership, and Adam Jaworski, Vice President of Pearson Science Editorial, who displays unwavering commitment to high-quality science publishing.

The editorial team was skillfully directed by Executive Editorial Manager Ginnie Simione Jutson during the early stages of the project. Program Manager Anna Amato's superb organizational skills and calm demeanor assured that all aspects of the process ran smoothly. Project Manager Mae Lum and Angel Chavez, Managing Editor of Integra, efficiently kept the mammoth project steadily rolling forward during production. Editorial Assistant Chloé Veylit gently but firmly kept all of us on track with deadlines and weekly conference calls. Development Editor Mary Hill worked magic to come up with visually aesthetic page layouts. Finally, we are deeply grateful for two key drivers of the Sixth Edition. Supervising Editor Sonia DiVittorio's remarkable vision and creativity; keen attention to detail, level, and clarity; and absolute insistence on excellence set the standard for us all. Senior Acquisitions Editor Michael Gillespie's unstoppable enthusiasm, invaluable skills at team building, upbeat attitude, and sharp intellect have energized and united the team while guiding the book through the hurdles to existence. The coauthor team gives many thanks to all these exceptional people for making the art and science of book writing a productive and exhilarating process.

1 Biology and the Tree of Life

This vervet monkey baby is exploring its new world and learning how to find food and stay alive. It represents one of the key characteristics of life introduced in this chapter—replication.

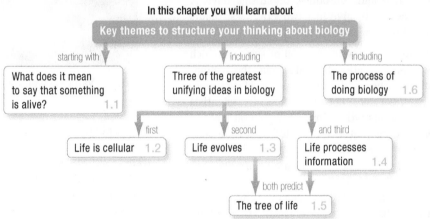

In this chapter you will learn about

Key themes to structure your thinking about biology

starting with

What does it mean to say that something is alive?   1.1

including

Three of the greatest unifying ideas in biology

including

The process of doing biology   1.6

first

Life is cellular   1.2

second

Life evolves   1.3

and third

Life processes information   1.4

both predict

The tree of life   1.5

This chapter is part of the Big Picture. See how on pages 16–17.

n essence, biological science is the study of life. It searches for ideas and observations that unify our understanding of the diversity of life—from bacteria living in hot springs to humans and majestic sequoia trees.

The goals of this chapter are to introduce the nature of life and explore how biologists go about studying it. The chapter also introduces themes that will resonate throughout this book:

- Analyzing how organisms work at the molecular level.

- Understanding organisms in terms of their evolutionary history.

- Helping you learn to think like a biologist.

Let's begin with what may be the most fundamental question of all: What is life?

1

1.1 What Does It Mean to Say That Something Is Alive?

An **organism** is a life-form—a living entity made up of one or more cells. Although there is no simple definition of life that is endorsed by all biologists, most agree that organisms share a suite of five fundamental characteristics. You can think of this text as one long exploration of these five traits.

- **Cells** Organisms are made up of membrane-bound units called **cells.** The membrane of a cell regulates the passage of materials between exterior and interior spaces.

- **Replication** One of the great biologists of the twentieth century, François Jacob, said that the "dream of a bacterium is to become two bacteria." Almost everything an organism does contributes to one goal: replicating itself.

- **Evolution** Organisms are the products of evolution, and their populations continue to evolve today.

- **Information** Organisms process hereditary, or genetic, information encoded in units called **genes.** Organisms also respond to information from the environment and adjust to maintain stable internal conditions. Right now, cells throughout your body are using information to make the molecules that keep you alive; your eyes and brain are decoding information on this page that will help you learn some biology, and if your room is too hot you might be sweating to cool off.

- **Energy** To stay alive and reproduce, organisms have to acquire and use energy. To give just two examples: plants absorb sunlight; animals ingest food.

Three of the greatest unifying ideas in all of science, which depend on the five characteristics just listed, laid the groundwork for modern biology: the cell theory, the theory of evolution, and the chromosome theory of inheritance. Formally, scientists define a **theory** as an explanation for a very general class of phenomena or observations that are supported by a wide body of evidence. Note that this definition contrasts sharply with the everyday usage of the word "theory," which often carries meanings such as "speculation" or "guess."

The cell theory, the theory of evolution, and the chromosome theory of inheritance address fundamental questions: What are organisms made of? Where do they come from? How is hereditary information transmitted from one generation to the next?

When these theories emerged in the mid-1800s, they revolutionized the way biologists think about the world. None of these insights came easily, however. The cell theory, for example, emerged after some 200 years of work. Let's examine some of the pivotal discoveries made along the way.

1.2 Life Is Cellular

In 1665 the Englishman Robert Hooke devised a crude microscope to examine the structure of cork (a bark tissue) from an oak tree. The instrument magnified objects to just 30× (30 times) their normal size, but it allowed Hooke to see something

(a) van Leeuwenhoek built his own microscopes—which, while small, were powerful. They allowed him to see, for example ...

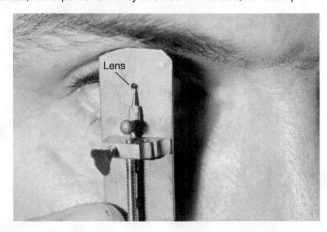

Lens

(b) ... human blood cells (this modern photo was shot through one of van Leeuwenhoek's original microscopes).

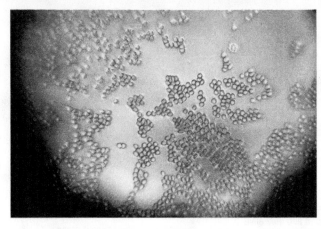

Figure 1.1 Van Leeuwenhoek's Microscope Made Cells Visible.

extraordinary. In the cork he observed small, pore-like compartments that were invisible to the naked eye. Hooke coined the term "cells" for these structures because he thought they resembled the cells inhabited by monks in a monastery.

Soon after Hooke published his results, the Dutch scientist Anton van Leeuwenhoek developed much more powerful microscopes, some capable of magnifications up to 300× (Figure 1.1). With these instruments, van Leeuwenhoek inspected samples of pond water and made the first observations of a dazzling collection of single-celled organisms that he called "animalcules."

In the 1670s an Italian researcher who was studying the leaves and stems of plants with a microscope concluded that plant tissues were composed of many individual cells. By the early 1800s, enough data had accumulated for a German biologist to claim that *all* organisms consist of cells. Did this claim hold up?

All Organisms Are Made of Cells

Advances in microscopy have made it possible to examine the amazing diversity and complexity of cells at higher and higher magnifications. Microscopes tens of thousands of times more powerful than van Leeuwenhoek's have revealed that cells are highly organized compartments separated from their environment by a membrane barrier. With these instruments, biologists have described over a million new species. The basic conclusion made in the 1800s remains intact: All organisms are made of cells.

The smallest organisms known today are bacteria that are barely 200 nanometers wide, or 200 *billionths* of a meter. (See BioSkills 1 to review the metric system.[1]) It would take 5000 of these organisms lined up side by side to span a millimeter. This is the distance between the smallest hash marks on a metric ruler. In contrast, sequoia trees can be over 100 meters tall, the equivalent of a 20-story building. Bacteria and sequoias are composed of the same fundamental building block, however—the cell. Bacteria consist of a single cell; sequoias are made up of trillions of cells.

The realization that all organisms are made of cells was fundamentally important, but it formed only the first part of the cell theory. In addition to understanding what organisms are made of, scientists wanted to understand how cells come to be.

Where Do Cells Come From?

In 1858, a German scientist named Rudolph Virchow proposed that all cells arise from cells already in existence. The complete **cell theory** builds on this concept: All organisms are made of cells, and all cells come from preexisting cells.

Two Hypotheses   The cell theory was a direct challenge to the prevailing explanation of where cells come from, called spontaneous generation. In the mid-1800s, most biologists believed that organisms could arise spontaneously under certain conditions.

---

[1]BioSkills are located after Chapter 1. They focus on general skills that you'll use throughout this course. More than a few students have found them to be a lifesaver. Please use them!

The bacteria and fungi that spoil foods such as milk and wine were thought to appear in these nutrient-rich media of their own accord—springing to life from nonliving materials. In contrast, the cell theory maintained that cells do not arise spontaneously but are produced only when preexisting cells grow and divide. The all-cells-from-cells explanation was a **hypothesis:** a testable statement to explain a phenomenon or a set of observations.

Biologists usually use the word "theory" to refer to proposed explanations for broad patterns in nature and prefer hypothesis to refer to explanations for more tightly focused questions. A theory serves as a framework for developing new hypotheses.

An Experiment to Settle the Question   Soon after Virchow's all-cells-from-cells hypothesis appeared in print, a French scientist named Louis Pasteur set out to test its predictions in an **experiment.** Experiments are a powerful scientific tool because they allow researchers to test the effect of a single, well-defined factor on a particular phenomenon. An experimental **prediction** describes a measurable or observable result that must be correct if a hypothesis is valid.

Pasteur wanted to determine whether organisms could arise spontaneously in a nutrient broth or whether they appear only when a broth is exposed to a source of preexisting cells. To address the question, he created two treatment groups that were identical in every respect but one: the factor being tested—in this case, a broth's exposure to preexisting cells.

Both treatments used glass flasks filled with the same amount of the same nutrient broth (Figure 1.2). Both flasks were boiled for the same amount of time to kill any existing organisms. After sterilization by boiling, however, any bacteria and fungi that cling to dust particles in the air could drop into the broth in the flask shown in Figure 1.2a because the neck of this flask was straight.

(a) Pasteur experiment with straight-necked flask:

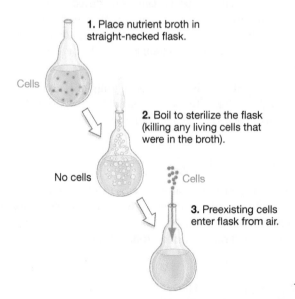

1. Place nutrient broth in straight-necked flask.

2. Boil to sterilize the flask (killing any living cells that were in the broth).

3. Preexisting cells enter flask from air.

Cells

No cells

Cells

(b) Pasteur experiment with swan-necked flask:

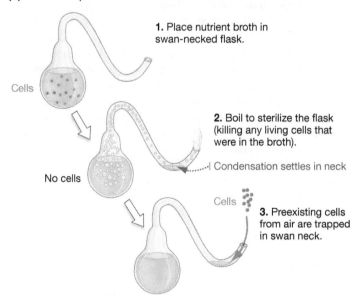

1. Place nutrient broth in swan-necked flask.

2. Boil to sterilize the flask (killing any living cells that were in the broth).

Condensation settles in neck

3. Preexisting cells from air are trapped in swan neck.

Cells

No cells

Cells

Figure 1.2 The Spontaneous Generation and All-Cells-from-Cells Hypotheses Were Tested Experimentally.

✔ **PROCESS OF SCIENCE** What problem would arise in interpreting these results if Pasteur had (1) put different types of broth in the two treatments, or (2) used a ceramic flask for one treatment and a glass flask for the other?

In contrast, in the flask with a long swan neck (Figure 1.2b), water would condense in the crook of the swan neck after boiling and this pool of water would trap any bacteria or fungi that entered on dust particles. Thus, the contents of the swan-necked flask were isolated from any source of preexisting cells even though they were still open to the air.

The spontaneous generation hypothesis predicted that cells would appear in both treatment groups. The all-cells-from-cells hypothesis predicted that cells would appear only in the treatment exposed to a source of preexisting cells.

And Pasteur's results? The broth in the straight-necked flask exposed to preexisting cells quickly filled with bacteria and fungi. This observation was important because it showed that the sterilization step had not altered the nutrient broth's capacity to support growth. The broth in the swan-necked flask remained sterile, however. Even when the flask was left standing for months, no organisms appeared in it. This result was inconsistent with the hypothesis of spontaneous generation.

Because Pasteur's data were so conclusive—meaning that there was no other reasonable explanation for them—the results persuaded most biologists that the all-cells-from-cells hypothesis was correct.

If all cells come from existing cells, where did the first cells come from? Biologists now have evidence that life arose from non-life early in Earth's history, through a process called **chemical evolution.**

Life Replicates Through Cell Division

For life on Earth to continue to exist, cells must replicate. Most cells are capable of reproducing by dividing—in effect, by making a copy of themselves. As predicted by the cell theory, all the cells present in your body and in most other multicellular individuals are descended from preexisting cells, tracing back to a fertilized egg. A fertilized egg is a cell created by the fusion of sperm and egg—cells that formed in individuals of the previous generation.

New cells arise when preexisting cells split. In multicellular organisms they become specialized for particular functions by intricate processes. In this way, all the cells in a multicellular organism are connected by a common lineage. Is the tremendous diversity among organisms also related to common ancestry?

The second great founding idea in biology, published the same year as the all-cells-from-cells hypothesis, provided an answer. This was the realization, made independently by the English scientists Charles Darwin and Alfred Russel Wallace, that all the diverse **species**—all distinct, identifiable types of organisms—are connected by common ancestry.

1.3 Life Evolves

In 1858 short papers written separately by Darwin and Wallace were read to a small group of scientists attending a meeting of the Linnean Society of London. A year later, Darwin published a book that expanded on the idea summarized in those brief papers. The book was called *On the Origin of Species*. The first edition sold out in a day.

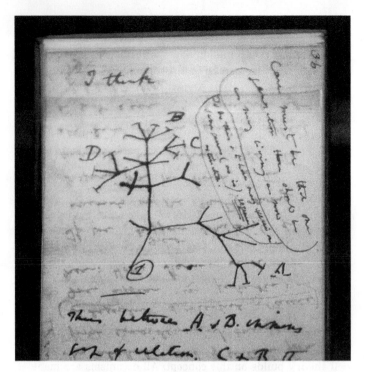

Figure 1.3 Sketch from Darwin's Notebook Dated 1837. Darwin wrote this in the notes that follow: "Thus genera would be formed. Bearing relation to ancient types with several extinct forms."

What Is Evolution?

Darwin and Wallace's theory made two important claims concerning patterns that exist in the natural world.

1. Species are related by common ancestry (**Figure 1.3**). This idea contrasted with the prevailing view in science at the time, which was that species represent independent entities created separately by a divine being.

2. The characteristics of species can be modified from generation to generation. Darwin called this process descent with modification. This claim argued against the popular view at the time that species do not change.

   Evolution is a change in the characteristics of a population over time. A **population** is defined as a group of individuals of the same species living in the same area at the same time. To put it another way, species are related to one another and can change through time.

What Is Natural Selection?

Several other scientists had already come to the same conclusions as Darwin and Wallace about the relationships between species. The great insight by Darwin and Wallace was in proposing a process, called **natural selection,** that explains *how* evolution occurs.

Two Conditions of Natural Selection Natural selection occurs whenever two conditions are met.

1. Individuals within a population vary in characteristics that are **heritable**—meaning, traits that can be passed on to offspring.

2. In a particular environment, certain versions of these heritable traits help individuals survive better or reproduce more than do other versions.

If certain heritable traits lead to increased success in producing offspring, then those traits become more common in the population over time. In this way, the population's characteristics change as a result of natural selection acting on individuals. This is a key insight: Natural selection acts on individuals, but evolutionary change occurs in populations.

Evolution occurs when heritable variation leads to differential success in reproduction. Individual populations change through time in response to natural selection. But over the past several decades, biologists have also documented dozens of cases in which natural selection has caused populations of one species to diverge and form new species. This divergence process is called **speciation.**

Research on speciation has two important implications: All species come from preexisting species, and all species, past and present, trace their ancestry back to a single common ancestor.

Fitness and Adaptation
Darwin also introduced some new terminology to identify what happens during natural selection.

- In everyday English, "fitness" means "health and well-being." But in biology, **fitness** means "an individual's ability to produce viable offspring." Individuals with high fitness produce many surviving offspring.

- In everyday English, "adaptation" means that an individual is adjusting and changing to function in new circumstances. But in biology, an **adaptation** is a trait that increases the fitness of an individual in a particular environment.

Darwin and Wallace's ideas arose from their observations of nature. For example, in finches from the Galápagos Islands Darwin noted the remarkable variation in beak size and shape in species that otherwise appeared similar. He proposed that the birds on different islands in the chain were similar because they descended from a common ancestor—the finch populations that colonized different islands had changed through time and formed new species with distinct beaks.

Long-term studies by biologists over the past several decades have documented dramatic changes in a population of finches on one of the Galápagos Islands (you will learn more about this study in Chapter 22). When small, soft seeds were abundant there due to increased rainfall, finches with small, pointed beaks produced more offspring and had higher fitness than individuals with large, deep beaks. In this population and with this food source, a small, pointed beak was an adaptation that allowed certain individuals to thrive, and the incidence of finches with such beaks increased in the population.

Note that during this process, the beak shape of any individual finch did not change within its lifetime—the change occurred in the characteristics of the population over time. Darwin's finches continue to evolve today in response to changes in the environment.

Together, the cell theory and the theory of evolution provided the young science of biology with two central, unifying ideas:

1. The cell is the fundamental structural unit in all organisms.

2. All species are related by common ancestry and have changed over time in response to natural selection.

But what was the source of the heritable variation in traits? And how was information stored and transmitted from one generation to the next? The third unifying idea—the chromosome theory of inheritance—provided the foundation for biologists to answer these questions.

1.4 Life Processes Information

After Walter Sutton and Theodor Boveri proposed the **chromosome theory of inheritance** in 1902, the pieces of the genetic puzzle began to fall into place. The key point? Inside cells, hereditary or genetic information is encoded in genes, the units located on chromosomes.

But it wasn't until experiments were carried out in the 1950s that biologists figured out the molecular nature of the genetic material—a **chromosome** consists of a molecule of **deoxyribonucleic acid,** or **DNA.** To sum up, DNA is the heredity material. Genes consist of specific segments of DNA that code for products in the cell.

The Central Dogma

In what is considered one of the greatest scientific breakthroughs of biology, James Watson and Francis Crick proposed that DNA is a double-stranded helix (**Figure 1.4**). Crucial insights that led to this model came from structural analyses performed by Rosalind Franklin in Maurice Wilkins' laboratory.

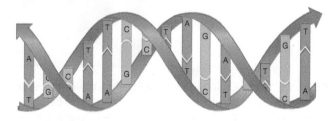

Figure 1.4 DNA Is a Double Helix.

Each strand of the **double helix** is made up of varying sequences of four different kinds of building blocks. In terms of structure, on each strand of the helix the building blocks of DNA are connected one to another linearly. In terms of function, they are like letters of the alphabet—the four different kinds of molecular building blocks are symbolized by the letters A, T, C, and G. A sequence of this letter code is like the sequence of letters in a word—it has meaning. In this way, DNA carries, or encodes, the information required for an organism's growth and reproduction.

The two strands of the double helix are joined by connections between the building blocks that occur only between certain letters: A always pairs with T, and C always pairs with G (see Figure 1.4). This pairing is key: DNA can be copied, and the information encoded in the DNA is faithfully preserved. The pairs are arranged much like the rungs on a ladder, with the strands acting as the sides of the ladder.

How is this information transmitted? The **central dogma**—first articulated by Crick—describes the flow of information in cells. In this context, the term "dogma" means a framework for understanding. Put simply, DNA codes for RNA, which codes for proteins (**Figure 1.5**).

Molecular machinery in cells makes a copy of a particular gene's information in the form of a closely related molecule called **ribonucleic acid,** or **RNA.** RNA molecules carry out a number of specialized functions in cells. For example, molecular machinery reads a messenger RNA molecule to determine what building blocks to use to make a **protein.** Proteins are crucial to most tasks required for a cell to exist, from forming structural components to promoting the chemical reactions that sustain life.

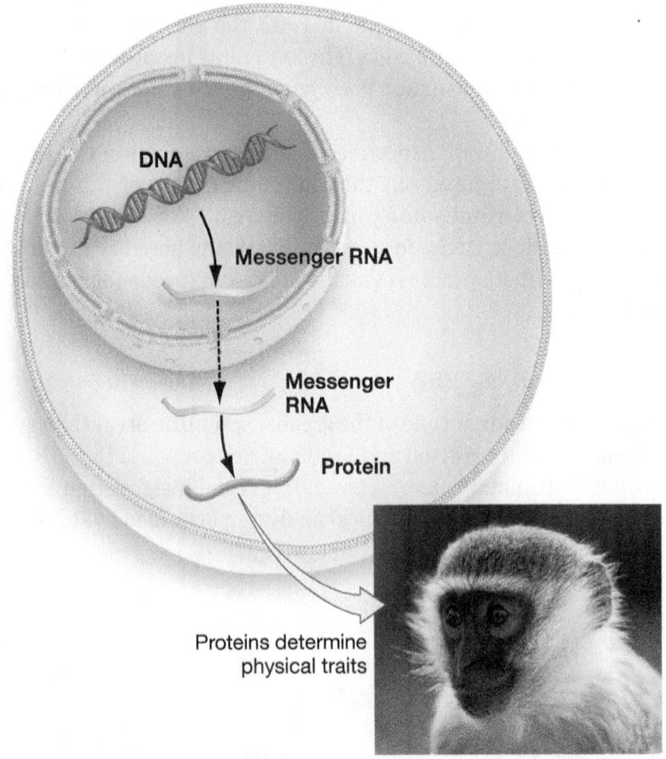

Understanding the structure of DNA provided insight into how genetic information is passed from cell to cell or from one organism to its offspring. Making a copy of DNA in a cell is a highly accurate process, but mistakes can occur. What happens when a mistake is made? Differences in DNA sequences may lead to differences in the sequence of building blocks of proteins.

The implications are profound: The outward appearance of an organism is a product of the proteins produced by its molecular machinery, so differences in DNA sequences might lead to a difference, for example, in finch beak size and shape, or in the length of a giraffe's neck. At the level of individuals, such changes might increase or decrease fitness. At the population level, changes in sequence lead to the heritable variations that underlie the diversity of life and make evolution possible.

Life Requires Energy

The chemical reactions that sustain the diversity of life take place inside cells. Transmitting genetic information, and the other work carried out by cells, requires energy. Organisms—whether single-celled or multicellular—are capable of living in a wide array of environments because they vary in cell structure and how they acquire and use energy.

Organisms have two fundamental nutritional needs—acquiring chemical energy in the form of a molecule called **ATP** (or **adenosine triphosphate**) and obtaining molecules that can be used as building blocks for the synthesis of DNA, RNA, proteins, the cell membrane, and other large, complex compounds required by the cell. How organisms do this—whether acquiring energy from the sun or through chemical compounds—is central to the tremendous diversification of life after it first arose on Earth.

1.5 The Tree of Life

The theory of evolution by natural selection predicts that biologists should be able to construct a **tree of life**—a family tree of organisms. If life on Earth arose just once, then such a diagram would describe the genealogical relationships between species with a single, ancestral species at its base. Has this task been accomplished? If the tree of life exists, what does it look like?

Using Molecules to Understand the Tree of Life

One of the great breakthroughs in research on the tree of life occurred when American biologist Carl Woese (pronounced *woze*) and colleagues began analyzing the molecular components of organisms as a way to understand their evolutionary relationships. Their goal was to understand the **phylogeny** of all organisms—their actual genealogical relationships. Translated literally, "phylogeny" means "tribe-source."

To understand which organisms are closely versus distantly related, Woese and co-workers needed to study a molecule found in all organisms. They selected an RNA molecule, an essential

DNA

Messenger RNA

Messenger RNA

Protein

Proteins determine physical traits

Figure 1.5 The Central Dogma Describes the Flow of Genetic Information. Genetic information flows from DNA to RNA to proteins. Differences in DNA sequences may lead to different physical traits.

part of the machinery that all cells use to grow and reproduce. The researchers based their initial work on the sequence of building blocks observed in this RNA molecule. At the time it was not yet possible to easily analyze DNA sequences. With advances in technology, biologists now use DNA sequences to investigate phylogenetic relationships.

Analyzing Genetic Variation   Why might DNA (or RNA) be useful for understanding the relationships between organisms? The answer is that the sequence of building blocks in DNA is a trait that can change during the course of evolution. Although a gene may code for an RNA or protein molecule that performs the same function in all organisms, the corresponding DNA sequence is not identical among species.

How is such genetic variation analyzed? Recall that the building blocks in DNA are symbolized by the letters A, T, C, and G. Biologists use this letter code to depict DNA sequences (**Making Models 1.1**). In land plants, for example, a section of DNA might start with the sequence A-T-A-T-**C**-G-A-G. In green algae, which are closely related to land plants, the same section of the molecule might contain A-T-A-T-**G**-G-A-G. But in brown algae, which are not closely related to green algae or to land plants, the same part of the molecule might consist of A-**A**-A-T-**G**-G-A-**C**.

The next step in analyzing genetic variation is to consider what the similarities and differences in the sequences imply about relationships between species. The goal is to produce a diagram that describes the phylogeny of the organisms being compared.

A diagram that depicts evolutionary history in this way is called a **phylogenetic tree.** (For help in learning how to read a phylogenetic tree, see BioSkills 13.) Just as a family tree shows relationships between individuals, a phylogenetic tree shows relationships between species. On a phylogenetic tree, branches that share a recent common ancestor—that is, an ancestral population—represent species that are closely related; branches that don't share recent common ancestors represent species that are more distantly related.

🖉 **Making Models 1.1** Tips on Drawing DNA Sequences

In models focused on the information content in DNA, structural details can be left out and the double-stranded DNA double helix simplified to show the letter code on one strand only. Sequences can then be compared for similarities and differences.

Land plant DNA   A—T—A—T—[C]—G—A—G

Green algal DNA   A—T—A—T—[G]—G—A—G

Different sequence
at the same location

MODEL Suppose that in the same section of DNA, molds and other fungi have the sequence A-T-A-T-G-G-A-C. Draw a model that compares the sequences. Are fungi more closely related to green algae or to land plants? Explain your logic.

To see this model in action, go to https://goo.gl/rXkXrM

The Tree of Life Estimated from Genetic Data   To construct a phylogenetic tree, such as the one shown in **Figure 1.6**, researchers use sophisticated computer programs to find the arrangement of branches that is most consistent with the similarities and differences observed in the genetic data.

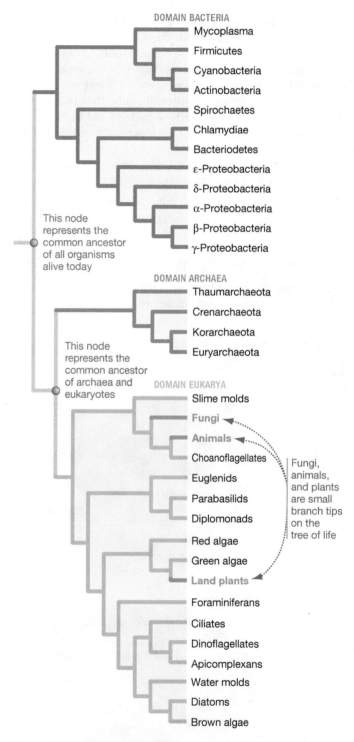

Figure 1.6 **The Tree of Life Was Produced by Comparing Genetic Sequence Data.** The three domains of life revealed by the analysis are labeled. Common names are given for lineages in the domains Bacteria and Eukarya. Phyla names are given for lineages in the domain Archaea, because most of them have no common names.

Because this tree includes such a diverse array of species, it is often called the universal tree, or the tree of life. Notice that the tree's main node is the common ancestor (ancestral population) of all living organisms. Researchers who study the origin of life propose that the tree's root extends even further back to the "*last universal common ancestor*" of cells, or **LUCA.**

The tree of life implied by genetic sequence data established that there are three fundamental groups or lineages of organisms: **(1)** the Bacteria, **(2)** the Archaea, and **(3)** the Eukarya. In all **eukaryotes** (literally, "true kernel"), cells have a prominent component called the nucleus (**Figure 1.7a**). Because the vast majority of bacterial and archaeal cells lack a nucleus, they are referred to as **prokaryotes** (literally, "before-kernel"; see **Figure 1.7b**). The vast majority of bacteria and archaea are unicellular ("one-celled"); many eukaryotes are multicellular ("many-celled").

When results based on genetic data were first published, biologists were astonished. For example:

- Prior to Woese's work and follow-up studies, biologists thought that the most fundamental division among organisms was between prokaryotes and eukaryotes. The Archaea were virtually unknown—much less recognized as a major and highly distinctive branch on the tree of life.

- Fungi were thought to be closely related to plants. Instead, they are actually much more closely related to animals.

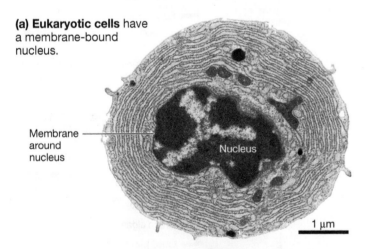

(a) Eukaryotic cells have a membrane-bound nucleus.

Membrane around nucleus

Nucleus

1 μm

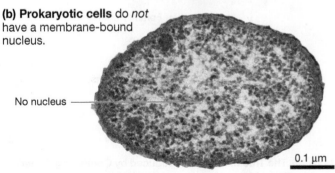

(b) Prokaryotic cells do *not* have a membrane-bound nucleus.

No nucleus

0.1 μm

Figure 1.7 Eukaryotic and Prokaryotic Cells Differ in Structure.

✔ **QUANTITATIVE** How many times larger is the eukaryotic cell in this figure than the prokaryotic cell? (Hint: Study the scale bars.)

- Traditional approaches for classifying organisms—including the system of five kingdoms divided into various classes, orders, and families that you may have learned in high school—are inaccurate in many cases, because they do not reflect the actual evolutionary history of the organisms involved.

The Tree of Life Is a Work in Progress Just as researching your family tree can help you understand who you are and where you came from, so the tree of life helps biologists understand the relationships between organisms and the history of species. The discovery of the Archaea and the accurate placement of lineages such as the fungi qualify as exciting breakthroughs in our understanding of evolutionary history and life's diversity.

Work on the tree of life continues at a furious pace, however, and the location of certain branches on the tree is hotly debated. As databases expand and as techniques for analyzing data improve, the shape of the tree of life will undoubtedly change. Our understanding of the tree of life, like our understanding of every other topic in biological science, is dynamic.

How Should We Name Branches on the Tree of Life?

In science, the effort to name and classify organisms is called **taxonomy.** Any named group is called a **taxon** (plural: **taxa**). Currently, biologists are working to create a taxonomy, or naming system, that accurately reflects the phylogeny of organisms. Based on the tree of life, Woese proposed a new taxonomic category called the **domain.** He designated the Bacteria, Archaea, and Eukarya as the three domains of life.

Biologists often use the term **phylum** (plural: **phyla**) to refer to major lineages within each domain. Although the designation is somewhat arbitrary, each phylum is considered a major branch on the tree of life. Within the lineage called animals, biologists currently name 30–35 phyla—each of which is distinguished by distinctive aspects of its body structure as well as by distinctive gene sequences. For example, the mollusks (clams, squid, octopuses) constitute a phylum, as do chordates (the vertebrates and their close relatives).

Because the tree of life is so new, though, naming systems are still being worked out. For example, recent genetic data have fueled an ongoing debate about whether there are only two domains of life: Bacteria as one domain, and the rest of life the other. One thing that hasn't changed for centuries, however, is the naming system for individual species.

Scientific (Latin) Names In 1735, a Swedish botanist named Carolus Linnaeus established a system for naming species that is still in use today. Linnaeus created a two-part name unique to each type of organism.

- *Genus* The first part indicates the organism's **genus** (plural: **genera**). A genus is made up of a closely related group of species. For example, Linnaeus put humans in the genus *Homo.* Although humans are the only living species in this genus, at least six extinct organisms, all of which walked upright and made extensive use of tools, were later also assigned to *Homo.*

- *Species* The second term in the two-part name identifies the organism's species. Linnaeus gave humans the species name *sapiens*. A species name is always preceded by its genus.

An organism's genus and species designation is called its **scientific name** or Latin name. Scientific names are always italicized. Genus names are always capitalized, but species names are not—as in *Homo sapiens*.

Linnaeus maintained that different types of organisms should not be given the same genus and species names. Other species may be assigned to the genus *Homo* (from the Latin for "man"), and members of other genera may be named *sapiens* (from the Latin for "wise" or "knowing"), but only humans are named *Homo sapiens*. Each scientific name is unique.

Scientific Names Are Often Descriptive Scientific names and terms are often based on Latin or Greek word roots that are descriptive. For example, consider the yeast *Saccharomyces cerevisiae*. *Saccharomyces* is aptly named—the domesticated strains of yeast used in commercial baking and brewing are often fed sugar (Greek root *saccharo*), and yeast is a fungus (Greek root *myces*). The species name of this organism, *cerevisiae*, is Latin for "beer." Loosely translated, then, the scientific name of brewer's yeast means "sugar-fungus for beer."

Scientific names and terms often seem daunting at first glance. So, most biologists find it extremely helpful to memorize some of the common Latin and Greek roots. To aid you in this process, new terms in this text are often accompanied by a translation of their Latin or Greek word roots in parentheses. (A glossary of common root words with translations and examples is also provided in BioSkills 15.)

CHECK YOUR UNDERSTANDING

If you understand that …

- A phylogenetic tree shows the evolutionary relationships between species.
- To infer where species belong on a phylogenetic tree, biologists examine their genetic and other characteristics. Closely related species should have similar characteristics, while less closely related species should be less similar.

✔ **You should be able to …**

Examine the following DNA sequences and determine which two species would be closest on a phylogenetic tree.

Species A: A A C T A G C G C G A T
Species B: A A C T A G C G C C A T
Species C: T T C T A G C G G T A T

Answers are available in Appendix A.

1.6 Doing Biology

This chapter has introduced some of the great ideas in biology. The development of the cell theory, the theory of evolution, and the chromosome theory of inheritance provided cornerstones when the science was young. The central dogma explained the flow of information from DNA to physical traits of an organism,

and the more recent insights of the tree of life have revolutionized our understanding of life's diversity.

These three unifying ideas are considered great because they explain fundamental aspects of nature, and because they have consistently been shown to be correct. They are considered correct because they have withstood extensive testing.

How do biologists go about testing their ideas? Before answering this question, let's step back a bit and consider the types of questions that researchers can and cannot ask.

The Nature of Science

Biologists ask questions about organisms, just as physicists and chemists ask questions about the physical world or geologists ask questions about Earth's history and the processes that shape landforms. No matter what their field, all scientists ask questions that can be answered by observing or measuring things—by collecting data. Conversely, scientists cannot address questions that can't be answered by observing or measuring things.

This distinction is important. It is at the root of continuing controversies about teaching evolution in publicly funded schools. In the United States and in Turkey, in particular, some Christian and Islamic leaders have been particularly successful in pushing their claim that evolution and religious faith are in conflict. Even though the theory of evolution is considered one of the most successful and best-substantiated ideas in the history of science, they object to teaching it.

The vast majority of biologists and many religious leaders reject this claim; they see no conflict between evolution and religious faith. Their view is that science and religion are compatible because they address different types of questions.

- Science is about formulating hypotheses and finding evidence that supports or conflicts with those hypotheses.

- Religious faith addresses questions that cannot be answered by data. The questions addressed by the world's great religions focus on why we exist and how we should live.

So how do biologists go about answering questions? After formulating hypotheses, biologists perform studies that yield experimental data or descriptive data, such as observing a behavior, characterizing a structure within a cell by microscopy, or sequencing DNA. Let's consider two examples of this process.

Why Do Giraffes Have Long Necks?
An Introduction to Hypothesis Testing

If you were asked why giraffes have long necks, you might say based on your observations that long necks enable giraffes to reach food that is unavailable to other mammals. This hypothesis is expressed in African folktales and has traditionally been accepted by many biologists. The food competition hypothesis is so plausible, in fact, that for decades no one thought to test it.

In the mid-1990s, however, Robert Simmons and Lue Scheepers assembled data suggesting that the food competition hypothesis is only part of the story. Their analysis supports an alternative hypothesis: Long necks allow giraffes to use their heads as effective weapons for battering their opponents, and longer-necked giraffes have a competitive advantage in fights.

(a) Most feeding is done at about shoulder height.

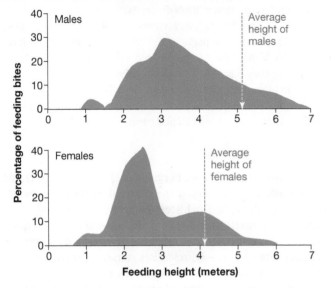

(b) Typical feeding posture in giraffes

Figure 1.8 Giraffes Do Not Usually Extend Their Necks Upward to Feed.

DATA: Young, T. P., and L. A. Isbell. 1991. *Ethology* 87: 79–89.

✔ **QUANTITATIVE** At what height of vegetation do male and female giraffes spend most of their time feeding?

Before exploring these alternative explanations, it's important to recognize that hypothesis testing is a two-step process:

Step 1 State the hypothesis as precisely as possible and list the predictions it makes.

Step 2 Design an observational or experimental study that is capable of testing those predictions.

If the predictions are accurate, the hypothesis is supported. If the predictions are not met, then researchers do further tests, modify the original hypothesis, or search for alternative explanations. But the process does not end here. Biologists communicate their results to the scientific community and beyond; for example, via informal conversations, scientific meetings, or publications. (You can see the Big Picture of Doing Biology on pages 16–17.)

Now that you understand more about hypothesis testing, let's return to the giraffes. How did biologists test the food competition hypothesis? What data support their alternative explanation?

The Food Competition Hypothesis: Predictions and Tests The food competition hypothesis claims that giraffes compete for food with other species of mammals. When food is scarce, as it is during the dry season, giraffes with longer necks can reach food that is unavailable to other species and to giraffes with shorter necks. As a result, the longest-necked individuals in a giraffe population survive better and produce more young than do shorter-necked individuals, and average neck length of the population increases with each generation.

To use the terms introduced earlier, long necks are adaptations that increase the fitness of individual giraffes during competition for food. This type of natural selection has gone on so long that the population has become extremely long necked.

The food competition hypothesis makes several explicit predictions. For example, it predicts that

- neck length is variable among giraffes;
- neck length in giraffes is heritable; and
- giraffes feed high in trees, especially during the dry season, when food is scarce and the threat of starvation is high.

The first prediction is correct. Studies in zoos and natural populations confirm that neck length is variable among individuals. The researchers were unable to test the second prediction, however, because they studied giraffes in a natural population and could not do breeding experiments. As a result, they simply had to accept this prediction as an assumption. In general, though, biologists prefer to test every assumption behind a hypothesis.

What about the prediction regarding feeding high in trees? According to Simmons and Scheepers, this is where the food competition hypothesis breaks down.

Consider, for example, data collected by a different research team on the amount of time that giraffes spend feeding in vegetation of different heights (Figure 1.8a). Note that this graph plots the height of vegetation on the *x*-axis, starting from ground level (0 meters on the graph) and continuing up to 7 meters. The percentage of bites taken by a giraffe is plotted on the *y*-axis, for males and for females from the same population in Kenya. The dashed line on each graph indicates the average height of a male or female in this population. (For more help on reading graphs, see BioSkills 2.)

Note that the average height of a giraffe in this population is much greater than the height where most feeding takes place. In this population, both male and female giraffes spend most of their feeding time eating vegetation that averages just 60 percent of their full height. Studies on other populations of giraffes, during both the wet and dry seasons, are consistent with these data. Giraffes usually feed with their necks bent (**Figure 1.8b**).

These data cast doubt on the food competition hypothesis, because one of its predictions does not appear to hold. Biologists have not abandoned this hypothesis completely, though, because feeding high in trees may be particularly valuable during extreme droughts, when a giraffe's ability to reach leaves far above the ground could mean the difference between life and death. Still, Simmons and Scheepers have offered an alternative explanation for why giraffes have long necks. The new hypothesis is based on the mating system of giraffes.

The Sexual Competition Hypothesis: Predictions and Tests

Giraffes have an unusual mating system. Breeding occurs year-round rather than seasonally. To determine when females are coming into estrus or "heat" and are thus receptive to mating, the males nuzzle the rumps of females. In response, the females urinate into the males' mouths. The males then tip their heads back and pull their lips to and fro, as if tasting the liquid. Biologists who have witnessed this behavior have proposed that the males taste the females' urine to detect whether estrus has begun.

Once a female giraffe enters estrus, males may fight among themselves for the opportunity to mate, though confrontation often is resolved by the males standing very tall and staring hard at each other until one male turns and runs away. When combat does occur, it is spectacular. The bulls stand next to one another, swing their necks, and strike thunderous blows with their heads. Researchers have seen males knocked unconscious for 20 minutes after being hit and have cataloged numerous instances in which the loser died.

These observations inspired a new explanation for why giraffes have long necks. The sexual competition hypothesis is based on the idea that longer-necked giraffes are able to strike harder blows during combat than can shorter-necked giraffes. In engineering terms, longer necks provide a longer "moment arm." A long moment arm increases the force of an impact. (Think about the type of sledgehammer you'd use to bash down a concrete wall—one with a short handle or one with a long handle?)

The idea here is that longer-necked males should win more fights and, as a result, father more offspring than shorter-necked males do. If neck length in giraffes is inherited, then the average neck length in the population should increase over time. Under the sexual competition hypothesis, long necks are adaptations that increase the fitness of males during competition for females.

Although several studies have shown that long-necked males are more successful in fighting and that the winners of fights gain access to estrous females, the question of why giraffes have long necks is not closed. With the data collected to date, many biologists would probably conclude that both the food competition hypothesis and the sexual competition hypothesis need further testing and refinement. It could be that both hypotheses are correct. For our purposes, the important take-home message is that all hypotheses must be tested rigorously.

In many cases in biological science, testing hypotheses rigorously involves experimentation. Experimenting on giraffes is difficult. But in the case study considered next, biologists were able to test an interesting hypothesis experimentally.

How Do Ants Navigate? An Introduction to Experimental Design

Let's consider a question that is easier to test than the one about factors that determine giraffe neck length: When ants leave their nest to search for food, how do they find their way back?

The Saharan desert ant lives in colonies and makes a living by scavenging the dead carcasses of insects. Individuals leave the burrow and wander about searching for food at midday, when temperatures at the surface can reach 60°C (140°F) and predators are hiding from the heat. Foraging trips can take the ants hundreds of meters—an impressive distance when you consider that the ants are only about a centimeter long. But when an ant returns, it doesn't follow the same wandering route it took away from the nest. Instead, its return path is a straight line (**Figure 1.9**).

Once individuals are close to the nest, they engage in a characteristic set of back-and-forth U-turns until they find their nest hole. How do they do know how far they are from the nest?

The Pedometer Hypothesis   Early work on navigation in desert ants showed that they use the Sun's position as a compass—meaning that they always know the approximate direction of the nest relative to the Sun. But how do they know how far to go?

Experiments had shown that the ants do not use landmarks to navigate, so Matthias Wittlinger and co-workers set out to test a novel idea. The biologists proposed that these ants know how far they are from the nest by using information from leg movements.

According to this pedometer hypothesis, the ants always know how far they are from the nest because they track the number of steps they have taken and their stride length. The idea is that they can make a beeline back toward the burrow because they integrate information on the angles they have traveled *and* the distance they have gone—based on step number and stride length.

If the pedometer hypothesis is wrong, however, then stride length and step number should have no effect on the ability of an ant to get back to its nest. This latter possibility is called a **null hypothesis.** A null hypothesis specifies what should be observed when the hypothesis being tested isn't correct.

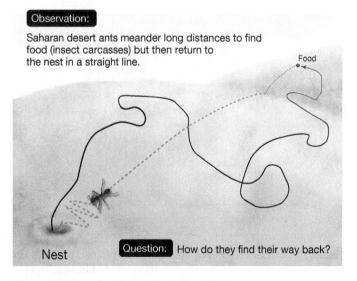

Observation:

Saharan desert ants meander long distances to find food (insect carcasses) but then return to the nest in a straight line.

Food

Question: How do they find their way back?

Nest

Figure 1.9 Foraging Desert Ants Can Navigate.

Testing the Hypothesis To test their idea, Wittlinger's group allowed ants to walk from a nest to a feeder through a channel—a distance of 10 m. Then they caught ants at the feeder and created three test groups, each with 25 individuals (Figures 1.10 and 1.11):

- **Stumps** By cutting the lower legs of some individuals off, the biologists created ants with shorter-than-normal legs.

- **Normal** Some individuals were left alone, meaning that they had normal leg length.

- **Stilts** By gluing pig bristles onto each leg, the biologists created ants with longer-than-normal legs.

Next they put the ants in a different channel and recorded how far they traveled in a direct line before starting their nest-searching behavior. To see the data they collected, look at the graph on the left side of the "Results" section in Figure 1.10.

- **Stumps** The ants with stumps stopped short, by about 5 m, before starting to search for the nest opening.

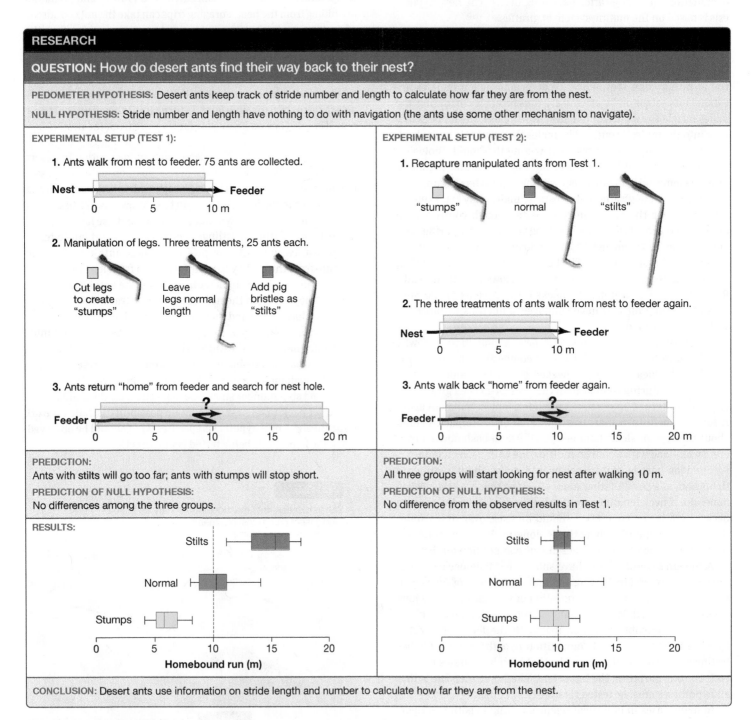

RESEARCH

QUESTION: How do desert ants find their way back to their nest?

PEDOMETER HYPOTHESIS: Desert ants keep track of stride number and length to calculate how far they are from the nest.

NULL HYPOTHESIS: Stride number and length have nothing to do with navigation (the ants use some other mechanism to navigate).

EXPERIMENTAL SETUP (TEST 1):

1. Ants walk from nest to feeder. 75 ants are collected.

Nest ——————————→ Feeder
0   5   10 m

2. Manipulation of legs. Three treatments, 25 ants each.

Cut legs to create "stumps"   Leave legs normal length   Add pig bristles as "stilts"

3. Ants return "home" from feeder and search for nest hole.

Feeder
0   5   10   15   20 m

EXPERIMENTAL SETUP (TEST 2):

1. Recapture manipulated ants from Test 1.

"stumps"   normal   "stilts"

2. The three treatments of ants walk from nest to feeder again.

Nest ——————————→ Feeder
0   5   10 m

3. Ants walk back "home" from feeder again.

Feeder
0   5   10   15   20 m

PREDICTION:
Ants with stilts will go too far; ants with stumps will stop short.

PREDICTION OF NULL HYPOTHESIS:
No differences among the three groups.

PREDICTION:
All three groups will start looking for nest after walking 10 m.

PREDICTION OF NULL HYPOTHESIS:
No difference from the observed results in Test 1.

RESULTS:

Stilts
Normal
Stumps
0   5   10   15   20
Homebound run (m)

Stilts
Normal
Stumps
0   5   10   15   20
Homebound run (m)

CONCLUSION: Desert ants use information on stride length and number to calculate how far they are from the nest.

Figure 1.10 An Experimental Test: Do Desert Ants Use a "Pedometer"?

SOURCE: Wittlinger, M., R. Wehner, and H. Wolf. 2006. The ant odometer: Stepping on stilts and stumps. *Science* 312: 1965–1967.

✔ **PROCESS OF SCIENCE** What is the advantage of using 25 ants in each group instead of just one?

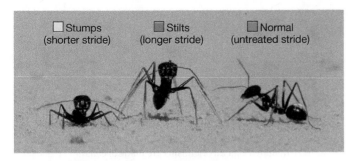

Figure 1.11 Manipulating Desert Ant Legs Changes Stride Length.

- *Normal* The normal ants walked the correct distance—about 10 m.

- *Stilts* The ants with stilts walked about 5 m too far before starting to search for the nest opening.

To check the validity of this result, the researchers put the test ants back in the nest and recaptured them one to several days later, when they had walked to the feeder on their stumps, normal legs, or stilts. Now when the ants were put into the other channel to "walk back," they all traveled the correct distance—10 m—before starting to search for the nest (see the graph on the right side of the "Results" section in Figure 1.10).

The graphs in the "Results" display "box-and-whisker" plots that allow you to easily see where most of the data fall. Each box indicates the range of distances where 50 percent of the ants stopped to search for the nest. The whiskers indicate the lower extreme (stopping short of the nest location) and the upper extreme (going too far) of where the ants stopped to search. The vertical line inside each box indicates the median—meaning that half the ants stopped above this distance and half below. (For more details on how biologists report medians and indicate the variability and uncertainty in data, see BioSkills 3.)

Interpreting the Results The pedometer hypothesis predicts that an ant's ability to walk home depends on the number and length of steps taken on its outbound trip. Recall that a prediction specifies what we should observe if a hypothesis is correct. Good scientific hypotheses make testable predictions—predictions that can be supported or rejected by collecting and analyzing data. In this case, the researchers tested the prediction by altering stride length and recording the distance traveled on the return trip. Under the null hypothesis in this experiment, all the ants—altered and unaltered—should have walked 10 m in the first test before they started looking for their nest.

Important Characteristics of Good Experimental Design This study illustrates several important points related to designing effective experiments:

- It is critical to include a **control.** A control checks for factors, other than the one being tested, that might influence the experiment's outcome. In this case, there were two controls. Including a normal, unmanipulated individual controlled for the possibility that switching the individuals to a new channel altered their behavior. In addition, the researchers had to

control for the possibility that the manipulation itself—and not the change in leg length—affected the behavior of the stilts and stumps ants. This is why they did the second test, where the outbound and return runs were done with the same legs.

- The experimental conditions must be as constant or equivalent as possible. The investigators used ants of the same species, from the same nest, at the same time of day, under the same humidity and temperature conditions, at the same feeders, in the same channels. Controlling all the variables except one—leg length in this case—is crucial because it eliminates alternative explanations for the results.

- Repeating the test is essential. It is almost universally true that larger sample sizes in experiments are better. By testing many individuals, researchers can reduce the amount of distortion or "noise" in the data caused by unusual individuals or circumstances.

From the outcomes of these experiments, the researchers concluded that desert ants use stride length and number to measure how far they are from the nest. They interpreted their results as strong support for the pedometer hypothesis.

The giraffe and ant studies demonstrate a vital point: Biologists practice evidence-based decision making. They ask questions about how organisms work, pose hypotheses to answer those questions, and use experimental or observational evidence to decide which hypotheses are correct.

The data on giraffes and ants offer a taste of things to come. In this text you will encounter hypotheses and research on questions ranging from how water gets to the top of 100-meter-tall sequoia trees to how the bacterium that causes tuberculosis has become resistant to antibiotics. As you work through this book, you'll get lots of practice thinking about hypotheses and predictions, analyzing the nature of control treatments, and interpreting graphs.

A commitment to tough-minded hypothesis testing and sound experimental design is a hallmark of biological science. Understanding their value is an important first step in becoming a biologist.

CHECK YOUR UNDERSTANDING

If you understand that …

- Hypotheses are proposed explanations that make testable predictions.
- Predictions describe observable outcomes of particular conditions.
- Well-designed experiments alter just one condition—a condition relevant to the hypothesis being tested.

✔ **You should be able to …**

PROCESS OF SCIENCE Design an experiment to test the hypothesis that desert ants feed during the hottest part of the day because it allows them to avoid being eaten by lizards. Then answer the following question about your experimental design: How are experimental conditions controlled or standardized in a way that precludes alternative explanations of the data?

Answers are available in Appendix A.

1.1 What Does It Mean to Say That Something Is Alive?

- There is no single, well-accepted definition of life. Instead, biologists point to five characteristics that organisms share.
- Three of the greatest unifying ideas in biology are the cell theory, the theory of evolution, and the chromosome theory of inheritance.

1.2 Life Is Cellular

- The cell theory identified the fundamental structural unit common to all life.

1.3 Life Evolves

- The theory of evolution states that all organisms are related by common ancestry.
- Natural selection is a well-tested explanation for why species change through time and why they are so well adapted to their habitats.

1.4 Life Processes Information

- The chromosome theory of inheritance states that genes are located on chromosomes.
- A chromosome consists of a molecule of DNA—the hereditary material. Genes, located on chromosomes, consist of specific segments of DNA that code for products in the cell.
- The flow of information from DNA to RNA to protein is called the central dogma.
- Organisms are highly diverse in how they acquire and use energy.

1.5 The Tree of Life

- The theory of evolution predicts that all organisms are part of a genealogy of species, and that all species trace their ancestry back to a single common ancestor.
- To construct this phylogeny, biologists have analyzed the sequences in an array of genetic material found in all cells.
- A tree of life, based on similarities and differences in these molecules, has three fundamental lineages, or domains: the Bacteria, the Archaea, and the Eukarya.

1.6 Doing Biology

- Biology is a hypothesis-driven, experimental science.

Answers are available in Appendix A

✓ TEST YOUR KNOWLEDGE

1. Anton van Leeuwenhoek made an important contribution to the development of the cell theory. How?
   a. He articulated that all organisms are made of cells.
   b. He articulated that all cells come from preexisting cells.
   c. He invented the first microscope and saw the first cell.
   d. He invented more powerful microscopes and was the first to describe the diversity of cells.

2. **PROCESS OF SCIENCE** What does it mean to say that experimental conditions are controlled?
   a. The test groups consist of the same individuals.
   b. The null hypothesis is correct.
   c. There is no difference in outcome between the control and experimental treatment.
   d. All physical conditions except for one are identical for all groups tested.

3. What does it mean to say that a characteristic is heritable?
   a. The characteristic evolves.
   b. The characteristic can be passed on to offspring.
   c. The characteristic is advantageous to the organism.
   d. The characteristic does not vary in the population.

4. Could *both* the food competition hypothesis and the sexual competition hypothesis explain why giraffes have long necks? Why or why not?

✓ TEST YOUR UNDERSTANDING

5. What would researchers have to demonstrate to convince you that they had discovered life on another planet?

6. What did Linnaeus' system of naming organisms ensure?
   a. Two different organisms never end up with the same genus and species name.
   b. Two different organisms have the same genus and species name if they are closely related.
   c. The genus name is different for closely related species.
   d. The species name is the same for each organism in a genus.

7. What is "selected" during natural selection? Explain your answer.

8. **PROCESS OF SCIENCE** Explain why researchers formulate a null hypothesis in addition to a hypothesis when designing an experimental study.

✓ TEST YOUR PROBLEM-SOLVING SKILLS

9. **CAUTION** A friend tells you that the theory of evolution is just an educated guess by biologists about how things work. Evaluate this statement.

10. Some humans have genes that make them resistant to infection by HIV. Would human populations likely evolve differently in areas of the world where HIV infection rates are high? Explain your logic.

✔ PUT IT ALL TOGETHER: Case Study

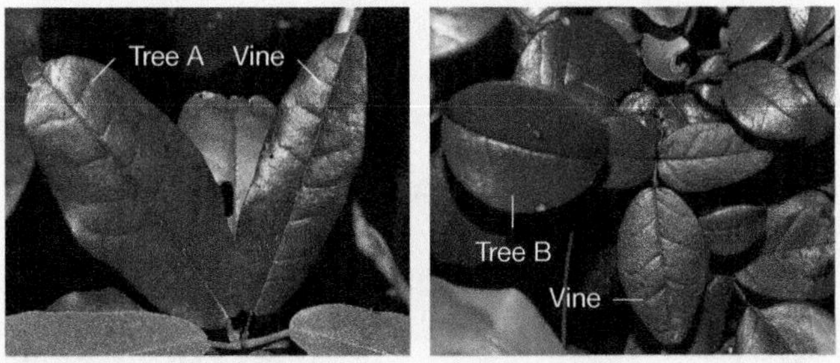

Can a plant act like a chameleon?

You may be familiar with chameleons turning different colors to blend in with their environment. Now biologists have observed that *Boquila trifoliolata*, a climbing vine found in the rain forest of southern Chile, can mimic the leaves of a dozen host species. When the vine climbs up a leafy tree, it adjusts the size, shape, and color of its own leaves to match that tree's leaves. But when a vine climbs up a bare tree trunk, it looks exactly the same as one that creeps along the rain forest floor.

11. Outline the flow of information from the genetic material to the physical appearance of the vine pictured earlier.

12. What does the species name of *Boquila trifoliolata* mean? Why is this name appropriate? (Hint: See BioSkills 15.)

13. **QUANTITATIVE** Researchers hypothesized that leaf mimicry by *B. trifoliolata* provides protection from plant-eating animals (herbivores). The results of a study of 45 individual vines are shown in the following graph. Light conditions were very similar in all cases. Researchers compared the level of leaf damage by plant eaters (herbivory index) in vines climbing leafy host trees, vines creeping on the ground with no support, and vines climbing on bare tree trunks. Use the *P* values provided to determine if the differences are significant or not (*** means $P < 0.001$, see BioSkills 3). What conclusion, if any, can be drawn about leaf mimicry from this study? What might the researchers do next to further explore the role of leaf mimicry?

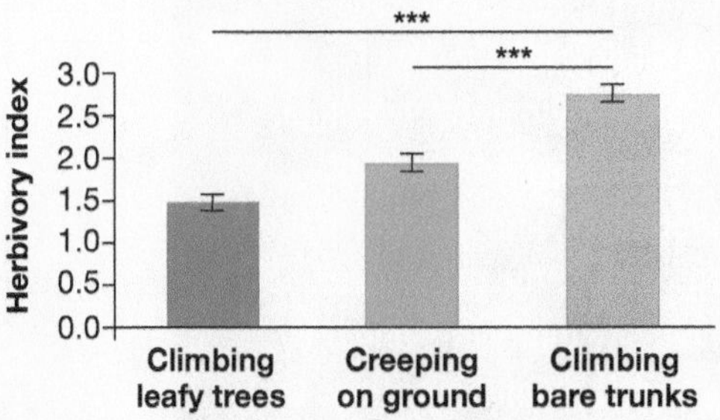

Source: Gianoli, E., and F. Carrasco-Urra. 2014. *Current Biology* 24: 984–987.

14. **PROCESS OF SCIENCE** If the researchers had compared vines growing under variable light conditions, how might this have changed their interpretation of the data?

15. **PROCESS OF SCIENCE** What was the purpose of including bare tree trunks in the study?

16. By avoiding being eaten, *B. trifoliolata* individuals would have increased fitness. In biology, what does the term "fitness" mean?

MasteringBiology®

Students Go to MasteringBiology for assignments, the eText, and the Study Area with animations, practice tests, and activities.

Professors Go to MasteringBiology for automatically graded tutorials and questions that you can assign to your students, plus Instructor Resources.

THE BIG PICTURE

BIG PICTURE

Big Picture activities are available at MasteringBiology **MB**

Biologists study the characteristics of life. The cell theory, the theory of evolution by natural selection, the chromosome theory of inheritance, and the tree of life are some of the great ideas in biology that came about by biologists asking questions that can be answered by observing or measuring things—that is, by collecting data.

Notice that the study of life is not a series of linear steps with a beginning and an end. Instead, the process of doing biology is dynamic and ongoing. The answer to one question may lay the foundation for 20 more questions. Working together, biologists from different disciplines integrate data across many levels, from atoms to the biosphere.

Note that the gray numbers in boxes tell you where to go in the book for more information. Also, be sure to do the blue exercises in the Check Your Understanding box below.

focuses on

Characteristics of living things
- Cells
- Replication
- Evolution
- Information
- Energy

1.1

Text section where you can find more information

Scientists regularly integrate across many of these levels

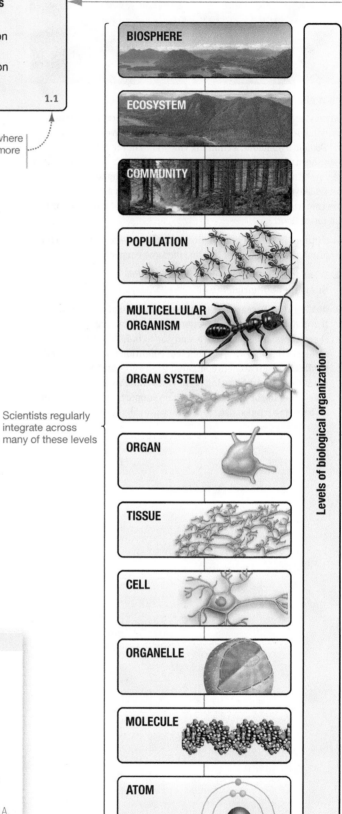

Levels of biological organization

BIOSPHERE

ECOSYSTEM

COMMUNITY

POPULATION

MULTICELLULAR ORGANISM

ORGAN SYSTEM

ORGAN

TISSUE

CELL

ORGANELLE

MOLECULE

ATOM

CHECK YOUR UNDERSTANDING

If you understand the big picture ...

✔ You should be able to ...

1. **PROCESS OF SCIENCE** Describe how biologists go about testing their ideas.
2. Provide an example of how an experimental study could span more than one level of biological organization.
3. Compare and contrast a hypothesis with a theory.
4. **PROCESS OF SCIENCE** Propose the next step to take if data support the hypothesis you are testing.

Answers are available in Appendix A.

16

DOING BIOLOGY

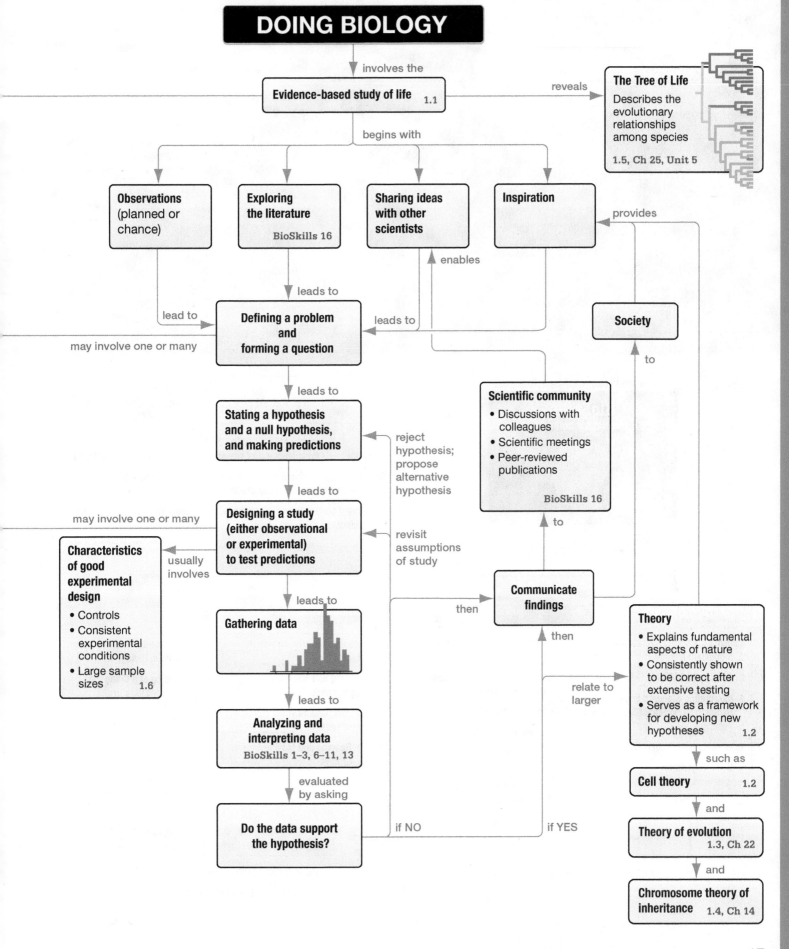

Evidence-based study of life 1.1

involves the

reveals

The Tree of Life
Describes the evolutionary relationships among species
1.5, Ch 25, Unit 5

begins with

Observations (planned or chance)

Exploring the literature
BioSkills 16

Sharing ideas with other scientists

Inspiration

provides

lead to

leads to

enables

Defining a problem and forming a question

leads to

may involve one or many

leads to

Society

to

leads to

Stating a hypothesis and a null hypothesis, and making predictions

reject hypothesis; propose alternative hypothesis

Scientific community
• Discussions with colleagues
• Scientific meetings
• Peer-reviewed publications
BioSkills 16

leads to

may involve one or many

Designing a study (either observational or experimental) to test predictions

usually involves

revisit assumptions of study

to

Characteristics of good experimental design
• Controls
• Consistent experimental conditions
• Large sample sizes 1.6

leads to

Gathering data

then

Communicate findings

then

Theory
• Explains fundamental aspects of nature
• Consistently shown to be correct after extensive testing
• Serves as a framework for developing new hypotheses 1.2

relate to larger

leads to

Analyzing and interpreting data
BioSkills 1–3, 6–11, 13

such as

Cell theory 1.2

evaluated by asking

and

Do the data support the hypothesis?

if NO

if YES

Theory of evolution 1.3, Ch 22

and

Chromosome theory of inheritance 1.4, Ch 14

17

BioSkills

In this book you will learn that

BioSkills
are essential for doing biology

starting with

then using this BioSkills section to review and practice with

Asking Questions and Designing Studies

Chapter 1: Introduces core principles and best practices

Big Picture 1: Provides a visual summary of how to think like a biologist

The narrative throughout the text models how to think like a biologist, including end-of-chapter case studies.

Experiment boxes, graphs, and other visual models in each chapter help you to visualize scientific ideas.

Quantifying Biology

1: Using the Metric System and Significant Figures

2: Reading and Making Graphs

3: Interpreting Standard Error Bars and Using Statistical Tests

4: Working with Probabilities

5: Using Logarithms

Using Common Lab Tools

6: Separating and Visualizing Molecules

7: Separating Cell Components by Centrifugation

8: Using Spectrophotometry

9: Using Microscopy

10: Using Molecular Biology Tools and Techniques

11: Using Cell Culture and Model Organisms as Tools

Visualizing Biology

12: Reading and Making Visual Models

13: Reading and Making Phylogenetic Trees

14: Reading Chemical Structures

See 2: Reading and Making Graphs

Reading Biology

15: Translating Greek and Latin Roots in Biology

16: Reading and Citing the Primary Literature

where success requires

where success requires

where success requires

Monitoring Your Own Learning

17: Recognizing and Correcting Misconceptions

18: Using Bloom's Taxonomy for Study Success

BioSkill 1 Using the Metric System and Significant Figures

Scientists ask questions that can be answered by observing or measuring things—by collecting data. What units are used to make measurements? When measurements are reported, how can you tell how reliable the data are?

Metric System Units and Conversions

The metric system is the system of units of measure used in every country of the world but three (Liberia, Myanmar, and the United States). It is also the basis of the SI system—the International System of Units (abbreviated from the French, *Système international d'unités*)—used in scientific publications.

The popularity of the metric system is based on its consistency and ease of use. These attributes arise from the system's use of the base 10. For example, each unit of length in the system is related to all other measures of length in the system by a multiple of 10. There are 10 millimeters in a centimeter, 100 centimeters in a meter, and 1000 meters in a kilometer.

Measures of length in the English system, in contrast, do not relate to each other in a regular way. Inches are routinely divided into 16ths; there are 12 inches in a foot, 3 feet in a yard, and 5280 feet (or 1760 yards) in a mile.

If you have grown up in the United States and are accustomed to using the English system, it is extremely important that you begin developing a working familiarity with metric units and values. Tables B1.1 and B1.2 should help you get started with this process.

As an example, consider the following question: An American football field is 120 yards long, while rugby fields are 144 meters long. In meters, how much longer is a rugby field than an American football field? To solve this problem, first convert yards to meters:

$$120 \text{ yards} \times \text{m}/1.09 \text{ yards} = 110 \text{ m}$$

Note that the unit "yards" cancels out. The difference in meters is thus $144 - 110 = 34$ m. If you did the unit conversion calculation on a calculator, you might have come up with 110.09 m. Why was the number of meters rounded off? The answer lies in significant figures. Let's take a closer look.

Table B1.1 Metric System Units and Conversions

Measurement	Unit of Measurement and Abbreviation	Metric System Equivalent	Converting Metric Units to English Units
Length	kilometer (km)	1 km = 1000 m = 10^3 m	1 km = 0.62 mile
	meter (m)	1 m = 100 cm	1 m = 1.09 yards = 3.28 feet = 39.37 inches
	centimeter (cm)	1 cm = 0.01 m = 10^{-2} m	1 cm = 0.3937 inch
	millimeter (mm)	1 mm = 0.001 m = 10^{-3} m	1 mm = 0.039 inch
	micrometer (µm)	1 µm = 10^{-6} m = 10^{-3} mm	
	nanometer (nm)	1 nm = 10^{-9} m = 10^{-3} µm	
Area	hectare (ha)	1 ha = 10,000 m^2	1 ha = 2.47 acres
	square meter (m^2)	1 m^2 = 10,000 cm^2	1 m^2 = 1.196 square yards
	square centimeter (cm^2)	1 cm^2 = 100 mm^2 = 10^{-4} m^2	1 cm^2 = 0.155 square inch
Volume	liter (L)	1 L = 1000 mL	1 L = 1.06 quarts
	milliliter (mL)	1 mL = 1000 µL = 10^{-3} L	1 mL = 0.034 fluid ounce
	microliter (µL)	1 µL = 10^{-6} L	
Mass	kilogram (kg)	1 kg = 1000 g	1 kg = 2.20 pounds
	gram (g)	1 g = 1000 mg	1 g = 0.035 ounce
	milligram (mg)	1 mg = 1000 µg = 10^{-3} g	
	microgram (µg)	1 µg = 10^{-6} g	
Temperature	Kelvin (K)*		$K = {}^\circ C + 273.15$
	degrees Celsius (°C)		$^\circ C = \dfrac{5}{9}(^\circ F - 32)$
	degrees Fahrenheit (°F)		$^\circ F = \dfrac{9}{5}(^\circ C + 32)$

*Absolute zero is −273.15°C = 0 K.

Table B1.2 Prefixes Used in the Metric System

Prefix	Abbreviation	10^n	Decimal	English expression
pico–	p	10^{-12}	0.000000000001	one trillionth
nano–	n	10^{-9}	0.000000001	one billionth
micro–	μ	10^{-6}	0.000001	one millionth
milli–	m	10^{-3}	0.001	one thousandth
centi–	c	10^{-2}	0.01	one hundredth
deci–	d	10^{-1}	0.1	one tenth
–	–	10^0	1	one
deca–	da	10^1	10	ten
hecto–	h	10^2	100	one hundred
kilo–	k	10^3	1000	one thousand
mega–	M	10^6	1,000,000	one million
giga–	G	10^9	1,000,000,000	one billion
tera–	T	10^{12}	1,000,000,000,000	one trillion

Significant Figures

Significant figures, or "sig figs," are critical when reporting scientific data. The number of significant figures in a measurement, such as 3.524, is the number of digits that are known with some degree of confidence (3, 5, and 2) plus the last digit (4), which is an estimate or approximation. How do scientists know how many digits to include when reporting a measurement?

Rules for Working with Significant Figures   The rules for counting significant figures in a reported measurement are:

- All nonzero numerals are always significant.
- Leading zeros are never significant; these zeros do nothing but set the decimal point.
- Embedded zeros are always significant.
- Trailing zeros are significant *only* if the decimal point is specified (Hint: Change the number to scientific notation. It is easier to see the "trailing" zeros.)

Table B1.3 shows examples of how to apply these rules. The bottom line? Significant figures indicate the accuracy of measurements.

Using Scientific Notation   Scientific notation is the way that biologists deal with very large or very small numbers. For example, instead of writing 0.00027, you could write this value as the product of two numbers: 2.7 (the digit term) and 10^{-4} (the exponential term), or 2.7×10^{-4}. The digit term shows the number of significant figures, and the exponential term places the decimal point. A negative exponent of 10 shows that to write the number in long form, you should shift the decimal point that number of places to the left. A positive exponent shows that the decimal point should be shifted that number of places to the right.

Precision versus Accuracy   If biologists count the number of bird eggs in a nest, they report the data as an exact number—say, 3 eggs. But if the same biologists are measuring the diameter of the eggs, the numbers will be inexact. Just how inexact they are depends on the equipment used to make the measurements.

If you measure the width of your textbook with a ruler several times, you'll get essentially the same measurement again and again with some variation. See Figure B1.1 for a graphical representation of this. Precision refers to how closely individual measurements agree with each other. You may have determined

Table B1.3 Rules for Working with Significant Figures

Example	Number of Significant Figures	Scientific Notation	Rule
35,214	5	3.5214×10^4	All nonzero numbers are always significant.
0.00352	3	3.52×10^{-3}	Leading zeros are not significant.
1.035	4	$1.035 (\times 10^0)$	Imbedded zeros are always significant.
200	1	2×10^2	Trailing zeros are significant only if the decimal point is specified.
200.0	4	2.000×10^2	Trailing zeros are significant only if the decimal point is specified.

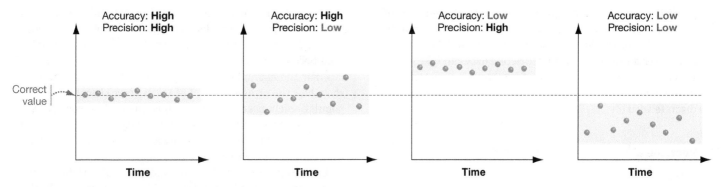

Figure B1.1 Accuracy Versus Precision in Measurement. The dashed line shows the correct value (in the example given, the actual width of your textbook), and the red dots indicate measurements made over time.

the book's width with precision, but how do you know if your ruler is accurate?

Accuracy refers to how closely a measured value agrees with the correct value. You don't know the accuracy of a measuring device unless you calibrate it. For instance, you could calibrate your ruler by comparing it against a ruler that is known to be accurate. As the sensitivity of equipment used to make a measurement increases, the number of significant figures increases. For example, if you used a kitchen scale to weigh some sodium chloride, you might obtain a weight of 3 ± 1 g (an accuracy of 1 significant figure); but an analytical balance in the lab might give a value of 3.524 ± 0.001 g (an accuracy of 4 significant figures).

It is important to follow the "sig fig rules" when reporting a measurement, so that data do not appear to be more accurate than the equipment allows.

Combining Measurements How do you deal with combining measurements with different degrees of accuracy and precision? A simple rule to follow when combining measurements is that the accuracy of the final answer can be no greater than the least accurate measurement. When you multiply or divide measurements, the answer can have no more significant figures than the least accurate measurement. When you add or subtract measurements, the answer can have no more decimal places than the least accurate measurement.

As an example, consider adding the following measurements: 5.9522, 2.065, and 1.06. If you add these numbers with your calculator, the answer your calculator will give you is 9.0772. However, this is incorrect—you must round your answer off to 9.08, which has two decimal places, the least number of decimal places in your data.

It is important to practice working with metric units and to nail down the concept of significant figures. The Check Your Understanding questions in this BioSkill should help you get started with this process.

BioSkill 2 Reading and Making Graphs

Graphs are the most common way to report data, for a simple reason. Compared to reading raw numerical values in a table or list, a graph makes it much easier to understand what the data mean.

Learning how to read and interpret graphs is one of the most basic skills you'll need to acquire as a biology student. As when learning piano or soccer or anything else, you need to understand a few key ideas to get started and then have a chance to practice—a lot—with some guidance and feedback. At the same time, you'll also be developing the skills you need to make your own graphs.

Getting Started

To start reading a graph, you need to do three things: read the axes, figure out what the data points represent—that is, where they came from—and think about the overall message of the data. Let's consider each step in turn.

What Do the Axes Represent? Most graphs have two axes: one horizontal and one vertical. The horizontal axis of a graph is also called the x-axis or the abscissa. The vertical axis of a graph is also called the y-axis or the ordinate. Each axis represents a variable that takes on a range of values. These values are indicated by the tick marks and labels on the axis. Note that each axis should *always* be clearly labeled with the unit or treatment it represents.

CHECK YOUR UNDERSTANDING

If you understand BioSkill 1

✔ You should be able to ...

1. **QUANTITATIVE** Calculate how many miles a runner completes in a 5.0-kilometer run.
2. **QUANTITATIVE** Calculate your normal body temperature in degrees Celsius. (Normal body temperature is 98.6 °F.)
3. **QUANTITATIVE** Calculate your current weight in kilograms.
4. **QUANTITATIVE** Calculate how many liters of milk you would need to buy to get approximately the same volume as a gallon of milk.
5. **QUANTITATIVE** Multiply the measurements 2.8723 and 1.6. How many significant figures does your answer have? Why?

Answers are available in Appendix A.

Figure B2.1 shows the steps in reading a *scatterplot*—a type of graph where continuous data are graphed on each axis and individual data points are plotted. Continuous data can take an array of values over a range. In contrast, discrete data can take only a restricted set of values. In a graph of the average height of men and women in your class, height is a continuous variable, but sex is a discrete variable.

(a) Read the axes—what is being plotted?

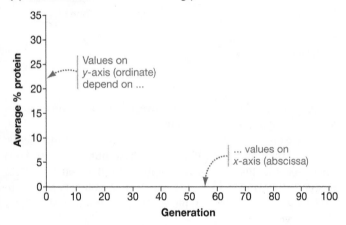

(b) Look at the data points (or bars)—what do they represent?

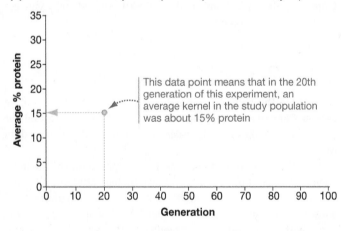

(c) What's the punch line?

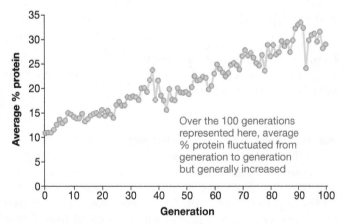

Figure B2.1 Scatterplots Are Used to Graph Continuous Data.

To create a graph, researchers plot the independent variable on the *x*-axis and the dependent variable on the *y*-axis (Figure B2.1a). The terms "independent" and "dependent" are used because the values on the *y*-axis *depend* on the *x*-axis values. For the example in this figure, the researchers wanted to show how the protein content of maize (corn) kernels in a study population changed over time. Thus, the protein concentration plotted on the *y*-axis depended on the generation plotted on the *x*-axis. The value on the *y*-axis always depends on the value on the *x*-axis, but not vice versa.

In many graphs in biology, the independent variable is either time or the various treatments used in an experiment. In these cases, the *y*-axis records how some quantity changes as a function of time or as the outcome of the treatments applied to the experimental cells or organisms.

What Do the Data Points Represent? Once you've read the axes, you need to figure out what each data point is. In our maize kernel example, the data point in Figure B2.1b represents the average percentage of protein found in a sample of kernels from a study population in a particular generation.

If it's difficult to figure out what the data points are, ask yourself where they came from—meaning how the researchers got them. You can do this by understanding how the study was done and by understanding what is being plotted on each axis. The *y*-axis will tell you what the researchers measured; the *x*-axis will usually tell you when they measured it or what group they measured. In some cases—for example, in a plot of average body size versus average brain size in primates—the *x*-axis will report a second variable that was measured.

In other cases, a data point on a graph may represent a relative or arbitrary unit of measurement, such as the amount of gene expression relative to a control, with the control set at an arbitrary value of 1.0 (for an example, see Figure 19.5). The data point shows the ratio of the amount of a substance, intensity, or other quantity, relative to a predetermined reference measurement. For example, the *y*-axis might show the percentage of relative activity of an enzyme—the rate of the enzyme-catalyzed reaction, scaled to the highest rate of activity observed (100 percent)—in experiments conducted under conditions that are identical except for one variable, such as pH or temperature (see Figure 8.15).

What Is the Overall Trend or Message? Look at the data as a whole, and figure out what they mean. Figure B2.1c suggests an interpretation of the maize kernel example. If the graph shows how some quantity changes over time, ask yourself if that quantity is increasing, decreasing, fluctuating up and down, or staying the same. Then ask whether the pattern is the same over time or whether it changes over time.

When you're interpreting a graph, it's extremely important to limit your conclusions to the data presented. Don't extrapolate beyond the data, unless you are explicitly making a prediction based on the assumption that present trends will continue. For example, you can't say that the average percentage of protein content was increasing in the population before the experiment started, or that it will continue to increase in the future. You can say only what the data tell you.

Types of Graphs

Many of the graphs in this text are scatterplots like the one shown in Figure B2.1c. But you will also come across other types of graphs in this text. When creating your own graphs, you'll want to think carefully about which type of graph is the most appropriate to use for a particular data set.

Scatterplots, Lines, and Curves Some scatterplots, like the one in Figure B2.1c, have data points that are connected by dot-to-dot lines to help make the overall trend clearer. In other scatterplots, the data points are unconnected or have a smooth line drawn through them.

A *smooth line* through data points—sometimes straight, sometimes curved—is a "line of best fit." It represents a mathematical function that summarizes the relationship between the x and y variables. It is "best" in the sense of fitting the data points most accurately. The line may intersect with some of the points, none of the points, or all of the points.

Curved lines often take on characteristic shapes depending on the relationships between the x and y variable. For example, bell-shaped curves typically fit data from studies on enzyme kinetics (see Chapter 8), while sigmoid, or S-shaped, curves fit data from many studies on oxygen–hemoglobin dissociation (see Chapter 42) and population growth (see Chapter 51).

Bar Charts, Histograms, and Box-and-Whisker Plots Scatterplots, or line-of-best-fit graphs, are the most appropriate type of graph when the data have a continuous range of values and you want to show individual data points. But other types of graphs are used to represent different types of data distributions:

- *Bar charts* plot data that have discrete or categorical values instead of a continuous range of values. In many cases the bars might represent different treatment groups in an experiment, as in Figure B2.2a. In this graph, the height of the bar indicates the mean value. To interpret the graph, ask yourself how different the values are. If the bar chart reports means over discrete ranges of values, ask what trend is implied—as you would for a scatterplot.

- *Histograms* illustrate frequency data and can be plotted as numbers or percentages. Figure B2.2b shows an example where height (in inches) is plotted on the x-axis, and the number of students in a population in the United States is plotted on the y-axis. Each bar indicates the number of individuals in each interval of height, which reflects the relative frequency, in this population, of people whose heights are in that interval. The measurements could also be recalculated so that the y-axis reported the percentage of the population in each interval. Then the total percentage for all the bars would equal 100 percent. Note that if you were to draw a smooth curve connecting the tops of the bars in this histogram, the curve would be roughly bell shaped. To interpret a histogram, ask whether there is a "hump" in the data—indicating a group of values on the x-axis that are more frequent than others. If so, what does it mean? Is the hump in the center of the distribution of values, toward the left, or toward the right?

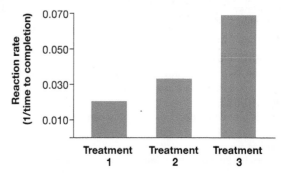

(a) Bar chart

(b) Histogram

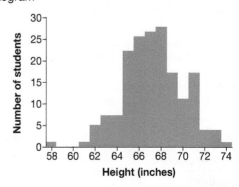

Figure B2.2 Bar Charts and Histograms. (a) Bar charts are used to graph data that are discontinuous or categorical. **(b)** Histograms show the distribution of frequencies or values in a population.

- *Box-and-whisker plots* allow you to easily see where most of the data fall (see Figure 1.10 for an example). Each box indicates where half of the data numbers are. The whiskers indicate the lower extreme and the upper extreme of the data. The vertical line inside each box indicates the median—meaning that half of the data are greater than this value and half are less. To interpret a box-and-whisker plot, ask yourself what information the graph gives you. What is the range of values for the data? Where are half the data points? Below what value is three quarters of the data?

In all types of graphs, statistical tests can be used to determine whether a difference between treatment groups, or a difference in the relationship between two continuous ranges of values, is significant. If differences are statistically significant, it means that they are not likely to have occurred by chance, but rather are likely to be attributable to a specific variable (see BioSkill 3).

Getting Practice

Working with this text will give you lots of practice with reading and interpreting graphs—they appear in almost every chapter. In many graphs, arrows and labels have been added to suggest an interpretation or draw your attention to an important point on the graph. In other graphs, you should be able to figure out what the data mean on your own or with the help of other students or your instructor.

BioSkill 3 Interpreting Standard Error Bars and Using Statistical Tests

When biologists do an experiment, they collect data on individuals or samples in a treatment group and a control group, or several such comparison groups. Then they typically test whether the mean (average) values of the dependent variable are different in two (or more) of the groups.

Standard Error Bars

For example, in one experiment student researchers measured how fast a product formed when they set up a reaction with three concentrations of reactants (see Figure 8.4). Each treatment—meaning each combination of reactant concentrations—was replicated many times.

Figure B3.1 graphs the mean reaction rate for each of the three treatments in the students' experiment. Note that Treatments 1, 2, and 3 represent increasing concentrations of reactants. The thin "I-beams" at the top of each bar indicate the standard error of each mean. The standard error of the mean is a quantity that indicates the uncertainty in a calculated mean. In effect, it quantifies how confident you are that the mean you've calculated is the mean you'd observe if you did the experiment under the

same conditions an extremely large number of times. It is a measure of precision (see BioSkill 1).

Note that sometimes the error bars represent the confidence interval of the mean. A *confidence interval* gives an estimated range of values that is likely to include the population parameter being studied, such as the survival rate of animals after exposure to a pathogen. The estimated range is calculated from a given set of sample data. A 95 percent confidence level means that 95 percent of the confidence intervals would include the population parameter. You might also have heard the term "standard deviation." How are standard error and standard deviation related? When biologists calculate the standard deviation of a sample, they are using it as an estimate of the variability of the population that the sample was taken from. For data with a normal distribution, about 95 percent of individuals will have values within two standard deviations of the mean. The standard deviation will not tend to change as sample size increases.

In contrast, the standard error of the mean (SEM) depends on both the standard deviation (SD) and the sample size:

$$\text{SEM} = \frac{\text{SD}}{\sqrt{\text{sample size}}}$$

The standard error decreases as the sample size increases, because the extent of chance variation is reduced.

Let's consider again the experiment carried out by the student researchers (see Figure B3.1). Suppose two trials with the same concentration of reactants had a reaction rate of 0.075, and two other trials had a reaction rate of 0.025. The mean reaction rate of all four trials would be 0.050. In this case, the standard error would be large. But what if two trials had a reaction rate of 0.051 and two had a reaction rate of 0.049? The mean would still be 0.050, but the standard error would be small.

Once they had calculated these means and standard errors, the student researchers wanted to answer a question: Does reaction rate increase when reactant concentration increases? After looking at the data, you might conclude that the answer is yes. But how could you come to a conclusion like this objectively, instead of subjectively? The answer is to use a statistical test to determine, for example, whether the difference between the rate

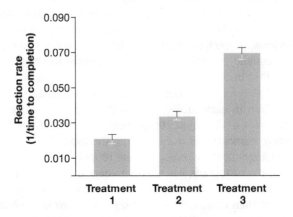

Figure B3.1 Standard Error Bars Indicate the Uncertainty in a Mean.

at the highest reactant concentration and the rate at the lowest reactant concentration is significant. If the difference is found to be statistically significant, then it is not likely to have occurred by chance—it's likely to be attributable to the change in reactant concentration. Let's take a closer look at using and interpreting statistical tests.

Using Statistical Tests

If you take a statistics course, you'll learn which statistical tests are most appropriate for analyzing different types of data. Three commonly used statistical tests are the chi-square test, t-test, and analysis of variance. Other tests examine regression and correlation:

- *Chi-square* tests are used to compare observed data with data you would expect to obtain according to a specific hypothesis. For example, if, according to Mendel's laws (see Chapter 14), you expected equal numbers of male and female offspring from a cross but you observed 9 males and 23 females, you might want to know whether the difference between the observed and expected numbers was due to chance or to other factors. How much of a difference can occur before you must conclude that something other than chance is at work? The chi-square test always tests the null hypothesis (see Chapter 1), which states that there is no significant difference between the observed and expected results.

- *T-tests* are used to determine if there is a significant difference between the mean values of two groups, such as the mean body sizes of mainland and island tortoises (see Chapter 39). In this case, the null hypothesis would be that there is no significant difference between the means of the two data sets.

- *Analysis of variance (ANOVA)* compares the means of two or more sets of data by calculating how widely individual values in each data set vary. If they vary greatly from the mean, the variance is large, and vice versa. When applied to only two data sets, ANOVA will give the same result as a t-test. ANOVA is a powerful statistical test because it allows you to test for each factor while controlling for others and to detect whether one variable affects another. As an example, if you were comparing the activity of a particular enzyme in mainland and island tortoises, you might want to determine whether sex affects enzyme activity, so you could also separate the data sets by sex.

- *Regression and correlation* analyses are done when a researcher wants to know whether there is a relationship or correlation between two variables and, if so, is it positive (positive slope) or negative (negative slope). For example, when patients are given increasing amounts of a drug, does their blood pressure increase or decrease proportionally? Correlation is a way to express the relationship between two variables, whereas linear regression is about the best fit line in a graph (see BioSkill 2).

You'll likely do statistical tests early in your undergraduate career. To use this textbook, though, you need to know only what statistical testing does and how to interpret a test statistic—a number that characterizes the size of the difference among the data sets.

Interpreting *P* Values and Statistical Significance

How do you use a statistical test to determine if differences are significant? Let's return to the experiment shown in Figure B3.1 and work through a three-step process:

1. Specify the null hypothesis, which is that reactant concentration has no effect on reaction rate.

2. Calculate a test statistic. In this experiment, the test statistic compares the actual differences in reaction rates at the three reactant concentrations to the difference predicted by the null hypothesis. The null hypothesis predicts that there should be no difference.

3. Determine the probability (see BioSkill 4) of getting by chance a test statistic at least as large as the one calculated. This probability, called the **P value,** comes from a reference distribution—a mathematical function that specifies the probability of getting various values of the test statistic if the null hypothesis is correct. The *P* value is the estimated probability of rejecting the null hypothesis when that hypothesis is correct. For example, a *P* value of 0.01 means that there is a 1 percent chance that the null hypothesis has been rejected when it is actually correct. One percent is considered a very small chance of making such an error; thus, very small *P* values indicate that researchers have high confidence in the significance of differences in their data.

By convention, most researchers consider a difference among treatment groups to be *statistically significant* if there is less than a 5 percent probability (P) of observing it by chance, or $P < 0.05$. When presenting *P* values in the scientific literature, researchers often use an asterisk rating system as well as quoting the *P* values (Table B3.1).

Table B3.1 **Asterisk Rating System for *P* Values and Statistical Significance**

P Value	Asterisk Rating	Statistical Significance Level	Meaning
$P > 0.05$	None	Not significant	Greater than a 1 in 20 chance of being wrong (i.e., incorrect rejection of the null hypothesis)
$P < 0.05$	*	Statistically significant	Less than a 1 in 20 chance of being wrong
$P < 0.01$	**	Statistically significant	Less than a 1 in 100 chance of being wrong
$P < 0.001$	***	Statistically significant	Less than a 1 in 1000 chance of being wrong

CHECK YOUR UNDERSTANDING

If you understand BioSkill 3

✔ You should be able to ...

1. **QUANTITATIVE** Determine which of the following tests used to estimate the average height of individuals in a class is likely to have the smaller standard error, and why.
   - Test 1: Measuring the height of two individuals chosen at random
   - Test 2: Measuring the height of every student who showed up for class on a particular day

2. Interpret data from a recent study in which researchers investigated the evolution of sweet taste perception in hummingbirds. Captive hummingbirds were presented with a control solution (sucrose) and a test solution (either water, the artificial sweetener aspartame, or erythritol, a substance that stimulates the sweet taste receptor). The length of time the birds spent drinking each solution was recorded. What can you conclude from the data shown in the graph below? (Hint: Consult Table B3.1 on the asterisk rating system for *P* values).

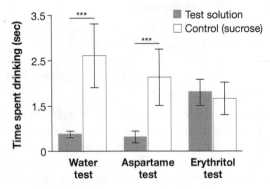

DATA: Baldwin, M. W., et al. 2014. *Science* 345: 929–933.

Answers are available in Appendix A.

You are very likely to see small differences among treatment groups just by chance. If you flipped a coin ten times, for example, you are unlikely to get exactly five heads and five tails, even if the coin is fair. A reference distribution tells you how likely you are to get, by chance, each of the possible outcomes, such as six heads and four tails.

In the case of the student researchers' experiment (see Figure B3.1), the reference distribution indicated that if the null hypothesis of no difference in reaction rates is correct, you would see differences at least as large as those observed only 0.01 percent of the time by chance ($P < 0.0001$). Because 0.0001 is less than 0.05, the students were able to conclude that the null hypothesis—that reactant concentration has no effect on reaction rate—is not correct. According to their data, the reaction they studied really does happen more rapidly when reactant concentration increases.

What does a result that is not statistically significant mean ($P > 0.05$)? You can conclude that no effect of the treatment was detected in the experiment. However, this doesn't necessarily mean there was no underlying effect. If the sample size in a study is small—particularly in a population with lots of natural

variability—researchers may not detect an effect of a particular treatment, even when an effect is actually there.

When reading graphs in this book, you should take care to inspect the standard error bars. As a *very* rough rule of thumb, means often turn out to be significantly different, according to an appropriate statistical test, if there is no overlap between two times the standard errors. When you are asked to make conclusions about the significance of data shown in a graph, however, you will be provided with *P* values to interpret.

BioSkill 4 Working with Probabilities

What is probability? Probability is the chance or likelihood that an event will occur or that a hypothesis or scientific prediction is correct. In biology, probability is used to evaluate the significance of experimental results and to predict the outcome of genetic crosses.

To answer certain questions, biologists sometimes need to combine the probabilities of different events. You'll encounter examples of this when you solve genetics problems (see Chapter 14) and analyze changes in allele frequencies using the Hardy–Weinberg principle (see Chapter 23).

Two fundamental rules apply when probabilities are combined. Each rule pertains to a distinct situation.

The Both-And Rule

The both-and rule—also known as the product rule or multiplication rule—applies when you want to know the probability of two or more independent events occurring together. Let's use the rolling of two dice as an example. What is the probability of rolling two sixes? These two events are independent, because the probability of rolling a six on one die has no effect on the probability of rolling a six on the other die.

The probability of rolling a six on the first die is ⅙. The probability of rolling a six on the second die is also ⅙. The probability of rolling a six on *both* dice, then, is ⅙ × ⅙ = 1/36. In other words, if you rolled two dice 36 times, on average you would expect to roll two sixes once.

In the case of a cross between two parents heterozygous for the *R* gene (genotype *Rr*), the probability of getting a gamete (egg or sperm) with allele *R* from one parent has no effect on the probability of getting a gamete with allele *R* from the other parent. Gametes fuse randomly. The probability of a child getting allele *R* from the father is ½, and the probability of the child getting allele *R* from the mother is ½. Thus, the probability of getting both *R* alleles and having the genotype *RR* is ½ × ½ = ¼.

The Either-Or Rule

The either-or rule—also known as the sum rule or addition rule—applies when you want to know the probability of an event happening when there are two or more alternative ways for that event to occur. In this case, the probability that the event will occur is the sum of the probabilities of each way that it can occur.

For example, suppose you wanted to know the probability of rolling either a one or a six when you toss a die. The probability of rolling each number is $\frac{1}{6}$, so the probability of rolling one or the other is $\frac{1}{6} + \frac{1}{6} = \frac{1}{3}$. If you rolled a die three times, on average you'd expect to roll a one or a six once.

In the case of a cross between two parents heterozygous for the R gene, the probability of getting an R allele from the father and an r allele from the mother is $\frac{1}{2} \times \frac{1}{2} = \frac{1}{4}$. Similarly, the probability of getting an r allele from the father and an R allele from the mother is $\frac{1}{2} \times \frac{1}{2} = \frac{1}{4}$. Thus, the combined probability of getting the Rr genotype in either of the two ways is $\frac{1}{4} + \frac{1}{4} = \frac{1}{2}$.

CHECK YOUR UNDERSTANDING

If you understand BioSkill 4

✔ You should be able to . . .

1. **QUANTITATIVE** Calculate the probability of getting four "tails" if four students each toss a coin.
2. **QUANTITATIVE** Calculate the probability of getting a two, a three, or a six after a single roll of a die.

Answers are available in Appendix A.

BioSkill 5 Using Logarithms

You will encounter logarithms at several points in this text. Logarithms are a way of working with powers—numbers that are multiplied by themselves one or more times.

Logarithms are useful when you are studying something that can have a large range of values, like the concentration of hydrogen ions in a solution or the intensity of sound that the human ear can detect. In cases like these, it's convenient to express the numbers involved as exponents. Using exponents makes a large range of numbers more manageable. For example, instead of saying that the hydrogen ion concentration in a solution can range from 10^0 to 10^{-14}, the logarithmic pH scale allows you to simply say that it ranges from 0 to 14. Instead of giving the actual value, the pH scale expresses concentration as an exponent.

Scientists use exponential notation to represent powers. For example,

$$a^x = y$$

means that if you multiply a by itself x times, you get y. In exponential notation, a is called the base and x is called the exponent. The entire expression is called an exponential function.

What if you know y and a, and you want to know x? This is where logarithms come in. You can solve for exponents by using logarithms:

$$x = \log_a y$$

This equation reads that x is equal to the logarithm of y to the base a. Logarithms are a way of working with exponential functions. They are important because so many processes in biology (and in chemistry and physics, for that matter) are exponential. To understand what's going on, you have to describe the process with an exponential function and then use logarithms to work with that function.

Although a base can be any number, most scientists use just two bases when they employ logarithmic notation: 10 and e (sometimes called Euler's number after Swiss mathematician Leonhard Euler). What is e? It is the limit of $(1 + \frac{1}{n})^n$ as n tends to infinity. Mathematicians have shown that the base e is an irrational number (like π) that is approximately equal to 2.718. Like 10, e is just a number; $10^0 = 1$ and, likewise, $e^0 = 1$. Both 10 and e have qualities that make them convenient to use in science.

Logarithms to the base 10 are so common that they are usually symbolized in the form $\log y$ instead of $\log_{10} y$. A logarithm to the base e is called a natural logarithm and is symbolized as ln (pronounced *EL-EN*) instead of log. You write "the natural logarithm of y" as $\ln y$.

Most scientific calculators have keys that allow you to solve problems involving base 10 and base e. For example, if you know y, they'll tell you what $\log y$ or $\ln y$ are—meaning that they'll solve for x in our first example equation. They'll also allow you to find a number when you know its logarithm to base 10 or base e. Stated another way, they'll tell you what y is if you know x, and y is equal to e^x or 10^x. This process is called finding an antilog. In most cases, you'll use the inverse or second function button on your calculator to find an antilog (above the log or ln key).

To get some practice with your calculator, consider this equation:

$$10^2 = 100$$

If you enter 100 in your calculator and then press the log key, the screen should say 2. The logarithm tells you what the exponent is. Now press the antilog key while 2 is on the screen. The screen should return to 100. The antilog solves the exponential function, given the base and the exponent.

If your background in algebra isn't strong, you'll want to get more practice working with logarithms because you'll see them frequently during your undergraduate career. Remember that once you understand the basic notation, there's nothing mysterious about logarithms. They are simply a way of working with exponential functions, which describe what happens when something is multiplied by itself a number of times—like cells that replicate and then replicate again and then again.

CHECK YOUR UNDERSTANDING

If you understand BioSkill 5

✔ You should be able to . . .

For questions 1 and 2, use the equation $N_t = N_0 e^{rt}$ (see Chapter 51).

1. Identify the type of function this equation describes.
2. **QUANTITATIVE** Rewrite this equation after taking the natural logarithm of both sides.

For questions 3 and 4, use the equation pH $= -\log [H^+]$ (see Chapter 2).

3. **QUANTITATIVE** Calculate the pH of a solution whose $[H^+]$ is 2.75×10^{-4}.
4. **QUANTITATIVE** Determine the $[H^+]$ of a solution whose pH is 5.43.

Answers are available in Appendix A.

BioSkill 6 Separating and Visualizing Molecules

To study a molecule, you have to be able to isolate it. Isolating a molecule is a two-step process: The molecule has to be separated from other molecules in a mixture and then physically picked out or located in a purified form. Let's explore the techniques that biologists use to separate proteins and nucleic acids and then find the particular one they are interested in.

Using Electrophoresis to Separate Molecules

In molecular biology, the standard technique for separating proteins and nucleic acids is called gel electrophoresis or, simply, electrophoresis (literally, "electricity-moving"). You may be using electrophoresis in a lab for this course, and you will be analyzing data derived from electrophoresis in this text.

The principle behind electrophoresis is simple. Nucleic acids carry a negative charge, as do proteins when they are denatured and coated with a charged (ionic) detergent. As a result, these molecules move when placed in an electric field. Negatively charged molecules move toward the positive electrode; positively charged molecules move toward the negative electrode.

An Example "Run" **Figure B6.1** shows an electrophoresis setup. To separate a mixture (sample) of macromolecules so that each one can be isolated and analyzed, researchers add the sample to a gelatinous substance ("gel") consisting of long molecules that form a matrix of fibers. The matrix has pores that act like a sieve through which the molecules in the sample can pass.

As shown in step 1, each sample is placed in a slot ("well") in a sheet or slab of the gel. In many cases, researchers also fill a well with a sample containing proteins or DNA molecules of known size, called a size standard or "ladder."

In step 2, the gel is immersed in a solution that conducts electricity. When an electric field is applied across the gel, the molecules in each well move through the gel toward the positive electrode, forming a lane. Molecules that are smaller or more highly charged for their size move faster through the sieve than do larger or less highly charged molecules. As they move, then, the molecules separate by size or by charge. Small or highly charged molecules end up near the bottom of the gel; large or less-charged molecules remain near the top.

Once molecules of different size or charge have separated from one another, the electric field is removed by turning off the power supply (step 3).

Is charge or size more important in separating molecules by electrophoresis? When it comes to nucleic acids, the answer is size. The same is true for proteins that are treated with a charged detergent before they are run on a gel. In these cases, there is a fixed amount of charge for a given length of the molecule. This means that the size of the molecule determines how fast it runs on the gel. For proteins that are run without treatment with a charged detergent, size and charge work together to determine how fast they separate on a gel.

Why Do Separated Molecules Form Bands? When researchers visualize a particular molecule on a gel, using techniques described later in this BioSkill, the image that results consists of bands: lines of varying thickness that are as wide as a lane in the gel. Why?

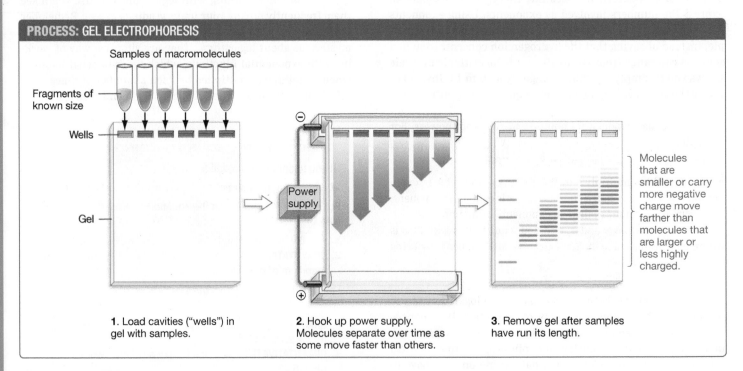

PROCESS: GEL ELECTROPHORESIS

Samples of macromolecules

Fragments of known size

Wells

Gel

Power supply

Molecules that are smaller or carry more negative charge move farther than molecules that are larger or less highly charged.

1. Load cavities ("wells") in gel with samples.

2. Hook up power supply. Molecules separate over time as some move faster than others.

3. Remove gel after samples have run its length.

Figure B6.1 Macromolecules Can Be Separated via Gel Electrophoresis.

✔ DNA and RNA move toward the positive electrode. What makes these molecules negatively charged?

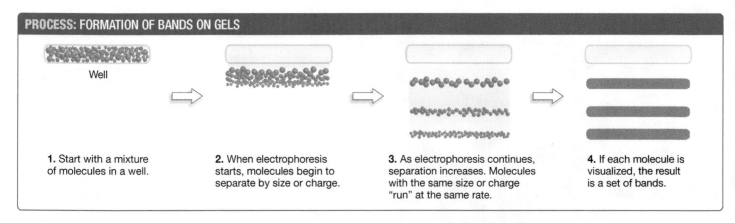

PROCESS: FORMATION OF BANDS ON GELS

Well

1. Start with a mixture of molecules in a well.

2. When electrophoresis starts, molecules begin to separate by size or charge.

3. As electrophoresis continues, separation increases. Molecules with the same size or charge "run" at the same rate.

4. If each molecule is visualized, the result is a set of bands.

Figure B6.2 On a Gel, Molecules That Are Alike Form Bands.

To understand the answer, study **Figure B6.2**. The left panel shows the original mixture of molecules. In this diagram, the size of each dot represents the size of each molecule. The key is to realize that the original sample contains many copies of each specific molecule, and that these copies run down the length of the gel together—meaning, at the same rate—because they have the same size or charge.

It's that simple: Molecules that are alike form a band because they stay together.

Using Thin Layer Chromatography to Separate Molecules

Gel electrophoresis is one of many ways to separate molecules. Another common method is called thin layer chromatography. This method was developed in the early 1900s by botanists who were analyzing the different-colored pigments from leaves of a plant (see Chapter 10). The name chromatography comes from the Greek words *khroma* for "color" and *graphein*, "to write."

In this method, rather than loading samples into wells in a gel, the samples are deposited or "spotted" near the bottom of a stiff support, either glass or plastic, that is coated with a thin layer of silica gel, cellulose, or a similar porous material. The coated support is then placed in a solvent. As the solvent moves up through the coating by capillary action, it carries the molecules in the samples with it. Molecules are carried at different rates, based on their size and solubility in the solvent.

Visualizing Molecules

Once molecules have been separated using electrophoresis or thin layer chromatography, they have to be detected. Although plant pigments are colored, nucleic acids and most proteins are invisible unless they are labeled in some way.

Using Radioactive Isotopes When molecular biology was getting under way, the first types of labels in common use were radioactive isotopes—forms of atoms that are unstable and release energy in the form of radiation. Radioactive isotopes can be incorporated into proteins or nucleic acids, and the radiation then can be used to detect the labeled macromolecules.

Once electrophoresis is complete, the labeled proteins or nucleic acids can be visualized by laying X-ray film over the gel. Because radiation exposes film, a black dot appears wherever a radioactive atom is located in the gel. So many black dots occur so close together that they form a dark band. This technique for visualizing macromolecules is called autoradiography.

Advances in technology have led to the development of another technique for visualizing labeled proteins or nucleic acids. In this technique, called phosphorimaging, the gel is placed on a specially coated plate in a laser scanner that then produces a digital image of the gel.

Using Fluorescent Tags Starting in the late 1990s and early 2000s, it became much more common to label macromolecules with fluorescent tags. Once electrophoresis is complete, fluorescence can be detected by exposing the gel to an appropriate wavelength of light; the fluorescent tag fluoresces, or glows, in response. (Fluorescence is explained in Chapter 10.)

Fluorescent tags have important advantages over radioactive isotopes: **(1)** They are safer to handle. **(2)** They are faster—you don't have to wait hours or days for the radioactive isotope to expose a film. **(3)** They come in multiple colors, so you can label several different molecules in the same experiment and detect them independently.

Using Nucleic Acid and Protein Stains DNA and RNA can be stained with a fluorescent dye such as ethidium bromide (EtBr). Ethidium bromide fits in and binds between the bases, causing nucleic acids to fluoresce orange when illuminated by ultraviolet light. Proteins can be detected by using silver stain or dyes such as Coomassie blue that bind to proteins in the gel.

An example of an EtBr-stained gel is shown in **Figure B6.3** on page 30. In this experiment, researchers wanted to determine the optimal temperature for primer annealing in a polymerase chain reaction (PCR; see **BioSkill 10**). The far-left lane contains DNA fragments of known size; this lane is used to estimate the size of the molecules in the other lanes, which are numbered: Lane 1 is a control sample containing no DNA template; lanes 2 through 8 are samples in which the primer annealing temperature was varied incrementally from 71°C to 51°C.

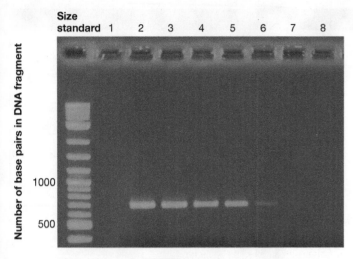

Figure B6.3 **Ethidium Bromide Staining Is a Technique for Visualizing Nucleic Acids.** The DNA molecules in this gel were stained with ethidium bromide and illuminated by ultraviolet light.

Reading a Gel One of the keys to interpreting, or "reading," a gel or an image of a gel is to realize that brighter or more intense bands contain more of the stain or label, indicating a greater amount of the stained or labeled molecule. Fainter bands contain less of the molecule.

To read a gel, then, you look for **(1)** the presence or absence of bands in some lanes—meaning some experimental samples—and **(2)** differences in the intensity of the bands—reflecting differences in the amount of DNA or protein present.

For example, several conclusions can be drawn from the data in Figure B6.3. A DNA fragment containing about 700 base pairs was amplified over a range of annealing temperatures (lanes 2–6). Lane 6 contained less of this fragment than lanes 2–5, and lanes 7 and 8 contained none at all. The fragment was not amplified in the absence of the DNA template (lane 1), indicating that it was specific for the DNA template used.

Using Nucleic Acid Probes In many cases, researchers want to find one specific molecule—a certain DNA sequence, for example—in a collection of molecules. How is this possible? The answer hinges on using a particular molecule as a probe. A probe is a labeled molecule that binds specifically to the molecule of interest. The label is often a radioactive atom, a fluorescent tag, or an enzyme that catalyzes a color-forming or light-emitting reaction.

For example, a nucleic acid probe is a single-stranded fragment of DNA or RNA that will bind to a particular single-stranded complementary sequence in a mixture of DNA or RNA molecules. By binding to the target sequence, the probe marks the fragment containing that sequence, distinguishing it from all the other nucleic acid fragments in the mixture. As **Figure B6.4** shows, a nucleic acid probe—in this case a labeled DNA probe—can be found after it has bound to the complementary sequence in the large mixture of fragments.

If you are looking for a particular DNA or RNA sequence on a gel, you will first need to transfer the nucleic acids to a nylon membrane by a technique called blotting.

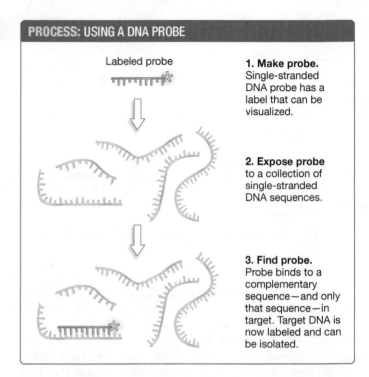

Figure B6.4 **DNA Probes Bind to and Identify Specific Target Sequences.**

✔ If you understand the concept of a DNA probe, you should be able to explain why the probe must be single stranded and labeled in order to work, and why it binds to just one specific fragment. You should also be able to indicate where a probe with the sequence AATCG will bind to a target DNA strand with the sequence TTTTACCCATTTACGATTGGCCT. (Recall that sequences are always written $5' \rightarrow 3'$.)

- *Southern blotting*, invented by Edwin Southern, is a technique for identifying DNA segments of interest in a mixed sample. This involves making DNA fragments that have been run on a gel single stranded, transferring them from the gel to a nylon membrane, and then exposing the membrane to a single-stranded probe that binds to the target sequence by complementary base pairing. Once the probe has bound, you can detect the band that contains it through autoradiography, fluorescence, or a color change.

- *Northern blotting* is a technique for detecting target RNA segments. It involves transferring RNA fragments from a gel to a nylon membrane and then probing them to detect the segment of interest. The name is a play on Southern blotting, the protocol that it was derived from.

Using Antibody Probes How can researchers find a particular protein out of a large collection of different proteins? The answer is to use an antibody. An antibody is a protein that binds specifically to a section of a different protein (see Chapter 48 for more details on antibodies).

To use an antibody as a probe, investigators attach a tag molecule—often an enzyme that catalyzes a color-forming or light-emitting reaction—to the antibody and then add the tagged antibody to the collection of proteins. The antibody will bind to its target protein and can be visualized thanks to the tag it carries.

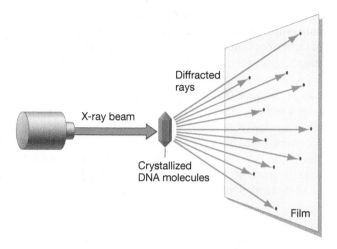
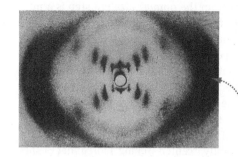

The pattern is determined by the structure of the molecules within the crystal

Figure B6.5 X-Ray Crystallography. When crystallized molecules are bombarded with X-rays, the radiation is scattered in distinctive patterns. The photograph at the right, obtained by Rosalind Franklin in 1953, shows an X-ray film that recorded the pattern of scattered radiation from DNA molecules.

If the proteins in question have been separated by gel electrophoresis and transferred to a membrane, the result is called a western blot. The name is an extension of the naming pattern for Southern and northern blots.

Using Radioimmunoassay and ELISA to Measure Amounts of Molecules Another important method that makes use of antibodies is called a radioimmunoassay. This method is used when investigators want to measure tiny amounts of a molecule, such as a hormone in the blood. In this case, a known quantity of a hormone is labeled with a radioactive isotope. This labeled hormone is then mixed with a known amount of antibody, and the two bind to one another. Next, a sample of blood, containing an unknown quantity of the same hormone, is added. The hormone from the blood and the radiolabeled hormone compete for antibody binding sites.

As the concentration of unlabeled hormone increases, more of it binds to the antibody, displacing more of the radiolabeled hormone. The amount of unbound radiolabeled hormone is then measured. Using known standards as a reference, the amount of hormone in the blood can be determined.

A commonly used technique based on similar principles is called enzyme-linked immunosorbent assay (ELISA). In ELISA, the amount of a particular molecule is measured using colorimetric signals instead of a radioactive signal.

Using X-ray Crystallography to Visualize Macromolecules To understand what the 3-D structure of individual macromolecules or macromolecular machines look like, researchers use a technique called X-ray crystallography, or X-ray diffraction analysis. The procedure is based on bombarding crystals of a molecule with X-rays. X-rays are scattered in precise ways when they interact with the atoms in a crystal, producing a diffraction pattern that can be recorded on X-ray film or other types of detectors (**Figure B6.5**).

By varying the orientation of the X-ray beam as it strikes a crystal and documenting the diffraction patterns that result, researchers can construct a map representing the density of

electrons in the crystal. Relating these electron-density maps to information about the primary structure of the nucleic acid or protein allows researchers to build a 3-D model of the molecule. Virtually all of the molecular models used in this book were built from X-ray crystallographic data.

CHECK YOUR UNDERSTANDING

If you understand BioSkill 6

✔ **You should be able to ...**

1. Consider a gel that has been stained for DNA products from a polymerase chain reaction using ethidium bromide. One lane contains no bands. Two lanes have a band in the same location, but one of the bands is very faint and the other is extremely bright. Interpret these results.

2. Explain why the effort to understand the structure of biological molecules is worthwhile even though X-ray crystallography is time-consuming and technically difficult. What's the payoff?

Answers are available in Appendix A.

BioSkill 7 Separating Cell Components by Centrifugation

Biologists use a technique called differential centrifugation to isolate specific cell components. A centrifuge accomplishes this task by spinning a cell sample in a solution that allows cell components to separate according to their density or size and shape. The individual parts of the cell can then be purified and studied in detail, in isolation from other parts of the cell.

The first step in preparing a cell sample for centrifugation is to release the cell components by breaking the cells apart. This can be done by putting them in a dilute (hypotonic) solution, by exposing them to high-frequency vibration, by treating them with a detergent, or by grinding them up. Each of these methods breaks apart plasma membranes and releases the contents of the cells.

The resulting pieces of plasma membrane quickly reseal to form small vesicles, often trapping cell components inside. The suspension that results from the homogenization step is a mixture of these vesicles, free-floating macromolecules released from the cells, and organelles. A suspension like this is called a cell extract or cell homogenate.

When a cell homogenate is placed in a centrifuge tube and spun at high speed, the suspended components move toward the bottom of the tube, along the red arrows in Figure B7.1a. The effect is similar to a merry-go-round, which seems to push you away from the spinning platform. At the same time, the solution in the tube exerts a centripetal (literally, "center-seeking") force that pushes the homogenate away from the bottom of the tube. Larger, denser components resist this inward force more readily than do smaller, less dense ones and so reach the bottom of the tube faster.

To separate the components of a cell extract, researchers often perform a series of centrifuge runs. Steps 1 and 2 of Figure B7.1b illustrate how an initial run at low speed causes larger, heavier parts of the homogenate to move below smaller, lighter parts. The material that collects at the bottom of the tube is called the pellet, and the solution and components left behind form the supernatant ("above-swimming"). The supernatant is placed in a fresh tube and centrifuged at increasingly higher speeds and longer durations. Each centrifuge run continues to separate cell components based on their size and density.

To separate macromolecules or organelles (for a list of eukaryotic cell components, see Summary Table 7.2), researchers carry out centrifugation at extremely high speeds. They also may fill the centrifuge tube with a series of sucrose solutions of decreasing density, starting with the highest density at the bottom of the tube (Figure B7.1c). The resulting density gradient allows cell components to separate on the basis of small differences in size, shape, and density. When the centrifuge run is complete, each cell component occupies a distinct band of material in the tube, based on where that component settled in the density gradient. A researcher can collect the material in each band for further study.

CHECK YOUR UNDERSTANDING

If you understand BioSkill 7

✔ You should be able to …

1. List the physical properties of molecules or cell components that allow their separation via centrifugation.
2. State which cell component—ribosomes or mitochondria— you would expect to form a pellet more quickly when you centrifuge a cell homogenate at medium speed using the method shown in Fig. B7.1b. Explain why.

Answers are available in Appendix A.

(a) How a centrifuge works

When the centrifuge spins, the cell components tend to move toward the bottom of the centrifuge tube (red arrow)

The solution in the tube exerts a centripetal force, which resists movement of the components to the bottom of the tube (blue arrow)

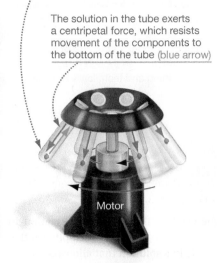

Very large or dense components overcome the centripetal force more readily than smaller, less dense ones. As a result, larger, denser components move toward the bottom of the tube faster.

(b) PROCESS: DIFFERENTIAL CENTRIFUGATION

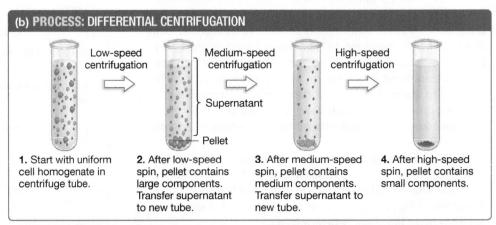

Low-speed centrifugation → Medium-speed centrifugation → Supernatant / Pellet → High-speed centrifugation

1. Start with uniform cell homogenate in centrifuge tube.
2. After low-speed spin, pellet contains large components. Transfer supernatant to new tube.
3. After medium-speed spin, pellet contains medium components. Transfer supernatant to new tube.
4. After high-speed spin, pellet contains small components.

(c) PROCESS: SUCROSE DENSITY–GRADIENT CENTRIFUGATION

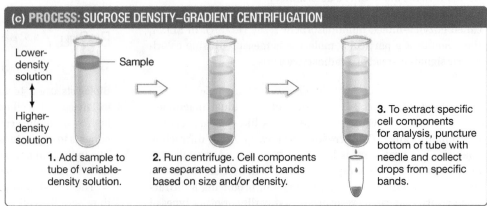

Lower-density solution / Higher-density solution — Sample

1. Add sample to tube of variable-density solution.
2. Run centrifuge. Cell components are separated into distinct bands based on size and/or density.
3. To extract specific cell components for analysis, puncture bottom of tube with needle and collect drops from specific bands.

Figure B7.1 **Cell Components Can Be Separated by Centrifugation. (a)** The forces inside a centrifuge tube allow cell components to be separated. **(b)** Through a series of centrifuge runs made at increasingly higher speeds, an investigator can separate fractions of a cell homogenate by size via differential centrifugation. **(c)** A high-speed centrifuge run can achieve extremely fine separation among cell components by sucrose density–gradient centrifugation.

BioSkill 8 Using Spectrophotometry

Spectrophotometry is a versatile technique in which an instrument called a spectrophotometer measures light absorbance by a substance. This measurement can be used to determine the concentration of the substance. In the spectrophotometer, light is passed from a lamp through a prism or diffraction grating, which splits the light into individual wavelengths (**Figure B8.1**). A moveable slit is then positioned to allow only light of a single wavelength to reach the sample, which is placed in the light path in a transparent cuvette or test tube. On the other side of the sample holder is a detector that measures the amount of transmitted light that got through the sample. This value is then converted into the amount of light absorbance.

In the lab, you may use spectrophotometry in the following tasks: **(1)** calculating the concentration of DNA, RNA, or proteins in a solution; **(2)** following the growth of bacterial cells; **(3)** quantifying the amount of photosynthesis occurring in chloroplasts, or **(4)** determining the rate of an enzyme-catalyzed reaction. Let's examine the last example in more detail.

If an enzyme-catalyzed reaction produces a colored product or destroys a colored substrate, a spectrophotometer can measure how much of that product or substrate is present and thereby quantify the activity of the enzyme. How does this work?

Suppose an enzyme-catalyzed reaction produces a green product that absorbs light best at a wavelength of 475 nm (blue light). If a solution containing this product is placed in a spectrophotometer and illuminated with light of this wavelength, the solution will absorb most of the blue light and transmit only some of it (see Figure B8.1). A more concentrated solution will absorb more blue light than a less concentrated one, so the more colored product a solution contains, the darker it looks.

Even solutions that appear colorless may absorb specific wavelengths of light. For instance, a solution of DNA absorbs light best at a wavelength of 260 nm, which is in the ultraviolet range. There are no units for absorbance, but you should always state the wavelength used, for example, "absorbance at 260 nm."

> ### CHECK YOUR UNDERSTANDING
>
> **If you understand BioSkill 8**
>
> ✔ **You should be able to ...**
>
> Explain the relationship between absorbance and transmittance of light through the sample in the spectrophotometer shown in Figure B8.1.
>
> Answers are available in Appendix A.

BioSkill 9 Using Microscopy

A lot of biology happens at levels that can't be detected with the naked eye. Biologists use an array of microscopes to study small multicellular organisms, individual cells, and the contents of cells.

You'll probably use dissecting microscopes and compound light microscopes to view specimens during your labs for this course, and throughout this text you'll see images generated from other types of microscopy. The key is to recognize that each approach for visualizing microscopic structures has strengths and weaknesses. As a result, each technique is appropriate for studying certain types or aspects of cells or molecules.

Light and Fluorescence Microscopy

If you use a dissecting microscope during labs, you'll recognize that it works by magnifying light that bounces off a whole specimen—often a live organism. You'll be able to view the specimen in three dimensions, which is why these instruments are sometimes called stereomicroscopes, but the maximum magnification possible is only about 20 to 40 times normal size (20× to 40×).

To view smaller objects, such as wet mounts or prepared slides of specimens, you'll probably use a compound microscope. Compound microscopes magnify light that passes *through* a specimen. The instruments used in introductory labs are usually capable of 400× magnification; the most sophisticated compound microscopes available can achieve magnifications of about 2000×. This is enough to view individual bacterial or eukaryotic cells and see large structures inside cells, like condensed chromosomes (see Chapter 12).

To prepare a specimen for viewing under a compound light microscope, researchers may need to slice the tissues or cells to create a section thin enough for light to pass through. The section is often stained to increase contrast and make structures visible. In many cases, different types of dyes are used to highlight different types of structures.

To visualize the location of specific proteins, such as structural or regulatory proteins, or to visualize organelles, such as mitochondria, researchers use a technique called immunostaining. After tissues or cells are prepared for viewing, the specimen is stained with fluorescently tagged antibodies. In this case, the cells are viewed under a fluorescence microscope. The fluorescing tag emits visible light when ultraviolet or other wavelengths of light are passed through the specimen. The result? Beautiful cells that glow green, red, or blue.

Figure B8.1 How a Spectrophotometer Works.

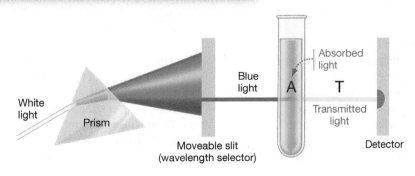

(a) Transmission electron microscopy: High magnification of cross sections

(b) Scanning electron microscopy: Lower magnification of surfaces

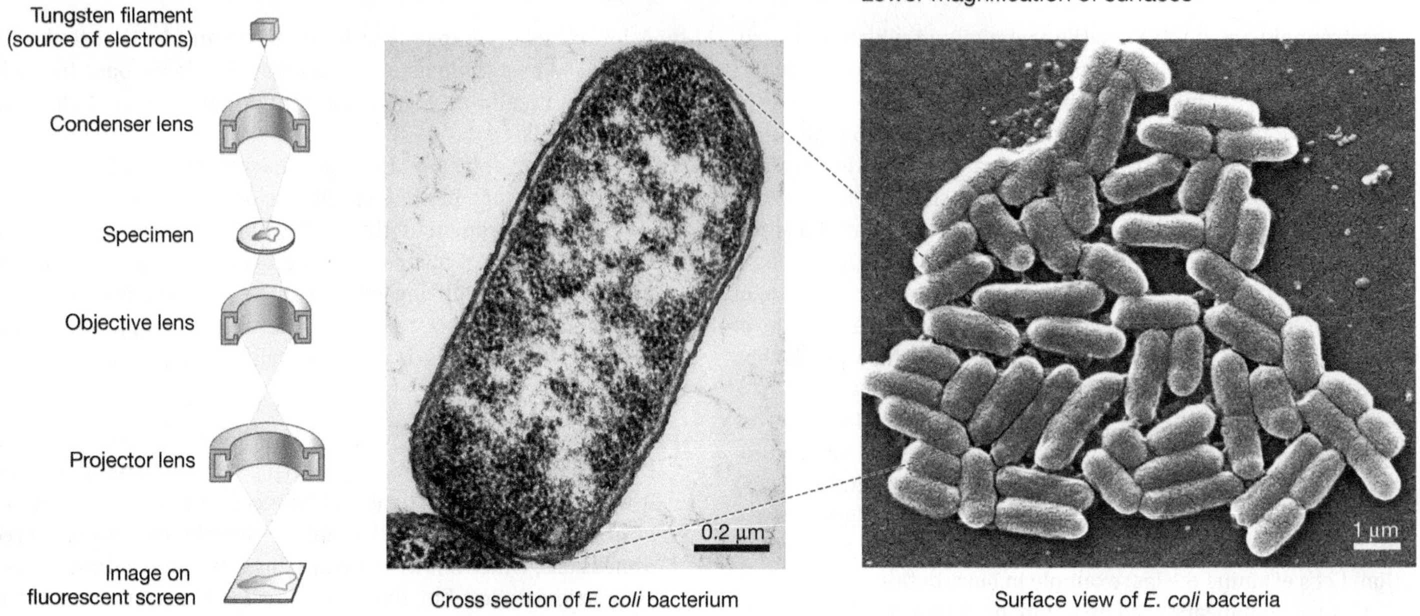

Tungsten filament (source of electrons)

Condenser lens

Specimen

Objective lens

Projector lens

Image on fluorescent screen

0.2 µm

Cross section of *E. coli* bacterium

1 µm

Surface view of *E. coli* bacteria

Figure B9.1 There Are Two Basic Types of Electron Microscopy.

Electron Microscopy

Until the 1950s, the compound microscope was the biologist's only tool for viewing cells directly. But the invention of the electron microscope provided a new way to view specimens. Two basic types of electron microscopy are now available: one that allows researchers to examine very thin cross sections of cells at extremely high magnification, and one that offers a view of surfaces at somewhat lower magnification.

Transmission Electron Microscopy The transmission electron microscope (TEM) is an extraordinarily effective tool for viewing cell structure at high magnification. TEM forms an image from electrons that pass through a specimen, just as a light microscope forms an image from light rays that pass through a specimen.

Biologists who want to view a cell under a transmission electron microscope begin by "fixing" the cell, meaning that they treat it with a chemical agent that stabilizes the cell's structure and contents while disturbing them as little as possible. Then the researcher permeates the cell with an epoxy plastic that stiffens the structure. Once this epoxy hardens, the cell can be cut into extremely thin sections with a glass or diamond knife. Finally, the sectioned specimens are saturated with a metal—often lead. (The reason for this last step is explained shortly.)

Figure B9.1a outlines how the transmission electron microscope works. A beam of electrons is produced by a tungsten filament at the top of a column and directed downward. (All of the air is pumped out of the column, so that the electron beam isn't scattered by collisions with air molecules.) The electron beam passes through a series of lenses and through the specimen. The lenses are actually electromagnets, which alter the path of the beam much like a glass lens in a dissecting or compound microscope bends light. The electromagnet lenses magnify and

focus the image on a screen at the bottom of the column. There the electrons strike a coating of fluorescent crystals, which emit visible light in response. The light can be detected by a digital camera; the result is a micrograph—a photograph of an image produced by microscopy.

The image itself is created by electrons that pass through the specimen. If no specimen were in place, all the electrons would pass through and the screen (and micrograph) would be uniformly bright. However, cell materials by themselves would also appear fairly uniform and bright. This is because an atom's ability to deflect electrons depends on its mass, and the hydrogen, carbon, oxygen, and nitrogen atoms that dominate biological molecules have low masses. This is why cell biologists must saturate cell sections with solutions containing heavy metals such as lead. These metals have high atomic masses and scatter electrons effectively. Different macromolecules take up the metal atoms in different amounts, so the metals function as "stains" that produce contrast for different structures. With TEM, areas that take up the most metal atoms scatter the electron beam most, producing dark areas in micrographs.

The advantage of TEM is that it can magnify objects up to 250,000×, making intracellular structures clearly visible. The downsides are that researchers are restricted to observing dead, sectioned material, and that they must take care not to distort the specimen during the preparation process.

Scanning Electron Microscopy The scanning electron microscope (SEM) is the most useful tool biologists have for looking at the surfaces of structures. Materials are prepared for scanning electron microscopy by coating their surfaces with a layer of metal atoms. To create an image of this surface, the microscope scans the surface with a narrow beam of electrons. Electrons that are reflected back from the surface or that are emitted by the metal atoms in response to the beam then strike a detector. The detector counts these electrons and sends the signals to an amplifier. The final image is built up from the number of electrons emitted from each spot on the sample and is displayed on a screen, magnified up to 50,000×. The image is captured directly in a computer.

Because SEM records shadows and highlights, it provides images with a three-dimensional appearance (**Figure B9.1b**). It cannot magnify objects nearly as much as TEM can, however.

Studying Live Cells and Real-Time Processes

Until the 1960s, biologists were unable to get clear, high-magnification images of living cells. But a series of innovations over the past 50 years has made it possible to observe organelles and subcellular structures in action.

The development of digital imaging proved revolutionary. It allowed specimens to be viewed at higher magnification, because digital cameras are more sensitive to small differences in contrast than are the human eye. It also made it easier to keep live specimens functioning normally, because the increased light sensitivity of digital cameras allows them to be used with low illumination, so specimens don't overheat. Digital imaging also made possible the use of computers to remove out-of-focus background material and increase image clarity.

A more recent innovation was the use of a fluorescent molecule called green fluorescent protein, or GFP, which allows researchers to tag specific molecules or structures and follow their movement in live cells over time. This was a major advance over immunostaining, in which cells have to be fixed. GFP is naturally synthesized in certain species of jellyfish. By affixing GFP to another protein (using genetic engineering techniques described in Chapter 20) and expressing that protein in a live cell, investigators can follow the protein's fate over time and record its movement. For example, researchers have made video recordings of GFP-tagged proteins being transported from

the rough ER through the Golgi apparatus and out to the plasma membrane. This is cell biology: the movie.

GFP's influence has been so profound that the researchers who developed its use in microscopy were awarded the 2008 Nobel Prize in Chemistry. Many other fluorescent proteins have since been developed with colors ranging from cyan (greenish blue) to yellow to red.

Visualizing Cellular Structures in 3-D

The world is three-dimensional. To understand how microscopic structures work, it is essential to understand their shapes and spatial relationships. Consider two techniques currently being used to analyze the 3-D structure of cells and organelles.

- *Confocal microscopy* is carried out by mounting a specimen that has been treated with one or more fluorescent tags on a microscope slide and then focusing a beam of light at a certain wavelength through a pinhole at a specific depth within the specimen. The tag emits light at a different wavelength in response. A detector is set up at exactly the position where the emitted light comes into focus. The result is a sharp image of a precise plane in the tissue being studied (**Figure B9.2a**). Note that if you viewed the same specimen under a conventional fluorescence microscope, the image would be blurry because it results from light emitted by the entire specimen (**Figure B9.2b**). By altering the focal plane, a researcher can record images from an array of depths in the specimen; a computer can then be used to generate a 3-D image of a cell or tissue (**Figure B9.2c**).

- *Electron tomography* uses a transmission electron microscope to generate a 3-D image of an organelle or other subcellular structure. The specimen is rotated around a single axis while the researcher takes many "snapshots." The individual images are then pieced together with a computer. This technique has provided a much more accurate view of mitochondrial structure than was possible using traditional TEM (see Figure 9.8).

(a) Confocal fluorescence image of mouse intestine

(b) Conventional fluorescence image of same tissue as in (a)

(c) Confocal 3-D image of cells forming a blood vessel

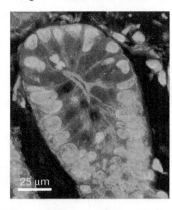 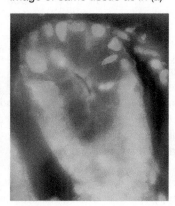 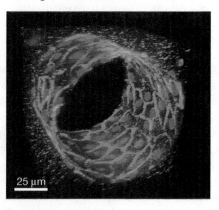

Figure B9.2 Confocal Microscopy Provides Sharp Images of Living Tissues. (a) The confocal image of this mouse intestine is sharp because it results from light emitted at a single plane within the tissue. **(b)** The conventional image of this same tissue is blurred because it results from light emitted by the entire tissue. **(c)** This 3-D confocal image was reconstructed from optical "sections" of cells forming a blood vessel.

If you understand BioSkill 9

✔ You should be able to ...

Interpret whether the absence of mitochondria in a transmission electron micrograph of a cancerous human liver cell means that the cell lacks mitochondria.

Answers are available in Appendix A.

BioSkill 10 Using Molecular Biology Tools and Techniques

The basic tools and techniques of genetic engineering and genome analysis are revolutionary. (Some of the major breakthroughs achieved by molecular biologists are highlighted in Chapter 20). But unless you are doing research in the lab, it can be difficult to fully appreciate all the details underlying the methods employed by molecular biologists. The key is to understand some of the basic principles and steps in each technique, and then to recognize how biologists can use each technique to answer distinct questions.

Often in a molecular biology study, some of the first tools and techniques used are associated with cloning. Biologists clone a DNA region of interest to obtain millions of copies of that region for further analysis. One traditional approach is to make a collection of DNA sequences called a DNA library. Let's take a closer look.

Making and Using DNA Libraries

A collection of DNA sequences, each of which is inserted into a vector, is called a DNA library. DNA libraries are made up of cloned genes or portions of genes. Each gene can be produced in large quantity and isolated in pure form. If the sequences are fragments of DNA from the genome of an individual, the library is called a genomic library. If the sequences are complementary DNA (cDNA)—DNA copies of mRNAs made by a particular cell type or tissue—the library is called a cDNA library. How is a cDNA library made?

Creating a cDNA Library The enzyme reverse transcriptase catalyzes the synthesis of cDNA from an RNA template. This cDNA can then be used to make a cDNA library, as shown in **Figure B10.1**. The end result, shown in step 5, is a collection of transformed bacterial cells. Each of the cells contains a plasmid with one cDNA from the initial mRNAs isolated from a particular cell type or tissue.

DNA libraries are important because they give researchers a way to store DNA fragments from a particular cell type or genome in a form that is accessible for gene cloning. But like a college library, a DNA library isn't very useful unless there is a way to retrieve specific pieces of information. At your school's

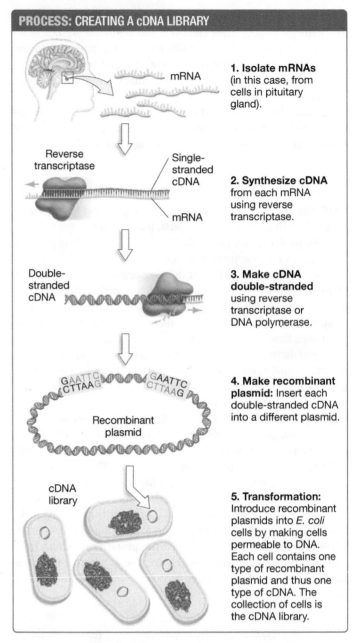

PROCESS: CREATING A cDNA LIBRARY

mRNA

1. Isolate mRNAs (in this case, from cells in pituitary gland).

Reverse transcriptase

Single-stranded cDNA

mRNA

2. Synthesize cDNA from each mRNA using reverse transcriptase.

Double-stranded cDNA

3. Make cDNA double-stranded using reverse transcriptase or DNA polymerase.

GAATTC CTTAAG   GAATTC CTTAAG

Recombinant plasmid

4. Make recombinant plasmid: Insert each double-stranded cDNA into a different plasmid.

cDNA library

5. Transformation: Introduce recombinant plasmids into *E. coli* cells by making cells permeable to DNA. Each cell contains one type of recombinant plasmid and thus one type of cDNA. The collection of cells is the cDNA library.

Figure B10.1 Complementary DNA (cDNA) Libraries Represent a Collection of the mRNAs in a Cell.

✔ Would each type of cDNA in the library be represented just once? Why or why not?

library, you use call numbers or computer searches to retrieve a particular book or article.

How do you go about retrieving a particular cDNA from a library?

Finding a Particular cDNA in a Library Molecular biologists are often faced with the task of finding one specific cDNA or gene in a large collection of DNA fragments. To do this requires a probe—a labeled molecule that binds to the molecule the biologist is looking for (see BioSkill 6).

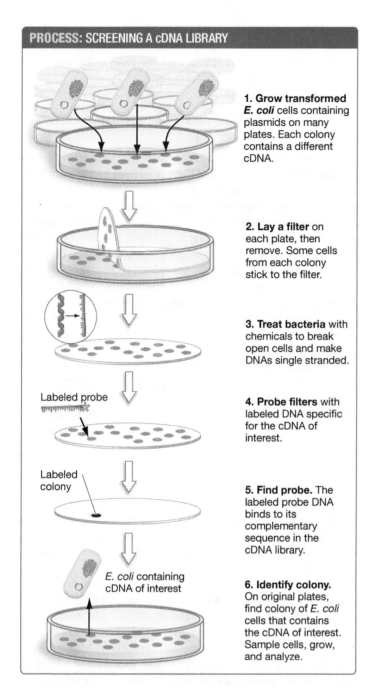

PROCESS: SCREENING A cDNA LIBRARY

1. Grow transformed *E. coli* cells containing plasmids on many plates. Each colony contains a different cDNA.

2. Lay a filter on each plate, then remove. Some cells from each colony stick to the filter.

3. Treat bacteria with chemicals to break open cells and make DNAs single stranded.

Labeled probe

4. Probe filters with labeled DNA specific for the cDNA of interest.

Labeled colony

5. Find probe. The labeled probe DNA binds to its complementary sequence in the cDNA library.

E. coli containing cDNA of interest

6. Identify colony. On original plates, find colony of *E. coli* cells that contains the cDNA of interest. Sample cells, grow, and analyze.

Figure B10.2 Finding a Specific cDNA by Probing a cDNA Library.

Figure B10.2 shows how researchers use a probe to find a particular plasmid in a cDNA library. The labeled probe will bind to its complementary sequence in the library. In this way, the recombinant cell that contains the specific cDNA of interest can be identified by the researchers.

Another powerful technique for making lots of identical copies of (amplifying) a particular region of DNA is the polymerase chain reaction. The amplified DNA can be used for cloning into a plasmid vector or for many other types of analyses (see Chapter 20).

Let's examine how PCR works.

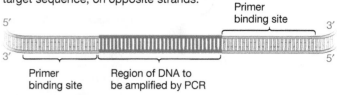

(a) PCR primers must bind to sequences on either side of the target sequence, on opposite strands.

Primer binding site

Primer binding site

Region of DNA to be amplified by PCR

(b) When target DNA is made single stranded, primers bind and allow DNA polymerase to work.

Primer

Primer

Figure B10.3 The Polymerase Chain Reaction Requires Appropriate Primers. (a) To design an appropriate primer, the base sequences at the primer binding sites must be known. **(b)** The primers bind by complementary base pairing to single-stranded target DNA.

✔ **MODEL** Indicate where DNA polymerase would begin to work on each strand; add an arrow indicating the direction of DNA synthesis.

Amplifying DNA Using the Polymerase Chain Reaction (PCR)

The polymerase chain reaction (PCR) is an in vitro DNA synthesis reaction that uses DNA polymerase to replicate a specific section of DNA over and over.

DNA polymerase cannot work without a primer (see Chapter 15). As **Figure B10.3a** shows, the primer sequences used must be complementary to bases on either side of the target region—the DNA you want to copy. One primer is complementary to a sequence on one side of the target DNA; the other primer is complementary to a sequence on the opposite strand of DNA, on the other side of the target region. If the target DNA molecule is made single stranded, then the primers will bind to their complementary sequence, as shown in **Figure B10.3b**. Once the primers are bound, DNA polymerase can extend each new strand of DNA in the 5′ → 3′ direction.

Figure B10.4 on page 38 shows the steps involved in the polymerase chain reaction.

Step 1 The researcher creates a reaction mix containing an abundant supply of the four deoxyribonucleoside triphosphates (dNTPs; see Chapter 15), a DNA sample that includes the target DNA of interest, many copies of the two primers, and a heat-resistant DNA polymerase.

Step 2 The reaction mix is heated to 95°C. At this temperature, double-stranded DNA denatures. This means that the two DNA strands separate, forming single-stranded templates.

Step 3 The mixture is allowed to cool to 50°C–72°C, depending on the polymerase used and the primer sequences. In this temperature range, the primers bind, or anneal, to complementary portions of the single-stranded template DNA. This step is called primer annealing.

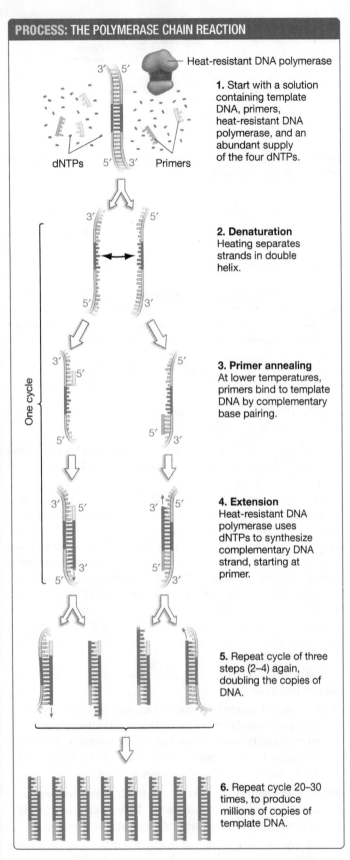

PROCESS: THE POLYMERASE CHAIN REACTION

Heat-resistant DNA polymerase

dNTPs   5′ 3′   Primers

1. Start with a solution containing template DNA, primers, heat-resistant DNA polymerase, and an abundant supply of the four dNTPs.

2. Denaturation Heating separates strands in double helix.

One cycle

3. Primer annealing At lower temperatures, primers bind to template DNA by complementary base pairing.

4. Extension Heat-resistant DNA polymerase uses dNTPs to synthesize complementary DNA strand, starting at primer.

5. Repeat cycle of three steps (2–4) again, doubling the copies of DNA.

6. Repeat cycle 20–30 times, to produce millions of copies of template DNA.

Figure B10.4 The Polymerase Chain Reaction Produces Many Copies of a Specific Sequence. Each PCR cycle (denaturation, primer annealing, and extension) results in a doubling of the number of target sequences.

Step 4 The reaction mix is heated to 72°C. At this temperature, the heat-resistant DNA polymerase efficiently synthesizes the complementary DNA strand from the dNTPs, starting at the primer. This step is called extension.

Step 5 Repeat steps 2 through 4.

Step 6 Continue repeating steps 2 through 4 until the necessary number of copies is obtained.

The temperature changes required in each step are controlled by automated PCR machines, and there is no need to add more components once the reaction starts.

The denaturation, primer annealing, and extension steps constitute a single PCR cycle. If one copy of the template sequence existed in the original sample, then two copies are present at the end of the first cycle (see step 4 in Figure B10.4). These two copies then act as templates for the second cycle—another round of denaturation, primer annealing, and extension—after which four copies of the target DNA are present (see step 5).

Each time the cycle repeats, the number of copies of template sequence in the reaction mixture doubles (step 6). Doubling occurs because each newly synthesized segment of DNA serves as a template in the subsequent cycle, along with the previously synthesized segments. Starting with a single copy, successive cycles result in the production of 2, 4, 8, 16, 32, 64, 128, 256 copies, and so on. A total of n cycles can generate 2^n copies. In just 20 cycles, one sequence can be amplified to over a million copies.

Dideoxy Sequencing

After cloning a gene or amplifying a region of DNA by PCR, molecular biologists often want to determine the DNA's base sequence. One way to do this, called dideoxy sequencing, is a clever variation on the basic in vitro DNA synthesis reaction (**Figure B10.5**).

The key is to use monomers for DNA synthesis called dideoxyribonucleoside triphosphates (ddNTPs) along with the normal deoxyribonucleoside triphosphates (dNTPs) in the reaction mix (see Chapter 15). The ddNTPs are identical to dNTPs, except they lack a hydroxyl group at their 3′ carbon. Four types of ddNTPs are used in dideoxy sequencing, each named according to whether it contains adenine (ddATP), thymine (ddTTP), cytosine (ddCTP), or guanine (ddGTP). The use of ddNTPs inspired the name dideoxy sequencing.

If a ddNTP is added to a growing DNA strand, it terminates synthesis. Why? After a ddNTP is added, no hydroxyl group is available on a 3′ carbon to link to the 5′ carbon on an incoming dNTP monomer. As a result, DNA polymerization stops once a ddNTP is added.

Every time a ddNTP is added to a growing strand, the result is a fragment with a length corresponding to the position in the template of a base complementary to the ddNTP. To produce these fragments, biologists create a reaction mix containing many copies of **(1)** the template DNA, **(2)** a primer, and **(3)** DNA polymerase, as well as **(4)** a large supply of the four dNTPs and **(5)** a small amount of the four ddNTPs (Figure B10.5, step 1). Each of the four ddNTPs carries a different fluorescent tag.

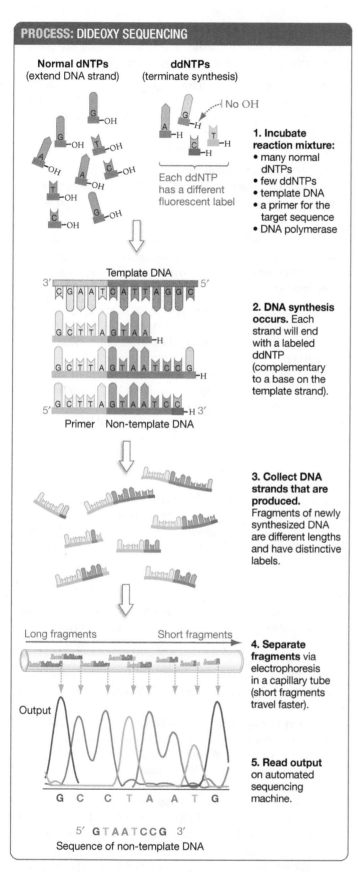

PROCESS: DIDEOXY SEQUENCING

Normal dNTPs
(extend DNA strand)

ddNTPs
(terminate synthesis)

No OH

Each ddNTP has a different fluorescent label

1. Incubate reaction mixture:
- many normal dNTPs
- few ddNTPs
- template DNA
- a primer for the target sequence
- DNA polymerase

Template DNA

3′ C G A A T C A T T A G G C 5′

G C T T A G T A A —H

G C T T A G T A A T C C G —H

5′ G C T T A G T A A T C C —H 3′

Primer   Non-template DNA

2. DNA synthesis occurs. Each strand will end with a labeled ddNTP (complementary to a base on the template strand).

3. Collect DNA strands that are produced. Fragments of newly synthesized DNA are different lengths and have distinctive labels.

Long fragments   Short fragments

4. Separate fragments via electrophoresis in a capillary tube (short fragments travel faster).

Output

G C   C T A A T G

5. Read output on automated sequencing machine.

5′ **G T A A T C C G** 3′
Sequence of non-template DNA

Figure B10.5 Dideoxy Sequencing Can Determine the Base Sequence of DNA.

Fluorescent molecules absorb light at one wavelength and reemit the light at a longer wavelength. As described in BioSkill 6, they provide a very sensitive way of detecting molecules.

Under these conditions, many daughter strands of different lengths are synthesized. All fragments that are the same length end in the same kind of ddNTP.

Step 2 in Figure B10.5 shows why:

- DNA polymerase synthesizes a complementary strand from each template in the reaction mix.

- The synthesis of each one of these complementary strands starts at the same point—the primer.

- Because there are many dNTPs and relatively few ddNTPs in the reaction mix, dNTPs are usually incorporated opposite each complementary base on the template strand as DNA polymerase works its way along the template strand. Incorporating a dNTP allows DNA synthesis to continue.

- Occasionally, one of the few ddNTPs is incorporated into the growing strand, opposite the corresponding base in the template. The complementary base in the template strand pairs randomly with either a ddNTP or a dNTP.

- The addition of the ddNTP stops further elongation.

- "Stops" of this kind happen for each base in the template strand. As a result, the overall reaction produces a collection of newly synthesized strands (fragments) whose various lengths correspond to the location of each base in the template strand (see step 3 in Figure B10.5). Each fragment will fluoresce in the color of its ddNTP.

Using gel electrophoresis in a capillary tube (step 4 in Figure B10.5), biologists can line up the fragments in order of size. When the fragments are lined up by size, the incorporated dideoxy nucleotides on the successive fragments reveal the sequence of bases in the template DNA. As step 5 shows, a machine can read the pattern of fluorescence, indicating the sequence of bases in the newly synthesized strand.

Sequencing a cDNA clone or PCR product is technically straightforward, but how can researchers sequence an entire genome?

Shotgun Sequencing

When researchers first set out to sequence the genome of a species, they usually relied on an approach known as shotgun sequencing. Molecular biologists still use shotgun sequencing, although newer sequencing technologies are streamlining the process. Let's take a look at key steps in the traditional method:

Step 1 Application of high-frequency sound waves, or sonication, is used to break a genome randomly into pieces about 160 kilobases (kb) long (1 kb = 1000 bases).

Step 2 Each 160-kb piece is inserted into an engineered version of a bacterial chromosome, called a bacterial artificial chromosome (BAC), that can be used as a cloning vector. BACs are able to replicate large segments of DNA. Each BAC is then inserted into a different bacterial cell. By allowing each cell to grow into a colony, researchers can isolate large numbers of each 160-kb fragment.

Step 3 After many copies of each 160-kb fragment have been produced, each cloned DNA is again broken into fragments—but this time, the fragments are about 1 kb long.

Step 4 These small fragments are then inserted into plasmids and placed inside bacterial cells. The plasmids are copied many times as each cell grows into a large population.

Step 5 Next, the cloned 1-kb fragments from each 160-kb BAC clone are sequenced, and computer programs analyze regions where the ends of different 1-kb fragments overlap. Overlaps occur because many copies of each 160-kb segment were made and then fragmented randomly by sonication.

Step 6 Based on the overlaps between 1-kb fragments from a single BAC clone, the computer stitches the sequences together until a continuous sequence across the BAC has been reconstructed.

Step 7 The ends of the reconstructed BACs are analyzed in a similar way. The goal is to link sequences from each 160-kb segment based on regions of overlap until the sequence of an entire genome is assembled.

In essence, the shotgun strategy consists of breaking a genome into many small fragments, sequencing each fragment, and then putting the sequence data back in the correct order. Whether the approach is traditional or modern, this principle holds.

Once genes are cloned and sequenced, researchers can then begin to address important questions about how genes function. (Chapter 20 covers some exciting recent discoveries.) Let's examine one method that allows researchers to find out how and when all the genes in an organism are expressed.

DNA Microarray

A DNA microarray lets researchers study the expression of thousands of genes at a time. The microarray consists of as many as 1 million different single-stranded DNA segments that are permanently attached at one end to a glass slide or silicon chip. The DNA sequence of each segment is known, as is its location on the slide or chip. Each segment serves as a probe for a specific transcript.

A typical experiment done with a DNA microarray follows the steps outlined in **Figure B10.6**. For example, suppose researchers wanted to learn how gene expression in a certain kind of cell is altered to meet the challenges of heat stress. They would begin by isolating mRNAs produced in control cells functioning at normal temperature and in cells of the same kind exposed to high temperatures (step 1).

Once they purified mRNAs from the two populations of cells, the researchers would use reverse transcriptase to make a single-stranded cDNA version of each RNA in the two samples. One of the nucleotides in the cDNA would carry a fluorescent tag (step 2). The tag used for the control cells would fluoresce one color (let's say green), while the tag for the heat-stressed cells would fluoresce another color (let's say red). The labeled cDNAs of both colors would then be added to the microarray, where they would bind to complementary DNA probes (step 3). This step is called hybridization because hybrids would form between probe DNAs and cDNAs.

Out of all the probes present on the microarray, then, only those that represent genes being expressed by the two populations of cells will be labeled on the microarray. In this example,

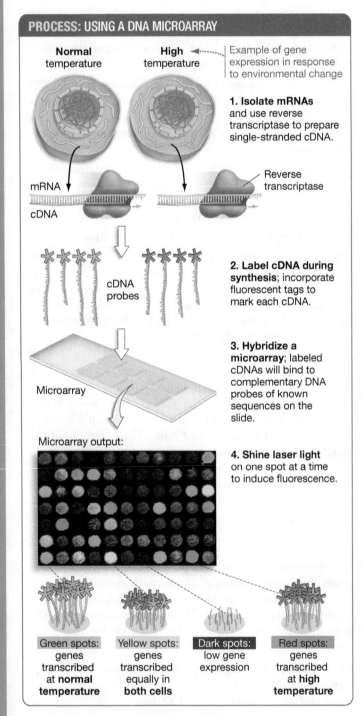

PROCESS: USING A DNA MICROARRAY

Normal temperature   **High** temperature — Example of gene expression in response to environmental change

1. Isolate mRNAs and use reverse transcriptase to prepare single-stranded cDNA.

mRNA
cDNA
Reverse transcriptase

cDNA probes

2. Label cDNA during synthesis; incorporate fluorescent tags to mark each cDNA.

Microarray

3. Hybridize a microarray; labeled cDNAs will bind to complementary DNA probes of known sequences on the slide.

Microarray output:

4. Shine laser light on one spot at a time to induce fluorescence.

| Green spots: genes transcribed at **normal** temperature | Yellow spots: genes transcribed equally in **both cells** | Dark spots: low gene expression | Red spots: genes transcribed at **high** temperature |

Figure B10.6 DNA Microarrays Can Be Used to Study Changes in Gene Expression. By hybridizing a microarray with labeled cDNAs synthesized from mRNAs, researchers can identify which sequences are being transcribed. Here cDNAs made from cells growing at normal temperature have a green tag, while cDNAs made from cells growing at high temperature have a red tag.

genes that are expressed by the control cells at the normal temperature will be labeled green, while those expressed by the cells during heat stress will be labeled red. If a gene is expressed under both sets of conditions, then both green- and red-labeled cDNAs will bind to the DNA in that spot on the microarray, and the spot will appear yellow (step 4).

CHECK YOUR UNDERSTANDING

If you understand BioSkill 10

✔ You should be able to ...

1. Explain why no further nucleotides can be added after a ddNTP molecule is added to a growing chain of DNA.
2. Consider the following scenario: Suppose a friend of yours is doing a series of PCRs and comes to you for advice. She purchased two sets of primers, hoping that one set would amplify the template sequence shown here. (The dashed lines in the template sequence stand for a long sequence of unspecified bases in the target gene.) Neither of the primer pairs produced any product DNA, however.

	Primer a	Primer b
Primer Pair 1:	5'-CAAGTCC-3' and	5'-GCTGGAC-3'
Primer Pair 2:	5'-GGACTTG -3' and	5'-GTCCAGC-3'
Template:	5'-ATTCGGACTTG—GTCCAGCTAGAGG-3'	
	3'-TAAGCCTGAAC—CAGGTCGATCTCC-5'	

  a. Explain why each primer pair didn't work. Indicate whether both primers are at fault, or just one of them.
  b. Your friend doesn't want to buy new primers. She asks you whether she can salvage this experiment. What should you tell her to do?
3. Explain how you would use a DNA microarray to compare the genes expressed in human brain cells with those expressed in human liver cells.

Answers are available in Appendix A.

BIOSKILL 11 Using Cell Culture and Model Organisms as Tools

Research in biological science starts with a question. In most cases, the question is inspired by an observation about a cell or an organism. To answer it, biologists often study cells or tissues in culture. At other times, they perform experiments on model organisms—aptly named because these organisms are intended to serve as models for what is going on in a wide array of species. Let's look at each approach in turn.

Cell and Tissue Culture Methods

For researchers, there are important advantages to culturing plant and animal cells and tissues. Culturing involves growing a cell or tissue outside the organism itself. Cell and tissue cultures produce large populations of a single type of cell or tissue and enable biologists to control experimental conditions precisely.

Animal Cell Culture In 1907, a researcher successfully cultivated amphibian nerve cells in a drop of fluid from the spinal cord, but biologists weren't able to routinely culture animal cells in the laboratory until the 1950s and 1960s. It took years to figure out how to re-create the conditions that exist in the intact organism precisely enough for cells to grow normally.

To grow in culture, animal cells must be provided with a liquid mixture containing the nutrients, vitamins, and hormones that stimulate growth. Typically, this mixture is serum, the liquid portion of blood. Serum-free media that are much more precisely defined chemically are available for certain cell types.

Moreover, many types of animal cells will not grow in culture unless they are on a solid surface that mimics the types of surfaces they would adhere to in the intact animal. As a result, animal cells are typically cultured in flasks with special coatings (**Figure B11.1a**, left).

(a) Animal cell culture: immortal HeLa cancer cells

 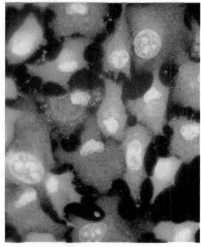

(b) Plant tissue culture: tobacco callus

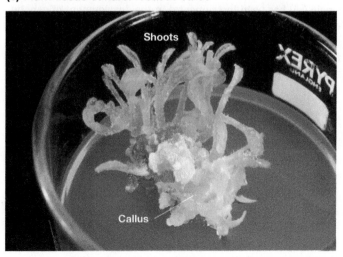

Figure B11.1 Animal and Plant Cells Can Be Grown in the Lab.

Even under optimal conditions, though, normal cells have a finite life span in culture. In contrast, many cultured cancerous cells grow indefinitely. This characteristic correlates with a key feature of cancerous cells in organisms: Their growth is continuous and uncontrolled.

The first human cell type to be grown in culture was isolated in 1951 from a woman with a malignant tumor of the uterine cervix. These cells are called HeLa cells in honor of their donor, Henrietta Lacks, who died soon after from her cancer. HeLa cells continue to grow in laboratories around the world (see the micrograph on the right in Figure B11.1a).

Because of their immortality and relative ease of growth, cultured cancer cells are commonly used in research on basic aspects of cell structure and function.

Plant Tissue Culture Certain cells found in plants are totipotent—meaning that they retain the ability to divide and differentiate into a complete, mature plant, including new types of tissue. These cells, called parenchyma cells, are important in wound healing and asexual reproduction. They also allow researchers to grow complete adult plants in the laboratory, starting with a small number of parenchyma cells.

Biologists who grow plants in tissue culture begin by placing parenchyma cells in a liquid or solid medium containing all the nutrients required for cell maintenance and growth. In the early days of plant tissue culture, as for animal cells, investigators found that successful growth and differentiation depended not only on the presence of specific hormones but also on their relative abundance.

The earliest experiments on hormone interactions in plant tissue cultures were done with tobacco cells in the 1950s. Researchers found that when they added roughly equal amounts of the hormones auxin and cytokinin to the cells, the cells began to divide and eventually formed an undifferentiated mass of parenchyma cells called a callus. By varying the proportion of auxin to cytokinin in different parts of the callus and through time, researchers could stimulate the growth and differentiation of root and shoot systems and produce whole new plants (Figure B11.1b).

The ability to grow a whole plant in tissue culture from a single cell has been instrumental in the development of genetic engineering (see Chapter 20). Researchers insert recombinant genes into target cells, test the cells to identify those that successfully express the recombinant genes, and then use tissue culture techniques to grow those cells into adult individuals with novel genotypes and phenotypes.

Model Organisms

Model organisms are chosen because they are convenient to study, and because they each have attributes that make them appropriate for the particular type of research proposed. They tend to have some common characteristics:

- **Short generation time and rapid reproduction** This trait is important because it makes it possible to produce offspring quickly and perform many experiments in a short amount of time—you don't have to wait long for individuals to grow.

- **Large numbers of offspring** This trait is particularly important in genetics, where many offspring phenotypes and genotypes need to be assessed to get a large sample size.

- **Small size and simple feeding and habitat requirements** These attributes make it relatively cheap and easy to maintain individuals in the lab.

The following examples highlight just a few model organisms supporting current work in biological science.

Escherichia coli Of all model organisms in biology, perhaps none has been more important than the bacterium *Escherichia coli*—a common inhabitant of the human gut. The strain that is most commonly worked on today, called K-12 (Figure B11.2a), was originally isolated from a hospital patient in 1922.

During the last half of the twentieth century, key results in molecular biology originated in studies of *E. coli*. These results include the discovery of enzymes such as DNA polymerase, RNA polymerase, DNA repair enzymes, and restriction endonucleases; the elucidation of ribosome structure and function; and the initial characterization of promoters, regulatory transcription factors, regulatory sites in DNA, and operons. In many cases, initial discoveries made in *E. coli* allowed researchers to confirm that homologous enzymes and processes existed in an array of organisms, ranging from other bacteria to yeast, mice, and humans.

The success of *E. coli* as a model for other species inspired Jacques Monod's claim that "Once we understand the biology of *Escherichia coli*, we will understand the biology of an elephant." The genome of *E. coli* K-12 was sequenced in 1997, and the strain continues to be a workhorse in studies of gene function, biochemistry, and particularly biotechnology.

In the lab, *E. coli* is usually grown in suspension culture, where cells are introduced to a liquid nutrient medium, or on plates containing agar—a gelatinous mix of polysaccharides. Under optimal growing conditions—meaning before cells begin to get crowded and compete for space and nutrients—a cell takes just 30 minutes on average to grow and divide. At this rate, a single cell can produce a population of over a million descendants in just 10 hours. Unless they have new mutations, all of the descendant cells are genetically identical.

Dictyostelium discoideum The cellular slime mold *Dictyostelium discoideum* is not always slimy, and it's not a mold—which is a type of fungus. Instead, it is an amoeba. Amoeba is a general term that biologists use to characterize a unicellular eukaryote that lacks a cell wall and is extremely flexible in shape. *Dictyostelium* has long fascinated biologists because it is a social organism. Independent cells sometimes aggregate to form a multicellular structure.

Under most conditions, *Dictyostelium* cells are haploid (*n*) and move about in decaying vegetation on forest floors or other habitats. They feed on bacteria by engulfing them whole. When these cells reproduce, they can do so sexually by fusing with another cell and then undergoing meiotic cell division, or asexually by mitotic cell division, which is more common. If food begins to run out, the cells begin to aggregate. In many cases, tens

(a) Bacterium *Escherichia coli* (strain K-12)

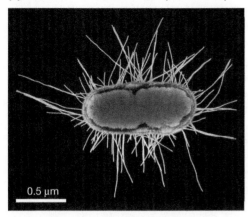

0.5 μm

(b) Slime mold *Dictyostelium discoideum*

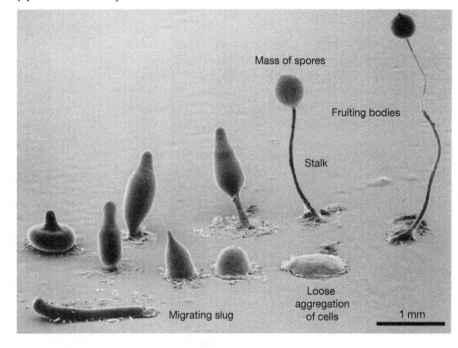

Mass of spores

Fruiting bodies

Stalk

Migrating slug

Loose aggregation of cells

1 mm

(c) Thale cress *Arabidopsis thaliana*

5 cm

(e) Fruit fly *Drosophila melanogaster*

0.5 mm

(f) Roundworm *Caenorhabditis elegans*

0.1 mm

(d) Yeast *Saccharomyces cerevisiae*

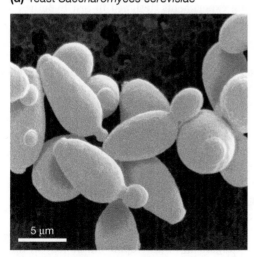

5 μm

(g) Mouse *Mus musculus*

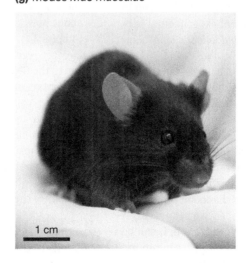

1 cm

Figure B11.2 Model Organisms.

of thousands of cells cohere to form a 2-mm-long mass called a slug (Figure B11.2b). (Note that this is not a slug that is related to snails.)

After migrating to a sunlit location, the slug stops, and individual cells differentiate according to their position in the slug. Some form a stalk; others form a mass of spores at the tip of the stalk. (A spore is a single cell that develops into an adult organism, but it is not formed from gamete fusion like a zygote is.) The entire structure, stalk plus mass of spores, is called a fruiting body.

Cells of *Dictyostelium* that form spores secrete a tough coat and represent a durable resting stage. The fruiting body eventually dries out, and the wind disperses the spores to new locations, where more food might be available.

Dictyostelium has been an important model organism for investigating questions about eukaryotes:

- Cells in a slug are initially identical in morphology but then differentiate into distinctive stalk cells and spores. Studying this process helped biologists better understand how cells in plant and animal embryos differentiate into distinct cell types.

- The process of slug formation has helped biologists study how animal cells move and how they aggregate as they form specific types of tissues.

- When *Dictyostelium* cells aggregate to form a slug, they stick to each other. The discovery of membrane proteins responsible for cell–cell adhesion helped biologists understand some of the general principles of multicellular life (highlighted in Chapter 11).

Arabidopsis thaliana   In the early days of biology, the best-studied plants were agricultural varieties such as maize (corn), rice, and garden peas. When biologists began to unravel the mechanisms responsible for oxygenic photosynthesis in the early to mid-1900s, they relied on green algae that were relatively easy to grow and manipulate in the lab—often the unicellular species *Chlamydomonas reinhardii*.

Although crop plants and green algae continue to be the subject of considerable research, a new model organism emerged in the 1980s and now serves as the preeminent experimental subject in plant biology. That organism is *Arabidopsis thaliana*, commonly known as thale cress or wall cress (Figure B11.2c).

Arabidopsis is a member of the mustard family, or Brassicaceae, so it is closely related to radishes and broccoli. In nature it is a weed—meaning a species that is adapted to thrive in habitats where soils have been disturbed.

One of the most attractive aspects of working with *Arabidopsis* is that individuals can grow from a seed into a mature, seed-producing plant in just four to six weeks. Several other attributes make it an effective subject for study: It has just five chromosomes and a relatively small genome, which has been completely sequenced and has limited numbers of repetitive sequences; it can self-fertilize as well as undergo cross-fertilization; it can be grown in a relatively small amount of space and with a minimum of care in the greenhouse; and it produces up to 10,000 seeds per individual per generation.

Arabidopsis has been instrumental in a variety of studies in plant molecular genetics and development, and it is becoming increasingly popular in ecological and evolutionary studies.

Saccharomyces cerevisiae   When biologists want to answer basic questions about how eukaryotic cells work, they often turn to a fungus, the yeast *Saccharomyces cerevisiae*.

S. cerevisiae is unicellular and relatively easy to culture and manipulate in the lab (Figure B11.2d). In good conditions, yeast cells grow and divide almost as rapidly as bacteria. As a result, the species has become the organism of choice for experiments on control of the cell cycle and regulation of gene expression in eukaryotes. For example, research has confirmed that several of the genes controlling cell division and DNA repair in yeast have homologs in humans; when mutated, these homologs contribute to cancer in humans. Strains of yeast that carry the homologous mutations are now being used to test drugs that might be effective against cancer.

S. cerevisiae was the first eukaryote with a sequenced genome, and it has become even more important in efforts to interpret the genomes of organisms like rice, mice, zebrafish, and humans. It is much easier to investigate the function of particular genes in *S. cerevisiae* by creating mutants or transferring specific alleles among individuals than it is to do the same experiments in mice or zebrafish. Once the function of a gene has been established in yeast, biologists can look for the homologous gene in other eukaryotes. If such a gene exists, they can usually infer that it has a function similar to its role in *S. cerevisiae*.

Drosophila melanogaster   If you walk into a biology building on any university campus around the world, you are almost certain to find at least one lab where the fruit fly *Drosophila melanogaster* is being studied (Figure B11.2e).

Drosophila has been a key experimental subject in genetics since the early 1900s. T. H. Morgan was the first to choose this organism as a focus for study, because it can be reared in the laboratory easily and inexpensively, matings can be arranged, the life cycle is completed in less than two weeks, and females lay a large number of eggs. These traits made fruit flies valuable subjects for breeding experiments designed to test hypotheses about how traits are transmitted from parents to offspring (see Chapter 14).

More recently, *Drosophila* has also become a key model organism in the field of developmental biology. The use of flies in developmental studies was inspired largely by the work of Christiane Nüsslein-Volhard and Eric Wieschaus, who in the 1980s isolated flies with genetic defects in early embryonic development. By investigating the nature of these defects, researchers have gained valuable insights into how various gene products influence the development of eukaryotes (see Chapter 21). The complete genome sequence of *Drosophila* has been available to investigators since the year 2000.

Caenorhabditis elegans   The roundworm *Caenorhabditis elegans* emerged as a model organism in developmental biology in the 1970s, due largely to work by Sydney Brenner and colleagues. (*Caenorhabditis* is pronounced *see-no-rab-DIE-tiss*.)

C. elegans was chosen for three reasons: **(1)** Its cuticle (soft outer layer) is transparent, making individual cells relatively easy to observe (**Figure B11.2f**); **(2)** adults have exactly 959 nonreproductive cells; and, most important, **(3)** the fate of each cell in an embryo can be predicted because cell fates are invariant among individuals. For example, when researchers examine a 33-cell *C. elegans* embryo, they know exactly which of the 959 cells in the adult will be derived from each of those 33 embryonic cells.

In addition, *C. elegans* is small (less than 1 mm long), can self-fertilize or cross-fertilize, and undergoes early development in just 16 hours. The genome of *C. elegans* was fully sequenced by 2002.

Mus musculus The house mouse *Mus musculus* is the most important model organism among mammals. For this reason, it is especially prominent in biomedical research, where researchers need to work on animals with strong genetic and developmental similarities to humans.

The house mouse was an intelligent choice for a model organism in mammals: It is small and thus relatively inexpensive to maintain in captivity, and it breeds rapidly. A litter can contain 10 offspring, and generation time is only 12 weeks—meaning that several generations can be produced in a year. Descendants of wild house mice have been selected for docility and other traits that make them easy to handle and rear; these populations are referred to as laboratory mice (**Figure B11.2g**).

Some of the most valuable laboratory mice are strains with distinctive, well-characterized genotypes. Inbred strains are virtually homogenous genetically and are useful in experiments where gene-by-gene or gene-by-environment interactions have to be controlled. Other populations carry mutations that knock out genes and cause diseases similar to those observed in humans. These populations are useful for identifying the causes of genetic diseases and for testing drugs or other types of therapies.

CHECK YOUR UNDERSTANDING

If you understand BioSkill 11

✔ You should be able to ...

1. Identify a limitation in interpreting experiments on HeLa cells.
2. Determine which model organisms described in BioSkill 11 would be the best choice for the following studies. In each case, explain your reasoning: (a) a study of how specific cells in an embryo become specialized for a particular fate at certain points in normal development; (b) a study of proteins that are required for cells to adhere to each other in multicellular organisms.

Answers are available in Appendix A.

BioSkill 12 Reading and Making Visual Models

Biology is a visual discipline—it's hard to imagine learning biology without illustrations such as the figures in this text. While some illustrations are designed to show structures as realistically as possible (such as a bluebird in a field guide), most illustrations in biology are *visual models*—drawings that are purposefully

simplified or abstracted to show a concept, process, or relationship clearly. Visual models help you see what is too small, too large, too complex, too hidden, or too conceptual to be seen otherwise.

Since the topics in biology are diverse, the types of visual models are diverse too. They include graphs (see BioSkill 2), phylogenetic trees (see BioSkill 13), and chemical structures (see BioSkill 14). Scientists make models to help them form hypotheses, design experiments, visualize data, and communicate with others. Making your own visual models is a skill that will help you learn biology and become a biologist. But like interpreting models, making models takes practice.

Tips for Interpreting Models

Each figure in this text was designed to focus on a specific take-home message about biology, and many are, by necessity, abstractions of reality. Table B12.1 on page 46 lists some basic tips to help you practice interpreting these models. As you examine the table, take your time and ask yourself these five questions:

1. *Have I read the figure legend and the section of text where the figure is called out? Do I understand what the words mean?* The text provides additional information that will help walk you through a complex model, step by step. Look for definitions of key terms and consult the glossary.

2. *Are all the parts of the figure at the same scale, or different scales? At one time, or at different times?* Different elements of a model may be shown at different scales to make them visible. A double strand of uncondensed DNA is so thin that it would not be visible in a model of a cell if not adjusted in size. Sometimes, one part of a model is an enlarged section of another part. Look for arrows and lines that indicate these connections.

3. *Do I understand what the symbols in the figure represent?* Sometimes different symbols are used for the same concept in different contexts due to the amount (or type) of detail needed—DNA, lipid bilayers, and cells are good examples. Or sometimes symbols such as arrows can have different meanings in different contexts. Take your time in mentally "translating" these symbols to make sure that you are not carrying a previous meaning into a new context.

4. *Do I understand the use of color?* Artificial coloration is an important aspect of models. For example, DNA and RNA are colorless in real life, but in this book, the default color for DNA is red and the default color for RNA is yellow. Color can also be used for emphasis to draw your attention to certain features. Bright red is more likely to grab your attention than pale gray, so red is often used for important information and gray for supporting information.

5. *What seems to be the most important part of the figure? What is the take-home message of the figure?* Many of the figures in this book have blue questions in the captions. You can use these questions (and the answers in **Appendix A**) to check that you are interpreting the figures appropriately.

Tips for Interpreting Visual Models	Example
Simplicity Visual models simplify reality to focus your attention on a specific concept. **1.** What is the focus of this model? What is *not* shown for simplicity?	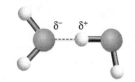
Color use Color coding helps to identify structures and emphasize certain parts of models. **2.** What do the red balls represent? Are they red in real life?	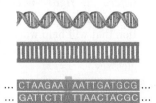
Same concept, different symbols Different symbols may be used to represent the same concept in different contexts, such as at different scales. **3.** What do these three symbols represent?	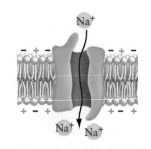
Same symbol, different meanings Some symbols, such as arrows, may have very different meanings in different contexts. **4.** Does this arrow represent a transformation of one thing to another, a movement, a passage of time, or something else?	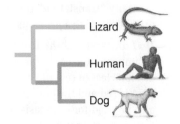
Scale flexibility Different components of a model may be shown at different scales to make them more visible. **5.** Estimate the size of the lizard relative to the human in real life.	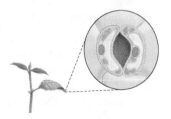
Scale connections Lines and arrows may be used to show that one part of a figure is an enlargement of another. **6.** Why are the stomata cells not shown directly on the leaf?	

Tips for Making your Own Models

You may be excited by the opportunity to draw models, or you may feel intimidated by the task. Either way, you have lots of company. The **Making Models** boxes throughout the book give you specific tips on how to make and use different types of visual models in biology—such as pedigrees, membrane models, phylogenetic trees, graphs, and food webs (see the inside back cover for a complete list of Making Models boxes). Here, let's consider four general tips to help you get started:

1. ***You don't have to be an artist to make good models.*** Models are often most effective when they are simple. Remember, the goal is to make tools to think with, not realistic art. The figure below shows an example of how your hand-drawn models may differ from typical textbook figures.

 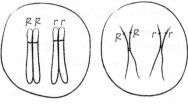

Textbook figure   Hand-drawn models

2. ***Focus on the important ideas.*** If you are drawing a model to show the relationship between cellular respiration and photosynthesis in an ecosphere that includes shrimp, algae, and bacteria, don't spend a lot of time drawing shrimp legs. You could simply use an oval containing the word "shrimp."

3. ***Practice using standard symbols.*** Translating from verbal to visual and visual to verbal is like translating between two languages. Learn the meaning of commonly used symbols in biology, such as the circles and squares in pedigrees, the axes in graphs, and the lines in phylogenetic trees.

4. ***Process is as important as product.*** Don't be afraid to change your model or start over. Since models are thinking tools, you should expect to make as many drafts of a model as you need to until you understand an idea or solve a problem.

Let's apply these ideas to one kind of model that you will be prompted to draw in this book: a concept map.

Concept Maps

Concept maps are devices for organizing and expressing what you know about a topic. They have been proven to be an effective studying and learning tool.

Concept maps have two main elements: **(1)** concepts that are identified by words or short phrases and placed in a box or circle (you can think of these as the "nouns"), and **(2)** labeled arrows that physically link two or more concepts and explain the relationship between them (you can think of these as the "verbs"). The concepts can be arranged in different patterns on the page depending on the content. Concept maps may be organized as a hierarchy starting with the big idea at the top and moving down to details, or they may be organized in a time sequence or cycle.

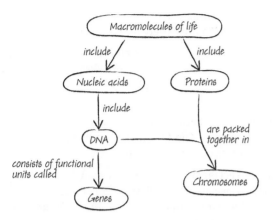

Figure B12.1 A Concept Map of the Relationships between Nucleic Acids and Proteins.

One example of a simple concept map is shown in **Figure B12.1**. Other types of concept maps that you will encounter in this textbook are the road maps that introduce each chapter and the Big Picture concept maps that show how material in multiple chapters is related. When you draw your own concept maps, note how the general principles of model making apply:

- Since concept maps are built using geometric shapes, arrows, and words, you don't need to be an artist to make them.
- The key to good concept maps is focusing on the important ideas and how they are related. Make sure that your connections are accurate.
- It may take time for you to get used to "concept map language," but you will become fluent with practice.
- Your first draft of a map might be a mess. Once you get your ideas down on paper, you may need to create a cleaner draft so that you can read the map easily.

Remember, interpreting and making visual models are skills that can be learned. These skills are valuable not only in your biology class but also in your other science classes and beyond.

CHECK YOUR UNDERSTANDING

If you understand BioSkill 12

✔ You should be able to ...

1–6. Answer the questions in Table B12.1.

7. MODEL Find a way to add "alleles" to the concept map in Figure B12.2.

Answers are available in Appendix A.

BioSkill 13 Reading and Making Phylogenetic Trees

Phylogenetic trees show the hypothesized evolutionary relationships among species or other taxa. A taxon is any named group of organisms, such as a population, a species, or a larger group (see Chapter 1). Phylogenetic trees are a type of visual model (see BioSkill 12) that can take some practice to interpret and draw correctly.

Anatomy of a Phylogenetic Tree

At first glance, a phylogenetic tree may look like just a bunch of lines. But the lines have very specific meanings that include some types of information and not others.

Let's start by examining the tree in **Figure B13.1** and considering each component.

- A *root* is the most ancestral branch in a phylogenetic tree—where the tree originates. In this text, most of the trees are rooted on the left with the branches facing right because this orientation is easy to label and read. You may see other orientations in other sources.

- *Branches* represent populations through time. For ease of interpretation in this text, most branches are drawn as horizontal lines with vertical connectors, and the branches have arbitrary lengths. You may also see trees whose branch lengths are proportional to time or to the extent of genetic difference among populations (indicated by a scale bar at the bottom of the tree; see Chapter 25). In other sources, branches may be drawn as diagonal or curved lines.

- *Nodes* (also called forks) occur where a hypothetical ancestral group splits into two or more descendant groups. In such cases, each node represents the most recent common ancestor of the descendant populations that emerge from it.
- *Tips* (also called terminal nodes) are the tree's endpoints. Each name on a tip represents a taxon of organisms living today or in the past. Taxa on tips connected by a single node are called sister taxa.
- A *monophyletic group* (also called a lineage or clade) consists of an ancestral species and all of its descendants. Monophyletic

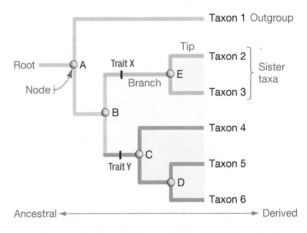

Figure B13.1 A Phylogenetic Tree Has a Root, Branches, Nodes, and Tips

groups can be identified using the "one-snip test": If you cut any branch on a phylogenetic tree, all of the branches and tips that fall off represent a monophyletic group. Using the one-snip test, you should be able to convince yourself that each of the tips is itself a monophyletic group.

- A *trait* is indicated by a black hash mark. An ancestral trait is a characteristic that existed in an ancestor; a derived trait is a characteristic that is a modified form of the ancestral trait, found in a descendant. A shared, derived trait (called a synapomorphy) occurs in all the branches to the right of the hash mark. A trait can be a characteristic that is *gained* (such as the origin of hair in mammals), or it can be a characteristic that is *lost* (such as legs in snakes).

- An *outgroup* is a taxon that is known to have diverged before the rest of the taxa shown in the tree. Outgroups are used to establish whether a trait is ancestral or derived.

How to Read a Phylogenetic Tree

The key to reading relationships in a phylogenetic tree is to examine which groups share most recent common ancestors. In Figure B13.1, for example, taxa 5 and 6 are more closely related to each other than either is to taxon 4, because taxa 5 and 6 share common ancestor D. Consider two important characteristics of phylogenetic trees:

1. **The branches can rotate at each node.** Imagine that a tree is like a mobile hanging by its root from the ceiling. If you were to look up at it, you would see that the taxa at the tips can spin around but the connections—which represent the relationships—don't change. For example, the following two trees are equivalent to the tree in Figure B13.1—although the pattern looks different, the relationships are the same:

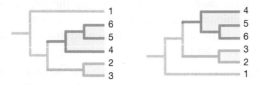

2. **Branches can be added or removed without changing the relationships of the other branches.** The taxa included in a tree often represent just a sample of the diversity of life that exists. Individual branches can be "expanded" to include more taxa or "collapsed" to include fewer taxa. For example, the following two trees include different numbers of taxa: 1 beetle + 5 butterflies, or 5 beetles + 1 butterfly:

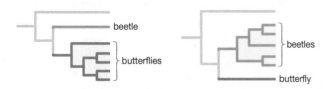

This example shows that counting the number of nodes is not a valid way to decide how closely or distantly related two taxa are—the number of nodes will depend on the number of taxa included in a particular part of a tree.

Let's apply these insights to a question regarding Figure B13.1: Is taxon 3 more closely related to taxon 4, 5, or 6?

- Even though taxa 3 and 4 are closest together on the page, this does not mean that they are more closely related. Remember, the branches can be rotated.

- Even though there are only three nodes between taxa 3 and 4 and four nodes between taxon 3 and taxon 5 or 6, this does not mean that taxa 3 and 4 are more closely related. Remember, the removal of taxon 5 or 6 from the analysis would remove node D.

- The correct answer: Taxon 3 is equally related to taxa 4, 5, and 6 because they all share a common ancestor, B. The branching events that occurred after this ancestor do not affect the underlying relationship.

It takes practice to use these visual models as tools and to draw them correctly. Drawing your own phylogenetic trees can help you improve your skill at interpreting phylogenetic trees.

How to Draw a Phylogenetic Tree

Some of the **Making Models** boxes throughout this book give you specific tips on how to make and use phylogenetic trees. (See the list of Making Models boxes on the inside back cover; also, Chapter 25 demonstrates how to build a phylogenetic tree based on a data matrix.) Note that many trees in the book are color-coded or include icons of the organisms to make them easier to read. Your hand-drawn trees can be much simpler and still be effective.

CHECK YOUR UNDERSTANDING

If you understand BioSkill 13

✔ You should be able to ...

Use the tree below to answer the questions.

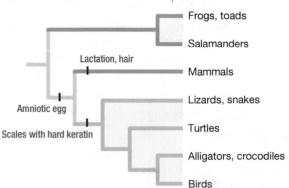

1. **MODEL** Draw a node on the tree that represents the most recent common ancestor of frogs and birds.
2. Determine which taxa have amniotic eggs.
3. **MODEL** Add a trait hash mark showing the origin of limbs. How could you modify the tree to show the loss of limbs in snakes?
4. **MODEL** Draw what the tree would look like if you collapsed all the reptile branches into one branch and included two branches of mammals: placentals and marsupials.
5. Determine whether mammals are more closely related to lizards or turtles.

Answers are available in Appendix A.

BioSkill 14 Reading Chemical Structures

If you haven't had much chemistry yet, learning basic biological chemistry can be a challenge. One stumbling block is simply being able to read chemical structures and understand what they mean. This task will become much easier once you have a little notation under your belt and you understand some basic symbols. Atoms are the basic building blocks of everything in the universe, just as cells are the basic building blocks of your body. Every atom has a one- or two-letter symbol.

Table B14.1 shows the symbols for most of the atoms you'll encounter in this book. You should memorize these symbols. The table also offers details on the number of bonds each atom can form, as well as how the atoms are represented in some visual models.

When atoms attach to each other by covalent bonding, a molecule forms. Table B14.1 also includes atoms such as chlorine and potassium that are joined by ionic bonds to form ionic compounds (see Chapter 2), but the focus here is on atoms that form molecules. Biologists have a couple of different ways of representing molecules—you'll see each of these in the book and in class.

- *Molecular formulas* like the one for the amino acid glycine (see Chapter 3) in Figure B14.1a simply list the atoms present in a molecule. Subscripts indicate how many of each atom are present. If the formula has no subscript, only one atom of each type is present. A methane (natural gas) molecule, for example, is written as CH_4. It consists of one carbon atom and four hydrogen atoms.

- *Structural formulas* like the one for glycine in Figure B14.1b show which atoms in a molecule are bonded to each other. Each bond is indicated by a dash. Single covalent bonds are symbolized by a single dash, as in the bonds between the hydrogen atoms and the nitrogen atom in glycine. Double bonds are indicated by two dashes, as in the covalent bond between a carbon atom and an oxygen atom in glycine. Triple bonds are indicated by three dashes, as in the structural formula for molecular nitrogen (N_2), which is written as $N \equiv N$.

Even simple molecules have distinctive shapes, because different atoms make covalent bonds at different angles. Ball-and-stick and space-filling models show the geometry of the bonds in a molecule accurately, while ribbon models are used to depict the way large molecules fold.

- *Ball-and-stick models* are not as realistic as space-filling models, but they make the bonding arrangement of atoms easier to see because the bonds are represented as sticks. Ball-and-stick models provide information on the three-dimensional shape of molecules and, in some cases, they show the relative sizes of the atoms (colored balls) involved (Figure B14.1c and Figure B14.2a on page 50).

- *Space-filling models* are the most realistic, with a sphere drawn around each atom to show its relative size. The models depict the spatial relationship between atoms—for example, how closely two atoms can approach each other

Table B14.1 **Some Attributes of Atoms Found in Organisms**

Atom	Symbol	Number of Bonds It Can Form	Standard Color Code*
Hydrogen	H	1	white
Carbon	C	4	black
Nitrogen	N	3	blue
Oxygen	O	2	red
Sodium	Na	1	—
Magnesium	Mg	2	—
Phosphorus	P	5	orange or purple
Sulfur	S	2	yellow
Chlorine	Cl	1	—
Potassium	K	1	—
Calcium	Ca	2	—

*In ball-and-stick or space-filling models.

(a) Molecular formula: NH_2CH_2COOH
(glycine)

(b) Structural formula:

(c) Ball-and-stick model:

(d) Space-filling model:

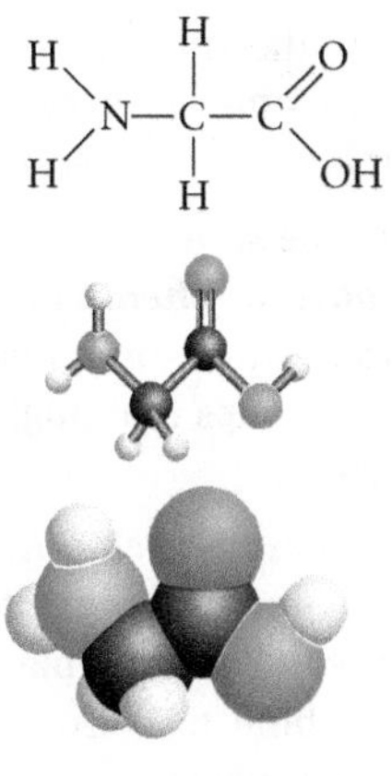

Figure B14.1 A Molecule Can Be Represented in Several Different Ways. The amino acid glycine consists of one nitrogen atom, two carbon atoms, five hydrogen atoms, and two oxygen atoms.

✔ **MODEL** Carbon dioxide consists of a carbon atom that forms a double bond with each of two oxygen atoms, for a total of four bonds. It is a linear molecule. Write carbon dioxide's molecular formula and then draw its structural formula, a ball-and-stick model, and a space-filling model.

when they are not linked by a covalent bond (Figure B14.1d and Figure B14.2b).

- *Ribbon models* are very schematic (Figure B14.2c). They are commonly used to highlight a few major features of protein structure. For example, α-helices are depicted as spring-like coils, β-pleated sheets as flat arrows, and loops as simple lines (see Chapter 3).

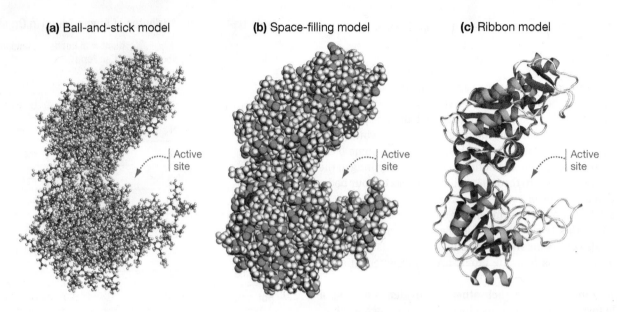

(a) Ball-and-stick model   **(b)** Space-filling model   **(c)** Ribbon model

Active site   Active site   Active site

Figure B14.2 Three Different Models of an Enzyme. The enzyme phosphoglycerate kinase catalyzes step 7 in glycolysis (see Chapter 9). The active site appears as a deep cleft.

To learn more about a molecule when you look at a chemical structure, ask yourself three questions:

1. *Is the molecule polar—meaning that some parts are more negatively or positively charged than others?* Molecules that contain nitrogen or oxygen atoms are often polar because these atoms are very electronegative (see Chapter 2). This trait is important because polar molecules dissolve in water.

2. *Does the structural formula show atoms that might participate in chemical reactions?* For example, are there charged atoms or amino ($-NH_2$) or carboxyl ($-COOH$) functional groups that might make the molecule act as a base or an acid?

3. *In ball-and-stick and especially space-filling models of large molecules, are there interesting aspects of overall shape?* For example, is there a groove where a protein might bind to DNA, or a cleft (as shown in Figure B14.2) where a substrate might undergo a reaction in an enzyme?

BioSkill 15 Translating Greek and Latin Roots in Biology

Use the common Greek and Latin roots shown in Table B15.1, to help interpret unfamiliar biological terms and come up with a literal translation that will help you remember its meaning.

CHECK YOUR UNDERSTANDING

If you understand BioSkill 15

✔ You should be able to ...

Provide literal translations of the following terms:
1. heterozygote **2.** glycolysis **3.** morphology **4.** trisomy

Answers are available in Appendix A.

BioSkill 16 Reading and Citing the Primary Literature

As part of the process of doing science, biologists communicate their results to the scientific community through publications in scientific journals that report on their original research discoveries (see Chapter 1). These published reports are referred to, interchangeably, as the primary literature, research papers, or primary research articles.

What Is the Primary Literature?

Scientists publish "peer-reviewed" papers. This means that several experts in the field have carefully read the paper and considered its strengths and weaknesses. Reviewers write a critique of the paper and make a recommendation to the journal editor as to whether the paper should be published. Often reviewers will suggest additional experiments that need to be completed before a paper is considered acceptable for publication. The peer review process means that research discoveries are carefully vetted before they go to press.

You can distinguish a primary research paper from secondary sources—such as review articles, textbooks, and magazine articles—by looking for key characteristics. A primary research paper includes a detailed description of methods and results, written by the researchers who did the work. As described in Table B16.1, it is typically divided into several sections, including the Title, Abstract, Introduction, Materials and Methods (or Experimental Design), Results and Discussion, and References (or Literature Cited), although the order and name of the sections varies among journals.

Getting Started

At first, trying to read the primary literature may seem like a daunting task. A paper may be peppered with unfamiliar terms and abbreviations. If you tried to read a research paper from start

Table B15.1 Some Common Greek and Latin Roots

Greek or Latin Root	English Translation	Example Term	Greek or Latin Root	English Translation	Example Term
a, an	not	anaerobic	*hyper*	over, more than	hypertonic
aero	air	aerobic	*hypo*	under, less than	hypotonic
allo	other	allopatric	*inter*	between	interspecific
amphi	on both sides	amphipathic	*intra*	within	intraspecific
anti	against	antibody	*iso*	same	isotonic
auto	self	autotroph	*logo, logy*	study of	morphology
bi	two	bilateral symmetry	*lyse, lysis*	loosen, burst	glycolysis
bio	life, living	bioinformatics	*macro*	large	macromolecule
blast	bud, sprout	blastula	*meta*	change, beyond	metamorphosis
co	with	cofactor	*micro*	small	microfilament
cyto	cell	cytoplasm	*morph*	form	morphology
di	two	diploid	*oligo*	few	oligopeptide
ecto	outer	ectoparasite	*para*	beside	parathyroid gland
endo	inner, within	endoparasite	*photo*	light	photosynthesis
epi	outer, upon	epidermis	*poly*	many	polymer
exo	outside	exothermic	*soma*	body	somatic cells
foli	leaf	foliage	*sym, syn*	together	symbiotic, synapsis
glyc	sugary	glycolysis	*trans*	across	translation
hetero	different	heterozygous	*tri*	three	trisomy
homo	alike	homozygous	*zygo*	yoked together	zygote
hydro	water	hydrolysis	*zym*	ferment	enzyme

to finish, like you might read a chapter in this textbook, it would be a frustrating experience. But, with practice, the scientific literature becomes approachable, and reading it is well worth the effort. The primary literature is the cutting edge, the place to read firsthand about the process of doing science. Becoming skilled at reading and evaluating scientific reports is a powerful way to learn how to think critically—to think like a biologist.

To get started, try breaking down the process of reading a primary research article into a series of steps:

1. Read the authors' names. Where are they from? Are they working as a team or alone? After you delve into the literature, certain familiar names will crop up again and again. You'll begin to recognize the experts in a particular field.

2. Read the title. It should summarize the key finding of the paper and tell you what you can expect to learn from the paper.

3. Read the abstract. The abstract summarizes the entire paper in a short paragraph. At this point, it might be tempting

Table B16.1 Sections of a Primary Research Paper

Section	Characteristics
Title	Short, succinct, descriptive
Abstract	Summary of Methods, Results, Discussion. Explains why the research was done and why the results are significant.
Introduction	Background information (what past work was done, why the work was important). States the objectives and hypotheses of the study and explains why the study is important.
Materials and Methods	Explains how and where the work was done.
Results	Presents the data from the study and explains what they show.
Discussion	Explains why the data show what they show, how the analysis relates to the objectives stated in the Introduction, the significance of the findings, and how they advance the field.
References	A list of all the literature cited in the research paper. All sources that served as a foundation for the work, including all the ideas and findings that are not those of the authors, should be cited.

to stop reading. But sometimes the abstract understates or overstates the significance and conclusions of the research. You should never cite an article as a reference after having read only the abstract.

4. Read the Introduction. The first couple of paragraphs should make it clear what the objectives or hypotheses of the paper are; the remaining paragraphs will give you the background information you need to understand the point of the paper.

5. Flip through the article and look at the figures and tables, including reading the legends.

6. Read the Results section carefully. Ask yourself these questions: Does this section accurately describe the data presented in the paper? Were all the appropriate controls carried out in an experiment? Are there additional experiments that you think should have been performed? Are the figures and tables clearly labeled?

7. Consult the Materials and Methods section to get help understanding the research design and the techniques used.

8. Read the Discussion. The first and last paragraphs usually summarize the key findings and state their significance. The Discussion is the part of the paper where the results are explained in the context of the scientific literature. The authors should explain what their results mean.

9. You don't need to read the reference list, but it will serve as a useful directory when you want to learn more about certain topics.

Citing Sources

Whether you're writing lab reports, poster presentations, or papers, it's important to get in the habit of citing your sources in the work you do for your biology classes. To avoid plagiarism, you need to credit the information that came from someone else. For those who read your work, citing references also assures them that the information you've used comes from reliable sources.

Your instructor may specify the exact format to use in citing references, but you can also see examples of how to format the reference list as you read the scientific literature. Note that the accepted style varies among journals. Take a moment to look at examples of citations in this textbook—wherever data are shown, a source for the data is provided (see BioSkill 3 for one example).

Getting Practice

The best way to get practice is to read the scientific literature as often as possible. You could begin by reading some of the references cited in this textbook. You can get an electronic copy of most articles through online databases such as PubMed, Science-Direct, or Google Scholar, or through your institution's library.

After reading a primary research paper, you should be able to paraphrase the significance of the paper in a few sentences, free of technical jargon. As you become more familiar with reading the scientific literature, you're likely to start thinking about what questions remain to be answered. You may even come up with "the next experiment."

BioSkill 17 Recognizing and Correcting Misconceptions

Have you ever felt confident that you understood a concept in a science class, and then been surprised to get a question wrong on a quiz? To avoid such unpleasant surprises, you can begin by mastering a certain learning skill—recognizing when everyday ways of thinking and everyday uses of words are not a good fit in a scientific context.

Table B17.1 summarizes some common ways that your experiences outside of your biology class might hinder your understanding of biology, leading to misconceptions—incorrect ideas, which can be very common among students. With some practice, though, you can learn to identify the common types of misconceptions and steer your thinking accordingly. Use the following three steps as a starting place:

1. *Study Table B17.1 to familiarize yourself with common categories of misconceptions.* Are any of them familiar to you already?

2. *Answer in-chapter and end-of-chapter questions that have a CAUTION tag.* You will see this tag on some questions throughout the book. The **CAUTION** tag is a prompt to alert you that the question addresses a concept that is often the source of a misconception.

3. *Check your answers in the Appendix.* If you missed a question with a **CAUTION** tag, look at Table B17.1 and identify the category of misconception that made it challenging to answer the question.

Becoming aware of how experiences in everyday life can hinder learning in biology will help you learn to think like a biologist. By learning to think like a biologist, you can maximize your study success.

Table B17.1 Common Categories of Misconceptions

Category	Description	Examples
Different meaning of terms	Some terms have a different meaning in everyday use than they do in biology.	theory, fitness, adaptation, selection, "using up" energy, "producing" energy, climate, germ
Goal-oriented thinking	Humans have a natural tendency to assign purpose or reason to events, but most biological processes are not goal driven.	"Plants produce oxygen so that animals can breathe." "Roses evolved thorns so that herbivores wouldn't eat them."
Human-centered thinking	Humans have a natural tendency to view the world from a human perspective, but our personal experiences often do not apply to other biological contexts.	"Plants suck up food through their roots." "Mutations are bad." "Disturbance in communities is bad."
Simplistic thinking	Humans have a natural tendency to mentally simplify complex systems to make sense of them, but this can lead to oversimplification.	"Eye genes occur only in eye cells." "All members of a species are alike."

BIOSKILL 18 Using Bloom's Taxonomy for Study Success

At one time or another, you may have wondered why a particular question on an exam seemed so hard while others seemed easy. The explanation has much to do with the type of cognitive skill required to answer the question.

Let's take a closer look.

Categories of Human Cognition

Bloom's Taxonomy is a classification system that instructors use to identify the cognitive skill levels at which they are asking students to work, particularly on practice problems and exams. Bloom's Taxonomy is also a very useful tool for you to know—it can help you figure out the appropriate level at which you should be studying to succeed in a course.

Bloom's Taxonomy distinguishes six categories of human thinking: *Remember, Understand, Apply, Analyze, Evaluate*, and *Create*. One of the most useful distinctions lies not in the differences among these six categories, but rather in the difference between what are classified as high-order cognitive (HOC) and low-order cognitive (LOC) skills. **Figure B18.1** shows how the six categories of the taxonomy can be broken into HOC and LOC skills.

Skills that hallmark LOCs include recall, explanation (*Remember, Understand*), and use of knowledge in the exact way that you have used it before (*Apply*). Note, however, that when knowledge is used in a new way, *Apply* is considered an HOC skill.

Other skills that typify HOCs include the breakdown, critique, and creation of information (*Analyze, Evaluate, Create*). Most college instructors will assume you are proficient at solving LOC questions and will expect you to frequently work at the HOC levels. The good news is that HOC problems usually require use of basic vocabulary and applying knowledge in a new way. Thus, working at the HOC levels has an added benefit—it also helps you to master the LOC levels.

Six Study Steps to Success

You can use Bloom's Taxonomy along with questions in this textbook to prepare for an exam, by following six study steps to success:

1. *Answer in-chapter questions while reading the chapter.* All questions in this book have been assigned Bloom's levels, so you can review the question answers and the Bloom's level while you study.

2. *Identify the Bloom's level(s) of the questions that you are having greatest difficulty answering.* While working through the text, take note of the content and Bloom's level(s) that you find the most challenging.

3. *Use the Bloom's Taxonomy Study Guide (Table B18.1 on page 54) to focus your study efforts at the appropriate Bloom's level.* Table B18.1 lists specific study methods that can help you practice your understanding of the material at both the LOC and HOC levels, whether you are studying alone or with a study group.

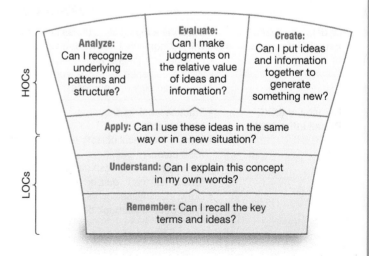

Figure B18.1 **Bloom's Taxonomy.**

4. **Complete the end-of-chapter questions as if you're taking an exam, without looking for the answers.** If you look at the chapter text or jump to the answers, then you really aren't testing your ability to work with the content and have reduced the questions to the lowest Bloom's level of *Remember*.

5. **Grade your answers to the end-of-chapter questions and note the Bloom's level of the questions you got wrong.** At what level of Bloom's Taxonomy were the questions you missed?

6. **Use the Bloom's Taxonomy Study Guide to focus your study efforts at the appropriate Bloom's level.** If you missed a lot of questions, then revisit Table B18.1 to review suggestions for study activities, spend more time studying the material, and find other resources for quizzing yourself, such as online problem sets.

By following these six steps and studying at both the LOC and HOC levels, you should succeed in answering questions on in-class exams.

Table B18.1 **Bloom's Taxonomy Study Guide**

	Individual Study Activities	Group Study Activities
Create (HOC) **Generate something new**	• Generate a hypothesis or design an experiment based on information you are studying. • Create a model based on a given data set. • Create summary sheets that show how facts and concepts relate to each other. • Create questions at each level of Bloom's Taxonomy as a practice test and then take the test.	• Have each student put forward a hypothesis about a biological process and design an experiment to test it, then have your peers critique the hypotheses and experiments. • Create a new model/summary sheet/concept map that integrates each group member's ideas.
Evaluate (HOC) **Defend or judge a concept or idea**	• Provide a written assessment of the strengths and weaknesses of your peers' work or understanding of a given concept based on previously determined criteria.	• Provide a verbal assessment of the strengths and weaknesses of your peers' work or understanding of a given concept based on previously described criteria, and have your peers critique your assessment.
Analyze (HOC) **Distinguish parts and make inferences**	• Analyze and interpret data in primary literature or a textbook without reading the author's interpretation and then compare the authors' interpretation with your own. • Analyze a situation and then identify the assumptions and principles of the argument. • Compare and contrast two ideas or concepts. • Construct a map of the main concepts by defining the relationships of the concepts using one- or two-way arrows.	• Work together to analyze and interpret data in primary literature or a textbook without reading the author's interpretation, and defend your analysis to your peers. • Work together to identify all of the concepts in a paper or textbook chapter, construct individual maps linking the concepts together with arrows and words that relate the concepts, and then grade each other's concept maps.
Apply (HOC or LOC) **Use information or concepts in new ways (HOC) or in the same ways (LOC)**	• Review each process you have learned and then ask yourself: What would happen if you increase or decrease a component in the system, or what would happen if you alter the activity of a component in the system? • If possible, graph a biological process and create scenarios that change the shape or slope of the graph.	• Practice writing out answers to old exam questions on the board, and have your peers check to make sure you don't have too much or too little information in your answer. • Take turns teaching your peers a biological process while the group critiques the content.
Understand (LOC) **Explain information or concepts**	• Describe a biological process in your own words without copying it from a book or another source. • Provide examples of a process. • Write a sentence using the word. • Give examples of a process.	• Discuss content with peers. • Take turns quizzing each other about definitions, and have your peers check your answers.
Remember (LOC) **Recall information**	• Practice labeling diagrams. • List characteristics. • Identify biological objects or components from flash cards. • Quiz yourself with flash cards. • Take a self-made quiz on vocabulary. • Draw, classify, select, or match items. • Write out the textbook definitions.	• Check a drawing that another student labeled. • Create lists of concepts and processes that your peers can match. • Place flash cards in a bag and take turns selecting one for which you must define a term. • Do the preceding activities, and have peers check your answers.

2 Water and Carbon: The Chemical Basis of Life

These deep-sea hydrothermal vents produce hydrogen-rich, highly basic fluids at temperatures that range from 40° to 90°C. It has been proposed that life emerged from similar seafloor chimneys early in Earth's history via chemical evolution.

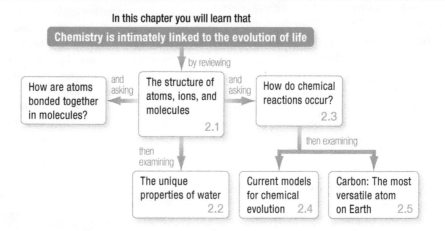

In this chapter you will learn that

Chemistry is intimately linked to the evolution of life

by reviewing

How are atoms bonded together in molecules? ← and asking — **The structure of atoms, ions, and molecules** 2.1 — and asking → How do chemical reactions occur? 2.3

then examining

The unique properties of water 2.2

then examining

Current models for chemical evolution 2.4

Carbon: The most versatile atom on Earth 2.5

This chapter is part of the Big Picture. See how on pages 140–141.

A classic experiment on spontaneous generation by Louis Pasteur tested the idea that organisms arise from nonliving materials (see Chapter 1). The results of this work helped build a consensus that spontaneous generation does not occur. But for life to exist, it must have evolved from non-living materials at least once early in Earth's history.

How did life begin? This simple query has been called "the mother of all questions." This chapter examines the leading scientific explanation for the origin of life—the theory of **chemical evolution.** The theory maintains that inputs of energy led to the formation of increasingly complex carbon-containing substances, culminating in a molecule that could replicate itself. At this point, there was a switch from chemical evolution to biological evolution.

As the original molecule multiplied, the process of evolution by natural selection took over. Eventually a descendant of the original molecule became metabolically active and acquired a membrane. When this occurred, the five attributes of life (discussed in Chapter 1) were fulfilled. Life had begun.

At first glance, the theory of chemical evolution may seem implausible. But is it? What evidence do biologists have that chemical evolution occurred? What approaches do they take to gathering this evidence? Let's start with the fundamentals—atoms and molecules that would have combined to get chemical evolution started.

2.1 Atoms, Ions, and Molecules: The Building Blocks of Chemical Evolution

Just four types of atoms—hydrogen, carbon, nitrogen, and oxygen—make up 96 percent of all matter found in organisms today. Many of the molecules found in your cells contain thousands, or even millions, of these atoms bonded together. But early in Earth's history, these atoms existed only in simple substances such as water and carbon dioxide, which contain just three atoms apiece.

Two questions are fundamental to understanding how these simple substances could have evolved into the more complex structures found in living cells:

1. What is the physical structure of the hydrogen, carbon, nitrogen, and oxygen atoms found in living cells?

2. What is the structure of the simple molecules—water, carbon dioxide, and others—that served as the building blocks of chemical evolution?

The focus on structure follows from one of the most central themes in biology: *Structure affects function.* To understand how a molecule affects your body or the role it played in chemical evolution, you have to understand how it is put together.

Basic Atomic Structure

Figure 2.1a shows a simple way of depicting the structure of an atom, using hydrogen and carbon as examples. Extremely small particles called electrons orbit an atomic nucleus made up of larger particles called protons and neutrons. Every element except hydrogen has one or more neutrons in its nucleus. Figure 2.1b provides a sense of scale at the atomic level.

Protons have a positive electric charge (+1), neutrons are electrically neutral, and electrons have a negative electric charge (−1). When the number of protons and the number of electrons in an atom are the same, the charges balance and make the entire atom electrically neutral.

Figure 2.2 shows a segment of the periodic table of the elements. Notice that each atom of a given **element** contains a characteristic number of protons, called its **atomic number.** The atomic number is written as a subscript to the left of an element's symbol in Figure 2.2. The sum of the protons and neutrons in an atom is called its **mass number** and is written as a superscript to the left of its symbol.

Although the masses of protons, neutrons, and electrons can be measured in grams, the numbers involved are so small that biologists prefer to use a special unit called the **dalton (Da).** This unit of measure was named after John Dalton, who is responsible for formulating the atomic theory. The masses of protons and neutrons are virtually identical and are routinely rounded to 1 Da each. The mass of an electron is so small that it is normally ignored. So, the mass of an atom is equal to its mass number.

The number of protons in an element does not vary—if the atomic number of an atom changes, then it is no longer the same element. The number of neutrons present in an element can vary, however. Forms of an element with different numbers of neutrons are known as **isotopes** (literally, "equal-places" in regard to position in the periodic table).

Isotopes of the same element have different masses because they have different numbers of neutrons. All atoms of the element carbon have 6 protons, for example, but naturally occurring isotopes of carbon can have 6, 7, or even 8 neutrons, giving them masses of 12, 13, or 14 Da, respectively. The **atomic weight** of an element is an average of all the masses of the naturally occurring isotopes based on their abundance. This is why the atomic weights for elements are often slightly different from

(a) Diagrams of atoms

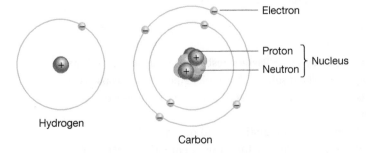

Hydrogen

Carbon

Electron

Proton

Neutron } Nucleus

(b) Most of an atom's volume is empty space.

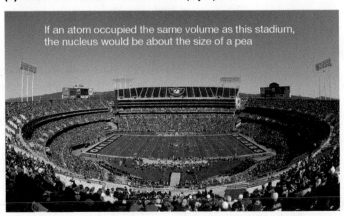

If an atom occupied the same volume as this stadium, the nucleus would be about the size of a pea

Figure 2.1 Parts of an Atom. A simplified model of an atom with its nucleus, made up of protons and neutrons—or a single proton in the case of hydrogen—surrounded by orbiting electrons. In reality, electrons are not evenly spaced, nor do they orbit the nucleus in concentric circles; their actual orbits are complex.

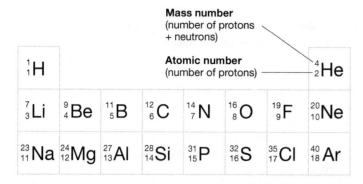

Mass number
(number of protons
+ neutrons)

Atomic number
(number of protons)

$^{1}_{1}H$							$^{4}_{2}He$
$^{7}_{3}Li$	$^{9}_{4}Be$	$^{11}_{5}B$	$^{12}_{6}C$	$^{14}_{7}N$	$^{16}_{8}O$	$^{19}_{9}F$	$^{20}_{10}Ne$
$^{23}_{11}Na$	$^{24}_{12}Mg$	$^{27}_{13}Al$	$^{28}_{14}Si$	$^{31}_{15}P$	$^{32}_{16}S$	$^{35}_{17}Cl$	$^{40}_{18}Ar$

Figure 2.2 A Portion of the Periodic Table. Each element has a unique atomic number and is represented by a unique one- or two-letter symbol. The mass numbers given here are the most common for each element. (Appendix B provides a complete periodic table.)

the mass numbers. For example, the atomic weight of carbon is 12.01, which reflects that the most abundant isotope has 6 neutrons and a mass of 12 daltons (^{12}C).

Most isotopes are stable, but not all. For example, ^{14}C, with 8 neutrons, represents an unstable **radioactive isotope.** Its nucleus will eventually decay and release energy (radiation). When ^{14}C decays, one of its neutrons changes into a proton, converting ^{14}C to the stable ^{14}N isotope of nitrogen, with 7 protons and 7 neutrons. Timing of decay is specific to each radioisotope, a fact that has been very useful in estimating the dates of key events in Earth's history (see Chapter 22).

To understand how the structures of atoms differ, take a moment to study **Figure 2.3**. This chart highlights in blue the elements that are most abundant in living cells. The elements C, H, N, O, P, and S make up over 99 percent of the atoms in your body. The arrangement of electrons around the nucleus is key to understanding how different elements behave.

- Electrons move around atomic nuclei in specific regions called **orbitals.**
- Each orbital can hold up to two electrons.
- Orbitals are grouped into levels called **electron shells.**
- Electron shells are numbered 1, 2, 3, and so on, to indicate their relative distance from the nucleus. Smaller numbers are closer to the nucleus.
- Each electron shell contains a specific number of orbitals. Each orbital in a shell is loaded with one electron before any orbital is filled with a paired electron.
- The electrons of an atom fill the innermost shells first, before filling outer shells.

Now focus on the outermost shell of each element. This is the atom's **valence shell.** The electrons found in this shell are referred to as **valence electrons.** Note that in each of the highlighted elements, the outermost electron shell is not full—there is at least one orbital with an unpaired valence electron. The number of unpaired valence electrons varies among elements. Carbon, for example, has four valence electrons, all unpaired. Oxygen has six valence electrons; four are paired, two are not. The number of unpaired electrons found in an atom's valence shell is called its **valence.** Carbon's valence is four, oxygen's is two.

These observations are significant because an atom is most stable when its valence shell is filled. One way that shells can be filled is through the formation of strong **chemical bonds**—attractions that bind atoms together. A strong attraction where two atoms share electrons is called a **covalent bond.**

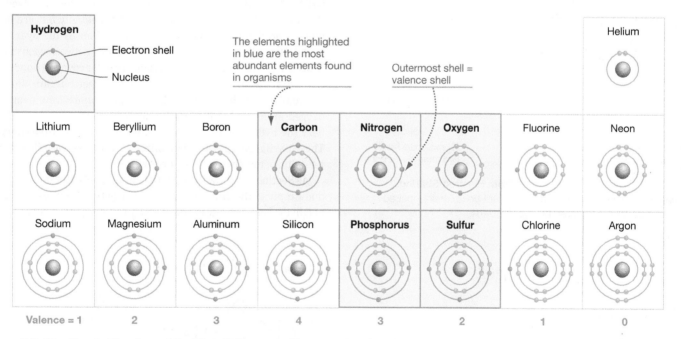

Figure 2.3 The Atomic Structure of the First 18 Elements. The most abundant elements in organisms are highlighted in blue.

✔ **MODEL** Use the atomic structure of phosphorus to determine the number of electrons, electron shells, and orbitals present in the outer shell of this element. Which, if any, of these values would differ between different isotopes?

How Does Covalent Bonding Hold Molecules Together?

To understand how atoms can become more stable by making covalent bonds, consider hydrogen. The hydrogen atom has just one electron, which resides in a shell that can hold two electrons.

Because it has an unpaired valence electron, the hydrogen atom does not have a full valence shell and is not very stable. But when two atoms of hydrogen come into contact, the two electrons become shared by the two nuclei as shown in Figure 2.4. This in effect gives each atom a filled outer shell. Together, the hydrogen atoms are more stable than the two individual hydrogen atoms.

Shared electrons "glue" atoms together. Substances held together by covalent bonds are called **molecules.** In the case of two hydrogen atoms, the bonded atoms form a single molecule of hydrogen, written as H—H or H_2.

Nonpolar and Polar Bonds In Figure 2.5a, the covalent bond between hydrogen atoms is represented by a dash and the electrons are drawn as dots halfway between the two nuclei. This depiction shows that the electrons are shared equally between the two hydrogen atoms, resulting in a covalent bond that is symmetrical.

It's important to note, though, that the electrons participating in a covalent bond are not always shared equally between the atoms involved. This may occur in **compounds,** where atoms of different elements are bonded together. When atoms of different elements form a bond, they may pull shared electrons toward their nuclei with varying strengths. Chemists call this property **electronegativity.**

What is responsible for an atom's electronegativity? It's a combination of two things—the number of protons in the nucleus and the distance between the nucleus and the valence shell. If you return to Figure 2.3 and move your finger along a row from left to right, you will be moving toward elements that increase in protons and in electronegativity (ignoring those with full outer shells in the far right column). Each row in the table represents a shell of electrons. As your finger moves down the table, it passes over elements with more shells and less electronegativity. In Figure 2.3, fluorine would have the highest electronegativity and sodium would have the lowest.

Oxygen, which has eight protons and only two electron shells, is among the most electronegative of all elements. It attracts covalently bonded electrons more strongly than does any other atom commonly found in organisms. Nitrogen, which has one fewer proton, has a somewhat lower electronegativity than oxygen. Sulfur, carbon, hydrogen, and phosphorus, in turn, have relatively low and approximately equal electronegativities. Thus, the electronegativities of the six most abundant elements in organisms are related as follows: $O > N > S \cong C \cong H \cong P$.

Because carbon and hydrogen have approximately equal electronegativity, the electrons in a C—H bond are shared equally or symmetrically. A bond that involves equally shared electrons is called a **nonpolar covalent bond.** In contrast, asymmetric sharing of electrons results in a **polar covalent bond.** The electrons in a polar covalent bond spend most of their time close to the nucleus of the more electronegative atom. Why is this important?

Polar Bonds Produce Partial Charges on Atoms To understand the consequences of differences in electronegativity and the formation of polar covalent bonds, consider the water molecule. Water consists of an oxygen atom bonded to two hydrogen atoms, and is written H_2O. As Figure 2.5b illustrates, the electrons involved in the covalent bonds in water are not shared equally but are held much more tightly by the oxygen nucleus than by the hydrogen nuclei. Hence, both bonds in a water molecule, between each of the hydrogen atoms and the oxygen atom, are polar covalent bonds.

Here's the key observation: Because electrons are shared unequally in each O—H bond, they spend more time near the oxygen atom, giving it a partial negative charge, and less time near the hydrogen atoms, giving them a partial positive charge. These partial charges are symbolized by the lowercase Greek letter delta, δ, together with a $+$ or $-$ sign.

As Section 2.2 shows, the partial charges on water molecules—due simply to the difference in electronegativity between oxygen and hydrogen—are one of the primary reasons that life exists.

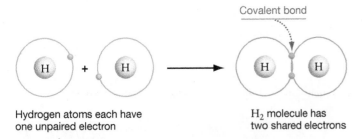

(a) Nonpolar covalent bond in hydrogen molecule

Covalent bond

Hydrogen atoms each have one unpaired electron

H_2 molecule has two shared electrons

Figure 2.4 Covalent Bonds Result from Electron Sharing. When two hydrogen atoms form a covalent bond, their unpaired valence electrons are shared by each nucleus.

H——H
Electrons are halfway between the two atoms, shared equally

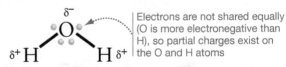

(b) Polar covalent bonds in water molecule

δ^-
O
δ^+ H   H δ^+

Electrons are not shared equally (O is more electronegative than H), so partial charges exist on the O and H atoms

Figure 2.5 Electron Sharing and Bond Polarity. Electrons in a covalent bond can be **(a)** shared equally, resulting in nonpolar bonds, or **(b)** shared unequally, resulting in polar bonds. Delta symbols δ^+ and δ^- associated with polar covalent bonds refer to partial charges that arise owing to unequal electron sharing.

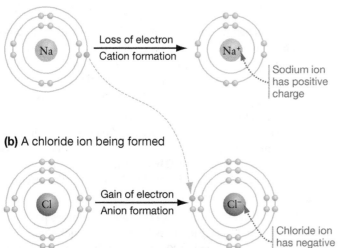

(a) A sodium ion being formed

Loss of electron
Cation formation

Sodium ion has positive charge

(b) A chloride ion being formed

Gain of electron
Anion formation

Chloride ion has negative charge

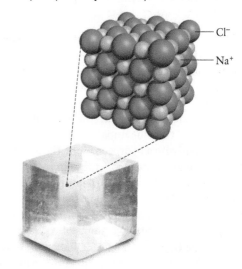

(c) Table salt (NaCl) is a crystal composed of two ions.

Cl⁻
Na⁺

Figure 2.6 Ion Formation and Ionic Bonding. The sodium ion (Na^+) and the chloride ion (Cl^-) are stable because they have full valence shells. In table salt (NaCl), sodium and chloride ions pack into a crystal structure held together by electrical attraction between their positive and negative charges.

Ionic Bonding, Ions, and the Electron-Sharing Continuum

Ionic bonds are similar in principle to covalent bonds, but instead of being shared between two atoms, the electrons in ionic bonds are completely transferred from one atom to the other. The electron transfer occurs because it gives the resulting atoms a full valence shell.

Sodium atoms (Na), for example, have three electron shells with a lone electron in its valence shell. These atoms tend to lose an electron, leaving them with a full second shell—a much more energetically stable arrangement (**Figure 2.6a**). The atom that results has a net electric charge of +1, because it has one more proton than it has electrons.

An atom or molecule that carries a full charge, rather than the partial charges that arise from polar covalent bonds, is called an **ion.** The sodium ion is written Na^+ and, like other positively charged ions, is called a **cation** (pronounced *KAT-eye-un*).

Chlorine atoms (Cl), in contrast, tend to gain an electron, filling their outermost shell (**Figure 2.6b**). The resulting ion has a net charge of −1, because it has one more electron than protons. This negatively charged ion, or **anion** (pronounced *AN-eye-un*), is written Cl^- and is called chloride.

When sodium and chlorine combine to form sodium chloride (NaCl, common table salt), they pack into a crystal structure consisting of sodium cations and chloride anions (**Figure 2.6c**). The electrical attraction between the ions is so strong that salt crystals are difficult to break apart.

This discussion of covalent and ionic bonding supports an important general observation: The degree to which electrons are shared in chemical bonds forms a continuum from equal sharing in nonpolar covalent bonds to unequal sharing in polar covalent bonds to the transfer of electrons in ionic bonds (**Figure 2.7**). Most of the compounds that are present in living organisms are formed from either nonpolar or polar covalent bonds. Let's look at how covalent bonds are used to hold atoms together in molecules.

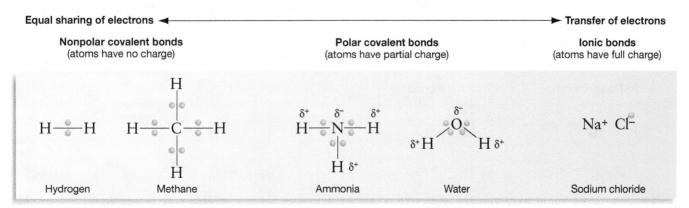

Equal sharing of electrons ◄──────────────────────────────► Transfer of electrons

| **Nonpolar covalent bonds** (atoms have no charge) | **Polar covalent bonds** (atoms have partial charge) | **Ionic bonds** (atoms have full charge) |

H—H

H—C—H (with H above and H below)

δ^+ H—N—H δ^+ with H δ^+ below, δ^- on N

δ^- O with δ^+ H and H δ^+

Na^+ Cl^-

Hydrogen   Methane   Ammonia   Water   Sodium chloride

Figure 2.7 The Electron-Sharing Continuum. The degree of electron sharing in chemical bonds can be thought of as a continuum, from equal sharing in nonpolar covalent bonds to complete electron transfer in ionic bonds.

✔ Why do most polar covalent bonds involve nitrogen or oxygen?

Some Simple Molecules Formed from C, H, N, and O

Look back at Figure 2.3 and count the number of unpaired electrons in the valence shells of carbon, nitrogen, oxygen, and hydrogen atoms. Each unpaired electron in a valence shell can make up half of a covalent bond. It should make sense to you that a carbon atom can form a total of four covalent bonds; nitrogen can form three; oxygen can form two; and hydrogen, one.

When each of the four unpaired electrons of a carbon atom covalently bonds with a hydrogen atom, the molecule that results is written CH_4 and is called methane (**Figure 2.8a**). Methane is the most common molecule found in natural gas. When a nitrogen atom's three unpaired electrons bond with three hydrogen atoms, the result is NH_3, or ammonia. Similarly, an atom of oxygen can form covalent bonds with two atoms of hydrogen, resulting in a water molecule (H_2O). As Figure 2.4 showed, a hydrogen atom can bond with another hydrogen atom to form hydrogen gas (H_2).

Atoms with more than one unpaired electron in the valence shell can also form double bonds or triple bonds. **Figure 2.8b** shows how carbon forms double bonds with oxygen atoms to produce carbon dioxide (CO_2). Triple bonds result when three pairs of electrons are shared. **Figure 2.8c** shows the structure of molecular nitrogen (N_2), which forms when two nitrogen atoms establish a triple bond.

✔ If you understand how electronegativity affects covalent bonds, you should be able to draw arrows between the atoms in each molecule shown in Figure 2.8 to indicate the relative position of the shared electrons. If they are equally shared, then draw a double-headed arrow.

Note that in each of the molecules in Figure 2.8, the single, double, or triple covalent bonds have the effect of giving each atom a full outer shell. Each nitrogen atom in N_2, for example, has one unshared pair of electrons and three shared electron pairs to fill its valence shell with a total of eight electrons.

The Geometry of Simple Molecules

In many cases, the overall shape of a molecule dictates how it *behaves*. In chemistry and in biology, function is based on structure.

The shapes of the simple molecules you've just learned about are governed by the geometry of their bonds. The position of these bonds results from the repulsive forces between the negative charges in shared and unshared electron pairs in the valence shell.

- Nitrogen (N_2) and carbon dioxide (CO_2) have linear structures (see Figure 2.8). There are only two atoms in N_2, so the molecule can only be linear. The three atoms in CO_2 are linear because the electrons in the two $C=O$ bonds repel one another and are thus 180° apart, which maximizes the distance between them.

- Methane (CH_4) has a tetrahedral structure (**Figure 2.9a**). The tetrahedron forms because the repulsive forces push the four $C-H$ bonds as far apart as they can get, such that each bond to the carbon atom is 120° away from its neighboring bonds.

- Water (H_2O) has a planar, or two-dimensional, structure that is bent (**Figure 2.9b**). Why? The electrons in the four orbitals of oxygen's valence shell repulse each other, just as they do in methane. But in water, two of the orbitals are filled with unshared electron pairs from the oxygen atom. The remaining pairs form $O-H$ bonds that are 120° apart and result in a flat, V-shaped molecule.

Section 2.2 explores how water's shape, in combination with the partial charges on the oxygen and hydrogen atoms, makes it the most important molecule on Earth.

Representing Molecules

Molecules can be represented in a variety of increasingly complex ways—only some of which reflect their actual shape. Each method has advantages and disadvantages.

- **Molecular formulas** are compact, but don't contain a great deal of information—they indicate only the numbers and types of atoms in a molecule (**Figure 2.10a**).

- **Structural formulas** indicate which atoms in a molecule are bonded together. Single, double, and triple bonds are represented by single, double, and triple dashes, respectively. Structural formulas also indicate geometry in two dimensions (**Figure 2.10b**). This method is useful for planar molecules such as water and CO_2.

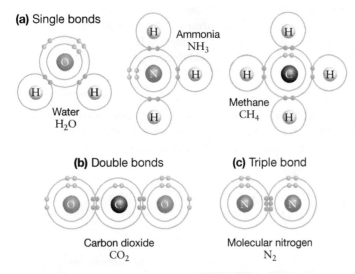

(a) Single bonds

Water H_2O

Ammonia NH_3

Methane CH_4

(b) Double bonds

Carbon dioxide CO_2

(c) Triple bond

Molecular nitrogen N_2

Figure 2.8 Unpaired Electrons in the Valence Shell Participate in Covalent Bonds. Covalent bonding is based on sharing of electrons in the outermost shell. Covalent bonds can be **(a)** single, **(b)** double, or **(c)** triple.

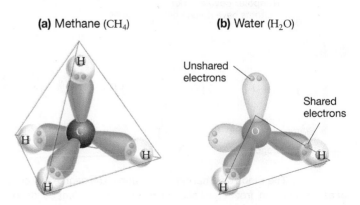

(a) Methane (CH_4)

(b) Water (H_2O)

Unshared electrons

Shared electrons

Figure 2.9 The Geometry of Methane and Water.

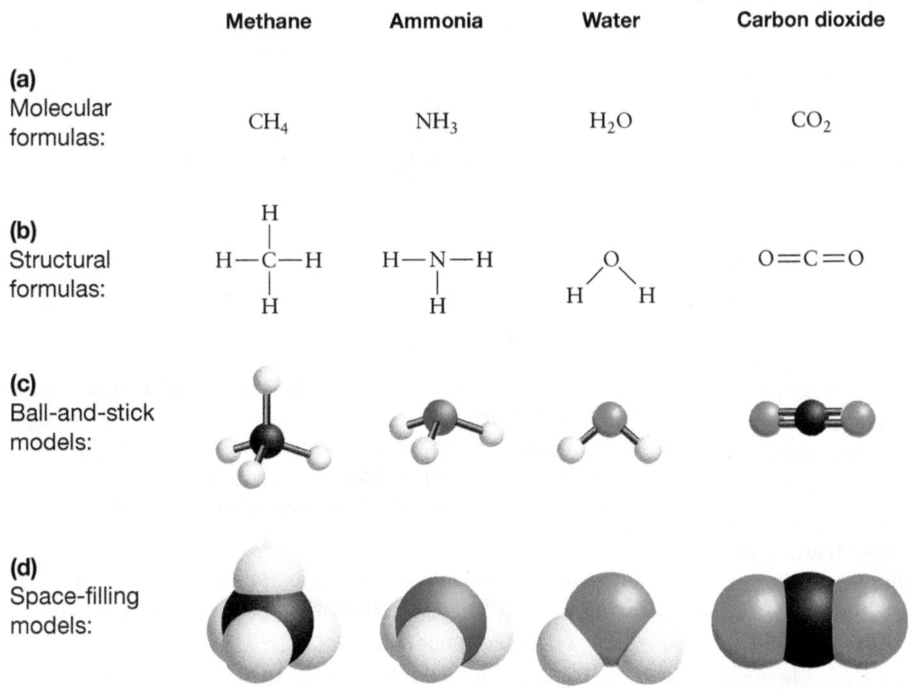

	Methane	Ammonia	Water	Carbon dioxide
(a) Molecular formulas:	CH_4	NH_3	H_2O	CO_2

Figure 2.10 Molecules Can Be Represented Several Ways. Each method of representing a molecule has particular advantages.

(b) Structural formulas:

Methane:
$$H-\underset{\underset{H}{|}}{\overset{\overset{H}{|}}{C}}-H$$

Ammonia:
$$H-\underset{\underset{H}{|}}{N}-H$$

Water:
$$\underset{H \qquad H}{\overset{O}{\diagdown}}$$

Carbon dioxide:
$$O=C=O$$

(c) Ball-and-stick models:

(d) Space-filling models:

- **Ball-and-stick models** take up more space than structural formulas, but provide information on the three-dimensional shape of molecules and indicate the relative sizes of the atoms involved (**Figure 2.10c**).

- **Space-filling models** are more difficult to read than ball-and-stick models but more accurately depict the relative sizes of atoms and their spatial relationships (**Figure 2.10d**).

In both ball-and-stick and space-filling models, biologists use certain colors to represent certain atoms. A black ball, for example, always symbolizes carbon. (For more information on interpreting chemical structures, see BioSkills 14.)

Some of the small molecules you've just learned about are found in volcanic gases, the atmospheres of nearby planets, and in deep-sea hydrothermal vents, like those shown in the photograph at the start of this chapter. Based on these observations, researchers claim that they were important components of

---

CHECK YOUR UNDERSTANDING

If you understand that ...

- Covalent bonds are formed when electrons are shared between atoms. Electron sharing allows atoms to fill all the orbitals in their valence shell, making them more stable.
- Covalent bonds can be nonpolar or polar, depending on whether the electronegativities of the two atoms involved are similar or not.

✓ **You should be able to ...**

MODEL Draw the structural formula of formaldehyde (CH_2O) with dots to indicate the relative locations of the electrons being shared in each covalent bond. Note any partial charges that may be associated with each atom based on the relative electronegativities of C, H, and O.

Answers are available in Appendix A.

Earth's ancient atmosphere and oceans. If so, then they provided the building blocks for chemical evolution. The question is: How did these simple building blocks combine to form more complex products early in Earth's history?

Researchers postulate that most of the critical reactions in chemical evolution occurred in an **aqueous,** or water-based, environment. To understand what happened and why, let's delve into the properties of water and then turn to analyzing the reactions that triggered chemical evolution.

2.2 Properties of Water and the Early Oceans

Life is based on water. It arose in an aqueous environment and remains dependent on water today. In fact, 75 percent of the volume in a typical cell is water; water is the most abundant molecule in organisms. You can survive for weeks without eating, but you aren't likely to live more than 3 or 4 days without drinking.

Water is vital for a simple reason: It is an excellent **solvent**—that is, an agent for dissolving, or getting substances into **solution.** Consider what happens when you add a packet of sugar to a cup of coffee. The sugar "disappears" as the sugar molecules disperse in the aqueous solution. The sugar molecules become separated from one another and interact with water's partial charges instead. Why is this so important?

The reactions that were responsible for chemical evolution some 3.5 billion years ago, like those occurring inside your body right now, depended on direct, physical interaction between molecules. Substances are most likely to come into contact with one another and react when they are **solutes**—meaning, when they are dissolved in a solvent like water. The formation of Earth's first ocean, about 3.8 billion years ago, was a turning point in chemical evolution because it gave the process a place to happen.

Why Is Water Such an Efficient Solvent?

To understand why water is such an effective solvent, recall that each of the covalent O—H bonds in a water molecule is polar, owing to the difference in the electronegativities of hydrogen and oxygen. As a result, the oxygen atom has a partial negative charge and each hydrogen atom has a partial positive charge. Also recall that water molecules have a bent geometry. Consequently, the partial negative charge on the oxygen atom sticks out, away from the partial positive charges on the hydrogen atoms, giving a water molecule an overall **polar** nature (Figure 2.11a). Like polar covalent bonds, when molecules are polar, they carry a partial positive charge on one side and a negative charge on the other.

Figure 2.11b illustrates how water's polarity affects its interactions with other water molecules. When two water molecules approach each other, the partial positive charge on hydrogen attracts the partial negative charge on oxygen. This weak electrical interaction is an example of a **hydrogen bond**—an attraction between a hydrogen atom with a partial positive charge and another atom, usually oxygen or nitrogen, with a partial negative charge.

✔ If you understand how water's structure makes hydrogen bonding possible, you should be able to (1) compare and contrast CO_2 and H_2O in terms of electronegativity, types of covalent bonds, and overall geometry; and (2) explain why electrical attractions between water molecules would be much weaker if their structure resembled CO_2.

In an aqueous solution, hydrogen bonds also form between water molecules and polar solutes, such as the sugar glucose (Figure 2.12a). Similar interactions occur between water and ions, such as Na^+ and Cl^- from dissolved table salt (Figure 2.12b). Ions and polar molecules stay in solution because of their interactions with water's partial charges. Substances that interact with water in this way are said to be **hydrophilic** ("water-loving"). These interactions make it possible for almost any ionic compound and polar molecule to dissolve in water.

Although individual hydrogen bonds are not as strong as covalent or ionic bonds, many of them occur in a solution. Hydrogen bonds, and other similar interactions between water

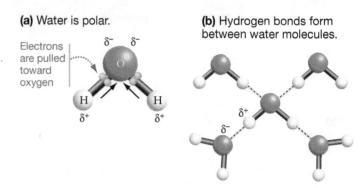

(a) Water is polar.

Electrons are pulled toward oxygen

(b) Hydrogen bonds form between water molecules.

Figure 2.11 Water Is Polar and Participates in Hydrogen Bonds. **(a)** The polar covalent bonds in water give the oxygen a partial negative charge and each hydrogen atom a partial positive charge. **(b)** The partial charges on water molecules can form up to four hydrogen bonds. The oxygen can form two; each hydrogen can form one.

and hydrophilic solutes, are extremely important in biology owing to their sheer number and their role in dissolving substances in an aqueous solution.

In contrast, nonpolar molecules do not interact with water and thus do not readily dissolve in in aqueous solutions. Substances that do not interact with water are said to be **hydrophobic** ("water-fearing"). Because their interactions with water are minimal or nonexistent, they are forced to interact with each other to minimize the disruption of the hydrogen bonds between water molecules (Figure 2.13). The interactions between nonpolar molecules that result from being caged together by surrounding water molecules are referred to as **hydrophobic interactions.**

What Properties Are Correlated with Water's Structure?

Water's small size, highly polar covalent bonds, and bent shape resulting in overall polarity are unique among molecules. Because the structure of molecules routinely correlates with their function, it's not surprising that water has some remarkable properties, in addition to its extraordinary capacity to act as a solvent.

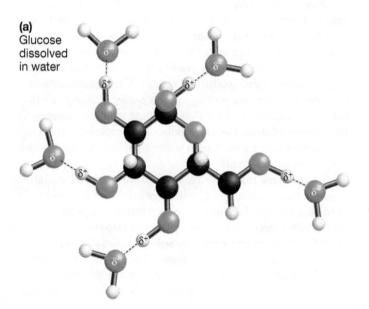

(a) Glucose dissolved in water

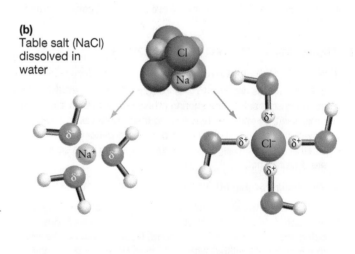

(b) Table salt (NaCl) dissolved in water

Figure 2.12 Polar Molecules and Ionic Compounds Dissolve Readily in Water. Water's polarity makes it a superb solvent.

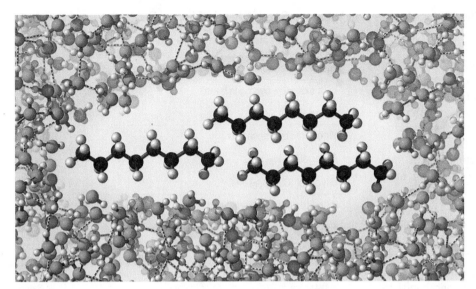

Figure 2.13 **Nonpolar Molecules Do Not Dissolve in Water.** In aqueous solution, nonpolar molecules such as octane (C_8H_{18})—a component of gasoline—are forced to interact with themselves. This occurs because water is much more stable when it interacts with itself rather than with the nonpolar molecules.

✔ Propose an explanation for the physical basis of the expression "Oil and water don't mix."

Cohesion, Adhesion, and Surface Tension   Attraction between like molecules is called **cohesion.** Water is cohesive—meaning that it stays together—because of the hydrogen bonds that form between individual molecules.

Attraction between unlike molecules, in contrast, is called **adhesion.** Adhesion is usually analyzed in regard to interactions between a liquid and a solid surface. Water adheres to surfaces that have any polar or charged components.

Cohesion and adhesion are important in explaining how water can move from the roots of plants to their leaves against the force of gravity (see Chapter 35). But you can also see them in action in the concave surface, or meniscus, that forms in a glass tube (**Figure 2.14a**). A meniscus forms as a result of

1. *Adhesion*   Partial positive charges on water molecules at the perimeter of the surface adhere to the negative charges on glass, resulting in an upward pull.

2. *Cohesion*   Water molecules at the surface hydrogen-bond with water molecules next to them and below them, resulting in a net lateral and downward pull that resists the upward pull of adhesion.

Cohesion is also instrumental in the phenomenon known as surface tension. **Surface tension** is the cohesive force caused by attraction between the molecules at the surface of a liquid. When water molecules are at the surface, there are no water molecules above them for hydrogen bonding. But hydrogen bonds do form between surface molecules and their nearest neighboring water molecules—next to and below them—resulting in tension that minimizes total surface area.

This fact has an important consequence: Water resists any force that increases its surface area. More specifically, any force that depresses a water surface meets with resistance. This resistance makes a water surface act like an elastic membrane (**Figure 2.14b**). Hydrogen bonds cause the "elastic membrane" of water to be stronger than that of other liquids. Water's extraordinarily high surface tension explains why it is better to cut the water's surface with your fingertips when you dive into a pool, instead of doing a belly flop.

(a) A meniscus forms where water meets a solid surface, as a result of two forces.

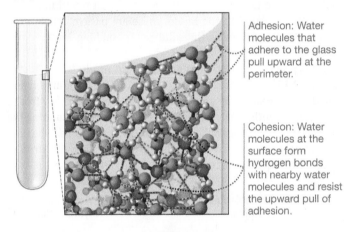

Adhesion: Water molecules that adhere to the glass pull upward at the perimeter.

Cohesion: Water molecules at the surface form hydrogen bonds with nearby water molecules and resist the upward pull of adhesion.

(b) Water has high surface tension.

Because of surface tension, light objects do not fall through the water's surface

Figure 2.14 **Cohesion, Adhesion, and Surface Tension.**
(a) Meniscus formation is based on hydrogen bonding and other interactions with glass that are represented here by highlighted dashed lines. **(b)** Water resists forces—like the weight of a spider—that increase its surface area. The resistance is great enough that light objects do not break the surface.

Water Is Denser as a Liquid than as a Solid When factory workers pour liquid metal or plastic into a mold and allow it to cool to a solid, the material shrinks. When molten lava pours out of a volcano and cools to solid rock, it shrinks. But when you fill an ice tray with water and put it in the freezer, the water expands as ice.

Unlike most substances, water is denser as a liquid than it is as a solid. In other words, there are more molecules of water in a given volume of liquid water than there are in the same volume of solid water, or ice. **Figure 2.15** illustrates why this is so.

Note that in ice, each water molecule participates in four hydrogen bonds. These hydrogen bonds cause the water molecules to form a regular and repeating lattice structure, or crystal (see Figure 2.15a). The crystal structure of ice is fairly open, meaning that there is a relatively large amount of space between molecules.

Normally, heating a substance causes it to expand because molecules begin moving faster and colliding more often and with greater force. But heating ice causes hydrogen bonds to break and the open crystal structure to collapse. Compare the arrangement of water molecules in ice with that of liquid water, illustrated in Figure 2.15b. In liquid water, hydrogen bonds are constantly being formed and broken, so the extent of hydrogen bonding in liquid water is much less than that found in ice. As a result, molecules in the liquid phase are packed much more closely together than in the solid phase, making liquid water denser than ice.

This property of water has an important result: Ice floats (see Figure 2.15c). If it didn't, ice would sink to the bottom of lakes, ponds, and oceans soon after it formed. The ice would stay frozen in the cold depths. Instead, ice serves as a blanket, insulating the liquid below from the cold air above. If water weren't so unusual, it is almost certain that Earth's oceans would have frozen solid before life had a chance to start.

Table 2.1 Specific Heats of Some Liquids

The specific heats reported in this table were measured at 25°C and are given in units of joules per gram of substance per degree Celsius. (The joule is a unit of energy.)

With extensive hydrogen bonding	Specific Heat
Water (H_2O)	4.18
With some hydrogen bonding	
Ethanol (C_2H_6O)	2.44
Glycerol ($C_3H_8O_3$)	2.38
With little or no hydrogen bonding	
Benzene (C_6H_6)	1.74
Xylene (C_8H_{10})	1.72

DATA: Lide, D. R. (ed.). 2008. Standard thermodynamic properties of chemical substances. In *CRC Handbook of Physics and Chemistry.* 89th ed. Boca Raton, FL: CRC Press.

Water Has a High Capacity for Absorbing Energy Hydrogen bonding is also responsible for another of water's remarkable physical properties: Water has a high capacity for absorbing energy.

Specific heat is the amount of energy required to raise the temperature of 1 gram of a substance by 1°C. Water has a high specific heat because when a source of energy hits it, hydrogen bonds must be broken before heat can be transferred and the water molecules begin moving faster. As **Table 2.1** indicates, as molecules increase in overall polarity, and thus in their ability to form hydrogen bonds, it takes an extraordinarily large amount of energy to change their temperature.

(a) In ice, water molecules form a crystal lattice.

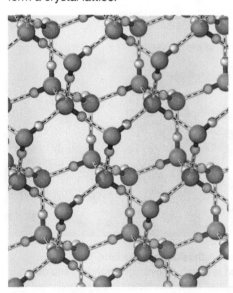

(b) In liquid water, no crystal lattice forms.

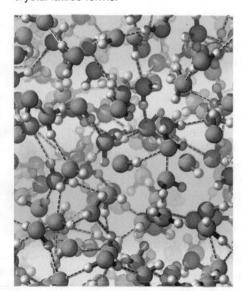

(c) Liquid water is denser than ice. As a result, ice floats.

Figure 2.15 Hydrogen Bonding in Ice and Water. (a) In ice, each molecule forms four hydrogen bonds (yellow dashed lines) at one time. **(b)** As a liquid, bonds are continually broken and formed, so no lattice develops. **(c)** As a result, ice is less dense than water.

Property	Cause	Biological Consequences
Solvent for charged or polar compounds	_____ _____ _____	Most chemical reactions important for life take place in aqueous solution.
Denser as a liquid than a solid	As water freezes, each molecule maintains four hydrogen bonds, leading to the formation of the low-density crystal structure called ice.	_____ _____ _____
High specific heat	Water molecules must absorb lots of heat energy to break hydrogen bonds and experience increased movement (and thus temperature).	Oceans absorb and release heat slowly, moderating coastal climates.
High heat of vaporization	_____	Evaporation of water from an organism cools the body.

✔ You should be able to fill in the missing cells in this table.

Similarly, it takes a large amount of energy to break the hydrogen bonds in liquid water and change the molecules from the liquid phase to the gas phase. Water's **heat of vaporization**—the energy required to change 1 gram of water from a liquid to gas—is higher than that of most molecules that are liquid at room temperature. To put it another way, water has to absorb a great deal of energy to evaporate. Water's high heat of vaporization is the reason that sweating is an effective way to cool off on a hot day. The water molecules in sweat absorb a great deal of energy from your body before they evaporate, so you lose heat.

Water's ability to absorb energy is critical to the theory of chemical evolution. Molecules that were formed in the ocean were well protected from sources of energy that could break them apart, such as intense sunlight. As a result, they would have persisted and slowly increased in concentration over time, making them more likely to react and continue the process. Table 2.2 summarizes some of the key properties of water.

The Role of Water in Acid–Base Chemical Reactions

You've seen that water's high specific heat and heat of vaporization tend to resist temperature and phase changes. One other aspect of water's chemistry is important for understanding chemical evolution and how organisms work: Water is not a completely stable molecule. In reality, water molecules continually undergo a chemical reaction with themselves.

When a **chemical reaction** occurs, one substance is combined with others or broken down into another substance. Atoms may also be rearranged; in most cases, chemical bonds are broken and new bonds form. Chemical reactions are written in a format similar to mathematical equations: The initial, or **reactant,** molecules are shown on the left and the resulting, or **product,** molecules are shown on the right. Arrows in between are like equal signs—the number of atoms of each element in the reactants must equal (be "balanced" with) the atoms of each element in the products. **Making Models 2.1** introduces some important conventions used to represent chemical reactions.

Making Models 2.1 Tips on Writing Chemical Equations

In chemical equations, arrows represent the direction of the reaction. Single arrows indicate a nonreversible reaction, where reactants are shown on the left and products on the right. Double arrows are used to show that a reaction is reversible—the reactants of the forward reaction can become the products in the reverse.

Number of reactant atoms = Number of product atoms

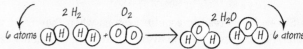

Reaction proceeds in only one direction

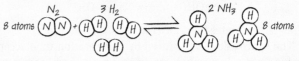

Reaction is reversible

MODEL When CH_4 and O_2 react, CO_2 and H_2O are produced. This reaction is not normally reversible. Draw the chemical equation of this reaction. Make sure your equation is balanced.

To see this model in action, go to https://goo.gl/bY5Zxw

The chemical reaction that takes place between water molecules is called a "dissociation" reaction. It can be written as follows:

$$H_2O \rightleftharpoons H^+ + OH^-$$

The products on the right-hand side of the expression are the **hydrogen ion** (H^+) and the **hydroxide ion** (OH^-). Note that this reaction is reversible. When the forward and reverse reactions proceed at the same rate, the quantities of reactants and products remain constant, although not necessarily equal. A dynamic but stable state such as this is termed a **chemical equilibrium.**

In a sample of pure water, the concentration of hydrogen ions is always equal to the concentration of hydroxide ions. Recall that a hydrogen ion is simply a proton (see Figure 2.1a). In reality, however, protons do not exist by themselves. In water, for example, protons associate with water molecules to form hydronium ions (H_3O^+). Thus, the dissociation of water is more accurately written as

$$2\,H_2O \rightleftharpoons H_3O^+ + OH^-$$

One of the water molecules on the left-hand side of the expression has given up a proton, while the other water molecule has accepted a proton.

Substances that give up protons during chemical reactions and raise the hydronium ion concentration of water are called **acids;** molecules or ions that acquire protons during chemical reactions and lower the hydronium ion concentration of water are called **bases.** Most acids act only as acids, and most bases act only as bases; but water can act as both an acid and a base.

A chemical reaction that involves a transfer of protons is called an acid–base reaction. Every acid–base reaction requires a proton donor and a proton acceptor—an acid and a base, respectively.

Water is an extremely weak acid and base—at any given moment, very few water molecules dissociate to form hydronium ions and hydroxide ions. In contrast, strong acids like the hydrochloric acid (HCl) in your stomach readily give up a proton to form hydronium ions when they react with water.

$$HCl + H_2O \rightleftharpoons H_3O^+ + Cl^-$$

Strong bases readily acquire protons when they react with water. For example, sodium hydroxide (NaOH, commonly called lye) dissociates completely in water to form Na^+ and OH^-.

$$NaOH(aq) \longrightarrow Na^+ + OH^-$$

(The "*aq*" indicates that NaOH is in aqueous solution.)

The hydroxide ion produced by that reaction then accepts a proton from a hydronium ion in the water, forming two water molecules.

$$OH^- + H_3O^+ \rightleftharpoons 2\,H_2O$$

To summarize, adding an acid to a solution increases the concentration of protons; adding a base to a solution lowers the concentration of protons. The stronger the acid or base, the more protons they donate or accept.

Determining the Concentration of Protons   In a solution, the tendency for acid–base reactions to occur is largely a function of the number of protons present. The problem is, there's no simple way to count the actual number of protons present in a sample. Researchers solve this problem using the mole concept.

A **mole** refers to the number 6.022×10^{23}—just as the unit called the dozen refers to the number 12 or the unit million refers to the number 1×10^6. The mole is a useful unit because the mass of one mole of an atom is the same as its atomic weight expressed in grams. The mass of one mole of a molecule, called its **molecular weight,** is the sum of the atomic weights of all the atoms in the molecule.

For example, to get the molecular weight of H_2O, you add the atomic weights of two atoms of hydrogen and one atom of oxygen. Since the atomic weights of hydrogen and oxygen are very close to their mass numbers (see Figure 2.2), the molecular weight of water would be $1 + 1 + 16$, or a total of 18. Thus, if you weighed a sample of 18 grams of water, it would contain around 6×10^{23} water molecules, or about 1 mole of water molecules.

When substances are dissolved in water, their concentration is expressed in terms of molarity (symbolized by "M"). **Molarity** is the number of moles of the solute present per liter of solution. A 1-molar solution of hydrogen ions in water, for example, means that 1 mole of protons is contained in 1 liter of solution.

The pH of a Solution Reveals Whether It Is Acidic or Basic   The concentration of protons in water is very low. In a sample of pure water at 25°C, the concentration of H^+ is 1.0×10^{-7} M, or 0.0000001 molar. Because exponential notation is cumbersome, scientists prefer to express the concentration of protons in a solution, and thus whether it is acidic or basic, with a logarithmic notation called **pH.** The term "pH" is derived from the French *puissance d'hydrogéne*, or "power of hydrogen."

By definition, pH is the negative of the base-10 logarithm, or log, of the molar concentration of hydrogen ions in a solution:

$$pH = -\log[H^+]$$

(The square brackets are a standard notation for indicating "concentration" of a substance in solution.) Chemists can measure the concentration of protons in a solution directly using an instrument called a pH meter. Recall that the concentration of H^+ in a sample of pure water is 1.0×10^{-7} M. Using the formula just considered, the pH of pure water is therefore 7. (To review logarithms, see BioSkills 5.)

Taking antilogs gives:

$$[H^+] = \text{antilog}(-pH) = 10^{-pH}$$

Solutions that contain acids have a proton concentration larger than 1×10^{-7} M and thus a pH < 7. This is because acidic molecules tend to release protons into solution. In contrast, solutions that contain bases have a proton concentration less than 1×10^{-7} M and thus a pH > 7. This is because basic molecules tend to accept protons from solution.

pH is a convenient way to indicate the concentration of protons in a solution, but take note of what the number represents. For example, a pH change from 7 to 5 might not seem like a big deal, but that change means that the sample contains 100 times more protons and has become 100 times more acidic.

Figure 2.16 shows the pH scale and reports the pH of some selected solutions. Pure water is used as a standard, or point of reference, for pH 7 on the pH scale. The solution inside living cells is about pH 7, which is considered neutral—neither acidic nor basic. The function of a cell is dependent on maintaining a neutral internal environment. What is responsible for regulating pH?

Buffers Protect against Damaging Changes in pH   Life is sensitive to changes in pH. Changes in proton concentration affect the structure and function of polar or charged substances as well as the tendency of acid–base reactions to occur.

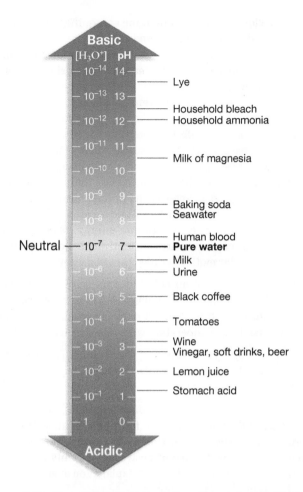

Figure 2.16 The pH Scale. Because the pH scale is logarithmic, a change in one unit of pH represents a change in the concentration of hydrogen ions equal to a factor of 10. Coffee has a hundred times more H^+ than pure water has.

✔ What happens to the concentration of protons in black coffee after you add milk?

Compounds that minimize changes in pH are called **buffers** because they reduce the impact of adding acids or bases on the overall pH of a solution. Buffers are important in maintaining relatively constant conditions, or **homeostasis,** in organisms.

Most buffers are weak acids, meaning that they are somewhat likely to give up a proton in solution, but once the proton concentration rises, the acid is regenerated. In cells and bodily fluids, a wide array of substances act as buffers. Your blood, for example, contains carbonic acid. To see how buffers work, consider the disassociation of carbonic acid in an aqueous solution to form bicarbonate ions and protons:

$$CH_2O_3(aq) \rightleftharpoons CHO_3^- + H^+$$
carbonic acid   bicarbonate

When carbonic acid and bicarbonate are present in about equal concentrations in a solution, such as blood, they function as a buffering system. If the concentration of protons increases slightly, the protons react with bicarbonate ions to form carbonic acid and pH does not change. If the concentration of protons decreases slightly, carbonic acid gives up protons and pH does not change. ✔ If you understand this concept, you should be able to predict what would happen to the concentration of bicarbonate ions if a strong base like sodium hydroxide (NaOH) were added to a solution of carbonic acid.

As chemical evolution began, then, water provided the physical environment for key reactions to take place. In some cases, water also acted as an important reactant. Although acid–base reactions were not critical to the initial stages of chemical evolution, they became extremely important once the process was under way. Now let's consider what happened in solution, some 3.5 billion years ago.

2.3 Chemical Reactions, Energy, and Chemical Evolution

Proponents of the theory of chemical evolution contend that simple molecules present in the atmosphere and oceans of early Earth participated in chemical reactions that eventually produced larger, more complex organic (carbon-containing) molecules— such as the proteins, nucleic acids, sugars, and lipids introduced in the next four chapters. Currently, researchers are investigating two environments where these reactions may have occurred:

1. *The atmosphere,* which was probably dominated by gases ejected from volcanoes. Water vapor, carbon dioxide (CO_2), and nitrogen (N_2) are the dominant gases ejected by volcanoes today; a small amount of molecular hydrogen (H_2) and carbon monoxide (CO) may also be present.

2. *Deep-sea hydrothermal vents,* where extremely hot rocks contact deep cracks in the seafloor. In addition to gases such as CO_2 and H_2, certain deep-sea vents are rich in minerals containing reactive metals such as nickel and iron.

When gases like CO_2, N_2, H_2, and CO are put together and allowed to interact on their own, however, very little happens. They do not suddenly link together to create large, complex substances like those found in living cells. Instead, their bonds remain intact. To understand why the bonds of these molecules remain unchanged, you must first learn more about how chemical reactions proceed.

How Do Chemical Reactions Happen?

The most common reaction in the mix of gases and water vapor that emerges from volcanoes results in the production of carbonic acid, which can be precipitated in rainwater:

$$CO_2(g) + H_2O(g) \rightleftharpoons CH_2O_3(aq)$$
carbonic acid

The physical state of each reactant and product is indicated as gas (*g*), liquid (*l*), solid (*s*), or in aqueous solution (*aq*).

Note that the expression is balanced; that is, on each side of the expression, there are 1 carbon, 3 oxygen, and 2 hydrogen atoms present. This illustrates the conservation of mass in closed systems—mass cannot be created or destroyed, but it may be rearranged through chemical reactions.

Changing the concentration of reactants or products can disturb a chemical equilibrium. For example, adding more CO_2 to the mixture would drive the reaction to the right, creating more CH_2O_3 until the equilibrium proportions of reactants and products are reestablished. Removing CO_2 or adding more CH_2O_3 would drive the reaction to the left.

A chemical equilibrium can also be altered by changes in temperature. For example, consider the following set of interacting components, or **system**, comprising a combination of liquid water and water vapor:

$$H_2O(l) \rightleftharpoons H_2O(g)$$

If this system absorbs enough thermal energy from the surrounding environment, the liquid water molecules will overcome the heat of vaporization and undergo a physical state change from liquid to gas. (Keep in mind that this would not represent a chemical reaction because the molecules are the same on both sides of the equation.) Such a change is termed **endothermic** ("within heating") because thermal energy is absorbed by the system during the process. In contrast, the transformation of water vapor to liquid water releases thermal energy to the environment and is **exothermic** ("outside heating"). This release of energy increases disorder of the surroundings at the same time that order is increased in the system by the formation of liquid water. Raising the temperature of this system drives the equilibrium to the right; cooling the system drives it to the left. This same type of energy transfer occurs in the phase change between liquid water and ice.

In addition to physical state changes, the transfer of energy is also required for chemical reactions to occur. To understand how life could have evolved from chemical reactions, you will first need a brief introduction to energy.

What Is Energy?

Energy can be defined as the capacity to do work or supply heat. This capacity exists in one of two ways—as a stored potential or as an active motion.

Stored energy is called **potential energy.** An object gains or loses its ability to store energy because of its position. In molecules, potential energy is related to the position of shared electrons in covalent bonds. When the shared electrons are far from the atomic nuclei, the bond is long and weak. If the electrons

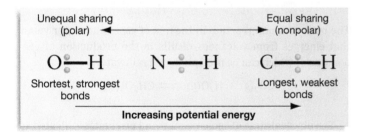

Figure 2.17 Potential Energy as a Function of Electron Sharing. Highly electronegative atoms, such as oxygen, pull shared electrons closer to their own nuclei, increasing bond strength and decreasing the potential energy of a molecule. Less electronegative atoms, such as carbon and hydrogen, share electrons more equally, decreasing bond strength and increasing potential energy.

are shifted closer to one or both of the atoms, the bond becomes shorter and stronger. Atoms bound together with weak bonds have a greater capacity to be broken apart to reform into new, stronger bonds during a reaction than do atoms held together by strong bonds. A molecule's potential to form stronger bonds is a type of potential energy called **chemical energy.**

What factors contribute to bond strength? Recall that the electronegativities of atoms affect the position of shared electrons. For example, the shared electrons in polar covalent bonds are pulled closer to the more electronegative atom, resulting in shorter, stronger bonds compared to what would be expected if the bond were nonpolar (Figure 2.17). Increased bond strength also occurs as more electron pairs are shared when double and triple bonds are formed.

Energy of motion is called **kinetic energy.** Molecules have kinetic energy because they are constantly in motion. The kinetic energy of molecular motion is called **thermal energy.**

- The **temperature** of an object is a measure of how much thermal energy its molecules possess. A cold object has a low temperature and it will consist of molecules that are moving slower than if the temperature were raised to make it hot.

- When two objects with different temperatures come into contact, thermal energy is transferred between them. This transferred energy is called **heat.**

There are many forms of potential energy and kinetic energy, and energy can change from one form into another. However, according to the **first law of thermodynamics,** energy is conserved—it cannot be created or destroyed, but only transferred and transformed. (A more thorough explanation of energy transformation is provided in Chapter 8.)

Energy transformation is the heart of chemical evolution. According to the best data available, molecules that were part of the early Earth were exposed to massive inputs of energy. Kinetic energy, in the form of heat, was present in the gradually cooling molten mass that initially formed the planet. The atmosphere and surface of the early Earth were also bombarded with electricity from lightening and radiation from the Sun. Energy that was stored in the chemical bonds of molecules was also abundant.

Now that you understand the different forms of energy that can be transferred in chemical reactions, a big question remains: What determines if a reaction will take place?

What Makes a Chemical Reaction Spontaneous?

When chemists say that a reaction is spontaneous, they have a precise meaning in mind: Chemical reactions are spontaneous if they are able to proceed on their own, without any continuous external influence, such as added energy. Two factors determine if a reaction will proceed spontaneously:

1. Reactions tend to be spontaneous when the product molecules are less ordered than the reactant molecules. For example, nitroglycerin is a single, highly ordered molecule. But when nitroglycerin explodes, it breaks up into gaseous products like carbon dioxide, nitrogen, oxygen, and water vapor. These molecules are much less ordered than the reactant nitroglycerin molecules. The amount of disorder in a system (or the surrounding environment) is called **entropy.** When the

(a) When hydrogen and oxygen gas react, the products have much lower potential energy than the reactants.

(b) The difference in potential energy is released as heat and light, which vaporizes the water produced.

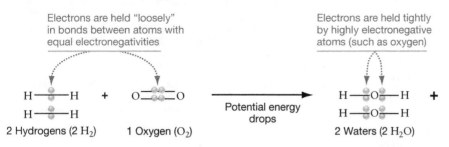

Electrons are held "loosely" in bonds between atoms with equal electronegativities

Electrons are held tightly by highly electronegative atoms (such as oxygen)

H—H
H—H   +   O=O   → Potential energy drops →   H—O—H
                                                          H—O—H   +

2 Hydrogens (2 H₂)   1 Oxygen (O₂)   2 Waters (2 H₂O)

Heat and light

Released energy

Figure 2.18 Potential Energy May Change during Chemical Reactions. In the Hindenburg disaster of 1937, hydrogen gas from a lighter-than-air craft reacted with oxygen in the atmosphere, with devastating results.

✔ In part (a) which electrons have relatively low potential energy and which electrons have relatively high potential energy?

products of a chemical reaction are less ordered than the reactant molecules are, entropy increases in the system.

2. Reactions tend to be spontaneous if the products have lower potential energy than the reactants—that is, when the shared electrons in the reaction products are held more tightly than those in the reactants. For example, when hydrogen and oxygen gases react, water is produced spontaneously:

$$2 H_2(g) + O_2(g) \longrightarrow 2 H_2O(g)$$

The electrons involved in the O—H bonds of water are held much more tightly by the more electronegative oxygen atom than when they were shared equally in the H—H and O=O bonds (**Figure 2.18a**). As a result, the products have much lower potential energy than the reactants.

It is important to note that spontaneous reactions can occur without appearing to increase entropy in the system. For example, the reaction just discussed converts three molecules of gas into two molecules of water vapor, an apparent decrease in entropy. However, the difference in chemical energy between reactants and products is given off as heat. This released thermal energy results in an overall *increase* in entropy when you include its effect on the surrounding environment. The **second law of thermodynamics,** in fact, states that in all spontaneous reactions, entropy always increases when both the system and its environment are taken into account. The Hindenburg disaster of 1937 illustrates the large and terrifying amount of heat that is given off from this relatively simple reaction (**Figure 2.18b**).

To summarize: Physical and chemical changes tend to proceed in the direction that results in increased entropy and lower potential energy (**Figure 2.19**). Potential energy and entropy are used to figure out whether a reaction is spontaneous or not. Were the reactions that led to chemical evolution spontaneous? Section 2.4 explores how researchers have tried to address this question.

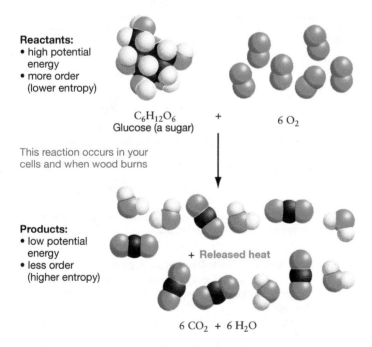

Reactants:
• high potential energy
• more order (lower entropy)

C₆H₁₂O₆
Glucose (a sugar)   +   6 O₂

This reaction occurs in your cells and when wood burns

Products:
• low potential energy
• less order (higher entropy)

+ Released heat

6 CO₂ + 6 H₂O

Figure 2.19 Spontaneous Processes Result in Lower Potential Energy, Increased Disorder, or Both.

CHECK YOUR UNDERSTANDING

If you understand that …
• Chemical reactions transform energy, either through the release of energy stored in chemical bonds or the uptake of energy from external sources.
• Chemical reactions tend to be spontaneous if they lead to lower potential energy and higher entropy (more disorder).

You should be able to …

1. Explain how the positions of the valence electrons in carbon and hydrogen change as methane (CH_4) reacts with oxygen (O_2) to produce carbon dioxide and water in the following reaction:

$$CH_4 + 2 O_2 \longrightarrow CO_2 + 2 H_2O$$

2. Determine if the reaction above is spontaneous or not, addressing both potential energy and entropy.

Answers are available in Appendix A.

2.4 Model Systems for Investigating Chemical Evolution

To probe the kinds of reactions that may have set chemical evolution in motion, many researchers have focused on the small molecules and environmental conditions that were present in early Earth. Two different model systems have arisen from this work:

1. The **prebiotic soup model** proposes that certain molecules were synthesized from gases in the atmosphere or arrived via meteorites. Afterward they would have condensed with rain and accumulated in oceans. This process would result in an "organic soup" that allowed for continued construction of larger, even more complex molecules.

2. The **surface metabolism model** suggests that dissolved gases came in contact with minerals lining the walls of deep-sea vents and formed more complex organic molecules.

Since it is impossible to directly examine how and where chemical evolution occurred, the next best thing is to re-create the conditions in the lab and test predictions made by these models. In the following sections, you will learn about how biologists used simulations of early Earth conditions to identify reactions that support each of these models for chemical evolution.

Early Origin-of-Life Experiments

Chemical evolution was first proposed by Alexander I. Oparin in 1924. The hypothesis was published again—independently and five years later—by J. B. S. Haldane. Today, the Oparin–Haldane proposal is considered a formal scientific theory (see Chapter 1). At the time, however, since Oparin and Haldane were unable to conduct definitive experiments, their proposal remained an untested hypothesis. Chemical evolution was first taken seriously in 1953 when a graduate student named Stanley Miller performed a breakthrough experiment testing the prebiotic soup model.

Miller wanted to answer a simple question: Can complex organic compounds be synthesized from the simple molecules present in Earth's early atmosphere? In other words, is it possible to re-create the first steps in chemical evolution by simulating early-Earth conditions in the laboratory?

Miller's experimental setup (**Figure 2.20**) was designed to produce a microcosm of early Earth. The large glass flask represented the atmosphere and contained the gases methane (CH_4), ammonia (NH_3), and hydrogen (H_2), all of which have high potential energy. This large flask was connected to a smaller flask by glass tubing. The small flask held a tiny ocean—200 milliliters (mL) of liquid water.

To connect the mini-atmosphere with the mini-ocean, Miller boiled the water constantly. This added water vapor to the mix of gases in the large flask. As the vapor cooled and condensed, it flowed back into the smaller flask, where it boiled again. In this way, water vapor circulated continuously through the system. This was important: If the molecules in the simulated atmosphere reacted with one another, the "rain" would carry them into the mini-ocean, forming a simulated version of the prebiotic soup.

Had Miller stopped at merely boiling the molecules, little or nothing would have happened. Even at the boiling point of

---

RESEARCH

QUESTION: Can simple molecules and kinetic energy lead to chemical evolution?

HYPOTHESIS: If kinetic energy is added to a mix of simple molecules, reactions will occur that produce more complex molecules, perhaps including some with C–C bonds.

NULL HYPOTHESIS: Chemical evolution will not occur, even with an input of energy.

EXPERIMENTAL SETUP:

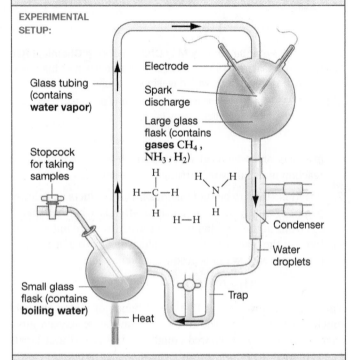

PREDICTION: Complex organic compounds will be found in the liquid water.

PREDICTION OF NULL HYPOTHESIS: Only the starting molecules will be found in the liquid water.

RESULTS

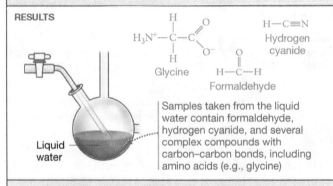

Samples taken from the liquid water contain formaldehyde, hydrogen cyanide, and several complex compounds with carbon–carbon bonds, including amino acids (e.g., glycine)

CONCLUSION: Chemical evolution occurs readily if simple molecules with high free energy are exposed to a source of kinetic energy.

Figure 2.20 Miller's Spark-Discharge Experiment. The arrows in the "Experimental Setup" diagram indicate the flow of water vapor or liquid. The condenser is a jacket with cold water flowing through it.

SOURCE: Miller, S. L. 1953. A production of amino acids under possible primitive Earth conditions. *Science* 117: 528–529.

✔ **PROCESS OF SCIENCE** Which parts of the apparatus mimic the ocean, atmosphere, rain, and lightning?

water (100°C), the starting molecules used in the experiment are stable and do not undergo spontaneous chemical reactions. A different form of energy would be required for these substrates to react.

Something did start to happen in the apparatus, however, when Miller sent electrical discharges across the electrodes he'd inserted into the atmosphere. These miniature "lightning bolts" added a crucial component to the reaction mix—pulses of intense electrical energy. After a day of continuous boiling and sparking, the solution in the boiling flask began to turn pink. After a week, it was deep red and cloudy.

When Miller analyzed samples from the mini-ocean, he found large quantities of hydrogen cyanide and formaldehyde. Although these chemicals are poisonous, they are also highly reactive and can promote the synthesis of larger, more complex compounds. Even more exciting, the samples also contained newly synthesized amino acids, which are the building blocks of proteins (see Chapter 3).

Recent Origin-of-Life Experiments

The production of more complex molecules from simple molecules in Miller's experiment supported his claim that the formation of a prebiotic soup was possible. The results came under fire, however, when other researchers pointed out that the early atmosphere was dominated by volcanic gases like CO, CO_2, and H_2, not the CH_4 and NH_3 used in Miller's experiment.

This controversy stimulated a series of follow-up experiments, which showed that the assembly of small molecules into more complex molecules could also occur under more realistic early Earth conditions.

Synthesis of Precursors Using Light Energy
One such reaction that may have played a role in chemical evolution is the synthesis of formaldehyde (CH_2O) from carbon dioxide and hydrogen:

$$CO_2(g) + 2H_2(g) \longrightarrow CH_2O(g) + H_2O(g)$$
$$\text{formaldehyde}$$

Researchers have shown that molecules of formaldehyde can react with one another to produce larger organic compounds, including energy-rich molecules like sugars (see Chapter 5). This reaction does not occur spontaneously—it requires a large input of energy, in the form of heat or light, for example.

To explore the possibility of early formaldehyde synthesis, a research group constructed a computer model of Earth's early atmosphere. The model consisted of a list of all possible chemical reactions that can occur among the molecules now thought to have dominated the early atmosphere: CO_2, H_2O, N_2, CO, and H_2. In this model, they included reactions that occur when these molecules are struck by sunlight. This was crucial because sunlight represents a source of energy.

Sunlight strikes Earth in the form of packets of light energy called **photons.** Today, Earth is protected by a blanket of ozone (O_3) in the upper atmosphere that absorbs most of the higher-energy photons in sunlight. But ozone was not among the volcanic gases released as the molten planet cooled, so it is extremely unlikely that appreciable quantities of protective ozone existed in Earth's early atmosphere. Based on this logic, researchers

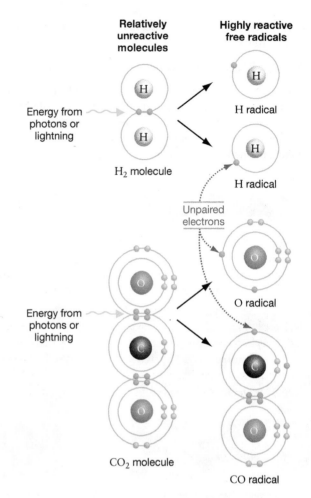

Figure 2.21 Free Radicals Are Extremely Reactive. When high-energy photons or the electrical energy from lightning strike molecules of hydrogen or carbon dioxide, free radicals can be created. Formation of free radicals is thought to be responsible for some key reactions in chemical evolution.

infer that when chemical evolution was occurring, large quantities of high-energy photons bombarded the planet.

To understand why high-energy photons were so important, recall that the atoms in hydrogen molecules and carbon dioxide molecules have full valence shells through covalent bonding. This arrangement makes these molecules largely unreactive. However, energy in the form of photons or the intense electrical energy in lightning that was modeled in Miller's experiment (Figure 2.20) can break up molecules by knocking apart shared electrons. The fragments that result, called **free radicals,** have unpaired electrons in their outermost shells and are extremely reactive (**Figure 2.21**).

To mimic the conditions on early Earth more accurately, the computer model included several reactions that produce highly reactive free radicals. The researchers calculated that, under conditions accepted as reasonable approximations of early Earth by most scientists, appreciable quantities of formaldehyde would have been produced. Thus, the energy in sunlight could be converted into chemical energy by generating radicals that spontaneously form new bonds in formaldehyde.

The complete reaction that results in the formation of formaldehyde is written as

$$CO_2(g) + 2\,H_2(g) + \text{sunlight} \longrightarrow CH_2O(g) + H_2O(g)$$

Not only is this reaction balanced in terms of atoms, it is also balanced in terms of the energy involved. The sunlight on the reactant side balances the higher energy required for the formation of formaldehyde and water. This result makes sense if you take a moment to think about it. Energy is the capacity to do work, and building larger, more complex molecules requires work to be done.

Using a similar model, other researchers have shown that hydrogen cyanide (HCN)—another important precursor of molecules required for life—could also have been produced in the early atmosphere. According to this research, large quantities of potential precursors for chemical evolution would have formed in the atmosphere and rained out into the early oceans. As a result, organic compounds with relatively high potential energy

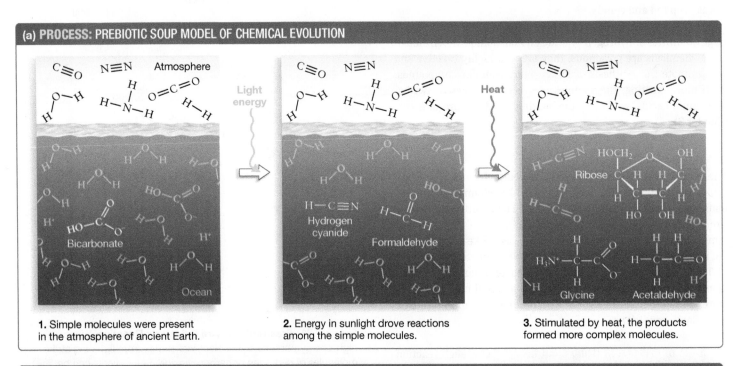

(a) PROCESS: PREBIOTIC SOUP MODEL OF CHEMICAL EVOLUTION

1. Simple molecules were present in the atmosphere of ancient Earth.

2. Energy in sunlight drove reactions among the simple molecules.

3. Stimulated by heat, the products formed more complex molecules.

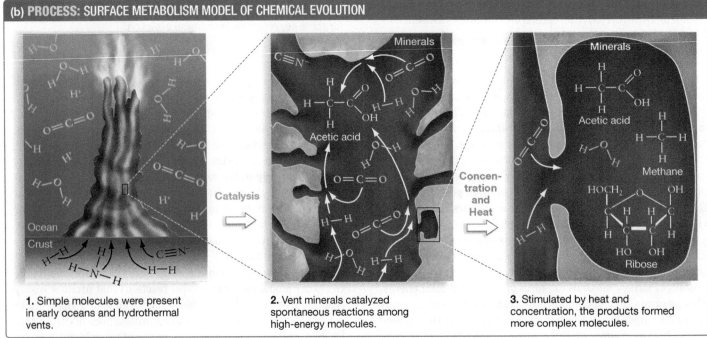

(b) PROCESS: SURFACE METABOLISM MODEL OF CHEMICAL EVOLUTION

1. Simple molecules were present in early oceans and hydrothermal vents.

2. Vent minerals catalyzed spontaneous reactions among high-energy molecules.

3. Stimulated by heat and concentration, the products formed more complex molecules.

Figure 2.22 **The Start of Chemical Evolution—Two Models.** The prebiotic soup and surface metabolism models illustrate how simple molecules containing C, H, O, and N reacted to form organic compounds that served as building blocks for more complex molecules.

could have accumulated, and the groundwork would have been in place for the prebiotic soup model of chemical evolution to take off (Figure 2.22a).

Concentration and Catalysis in Hydrothermal Vents A major stumbling block in the prebiotic soup model is that precursor molecules would have become diluted when they entered the early oceans. Without some means of localized concentration, the formaldehyde and hydrogen cyanide would have been unlikely to meet and react to form larger, more complex molecules. The surface metabolism model offers one possible solution to this dilution effect.

In the surface metabolism model, reactants are recruited to a defined space—a layer of reactive minerals deposited on the walls of deep-sea vent chimneys. Dissolved gases would be attracted by the minerals and concentrated on vent-wall surfaces (Figure 2.22b).

Here's a key point of this model: Not only would vent-wall minerals bring reactants together, they would also be critical to the rate at which reaction products formed. Even if a potential reaction were spontaneous, it would probably not occur at a level useful for chemical evolution without the support of a catalyst. A catalyst provides the appropriate chemical environment for reactants to interact with one another effectively. (You will learn in Chapter 8 that a catalyst only influences the rate of a reaction—it does not provide energy or alter spontaneity.)

A reaction that provides an example of the role catalysts may have played during chemical evolution is the synthesis of acetic acid (CH_3COOH) from carbon dioxide and hydrogen:

$$2\,CO_2(aq) + 4\,H_2(aq) \longrightarrow CH_3COOH(aq) + 2\,H_2O(l)$$
acetic acid

This spontaneous reaction is driven by chemical energy stored in one of the reactants—H_2. It is employed by certain groups of bacteria and archaea today as a step toward building even more complex organic molecules.

This reaction has grabbed wide attention among the chemical evolution research community, for two reasons in particular: (1) Acetic acid can be formed under conditions that simulate a hydrothermal vent environment. (2) It is a key intermediate in an ancient metabolic pathway that produces acetyl CoA, which is a molecule used by cells throughout the tree of life. (The role of acetyl CoA in modern cells is discussed in Chapter 9.)

Did vent minerals serve as catalysts in the synthesis of acetic acid in early Earth? Evidence from modern cells suggests the answer may be yes. The catalysts that perform the same reaction in modern cells contain minerals similar to those found in hydrothermal vents. These minerals may represent a form of molecular luggage taken from the deep-sea hydrothermal vents as the last universal common ancestor (LUCA; introduced in Chapter 1) evolved its independence.

Research is currently under way to establish laboratory systems that more closely mimic surface metabolism conditions in hydrothermal vents. Preliminary results show that in addition to the production of acetic acid, a variety of larger carbon-based molecules can be formed under early Earth conditions. Among

these are precursors for the synthesis of nucleotides, the building blocks for the molecules of inheritance used by every living organism on Earth (see Chapter 4).

2.5 The Importance of Organic Molecules

Life has been called a carbon-based phenomenon, and with good reason. Except for water, almost all of the molecules found in organisms contain this atom. Many molecules that contain carbon bonded to other elements, such as hydrogen, are called **organic compounds.** (Other types of molecules are referred to as being *inorganic.*)

Carbon has great importance in biology because it is the most versatile atom on Earth. Because of its four valence electrons, it will form four covalent bonds. The formation of carbon–carbon bonds was an important event in chemical evolution: It represented a crucial step toward the production of organic molecules found in living organisms. As a result, organic molecules come in an almost limitless array of molecular shapes, made possible by different combinations of single and double bonds.

Linking Carbon Atoms Together

You have already examined the shapes of single-carbon molecules such as carbon dioxide, which is linear, and methane, which is tetrahedral (see Figure 2.8 and Figure 2.10). In molecules that contain more than one carbon atom, the shapes can become much more complex. For example, several carbon and hydrogen atoms can bond to one another to form long hydrocarbon chains, as in octane (C_8H_{18}; Figure 2.23a). In glucose ($C_6H_{12}O_6$; Figure 2.23b), a ring structure is formed from carbon, hydrogen, and oxygen atoms that are bonded together. Octane is one of the primary components in gasoline, and the sugar glucose is the primary energy storage molecule for organisms (see Chapter 5).

(a) Carbons linked in a chain   **(b)** Carbons linked in a ring

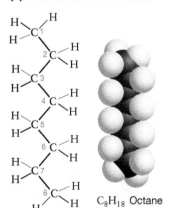
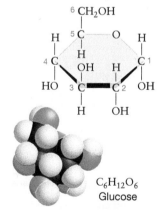

Figure 2.23 The Shapes of Carbon-Containing Molecules.
(a) Octane is a hydrocarbon chain present in gasoline. **(b)** Glucose is a sugar that can form a ring-like structure.

Functional Group	Formula*	Family of Molecules	Properties of Functional Group	Example
Amino		Amines	Acts as a base—tends to attract a proton to form:	Glycine (an amino acid)
Carboxyl		Carboxylic acids	Acts as an acid—tends to lose a proton in solution to form:	Acetic acid
Carbonyl		Aldehydes	Aldehydes, especially, react with certain compounds to produce larger molecules to form:	Acetaldehyde
		Ketones		Acetone
Hydroxyl	R—OH	Alcohols	Highly polar, so makes compounds more soluble through hydrogen bonding with water; may also act as a weak acid and drop a proton	Ethanol
Phosphate		Organic phosphates	Molecules with more than one phosphate linked together store large amounts of chemical energy	3–Phosphoglyceric acid
Sulfhydryl	R—SH	Thiols	When present in proteins, can form disulfide (S–S) bonds that contribute to protein structure	Cysteine

*In these structural formulas, "R" stands for the rest of the molecule.

✔ Based on the relative electronegativities of the atoms involved, predict whether each functional group is polar or nonpolar.

Functional Groups

In general, the carbon atoms in an organic molecule furnish a skeleton that gives the molecule its overall shape. But the chemical behavior of the compound—meaning the types of reactions that it participates in—is dictated by groups of H, N, O, P, or S atoms that are bonded to one of the carbon atoms in a specific way.

The critically important H-, N-, O-, P-, and S-containing groups found in organic compounds are called **functional groups.** The composition and properties of six prominent functional groups that are commonly found in organic molecules and recognized by organic chemists are summarized in Table 2.3. To understand the role that organic compounds play in organisms, it is important to analyze how these functional groups behave.

- *Amino and carboxyl functional groups* tend to attract or release a hydrogen ion (proton), respectively, when in solution. Amino groups function as bases; carboxyl groups act as acids. During chemical evolution and in organisms today, the most important types of amino- and carboxyl-containing molecules are the amino acids (analyzed in detail in Chapter 3). Amino acids contain both an amino group and a carboxyl group. Amino acids can be linked together by covalent bonds that form between amino and carboxyl groups. In addition, both of these functional groups participate in hydrogen bonding.

- *Carbonyl groups* are found on molecules such as formaldehyde, acetaldehyde, and acetone. This functional group is the site of reactions that link these molecules into larger, more complex organic compounds.

- *Hydroxyl groups* are important because they act as weak acids. In many cases, the protons involved in acid–base reactions that occur in cells come from hydroxyl groups on organic compounds. Because hydroxyl groups are polar, molecules containing hydroxyl groups will form hydrogen bonds and tend to be soluble in water.

- *Phosphate groups* carry two negative charges. When phosphate groups are transferred from one organic compound to another, the change in charge often dramatically affects the structure of the recipient molecule. In addition, phosphates that are bonded together store chemical energy that can be used in chemical reactions (some of these are discussed in Chapter 3).

- *Sulfhydryl groups* consist of a sulfur atom bonded to a hydrogen atom. They are important because sulfhydryl groups can link to one another via disulfide (S — S) bonds.

To summarize, functional groups make things happen. The number and types of functional groups attached to a framework of carbon atoms imply a great deal about how that molecule is going to behave.

When you encounter an organic compound that is new to you, it's important to do the following three things:

1. Examine the overall size and shape provided by the carbon framework.

2. Identify the types of covalent bonds present based on the electronegativities of the atoms. Use this information to estimate the polarity of the molecule and the amount of potential energy stored in its chemical bonds.

3. Locate any functional groups and note the properties these groups give to the molecule.

Understanding these three features will help you predict the molecule's role in the chemistry of life.

Once carbon-containing molecules with functional groups had appeared early in Earth's history, what happened next? For chemical evolution to continue, small carbon-based molecules had to form still larger, more complex molecules like those found in living cells. How were the molecules of life—proteins, nucleic acids, carbohydrates, and lipids—formed, and how do they function in organisms today? The rest of this unit explores the next steps in chemical evolution, culminating in the formation of the first living cell.

CHAPTER 2 REVIEW

For media, go to MasteringBiology

2.1 Atoms, Ions, and Molecules: The Building Blocks of Chemical Evolution

- When atoms participate in chemical bonds, the shared or transferred electrons often give the atoms full valence shells and thus contribute to the atoms' stability.

- The electrons in a covalent bond may be shared equally or unequally, depending on the relative electronegativities of the two atoms involved.

- Nonpolar covalent bonds result from equal sharing; polar covalent bonds are due to unequal sharing. Ionic bonds form when an electron is completely transferred from one atom to another.

2.2 Properties of Water and the Early Oceans

- The chemical reactions required for life take place in water.
- Water is polar—meaning that it has partial positive and negative charges—because it is bent and has two polar covalent bonds.

- Solutes dissolve in water. Water interacts with polar molecules via hydrogen bonding and ions via similar electrical attractions.

- Water's ability to participate in hydrogen bonding also gives it an extraordinarily high capacity to absorb heat and cohere to other water molecules.

- Water spontaneously dissociates into hydrogen ions (or protons, H^+) and hydroxide ions (OH^-). The concentration of protons in a solution determines the pH, which can be altered by acids and bases or stabilized by buffers.

2.3 Chemical Reactions, Energy, and Chemical Evolution

- The first step in chemical evolution was the formation of small organic compounds from molecules such as molecular hydrogen (H_2) and carbon dioxide (CO_2).

- Chemical reactions involve bonds being broken, atoms being rearranged, and new bonds being formed. This process involves energy from either the potential energy within bonds of the reactants or kinetic energy of external sources (e.g., thermal energy).

- Energy comes in different forms. Although energy cannot be created or destroyed, one form of energy can be transformed into another.

2.4 Model Systems for Investigating Chemical Evolution

- Experiments suggest that early in Earth's history, external sources of energy, such as sunlight or lightning, could have driven chemical reactions between simple molecules to form molecules with higher potential energy. In this way, energy in the form of radiation or electricity was transformed into chemical energy.

- The prebiotic soup and surface metabolism models for chemical evolution have been supported by the synthesis of organic molecules in laboratory simulations of the early Earth environment.

2.5 The Importance of Organic Molecules

- Carbon is the foundation of organic molecules based on its valence, which allows for the construction of molecules with complex shapes.

- Organic molecules are critical to life because they possess versatility of chemical behavior due to the presence of functional groups.

Answers are available in Appendix A

✓ TEST YOUR KNOWLEDGE

1. Which of the following occurs when a covalent bond forms?
   a. Electrons in valence shells are transferred from one atom to another.
   b. Electrons in valence shells are shared between atoms.
   c. Partial charges on polar molecules interact.
   d. Nonpolar molecules are pushed together.by surrounding water molecules.

2. If a reaction is exothermic, then which of the following statements is always true?
   a. The products have lower potential energy than the reactants.
   b. Energy must be added for the reaction to proceed.
   c. The products have lower entropy (are more ordered) than the reactants.
   d. It occurs extremely quickly.

3. Which of the following is most likely to have supplied the energy needed for the formation of acetic acid in deep-sea hydrothermal vents?
   a. heat from volcanoes
   b. photons from solar radiation
   c. chemical energy stored in the reactants
   d. kinetic energy released by the products

4. What factors determine whether a chemical reaction is spontaneous or not?

✓ TEST YOUR UNDERSTANDING

5. Which of the following molecules would you predict to have the largest number of polar covalent bonds based on their molecular formulas?
   a. C_2H_6O (ethanol)
   b. C_2H_6 (ethane)
   c. $C_2H_4O_2$ (acetic acid)
   d. C_3H_8O (propanol)

6. Locate fluorine (F) on the partial periodic table provided in Figure 2.2. Predict its relative electronegativity compared to hydrogen, sodium, and oxygen. State the number and type of bond(s) you expect it would form if it reacted with sodium (Na).

7. **QUANTITATIVE** If you were given a solution that has a pH of 8.5, what would be its concentration of protons? What is the difference in proton concentration between this solution and one that has a pH of 7?

8. Consider the reaction between carbon dioxide and water to form carbonic acid:

$$CO_2(g) + H_2O(l) \rightleftharpoons CH_2O_3(aq)$$

In the ocean, carbonic acid immediately dissociates to form a proton and bicarbonate ion, as follows:

$$CH_2O_3(aq) \rightleftharpoons H^+(aq) + CHO_3^-(aq)$$

If an underwater volcano bubbled additional CO_2 into the ocean, would this sequence of reactions be driven to the left or the right? How would this affect the pH of the ocean?

✓ TEST YOUR PROBLEM-SOLVING SKILLS

9. When H_2 and CO_2 react, acetic acid can be formed spontaneously while the production of formaldehyde requires an input of energy. Which of the following conclusions may be drawn from this observation?
   a. More heat is released when formaldehyde is produced compared to the production of acetic acid.
   b. Compared to the reactants that it is formed from, formaldehyde has more potential energy than does acetic acid.
   c. Entropy decreases when acetic acid is produced and increases when formaldehyde is produced.
   d. The mineral catalyst involved in acetic acid production provides energy to make the reaction spontaneous.

10. From what you have learned about water, why do coastal regions tend to have milder climates with cooler summers and warmer winters than do inland areas at the same latitude?

✓ PUT IT ALL TOGETHER: Case Study

How do organisms survive below freezing temperatures?

The winter flounder (*Pseudopleuronectes americanus*) lives in the Mid-Atlantic Ocean and along the New England coast, where frigid water temperatures would normally turn the water inside the flounder's cells into ice. Does the flounder produce some type of antifreeze compound that prevents it from freezing solid?

11. The flounder is able to survive in very cold water, but only when water is in its liquid state. What property of water prevents the ocean from freezing solid when the temperature in the air is well below water's freezing point?

12. The salty ocean has a higher level of entropy compared to fresh water due to the dissolved ions it contains, which interact with and disperse water molecules. For ice to form in the ocean, this entropy must be reduced to allow the crystalline structure shown in Figure 2.15a to form. If you were to break off a piece of this ice and melt it, would the water taste fresh or salty? Explain your answer.

13. **CAUTION** Evaluate the following statements related to the process of freezing water.
    T/F It does not follow the second law of thermodynamics.
    T/F It is exothermic.
    T/F It results in an overall increase in entropy.
    T/F It requires an input of energy.

14. **PROCESS OF SCIENCE** *P. americanus* produces a small antifreeze protein (AFP) that binds to ice crystals as they form. The structure of AFP has polar groups on one side and nonpolar groups on the other. Propose a hypothesis to explain how AFP prevents cells from freezing solid.

15. **PROCESS OF SCIENCE** The flounder AFP has been used to genetically modify plants to reduce tissue damage under freezing temperatures. The data from one experiment using a potato plant are provided below. What additional information is needed to determine if AFP is useful in protecting against frost damage?

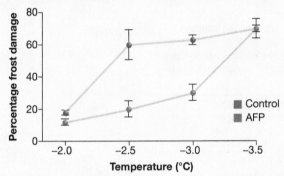

Source: Wallis, J. G., H. Wang, and D. J. Guerra. 1997. *Plant Molecular Biology* 35: 323–330.

16. **SOCIETY** Engineering potatoes, tomatoes, and strawberries to produce the flounder AFP has been a topic of heated debate. What do you think some of the pros and cons of producing these genetically modified organisms might be?

3 Protein Structure and Function

A molecular model of
hemoglobin—a protein
that is carrying oxygen
in your blood right now.

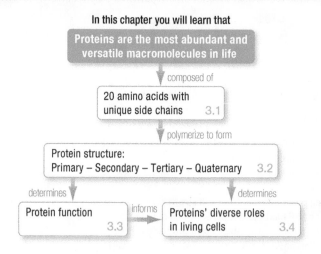

In this chapter you will learn that

> **Proteins are the most abundant and versatile macromolecules in life**

composed of

> **20 amino acids with unique side chains** 3.1

polymerize to form

> **Protein structure: Primary – Secondary – Tertiary – Quaternary** 3.2

determines — determines

> **Protein function** 3.3   informs   **Proteins' diverse roles in living cells** 3.4

This chapter is part of the
Big Picture. See how on
pages 140–141.

What type of molecule was responsible for the origin of life? Answering this question is a recurring theme in this and the next three chapters.

To address the question of life's origins, researchers designed experiments to identify the types of molecules that could have been produced in the waters of prebiotic Earth (Chapter 2). The early Earth simulations designed by Stanley Miller and others who followed up on his work sparked particular excitement for origin-of-life researchers, because the same molecules were repeatedly discovered among their products—amino acids.

Amino acids have also been found in meteorites and produced in experiments that approximate the environment of interstellar space. Taken together, these observations have led researchers to conclude that amino acids were present and probably abundant during chemical evolution. Because amino acids are the building blocks of proteins, and proteins are vital, tremendously versatile components of today's cells, many researchers have asked, Could a protein have been the initial spark of life? For the answer to be yes, or even maybe, proteins would need to possess three of the fundamental attributes of life, namely, information, replication, and evolution.

To determine if proteins do have these attributes, let's begin by looking at their basic structural unit, the amino acid, and at how amino acids link to form proteins.

3.1 Amino Acids and Their Polymerization

Modern cells, such as those that make up your body, produce tens of thousands of distinct proteins. Most of these molecules are composed of just 20 different building blocks, called **amino acids.** All 20 of these building blocks share a common core structure.

The Structure of Amino Acids

To understand how amino acids are put together, recall that carbon atoms have a valence of four—they can form up to four covalent bonds (Chapter 2). In all 20 amino acids, a central carbon atom (referred to as the α-carbon) bonds covalently to the four different atoms or groups of atoms listed here (see also **Figure 3.1a**):

1. H—a hydrogen atom
2. NH_2—an amino functional group
3. COOH—a carboxyl functional group
4. a distinctive "R-group" (often referred to as a "side chain")

The combination of amino and carboxyl functional groups is key to how these molecules behave. In water, which has a pH of 7, amino acids ionize. The concentration of protons at this pH causes the amino group to act as a base, and it attracts a proton to form NH_3^+ (**Figure 3.1b**, left). The carboxyl group, in contrast, acts as an acid. The two highly electronegative oxygen atoms in

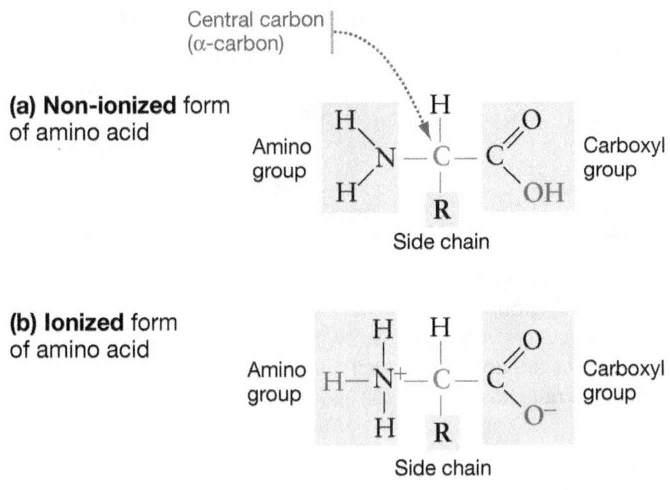

Central carbon (α-carbon)

(a) Non-ionized form of amino acid

Amino group

Carboxyl group

Side chain

(b) Ionized form of amino acid

Amino group

Carboxyl group

Side chain

Figure 3.1 All Amino Acids Have the Same Core Structure. The presence of amino (basic) and carboxyl (acidic) functional groups inspired the name *amino acid*.

this group pull the electron away from its hydrogen atom, which means that it is relatively easy for this group to lose a proton to form COO^- (**Figure 3.1b**, right).

The charges on these functional groups are important for two reasons: **(1)** They help amino acids stay in solution, where they can interact with one another and with other solutes, and **(2)** they affect the amino acid's chemical reactivity.

The Nature of Side Chains

What about the R-group? The **R-group,** or **side chain,** represents the part of the amino acid core structure that makes each of the 20 different amino acids unique. R-groups vary from a single hydrogen atom to large structures containing carbon atoms linked into rings. The properties of amino acids vary because their R-groups vary. **Figure 3.2** on page 80 highlights the R-groups on the 20 most common amino acids found in cells.[1]

Functional Groups Affect Reactivity   Several of the side chains found in amino acids contain carboxyl, sulfhydryl, hydroxyl, or amino functional groups. Under the right conditions, these functional groups can participate in chemical reactions. For example, amino acids with a sulfhydryl group (SH) in their side chains can form disulfide (S—S) bonds that help link different parts of large proteins. Such bonds naturally form between the proteins in your hair; curly hair contains many cross-links and straight hair far fewer.

In contrast, some amino acids contain side chains that are devoid of functional groups—consisting solely of carbon and hydrogen atoms. These R-groups rarely participate in chemical reactions. As a result, the influence of these amino acids on protein function depends primarily on their size and shape rather than reactivity.

The Polarity and Charge of R-Groups Affect Solubility   The nature of its R-group affects the solubility of an amino acid in in its natural environment—the aqueous interior of the cell.

*   Both polar and electrically charged R-groups interact readily with water and are **hydrophilic.** Hydrophilic R-groups dissolve easily in water.

*   Nonpolar R-groups lack charged or highly electronegative atoms capable of forming hydrogen bonds with water. These R-groups are **hydrophobic,** meaning that they do not interact with water. Instead of dissolving, hydrophobic R-groups tend to coalesce in aqueous solution.

Amino acid R-groups can be grouped into three general types: charged, which includes acidic and basic; uncharged polar; and nonpolar. If given the structural formula for an amino acid at cellular pH, as in Figure 3.2, you can determine which type of amino acid it is by asking three questions:

1. Does the R-group have a negative charge? If so, it is acidic and will lose a proton, like aspartate.

2. Does the R-group have a positive charge? If so, it is basic and will pick up a proton, like lysine.

---
[1]There are actually 22 amino acids found in proteins that occur in organisms, but two are very rare.

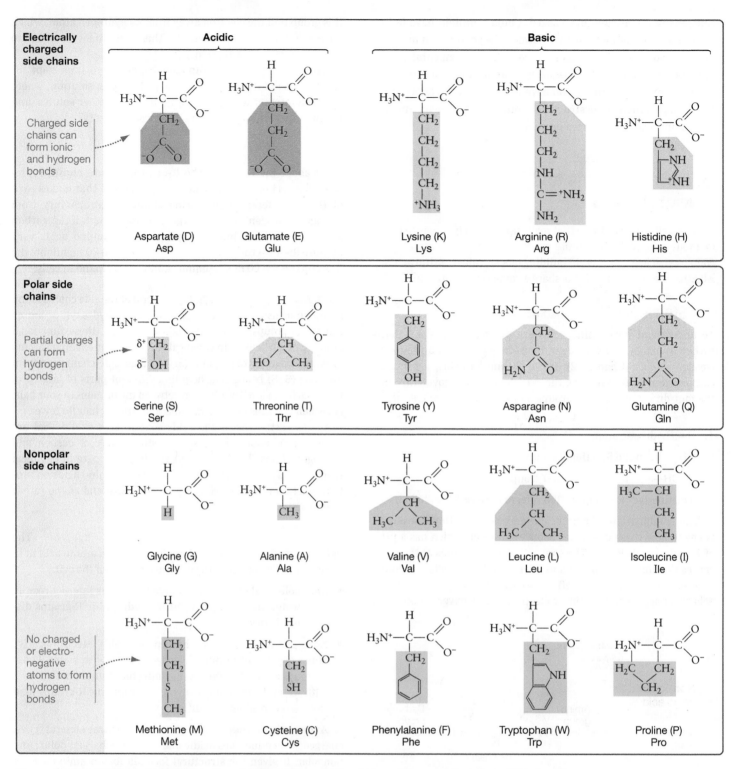

Figure 3.2 The 20 Major Amino Acids Found in Organisms. At the pH found in most cells (about pH 7), the 20 major amino acids found in organisms have the structural formulas shown here. Their R-groups (side chains) are highlighted, and standard single-letter and three-letter abbreviations for each amino acid are given. For clarity, the carbon atoms in the ring structures of phenylalanine, tyrosine, tryptophan, and histidine are not shown; each bend in a ring is the site of a carbon atom. The hydrogen atoms in these structures are also not shown. A double line inside a ring indicates a double bond.

✔ Based on the relative electronegativities of O, N, C, S, and H (see Chapter 2), explain why the R-groups highlighted in green are nonpolar and why R-groups highlighted in pink are polar.

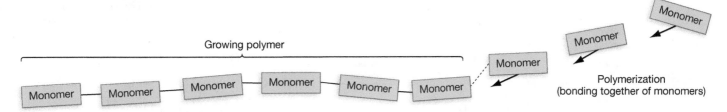

Figure 3.3 **Monomers Are the Building Blocks of Polymers.**

3. If the R-group is uncharged, does it have an oxygen atom? If so, then the highly electronegative oxygen will form a polar covalent bond in the R-group, thus making it uncharged polar like serine. (Although somewhat less electronegative, nitrogen atoms can also contribute polarity.) The overall polarity of an R-group is based on the number of highly polar covalent bonds relative to nonpolar bonds.

If the R-group in your amino acid does not have a negative charge, a positive charge, or an oxygen atom, then you are looking at a nonpolar amino acid, such as methionine.

✔ If you understand how the interaction between amino acids and water is affected by the side chains, you should be able to use Figure 3.2 to order the following amino acids from most hydrophilic to most hydrophobic: valine, aspartate, asparagine, and tyrosine. Explain how you determined the order of these amino acids.

Now that you have seen the diversity of structures in amino acids, let's put them together to make a protein.

How Do Amino Acids Link to Form Proteins?

Amino acids link to one another to form proteins. Proteins are **macromolecules**—large molecules made up of smaller molecular subunits joined together. In general, a molecular subunit used to build a macromolecule is called a **monomer** ("one-part").

When a large number of monomers are bonded together, the resulting structure is called a **polymer** ("many-parts"). The process of linking monomers together is called **polymerization** (Figure 3.3). Amino acids are the monomers that polymerize to form proteins. As you will learn in later chapters, other macromolecules of life—nucleic acids and carbohydrates—are also polymers formed by the linking together of monomers.

The theory of chemical evolution states that monomers in the prebiotic soup polymerized to form the larger and more complex macromolecules found in organisms. But according to

the second law of thermodynamics (see Chapter 2), a pool of free monomers would not be expected to spontaneously self-assemble into a polymer. The polymerization reaction organizes multiple simpler monomers into a single more complex and ordered structure. Stated another way, polymerization decreases the disorder, or entropy, of the molecules involved.

For monomers to link together and form macromolecules on early Earth, an input of energy would be required to offset the reduction in entropy and allow the reaction to become spontaneous. Recall that early Earth is thought to have been rich in chemical energy and constantly bombarded with photons and lightning (Chapter 2). Is it possible that one or more of these sources of energy drove the polymerization reactions that would be required for chemical evolution of proteins? What is necessary for linking together monomers?

Polymerization of Proteins in Early Earth Monomers polymerize through **condensation reactions,** also known as **dehydration reactions.** These reactions are aptly named because the newly formed bond results in the loss of a water molecule (Figure 3.4a). The reverse reaction, called **hydrolysis,** breaks polymers apart by adding a water molecule (Figure 3.4b). The water molecule reacts with the bond linking the monomers, separating one monomer from the polymer chain.

In a solution like the one described in the prebiotic soup model, condensation and hydrolysis represent the forward and reverse reactions of a chemical equilibrium:

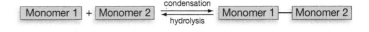

Based on what you have learned about chemical reactions, hydrolysis dominates because it both increases entropy and is favorable energetically.

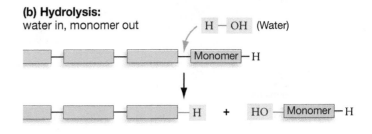

Figure 3.4 **Polymers Can Be Extended or Broken Apart.**

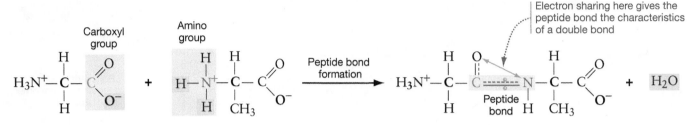

Figure 3.5 Peptide Bonds Form When the Carboxyl Group of One Amino Acid Reacts with the Amino Group of a Second Amino Acid.

This means that, in a prebiotic soup, polymerization would occur only if there were a very high concentration of amino acids to push the reaction toward condensation. Since the equilibrium favors free monomers over polymers even under concentrated conditions, a polymer is unlikely to have grown much beyond a short chain. However, according to recent experiments, there are several ways that amino acids could have polymerized early in chemical evolution.

- Researchers evaluating the surface metabolism model of chemical evolution (see Chapter 2) have been able to generate stable polymers in the laboratory by mixing free amino acids with a source of chemical energy and tiny mineral particles. Apparently, growing macromolecules are protected from hydrolysis if they cling, or adsorb, to a mineral surface.

- In conditions that simulate the hot, metal-rich environments of undersea volcanoes, researchers have observed the amino acids being formed and even polymerized.

- In other laboratory experiments, amino acids have also joined into polymers in cooler water if an energy-rich carbon- and sulfur-containing gas—one that is commonly ejected from undersea volcanoes—is present.

So, the current consensus is that several mechanisms could have led to polymerization reactions between amino acids early in chemical evolution. But what kind of bond is responsible for linking these monomers?

The Peptide Bond As **Figure 3.5** shows, amino acids polymerize when a bond forms between the carboxyl group of one amino acid and the amino group of another. The C–N covalent bond that results from this condensation reaction is called a **peptide bond.** When a water molecule is removed in the condensation reaction, the carboxyl group is converted to a carbonyl functional group (C=O) and the amino group becomes simply N–H in the resulting polymer.

Peptide bonds are unusually stable compared to linkages in other types of macromolecules. This is because a pair of valence electrons on the nitrogen is partially shared in the C–N bond (see Figure 3.5). The degree of electron sharing is great enough that peptide bonds actually have some of the characteristics of a double bond. For example, the peptide bond is planar, limiting the movement of the atoms participating in the peptide bond.

When amino acids are linked by peptide bonds into a chain, they are referred to as residues to distinguish them from free amino acid monomers. **Figure 3.6a** shows how the chain of peptide bonds in a short polymer gives the molecule a structural framework, or a "backbone." There are three key points to note about the peptide-bonded backbone:

1. **R-group orientation** The side chains of each residue extend out from the backbone, making it possible for them to interact with each other and with water.

2. **Directionality** There is an amino group ($-NH_3^+$) on one end of the backbone and a carboxyl group ($-COO^-$) on the

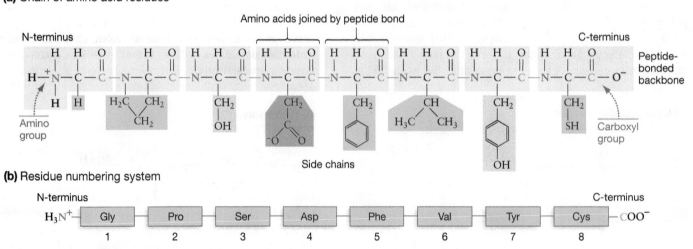

(a) Chain of amino acid residues

(b) Residue numbering system

Figure 3.6 Amino Acids Polymerize to Form Chains.

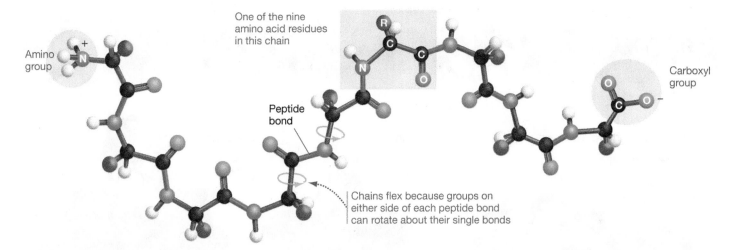

Amino group

One of the nine amino acid residues in this chain

Carboxyl group

Peptide bond

Chains flex because groups on either side of each peptide bond can rotate about their single bonds

Figure 3.7 **Amino Acid Chains Are Flexible.**

other. The end of the residue sequence that has the free amino group is called the N-terminus, or amino-terminus, and the end with the free carboxyl group is called the C-terminus, or carboxy-terminus. By convention, biologists always write amino acid residue sequences from the N-terminus to the C-terminus (**Figure 3.6b**), because the N-terminus is the start of the chain when proteins are synthesized in cells.

3. *Flexibility*   Although the peptide bond itself cannot rotate because of its double-bond nature, the single bonds on either side of the peptide bond can rotate. As a result, the structure as a whole is flexible (**Figure 3.7**).

Generally, when fewer than 50 amino acids are linked together in this way, the resulting polymer is called an **oligopeptide** ("few-peptides") or simply a **peptide.** Polymers that contain 50 or more amino acids are called **polypeptides** ("many-peptides").

The term **protein** is often used to describe any chain of amino acid residues. But in formal use, "protein" refers to the complete,

often functional form of the molecule. Most proteins are large enough to be considered polypeptides. In Section 3.2, you'll see that some proteins consist of a single polypeptide while others are functional only when multiple polypeptides are bonded to one another.

Proteins are the stuff of life. Let's take a look at how they are put together and then see what they do.

3.2 What Do Proteins Look Like?

Structure gives rise to function, and proteins have unparalleled diversity when it comes to their functional roles in life. The variability in protein size and shape, as well as in the chemical properties of their amino acid residues, is responsible for the diverse functions that proteins perform in cells.

Figure 3.8 on page 84 illustrates some of the variety in the shapes observed in proteins. Proteins that provide structural support for cells or tissues, such as the collagen triple helix in Figure 3.8a, often form long, cable-like fibers. In the case of the TATA box–binding protein in Figure 3.8b and the porin protein in Figure 3.8c, the shape of the molecule has a clear correlation with its function. The TATA box–binding protein has a groove where a molecule of DNA (a type of nucleic acid) fits; porin has a hole that forms a pore. The groove in the TATA box–binding protein interacts with specific regions of a DNA molecule to regulate gene activity while porin fits in cell membranes and allows certain hydrophilic molecules to pass through.

But many of the proteins found in cells do not have shapes that are noticeably correlated with their functions. For example, the chymotrypsin protein in Figure 3.8d has an overall globular shape that tells little about its function, which is to bind to and cleave the peptide bonds of other proteins.

How can biologists make sense of this diversity of protein size and shape? Initially, the amount of variation seems overwhelming. Fortunately, it is not. No matter how large or complex a protein may be, its underlying structure can be categorized into just four basic levels of organization.

| CHECK YOUR UNDERSTANDING

If you understand that ...

- Amino acids are small molecules with a central carbon atom bonded to a carboxyl group, an amino group, a hydrogen atom, and a side chain called an R-group.
- Each amino acid has distinctive chemical properties because each has a unique R-group.
- Proteins are polymers made up of amino acids.
- When the carboxyl group of one amino acid reacts with the amino group of another amino acid, a strong covalent bond called a peptide bond forms. Small chains are called oligopeptides; large chains are called polypeptides.

✔ **You should be able to ...**

MODEL Draw the structural formula for two glycine residues (glycine's R-group is an H) linked by a peptide bond, and label the amino- and carboxy-terminus.

Answers are available in Appendix A.

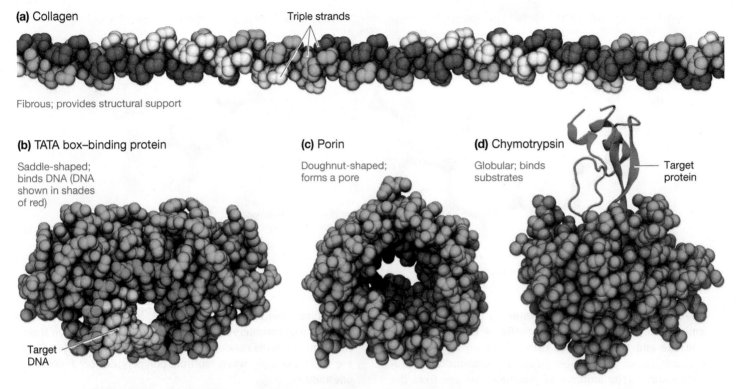

(a) Collagen

Triple strands

Fibrous; provides structural support

(b) TATA box–binding protein

Saddle-shaped; binds DNA (DNA shown in shades of red)

Target DNA

(c) Porin

Doughnut-shaped; forms a pore

(d) Chymotrypsin

Globular; binds substrates

Target protein

Figure 3.8 In Overall Shape, Proteins Are the Most Diverse Class of Molecules Known. Space-filling models are used here to illustrate the three-dimensional appearance of the proteins. Each atom is represented by a sphere with a diameter proportional to its size.

Primary Structure

Each protein has a unique sequence of amino acids. That simple conclusion was the culmination of 12 years of study by Frederick Sanger and co-workers during the 1940s and 1950s. Sanger's group worked out the first techniques for determining the amino acid sequence of insulin, a hormone that helps regulate sugar concentrations in the blood of humans and other mammals. When other proteins were analyzed, it rapidly became clear that each protein has a definite and distinct amino acid sequence.

Biochemists refer to the unique sequence of amino acids in a protein as its **primary structure.** With 20 types of amino acids available and chain lengths of up to tens of thousands of amino acid residues, the number of primary structures that are possible is practically limitless. There may, in fact, be 20^n different combinations of amino acid residues for a polymer with a given length of n. For example, a chain of just 10 amino acids has 20^{10} possible sequences. This is over 10,000 billion variations.

Why is the order and type of residues in the primary structure of a protein important? Recall that the R-groups present on each amino acid affect its chemical reactivity and solubility. It's therefore reasonable to predict that the order of the R-groups present in a polypeptide will affect that molecule's properties and function. This prediction is correct. In some cases, even a single change in the sequence of amino acids can cause striking changes in the way the protein as a whole behaves.

As an example, consider hemoglobin, an oxygen-binding protein in human red blood cells. In some individuals, one of the two different polypeptide sequences that make up hemoglobin (see section on quaternary structure) has a valine instead of a glutamate at the 6th position (Figure 3.9a). Valine and glutamate have radically different side chains. The change in R-group produces hemoglobin molecules that stick to one another and form fibers when oxygen concentrations in the blood are low. Red blood cells that carry these fibers adopt a sickle-like shape (Figure 3.9b).

Figure 3.9 Changes in Primary Structure Affect Protein Function. Compare the primary structure of normal hemoglobin **(a)** with that of hemoglobin molecules in people with sickle-cell disease **(b).** The single amino acid change causes red blood cells to change from their normal disc shape in (a) to a sickled shape in (b) when oxygen concentrations are low.

(a) Normal sequence of residues

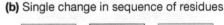

Pro	Glu	Glu
5	6	7

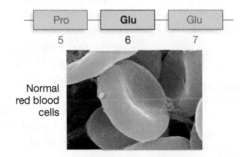

Normal red blood cells

(b) Single change in sequence of residues

Pro	Val	Glu
5	6	7

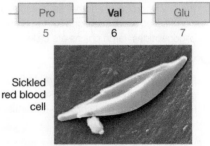

Sickled red blood cell

Sickled red blood cells get stuck in small blood vessels called capillaries, thereby starving downstream cells of oxygen. A debilitating illness called sickle-cell disease results.

A protein's primary structure is fundamental to its function. Primary structure is also fundamental to the higher levels of protein structure: secondary, tertiary, and quaternary.

Secondary Structure

Even though variation in the amino acid sequence of a protein is virtually limitless, it is only the tip of the iceberg in terms of generating structural diversity.

The next level of organization in proteins—**secondary structure**—is created in part by interactions between functional groups in the peptide-bonded backbone. Secondary structures are distinctively shaped sections that are stabilized largely by hydrogen bonding that occurs between the oxygen on the C=O group of one amino acid residue and the hydrogen on the N—H groups of another (**Figure 3.10a**). The oxygen atom in the C=O group has a partial negative charge due to its high electronegativity, while the hydrogen atom in the N—H group has a partial positive charge because it is bonded to nitrogen, which also has high electronegativity.

Note a key point: Hydrogen bonding between sections of the same backbone is possible only when a polypeptide bends in a way that puts C=O and N—H groups close together. In most proteins, these polar groups are aligned and form hydrogen bonds with one another when the backbone bends to form one of two possible structures:

1. an **α-helix** (alpha-helix), in which the polypeptide's backbone is coiled (**Figure 3.10b**, left); or

2. a **β-pleated sheet** (beta-pleated sheet), in which segments of a peptide chain bend 180° and then fold in the same plane (**Figure 3.10b**, right).

In both structures, the residues that hydrogen-bond to one another are often close together in the linear sequence of a polypeptide's primary structure. In an α-helix, H-bonds form between residues that are just four linear positions apart (see Figure 3.10a). The distance between residues that form a β-pleated sheet may be larger because folds in the chain can bring them close enough to bond in three-dimensional space.

Biologists use illustrations called ribbon diagrams to reveal the secondary structures within the overall shape of a protein. Ribbon diagrams represent α-helices as coils and β-pleated sheets as groups of arrows in a plane (**Figure 3.10c**). Unlike space-filling models, ribbon diagrams don't show the presence of each atom and its volume—only the underlying structure of the protein backbone.

Which secondary structures form, if either, depend on the molecule's primary structure—specifically, the geometry and properties of the amino acids in the sequence. Certain amino acids are more likely to be involved in α-helices than in β-pleated sheets, and vice versa, due to the specific geometry of their side chains. Proline, for example, is rarely found in α-helices due to its unusual R-group, which bonds not only to the central carbon, but to the nitrogen of the core amino group, too (see residue 2 in Figure 3.6a). This structure often introduces kinks in the peptide-bonded backbone that do not conform to the shape of the helix.

(a) Hydrogen bonds can form between nearby amino and carbonyl groups on the same polypeptide chain.

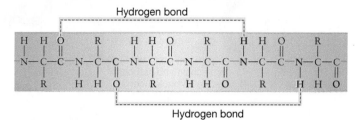

(b) Secondary structures of proteins result.

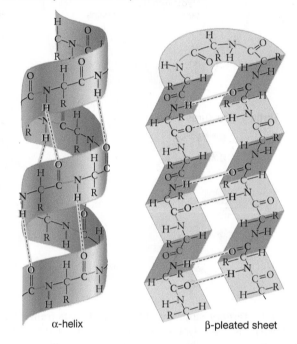

α-helix   β-pleated sheet

(c) Ribbon diagrams of secondary structure

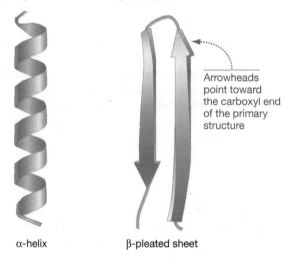

Arrowheads point toward the carboxyl end of the primary structure

α-helix   β-pleated sheet

Figure 3.10 **Secondary Structures of Proteins. (a)** Neighboring regions in a polypeptide chain can form hydrogen bonds between N—H and C=O groups in the peptide-bonded backbone. **(b)** These interactions can result in helical coils or folds that form pleated-sheet structures in the polypeptide. **(c)** Ribbon diagrams represent secondary structures using coils for helices and parallel arrows for pleated sheets.

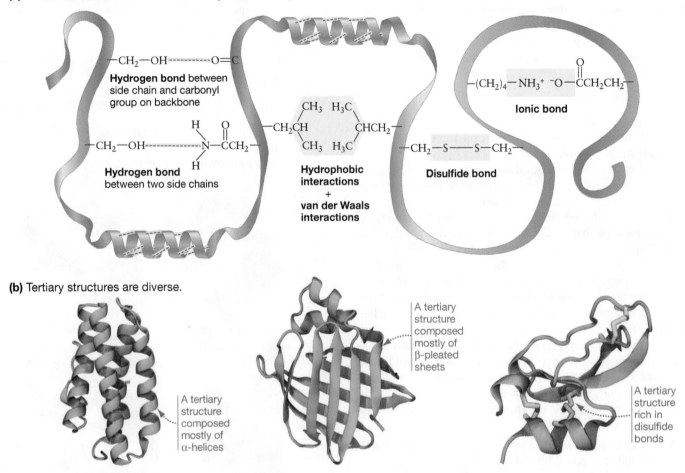

(a) Interactions that determine the tertiary structure of proteins

Hydrogen bond between side chain and carbonyl group on backbone

Hydrogen bond between two side chains

Hydrophobic interactions + **van der Waals interactions**

Disulfide bond

Ionic bond

(b) Tertiary structures are diverse.

A tertiary structure composed mostly of α-helices

A tertiary structure composed mostly of β-pleated sheets

A tertiary structure rich in disulfide bonds

Figure 3.11 Tertiary Structure of Proteins Results from Interactions Involving R-Groups. (a) The overall folded shape of a complete polypeptide gives a protein its tertiary structure. This level of structure is stabilized by bonds and other interactions. **(b)** These different examples of tertiary structure include interactions between α-helices and β-pleated sheets (secondary structures).

Although each of the hydrogen bonds in an α-helix or a β-pleated sheet is weak relative to a covalent bond, the large number of hydrogen bonds in these secondary structures makes them highly stable. As a result, they increase the stability of the molecule as a whole and help define its shape. In terms of overall shape and stability, though, the tertiary structure of a protein is even more important.

Tertiary Structure

A protein's distinctive three-dimensional shape, or **tertiary structure,** results from interactions between residues that are brought together as the chain bends and folds in space. The residues that interact with one another are often far apart in the linear sequence. In contrast to secondary structures, which involve only hydrogen bonds between backbone components, tertiary structures form using a variety of bonds and interactions between R-groups or between R-groups and the backbone.

Five types of interactions involving R-groups are particularly important:

1. **Hydrogen bonding** Hydrogen bonds form between polar side chains and opposite partial charges either in the peptide backbone or other R-groups.

2. **Hydrophobic interactions** In an aqueous solution, water molecules interact with the hydrophilic polar side chains of a polypeptide, forcing the hydrophobic nonpolar side chains to coalesce into globular masses. When these nonpolar R-groups come together, the surrounding water molecules form more hydrogen bonds with each other and the polar residues on the surface of the protein, increasing the stability of their own interactions and the disorder of the aqueous solution.

3. **van der Waals interactions** Once hydrophobic side chains are close to one another, their association is further stabilized by electrical attractions known as **van der Waals interactions.** These weak attractions occur because the constant motion of electrons gives molecules a tiny asymmetry in charge that changes with time. If nonpolar molecules get extremely close to each other, the minute partial charge on one molecule induces an opposite partial charge in the nearby molecule and causes an attraction. Although the interaction is very weak relative to covalent bonds or even

(a) Cro protein, a dimer

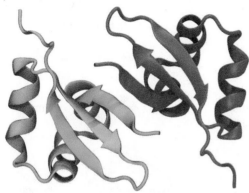

(b) Hemoglobin, a tetramer

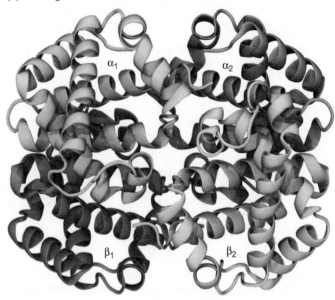

Figure 3.12 Proteins with Quaternary Structure Have Multiple Polypeptides. (a) The Cro protein is a dimer—it consists of two identical polypeptide subunits, colored light and dark green in this figure. **(b)** Hemoglobin is a tetramer—it consists of four polypeptide subunits. Two identical α subunits (light and dark green) and two identical β subunits (light and dark blue).

hydrogen bonds, a large number of van der Waals interactions can significantly increase the stability of the structure.

4. *Covalent bonding* Covalent bonds can form between the side chains of two cysteines through a reaction between the sulfhydryl groups. These **disulfide** ("two-sulfur") **bonds** are frequently referred to as bridges, because they create strong links between distinct regions of the same polypeptide or two separate polypeptides.

5. *Ionic bonding* Ionic bonds may form between groups that have full and opposing charges, such as the ionized acidic and basic side chains highlighted on the right in **Figure 3.11a**.[2]

In addition, the tertiary structure of many proteins depends in part on the presence of secondary structures like α-helices and β-pleated sheets (**Figure 3.11b**). Thus, tertiary structure depends on both primary and secondary structures.

With so many interactions possible between side chains and peptide-bonded backbones, it's not surprising that proteins vary in shape from rod-like filaments to ball-like masses.

Quaternary Structure

The first three levels of protein structure involve single polypeptides. But some proteins contain multiple polypeptides that interact to form a single functional structure. The combination of polypeptides, referred to as subunits, gives some proteins **quaternary structure.** The individual polypeptides are held together by the same types of bonds and interactions found in the tertiary level of structure.

In the simplest case, a protein with quaternary structure can consist of just two subunits that are identical. The Cro protein found in a virus called bacteriophage λ (pronounced *LAMB-da*)

is an example (**Figure 3.12a**). Proteins with two polypeptide subunits are called dimers ("two-parts").

The quaternary structure of a protein may also include polypeptides that are distinct in primary, secondary, and tertiary structures. For example hemoglobin consists of four polypeptides: two identical copies of an α subunit and two identical copies of a β subunit (**Figure 3.12b**). Hemoglobin is an example of a tetramer ("four-parts").

In addition, cells contain **macromolecular machines:** groups of multiple proteins that assemble to carry out a particular function. Some proteins are also found in complexes that include other types of macromolecules. The ribosome (introduced in Chapter 7) provides an example; it consists of several nucleic acid molecules and over 50 different proteins.

CHECK YOUR UNDERSTANDING

If you understand that …
- Proteins have up to four levels of structure.
- Primary structure is the sequence of amino acids.
- Secondary structure results from hydrogen bonds between atoms in the peptide-bonded backbone of the same polypeptide. These bonds produce structures such as α-helices and β-pleated sheets.
- Tertiary structure is the overall folded shape of a single polypeptide. Most tertiary structure is a consequence of bonds or other interactions between R-groups or between R-groups and the peptide-bonded backbone.
- Quaternary structure occurs when multiple polypeptides interact to form a single protein.

✓ You should be able to …
1. Explain how secondary, tertiary, and quaternary levels of structure depend on primary structure.
2. Predict where amino acid residues with nonpolar R-groups would be found within the overall structure of a protein such as chymotrypsin, shown in Figure 3.8d.

Answers are available in Appendix A.

---

[2]Ionic bonding is rare in proteins unless ionized R-groups are located in the interior where there is little water. Ionized groups on the exterior are normally exposed to the aqueous environment and enveloped by a shell of water, which prevents them from interacting with one another.

Level	Description	Stabilized by	Example: Hemoglobin		
Primary	The sequence of amino acids in a polypeptide	Peptide bonds	Gly — Ser — Asp — Cys		
Secondary	Formation of α-helices and β-pleated sheets in a polypeptide (depends on primary structure)	Hydrogen bonding between groups along the peptide-bonded backbone			One α-helix
Tertiary	Overall three-dimensional shape of a polypeptide (includes contribution from secondary structures)	Bonds and other interactions between R-groups, or between R-groups and the peptide-bonded backbone			One of hemoglobin's subunits
Quaternary	Shape produced by combinations of polypeptides (thus, combinations of tertiary structures)	Bonds and other interactions between R-groups, and between peptide backbones of different polypeptides			Hemoglobin consists of four polypeptide subunits

Table 3.1 summarizes the four levels of protein structure, using hemoglobin as an example. The key thing to note is that protein structure is hierarchical. The order and type of amino acids in the primary structure is responsible for the secondary structures, which then fold up to form tertiary structure. Quaternary structure (if present) is based on interactions between the tertiary structures of the polypeptide subunits.

The summary table and preceding discussion convey three important messages:

1. The combination of primary, secondary, tertiary, and quaternary levels of structure is responsible for the fantastic diversity of sizes and shapes observed in proteins.

2. Protein folding is directed by the sequence of amino acids present in the primary structure.

3. Most elements of protein structure are the result of folding polypeptide chains.

Does protein folding occur spontaneously? What happens to the function of a protein if normal folding is disrupted? Let's use these questions as a guide to dig deeper into how proteins fold.

3.3 Folding and Function

If you were able to synthesize one of the polypeptides in hemoglobin from individual amino acids, and you then placed the resulting chain in an aqueous solution, it would spontaneously fold into the shape of the tertiary structure shown in Table 3.1.

In terms of entropy, this result may seem to be in conflict with the second law of thermodynamics. Because an unfolded protein has many more ways to move about, it has much higher entropy than the folded version. Unlike polymerization, however, folding

does tend to be spontaneous because the chemical bonds and interactions that occur release enough energy to overcome this decrease in entropy and will also increase entropy in the surrounding environment. As a result, the folded molecule has less potential energy and is thus more stable than the unfolded molecule.

Folding is also crucial to the function of a completed protein. This relationship between protein structure and function was hammered home in a set of classic experiments by Christian Anfinsen and colleagues during the 1950s.

Normal Folding Is Crucial to Function

Anfinsen studied a protein called ribonuclease that cleaves ribonucleic acid (RNA) polymers. He found that ribonuclease could be unfolded, or **denatured,** by treating it with compounds that break hydrogen bonds and disulfide bonds. The denatured ribonuclease was unable to function normally—it could no longer break apart nucleic acids.

When the chemical denaturing agents were removed, however, ribonuclease refolded spontaneously and began to function normally again (**Figure 3.13**). These experiments confirmed that the primary sequence contains all the information required for folding and that folding is essential for protein function.

More recent work has shown that cells contain special proteins called **molecular chaperones** that can facilitate protein folding. Many molecular chaperones belong to a family of molecules called the heat-shock proteins, because they are produced in large quantities after cells experience the denaturing effects of high temperatures. Chaperones recognize unfolded proteins by binding to hydrophobic patches that are not normally exposed when the proteins are folded properly. This interaction prevents the unfolded proteins from clumping together, allowing them to fold into the shape specified by their primary sequence. In this

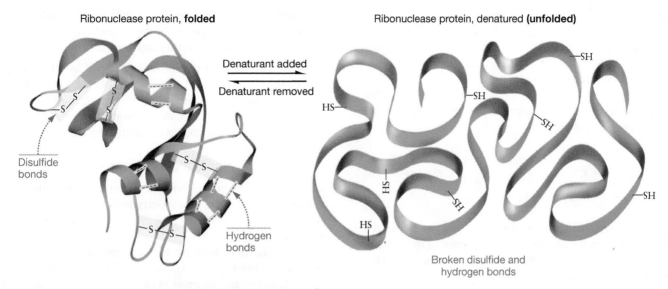

Ribonuclease protein, **folded**   Ribonuclease protein, denatured **(unfolded)**

Denaturant added

Denaturant removed

Disulfide bonds

Hydrogen bonds

HS

SH

SH

SH

HS

SH

HS

SH

Broken disulfide and hydrogen bonds

Figure 3.13 Protein Structure Determines Function. (left) Ribonuclease is functional when properly folded via hydrogen and disulfide bonds. **(right)** When the disulfide and various noncovalent bonds are broken, ribonuclease is no longer able to function. The double arrow indicates that in this case, the process is reversible.

way, chaperones help fold new proteins, and in some cases denatured proteins, before these unfolded aggregates can form.

So what is the "normal shape" of a protein? Is only one shape possible for each protein, or could there be several different folded shapes?

Protein Shape Is Flexible

Although each protein has a characteristic folded shape that is necessary for its function, most proteins maintain a flexible and dynamic shape when they are not actively performing that function. Over half of the proteins that have been analyzed to date have disordered regions lacking any apparent structure when they are in an inactive state. Each of these proteins will exist in an assortment of shapes until they are prompted to adopt a single folded and functional form. This step is often accomplished when the proteins interact with particular ions or molecules, or when they are chemically modified.

Protein Folding Is Often Regulated Since the function of a protein is dependent on its shape, controlling when or where it is folded into its active shape will regulate the protein's activity. Proteins involved in cell signaling, for example, are often regulated in this way. Many of these proteins are disordered and do not complete their folding until after binding to ions or other molecules that are present only during a signaling event. This interaction induces the protein to fold into an ordered, active conformation. Such regulated folding plays a major role in controlling and coordinating cellular activities (see Chapter 11).

Folding Can Be "Infectious" In 1982, Stanley Prusiner published what may be the most surprising result to emerge from research on protein folding: Certain normal proteins can be induced to fold into infectious, disease-causing agents. These proteins are called **prions** (pronounced *PREE-ons*), or proteinaceous infectious particles.

Infectious prions are alternately folded forms of normal proteins that are present in healthy individuals. These infectious and normal proteins do not differ in their primary structure, but their *shapes* are radically different. **Figure 3.14** illustrates the differences in shape observed between the normal and infectious forms of the prion protein (PrP) responsible for "mad cow disease" in cattle. Figure 3.14a shows the normal folded form seen in healthy cattle cells. The infectious version of this protein is shown in Figure 3.14b.

Mad cow disease is one of a family of diseases caused by prions known as the spongiform encephalopathies—literally, "sponge-brain-illnesses." Cows, sheep, goats, and humans afflicted with these diseases undergo massive degeneration of the brain. Although some spongiform encephalopathies can be inherited, in many cases the disease is transmitted when individuals eat tissues containing the infectious form of PrP. All the prion illnesses are fatal.

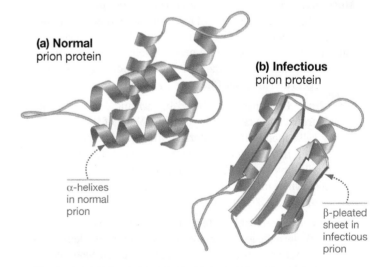

(a) Normal prion protein

(b) Infectious prion protein

α-helixes in normal prion

β-pleated sheet in infectious prion

Figure 3.14 Prion Infectivity Is Linked to Structure. Ribbon diagram of **(a)** a normal, noninfectious prion protein with α-helices; and **(b)** the infectious form with β-pleated sheets that causes mad cow disease in cattle.

Infectious prions propagate by binding to normal prions and inducing conformational changes that cause them to adopt the alternate, infectious shape. This shape change stabilizes the interactions between prion proteins, resulting in the assembly of long fibrils that often leads to cell death.

Prions are a particularly dramatic example of how a protein's function depends on its shape as well as how the final shape of a protein depends on folding.

3.4 Protein Functions Are as Diverse as Protein Structures

As a group, proteins perform more types of cell functions than any other type of molecule does. It makes sense to hypothesize that life began with proteins, simply because proteins are so vital to the life of today's cells.

Consider the red blood cells that are moving through your veins and arteries right now. Each of these cells contains about 300 million copies of hemoglobin. Hemoglobin carries oxygen from your lungs to cells throughout the body. But every red blood cell also has thousands of copies of a protein called carbonic anhydrase, which is important for moving carbon dioxide from cells back to the lungs, where it can be breathed out. These are just two examples of the incredible variety of proteins in your body. Proteins are crucial to most tasks required for cells to exist:

- *Catalysis* Many proteins are specialized to **catalyze,** or speed up, chemical reactions. A protein that functions as a catalyst is called an **enzyme.** The carbonic anhydrase molecules in red blood cells are catalysts. So is the salivary amylase protein in your mouth. Salivary amylase begins the digestion of starch into simple sugars. Most chemical reactions that make life possible depend on enzymes (see Chapters 8, 9, and 10).

- *Defense* Proteins called antibodies attack and destroy viruses and bacteria that cause disease (see Chapter 48).

- *Movement* Motor proteins and contractile proteins are responsible for moving the cell itself, or for moving large molecules and other types of cargo inside the cell. As you turn this page, for example, specialized proteins called actin and myosin will slide past one another to flex or extend muscle cells in your fingers and arm (see Chapters 7 and 45).

- *Signaling* Proteins are involved in carrying and receiving signals from cell to cell inside the body. Many of them reside on the cell's membrane to interact with neighboring cells. If sugar levels in your blood are low, a small peptide called glucagon will bind to receptor proteins on your liver cells, triggering enzymes inside to release sugar into your bloodstream (see Chapters 11, 37, and 46).

- *Structure* Structural proteins make up body components such as fingernails and hair, and form the internal "skeleton" of individual cells. Structural proteins keep red blood cells flexible and in their normal disc-like shape (see Chapter 7).

- *Transport* Proteins allow particular molecules to enter and exit cells or carry them throughout the body. Hemoglobin is

a particularly well-studied transport protein, but virtually every cell is studded with membrane proteins that control the passage of specific molecules and ions (see Chapter 6).

Of all the functions that proteins perform in cells, catalysis may be the most important. The reason is speed. Life, at its most basic level, consists of chemical reactions. But most don't occur fast enough to support life unless a catalyst is present. Enzymes are the most effective catalysts on Earth. Why is this so?

Why Are Enzymes Good Catalysts?

Catalyzed reactions involve one or more reactants, called **substrates.** Part of the reason enzymes are such effective catalysts is that they hold substrates in a precise orientation so they can react.

The initial hypothesis for how enzymes work was proposed by Emil Fischer in 1894. According to Fischer's "lock-and-key" model, enzymes are analogous to a lock and the keys are substrates that fit into the lock and then react. Several important ideas in this model have stood the test of time. For example, Fischer was correct in proposing that enzymes bring substrates into a precise orientation that makes reactions more likely. His model also accurately explained why most enzymes effectively catalyze one specific reaction. Enzyme specificity is a product of the geometry and types of functional groups in the sites where substrates bind.

As researchers began to test Fischer's model, the location where substrates bind and react became known as the enzyme's **active site.** The active site is where catalysis actually occurs.

When techniques for solving the three-dimensional structure of enzymes became available, the active sites were identified as clefts or cavities within the overall shapes. The digestive enzyme chymotrypsin, which is at work in your body now, is a good example. The active site in chymotrypsin contains three key amino acid residues, called a triad, with functional groups that catalyze the cleavage of peptide bonds in other proteins (**Figure 3.15**).

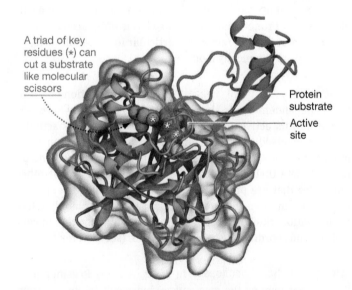

A triad of key residues (∗) can cut a substrate like molecular scissors

Protein substrate

Active site

Figure 3.15 Substrates Bind to a Specific Location in an Enzyme Called the Active Site. The active site in chymotrypsin, as in many enzymes, contains key amino acid residues that bind substrates and catalyze a reaction.

No other class of macromolecules can match proteins for their catalytic potential. The variety of reactive functional groups present in amino acids is much better suited for this activity than those found in nucleotides or sugars.

The role of enzymes in catalyzing reactions is discussed in more detail in the next unit (see Chapter 8). There you will see that Fischer's model had to be modified as research on enzyme action progressed.

Did Life Arise from a Self-Replicating Enzyme?

Several observations in the preceding sections could argue that a protein catalyst was the first molecule capable of replication. Experimental studies have shown that amino acids were likely abundant during chemical evolution and that they could have polymerized to form small proteins. To date, however, attempts to simulate the origin of life with proteins alone have not been successful.

Although it is too early to arrive at definitive conclusions, most origin-of-life researchers are skeptical that life began with

a protein. To achieve the attributes of life, proteins would need to possess information, replicate, and evolve. The information carried in proteins is necessary for their function, but it cannot be used as a template or mold for their own replication. If they cannot replicate, then they cannot evolve on their own. Nucleic acids, in contrast, *do* carry this type of information. How they use it is the subject of the next chapter.

CHECK YOUR UNDERSTANDING

If you understand that …

- Proteins carry out a wide variety of functions in cells, and each function is directly connected to structure.
- Enzymes speed up chemical reactions by binding substrates at their active site, where catalysis takes place.

✔ **You should be able to …**

Explain how the primary and tertiary levels of protein structure relate to enzyme-substrate specificity.

Answers are available in Appendix A.

For media, go to MasteringBiology

3.1 Amino Acids and Their Polymerization

- Amino acids have a central carbon bonded to an amino group, a hydrogen atom, a carboxyl group, and an R-group.
- The structure of the R-group affects the chemical reactivity and solubility of the amino acid.
- In proteins, amino acids are joined by a peptide bond between the carboxyl group of one amino acid and the amino group of another amino acid.

3.2 What Do Proteins Look Like?

- A protein's primary structure, or sequence of amino acids, is responsible for most of its chemical properties.
- Interactions that take place between C=O and N–H groups in the same peptide-bonded backbone create secondary structures, which are stabilized by hydrogen bonding.
- Tertiary structure results from interactions between R-groups—or R-groups and the peptide-bonded backbone—that stabilize a complete polypeptide into an overall three-dimensional shape.
- In many cases, a complete protein consists of several different polypeptides, bonded together. The combination of polypeptides represents the protein's quaternary structure.

3.3 Folding and Function

- Protein folding is a spontaneous process.
- A protein's overall folded shape is essential to its function.
- Many proteins must first bind to other molecules or ions before they can adopt their active conformation.
- Improperly folded proteins can be detrimental to life, and certain folded variations of proteins can cause deadly infectious diseases.

3.4 Protein Functions Are as Diverse as Protein Structures

- In organisms, proteins function in catalysis, defense, movement, signaling, structural support, and transport of materials.
- Proteins can have diverse functions in cells because they have such diverse structures and chemical properties.
- Catalysis takes place at the enzyme's active site, which has unique chemical properties and a distinctive size and shape that is specific to its substrates.

Answers are available in Appendix A

✔ TEST YOUR KNOWLEDGE

1. What two functional groups are bound to the central carbon of every free amino acid monomer?
   a. an R-group and a hydroxyl group
   b. an N–H group and a carbonyl group
   c. an amino group and a hydroxyl group
   d. an amino group and a carboxyl group

2. What type of bond is directly involved in the formation of an α-helix?
   a. peptide bonds between amino acid residues
   b. hydrogen bonds between amino acid residues
   c. van der Waals interactions between nonpolar residues
   d. disulfide bonds that form between cysteine residues

3. What type of information is used to direct different polypeptides to fold into different shapes?

4. What is an active site?
   a. the location in an enzyme where substrates bind and react
   b. the place where a molecule or ion binds to an inactive protein to induce a shape change
   c. the portion of a motor protein involved in moving cargo in a cell
   d. the site on an antibody where it binds to bacterial cells or viruses

✓ TEST YOUR UNDERSTANDING

5. **QUANTITATIVE** If a cell were to use only 10 of the 20 possible amino acids, how much of an effect would you expect this to have on protein diversity? Calculate and compare the number of different sequences that can be generated by randomly assembling either 10 or 20 amino acids into peptides that are five residues long.

6. Explain how molecular chaperones facilitate protein folding in many different polypeptides, each with their own specific shape.

7. Why are proteins not considered to be a good candidate for the first living molecule?
   a. Their catalytic capability is not sufficient for most biological reactions.
   b. Their amino acid monomers were not likely present in the prebiotic soup.
   c. They cannot serve as a template for replication.
   d. They could not have polymerized from amino acid monomers under early Earth conditions.

8. If proteins could fold only into rigid, inflexible structures, how might this affect the cell's ability to regulate their function?

✓ TEST YOUR PROBLEM-SOLVING SKILLS

9. Based on what you know of the peptide bonds that link together amino acid residues, why would proline's side chain reduce the flexibility of the backbone?

10. Make a concept map (see BioSkills 12) that relates the four levels of protein structure and shows how they can contribute to the formation of hemoglobin. Your map should include the following boxed terms: Primary structure, Secondary structure, Tertiary structure, Quaternary structure, Active site, Amino acid sequence, R-groups, α-Helices.

✓ PUT IT ALL TOGETHER: Case Study

Why do so many people avoid eating gluten?

Gluten is a mixture of proteins abundant in wheat, barley, and rye. Although these grains are staples in the Western diet, almost 1 percent of Americans have celiac disease—a disorder of the intestines caused by an abnormal immune response after eating gluten. This immune response damages the fingerlike villi of the small intestine, which can lead to intestinal upset and malnourishment. Currently, the only treatment is to maintain a strict gluten-free diet.

11. The typical college student diet is rich in gluten-containing foods. Make a list of six items that you would not be able to eat if you were diagnosed with celiac disease.

12. When you eat gluten, enzymes present in your stomach and intestines digest all but a few short peptides. How do enzymes accomplish this activity?
   a. The active site of an enzyme binds to a gluten protein and facilitates the hydrolysis reaction that breaks apart peptide bonds.
   b. An enzyme binds to the active site of a gluten protein and speeds up the condensation reaction that breaks apart peptide bonds.
   c. The active site of an enzyme binds to a gluten protein and reacts with it to break apart hydrogen bonds.
   d. An enzyme binds to the active site of a gluten protein and catalyzes the reactions that break apart hydrogen bonds.

13. **QUANTITATIVE** One of the peptides that can be recovered after gluten digestion is 33 residues long; 13 of the 33 residues are proline. How many times would you expect proline to appear in this peptide if it were made up of a completely random assortment of the 20 most common amino acids?

14. Recall that proline often introduces kinks in the backbone of a polypeptide. These kinks make it difficult for enzymes in your gut to fully digest gluten. In people with celiac disease, certain proline-rich peptides left over after gluten digestion will trigger an abnormal immune response. Researchers have identified a mold enzyme called AN-PEP that effectively digests proline-rich peptides. Predict where the structural differences would occur between AN-PEP and other enzymes that do not digest the peptides.

15. **PROCESS OF SCIENCE** AN-PEP was tested for its ability to digest gluten peptides in a system that mimics the human stomach. White bread was loaded into the artificial stomach with or without AN-PEP. The following graph shows the experiment results. Interpret the effect of AN-PEP on the accumulation of proline-rich gluten peptides. Explain why the peptide concentration increases in the negative control.

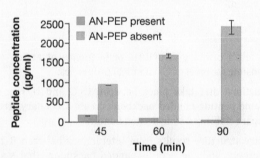

Source: Mitea, C., et al. 2008. *Gut* 57:25–32.

16. **SOCIETY** Based on the experiment in question 15, propose how AN-PEP might be used to treat celiac disease.

4 Nucleic Acids and the RNA World

This is part of the sheet-metal-and-wire model that James Watson and Francis Crick used to figure out the secondary structure of DNA. The large "T" stands for the nitrogen-containing base thymine.

In this chapter you will learn that

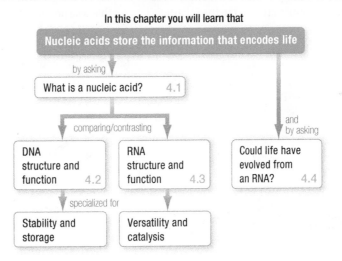

Nucleic acids store the information that encodes life

by asking

What is a nucleic acid?   4.1

comparing/contrasting

DNA structure and function   4.2

RNA structure and function   4.3

and by asking

Could life have evolved from an RNA?   4.4

specialized for

Stability and storage

Versatility and catalysis

This chapter is part of the Big Picture. See how on pages 140–141.

ife began when chemical evolution led to the production of a molecule that could promote its own replication. In today's cells, **deoxyribonucleic acid (DNA)** stores genetic information and is replicated using proteins. Relatively few researchers favor the hypothesis that life began as a DNA or protein molecule, however. Instead, the **RNA world hypothesis** proposes that there was a stage in the evolution of life when **ribonucleic acid (RNA)** both stored the genetic information and catalyzed its own replication.

There is compelling evidence that such an RNA world existed on early Earth. The nature of the first "living molecule," however, has been the subject of many investigations and heated debates. Did life on Earth begin with RNA first, or did some other replicating, evolving molecule come before RNA, just as RNA preceded DNA and proteins?

Regardless of the answer to this question, once the first self-replicating molecules evolved, chance errors in the copying process created variations that would undergo natural selection—the evolutionary process by which individuals, in this case molecules, with certain attributes reproduce more frequently than others (see Chapter 1). At this point, chemical evolution was over and biological evolution was off and running.

This chapter focuses on the structure and function of nucleic acids in today's cells, but also explores how they could have triggered the evolution of life on Earth. Let's begin with an analysis of nucleic acid monomers and how they are linked together into polymers.

4.1 What Is a Nucleic Acid?

Nucleic acids are polymers, just as proteins are polymers. But instead of being assembled from amino acids, **nucleic acids** are made up of monomers called **nucleotides.**

Figure 4.1a diagrams the three components of a nucleotide: **(1)** a phosphate group, **(2)** a five-carbon sugar, and **(3)** a nitrogenous (nitrogen-containing) base. The phosphate group is bonded to the sugar molecule, which in turn is bonded to the base.

The sugar is the central component of the nucleotide, much like the α-carbon in amino acids (see Chapter 3). The five carbons in this sugar are labeled with numbers and prime symbols (') to provide a frame of reference. For example, the base is attached to the 1' carbon and the phosphate group is attached to the 5' carbon.

Ribonucleotides are the monomers of ribonucleic acid (RNA), and **deoxyribonucleotides** are the monomers of deoxyribonucleic acid (DNA). In ribonucleotides, the sugar is ribose; in deoxyribonucleotides, it is deoxyribose (*deoxy* means "lacking oxygen"). As **Figure 4.1b** shows, both of these sugars have an —OH group bonded to the 3' carbon, but ribose has an —OH group bonded to the 2' carbon while deoxyribose has an H at the same location—a difference of just a single oxygen atom.

Ribonucleotides and deoxyribonucleotides also differ in one of their nitrogenous bases. These bases, diagrammed in **Figure 4.1c**, belong to structural groups called **purines** and **pyrimidines.** The purines are adenine (A) and guanine (G); the pyrimidines are cytosine (C), uracil (U), and thymine (T). Ribonucleotides use uracil (U), while deoxyribonucleotides use thymine (T).

Note that the two rings in adenine and guanine are formed from nine atoms, compared to the six atoms that make a single ring in each pyrimidine. This makes remembering which bases are purines easy, since both adenine and guanine include "nine" in their names.

To summarize: After the different sugars and bases are taken into account, eight different nucleotides are used to build nucleic acids—four ribonucleotides (A, G, C, and U) and four deoxyribonucleotides (A, G, C, and T). See **Making Models 4.1** to learn how simple models are commonly used to represent nucleotides.

If nucleic acids played any role in the chemical evolution of life, then at least some of these nucleotides must have been present in the prebiotic oceans. Is there any evidence to suggest that this was possible?

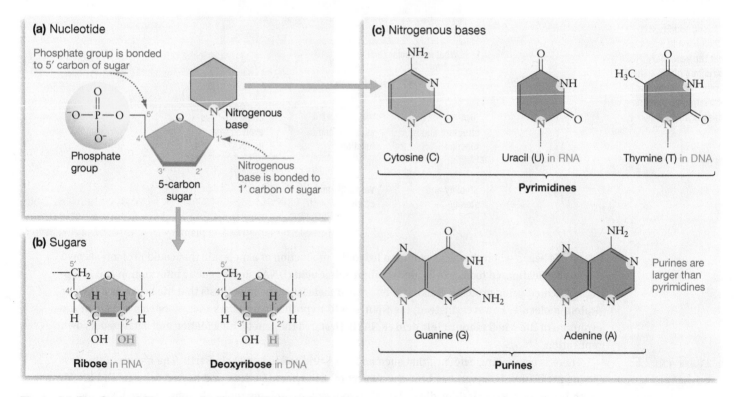

Figure 4.1 The General Structure of a Nucleotide. Note that in the bases, the nitrogen that bonds to the sugar is colored blue.

Making Models 4.1 Tips on Drawing Nucleotides

Models of complex chemical structures may be drawn by using simple shapes for the different components. Nucleotides are often drawn using a circle for the phosphate group, a pentagon with a tail for the sugar, and a hexagon for the base. Lines connecting the shapes represent covalent bonds.

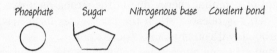

Phosphate   Sugar   Nitrogenous base   Covalent bond

MODEL Using the shapes above, draw two nucleotide models—one ribonucleotide and one deoxyribonucleotide. Label the 2′, 3′, and 5′ carbons on the sugars and show what is bonded to each carbon.

To see this model in action, go to https://goo.gl/nh62UZ

Could Chemical Evolution Result in the Production of Nucleotides?

Based on data from Stanley Miller and researchers who followed (Chapter 2), most biologists accept the idea that amino acids could have been synthesized early in Earth's history. The reactions behind the prebiotic synthesis of nucleotides, however, have been more difficult to identify.

Miller-like laboratory simulations have shown that nitrogenous bases and many different types of sugars, including ribose, can be synthesized readily under conditions that mimic the prebiotic soup. Recent work has focused on the conditions that exist in deep-sea hydrothermal vent systems (see Chapter 2). What they found was striking—the minerals preferentially bound to ribose, effectively enriching and concentrating ribose on their

surface from a pool of diverse sugars. Did this occur in the ancient vents? If so, the implications are exciting: A high concentration of ribose would be present in the same deep-sea vent environment where the evolution of life is thought to have taken place.

The production of nucleotides remains a serious challenge for the theory of chemical evolution. At this time, experiments that attempt to simulate early Earth environments have yet to synthesize complete nucleotides. But research on this issue continues.

In the meantime, let's consider the next question: Once nucleotides formed, how would they polymerize to form nucleic acids? This question has a definitive answer.

How Do Nucleotides Polymerize to Form Nucleic Acids?

As **Figure 4.2** shows, nucleotides polymerize via condensation reactions between the hydroxyl on the sugar component of one nucleotide and the phosphate group of another nucleotide. The reaction forms a new covalent bond—called a **phosphodiester linkage,** or a phosphodiester bond—between the nucleotides, and a molecule of water is released.

When phosphodiester linkages join ribonucleotides together, the polymer that is produced is RNA. Phosphodiester linkages between deoxyribonucleotides produce DNA.

DNA and RNA Strands Are Directional **Figure 4.3** on page 96 shows how the chain of phosphodiester linkages in a nucleic acid acts as a backbone, analogous to the peptide-bonded backbone found in proteins.

Like the peptide-bonded backbone of a polypeptide, the sugar–phosphate backbone of a nucleic acid is directional. In a strand of RNA or DNA, one end has an unlinked 5′ phosphate while the other end has an unlinked 3′ hydroxyl—meaning the groups are not bonded to another nucleotide.

The order of the different nucleotides forms the primary structure of the nucleic acid. When biologists write the primary structure of a stretch of DNA or RNA, they use shorthand and simply list the sequence of bases by their single-letter abbreviations. By convention, the sequence of bases found in an RNA or DNA strand is always written in the 5′ → 3′ direction. (This system is logical because in cells, RNA and DNA are always synthesized in this direction. Nucleotides are added only at the 3′ end of the growing molecule.) For example, a DNA sequence consisting of six nucleotides might be ATTAGC. It would take roughly 6 billion of these letters to write the primary structure of the DNA in most of your cells.

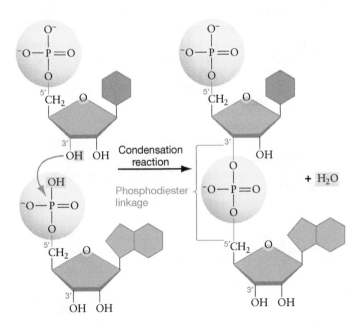

Figure 4.2 Nucleotides Polymerize via Phosphodiester Linkages. Nucleotides can polymerize via condensation reactions. The resulting phosphodiester linkage connects the 3′ carbon of one nucleotide and the 5′ carbon of another nucleotide. Ribonucleotides are shown here, but the same reaction occurs between deoxyribonucleotides.

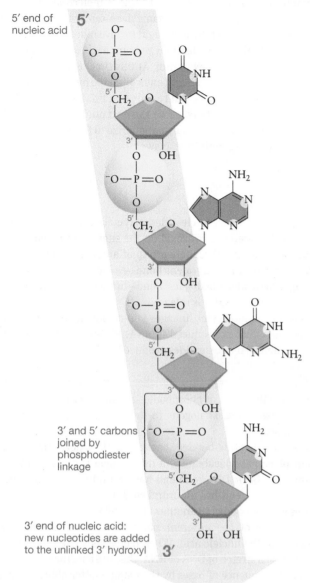

The sugar–phosphate backbone of RNA

5' end of nucleic acid

5'

3' and 5' carbons joined by phosphodiester linkage

3' end of nucleic acid: new nucleotides are added to the unlinked 3' hydroxyl

3'

Figure 4.3 Nucleic Acids Have a Sugar–Phosphate Backbone.

✔ Identify the four bases in this RNA strand, using Figure 4.1c as a key. Then write down the base sequence, starting at the 5' end.

Polymerization Requires an Energy Source In cells, the polymerization reactions that join nucleotides into nucleic acids are catalyzed by enzymes. As with other polymerization reactions, the joining of nucleotides dramatically decreases entropy and is thus not spontaneous. An input of energy is needed to tip the energy balance in favor of polymerization.

Polymerization can take place in cells because the potential energy of the nucleotide monomers is first raised by reactions that add two phosphate groups to the ribonucleotides or deoxyribonucleotides, creating nucleoside triphosphates.[1] In the case of nucleic acid polymerization, researchers refer to these

nucleoside triphosphates as "activated nucleotides." **Figure 4.4a** shows an example of an activated ribonucleotide; this molecule is called **adenosine triphosphate,** or **ATP.**

How do added phosphate groups raise the potential energy of a molecule? Recall that phosphates are negatively charged and that like charges repel (Chapter 2). Linking two or more phosphates together generates a covalent bond that carries a large amount of potential energy due to the strong repulsive forces. The energy is released when the phosphates form new, more stable bonds with other atoms (**Figure 4.4b**).

When activated nucleotides polymerize, the energy released from the condensation reaction compensates for the decrease in entropy, making the reaction spontaneous. You will see in later chapters that potential energy stored in ATP is also used to drive other cellular activities, independent of nucleotide polymerization. (Chapter 8 explains how this happens in more detail.)

Could Nucleic Acids Have Formed in the Absence of Cellular Enzymes? Accumulating data suggest that the answer is yes. Activation of nucleotides has been observed when prebiotic conditions are simulated experimentally. In follow-up experiments, researchers produced RNA molecules by incubating activated ribonucleotides with tiny mineral particles—in one case, molecules up to 50 nucleotides long were observed. These data would be in line with the surface metabolism model (introduced in Chapter 2) for the chemical evolution of nucleic acids.

Based on the results of many experiments, there is a strong consensus that if activated ribonucleotides and deoxyribonucleotides were able to form during chemical evolution, they could have polymerized into DNA and RNA without protein-based catalysts. Now, what do these nucleic acids look like, and what can they do? Let's analyze the structure and function of DNA first, and then dig into the structure and function of RNA.

CHECK YOUR UNDERSTANDING

If you understand that …

- Nucleotides are monomers that consist of a sugar, a phosphate group, and a nitrogen-containing base.
- Nucleotides polymerize to form nucleic acids through formation of phosphodiester linkages between the 3' hydroxyl on one nucleotide and the 5' phosphate on another.
- During polymerization, activated nucleotides are added to the 3' end of a nucleic acid strand.

✔ You should be able to …

1. **MODEL** Draw a simplified diagram of the phosphodiester linkage between two nucleotides, indicate the 5' → 3' polarity, and mark where the next nucleotide would be added to the growing chain.
2. Describe how nucleotides are activated in cells for incorporation into a polymer. Why is this activation required?

Answers are available in Appendix A.

---

[1] A molecule consisting of a sugar and one of the bases in Figure 4.1c is called a nucleoside (a nucleotide is a sugar, a base, and one or more phosphate groups). Thus, a sugar attached to a base and three phosphate groups is called a nucleoside triphosphate.

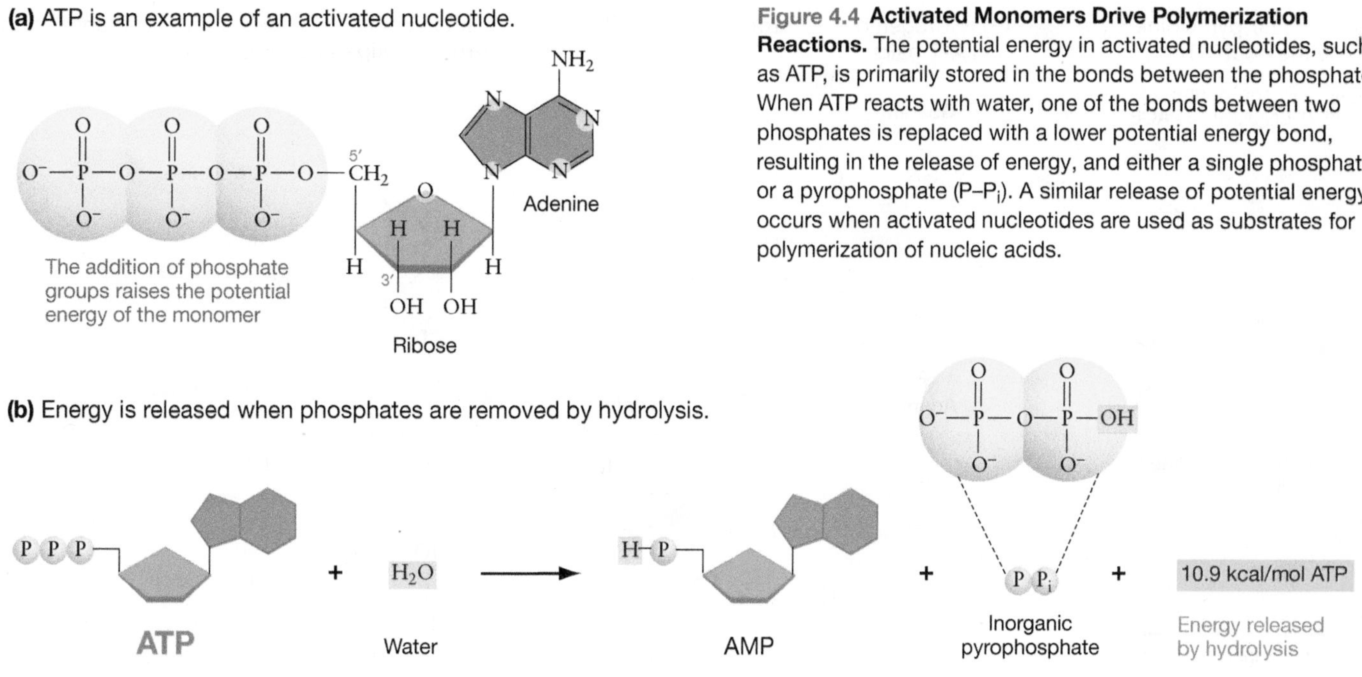

(a) ATP is an example of an activated nucleotide.

The addition of phosphate groups raises the potential energy of the monomer

Adenine

Ribose

Figure 4.4 Activated Monomers Drive Polymerization Reactions. The potential energy in activated nucleotides, such as ATP, is primarily stored in the bonds between the phosphates. When ATP reacts with water, one of the bonds between two phosphates is replaced with a lower potential energy bond, resulting in the release of energy, and either a single phosphate (P_i) or a pyrophosphate ($P–P_i$). A similar release of potential energy occurs when activated nucleotides are used as substrates for polymerization of nucleic acids.

(b) Energy is released when phosphates are removed by hydrolysis.

ATP + Water $\longrightarrow$ AMP + Inorganic pyrophosphate + 10.9 kcal/mol ATP

Energy released by hydrolysis

4.2 DNA Structure and Function

The primary structure of DNA is somewhat similar to the primary structure of proteins. Proteins have a peptide-bonded backbone with a series of R-groups that extend from it. DNA molecules have a sugar–phosphate backbone, created by phosphodiester linkages, and a sequence of any of four nitrogenous bases that extend from it.

Like proteins, DNA also has secondary structure. But while the α-helices and β-pleated sheets of proteins are formed by hydrogen bonding between groups in the backbone, the secondary structure of DNA is formed in a very different way. Let's look at details of this structure and how it relates to DNA's function as an information-carrying molecule.

What Is the Nature of DNA's Secondary Structure?

The discovery of DNA's secondary structure, announced in 1953, ranks among the great scientific breakthroughs of the twentieth century. James Watson and Francis Crick presented their celebrated model for the secondary structure of DNA in a single page that was published in the scientific journal *Nature*.

Early Data Provided Clues Watson and Crick's model was a hypothesis based on a series of results from other laboratories. They were trying to propose a secondary structure that could explain several important observations about the DNA found in cells:

- Chemists had worked out the structure of nucleotides and knew that DNA polymerized through the formation of phosphodiester linkages. Thus, Watson and Crick knew that the molecule had a sugar–phosphate backbone.

- By analyzing the nitrogenous bases in DNA samples from different organisms, Erwin Chargaff had established two empirical rules: **(1)** The number of purines in a given DNA molecule is equal to the number of pyrimidines, and **(2)** the DNA molecule has an equal number of T's and A's, and it has an equal number of C's and G's.

- By bombarding DNA with X-rays and analyzing how it scattered the radiation, Rosalind Franklin and Maurice Wilkins had calculated the distances between groups of atoms in the molecule. The technique they used is called **X-ray crystallography** (see BioSkills 6 for an introduction to this technique). The scattering patterns showed that three distances were repeated many times: 0.34 nanometer (nm), 2.0 nm, and 3.4 nm. Because the measurements repeated, the researchers inferred that DNA molecules had a regular and repeating structure. The pattern of X-ray scattering suggested that the molecule was helical, or spiral, in nature.

Based on this work, understanding DNA's structure boiled down to understanding the nature of the helix involved. What type of helix would have a sugar–phosphate backbone and explain both Chargaff's rules and the Franklin–Wilkins measurements?

DNA Strands Form an Antiparallel Double Helix Watson and Crick began by analyzing the size and geometry of the three nucleotide components: deoxyribose, phosphate, and base. The bond angles and measurements suggested that the distance of 2.0 nm represented the width of the helix and that 0.34 nm was likely to be the distance between bases stacked in a spiral.

How could they make sense of Chargaff's rules and the 3.4-nm distance, which appeared to be exactly 10 times the distance between a single pair of bases?

(a) Only purine-pyrimidine pairs fit inside the double helix.

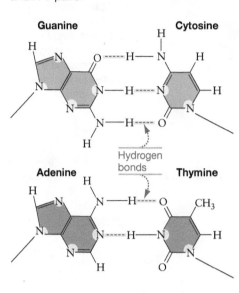

Purine-purine
NOT ENOUGH SPACE

Pyrimidine-pyrimidine
TOO MUCH SPACE

Purine-pyrimidine
JUST RIGHT

Space inside sugar-
phosphate backbones

(b) Hydrogen bonds form between G-C pairs and A-T pairs.

Guanine   Cytosine

Hydrogen bonds

Adenine   Thymine

(c) In double-stranded DNA, backbones must run in antiparallel directions.

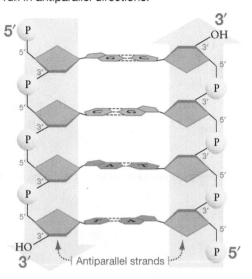

Antiparallel strands

Figure 4.5 **Complementary Base Pairing Is Based on Hydrogen Bonding.**

To solve this problem, Watson and Crick constructed a series of physical models that allowed them to tinker with different types of helical configurations. After many false starts, certain things started to click:

- They arranged two strands of DNA side by side with the sugar–phosphate backbones on the outside and the bases on the inside. If the bases extending from each backbone are to fit within the interior of a 2.0-nm-wide structure, then they have to form purine-pyrimidine pairs (see Figure 4.5a).

- Purine-pyrimidine pairing allows hydrogen bonds to form only between certain bases, said to be complementary. Adenine will form two hydrogen bonds with thymine, and guanine will form three hydrogen bonds with cytosine (Figure 4.5b). The third hydrogen bond in G-C pairs makes them slightly stronger than A-T pairs.

- The patterns of hydrogen bonding shown in Figure 4.5b could form only if the bases on opposite strands were flipped 180 degrees relative to one another. For this to happen, the two parallel strands of DNA must be oriented in opposite directions—meaning that one strand runs in the 5' → 3' direction while the other strand runs 3' → 5' (Figure 4.5c). Strands with this orientation are said to be **antiparallel.**

- After these parameters were in place, the antiparallel strands were predicted to be twisted together to form a **double helix.**

By creating this model, Watson and Crick had discovered **complementary base pairing** between the A-T and G-C bases. In fact, the term **Watson–Crick pairing** is now used interchangeably with the phrase "complementary base pairing." This discovery explains the purine-pyrimidine ratios that Chargaff observed.

Figure 4.6a shows that DNA is put together like a ladder. The antiparallel sugar–phosphate backbones form the supports of the ladder, and the base pairs form its rungs. The helical twisting of the strands allows the bases to line up in a way that makes hydrogen bonding between them possible. The physical restraints posed by these interactions result in a full helical turn every 10 bases—the 3.4-nm distance observed by Franklin and Wilkins.

Although each base has polar groups involved in the hydrogen bonds, the carbon-nitrogen ring structure is mostly nonpolar. This is a key point, because hydrophobic interactions cause double-stranded DNA to twist into a helix to minimize contact between the hydrophobic rings and surrounding water molecules. The paired strands are further stabilized by van der Waals interactions between the tightly packed bases. The negatively charged phosphate groups facing the exterior of the molecule make the double helix hydrophilic overall and thus soluble in aqueous solutions.

Figure 4.6b highlights additional features of DNA's secondary structure. It's important to note that the outside of the helical DNA molecule forms two types of grooves. The wider of the two is known as the major groove, and the narrower one is known as the minor groove. This groove asymmetry is vital for granting access to proteins that bind to particular base sequences in DNA (see Chapter 19 to learn more about the roles of these proteins).

As Figure 4.6 shows, the secondary structure of DNA can be illustrated at different levels of detail. In Making Models 4.2, you will learn how to draw highly simplified versions of DNA that can be used to model key concepts of its secondary structure.

Since Watson and Crick's model of the double helix was published, experimental tests have shown that the hypothesis is correct in almost every detail. To summarize:

(a) Schematic diagrams of DNA structure

(b) Space-filling model of DNA double helix

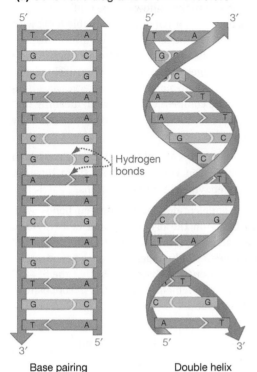

Hydrogen bonds

Base pairing

Double helix

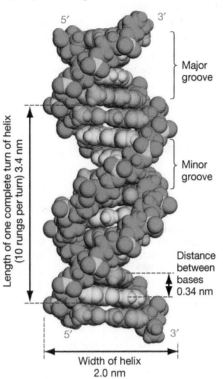

Length of one complete turn of helix (10 rungs per turn) 3.4 nm

Major groove

Minor groove

Distance between bases 0.34 nm

Width of helix 2.0 nm

Figure 4.6 The Secondary Structure of DNA Is a Double Helix. (a) The schematic diagrams illustrate complementary base pairing (yellow bands represent hydrogen bonding) and how strands are twisted into a double helix. **(b)** The space-filling model shows tight packing of the bases inside the double helix. The double-helix structure explains the measurements inferred from X-ray analysis of DNA molecules.

- DNA's secondary structure consists of two antiparallel strands twisted into a double helix.
- The double helix is shaped and stabilized by hydrophobic interactions, van der Waals interactions, and hydrogen bonding between the complementary base pairs A-T and G-C.

Up until now, the focus of this chapter has been on DNA's secondary structure. Does the DNA double helix also form tertiary structures?

Making Models 4.2 Tips on Drawing Nucleic Acids

When you're drawing models of DNA, the molecular details of the structure are not necessary. The sugar–phosphate backbone can be simplified to a single line with an arrowhead to identify the 3′ end. Base pairing is drawn as short lines and, if the sequence is part of the model, nucleotides are represented by letters.

DNA without sequence

Primary   Secondary

DNA with sequence

Primary   Secondary

G   G — C
G   G — C
T   T — A
C   C — G

MODEL Draw a double-stranded DNA molecule with the sequence A-G-C-T. Label the 5′ and 3′ ends, one of the sugar–phosphate backbones, and the hydrogen bonds involved in base pairing.

To see this model in action, go to https://goo.gl/e3zrah

The Tertiary Structure of DNA

Recall that the secondary structure of a protein often leads to a more compact tertiary structure by the polypeptide folding on itself (Chapter 3). It turns out that the DNA in cells is also normally found in more compact three-dimensional structures.

The tertiary level of structure in DNA is not as varied as seen in proteins, but two forms are commonly found in cells. When DNA becomes wound too tightly or loosely with respect to the number of base pairs per helical turn, it can twist on itself to form compact, three-dimensional structures called supercoils (see Chapter 7). In addition, DNA often forms highly organized tertiary structures by wrapping around certain proteins. These DNA-protein complexes compact the DNA into discrete, movable units during cell division (Chapter 12), and they also contribute to DNA's ability to store and transmit information (Chapter 19).

Now let's take a closer look at how the structure of DNA is involved in storing biological information.

DNA Functions as an Information-Containing Molecule

Watson and Crick's model created a sensation for a simple reason: It revealed how DNA could store and transmit biological information. In literature, information consists of letters on a page. In music, information is composed of the notes on a staff. But inside cells, information consists of a sequence of nucleotides in a nucleic acid. The four nitrogenous bases function like letters of the alphabet. A sequence of bases is like the sequence of letters in a word—it has meaning.

In all organisms that have been examined to date, from tiny bacteria to gigantic redwood trees, DNA stores the information required for the organism's growth and reproduction. Exploring how hereditary information is encoded and translated into action is the heart of several later chapters (Chapters 16 through 19). Here, however, our focus is on how life began. The theory of chemical evolution holds that life began once a molecule emerged that could make a copy of itself. Does the information contained within DNA allow it to be replicated?

Watson and Crick ended their paper on the double helix with one of the classic understatements in the scientific literature: "It has not escaped our notice that the specific pairing we have postulated immediately suggests a possible copying mechanism." Here's the key insight: DNA's primary structure serves as a template for the synthesis of a complementary strand, meaning that DNA contains the information required for a copy of itself to be made. **Figure 4.7** shows this process.

Step 1 The two strands of a DNA double helix can be separated by breaking the hydrogen bonds that hold them together using either heat or enzyme-catalyzed reactions.

Step 2 Free deoxyribonucleotides form hydrogen bonds with complementary bases on the original strand of DNA—also called a **template strand.** As they do, their sugar–phosphate groups form phosphodiester linkages to create a new strand—also called a **complementary strand.** Note that the 5′ → 3′ directionality of the complementary strand is the opposite to that of the template strand.

Step 3 Complementary base pairing allows each strand of a DNA double helix to be copied exactly, producing two identical daughter molecules.

DNA copying is the basis for one of the five characteristics of life (introduced in Chapter 1): replication. But can DNA catalyze the reactions needed to *self*-replicate? In today's cells and in laboratory experiments, the answer is no. Instead, the molecule is copied through a complicated series of reactions that are catalyzed by enzymes (see Chapter 15). Why can't DNA catalyze these reactions itself?

The DNA Double Helix Is a Stable Structure

The DNA double helix is highly structured. It is regular, symmetric, and held together by phosphodiester linkages, hydrogen bonding, and hydrophobic interactions. In addition, the double helix has few functional groups exposed that can participate in chemical reactions, making the molecule particularly stable and resistant to degradation.

Intact stretches of DNA have been recovered from fossils that are tens of thousands of years old. The molecules have the same sequence of bases as the organisms had when they were alive, despite death and exposure to a wide array of pH, temperature, and chemical conditions. DNA's stability is the key to its effectiveness as a reliable information-storage molecule. DNA's structure is consistent with its function in cells.

The orderliness and stability that make DNA such a dependable information repository also make it inept at catalysis. Recall that enzymes function by forming a structure that will specifically bind to a substrate and catalyze a reaction (Chapter 3). A wide variety of catalytic activities can be generated in protein enzymes thanks to variation in the reactivity among R-groups in amino acids and to the enormous diversity of shapes found in proteins. In comparison, the structure of DNA is simple and nonreactive. It's not surprising, then, that DNA has never been observed to catalyze any reaction in any organism.

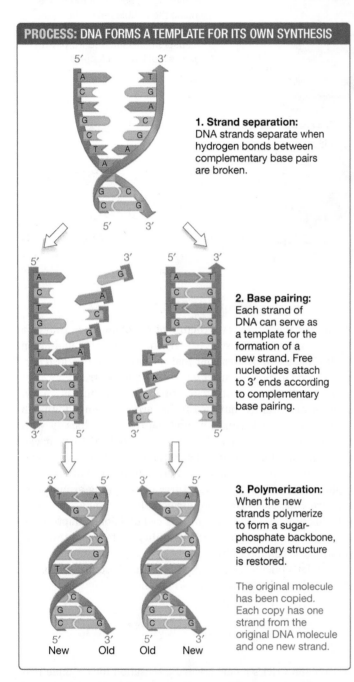

PROCESS: DNA FORMS A TEMPLATE FOR ITS OWN SYNTHESIS

1. Strand separation:
DNA strands separate when hydrogen bonds between complementary base pairs are broken.

2. Base pairing:
Each strand of DNA can serve as a template for the formation of a new strand. Free nucleotides attach to 3′ ends according to complementary base pairing.

3. Polymerization:
When the new strands polymerize to form a sugar-phosphate backbone, secondary structure is restored.

The original molecule has been copied. Each copy has one strand from the original DNA molecule and one new strand.

New   Old   Old   New

Figure 4.7 Making a Copy of DNA. If new bases are added to each of the two strands of DNA via complementary base pairing, a copy of the DNA molecule can be produced.

✔ When double-stranded DNA is heated to 95°C, the bonds between complementary base pairs break and single-stranded DNA results. Considering this observation, is the reaction shown in step 1 spontaneous?

In short, DNA furnishes an extraordinarily stable template for storing information encoded in a sequence of bases. But owing to DNA's inability to act as an effective catalyst and therefore to self-replicate, there is virtually no support for the hypothesis that the first life-form consisted of DNA alone. Instead, most biologists who are working on the origin of life support the hypothesis that life began with RNA.

4.3 RNA Structure and Function

The first living molecule would have needed to perform two key functions: carry information and catalyze reactions that promoted its own replication. At first glance, these two functions appear to conflict. Information storage requires regularity and stability; catalysis requires variation in chemical composition and flexibility in shape. How is it possible for a molecule to do both? The answer lies in structure.

Structurally, RNA Differs from DNA

How does the structure of RNA differ from DNA? To answer this question, let's take a closer look at the primary, secondary, and tertiary structures of RNA.

Primary Structure   Like DNA, RNA has a primary structure consisting of four types of nitrogenous bases extending from a sugar–phosphate backbone. But it's important to recall two significant differences between these nucleic acids:

1. The sugar in the sugar–phosphate backbone of RNA is ribose, not deoxyribose as in DNA.

2. The pyrimidine base thymine does not exist in RNA. Instead, RNA contains the closely related pyrimidine base uracil.

The first point is critical. Look back at Figure 4.1b and compare the functional groups attached to ribose and deoxyribose.

Notice the hydroxyl (—OH) group on the 2′ carbon of ribose. This additional hydroxyl is much more reactive than the hydrogen atom on the 2′ carbon of deoxyribose. When RNA molecules fold in certain ways, the hydroxyl group can attack the phosphate linkage between nucleotides, which would generate a break in the sugar–phosphate backbone. This —OH group makes RNA much less stable than DNA, but as you will see later, it can also support other catalytic activities.

Secondary Structure   Like DNA, most RNA molecules have secondary structure that results from complementary base pairing between purine and pyrimidine bases. In RNA, adenine forms two hydrogen bonds with uracil, and guanine again forms three hydrogen bonds with cytosine. (Other, non-Watson–Crick base pairs can occur, although less frequently.)

This hydrogen bonding should seem familiar, since DNA bonds together in a similar manner—so how do the secondary structures of RNA and DNA differ? In the vast majority of cases, the purine and pyrimidine bases in RNA undergo hydrogen bonding with complementary bases on the *same strand*, rather than forming hydrogen bonds with complementary bases on a different strand, as in DNA.

Figure 4.8 shows how within-strand base pairing works. The key is that when bases on one part of an RNA strand fold over and align with bases on another part of the same strand, the two sugar–phosphate strands are antiparallel. In this orientation, hydrogen bonding between complementary bases results in a helical structure that resembles the double helix of DNA—but unlike DNA, the RNA structure forms from a single nucleic acid strand.

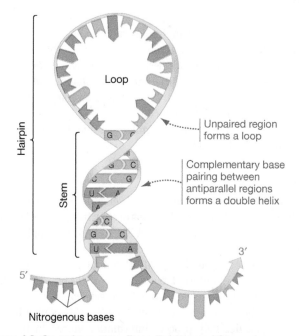

Figure 4.8 **Complementary Base Pairing and Secondary Structure in RNA: Stem-and-Loop Structures.** This RNA molecule has secondary structure. The structure formed by a double helical "stem" and unpaired "loop" is often described as a hairpin. The hydrogen-bonded bases in the stem are antiparallel.

Level of Structure	DNA		RNA	
Primary	Sequence of deoxyribonucleotides; bases are A, T, G, C		Sequence of ribonucleotides; bases are A, U, G, C	
Secondary	Two antiparallel strands twist into a double helix, stabilized by hydrogen bonding between complementary bases (A-T, G-C) and hydrophobic interactions		Most common are hairpins, formed when a single strand folds back on itself to form a double-helix "stem" and an unpaired "loop"	
Tertiary	Double helix forms compact structures by twisting into supercoils or wrapping around proteins	 DNA (red) + histones (green)	Secondary structures fold to form a wide variety of distinctive three-dimensional shapes	Example: tRNA

If the section where the fold occurs includes unpaired bases, then the stem-and-loop configuration shown in Figure 4.8 results. This type of secondary structure is called a **hairpin.** Several other types of RNA secondary structures are possible, each involving a different length and arrangement of base-paired segments.

Like the α-helices and β-pleated sheets observed in many proteins, RNA secondary structures will form spontaneously. The bases are brought together by hydrophobic interactions and stabilized by hydrogen bonding and van der Waals interactions.

Tertiary Structure RNA molecules can also have tertiary structure, which arises when secondary structures fold into more complex shapes. As a result, RNA molecules with different base sequences can have very different overall shapes and chemical properties. RNA molecules are much more diverse in size, shape, and reactivity than DNA molecules.

Table 4.1 summarizes the similarities and differences in the structures of RNA and DNA.

RNA's Versatility

In cells, RNA molecules are highly versatile, like a pocket tool with an array of functions. In terms of structure, you've seen that RNA is a nucleic acid like DNA, but RNA folds into complex three-dimensional shapes much like proteins.

The structural flexibility of RNA molecules allows them to perform many different tasks. Some of the most surprising results in the last decade of biological science, in fact, involve new insights into the diversity of roles that RNAs play in cells. These molecules help process information stored in DNA and synthesize proteins, among other things. (Functions of RNA are explored in more depth in Chapters 17, 18, and 19.)

Next let's focus on the roles that RNA may have played in the origin of life—as a catalyst and as an information-containing entity.

RNA Can Function as a Catalytic Molecule

In terms of diversity in chemical reactivity and overall shape, the four different nucleotides in RNA molecules are no match for the 20 different amino acid residues in proteins. Nevertheless, because RNA has a degree of structural and chemical complexity, it's capable of forming structures that catalyze a number of chemical reactions. Sidney Altman and Thomas Cech shared the 1989 Nobel Prize in chemistry for showing that organisms have catalytic RNAs. These RNAs are called **ribozymes,** or RNA enzymes, because they catalyze reactions similar to protein enzymes.

Figure 4.9 shows the structure of a ribozyme Cech isolated from a single-celled organism called *Tetrahymena*. This ribozyme catalyzes both the hydrolysis and the condensation of phosphodiester linkages in RNA. Researchers have since discovered a variety of ribozymes that catalyze several important reactions in cells. For example, ribozymes are responsible for the catalytic activity of the ribosomes that polymerize amino acids to form polypeptides. Ribozymes are at work in your cells right now.

The three-dimensional nature of ribozymes is vital to their catalytic activity. To catalyze a chemical reaction, substrates must be brought together in an environment that will promote the reaction. As with protein enzymes, the region of the ribozyme that is responsible for this activity is called the active site. When the *Tetrahymena* ribozyme was compared to enzymes that catalyze similar reactions, their active sites were found to be similar in structure. This observation about two very different molecules demonstrates the critical relationship between structure and function.

The discovery of ribozymes was a watershed event in origin-of-life research. Before Altman and Cech published their results, most biologists thought that the only molecules capable of catalyzing reactions in cells were proteins. The fact that a ribozyme

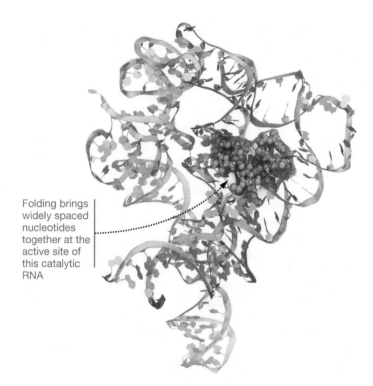

Folding brings widely spaced nucleotides together at the active site of this catalytic RNA

Figure 4.9 Tertiary Structure of the *Tetrahymena* Ribozyme. The folded structure brings together bases from distant locations in the primary structure to form the active site where catalysis occurs.

could catalyze the formation of a phosphodiester bond raised the possibility that an RNA molecule could polymerize a copy of itself. Such a molecule could qualify as the first living entity. Is there any experimental evidence to support this hypothesis?

4.4 In Search of the First Life-Form

The theory of chemical evolution maintains that life began as a naked self-replicator—a molecule that existed by itself in solution, without being enclosed in a membrane. To make a copy of itself, that first living molecule had to **(1)** provide a template that could be copied, and **(2)** catalyze polymerization reactions that would link monomers into a copy of that template. Because RNA is capable of both processes, most origin-of-life researchers propose that the first life-form was an RNA.

RNA contains a sequence of bases analogous to the letters in a word, so it can function as an information-containing molecule. Like DNA, the information stored in RNA can also be used to make copies of itself via complementary base pairing. In RNA, hydrogen bonding occurs between A-U pairs and G-C pairs. **Figure 4.10** illustrates how the information stored in an RNA molecule could have been used to direct its own replication on early Earth. This process still occurs today in some viruses where RNA serves as their hereditary information (see Chapter 33).

To replicate a single-stranded RNA, first a complementary copy of the RNA is made. Using the original strand as a template, free ribonucleotides form hydrogen bonds with complementary bases on the template. A new strand is polymerized when

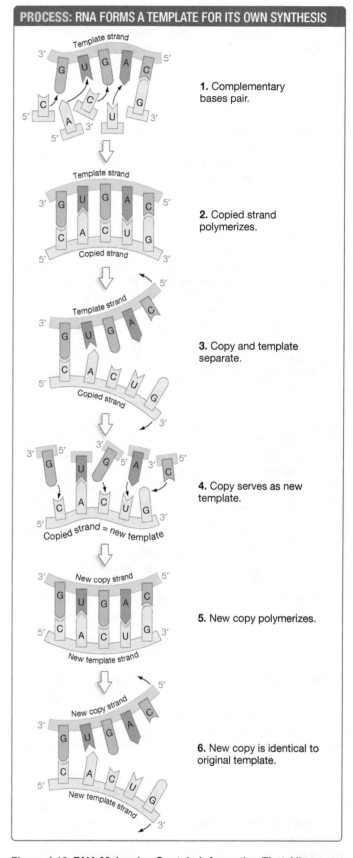

PROCESS: RNA FORMS A TEMPLATE FOR ITS OWN SYNTHESIS

1. Complementary bases pair.

2. Copied strand polymerizes.

3. Copy and template separate.

4. Copy serves as new template.

5. New copy polymerizes.

6. New copy is identical to original template.

Figure 4.10 RNA Molecules Contain Information That Allows Them to Be Replicated. For a single-stranded RNA to be copied, it must make a complementary strand and pass through double-stranded RNA intermediates.

3′ hydroxyls and 5′ phosphates on adjacent nucleotides are linked together via condensation reactions. The product is a double-stranded RNA molecule (steps 1 and 2 in Figure 4.10).

To make a copy of the original single-stranded RNA, the hydrogen bonds between the double-stranded product must first be broken by heating or by a catalyzed reaction (step 3). The newly made complementary RNA molecule now exists independently of the original template strand. If steps 1–3 were repeated with the new strand serving as a template (steps 4–6), the resulting molecule would be a copy of the original. This series of steps may repeat to make more copies of the template and complementary strands.

How Biologists Study the RNA World

Researchers test the RNA world hypothesis by establishing an environment in the laboratory that would select for ribozymes that catalyze key steps required for an RNA world. To understand how this is done, consider two experiments performed by researchers in David Bartel's laboratory.

In one study, the team attempted to generate an RNA molecule that could catalyze the kind of template-directed polymerization needed for RNA replication—an RNA "replicase." Starting with a ribozyme capable of joining two ribonucleotides together, they generated billions of copies into which random mutations were introduced.

Next they incubated the mutants with free ribonucleotides and began selecting for replicase activity. Molecules that exhibited such activity were isolated and copied. After two weeks and 18 rounds of selection, the team succeeded in isolating a ribozyme that could add 14 nucleotides to an existing RNA strand.

Note that the team's experimental protocol was designed to mimic the process of natural selection (introduced in Chapter 1). The population of RNAs from each round had variable characteristics that could be replicated and passed on to the next generation of ribozymes. In addition, the researchers were able to select the most efficient RNAs to be the "parents" of the next generation—and in the process introduce new mutations that potentially could make some of the "offspring" even better ribozymes.

The results from this research created considerable excitement among biologists interested in the origin of life. However, since the maximum product length generated was less than 10 percent of the ribozyme's own length, an RNA replicase capable of self-replication was far from being discovered. In fact, the difficulty in creating an effective RNA replicase has led many researchers to question the idea of a replicase being the first ribozyme to emerge in the RNA world.

In another study, Bartel's group asked a different question: Would it be possible to select for a ribozyme that could make ribonucleotides? This type of ribozyme has not been observed in cells, but it would be a key component in the RNA world.

Recall that the direction of a chemical reaction and how much product it makes is influenced by the amount of reactants present (Chapter 2). Since the production of nucleotides has been difficult

to demonstrate in experiments simulating early Earth conditions, nucleotides may have been a scarce resource. Ribozymes that could catalyze the production of nucleotides would be more likely to be copied due to local accumulation of monomers.

Starting with a large pool of randomly generated RNA sequences, the researchers selected for RNAs that could catalyze the addition of a uracil base to a ribose sugar. By round 11, the group had recovered ribozymes that were 50,000 times better at catalyzing the reaction than those found in the fourth round and over 1 million times more efficient than the uncatalyzed reaction. In effect, molecular evolution had occurred in the reaction tubes.

Thanks to similar efforts at other laboratories around the world, biologists have produced an increasingly impressive set of catalytic activities from RNA molecules. The results from each of these studies help clarify our view of what occurred in the RNA world. If a living ribozyme ever existed, then each round of simulated molecular evolution brings us closer to resurrecting it.

✔ If you understand how RNA could be considered as the first living molecule, you should be able to provide two examples of catalytic activities that would have been necessary for ribozymes to replicate in the RNA world.

The RNA World May Have Sparked the Evolution of Life

Most of the discovered ribozymes that continue to exist in modern cells play key roles in the synthesis of proteins. If these ribozymes were removed from cells, then proteins could no longer be made. This relationship suggests the order of events in chemical evolution—the RNA world preceded proteins.

The evolution of protein enzymes would have marked the end of the RNA world—providing the means for catalyzing reactions necessary for life to emerge in a cellular form. After this milestone, three of the five fundamental characteristics of life (see Chapter 1) were solidly in place:

1. *Information* Proteins and ribozymes were processing information stored in nucleic acids for the synthesis of more proteins.

2. *Replication* Enzymes, and possibly ribozymes, were replicating the nucleic acids that stored the hereditary information.

3. *Evolution* Random changes in the nucleic acids led to the synthesis of different proteins and ribozymes. Selective advantages resulting from some of these changes allowed for the evolution of new functions.

If these events occurred in a hydrothermal vent, the molecular assemblages of nucleic acids and proteins would have been constantly fed with thermal and chemical energy. To gain independence from their undersea hatchery, enzymes would have evolved to store this energy as something more portable—carbohydrates. The structure and function of carbohydrates will be the focus of the next chapter.

4.1 What Is a Nucleic Acid?

- Nucleic acids are polymers of nucleotide monomers, which consist of a sugar, a phosphate group, and a nitrogenous base. Ribonucleotide monomers polymerize to form RNA. Deoxyribonucleotide monomers polymerize to form DNA.

- Ribonucleotides have a hydroxyl (−OH) group on their 2′ carbon; deoxyribonucleotides have a hydrogen (−H) instead.

- Nucleic acids polymerize when condensation reactions join nucleotides together via phosphodiester linkages.

- Nucleic acids are directional: they have a 5′ end and a 3′ end. During polymerization, new nucleotides are added only to the 3′end.

4.2 DNA Structure and Function

- DNA's primary structure consists of a sequence of linked nucleotides.

- The secondary structure of DNA consists of two DNA strands running in opposite directions that are twisted into a double helix.

- The tertiary structure of DNA forms compact structures by twisting the double helix into supercoils or wrapping around proteins.

- DNA is an extremely stable molecule that serves as a superb archive for information in the form of base sequences. Its secondary structure is stabilized by hydrogen bonds, hydrophobic interactions, and van der Waals interactions that form between complementary bases stacked on the inside of the helix.

- DNA is readily copied via complementary base pairing. Complementary base pairing occurs between A-T and G-C pairs.

4.3 RNA Structure and Function

- Like DNA, RNA's primary structure consists of a sequence of linked nucleotides.

- RNA's secondary structure includes a variety of configurations including short regions of complementary base pairing that form double-helical stems and unpaired loops.

- The secondary structures of RNA can further fold into more complex shapes via complementary base pairing to give the molecule tertiary structure.

- RNA is versatile and can function as an information-carrying molecule and a catalyst.

4.4 In Search of the First Life-Form

- To test the RNA world hypothesis, researchers are attempting to synthesize new ribozymes in the laboratory. Using artificial selection strategies, they have succeeded in identifying RNAs that catalyze several different reactions.

- Ribozymes that catalyze reactions necessary for the production of nucleotides may have preceded the evolution of RNA replicases.

Answers are available in Appendix A

✓ TEST YOUR KNOWLEDGE

1. What are the four nitrogenous bases found in RNA?
   a. cytosine, guanine, thymine, uracil (C, G, T, U)
   b. adenine, cytosine, guanine, thymine (A, C, G, T)
   c. adenine, cytosine, guanine, uracil (A, C, G, U)
   d. alanine, cysteine, glycine, threonine (A, C, G, T)

2. What determines the primary structure of a DNA molecule?
   a. hairpins and supercoils
   b. complementary base pairing
   c. deoxyribonucleotide sequence
   d. hydrophobic interactions and hydrogen bonding

3. Which of the following describes the synthesis of nucleic acids?
   a. Nucleotides are added to the 5′ end of a single nucleic acid strand.
   b. Nucleic acids are polymerized by the formation of peptide bonds between nucleotides.
   c. Strands in a double helix are synthesized in a parallel direction such that one end of the molecule has two 3′ ends and other has two 5′ ends.
   d. Complementary pairing between bases is required for copying nucleic acids.

4. Single strands of nucleic acids are directional, meaning that there are two different ends. What functional groups define the two different ends of a strand?

✓ TEST YOUR UNDERSTANDING

5. What is responsible for the increased stability of DNA compared to RNA?

6. **QUANTITATIVE** If nucleotides from the DNA of a human were quantified and 30 percent of them contained the base adenine, what percentage of them would contain the base guanine?
   a. 20 percent
   b. 30 percent
   c. 40 percent
   d. 70 percent

7. What would be the sequence of the strand of DNA that is made from the following template: 5′-GATATCGAT-3′? (Your answer must be written 5′ → 3′.) How would the sequence be different if RNA were made from this DNA template?

8. According to the RNA world model, a ribozyme would replicate by creating a double-stranded RNA intermediate. Would you expect the intermediate to have the same catalytic activity as the original ribozyme? Justify your answer with an explanation.

✓ TEST YOUR PROBLEM-SOLVING SKILLS

9. Make a concept map (see BioSkills 12) that relates DNA's primary structure to its secondary structure. Your diagram should include deoxyribonucleotides, hydrophobic interactions, purines, pyrimidines, phosphodiester linkages, DNA primary structure, DNA secondary structure, complementary base pairing, and antiparallel strands.

10. **MODEL** In the field of nanotechnology, DNA is used like Velcro to assemble tiny particles into structures that are < 0.0001 mm in size. Draw a model to illustrate how two particles (a circle and a square) could be brought together by linking them to short single-stranded DNA molecules. If the DNA sequence linked to the circle is GGATC, then provide the sequence linked to the square and identify the 5′ and 3′ ends of each strand.

✔ PUT IT ALL TOGETHER: Case Study

Who deserves credit for discovering the structure of the double helix?

The famous model in the photo was built by Watson and Crick in 1953 to demonstrate the secondary structure of DNA. This was not the first attempt at modeling DNA's structure, however. Before 1953, there were several failed attempts. The accumulation of data from different research groups was key to arriving at the correct model. What were the incorrect versions of DNA structure, and how did Watson and Crick get it right?

11. Phoebus Levene was the first to describe the structure of nucleotides and how they were bonded together with phosphodiester linkages. In 1919, he incorrectly proposed the tetranucleotide hypothesis, which stated that nucleic acids were polymers consisting of GCTA repeated over and over. If his model had been correct, then how would it affect the information that could be stored in the DNA?

12. In the 1950s, the race to solve the secondary structure of DNA became intense. In an uncharacteristic rush to publish, Linus Pauling erroneously proposed a triple-stranded structure in February 1953. This model had the nitrogenous bases on the exterior and the sugar–phosphate backbones clustered in the middle. How does the orientation of the sugar–phosphate backbone in this model compare with the one proposed by Watson and Crick? Do you think Pauling's structure could exist in cells? Why or why not?

13. Rosalind Franklin was the first person to obtain X-ray crystallographic data on the form of DNA that is most commonly found in cells. Other researchers, including Pauling, used data from DNA samples that were more concentrated than Franklin's samples. Why would you expect the amount of water to affect the helical structure of DNA?

14. **QUANTITATIVE** In 1951, Erwin Chargaff was accumulating data on the molar ratios of nucleotides using DNA obtained from a variety of sources. Some of these data are provided in the following table:

Molar Ratios in DNA Preparations

Source	A:G	T:C	A:T	G:C	purines:pyrimidines
Ox	1.29	1.43	1.04	1.00	1.10
Human	1.56	1.75	1.00	1.00	1.0
Chicken	1.45	1.29	1.06	0.91	0.99
Salmon	1.43	1.43	1.02	1.02	1.02
Wheat	1.22	1.18	1.00	0.97	0.99
Yeast	1.67	1.92	1.03	1.20	1.0

Source: Chargaff, E. 1951. Federal Proceedings 10: 654–659.

Compare the molar ratios presented from each organism tested and between different organisms. Explain how these data could be used to show that Levene's tetranucleotide model is incorrect. What do they imply about the primary structure of DNA in different organisms?

15. Watson and Crick met with Chargaff to discuss his work in 1952. Explain how Chargaff's observations helped Watson and Crick to propose the complementary base pairing in their model of double-stranded DNA. Would you expect similar ratios of nucleotides if Chargaff had used RNA instead? Explain why or why not.

16. **PROCESS OF SCIENCE** Now that you have learned a little more of the history behind the elucidation of the secondary structure of DNA, what does it tell you about the role of the scientific community in advancing science? Were Watson and Crick solely responsible?

MasteringBiology®

Students Go to MasteringBiology for assignments, the eText, and the Study Area with animations, practice tests, and activities.

Professors Go to MasteringBiology for automatically graded tutorials and questions that you can assign to your students, plus Instructor Resources.

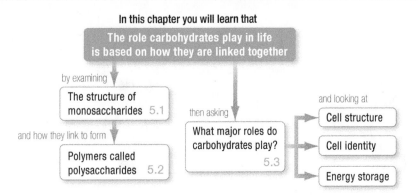

5 An Introduction
to Carbohydrates

A cross section
through a potato tuber.
Starch-filled structures
are stained red;
cellulose-rich cell walls
are stained green.
Starch is an energy-
storage carbohydrate;
cellulose is a structural
carbohydrate.

In this chapter you will learn that

The role carbohydrates play in life
is based on how they are linked together

by examining

The structure of
monosaccharides 5.1

and how they link to form

Polymers called
polysaccharides 5.2

then asking

What major roles do
carbohydrates play?
5.3

and looking at

Cell structure

Cell identity

Energy storage

This chapter is part of the
Big Picture. See how on
pages 140–141.

This unit highlights the four types of macromolecules that were key to the evolution of the cell: proteins, nucleic acids, carbohydrates, and lipids. Understanding the structure and function of macromolecules is a basic requirement for exploring how life began and how organisms work. Recall that proteins and nucleic acids could satisfy three of the five fundamental characteristics of life: information, replication, and evolution (Chapter 4). Carbohydrates, the subject of this chapter, play an important role in a fourth characteristic—energy.

The term **carbohydrate,** or **sugar,** encompasses the monomers called **monosaccharides** (literally, "one-sugar"), small polymers called **oligosaccharides** ("few-sugars"), and the large polymers called **polysaccharides** ("many-sugars"). The name "carbohydrate" is logical because the molecular formula of many of these molecules is $(CH_2O)_n$, where the n indicates the number of "carbon-hydrate" groups (recall that "hydrate" refers to water). The value of n can vary from 3, for the smallest sugar, to well over a thousand for some of the large polymers.

The name "carbohydrate" is a little misleading, though, because carbohydrates do not consist of carbon atoms bonded to water molecules. Instead, they are made up of a carbonyl group (C=O), several hydroxyl groups (–OH), along with multiple carbon–hydrogen bonds (C–H). Consider formaldehyde (CH_2O), which was introduced as one of the molecules present in early Earth (Chapter 2). Even though the molecular formula of formaldehyde fits the pattern of carbohydrates (with an n of 1), it does not contain a hydroxyl group and so it is not a carbohydrate.

Let's begin with monosaccharides and then put them together into oligosaccharides and polysaccharides. From there, you will then explore how carbohydrates figured in the origin of life and what they do in cells today. As you study this material, be sure to ask yourself the central question of biological chemistry: How does this molecule's structure relate to its properties and function?

5.1 Sugars as Monomers

Sugars are fundamental to life. They provide chemical energy in cells and furnish some of the molecular building blocks required for the synthesis of larger, more complex compounds. Monosaccharides were important during chemical evolution, early in Earth's history, too. For example, as you've seen, the sugar called ribose is required for the formation of the nucleotides that make up nucleic acids (Chapter 4).

What Distinguishes One Monosaccharide from Another?

Monosaccharides, or simple sugars, are the monomers of carbohydrates. **Figure 5.1** illustrates two of the smallest monosaccharides. Although these two sugars share the same molecular formula ($C_3H_6O_3$), their molecular structures are different. The carbonyl group that serves as one of monosaccharides' distinguishing features can be found either at the end of the molecule, forming an aldehyde sugar (an aldose), or within the carbon chain, forming a ketone sugar (a ketose).

The presence of a carbonyl group along with multiple polar hydroxyl groups means that even the simplest sugars have many reactive and hydrophilic functional groups. Based on this observation, it's not surprising that sugars are polar molecules that form hydrogen bonds with water and are easily dissolved in aqueous solutions.

The number of carbon atoms present also varies among monosaccharides. By convention, the carbons in a monosaccharide are numbered consecutively, starting with the end nearest the carbonyl group. Three-carbon sugars, such as those in Figure 5.1, are called **trioses.** Ribose, which acts as a building block for nucleotides, has five carbons and is called a **pentose;** the glucose that's coursing through your bloodstream right now is a six-carbon sugar, or a **hexose.**

Besides varying in the location of the carbonyl group and the total number of carbon atoms present, monosaccharides can vary in the spatial arrangement of their atoms. For example, **Figure 5.2**

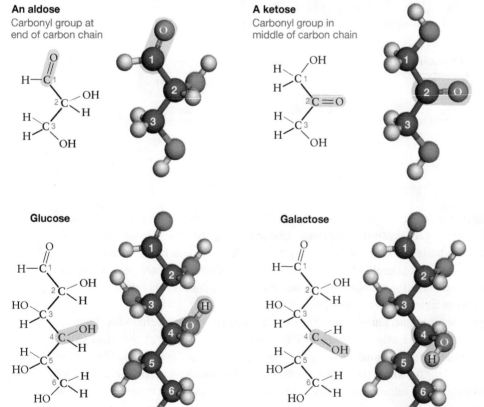

An aldose
Carbonyl group at end of carbon chain

A ketose
Carbonyl group in middle of carbon chain

Glucose

Galactose

Figure 5.1 The Carbonyl Group in a Sugar Occurs in One of Two Configurations.

Figure 5.2 Sugars May Vary in the Configuration of Their Hydroxyl Groups.
The two six-carbon sugars shown here vary only in the spatial orientation of their hydroxyl groups on carbon number 4.

✔ **MODEL** Mannose is a six-carbon sugar that is similar to glucose, except for the orientation of the hydroxyl (–OH) group on the second carbon. Draw the structural formula of mannose and circle carbon number 2 and the hydroxyl group.

illustrates the different structures of glucose and galactose. While these two aldose sugars have the same molecular formula ($C_6H_{12}O_6$), they differ in the spatial arrangement of the hydroxyl group on the fourth carbon (highlighted in blue in Figure 5.2).

This is a key point: Because the structures of glucose and galactose differ, their functions differ. In cells, glucose is both a source of carbon atoms that are used to construct other molecules and of chemical energy that sustains life. But because molecules interact in precise ways based on their shape, galactose must first be converted to glucose via an enzyme-catalyzed reaction to be used in these same ways. This example underscores a general theme: Even seemingly simple changes in structure—like the location of a single hydroxyl group—can have enormous consequences for function.

Although Figure 5.2 represents monosaccharides as linear chains, it's actually rare for sugars consisting of five or more carbons to exist in this form. In aqueous solution they spontaneously form ring structures when the carbonyl group bonds to a carbon with a hydroxyl group. An example of this process is shown in Figure 5.3. When glucose forms a ring, the C-1 carbon (the first carbon in the linear chain) forms a bond with the oxygen atom of the C-5 hydroxyl. The hydrogen displaced from the C-5 hydroxyl is transferred to the C-1 carbonyl. This transfer preserves the number of atoms and hydroxyls between the ring and linear forms.

When the ring structure is formed in sugars, the position of the newly formed C-1 hydroxyl group will be fixed in one of two possible orientations: below or above the plane of the ring. So there are two possible forms of glucose: α-glucose and β-glucose. The two forms exist in equilibrium, but β-glucose is more common because it is slightly more stable than α-glucose.

To summarize, many distinct monosaccharides exist because so many aspects of their structure are variable: aldose or ketose placement of the carbonyl group, the number of carbons, and the different arrangements of hydroxyl groups in space. Ring forms of the same molecule also have alternative forms. These variations give each monosaccharide a unique structure and function.

Can Monosaccharides Form by Chemical Evolution?

Laboratory simulations have shown that most monosaccharides are readily synthesized under conditions that mimic those predicted for early Earth (see Chapters 2 and 4). For example, when formaldehyde (CH_2O) molecules are heated in solution, they react with one another to form almost all the possible types of pentoses and hexoses. These reactions may have occurred in the hot water released from undersea volcanoes and hydrothermal vents.

In addition, researchers have discovered the three-carbon ketose illustrated in Figure 5.1, along with a wide array of compounds closely related to sugars, on a meteorite that struck Murchison, Australia, in 1969. Based on these observations, investigators suspect that sugars are synthesized on dust particles and other debris in interstellar space and could have rained down onto Earth as the planet was forming.

Most researchers interested in chemical evolution maintain that one or more of the above mechanisms led to the accumulation of monosaccharides in the early oceans.

Modern cells display a wide range of carbohydrates, including oligomers and polymers formed from linking together monosaccharides. How do these monomers join together to form polymers? Is the process similar to how amino acids link together to form proteins and how nucleotides join together to form nucleic acids? Let's explore how the functional groups in monosaccharides influence the polymerization of carbohydrates.

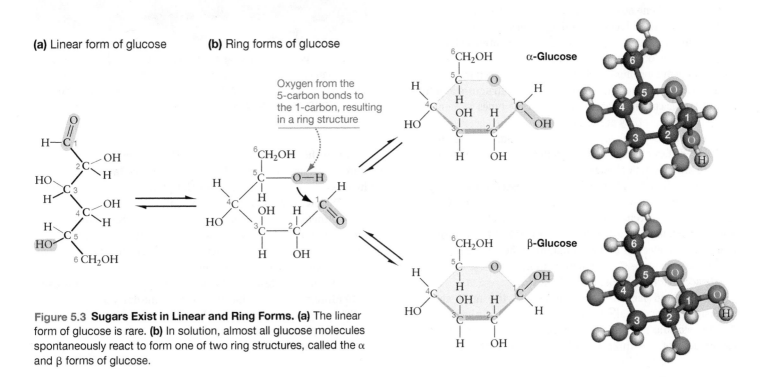

(a) Linear form of glucose **(b)** Ring forms of glucose

Oxygen from the 5-carbon bonds to the 1-carbon, resulting in a ring structure

α-Glucose

β-Glucose

Figure 5.3 Sugars Exist in Linear and Ring Forms. (a) The linear form of glucose is rare. **(b)** In solution, almost all glucose molecules spontaneously react to form one of two ring structures, called the α and β forms of glucose.

5.2 The Structure of Polysaccharides

Simple sugars covalently link to form chains of varying lengths called complex carbohydrates. These chains range in size from short oligosaccharides to long polysaccharides. When just two sugars link together, the resulting molecule is known as a **disaccharide.**

Monosaccharides polymerize when a condensation reaction occurs between two hydroxyl groups, resulting in a covalent bond called a **glycosidic linkage.** The inverse reaction, hydrolysis, cleaves these linkages. (To review condensation and hydrolysis reactions, see Chapter 3.)

Glycosidic linkages hold monomers together, just like the peptide bonds and phosphodiester linkages do for proteins and nucleic acids. There is an important difference, however. Peptide bonds and phosphodiester linkages form between the same locations in their monomers, giving proteins and nucleic acids a standard backbone structure, but this is not the case for carbohydrates. Because glycosidic linkages form between hydroxyl groups, and because every monosaccharide contains at least two hydroxyls, the location and geometry of glycosidic linkages can vary widely among oligosaccharides and polysaccharides.

Similar to proteins and nucleic acids, the structure and function of larger carbohydrates depends on the types of monomers involved and how they are linked together. The variation in how polysaccharides are formed allows organisms to use them in radically different ways. For example, polysaccharides may be used to store chemical energy in the cells of plants or provide structural support in the exoskeletons of insects (Figure 5.4).

The same principles that dictate the overall structure and function in polysaccharides hold true for small oligomers as well. For example, maltose, or malt sugar, is a disaccharide formed by two glucose molecules and is abundant in the starter liquid used to brew beer (Figure 5.5a). Lactose, an important sugar in milk, is a disaccharide of glucose and galactose (Figure 5.5b).

Maltose and lactose illustrate two of the most common glycosidic linkages, called the α-1,4-glycosidic linkage and the β-1,4-glycosidic linkage. The numbers refer to the carbons on either side of the linkage, indicating that both linkages are

(a) Starch—used for energy storage in plant cells

(b) Chitin—used for structural support in insect exoskeletons

Figure 5.4 Polysaccharides Are Used in Many Different Ways. The variation in carbohydrate monomers and the glycosidic linkages that bond them together result in very different structures, including **(a)** the starch in potatoes and **(b)** the exoskeleton of a cicada.

between the C-1 and C-4 carbons. Their geometry, however, is different: α and β refer to the contrasting orientations of the C-1 hydroxyls—on opposite sides of the plane of the glucose rings (i.e., "below" versus "above" the plane).

A functional consequence of the structural differences between maltose and lactose is that the enzymes used to hydrolyze maltose will not cleave lactose. Instead, lactose is digested by lactase—an enzyme that many humans stop secreting after childhood. Without lactase, adults may become lactose intolerant and suffer intestinal discomfort if they consume dairy products.

This is just one example of how the orientation of glycosidic linkages affects the structure, function, and durability of the carbohydrates.

(a) Formation of α-glycosidic linkage

α-Glucose   α-Glucose

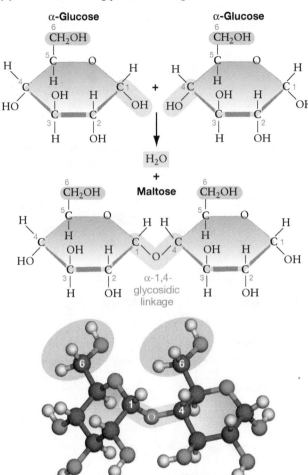

H₂O

+

Maltose

α-1,4-
glycosidic
linkage

(b) Formation of β-glycosidic linkage

β-Galactose   β-Glucose

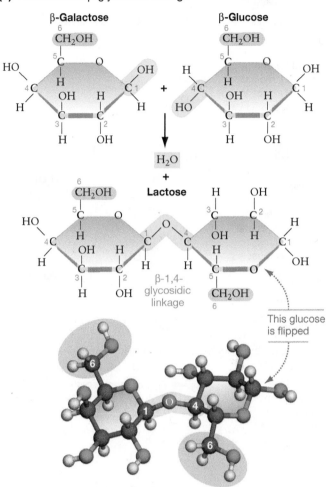

H₂O

+

Lactose

β-1,4-
glycosidic
linkage

This glucose
is flipped

Figure 5.5 Monosaccharides Polymerize through Formation of Glycosidic Linkages. A glycosidic linkage occurs when hydroxyl groups on two monosaccharides undergo a condensation reaction. Maltose and lactose are disaccharides.

Let's now consider the structures of the most common polysaccharides found in organisms today: starch, glycogen, cellulose, and chitin, along with a modified polysaccharide called peptidoglycan. As shown in **Table 5.1** (see page 112), each of these macromolecules is joined by particular α-1,4- or β-1,4-glycosidic linkages. These polysaccharides can consist of a few hundred to many thousands of residues.

As you learn more about each of these five carbohydrate polymers, pay special attention to how the different glycosidic linkages affect the structure of the molecule and its interaction with other molecules. The differences in their functions result directly from differences in their structures, and as Section 5.3 explains, these differences generally come down to a simple twist of a link.

Starch: A Storage Polysaccharide in Plants

In plant cells, some monosaccharides are polymerized and stored for later use in the form of starch. **Starch** consists entirely of α-glucose joined by glycosidic linkages. Most of these linkages

are between C-1 and C-4 carbons, and the angle of these bonds causes the chain of glucose residues to coil into a helix.

As shown in the top panel in Table 5.1, starch is made up of two types of polymers. One is an unbranched molecule called amylose, which contains only α-1,4-glycosidic linkages. The other is a branched molecule called amylopectin. Branching occurs when a glycosidic linkage forms between a C-1 carbon and a C-6 carbon (an α-1,6 linkage). In amylopectin, branching occurs at about one out of every 30 glucose residues.

Glycogen: A Highly Branched Storage Polysaccharide in Animals

Glycogen performs the same storage role in animals that starch performs in plants. In humans, for example, glycogen is stored in the cells of liver and muscle tissues. When you start exercising, enzymes begin breaking glycogen into glucose monomers, which are then processed in muscle cells to supply energy.

Polysaccharide	Chemical Structure	Three-dimensional Structure

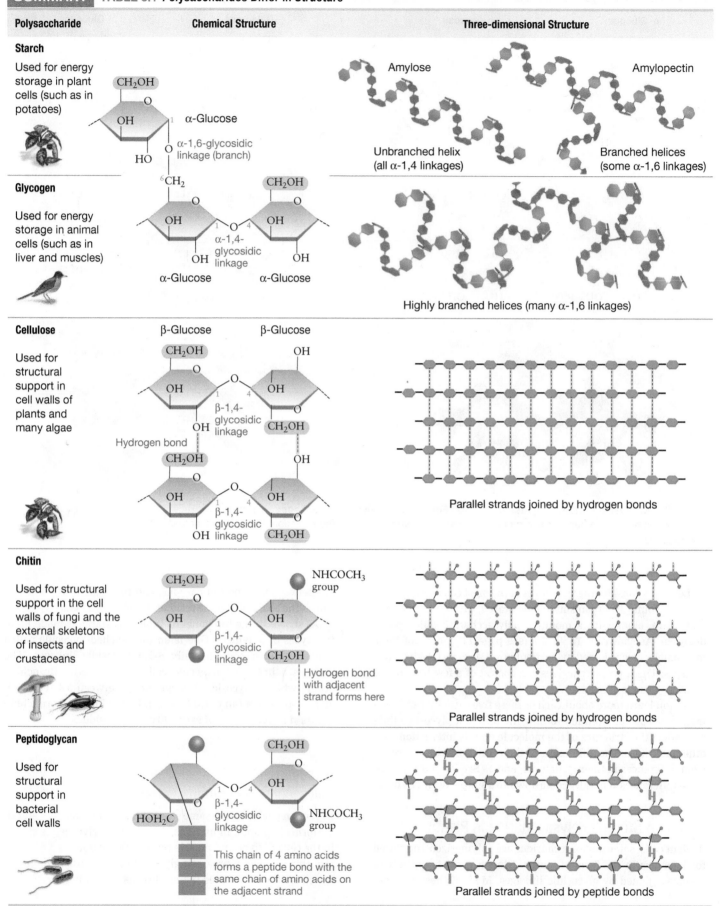

Starch

Used for energy storage in plant cells (such as in potatoes)

CH$_2$OH
O
OH 1 α-Glucose
α-1,6-glycosidic linkage (branch)
HO

Amylose — Amylopectin

Unbranched helix (all α-1,4 linkages) — Branched helices (some α-1,6 linkages)

Glycogen

Used for energy storage in animal cells (such as in liver and muscles)

^{6}CH$_2$
O
OH 1 O 4 OH
α-1,4-glycosidic linkage
OH   OH
α-Glucose   α-Glucose
CH$_2$OH
O

Highly branched helices (many α-1,6 linkages)

Cellulose

Used for structural support in cell walls of plants and many algae

β-Glucose   β-Glucose
CH$_2$OH   OH
O
OH   OH
β-1,4-glycosidic linkage
OH   O
CH$_2$OH
Hydrogen bond
CH$_2$OH   OH
O
OH   OH
β-1,4-glycosidic linkage
OH   O
CH$_2$OH

Parallel strands joined by hydrogen bonds

Chitin

Used for structural support in the cell walls of fungi and the external skeletons of insects and crustaceans

CH$_2$OH   NHCOCH$_3$ group
O
OH   OH
β-1,4-glycosidic linkage
CH$_2$OH

Hydrogen bond with adjacent strand forms here

Parallel strands joined by hydrogen bonds

Peptidoglycan

Used for structural support in bacterial cell walls

CH$_2$OH
O
1 O 4 OH
β-1,4-glycosidic linkage
HOH$_2$C   NHCOCH$_3$ group

This chain of 4 amino acids forms a peptide bond with the same chain of amino acids on the adjacent strand

Parallel strands joined by peptide bonds

Glycogen is a helical polymer of α-glucose and is nearly identical to the branched form of starch. However, instead of an α-1,6-glycosidic linkage occurring in about 1 out of every 30 residues in amylopectin, a branch occurs in about 1 out of every 10 glucose subunits (see Table 5.1).

Cellulose: A Structural Polysaccharide in Plants

All cells are enclosed by a membrane (Chapter 1), and the cells of most organisms are also surrounded by a protective layer of material called a **cell wall.** In plants, bacteria, fungi, and many other groups, the cell wall is composed primarily of one or more polysaccharides.

In plants, the major component of the cell wall is cellulose. **Cellulose** is a polymer made from β-glucose monomers joined by β-1,4-glycosidic linkages. As Table 5.1 shows, the geometry of the linkage is such that each glucose residue in the chain is flipped in relation to the adjacent residue. The flipped orientation is important because **(1)** it generates a linear molecule, rather than the helix seen in starch; and **(2)** it permits multiple hydrogen bonds to form between adjacent, parallel strands of cellulose. As a result, cellulose forms long, parallel strands that are joined by hydrogen bonds. The interacting cellulose fibers are strong and give the cell structural support.

Chitin: A Structural Polysaccharide in Fungi and Animals

Chitin is a polysaccharide that stiffens the cell walls of fungi. It's also found in a few types of protists and in many animals. It is, for example, the most important component of the external skeletons of insects and crustaceans.

Chitin is similar to cellulose, but instead of consisting of glucose residues, the monosaccharide involved is one called N-acetylglucosamine (abbreviated as NAG). These NAG monomers are joined by β-1,4-glycosidic linkages (see Table 5.1). As in cellulose, the geometry of these bonds results in every other residue being flipped in orientation. The NAG subunits in chitin also form hydrogen bonds between adjacent strands to produce a stiff protective armor.

Peptidoglycan: A Structural Polysaccharide in Bacteria

Most bacteria, like all plants and fungi, have cell walls. The primary structural component of bacterial cell walls consists of a polysaccharide called **peptidoglycan.**

Peptidoglycan is the most complex of the polysaccharides discussed so far. It has a long backbone formed by NAG and N-acetylmuramic acid (NAM) that alternate with each other and are linked by β-1,4-glycosidic linkages (see Table 5.1). In addition, a short chain of amino acids is attached at the C-3 carbon of NAM. When molecules of peptidoglycan align, peptide bonds link the amino acid chains on adjacent strands. These links serve the same purpose as the hydrogen bonds between the parallel strands of cellulose and chitin in the cell walls of other organisms.

Polysaccharides and Chemical Evolution

Cellulose is the most abundant organic compound on Earth today, and chitin is probably the second most abundant by weight. Virtually all organisms depend on glycogen or starch to store chemical energy, but despite their current importance to life, polysaccharides probably played little to no role in the origin of life. This conclusion is supported by several observations:

- ***No plausible mechanism exists for the polymerization of monosaccharides under conditions that prevailed early in Earth's history.*** In cells and in laboratory experiments, the glycosidic linkages illustrated in Figure 5.5 and Table 5.1 form only with the aid of protein enzymes. No enzyme-like RNAs are known to catalyze these reactions.

- ***To date, no polysaccharide has been discovered that can catalyze polymerization reactions.*** Even though polysaccharides contain reactive hydroxyl and carbonyl groups, they lack the structural and chemical complexity that makes proteins, and to a lesser extent RNA, effective catalysts.

- ***The monomers in polysaccharides are not capable of complementary base pairing.*** Unlike nucleic acids, polysaccharides cannot serve as templates for their own replication.

Even though polysaccharides probably did not play a significant role in the earliest forms of life, they became enormously important once cellular life evolved. In the next section, let's take a detailed look at how they function in today's cells.

CHECK YOUR UNDERSTANDING

If you understand that ...

- Polysaccharides form when enzymes catalyze the formation of glycosidic linkages between monosaccharides that are in the α or β form.
- Most polysaccharides are long chains of residues, but some branch extensively. Among linear forms, it is common for adjacent strands to be connected by hydrogen bonding or other types of linkages.

✔ You should be able to ...

Describe four structural differences that could result in different oligosaccharides consisting of two glucose residues and two galactose residues.

Answers are available in Appendix A.

5.3 What Do Carbohydrates Do?

One of the basic functions that carbohydrates perform in organisms is to serve as a substrate for synthesizing more-complex molecules. For example, recall that RNA contains the five-carbon sugar ribose ($C_5H_{10}O_5$) and DNA contains the modified sugar deoxyribose ($C_5H_{10}O_4$). The nucleotides that make up these polymers consist of the ribose or deoxyribose sugar, a phosphate group, and a nitrogenous base (Chapter 4). The sugar itself acts as a subunit of each of these monomers.

In addition, sugars frequently furnish the raw "carbon skeletons" that are used as building blocks in the synthesis of important molecules. Your cells are using sugars right now, for example, as a starting point for the synthesis of amino acids.

Carbohydrates have diverse functions in cells: In addition to serving as precursors to larger molecules, they (1) provide fibrous structural materials, (2) indicate cell identity, and (3) store chemical energy. Let's look at each function in turn.

Carbohydrates Can Provide Structural Support

Cellulose and chitin, along with the modified polysaccharide peptidoglycan, are key structural compounds. They form fibers that give cells and organisms strength and elasticity.

To appreciate why cellulose, chitin, and peptidoglycan are effective structural molecules, recall that they form long strands and that bonds can form between adjacent strands. In the cell walls of plants, for example, a collection of about 80 cellulose molecules are cross-linked by hydrogen bonding to produce a tough fiber. These cellulose fibers, in turn, crisscross to form a tough sheet that is able to withstand pulling and pushing forces—what an engineer would call tension and compression (see Chapter 11).

In addition to being tough, structural carbohydrates are durable. Almost all organisms produce enzymes that cleave the α-glycosidic linkages in starch and glycogen molecules, but only a few organisms have enzymes capable of digesting cellulose, chitin, or peptidoglycan. These fibers tend to be insoluble due to the strong interactions between strands consisting of β-1,4-glycosidic linkages. The exclusion of water within these fibers makes their hydrolysis more difficult so they are resistant to degradation and decay.

Ironically, the fact that cellulose is indigestible makes it extremely important for digestive health. The cellulose that you ingest when you eat plants—what biologists call dietary fiber—forms a porous mass that absorbs and retains water. This sponge-like mass adds moisture and bulk that helps fecal material move through the intestinal tract more quickly, preventing constipation and other problems.

The Role of Carbohydrates in Cell Identity

Structural polymers tend to be repetitive, made up of only one or two types of monosaccharides. The same is not true for all complex carbohydrates. Some polysaccharides exhibit enormous structural diversity, because their component monomers—and the linkages between them—vary a lot. As a result, they are capable of displaying information to other cells through their structure. More specifically, polysaccharides act as an identification badge on the outer surface of the plasma membrane that surrounds a cell. (Chapter 6 describes plasma membranes in detail.)

Figure 5.6 shows how this information about cell identity is displayed. Carbohydrates attached to lipids and proteins project outward from the cell surface into the surrounding environment. A **glycolipid** is a lipid that has been glycosylated, meaning it has one or more covalently bonded carbohydrates. A **glycoprotein** is

a protein that is similarly linked to carbohydrates—usually relatively short oligosaccharides.

Glycolipids and glycoproteins are key molecules in what biologists call cell–cell recognition and cell–cell signaling. Each cell in your body has carbohydrates on its surface that identify it as part of your body. For example, your blood type is determined by the type of oligosaccharides presented on the surface of your blood cells. The A, B, and O antigens arise from different modifications of the carbohydrates in glycolipids. In addition, each distinct type of cell in a multicellular organism—for example, the nerve cells and muscle cells in your body—displays a different set of glycoproteins on its surface. This identification information helps cells recognize and communicate with each other.

The key point here is to recognize that the variety in the types of monosaccharides and how they can be linked together makes it possible for an enormous number of unique carbohydrates—and therefore glycolipids and glycoproteins—to exist. As a result, each cell type and each species can display a unique identity.

Carbohydrates are at the root of one of the most important events in the life cycle of many multicellular organisms—sexual reproduction. During the 1980s, Paul Wassarman and colleagues investigated the role of glycoproteins in cell–cell recognition between sperm and egg during fertilization. This step guarantees specificity—sperm normally recognize and bind only to eggs of their own species.

In one experiment, the researchers mixed sperm with purified egg-surface glycoproteins and discovered that most of the sperm lost their ability to attach to eggs. Such loss of function is an example of what researchers call competitive inhibition. The glycoproteins had bound to—and thus blocked—the same structure on the sperm that it uses to bind to eggs. This result showed that sperm attach to eggs via egg glycoproteins.

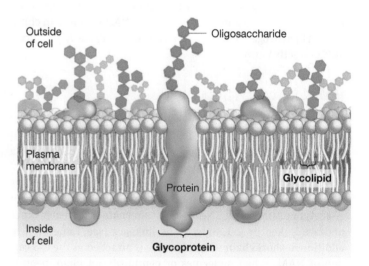

Figure 5.6 Carbohydrates Are an Identification Badge for Cells. Glycolipids and glycoproteins contain carbohydrates that project outside the cell from the surface of the plasma membrane enclosing the cell. These sugar groups have distinctive structures that identify the type or species of the cell.

QUESTION: What part of surface glycoproteins do sperm recognize when they attach to eggs?

HYPOTHESIS: Sperm attach to the carbohydrate component.

NULL HYPOTHESIS: Sperm attach to the protein component.

EXPERIMENTAL SETUP:

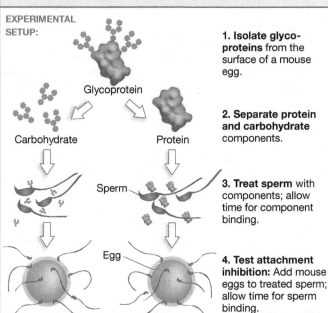

1. **Isolate glyco-proteins** from the surface of a mouse egg.

Glycoprotein

Carbohydrate   Protein

2. **Separate protein and carbohydrate** components.

Sperm

3. **Treat sperm** with components; allow time for component binding.

Egg

4. **Test attachment inhibition:** Add mouse eggs to treated sperm; allow time for sperm binding.

PREDICTION: The carbohydrate component of the glycoprotein will bind to sperm and block their attachment to eggs.

PREDICTION OF NULL HYPOTHESIS: The protein component of the glycoprotein will block sperm attachment to eggs.

RESULTS:

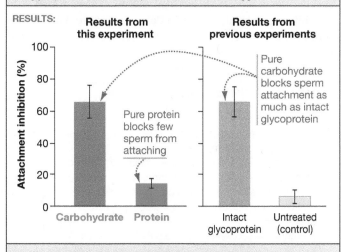

Results from this experiment

Results from previous experiments

Pure carbohydrate blocks sperm attachment as much as intact glycoprotein

Pure protein blocks few sperm from attaching

Attachment inhibition (%)

Carbohydrate   Protein

Intact glycoprotein   Untreated (control)

CONCLUSION: Sperm recognize and bind to the carbohydrates of egg-surface glycoproteins when they attach to egg cells.

Figure 5.7 Carbohydrates Are Required for Cellular Recognition and Attachment during Fertilization.

SOURCES: Florman, H. M., K. B. Bechtol, and P. M. Wassarman. 1984. Enzymatic dissection of the functions of the mouse egg's receptor for sperm. *Developmental Biology* 106: 243–255. Also Florman, H. M., and P. M. Wassarman. 1985. O-linked oligosaccharides of mouse egg ZP3 account for its sperm receptor activity. *Cell* 41: 313–324.

✔ **PROCESS OF SCIENCE** How would the bars change in each graph if sperm attachment required only the protein portion of egg glycoproteins?

But which part of the egg glycoproteins is essential for recognition and attachment—the protein or the carbohydrate? In follow-up experiments, Wassarman's group used the same type of competitive-binding assay to answer this question (**Figure 5.7**). When sperm were mixed with purified carbohydrates alone, most were unable to attach to eggs. In contrast, most sperm treated with purified protein alone were not inhibited and still attached to eggs. Both results show that the carbohydrate component plays a fundamental role in the process of egg-cell recognition.

Carbohydrates and Energy Storage

Candy-bar wrappers promise a quick energy boost, and ads for sports drinks claim that their products provide the "carbs" needed for peak activity. If you were to ask friends or family members what carbohydrates do in your body, they would probably say something like "They give you energy." And you'd agree, but only after pointing out that carbohydrates are also used in cell identity, as a structural material, and as a source of carbon atoms for the synthesis of other complex molecules.

Carbohydrates store and provide chemical energy in cells. What aspect of carbohydrate structure makes this function possible?

Carbohydrates Store Sunlight as Chemical Energy Recall that the essence of chemical evolution was energy transformations (Chapter 2). For example, it was proposed that the energy in sunlight may have been converted into chemical energy and stored in bonds of molecules such as formaldehyde (CH_2O).

This same type of transformation from light energy to chemical energy occurs in cells today, but instead of making formaldehyde, cells produce sugars. For example, plants harvest the energy in sunlight and store it in the bonds of carbohydrates by the process known as **photosynthesis.** (Photosynthesis is the focus of Chapter 10.)

Photosynthesis entails a complex set of reactions that can be summarized most simply as follows:

$$CO_2 + H_2O + sunlight \longrightarrow (CH_2O)_n + O_2$$

where $(CH_2O)_n$ represents a carbohydrate. The key to understanding the energy conversion that takes place during photosynthesis is to compare the positions of the electrons associated with carbon in the reactants to those in the products.

1. The electrons in the C=O bonds of carbon dioxide and the C–O bonds of carbohydrates are held tightly because of oxygen's high electronegativity. Thus, they have relatively low potential energy.

2. The electrons involved in the C–H bonds of carbohydrates are shared equally because the electronegativity of carbon and hydrogen is about the same. Thus, bonds are weaker and these electrons have relatively high potential energy.

3. Electrons are also shared equally in the carbon–carbon (C–C) bonds of carbohydrates—meaning that they, too, have relatively high potential energy.

So, because C–C and C–H bonds have much higher potential energy than C–O bonds have, carbohydrates store much more chemical energy than carbon dioxide does.

(a) Carbon dioxide

$$O = C = O$$

(b) A carbohydrate

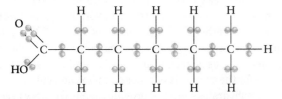

(c) A fatty acid (a component of fat molecules)

Figure 5.8 In Organisms, Potential Energy Is Stored in the Bonds of Molecules. (a) Carbon dioxide has low potential energy because the electrons involved in covalent bonds are held tightly by oxygen atoms. **(b)** Carbohydrates, such as the sugar shown here, have high potential energy because many of the covalent bonds are weak and the electrons are held equally between C and H atoms. **(c)** The fatty acids found in fat molecules have even more potential energy than carbohydrates because they have a higher ratio of C–H and C–C bonds to C–O bonds.

✔ Circle the bonds in this diagram that have high potential energy.

Figure 5.8 summarizes and extends these points. Start by comparing the structure of carbon dioxide in Figure 5.8a with the carbohydrate in Figure 5.8b. The main difference is the presence of C–C and C–H bonds in the carbohydrate. Now compare the carbohydrate in Figure 5.8b with the fatty acid—a subunit of a fat molecule—in Figure 5.8c. The ratio of C–C and C–H bonds to C–O bonds is much greater in fats than in carbohydrates.

This point is important. C–C and C–H bonds have high potential energy because the atoms have low electronegativities and share the electrons equally. C–O bonds, in contrast, have low potential energy because the highly electronegative oxygen atom holds the electrons so tightly, resulting in a stronger bond. Recall that the potential energy in bonds is released when they are broken and new, stronger bonds are formed (Chapter 2). Both carbohydrates and fats are used as fuel in cells, but fats store twice as much energy per gram compared with carbohydrates. (Fats are discussed in more detail in Chapter 6.)

Enzymes Hydrolyze Polysaccharides to Release Glucose Starch and glycogen are efficient energy-storage molecules because they polymerize via α-glycosidic linkages instead of the β-glycosidic linkages observed in the structural polysaccharides. The α-linkages in storage polysaccharides are readily hydrolyzed to release glucose, while the structural polysaccharides resist enzymatic degradation.

The most important enzyme involved in catalyzing the hydrolysis of α-glycosidic linkages in glycogen molecules is a protein called **phosphorylase.** Many of your cells contain phosphorylase, so they can break down glycogen to provide glucose on demand. The enzymes involved in breaking the α-glycosidic linkages in starch are called **amylases.** Your salivary glands and pancreas produce amylases that are secreted into your mouth and small intestine, respectively. These amylases are responsible for digesting the starch that you eat.

The glucose subunits that are hydrolyzed from glycogen and starch are processed in reactions that result in the production of chemical energy that can be used in the cell. Glycogen and starch are like a candy bar that has segments, so you can break off chunks whenever you need a boost.

Energy Stored in Glucose Is Used to Make ATP When a cell needs energy, reactions break down glucose and capture some of the released energy through synthesis of the nucleotide adenosine triphosphate (ATP) (introduced in Chapter 4). More specifically, the energy that's released when sugars are processed is used to synthesize ATP from a precursor called adenosine diphosphate (ADP) plus a free inorganic phosphate (P_i) molecule. The overall reaction can be written as follows:

$$(CH_2O)_n + O_2 + ADP + P_i \longrightarrow CO_2 + H_2O + ATP$$

To put this in terms of bonds, some of the chemical energy stored in the C–H and C–C bonds of carbohydrate is released as new C=O bonds are formed. This energy is then transferred to a new bond linking a third phosphate group to ADP to form ATP.

How much sugar does it take to form ATP? Not much! Consider this example: A cell can use the sugar stored in a single LifeSavers candy (about 15 Calories of energy) to produce approximately 3×10^{23} molecules of ATP. Although this sounds

---

CHECK YOUR UNDERSTANDING

If you understand that ...

- Carbohydrates provide raw materials for the synthesis of more complex compounds.
- Polysaccharides such as cellulose, chitin, and peptidoglycan form cell walls, which give cells structural strength.
- Glycoproteins and glycolipids project from cell surfaces and provide molecular badges that identify the cell's type or species.
- Starch and glycogen store sugars for later use in reactions that produce ATP. Sugars contain large amounts of potential energy in their C–H and C–C bonds.

✔ **You should be able to ...**

1. Identify two aspects of the structures of cellulose, chitin, and peptidoglycan that correlate with their function as structural molecules.
2. Describe how the various types of carbohydrates you ate during breakfast today are being used in your body right now.

Answers are available in Appendix A.

like a lot of ATP, an average person would burn through all of this ATP in less than 2 minutes! The energy in ATP drives reactions that are responsible for everything from polymerization to muscle movement.

Later chapters analyze in detail how cells capture and store energy in sugars and how these sugars are then broken down to provide cells with usable chemical energy in the form of ATP (Chapters 8, 9, and 10). For both of these processes to occur, however, a selectively permeable membrane barrier is required. The following chapter introduces the lipids needed to build these membranes and the role they played in the evolution of the first cell.

5.1 Sugars as Monomers

- Monosaccharides are organic compounds that have a carbonyl group and several hydroxyl groups. The molecular formula for a sugar is typically $(CH_2O)_n$, but the number of "carbon-hydrate" groups may vary between sugars, as indicated by the n.

- Monosaccharides have either an aldose or ketose configuration, depending on whether the carbonyl group is located at the end or middle of the carbon chain.

- Although some monosaccharides may have the same molecular formula, the spatial arrangement of their functional groups leads to differences in their molecular structures and therefore functions.

- Monosaccharides may form ring structures in solution that can differ from one another in the orientation of a hydroxyl group, even among molecules of the same monosaccharide.

5.2 The Structure of Polysaccharides

- Monosaccharides can be covalently bonded to one another via glycosidic linkages, which join hydroxyl groups on adjacent molecules.

- In contrast to proteins and nucleic acids, polysaccharides do not always form a single uniform backbone structure. The numerous hydroxyls found in each monosaccharide allow glycosidic linkages to form at different sites and new strands to branch from existing chains.

- The types of monomers involved and the geometries of the glycosidic linkages between monomers distinguish different polysaccharides from one another.

- The most common polysaccharides in organisms today are starch, glycogen, cellulose, and chitin; peptidoglycan is an abundant polysaccharide that consists of sugar monosaccharides and short chains of attached amino acids.

5.3 What Do Carbohydrates Do?

- In carbohydrates, as in proteins and nucleic acids, structure correlates with function.

- Cellulose, chitin, and peptidoglycan are polysaccharides that function in support. They are made up of monosaccharide monomers joined by β-1,4-glycosidic linkages. When individual molecules of these polysaccharides align side by side, bonds form between them—resulting in strong, flexible fibers or sheets that resist hydrolysis.

- The oligosaccharides on cell-surface glycoproteins and glycolipids can function as specific signposts or identity tags because their constituent sugar residues are so diverse in geometry and composition.

- Both starch and glycogen function as energy-storage molecules. They are made up of glucose molecules that are joined by α-glycosidic linkages. These linkages are readily hydrolyzed to release glucose for the production of ATP and raw materials for building new molecules.

Answers are available in Appendix A

✔ TEST YOUR KNOWLEDGE

1. What are three ways monosaccharides differ from one another?

2. What type of bond is formed between two sugars in a disaccharide?
   a. glycosidic linkage
   b. phosphodiester bond
   c. peptide bond
   d. hydrogen bond

3. What holds cellulose molecules together in bundles large enough to form fibers?
   a. the cell wall
   b. peptide bonds
   c. hydrogen bonds
   d. hydrophobic interactions

4. What are the primary functions of carbohydrates in cells?
   a. cell identity, energy storage, raw material source for synthesis, and structure
   b. catalysis, energy storage, metabolism, and structure
   c. catalysis, digestion, energy storage, and information storage
   d. energy storage, information storage, polymerization, and raw material source for synthesis

✔ TEST YOUR UNDERSTANDING

5. Which of the differences listed here could be found among molecules of the same monosaccharide?
   a. different orientations of a hydroxyl group in the linear form
   b. different numbers of carbons
   c. different orientations of a hydroxyl group in the ring form
   d. different positions of the carbonyl group in the linear form

6. What is the difference between linking glucose molecules with α-1,4-glycosidic linkages versus β-1,4-glycosidic linkages? What are the consequences?

7. Compare and contrast polysaccharides and nucleic acids (see Chapter 4) in terms of monomer diversity and how the monomers are joined together.

8. Lysozyme, an enzyme found in human saliva, tears, and other secretions, catalyzes the hydrolysis of the β-1,4-glycosidic linkages in peptidoglycan. Predict the effect of this enzyme on bacteria and how it may be involved in human health.

✔ TEST YOUR PROBLEM-SOLVING SKILLS

9. **SOCIETY** Galactosemia is a potentially fatal disease that occurs in humans who lack the enzyme that converts galactose to glucose. If you were a physician treating a person with this disease, which of the following would you have them exclude from their diet?
   a. maltose
   b. starch
   c. mannose
   d. lactose

10. If you hold a salty cracker in your mouth long enough, it will begin to taste sweet. What is responsible for this change in taste?

✔ PUT IT ALL TOGETHER: Case Study

Is the sugar in your soda affecting your mind?

A 20-ounce soda typically contains 15 teaspoons of either sucrose or high-fructose corn syrup. These sugary beverages are a leading source of calories in the American diet and have been correlated with obesity and diabetes. There may be even more to this sweet dilemma, however. Could the sugars found in soda be altering your brain function?

11. Sucrose is a disaccharide consisting of α-glucose and β-fructose. What type of glycosidic bond links these monosaccharides?

Sucrose

α-Glucose

β-Fructose

12. Sucrose is cleaved in your saliva by the enzyme sucrase to release glucose and fructose. Use the structural formula of sucrose to describe fructose using the terms that define its carbon number and placement of the carbonyl group.

13. You perceive the sweetness of sucrose based on a specific interaction between fructose and proteins on your tongue's taste buds. What structural difference between glucose and fructose would you predict to be responsible for the fact that fructose tastes sweeter?

14. High-fructose corn syrup is produced by converting starch from corn into a mixture of glucose and fructose monosaccharides. What two events must occur in this process in order to turn starch into these simple sugars?

15. **QUANTITATIVE** The effect of diet on human health is often evaluated using animal models. Researchers tested the impact of drinking fructose solutions on memory by using mice trained to find an escape chamber in a maze. The mice were fed diets consisting of control chow or chow that was supplemented with a fructose solution, omega-3 fatty acids, or both. After six weeks on the diets, the mice were tested again on the same maze with the results shown in the bar graph (* means $P < 0.05$ and ** means $P < 0.01$, see BioSkills 3). What can you conclude from these results about fructose-fed mice versus those without fructose? How did the omega-3 fatty acids affect memory in this test?

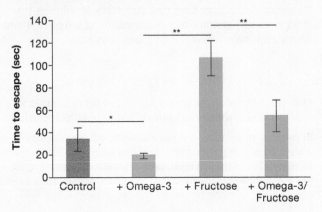

Source: Agrawal, R., and F. G. Pinilla 2012. *Journal of Physiology* 590: 2485–2499.

16. **SOCIETY** How might the results from this study influence your diet while studying biology?

6 Lipids, Membranes, and the First Cells

A space-filling model of a phospholipid bilayer with two phospholipids highlighted in blue. This cluster of molecules forms part of the boundary between life (inside the cell) and nonlife (outside the cell)— the cell membrane.

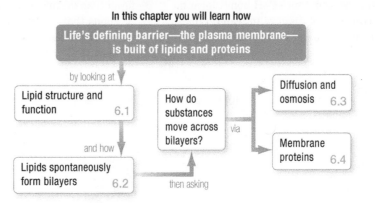

In this chapter you will learn how

Life's defining barrier—the plasma membrane— is built of lipids and proteins

by looking at

Lipid structure and function   6.1

and how

Lipids spontaneously form bilayers   6.2

then asking

How do substances move across bilayers?

via

Diffusion and osmosis   6.3

Membrane proteins   6.4

This chapter is part of the Big Picture. See how on pages 140–141.

Currently, most biologists support the hypothesis that biological evolution began with a molecule that could replicate itself. As the offspring of this molecule multiplied, natural selection would have favored the versions that reproduced most frequently. A second great milestone in the history of life occurred when descendants of these replicators became enclosed within a membrane.

Why was the emergence of a membrane so important? The **plasma membrane,** or often called the **cell membrane,** separates life from nonlife. It is a layer of molecules that surrounds and separates the cell interior from the environment.

- The plasma membrane serves as a selective barrier: It can keep damaging substances out of the cell and allow entry of substances needed by the cell.

- Because the plasma membrane sequesters the appropriate chemicals in an enclosed area, reactants collide more frequently, allowing the chemical reactions necessary for life to occur much more efficiently.

How do membranes form? Which ions and molecules can pass through a membrane and which cannot, and why? These are some of the most fundamental questions in all of biological science. Let's delve into them, beginning with the membrane's foundation—lipids.

6.1 Lipid Structure and Function

Lipid is a catchall term for carbon-containing compounds that are found in organisms and are largely nonpolar and hydrophobic—meaning that they do not dissolve readily in water. (Recall from Chapter 2 that water is a polar solvent.) Lipids do dissolve, however, in organic solvents consisting of nonpolar compounds like benzene (C_6H_6).

To understand why lipids are insoluble in water, examine the five-carbon compound, called isoprene, illustrated in **Figure 6.1a**. Note that isoprene consists entirely of carbon atoms bonded to hydrogen atoms. The figure also shows the structural formula of a chain of linked isoprenes, called an isoprenoid. Isoprenoids serve a wide range of functions in organism—from pigments and scents to vitamins and precursors of sex hormones. As you will see, they are also important building blocks for other, more complex lipids.

Molecules that contain only carbon and hydrogen are known as **hydrocarbons.** Hydrocarbons are nonpolar because electrons are shared equally in C–H bonds owing to the similar electronegativities of carbon and hydrogen. Since C–H bonds form no partial charges, hydrocarbons do not dissolve in water. Lipids, therefore, are mostly hydrophobic because they have a significant hydrocarbon component.

How Does Bond Saturation Affect Hydrocarbon Structure?

Figure 6.1b gives the structural formula of a **fatty acid,** a simple lipid consisting of a hydrocarbon chain bonded to a carboxyl (–COOH) functional group. Fatty acids typically contain a total of 14–20 carbon atoms, most found in their long hydrocarbon "tails." Like isoprenoids, fatty acids are also key building blocks of important lipids found in organisms. Let's look at how these molecules are put together.

Just as subtle differences in the orientation of hydroxyl (–OH) groups can lead to dramatic effects in the structure and function of sugars, the type of bond between carbons in hydrocarbon chains is a key factor in lipid structure and function.

When two carbon atoms form a double bond, the attached atoms are found in a plane instead of a three-dimensional tetrahedron (Chapter 2). The carbon atoms involved are also locked into place. They cannot rotate freely, as can carbons in C–C single bonds. As a result, certain double bonds between carbon atoms (called *cis* bonds) produce a "kink" in an otherwise straight hydrocarbon chain (compare the two structures in Figure 6.1b).

Hydrocarbon chains that consist of only single bonds between the carbons are called **saturated.** If one or more double bonds exist in the hydrocarbon chains, then they are **unsaturated.** The choice of terms is logical. If a hydrocarbon chain does not contain a double bond, it is saturated with the maximum number of hydrogen atoms that can attach to the carbon skeleton. If it is unsaturated, then a C–H bond is removed to form a C=C double bond, resulting in fewer than the maximum number of attached hydrogen atoms.

Foods that contain lipids with many double bonds are said to be polyunsaturated and are advertised as healthier than foods with saturated lipids. Some recent research suggests that

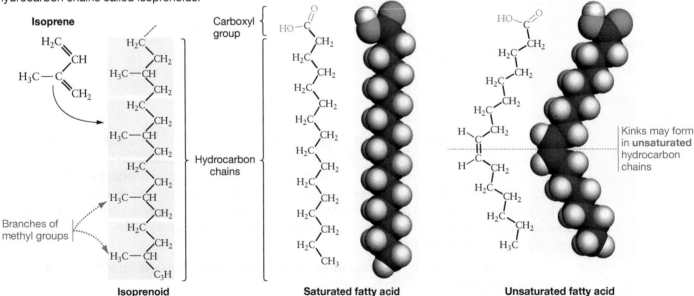

(a) Isoprenes can be linked into branched hydrocarbon chains called isoprenoids.

(b) Fatty acids are unbranched hydrocarbon chains joined to a carboxyl group.

Isoprene

Carboxyl group

Hydrocarbon chains

Branches of methyl groups

Isoprenoid

Saturated fatty acid

Kinks may form in **unsaturated** hydrocarbon chains

Unsaturated fatty acid

Figure 6.1 Hydrocarbon Structure. (a) Isoprene subunits, like the one shown to the left, can link to each other, end to end, to form long branched hydrocarbon chains called isoprenoids. **(b)** Fatty acids have unbranched hydrocarbon chains. Unsaturated hydrocarbons contain carbon–carbon double bonds; saturated hydrocarbons do not.

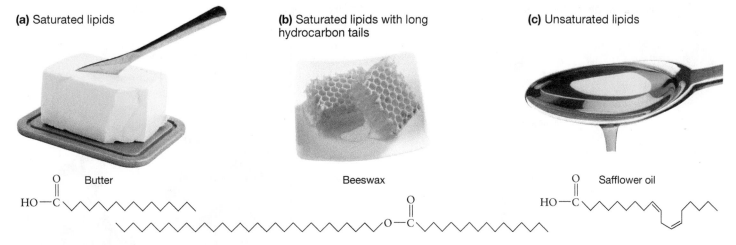

(a) Saturated lipids

Butter

(b) Saturated lipids with long hydrocarbon tails

Beeswax

(c) Unsaturated lipids

Safflower oil

Figure 6.2 The Fluidity of Lipids Depends on the Length and Saturation of Their Hydrocarbon Chains. (a) Butter consists primarily of saturated lipids. **(b)** Waxes are lipids with extremely long saturated hydrocarbon chains. **(c)** Oils are dominated by "polyunsaturates"—lipids with hydrocarbon chains that contain multiple C=C double bonds. **(d)** The product Crisco is made by converting polyunsaturates into saturated lipids by hydrogenation.

(d) Hydrogenation

polyunsaturated lipids may help protect the heart from disease. Exactly how this occurs is under investigation.

Bond saturation profoundly affects the physical state of lipids. Highly saturated lipids, such as in butter, have relatively high melting points and are solid at room temperature (≈ 20–$22°C$) (Figure 6.2a). Saturated lipids that have extremely long hydrocarbon tails, like **waxes,** form particularly stiff solids at room temperature (Figure 6.2b). Highly unsaturated lipids are liquid at room temperature (Figure 6.2c). Unsaturated oils may be converted to saturated lipids by breaking double bonds and adding hydrogen atoms via the process of hydrogenation (Figure 6.2d).

A Look at Three Types of Lipids Found in Cells

Unlike amino acids, nucleotides, and monosaccharides, lipids are characterized by a physical property—their insolubility in water—instead of by a shared chemical structure. This insolubility results from a high proportion of nonpolar C–C and C–H bonds relative to polar functional groups. These bonds and groups can be put together in more than one way, so lipid structures vary widely. For example, consider the most important types of lipids found in cells: steroids, fats, and phospholipids.

Steroids **Steroids** are a family of lipids distinguished by the bulky, four-ring structure shown in orange in Figure 6.3. The various steroids differ from one another by the functional groups or side groups attached to different carbons in those hydrophobic rings. Common steroids such as estrogen and testosterone are known for their role as hormones in cell signaling (see Chapter 11). The steroid shown in the figure is cholesterol, which has a hydrophilic hydroxyl group attached to the top ring and an isoprenoid "tail" attached at the bottom. Cholesterol is an important component of plasma membranes in many organisms.

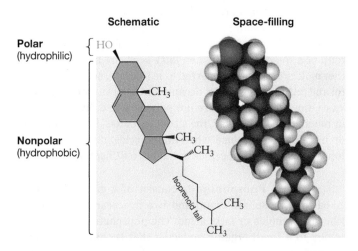

Figure 6.3 Steroids Are Defined by a Common Structure. All steroids have the distinctive four-ring structure shown in orange. Cholesterol has a polar hydroxyl group and an isoprenoid chain attached to these rings.

(a) Fats form via dehydration reactions.

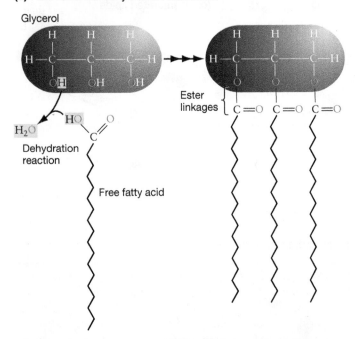

Glycerol

Ester linkages

H₂O

Dehydration reaction

Free fatty acid

(b) Phospholipids include a hydrophilic head.

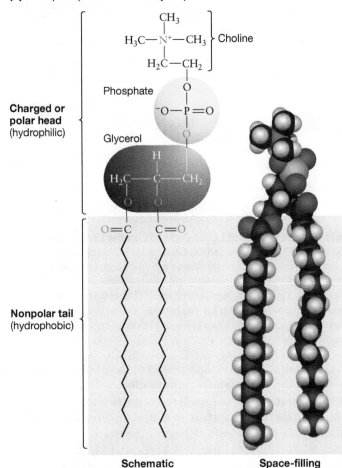

Choline

Phosphate

Charged or polar head (hydrophilic)

Glycerol

Nonpolar tail (hydrophobic)

Schematic   Space-filling

Figure 6.4 Fats and Phospholipids Differ in the Presence of a Hydrophilic Region. (a) Fats form when dehydration reactions connect glycerol to three fatty acids and produce ester linkages. **(b)** Most phospholipids consist of glycerol linked to only two fatty acid or isoprenoid chains. Unlike fats, the third hydroxyl in glycerol is attached to a phosphate group and a small polar or charged organic molecule (in this example, choline).

✔ Draw a circle around the part of the phospholipid model that would interact with water if it were placed in an aqueous solution.

Fats **Fats** are nonpolar molecules composed of three fatty acids that are linked to a three-carbon molecule called **glycerol.** Because of this structure, fats are also called triacylglycerols or triglycerides. (If the glycerol-linked fatty acids are polyunsaturated, the resulting triacylglycerols are liquid and called **oils.**) In organisms, the primary role of fats is energy storage.

As **Figure 6.4a** shows, fats form when a dehydration reaction occurs between a hydroxyl group of glycerol and the carboxyl group of a free fatty acid (when fatty acids are not attached to other molecules, they are referred to as free fatty acids). The glycerol and fatty acid molecules become joined by an **ester linkage.** Notice, however, that fats are not polymers, and fatty acids are not monomers. In this way, the structure of fats differs from the polymers that are formed when amino acids, nucleotides, and monosaccharides link together in chains (see Chapters 3–5).

Phospholipids **Phospholipids** consist of a glycerol that is linked to a phosphate group and two hydrocarbon chains of either isoprenoids or fatty acids. The phosphate group is also bonded to a small organic molecule that is charged or polar (**Figure 6.4b**).

Phospholipids with fatty acid tails are found in the domains Bacteria and Eukarya; phospholipids with isoprenoid tails are found in the domain Archaea. (The domains of life were introduced in Chapter 1.) In all three domains, phospholipids are crucial components of the plasma membrane. The branched isoprenoid chains in archaeal phospholipids provide greater membrane stability and protection in the extreme environments inhabited by certain archaea (see Chapter 26).

How Membrane Lipids Interact with Water

The lipids found in organisms have a wide array of functions. In addition to storing chemical energy, lipids act as pigments that capture or respond to sunlight, serve as signals between cells, form waterproof coatings on leaves and skin, and act as vitamins used in many cellular processes. The most prominent function of lipids, however, is their role in cell membranes. Not all lipids can form membranes, however.

In addition to the nonpolar, hydrophobic region that defines lipids, membrane-forming lipids have a polar, hydrophilic region. To better understand this structure, take another look at the phospholipid illustrated in Figure 6.4b. Notice that the molecule has a "head" region containing a negatively charged phosphate group attached to a polar group. The charges and polar bonds in the head region interact with water molecules when a phospholipid is placed in solution. In contrast, the long hydrocarbon tails of a phospholipid are nonpolar and hydrophobic.

Water molecules cannot form hydrogen bonds with the hydrocarbon tail, so they do not interact extensively with this part of the molecule.

Substances that contain both hydrophilic and hydrophobic regions are **amphipathic** (literally, "dual-sympathy"). Phospholipids are amphipathic. As Figure 6.3 shows, cholesterol is also amphipathic because it has a hydrophilic hydroxyl functional group attached to its hydrophobic rings. ✔ If you understand the criteria for amphipathy, you should be able to look back at Figure 6.1b and explain why free fatty acids are also amphipathic.

The amphipathic nature of lipids is far and away their most important feature biologically. It is responsible for life's defining barrier—the plasma membrane. If the membrane defines cellular life, then amphipathic lipids must have existed when life first originated during chemical evolution. Was that possible?

Were Lipids Present during Chemical Evolution?

Like amino acids, nucleic acids, and carbohydrates (Chapters 3–5), there is evidence that lipids were present during chemical evolution. Laboratory experiments have shown that simple lipids, such as fatty acids, can be synthesized from H_2 and CO_2 via reactions with mineral catalysts under conditions thought to be present in prebiotic hydrothermal vent systems (Chapter 2).

It's also possible that lipids literally fell from the sky early in Earth's history. Modern meteorites have been found to contain not only amino acids and carbohydrates but also lipids that exhibit amphipathic qualities. For example, lipids extracted from the meteorite that struck Murchison, Australia, in 1969 spontaneously formed lipid "bubbles" that resembled small cells. Why do amphipathic lipids do this?

6.2 Phospholipid Bilayers

Amphipathic lipids do not dissolve when they are placed in water. Their hydrophilic heads interact with water, but their hydrophobic tails do not. Instead of dissolving in water, amphipathic lipids assume one of two types of structures: micelles or lipid bilayers.

- Micelles (**Figure 6.5a**) are tiny aggregates created when the hydrophilic heads of a set of lipids face the water and form hydrogen bonds, while the hydrophobic tails interact with each other in the interior, away from the water.

- A **lipid bilayer** is created when lipid molecules align in paired sheets. As **Figure 6.5b** shows, the hydrophilic heads in each layer face the surrounding solution while the hydrophobic tails face one another inside the bilayer. In this way, the hydrophilic heads interact with water while the hydrophobic tails interact with one another.

Micelles tend to form from fatty acids or other simple amphipathic lipids with single hydrocarbon chains. Bilayers tend to form from phospholipids, which have bulkier two-hydrocarbon tails. For this reason, lipid bilayers are often called *phospho*lipid bilayers.

It's critical to recognize that micelles and phospholipid bilayers form spontaneously in water—no input of energy is required. However, at the level of lipid organization, it appears as if entropy decreases—because the lipids become less disordered as micelles and phospholipid bilayers form. How can this be explained if spontaneous processes tend to increase entropy?

To understand how amphipathic lipids aggregate, you must consider the organization of water molecules. Recall that hydrophobic interactions occur when nonpolar molecules are surrounded by a "cage" of highly organized water molecules (see Chapter 2). When amphipathic lipids are dispersed in an aqueous solution, these cages would form around each of the nonpolar tails. If the tails aggregate to form micelles and bilayers, then only the hydrophilic regions of the lipids would be exposed and the water cages would melt. This decrease in water molecule organization results in an overall increase in the entropy of the system.

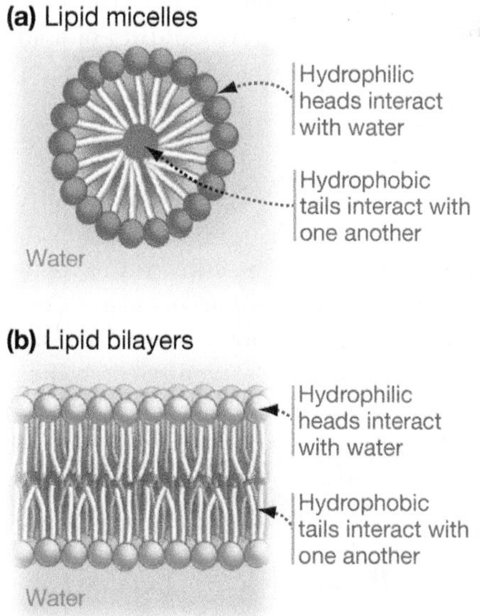

(a) Lipid micelles

Hydrophilic heads interact with water

Hydrophobic tails interact with one another

Water

(b) Lipid bilayers

Hydrophilic heads interact with water

Hydrophobic tails interact with one another

Water

Figure 6.5 Lipids Form Micelles and Bilayers in Solution.
In **(a)** a micelle or **(b)** a lipid bilayer, the hydrophilic heads of lipids face out, toward water; the hydrophobic tails face in, away from water. Lipid bilayers are the foundation of cellular membranes.

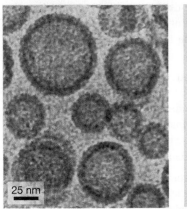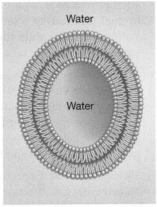

Water

Water

Figure 6.6 Liposomes Are Artificial Membrane-Bound Vesicles. Electron micrograph of liposomes in cross section (left) and a cross-sectional diagram of the lipid bilayer in a liposome (right).

Artificial Membranes as an Experimental System

To explore how membranes work, researchers began creating and experimenting with artificial membranes in the lab. In one method, phospholipids are added to an aqueous solution and agitated to form **vesicles**—small bubble-like structures consisting of lipid bilayers surrounding a small amount of aqueous solution. The hydrophobic tails are shielded from water, and the hydrophilic heads remain in contact with water on the inside or outside of the vesicle. Artificially generated membrane-bound vesicles like these are called **liposomes** (**Figure 6.6**). Liposomes provide a three-dimensional model that mimics a membrane-bound cell.

Another artificial membrane used in experiments is the planar bilayer, which provides a simpler, two-dimensional model. In this case, the lipid bilayer is constructed across a hole in a glass or plastic wall separating two aqueous solutions (**Figure 6.7a**). Some of the first questions scientists posed concerned the permeability of lipid bilayers. The **permeability** of a structure is its tendency to allow a given substance to pass through it.

Using liposomes and planar bilayers, researchers can study what happens when a known ion or molecule is added to one side of a lipid bilayer. **Figure 6.7b** shows how a planar bilayer could be used to answer experimental questions such as these: Does the substance cross the membrane and show up on the other side? If so, how rapidly does the movement take place? What happens when a different type of phospholipid is used to make the artificial membrane? Does the membrane's permeability change when proteins or other types of molecules become part of it?

Biologists describe such an experimental system as elegant and powerful because it lets them precisely control which factor changes from one experimental treatment to the next. Control, in turn, is why experiments are such an effective way to explore scientific questions. Recall that good experimental design allows researchers to alter one factor at a time and determine what effect, if any, each has on the process being studied (Chapter 1).

Selective Permeability of Lipid Bilayers

When researchers put molecules or ions in a solution containing liposomes, or on one side of a planar bilayer, and measure the rate at which the particles cross the membrane barrier, a clear pattern emerges: Lipid bilayers are highly selective.

Selective permeability means that some substances cross a membrane more easily than other substances do. Small nonpolar molecules, for example, move across bilayers quickly. If the small molecules are polar, the rate of transport decreases. Larger polar molecules and charged substances cross the membrane even slower, if at all. This difference in membrane permeability is a critical issue because controlling what passes between the exterior and interior environments is a key characteristic of cells.

According to the data in **Figure 6.8**, small nonpolar molecules such as oxygen (O_2) move across selectively permeable membranes more than a billion times faster than do chloride ions (Cl^-). In essence, ions cannot cross membranes at all—unless they have "help" in the form of membrane proteins introduced later in the chapter. Very small polar molecules, such as water

(a) Planar bilayer

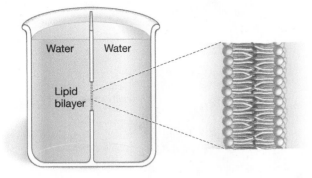

Water   Water

Lipid
bilayer

(b) Planar bilayer experiments

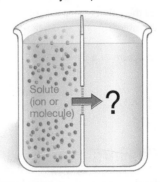

Solute
(ion or
molecule)   **?**

How rapidly can different solutes cross the membrane (if at all) when ...

1. Different types of phospholipids are used to make the membrane?

2. Proteins or other molecules are added to the membrane?

Figure 6.7 Use of Planar Bilayers in Experiments. (a) The construction of a planar bilayer across a hole in a wall separating two water-filled compartments. **(b)** A wide variety of experiments are possible with planar bilayers; a few experimental questions are suggested here.

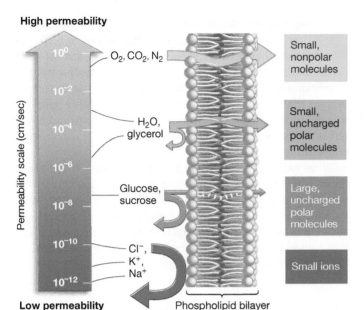

High permeability

Permeability scale (cm/sec)

10^0 — O_2, CO_2, N_2 — Small, nonpolar molecules

10^{-2}

10^{-4} — H_2O, glycerol — Small, uncharged polar molecules

10^{-6}

10^{-8} — Glucose, sucrose — Large, uncharged polar molecules

10^{-10} — Cl^-, K^+, Na^+ — Small ions

10^{-12}

Low permeability — Phospholipid bilayer

Figure 6.8 Lipid Bilayers Show Selective Permeability. Only certain substances cross lipid bilayers readily. Size and polarity or charge affect the rate of diffusion across a membrane.

(H_2O), can cross membranes while slightly larger polar molecules, such as glycerol, are less likely to cross.

The leading hypothesis to explain this emerging pattern is that charged substances and polar molecules above a certain size are more stable dissolved in water—a polar environment—than they would be in the nonpolar interior of membranes. ✔ If you understand this hypothesis, you should be able to predict where amino acids and nucleotides would be placed in Figure 6.8 and explain your reasoning.

How Does Lipid Structure Affect Membrane Permeability?

The amphipathic nature of phospholipids causes them to spontaneously form bilayers that are comprised of two lipid sheets held together by hydrophobic interactions. But not all phospholipid bilayers are the same. The length and saturation state of the hydrocarbon tails, in addition to the presence of cholesterol molecules, profoundly influences the physical properties of a membrane and its permeability.

Bond Saturation and Hydrocarbon Chain Length Affect Membrane Fluidity and Permeability   A phospholipid's degree of saturation—along with the length of its hydrocarbon tails—affects key aspects of its behavior in a membrane.

- When unsaturated hydrocarbon tails are packed into a lipid bilayer, kinks created by double bonds produce spaces among the tails. These spaces reduce the strength of van der Waals interactions (see Chapter 3) that help hold the hydrophobic tails together, weakening the barrier to solutes.

- Packed saturated hydrocarbon tails have fewer spaces and stronger van der Waals interactions. As the length of saturated hydrocarbon tails increases, the forces that hold them together also grow stronger, making the membrane even denser.

These factors profoundly affect membrane fluidity and permeability—two closely related properties. As **Figure 6.9** shows, lipid bilayers are more permeable as well as more fluid when they contain many short, kinked, unsaturated hydrocarbon tails. A largely unsaturated membrane allows more materials to pass because its interior is held together less tightly. Bilayers containing largely long, straight, saturated hydrocarbon tails are much less permeable and fluid.

Cholesterol Reduces Membrane Permeability   Cholesterol molecules are present, to varying extents, in the membranes of every cell in your body. What effect does adding cholesterol have on a membrane? Researchers have found that adding cholesterol molecules to artificial membranes dramatically reduces their permeability.

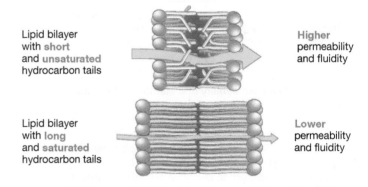

Lipid bilayer with **short** and **unsaturated** hydrocarbon tails — **Higher** permeability and fluidity

Lipid bilayer with **long** and **saturated** hydrocarbon tails — **Lower** permeability and fluidity

Figure 6.9 Degree of Hydrocarbon Saturation Affects the Permeability of Membranes. In general, phospholipids containing unsaturated hydrocarbon tails form bilayers that have more gaps and are more permeable than bilayers formed from phospholipids with saturated hydrocarbon tails.

QUESTION: Does adding cholesterol to a membrane affect its permeability?

HYPOTHESIS: Cholesterol reduces permeability.

NULL HYPOTHESIS: Cholesterol has no effect on permeability.

EXPERIMENTAL SETUP:

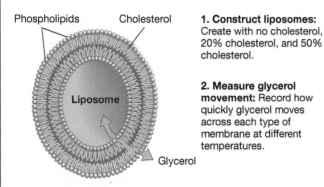

Phospholipids   Cholesterol

Liposome

Glycerol

1. Construct liposomes: Create with no cholesterol, 20% cholesterol, and 50% cholesterol.

2. Measure glycerol movement: Record how quickly glycerol moves across each type of membrane at different temperatures.

PREDICTION: Liposomes with higher cholesterol levels will have reduced permeability to glycerol.

PREDICTION OF NULL HYPOTHESIS: All liposomes will have reduced permeability to glycerol.

RESULTS:

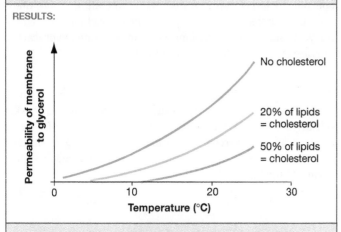

No cholesterol

20% of lipids = cholesterol

50% of lipids = cholesterol

CONCLUSION: Adding cholesterol to membranes decreases their permeability to glycerol. The permeability of all membranes analyzed in this experiment increases with increasing temperature.

Figure 6.10 The Permeability of a Membrane Depends on Its Lipid Composition.

SOURCE: de Gier, J., J. G. Mandersloot, L. L. M. Van Deenen. 1968. Lipid composition and permeability of liposomes. *Biochimica et Biophysica Acta* 150: 666–675.

✔ **QUANTITATIVE** Suppose the investigators had instead created a set of liposomes using phospholipids with fully saturated tails and compared them to two other sets of liposomes where either 20 percent or 50 percent of the phospholipids contained polyunsaturated tails. Label the three lines on the graph above with your prediction for the three different sets of liposomes in this new experiment.

Some data behind this conclusion are presented in **Figure 6.10**. To read the graph in the "Results" section of Figure 6.10, put your finger on the *x*-axis at the point marked 20°C, and note that permeability to glycerol is much higher at this temperature in membranes that contain no cholesterol versus 20 percent or 50 percent cholesterol. Repeating this procedure at other temperature points should convince you that membranes lacking cholesterol are more permeable than the other two membranes at every temperature tested in the experiment.

What explains this result? Cholesterol orients in the membrane with its hydrophobic steroid rings buried deeply in the hydrocarbon tails of the phospholipids. Its interaction with the tails increases their packing density. When cholesterol was added to the experimental membranes, the closer packing of the tails caused the membranes to become less fluid and decreased their permeability.

How Does Temperature Affect the Fluidity and Permeability of Membranes?

The phospholipids in the plasma membrane of a cell have a consistency resembling olive oil. This fluid physical state allows individual lipid molecules to move laterally within each layer (**Figure 6.11**), a little like a person moving about in a dense crowd. By tagging individual phospholipids and following their movement, researchers have clocked average speeds of 2 micrometers (µm) per second. At these speeds, a phospholipid could travel the length of a small bacterial cell in a second.

Recall that permeability is closely related to fluidity. As temperature drops, molecules in a bilayer move more slowly. As a result, the hydrophobic tails in the interior of membranes pack together more tightly. At very low temperatures, lipid bilayers even begin to solidify. As the "Results" in Figure 6.10 indicated, low temperatures can make membranes impervious to molecules that would cross them readily at more moderate temperatures. Put your finger at 0°C on the *x*-axis of that graph (just about the freezing point of water), and note that membranes that lack cholesterol are almost completely impermeable to glycerol. But if you trace any of the three data lines in the same figure to the right (increasing temperature), you will see that permeability increases.

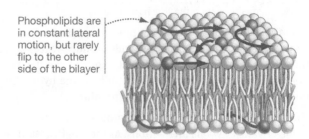

Phospholipids are in constant lateral motion, but rarely flip to the other side of the bilayer

Figure 6.11 Phospholipids Move within Membranes. Membranes are dynamic—in part because phospholipid molecules randomly move laterally within each layer in the structure.

If you understand that ...

• In water, phospholipids form bilayers that are selectively permeable—meaning that some substances cross them much more readily than others do.

• Membrane permeability depends on the degree of saturation and the length of the phospholipids' hydrocarbon tails, the amount of cholesterol in the membrane, and the temperature.

✔ **You should be able to ...**

Fill in a chart that has columns labeled Factor, Effect on permeability, and Reason and rows under the Factor column labeled Temperature, Cholesterol, Length of hydrocarbon tails, and Saturation of hydrocarbon tails.

Answers are available in Appendix A.

6.3 How Substances Move across Lipid Bilayers: Diffusion and Osmosis

Small uncharged molecules and hydrophobic compounds can cross membranes readily and spontaneously—without an input of energy. The question now is: How is this possible? What process is responsible for movement of molecules across lipid bilayers?

Diffusion

A thought experiment can help explain how substances can cross membranes spontaneously. Suppose you rack up a set of billiard balls in the middle of a pool table and then begin to vibrate the table.

1. Because of the vibration, the billiard balls will move about randomly. They will also bump into one another.

2. After these collisions, some balls will move outward—away from their original position.

3. As movement and collisions continue, the overall or net movement of balls will be outward. This occurs because the random motion of the balls disrupts their original, nonrandom position. As the balls move at random, they are more likely to move away from one another than to stay together.

4. Eventually, the balls will be distributed randomly across the table. The entropy of the billiard balls has increased. Recall that entropy is a measure of the randomness or disorder in a system (Chapter 2). The second law of thermodynamics states that in an isolated system, entropy always increases.

This hypothetical example illustrates how vibrating billiard balls move at random. More to the point, it also explains how substances located on one side of a lipid bilayer can move to the other side spontaneously—because like the billiard balls, dissolved solutes are in constant random motion due to their thermal energy. Spontaneous movement of molecules and ions is known as **diffusion.**

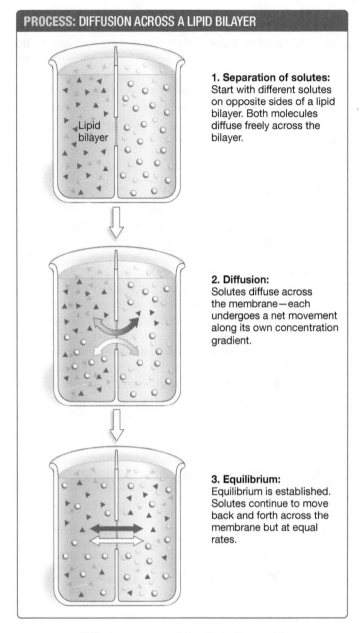

PROCESS: DIFFUSION ACROSS A LIPID BILAYER

1. Separation of solutes: Start with different solutes on opposite sides of a lipid bilayer. Both molecules diffuse freely across the bilayer.

Lipid bilayer

2. Diffusion: Solutes diffuse across the membrane—each undergoes a net movement along its own concentration gradient.

3. Equilibrium: Equilibrium is established. Solutes continue to move back and forth across the membrane but at equal rates.

Figure 6.12 Diffusion across a Selectively Permeable Membrane Establishes an Equilibrium.

A difference in solute concentrations creates what is called a **concentration gradient.** Solutes move randomly in all directions, but when a concentration gradient exists, there is a net movement from regions of high concentration to regions of low concentration. Diffusion down a concentration gradient, or away from the higher concentration, is a spontaneous process because it results in an increase in entropy.

Once the molecules or ions are randomly distributed throughout a solution, an equilibrium is established. For example, consider two aqueous solutions separated by a lipid bilayer. **Figure 6.12** shows how molecules that can pass through the bilayer diffuse to the other side. When substances diffuse across a membrane in the absence of an outside energy source, it is known as **passive transport.**

At equilibrium, movement across the membrane does not stop. Instead, these molecules continue to move back and forth across the membrane due to their constant random motion, but at equal rates because they are equally likely to move in any direction. This means that there is no longer a net movement of molecules across the membrane. ✔ If you understand passive transport, you should be able to predict how increasing the temperature would affect the rate of achieving equilibrium in Figure 6.12.

Osmosis

What about water? As the data in Figure 6.8 show, water moves across lipid bilayers relatively quickly. The movement of water is a special case of diffusion that is given its own name: **osmosis.** Osmosis occurs only when solutions are separated by a membrane that permits water to cross, but holds back some or all of the solutes—that is, a selectively permeable membrane.

It's important to note that some of the water molecules in a solution are unavailable to diffuse across the membrane. Recall that water molecules interact with charged particles and form hydrogen bonds with polar molecules (Chapter 2). If a solute can't cross the membrane, then any associated water molecules are also prevented from crossing. Thus, only unbound water molecules are able to diffuse across the membrane during osmosis. When they do, they flow from the solution with the lower solute concentration into the solution with the higher solute concentration.

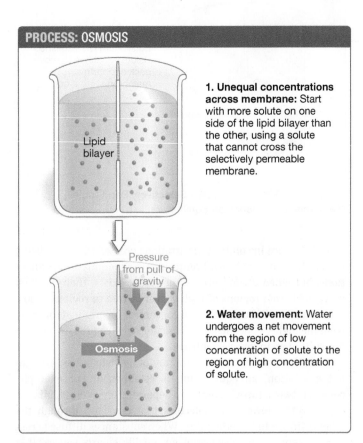

PROCESS: OSMOSIS

Lipid bilayer

1. **Unequal concentrations across membrane:** Start with more solute on one side of the lipid bilayer than the other, using a solute that cannot cross the selectively permeable membrane.

Pressure from pull of gravity

Osmosis

2. **Water movement:** Water undergoes a net movement from the region of low concentration of solute to the region of high concentration of solute.

Figure 6.13 Osmosis Is the Diffusion of Water across a Selectively Permeable Membrane.

To drive this point home, let's suppose the concentration of a particular solute is higher on one side of a selectively permeable membrane than it is on the other side (Figure 6.13, step 1). Further, suppose that this solute cannot diffuse through the membrane to establish equilibrium. What happens? Water will move from the side with a lower concentration of solute to the side with a higher concentration of solute (Figure 6.13, step 2). Osmosis dilutes the higher concentration of solute on the right side as water diffuses across the membrane. This directional movement is spontaneous because entropy will increase as the difference in solute concentrations decreases.

When water moves by osmosis, the solutions on both sides of the membrane experience a change in volume as well as a change in solute concentration. The greater the initial difference in solute concentration, the greater the volume change will be. However, opposing forces, such as the pressure resulting from the downward pull of gravity, exert resistance to the directional movement of water. ✔ **CAUTION** If you understand what forces contribute to osmosis, you should be able to predict whether or not the concentration of the solute in Figure 6.13 would be the same across the membrane after reaching equilibrium. Explain your answer.

Osmosis also affects the volume of a cell or membrane-bound vesicle. When water moves across membranes in cells and vesicles, the volume enclosed within the membrane will change based on the direction of movement. In a cell, a rapid change in volume by osmosis can be catastrophic. Consider the liposomes illustrated in **Figure 6.14.** (Remember that osmosis occurs only when a solute cannot pass through a separating membrane.)

- ***Left*** If the solution outside the membrane has a higher concentration of solutes than the interior has, water moves out of the vesicle into the solution outside. The solution outside is said to be **hypertonic** relative to the inside of the vesicle. As water leaves, the vesicle shrinks and the membrane shrivels.

- ***Middle*** If the solution outside the membrane has a lower concentration of solutes than the interior has, water moves into the vesicle via osmosis. The outside solution is said to be **hypotonic** relative to the inside of the vesicle. The incoming water causes the vesicle to swell, or even burst.

- ***Right*** If solute concentrations are equal on both sides of the membrane, the liposome maintains its size. When the inside solution does not affect the membrane's shape, that solution is called **isotonic.**

Note that the terms "hypertonic," "hypotonic," and "isotonic" are used only in referring to the effect of water movement into or out of a membrane-enclosed structure, such as a vesicle or cell. Tonicity defines how these structures are affected by water transport, where "tone" (from the Greek root *tonos*, meaning "to stretch") is referring to the firmness of the structure.

For example, if a cell is placed within a hypertonic solution, then the inside solution would be hypotonic ("lower tone") because the firmness of the structure is reduced. The opposite is true for vesicles placed in hypotonic solutions, where the inside solution would be hypertonic ("excess tone") and cause the vesicle to swell.

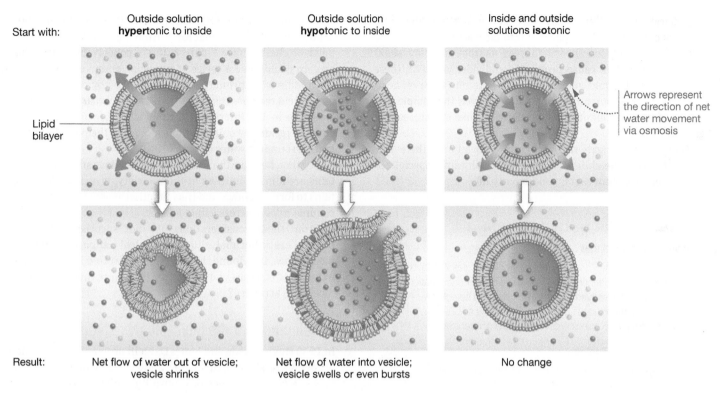

Start with:	Outside solution **hyper**tonic to inside	Outside solution **hypo**tonic to inside	Inside and outside solutions **iso**tonic

Arrows represent the direction of net water movement via osmosis

Lipid bilayer

Result:	Net flow of water out of vesicle; vesicle shrinks	Net flow of water into vesicle; vesicle swells or even bursts	No change

Figure 6.14 Osmosis Can Shrink or Burst Membrane-Bound Vesicles.

Membranes and Chemical Evolution

What do diffusion and osmosis have to do with the first membranes floating in the prebiotic soup? Both processes tend to *reduce* differences in chemical composition between the inside and outside of membrane-bound compartments.

If liposome-like structures first arose in the oceans of early Earth, their interiors probably didn't offer a radically different environment from the surrounding solution. In all likelihood, the primary importance of the first lipid bilayers was simply to provide a container for replicating RNA, the macromolecule most likely to have been the first "living" molecule (see Chapter 4). But ribonucleotide monomers would need to be available for these RNAs to replicate. Can negatively charged ribonucleotides get across lipid bilayers and inside lipid-bounded vesicles?

The answer is yes. Jack Szostak and colleagues first set out to study the permeability of membranes consisting of fatty acids and other simple amphipathic lipids thought to be present in the early oceans. Like phospholipids, fatty acids will assemble into lipid bilayers and water-filled vesicles. Their experiments showed that ions, and even ribonucleotides, can diffuse across the fatty acid vesicle membranes—meaning that monomers could have been available for RNA synthesis.

Lending support to this hypothesis, the same minerals found to catalyze the polymerization of RNA from activated nucleotides (see Chapter 4) will also promote the formation of fatty acid vesicles—and in the process, often end up on the inside along with RNA. Simple vesicle-like structures that harbor nucleic acids are referred to as **protocells** (Figure 6.15). Most origin-of-life researchers view protocells as possible intermediates in the evolution of the cell.

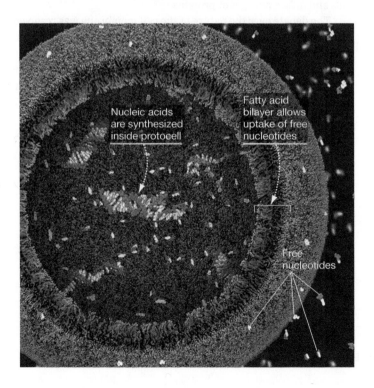

Nucleic acids are synthesized inside protocell

Fatty acid bilayer allows uptake of free nucleotides

Free nucleotides

Figure 6.15 Protocells May Have Had Simple, Permeable Membranes. This image shows a cross section of a computer model of a protocell. Like this model, the membranes of early cells may have been built of fatty acids. Passive transport of nucleotides across these membranes, as well as replication of nucleic acids inside, has been observed in the laboratory.

Laboratory simulations have also shown that free lipids and micelles can become incorporated into fatty acid bilayers, causing protocells to grow. Shearing forces, as from bubbling, shaking, or wave action, cause protocells to divide. Based on these observations, it is reasonable to hypothesize that once replicating RNAs became surrounded by a lipid bilayer, this simple life-form and its descendants would occupy cell-like structures that grew and divided.

Now let's investigate the next great innovation in the evolution of the cell: the ability to create and maintain a specialized internal environment that is conducive to life.

CHECK YOUR UNDERSTANDING

If you understand that ...

- Diffusion is the net movement of ions or molecules in solution from regions of high concentration to regions of low concentration.
- Osmosis is the movement of water across a selectively permeable membrane, from a region of low solute concentration to a region of high solute concentration.

✔ **You should be able to ...**

Make a concept map (see **BioSkills 12**) that includes the boxed terms water molecules, solute molecules, osmosis, diffusion, areas of high-to-low concentration, selectively permeable membranes, concentration gradients, hypertonic solutions, hypotonic solutions, and isotonic solutions.

Answers are available in Appendix A.

6.4 Proteins Alter Membrane Structure and Function

To be effective as a selective barrier, a plasma membrane needs to import ions and molecules necessary for life while excluding ions and molecules that might damage it. What sort of molecule could become incorporated into a lipid bilayer and affect the bilayer's permeability? The title of this section gives the answer away—proteins.

Proteins can be amphipathic because their monomers, amino acids, have side chains that range from highly nonpolar to highly polar or charged (see Figure 3.2). It's conceivable, then, that a protein could have a series of nonpolar amino acid residues in the middle of its primary structure flanked by polar or charged amino acid residues (**Figure 6.16a**). The nonpolar residues would be stable in the interior of a lipid bilayer, while the polar or charged residues would be stable alongside the polar lipid heads and surrounding water (**Figure 6.16b**).

Further, because the secondary and tertiary structures of proteins are almost limitless in their variety, it is possible for proteins to form openings and thus function as some sort of selective channel or pore across a lipid bilayer.

From these considerations, it's not surprising that when researchers began analyzing the chemical composition of plasma membranes, they found that proteins were often just as common, in terms of mass, as phospholipids. How were these two types of molecules arranged?

Development of the Fluid-Mosaic Model

In 1935 Hugh Davson and James Danielli proposed that cell membranes were structured like a sandwich in which hydrophilic proteins coat both sides of a pure lipid bilayer (**Figure 6.17a**). Early electron micrographs of plasma membranes seemed to be consistent with the sandwich model, and for decades it was widely accepted.

The realization that membrane proteins could be amphipathic, however, led S. Jon Singer and Garth Nicolson to suggest an alternative hypothesis. In 1972, they proposed that at least some proteins span the membrane instead of being found only outside the lipid bilayer. Their hypothesis was called the **fluid-mosaic model** (**Figure 6.17b**). Singer and Nicolson suggested that membranes are a dynamic and fluid mosaic of phospholipids and different types of proteins.

The debate over the nature of the cell membrane was resolved in the early 1970s with the development of an innovative technique for visualizing the surface of plasma membranes. The method is called freeze-fracture electron microscopy because the steps involve freezing and fracturing the membrane before

(a) Proteins can be amphipathic.

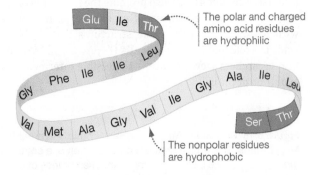

The polar and charged amino acid residues are hydrophilic

The nonpolar residues are hydrophobic

(b) Amphipathic proteins can integrate into lipid bilayers.

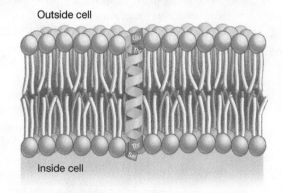

Outside cell

Inside cell

Figure 6.16 The Hydrophobic Region of an Amphipathic Protein Can Be Anchored into a Lipid Bilayer.

(a) Sandwich model

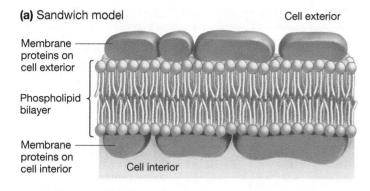

Cell exterior

Membrane proteins on cell exterior

Phospholipid bilayer

Membrane proteins on cell interior

Cell interior

(b) Fluid-mosaic model

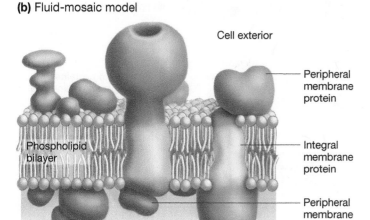

Cell exterior

Peripheral membrane protein

Phospholipid bilayer

Integral membrane protein

Peripheral membrane protein

Cell interior

Figure 6.17 Past and Current Models of Membrane Structure Differ in Where Membrane Proteins Reside. (a) The protein-lipid-lipid-protein sandwich model was the first hypothesis for the arrangement of lipids and proteins in cell membranes. **(b)** The fluid-mosaic model was a radical departure from the sandwich hypothesis.

examining it with a **scanning electron microscope (SEM),** which produces images of an object's surface (see BioSkills 9).

As Figure 6.18 shows, the freeze-fracture technique allows researchers to split cell membranes and view the middle of the structure. The scanning electron micrographs that result show pits and mounds studding the inner surfaces of the lipid bilayer. Researchers interpreted these structures as the locations of membrane proteins. As step 4 in the figure shows, the mounds represent proteins that remained attached to one side of the split lipid bilayer and the pits are the holes they left behind.

These observations conflicted with the sandwich model but were consistent with the fluid-mosaic model. Based on these and subsequent observations, the fluid-mosaic model is now widely accepted. This basic model of membrane structure has been expanded over the past 40 years as researchers have learned more about the organization and function of membrane lipids, proteins, and the carbohydrates that may be bound to them (see Chapters 5 and 7).

Notice in Figure 6.17b that some proteins span the membrane and have segments facing both the interior and the exterior of the cell. Proteins like these are called **integral membrane proteins,** or **transmembrane proteins.** Proteins that bind to

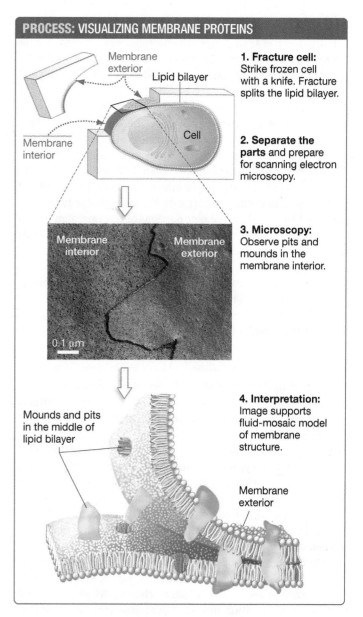

PROCESS: VISUALIZING MEMBRANE PROTEINS

Membrane exterior

Lipid bilayer

Membrane interior

Cell

1. Fracture cell: Strike frozen cell with a knife. Fracture splits the lipid bilayer.

2. Separate the parts and prepare for scanning electron microscopy.

Membrane interior

Membrane exterior

0.1 µm

3. Microscopy: Observe pits and mounds in the membrane interior.

Mounds and pits in the middle of lipid bilayer

4. Interpretation: Image supports fluid-mosaic model of membrane structure.

Membrane exterior

Figure 6.18 Freeze-Fracture Preparations Allow Biologists to View Membrane Proteins.

✔ **PROCESS OF SCIENCE** What would be an appropriate control to show that the pits and mounds were not simply irregularities in the lipid bilayer caused by the freeze-fracture process?

membrane lipids or integral membrane proteins without passing through it are called **peripheral membrane proteins.**

Certain peripheral membrane proteins are found only on the membrane surface facing the interior of the cell, while others are found only on the cell exterior. As a result, the interior and exterior surfaces of the plasma membrane are distinct—the peripheral membrane proteins and the ends of transmembrane proteins differ.

How do these proteins affect the permeability of membranes? The answer to this question starts with an investigation of the structure of proteins involved in the transport of molecules and ions across the plasma membrane.

Systems for Studying Membrane Proteins

The discovery of transmembrane proteins was consistent with the hypothesis that proteins affect membrane permeability. To test this hypothesis, researchers needed some way to isolate and purify membrane proteins.

Figure 6.19 outlines one method that researchers developed to separate proteins from membranes. The key to the technique is the use of detergents. A **detergent** is a small amphipathic molecule that can form micelles. However, unlike amphipathic lipids, detergents are water soluble. When detergents are added to the solution surrounding a lipid bilayer, the hydrophobic tails of the detergent molecule interact with the hydrophobic tails of the lipids and with the hydrophobic portions of transmembrane proteins. These interactions displace the membrane phospholipids and end up forming water-soluble detergent–protein complexes that can be isolated.

Since intensive experimentation on membrane proteins began, researchers have identified three broad classes of proteins that affect membrane permeability: channels, carriers, and pumps. Let's consider each class in turn.

Channel Proteins Facilitate Diffusion

As the data in Figure 6.8 showed, ions almost never cross pure phospholipid bilayers on their own. But in cells, ions routinely cross membranes by way of specialized transmembrane proteins called **ion channels.**

Ion channels form pores, or openings, in a membrane. Ions diffuse through these pores in a predictable direction: from regions of high concentration to regions of low concentration and from areas of like charge to areas of unlike charge.

In Figure 6.20, for example, a large concentration gradient across the membrane favors the movement of sodium ions from the region of higher sodium concentration to the region of lower sodium concentration. But in addition, the solution above the membrane has a net positive charge while the solution below the membrane has a net negative charge. When considered together, concentration and electrical gradients are called an **electrochemical gradient.**

In response to electrochemical gradients, ions will diffuse in a directional manner if an appropriate channel exists. For example, if a sodium ion channel were inserted into the membrane in Figure 6.20, the net movement of sodium ions would occur down the electrochemical gradient. At equilibrium, sodium ions would continue to move back and forth through the channel, but at equal rates.

✔ If you understand the basis of electrochemical gradients, you should be able to add another arrow to Figure 6.20 indicating the electrochemical gradient for chloride ions.

Is an Ion Channel Involved in Cystic Fibrosis? To understand the importance of ion channels, consider work on the cause of cystic fibrosis.

Cystic fibrosis (CF) is the most common genetic disease in humans of Northern European descent. It affects cells that produce mucus, sweat, and digestive juices. Normally these secretions are thin and slippery and act as lubricants. In individuals

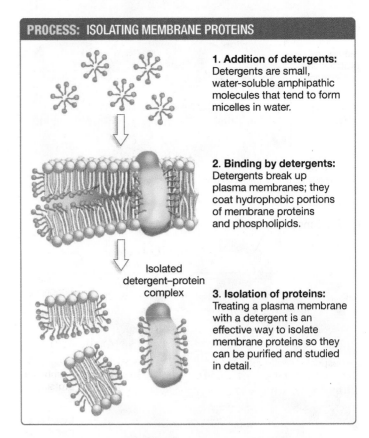

PROCESS: ISOLATING MEMBRANE PROTEINS

1. Addition of detergents: Detergents are small, water-soluble amphipathic molecules that tend to form micelles in water.

2. Binding by detergents: Detergents break up plasma membranes; they coat hydrophobic portions of membrane proteins and phospholipids.

Isolated detergent–protein complex

3. Isolation of proteins: Treating a plasma membrane with a detergent is an effective way to isolate membrane proteins so they can be purified and studied in detail.

Figure 6.19 **Detergents Can Be Used to Isolate Proteins from Membranes.**

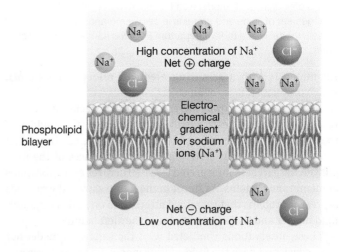

High concentration of Na⁺
Net ⊕ charge

Phospholipid bilayer

Electrochemical gradient for sodium ions (Na⁺)

Net ⊖ charge
Low concentration of Na⁺

Figure 6.20 **An Electrochemical Gradient Is a Combined Concentration and Electrical Gradient.** Electrochemical gradients are established when ions build up on one side of a membrane.

with CF, however, the secretions become abnormally concentrated and sticky, which can cause them to clog passageways in organs like the lungs.

Experiments published in 1983 suggested that cystic fibrosis is caused by defects in a transmembrane protein that allows passage of chloride ions (Cl^-). It was proposed that a reduced rate of chloride ion transport would account for the thick mucus.

How is the transport of chloride ions involved in mucus consistency? Water movement across cell membranes is largely determined by the presence of extracellular ions like chloride. If a defective channel prevents chloride ions from leaving cells, water isn't pulled from cells by osmosis to maintain the proper mucus consistency. In effect, the disease results from the mismanagement of osmosis.

Using molecular techniques introduced in Unit 3 (see Chapter 20), biologists were able to **(1)** find the gene that is defective in people suffering from CF and **(2)** isolate the gene from a healthy individual and use it to produce copies of the normal protein, which was called CFTR (short for cystic fibrosis transmembrane conductance regulator).

Is CFTR a chloride channel? To answer this question, researchers inserted purified CFTR into planar bilayers and measured the flow of electric current across the membrane. Because ions carry a charge, ion movement across a membrane produces an electric current.

The graphs in **Figure 6.21**, which plot the amount of current flowing across the membrane over time, show the results from this experiment. Notice that when CFTR was absent, no electric current passed through the membrane. But when CFTR was inserted into the membrane, current began to flow. This was strong evidence that CFTR was indeed a chloride ion channel.

Protein Structure Determines Channel Selectivity Subsequent research has shown that cells have many different types of pore-like **channel proteins** in their membranes. Some of these channel proteins are ion channels like CFTR, and others are channels for small polar molecules. A channel's pore is hydrophilic relative to the hydrophobic residues facing the hydrocarbon tails of the membrane.

Channel proteins are selective. Each channel protein has a structure that permits only a particular type of ion or small molecule to pass through it. For example, Peter Agre and co-workers discovered channels called **aquaporins** ("water-pores") that allow water to cross the plasma membrane but exclude other molecules and most ions. Although water can move across lipid bilayers without aquaporins, they are transported over 10 times faster when these channels are present. This increased rate of transport is particularly important for the absorption of water in your gastrointestinal tract.

Figure 6.22 on page 134 shows a cutaway view from the side of an aquaporin, indicating how it fits in a plasma membrane. Like other channels that have been studied in detail, aquaporins have a pore that is lined with polar functional groups that interact with water.

But how can aquaporin be selective for water and not other hydrophilic substances? The answer was found when researchers examined its structure. Key side chains in the interior of the pore

---

RESEARCH

QUESTION: Is CFTR a chloride channel?

HYPOTHESIS: CFTR increases the flow of chloride ions across a membrane.

NULL HYPOTHESIS: CFTR has no effect on membrane permeability.

EXPERIMENTAL SETUP:

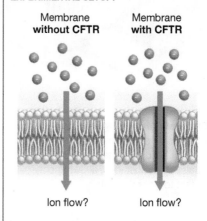

Membrane **without CFTR**

Membrane **with CFTR**

1. **Create planar bilayers** with and without CFTR.

2. **Add chloride ions** to one side of the planar bilayer to create an electrochemical gradient.

3. **Record electrical currents** to measure ion flow across the planar bilayers.

Ion flow?   Ion flow?

PREDICTION: Ion flow (current) will be higher in membrane with CFTR.

PREDICTION OF NULL HYPOTHESIS: Ion flow will be the same in both membranes.

RESULTS:

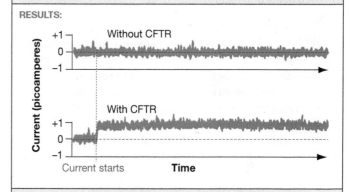

Current (picoamperes)

Without CFTR

With CFTR

Current starts   Time

CONCLUSION: CFTR facilitates diffusion of chloride ions along an electrochemical gradient. CFTR is a chloride channel.

Figure 6.21 Electric Current Measurements Indicate that Chloride Ions Flow through CFTR.

SOURCE: Bear, C. A., C. Li, N. Kartner, et al. (1992). Purification and functional reconstitution of the cystic fibrosis transmembrane conductance regulator (CFTR). *Cell* 68: 809–818.

✔ **PROCESS OF SCIENCE** The researchers repeated the "with CFTR" treatment 45 times, but recorded a current in only 35 of the replicates. Does this observation negate the conclusion? Explain why or why not.

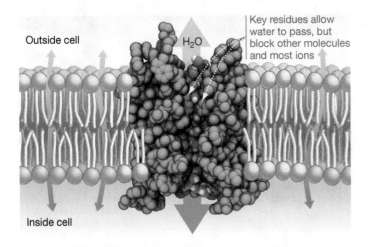

Figure 6.22 Membrane Channels Are Highly Selective.
A cutaway view looking at the inside of a membrane channel, aquaporin. The key residues identified in the space-filling model selectively filter other molecules and most ions, allowing only water (red and white structures) to pass through.

In figure: Outside cell / H₂O / Key residues allow water to pass, but block other molecules and most ions / Inside cell

function as a filter. The position of these groups across the channel allows only water molecules, which are capable of interacting with all of the functional groups in a precise manner, to pass through to the other side.

Movement through Many Membrane Channels Is Regulated

Recent research has shown that aquaporins and many ion channels are **gated channels**—meaning that they open or close in response to a signal, such as the binding of a particular substance or a change in the electrical voltage across the membrane.

As an example of how voltage-gated channels work, **Figure 6.23** shows a potassium channel in closed and open configurations. The electrical charge on the membrane is normally negative on the inside relative to the outside, which causes the channel to adopt a

closed shape that prevents potassium ions from passing through. When this charge asymmetry is reversed, the shape changes in a way that opens the channel and allows potassium ions to cross. The key point here is that in almost all cases, the flow of ions and small molecules through membrane channels is carefully controlled.

Whether gated or not, the movement of substances through channels is passive—meaning it does not require an input of energy. Channel proteins simply enable ions or small polar molecules to diffuse across lipid bilayers efficiently in response to an existing gradient. When transmembrane proteins assist the passive transport of substances that otherwise would not cross a membrane readily, the process is called **facilitated diffusion.**

Carrier Proteins Facilitate Diffusion

The movement of water and K^+ are examples of facilitated diffusion through channel proteins, but facilitated diffusion can also occur through specialized membrane proteins called **carrier proteins.**

The primary difference between channels and carrier proteins is the mechanism of transport. While channels allow movement through a selective pore, channel proteins undergo shape changes that selectively pick up a solute on one side of the membrane, then drop it off on the other side.

Perhaps the best-studied carrier protein is one that is involved in transporting glucose into cells.

The Search for a Glucose Carrier Next to ribose, the six-carbon sugar glucose is the most prevalent sugar found in organisms. Virtually all living organisms use glucose as a building block for important macromolecules and as a source of stored chemical energy (Chapter 5). But as Figure 6.8 shows, lipid bilayers are only moderately permeable to glucose. It is reasonable to expect, then, that plasma membranes have some mechanism for increasing their permeability to this sugar.

This prediction was supported in experiments on pure preparations of plasma membranes from human red blood cells. These

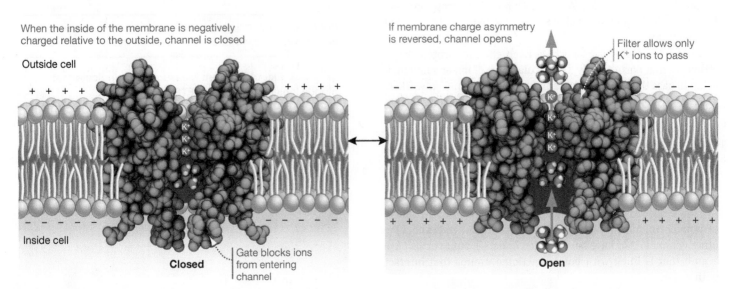

Figure 6.23 Some Membrane Channels Are Highly Regulated. A model of a voltage-gated K^+ channel in the closed and open configurations. The channel filter displaces water molecules that normally surround the K^+ ions in an aqueous solution.

In figure (left): When the inside of the membrane is negatively charged relative to the outside, channel is closed / Outside cell / Inside cell / **Closed** / Gate blocks ions from entering channel

In figure (right): If membrane charge asymmetry is reversed, channel opens / Filter allows only K^+ ions to pass / **Open**

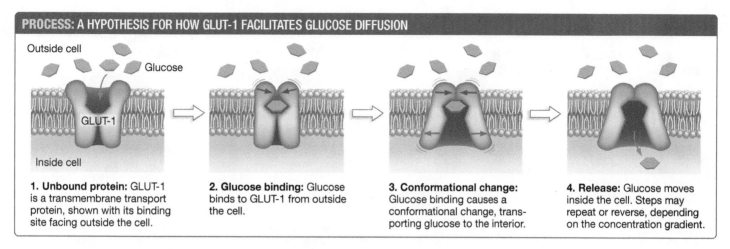

Outside cell

Glucose

GLUT-1

Inside cell

1. Unbound protein: GLUT-1 is a transmembrane transport protein, shown with its binding site facing outside the cell.

2. Glucose binding: Glucose binds to GLUT-1 from outside the cell.

3. Conformational change: Glucose binding causes a conformational change, transporting glucose to the interior.

4. Release: Glucose moves inside the cell. Steps may repeat or reverse, depending on the concentration gradient.

Figure 6.24 Carrier Proteins Move Substances via Structural Changes. This model shows that when GLUT-1 binds a glucose molecule, it undergoes a conformational change to move glucose across the membrane.

plasma membranes turned out to be much more permeable to glucose than are pure lipid bilayers. Why?

After isolating and analyzing many proteins from red blood cell membranes, researchers found one protein that specifically increases membrane permeability to glucose. When they added this purified protein to liposomes, the artificial membrane transported glucose at the same rate as a membrane from a living cell. This experiment convinced biologists that the membrane protein—now called GLUT-1 (short for glucose transporter 1)—was indeed responsible for transporting glucose across plasma membranes.

How Does GLUT-1 Work? Recall that proteins frequently change shape when they bind to other molecules and that such conformational changes are often a critical step in their function (see Chapter 3).

Figure 6.24 illustrates the current hypothesis for how GLUT-1 works to facilitate the movement of glucose. The idea is that when glucose binds to GLUT-1, it changes the shape of the protein in a way that moves the sugar through the hydrophobic region of the membrane and releases it on the other side.

What drives the movement of molecules through carriers? The answer is diffusion. GLUT-1 facilitates diffusion by allowing glucose to enter the carrier from either side of the membrane. Glucose will pass through the carrier in the direction dictated by its concentration gradient. A large variety of molecules move across plasma membranes via specific carrier proteins. To practice modeling the process of transport across a membrane, see **Making Models 6.1**.

Pumps Perform Active Transport

Diffusion—whether it is facilitated by proteins or not—is a passive process that moves substances in either direction across a membrane to make the cell interior and exterior environments more similar. But it is also possible for cells to move molecules or ions in a directed manner, often *against* an existing gradient. Accomplishing this task requires an input of energy to counteract the decrease in entropy that occurs when molecules or ions

Making Models 6.1 Tips on Drawing Membranes

Drawing models of membranes can help you understand membrane structure and transport, but the amount of detail you include depends on your goal. For example:

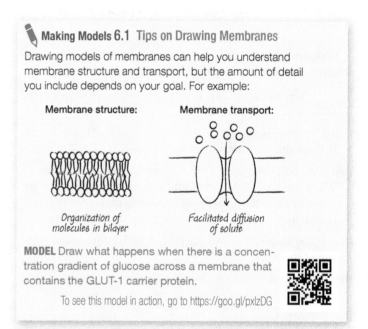

Membrane structure:

Membrane transport:

Organization of molecules in bilayer

Facilitated diffusion of solute

MODEL Draw what happens when there is a concentration gradient of glucose across a membrane that contains the GLUT-1 carrier protein.

To see this model in action, go to https://goo.gl/pxlzDG

are concentrated. It makes sense, then, that transport against a gradient is called **active transport.**

In cells, ATP (adenosine triphosphate) often provides the energy for active transport by transferring a phosphate group (HPO_4^{2-}) to an active transport protein called a **pump.** Recall that ATP contains three phosphate groups (Chapter 4), and that phosphate groups carry two negative charges (Chapter 2). When a phosphate group is transferred from ATP to a pump, its negative charges interact with charged amino acid residues in the protein pump. As a result, the pump's potential energy increases and its shape changes.

The Sodium–Potassium Pump A classic example of how structural changes can lead to active transport is provided in the **sodium–potassium pump,** or more formally, Na^+/K^+-ATPase. The Na^+/K^+ part of the name refers to the ions that are transported, ATP indicates that adenosine triphosphate is used, and —*ase* identifies the molecule as an enzyme.

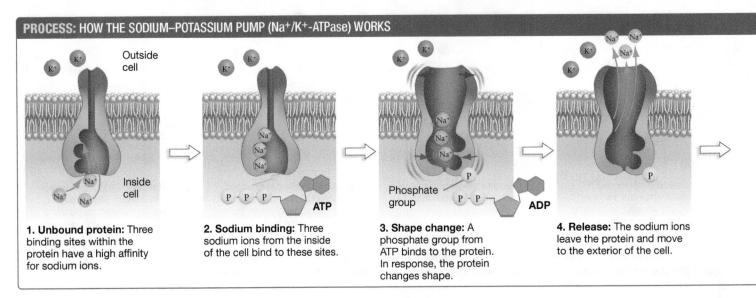

1. Unbound protein: Three binding sites within the protein have a high affinity for sodium ions.

2. Sodium binding: Three sodium ions from the inside of the cell bind to these sites.

3. Shape change: A phosphate group from ATP binds to the protein. In response, the protein changes shape.

4. Release: The sodium ions leave the protein and move to the exterior of the cell.

Figure 6.25 The Sodium–Potassium Pump Depends on an Input of Chemical Energy Stored in ATP.

As shown in **Figure 6.25**, sodium and potassium ions move in a multistep process:

Step 1 When Na+/K+-ATPase is in the conformation shown here, binding sites with a high affinity for sodium ions are available.

Step 2 Three sodium ions diffuse from the inside of the cell, bind to these sites, and activate the ATPase activity in the pump.

Step 3 A phosphate group from ATP is transferred to the pump. When the phosphate group attaches, the pump changes its shape in a way that opens the ion-binding pocket to the external environment and reduces its affinity for sodium ions.

Step 4 The sodium ions exit the protein and diffuse to the exterior of the cell.

Step 5 In this conformation, the pump has binding sites with a high affinity for potassium ions facing the external environment.

Step 6 Two potassium ions from outside the cell bind to the pump.

Step 7 When the potassium is bound, the phosphate group is cleaved from the protein and its structure changes in response—back to the original shape with the ion-binding pocket facing the interior of the cell.

Step 8 In this conformation, the pump has low affinity for potassium ions. The potassium ions exit the protein and diffuse into the interior of the cell. The cycle then repeats.

Other types of pumps move protons (H+), calcium ions (Ca2+), or other ions or molecules across membranes in a directed manner, regardless of the existing gradient. This is an important point. If the concentration gradient were to reverse, pumps would continue to use the same energy source to transport the solutes in the same direction, even if it is down the gradient.

As a result, cells can import and concentrate valuable nutrients and ions inside the cell despite their relatively low external concentration. They can also expel molecules or ions, even when a gradient favors diffusion of these substances into the cell.

Secondary Active Transport Approximately 30 percent of all the ATP generated in your body is used to drive the Na+/K+-ATPase cycle. With each cycle, three Na+ ions are exported for every two K+ ions imported. In this way, the outside of the membrane becomes positively charged relative to the inside. In other words, the sodium–potassium pump converts energy from ATP to an electrochemical gradient across the membrane that favors a flow of anions out of the cell and a flow of cations into the cell.

The electrochemical gradient established by Na+/K+-ATPase represents a form of stored energy, much like the electrical energy stored in a battery. Do cells use this energy?

Gradients are crucial to the function of the cell, in part because they make it possible for cells to engage in **secondary active transport**—also known as cotransport. When cotransport occurs, ATP is not directly used to power transport, but instead an ATP pump provides the energy in the form of a

---

CHECK YOUR UNDERSTANDING

If you understand that . . .

- Membrane proteins allow substances that ordinarily do not readily cross lipid bilayers to enter or exit cells.
- Substances may move across a membrane along a gradient, via facilitated diffusion through channel or carrier proteins. Or, they may move against a gradient through pumps or in combination with the cotransport of a substance along a gradient set up by a pump.

✔ You should be able to . . .

1. Explain what is passive about passive transport, active about active transport, and "co" about cotransport.
2. **MODEL** Draw a model to explain the process of secondary active transport of glucose. In this drawing, include the Na+/K+-ATPase and a Na+/glucose cotransporter, along with the relevant gradients across the membrane.

Answers are available in Appendix A.

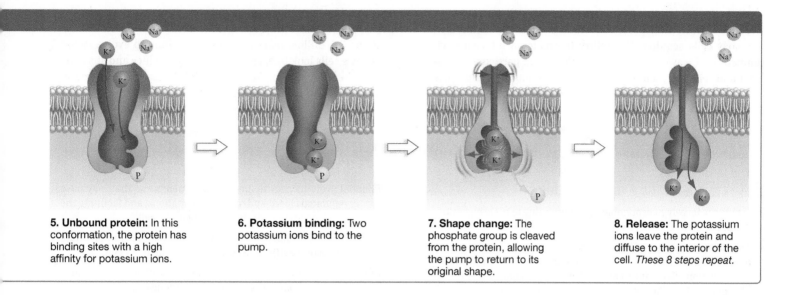

5. Unbound protein: In this conformation, the protein has binding sites with a high affinity for potassium ions.

6. Potassium binding: Two potassium ions bind to the pump.

7. Shape change: The phosphate group is cleaved from the protein, allowing the pump to return to its original shape.

8. Release: The potassium ions leave the protein and diffuse to the interior of the cell. *These 8 steps repeat.*

gradient that is used to power the movement of a different molecule against its particular gradient.

Recall that GLUT-1 facilitates the movement of glucose into or out of cells in the direction of its gradient. Can glucose be moved against its gradient? The answer is yes—a cotransport protein in your gut cells uses the Na^+ gradient created by Na^+/K^+-ATPases to import glucose against its chemical gradient. When Na^+ ions bind to this cotransporter, its shape changes in a way that allows glucose to bind. Once glucose binds, the cotransporter changes shape and transports both Na^+ ions and glucose to the inside of the cell. Note that in this case, Na^+ is moving down its gradient and the glucose is moving against its gradient. After dropping off Na^+ ions and glucose, the protein's original shape returns to repeat the cycle.

In this way, glucose present in the food you digest is actively transported into your body. The glucose molecules eventually diffuse into your bloodstream and are transported to your brain, where they provide the chemical energy you need to stay awake and learn some biology. (You will learn more about secondary active transport in Units 6 and 7.)

Plasma Membranes Define the Intracellular Environment

Taken together, the selective permeability of the lipid bilayer and the specificity of the proteins involved in passive transport and active transport enable cells to create an internal environment that is much different from the external one (**Figure 6.26**).

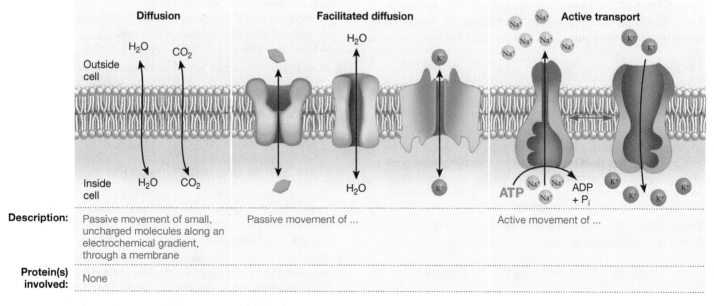

	Diffusion	Facilitated diffusion	Active transport
Description:	Passive movement of small, uncharged molecules along an electrochemical gradient, through a membrane	Passive movement of ...	Active movement of ...
Protein(s) involved:	None		

Figure 6.26 Summary of the Passive and Active Mechanisms of Membrane Transport.

✔ Complete the chart.

With the evolution of membrane proteins that either passively or actively transported substances across the membrane, the early cells acquired the ability to create an internal environment that was conducive to life. Cells with particularly efficient and selective membrane proteins that imported molecules required for manufacturing ATP and copying ribozymes would be favored by natural selection and would come to dominate the population. Cellular life had begun.

Some 3.5 billion years later, cells continue to evolve. What do today's cells look like, and how do they produce and store the chemical energy that makes life possible? Answering these and related questions is the focus of the following unit.

6.1 Lipid Structure and Function

- Lipids are largely hydrophobic compounds due to their high number of nonpolar C–H bonds.

- The three main types of lipids found in cells are fats, steroids, and phospholipids. These molecules vary considerably in structure and function. Fats store chemical energy; certain steroids and phospholipids are key components of cell membranes.

- In hydrocarbon chains, the length and degree of saturation have a profound effect on their physical properties.

- All lipids have a hydrophobic region, but amphipathic lipids also possess a distinct hydrophilic region containing polar or charged groups. Phospholipids have a polar or charged head and a nonpolar tail. The nonpolar tail usually consists of fatty acids or isoprenoids.

6.2 Phospholipid Bilayers

- In solution, phospholipids spontaneously assemble into bilayers that can serve as a physical barrier between an internal and external environment.

- Small nonpolar molecules tend to move directly across lipid bilayers readily; ions cross rarely, if at all.

- The permeability and fluidity of lipid bilayers depend on temperature, on the concentration of cholesterol, and on the chemical structure of the lipids present, such as the saturation status and length of the hydrocarbon chains. Phospholipids with longer or saturated tails form a dense and highly hydrophobic interior that lowers bilayer permeability, relative to phospholipids containing shorter or unsaturated tails.

6.3 How Molecules Move across Lipid Bilayers: Diffusion and Osmosis

- Diffusion is the random movement of ions or molecules owing to their thermal energy.

- If a membrane separates solutions that differ in concentration or charge, passive transport results in the net directional movement of solutes across the membrane that makes the environments on both sides of the membrane more similar. This is a spontaneous process driven by an increase in entropy.

- The diffusion of water across a membrane in response to a concentration gradient is called osmosis.

6.4 Proteins Alter Membrane Structure and Function

- The permeability of lipid bilayers can be altered significantly by membrane proteins.

- Channel proteins provide pores in the membrane that may have highly regulated closed and open conformations, and facilitate the diffusion of specific solutes into and out of the cell.

- Carrier proteins undergo conformational changes that facilitate the diffusion of specific molecules into and out of the cell.

- Pumps use energy to actively move ions or molecules in a single direction, often against the electrical or chemical gradient.

- In combination, the selective permeability of phospholipid bilayers and the specificity of transport proteins make it possible to create an environment inside a cell that is radically different from the exterior environment.

Answers are available in Appendix A

✔ TEST YOUR KNOWLEDGE

1. How do the phospholipids in archaea differ from those in other cells?
   a. They have tails made of unsaturated fatty acids instead of saturated fatty acids.
   b. They do not contain hydrocarbon chains.
   c. They have isoprenoid tails instead of fatty acid tails.
   d. They have two hydrocarbon chains instead of three hydrocarbon chains.

2. If a solution surrounding a cell is hypertonic relative to the inside of the cell, how will water move?
   a. It will move into the cell via osmosis.
   b. It will move out of the cell via osmosis.
   c. It will not move, because equilibrium exists.
   d. It will evaporate from the cell surface more rapidly.

3. What two conditions must be present for osmosis to occur?

4. Integral membrane proteins are anchored in lipid bilayers. Which of the following groups of amino acid residues (see Figure 3.2) would likely be found in the portion that crosses the lipid bilayer?
   a. acidic   c. polar uncharged
   b. basic   d. nonpolar

✔ TEST YOUR UNDERSTANDING

5. Cooking oil lipids consist of long, unsaturated hydrocarbon chains. Would you expect these molecules to form membranes spontaneously? Why or why not? Describe, on a molecular level, how you would expect these lipids to behave in water.

6. **MODEL** Draw and label the plasma membrane of a cell that is placed in a solution with concentrations of calcium ion and lactose that are greater than those on the inside of the cell. Use arrows to show the relevant gradients and the activity of the following membrane proteins: (1) a pump that exports protons; (2) a calcium channel; and (3) a lactose carrier.

7. In terms of structure, how do channel proteins differ from carrier proteins?

8. Suppose a cell is placed in a solution with a high concentration of potassium and no sodium. How would the cellular sodium–potassium pump function in this environment?
   a. It would stop moving ions across the membrane.
   b. It would continue using ATP to pump sodium out of the cell and potassium into the cell.
   c. It would move sodium and potassium ions across the membrane, but no ATP would be used.
   d. It would reverse the direction of sodium and potassium ions to move them against their gradients.

✔ TEST YOUR PROBLEM-SOLVING SKILLS

9. **PROCESS OF SCIENCE** In an experiment, you create two groups of liposomes in a solution containing 0.1 M NaCl—one made from red blood cell membranes and the other from frog egg cell membranes. When the liposomes are placed in water, those with red blood cell membranes burst more rapidly than those made from egg membranes. Evaluate each of the following statements and identify those that could explain these results.
   - **T/F** The red blood cell liposomes are more hypertonic relative to water than the frog egg liposomes.
   - **T/F** The red blood cell liposomes are more hypotonic relative to water than the frog egg liposomes.
   - **T/F** The red blood cell liposomes contain more aquaporins than the frog egg liposomes.
   - **T/F** The frog egg liposomes contain ion channels, which are not present in the red blood cell liposomes.

10. **QUANTITATIVE** Examine the experimental chamber in Figure 6.7a. If the lipid bilayer were to contain the CFTR molecule, what would pass through the membrane if you added a 1 M solution of sodium chloride on the left side and a 1.5 M solution of potassium ions on the right? Assume that there is an equal amount of water on each side at the start of the experiment.

✔ PUT IT ALL TOGETHER: Case Study

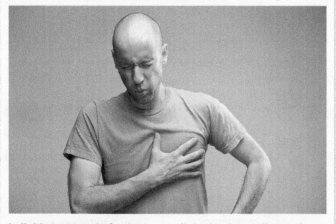

Is lipid structure in foods you eat linked to heart disease?

The media is full of advice on what you should and should not eat, but these recommendations often change from year to year. You may have heard that polyunsaturated fats are heart healthy and saturated fats are not, but is it really that simple?

11. How you prepare food can affect the amount of saturated fats that you eat. For example, if you cook meat on a grill, the product will have less saturated fat than if you were to eat the same meat raw. What occurs during the process of cooking the meat on a grill that would explain this result?

12. How is the chemical structure of saturated fats different from that of unsaturated fats? What physical property is often associated with these chemical differences?

13. An industrial process called hydrogenation is used to convert vegetable oil into a semisolid compound called margarine. Explain why hydrogenation is an appropriate term for this process.

14. A side effect of hydrogenation is that a small percentage of oil lipids retain their double bonds, but instead of causing kinks, they straighten out the hydrocarbon chain. These are called trans fats based on the configuration of the double bond (*cis* bonds generate kinks [see Figure 6.1b, right], but *trans* bonds do not). How do trans fats complicate the previous description of saturated and unsaturated fats?

15. **PROCESS OF SCIENCE** To study the effect of food on heart disease, researchers fed a variety of diets to mice and then examined them for atherosclerosis—the narrowing of arteries that is a leading cause of heart attacks. Data observed from mice fed with trans fats are provided below. Do these data identify the *cause* of atherosclerosis in the mice? Explain. (Note that "causation" means that one event is responsible for the occurrence of the other, while "correlation" means that the two events appear to occur together).

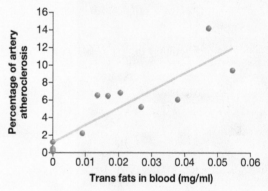

Source: C. M. C. Bassett, R. S. McCullough, A. L. Edel, et al. 2009. *Metabolism: Clinical and Experimental* 58: 1802–1808.

16. **SOCIETY** Recent studies on humans have shown that trans fats are correlated with heart disease while saturated fats are not. In addition to diet, what other factors should be evaluated before drawing conclusions on the health risk of trans fats?

MasteringBiology®

Students Go to MasteringBiology for assignments, the eText, and the Study Area with animations, practice tests, and activities.

Professors Go to MasteringBiology for automatically graded tutorials and questions that you can assign to your students, plus Instructor Resources.

THE BIG PICTURE

The first spark of life ignited when simple chemical reactions began to convert small molecules into larger, more complex molecules with novel 3-D structures and activities. According to the theory of chemical evolution, these reactions eventually led to the formation of the four types of macromolecules characteristic of life—proteins, nucleic acids, carbohydrates, and lipids.

As you look through this concept map, consider how the functions of the four types of macromolecules are determined by their structures, and how these structures stem from the chemical properties of the atoms and bonds used to build them.

Note that most boxes in the concept map indicate the chapters and sections where you can go for review. Also, be sure to do the blue exercises in the Check Your Understanding box below.

CHECK YOUR UNDERSTANDING

If you understand the big picture …

✔ You should be able to …

1. Explain how the relative electronegativities of atoms affect bonding within and among water molecules.
2. Describe the attributes of RNA that make it a candidate for the origin of life molecule. Why isn't DNA considered a viable candidate?
3. Circle the atoms in amino acids and nucleotides that engage in creating bonds that link monomers to form polymers.
4. Draw a protein in the lipid bilayer. What role might it play?

Answers are available in Appendix A.

THE CHEMISTRY OF LIFE

is based on the reactivity of

Atoms
- Carbon (C)
- Hydrogen (H) } 96% of atoms in living matter
- Oxygen (O)
- Nitrogen (N)
- Phosphorus (P)
- Sulfur (S)
- Others

2.1, 2.4

differ in

Electronegativity

$O > N > C \cong H$

Number of unpaired electrons:
- Hydrogen: 1
- Oxygen: 2
- Nitrogen: 3
- Carbon: 4

2.1

combine to form

Molecules 2.1   notably

have specific

3-D structure
- (may possess primary, secondary, tertiary, quaternary structure)

2.1, 3.1–3, 4.1–3, 5.1–2, 6.1

determines function

determine type and number of

influence

Polarity 2.1

affects

Molecular function
2.2, 3.1, 4.1, 5.1

depends on

Chemical bonds
- Nonpolar covalent bonds
- Polar covalent bonds
- Ionic bonds
- Hydrogen bonds

δ^- δ^+

2.1

including

formed and broken in

Chemical reactions 2.3

as demonstrated by

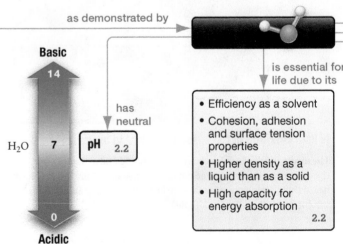

Basic
14

neutral

H_2O 7   **pH** 2.2

0
Acidic

has

is essential for life due to its

- Efficiency as a solvent
- Cohesion, adhesion and surface tension properties
- Higher density as a liquid than as a solid
- High capacity for energy absorption

2.2

Biological macromolecules

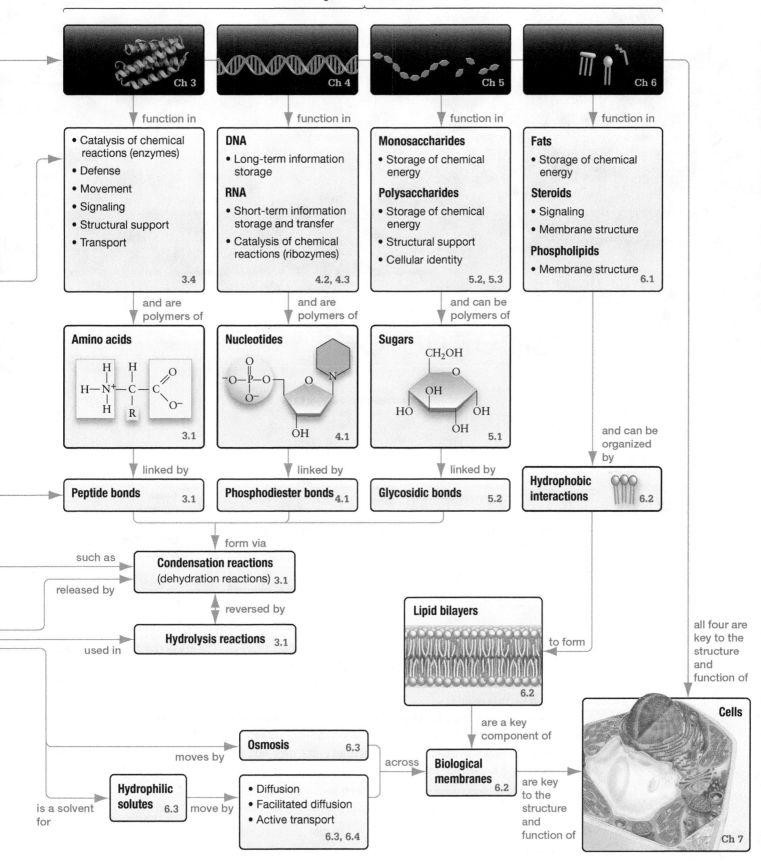

Ch 3 | Ch 4 | Ch 5 | Ch 6

function in

- Catalysis of chemical reactions (enzymes)
- Defense
- Movement
- Signaling
- Structural support
- Transport

3.4

function in

DNA
- Long-term information storage

RNA
- Short-term information storage and transfer
- Catalysis of chemical reactions (ribozymes)

4.2, 4.3

function in

Monosaccharides
- Storage of chemical energy

Polysaccharides
- Storage of chemical energy
- Structural support
- Cellular identity

5.2, 5.3

function in

Fats
- Storage of chemical energy

Steroids
- Signaling
- Membrane structure

Phospholipids
- Membrane structure

6.1

and are polymers of

Amino acids

3.1

and are polymers of

Nucleotides

4.1

and can be polymers of

Sugars

5.1

and can be organized by

linked by

Peptide bonds 3.1

linked by

Phosphodiester bonds 4.1

linked by

Glycosidic bonds 5.2

Hydrophobic interactions 6.2

form via

such as

Condensation reactions (dehydration reactions) 3.1

released by

reversed by

Hydrolysis reactions 3.1

used in

Lipid bilayers

6.2

to form

all four are key to the structure and function of

are a key component of

is a solvent for

Hydrophilic solutes 6.3

move by

Osmosis 6.3

moves by

- Diffusion
- Facilitated diffusion
- Active transport

6.3, 6.4

across

Biological membranes 6.2

are key to the structure and function of

Cells

Ch 7

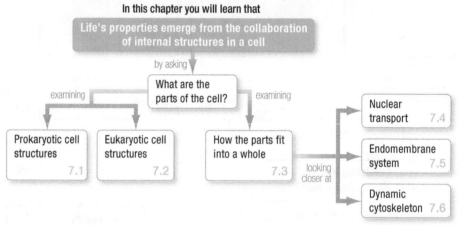

7 Inside the Cell

This cell has been treated with fluorescing molecules that bind to its fibrous cytoskeleton. Microtubules (large protein fibers) are yellow; actin filaments (smaller fibers) are blue. The cell's nucleus has been stained green.

In this chapter you will learn that

Life's properties emerge from the collaboration of internal structures in a cell

by asking ▼

What are the parts of the cell?

examining ◄   examining ►

| Prokaryotic cell structures 7.1 | Eukaryotic cell structures 7.2 | How the parts fit into a whole 7.3 |

looking closer at

Nuclear transport 7.4

Endomembrane system 7.5

Dynamic cytoskeleton 7.6

The cell theory states that all organisms consist of cells and all cells are derived from preexisting cells (Chapter 1). Since this theory was initially developed and tested in the 1850s, an enormous body of research has confirmed that the cell is the fundamental structural and functional unit of life. Life on Earth is cellular.

Previous chapters (Unit 1) delved into the fundamental attributes of life by looking at biologists' current understanding of how the cell evolved—from the early chemistry to the assembly and replication of a protocell. As the first cells left the hydrothermal vents, they took with them characteristics that are now shared among all known life-forms:

1. *proteins* that perform most of the cell's functions;

2. *nucleic acids* that store, transmit, and process information;

3. *carbohydrates* that provide chemical energy, carbon, support, and identity; and

4. a *plasma membrane*, which serves as a selectively permeable barrier.

Thanks to the selective permeability of phospholipid bilayers and the activity of membrane transport proteins, the plasma membrane creates an internal environment that differs from conditions outside the cell. Our task now is to explore the structures inside the cell to understand how the properties of life emerged from their collaboration.

Cells are divided into two fundamental types: eukaryotes and prokaryotes (see Chapter 1). This division is mostly based on cell **morphology** (meaning "form-science")—eukaryotic cells have a membrane-bound compartment called a nucleus, and prokaryotic cells do not.

But according to **phylogeny** (meaning "tribe-source"), or evolutionary history, organisms are divided into three broad domains called **(1)** Bacteria, **(2)** Archaea, and **(3)** Eukarya. Members of the Bacteria and Archaea are prokaryotic; members of the Eukarya—including algae, fungi, plants, and animals—are eukaryotic.

Let's begin by analyzing how the parts inside a cell function individually and then exploring how they work as a unit. This approach is analogous to studying individual organs in the body and then analyzing how they work together to form the nervous system or digestive system. As you study this material, keep asking yourself this key question: How does the structure of this part or group of parts correlate with its function?

7.1 Bacterial and Archaeal Cell Structures and Their Functions

For almost 200 years, biologists thought that prokaryotic cells were simple in terms of their morphology and that there was little structural diversity among species. This conclusion was valid at the time, given the resolution of the microscopes that were available and the number of species that had been studied. Recent improvements in microscopy and other research tools, however, have dramatically changed our view of prokaryotes.

A Revolutionary New View

Biologists are now convinced that prokaryotic cells, among which bacteria are the best understood, possess an array of distinctive structures and functions found among millions of species. This conclusion represents one of the most exciting discoveries in cell biology over the past two decades.

To start with the basics, **Figure 7.1** offers a low-magnification electron micrograph and a stripped-down diagram of a prokaryotic cell. This electron micrograph, along with others shown in this chapter, was generated using a transmission electron microscope (see BioSkills 9).

Prokaryotic Cell Structures: A Parts List

The labels in Figure 7.1 highlight the components common to most prokaryotes studied to date. Let's explore these parts one by one, starting from the inside and working out, and then look at more specialized structures found in particular species.

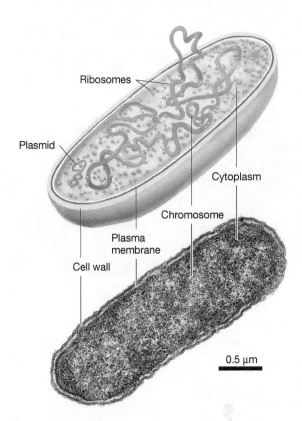

Figure 7.1 **Overview of a Prokaryotic Cell.** Prokaryotic cells are identified by a negative trait—the absence of a membrane-bound nucleus. Although there is wide variation in the size and shape of bacterial and archaeal cells, they all contain a plasma membrane, a chromosome, and protein-synthesizing ribosomes.

The Chromosome Is Organized in a Nucleoid The most prominent structure inside a prokaryotic cell is the **chromosome**, although it is often difficult to visualize by electron microscopy. Most bacterial and archaeal species have a single, circular chromosome that consists of a large DNA molecule associated with proteins. The DNA molecule contains information, and the proteins provide structural support for the DNA.

Recall that the information in DNA is encoded in its sequence of nitrogenous bases. Segments of DNA that contain information for building functional RNAs, some of which may be used to make polypeptides, are called **genes** (Chapter 4). Thus, chromosomes contain DNA, which contains genes.

In the well-studied bacterium *Escherichia coli*, the circular chromosome would be over 1 mm long if it were linear—500 times longer than the cell itself (see **Figure 7.2a** on page 144). This situation is typical in prokaryotes. To fit into the cell, the DNA double helix coils on itself with the aid of enzymes to form a compact, "supercoiled" structure. Supercoiled regions of DNA resemble a rubber band that has been held at either end and then twisted until it coils back upon itself (see Chapter 4).

The region of the cell where the circular chromosome is located is called the **nucleoid** (pronounced *NEW-klee-oyd*). The genetic material in the nucleoid is often organized by clustering loops of DNA into distinct domains, but it is not separated from the rest of the cell interior by a membrane. There is currently intense research into the functional role of this chromosomal organization and how it changes over time.

(a) Compared to the cell, chromosomal DNA is very long.

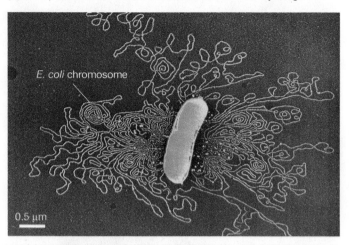

E. coli chromosome

0.5 μm

(b) DNA is packaged by supercoiling.

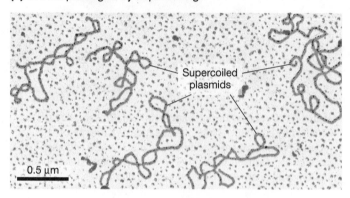

Supercoiled plasmids

0.5 μm

Figure 7.2 Prokaryotic DNA Is Supercoiled. (a) Chromosomes of bacteria and archaea are often over 500 times the length of the cell, as shown in this micrograph of *E. coli* that has been treated to release its DNA. To fit inside cells, this DNA must be highly compacted by supercoiling. **(b)** A colorized electron micrograph showing the effect of supercoiling on the DNA of isolated plasmids (colored green).

In addition to their chromosomes, prokaryotic cells may contain from one to about a hundred small, usually circular, supercoiled DNA molecules called **plasmids** (**Figure 7.2b**). Plasmids contain genes but are physically independent of the cellular chromosome. In many cases the genes carried by plasmids are not required under normal conditions; instead, they help cells adapt to unusual circumstances, such as the sudden presence of a poison in the environment. As a result, plasmids can be considered auxiliary genetic elements.

Ribosomes Manufacture Proteins **Ribosomes** are observed in all prokaryotic cells and are found throughout the cell interior. It is not unusual for a single cell to contain 10,000 ribosomes, each functioning as a protein-manufacturing center.

Ribosomes are complex structures composed of large and small subunits, each of which contains RNA and protein molecules. Biologists often refer to ribosomes, along with other multicomponent complexes that perform specialized tasks, as "macromolecular machines." (Chapter 17 analyzes the structure

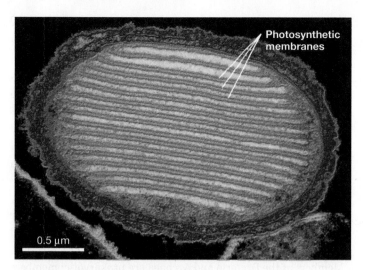

Photosynthetic membranes

0.5 μm

Figure 7.3 Photosynthetic Membranes in Bacteria. The green stripes in this photosynthetic bacterium are membranes that contain the pigments and enzymes required for photosynthesis. This photo has been colorized to enhance the membranes.

and function of ribosomes in detail.) While the ribosomes in bacteria and archaea are similar in size and function, the primary structures of the RNA and protein components are different.

Photosynthetic Species Have Internal Membrane Complexes In addition to the nucleoid and ribosomes found in all bacteria and archaea studied to date, it is common to observe extensive internal membranes in bacteria that perform photosynthesis. Photosynthesis is the set of chemical reactions responsible for converting the energy in sunlight into chemical energy stored in sugars. The photosynthetic membranes observed in bacteria develop as infoldings of the plasma membrane and contain the enzymes and pigment molecules required for these reactions to occur.

In some cases, vesicles pinch off as the plasma membrane folds in. In other cases, flattened stacks of photosynthetic membrane remain connected to the plasma membrane, like those shown in **Figure 7.3**. The extensive surface area provided by these internal membranes makes it possible for more photosynthetic reactions to occur and thus increases the cell's ability to make food.

Organelles Perform Specialized Functions Recent research indicates that several bacterial species have internal compartments that qualify as **organelles** (literally, "little organs"). An organelle is a membrane-bound compartment inside the cell that contains enzymes or structures specialized for a particular function.

Bacterial organelles perform specialized tasks, including

- storing calcium ions;

- holding crystals of the mineral magnetite, which function like a compass needle to help cells swim in a directed way; and

- organizing enzymes responsible for synthesizing complex carbon compounds from carbon dioxide.

The Cytoskeleton Structures the Cell Interior Researchers have also observed long, thin fibers in bacteria and archaea that serve a variety of roles inside the cell. All bacterial species, for example, contain protein fibers that are essential for cell division to take place. Some species also have protein filaments that help maintain cell shape. Protein filaments such as these form the basis of the **cytoskeleton** ("cell skeleton").

Current research has revealed a much more complex cytoskeletal network in prokaryotes than previously thought. Researchers are working to identify how these different filaments participate in cell morphology, growth, and division. (For more information about how the cytoskeleton participates in bacterial cell division, see Chapter 12.)

The Plasma Membrane Separates Life from Nonlife

The plasma membrane consists of a phospholipid bilayer and proteins that either span the bilayer or attach to one side. Inside the membrane, all the contents of a cell (excluding the nucleus in eukaryotes) are collectively termed the **cytoplasm** ("cell-formed").

The plasma membranes in archaea and bacteria share a common function—to create an internal environment that is distinct from the outside, nonliving environment. The combined effect of a lipid bilayer and membrane proteins prohibits the entry of many substances that would be dangerous to life while allowing the passage of molecules and ions required for life (see Chapter 6).

The phospholipid components of archaeal and bacterial membranes differ in their structure, however. Bacterial phospholipids consist of fatty acids bound to glycerol while archaeal phospholipids use highly branched isoprenoid chains bound to glycerol (see Chapter 6). These molecules also vary in the types of linkages used to form the phospholipids and the length of the hydrocarbon chains. A functional consequence of the archaeal membrane structure is that it is more stable in the extreme environments that are inhabited by certain species within this domain (see Chapter 26).

The Cell Wall Forms a Protective "Exoskeleton"

Because the cytoplasm contains a high concentration of solutes, it is hypertonic relative to the surrounding environment in most habitats. Under these conditions, water enters the cell via osmosis and makes the cell's volume expand. In most bacteria and archaea, this pressure is resisted by a stiff **cell wall.**

Bacterial and archaeal cell walls are a tough, fibrous layer that surrounds the plasma membrane. This structure protects the organisms and gives them shape and rigidity, much like the exoskeleton (external skeleton) of a crab or insect. In prokaryotes, the osmotic pressure that pushes the plasma membrane against the cell wall has a force similar to the pressure in an automobile tire.

The molecular structure of prokaryotic cell walls differs between bacteria and archaea. In most bacteria, peptidoglycan is the primary structural component of the cell wall, and some also include an outer membrane that consists of glycolipids. The cell walls of archaea are highly variable among the different species, but peptidoglycan is markedly absent among those studied to date.

External Structures Enable Movement and Attachment

Besides having a cell wall to provide protection, as just described, many prokaryotes also interact with their environment via structures that grow from the plasma membrane. The flagella and fimbriae

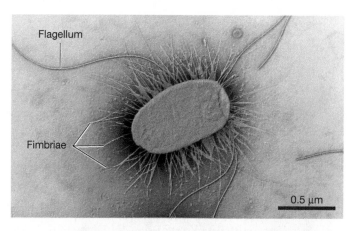

Figure 7.4 Extracellular Appendages Found on Prokaryotes. Some species of bacteria and archaea, such as the *E. coli* bacterial cell shown here, assemble large protein structures used for swimming through liquid (flagella) or adhering to surfaces (fimbriae).

shown in **Figure 7.4** are examples that are commonly found on bacterial surfaces. Archaea also have flagella and appendages similar to fimbriae, but they are structurally distinct from those found on bacteria.

A prokaryotic **flagellum** (plural: **flagella**) is assembled from many different proteins at the cell surface of certain species. The feature that is common to both archaeal and bacterial flagella is a molecular motor embedded in the plasma membrane. The proteins that comprise these motors and filaments differ between the two groups, but their functions are the same—to rotate a long rigid filament to propel the cell through water. At top speed, flagellar movement can drive a bacterial cell through water at 60 cell lengths per second. In contrast, the fastest animal in the ocean—the sailfish—can swim at a mere 10 body lengths per second.

A **fimbria** (plural: **fimbriae**) is a needlelike projection that extends from the plasma membrane of some bacteria and promotes attachment to other cells or surfaces. Similar, but unrelated structures are also found in archaea. These structures tend to be more numerous than flagella and may be distributed over the entire surface of the cell. Fimbriae are not involved in cell motility, but they are crucial to the establishment of many infections based on their ability to glue bacteria to the surface of tissues.

The painting in **Figure 7.5** on page 146 shows a cross section of a bacterial cell and provides a close-up view of the internal and external structures introduced in this section. One feature that prokaryotic and eukaryotic cells have in common: They are both packed with lively, highly integrated structures.

CHECK YOUR UNDERSTANDING

If you understand that ...

- Each structure in a prokaryotic cell performs a function vital to the cell.

✔ **You should be able to ...**

Describe the structure and function of the (1) ribosomes, (2) photosynthetic membranes, (3) flagella, and (4) cell wall.

Answers are available in Appendix A.

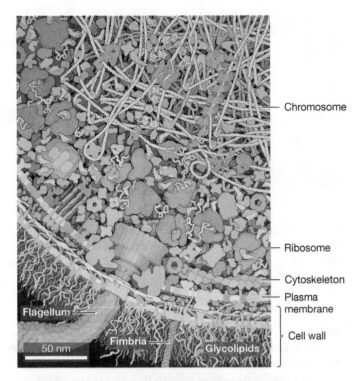

Chromosome

Ribosome

Cytoskeleton

Plasma membrane

Flagellum

Cell wall

Fimbria

Glycolipids

50 nm

Figure 7.5 Close-up View of a Prokaryotic Cell. This painting is David Goodsell's representation of a cross section through part of a bacterial cell. It is based on electron micrographs of bacterial cells and is drawn to scale. Note that the cell is packed with proteins, DNA, ribosomes, and other molecular machinery.

7.2 Eukaryotic Cell Structures and Their Functions

The Eukarya domain includes species that range from microscopic algae to 100-meter-tall redwood trees. Protists, fungi, plants, and animals are all eukaryotic. Although multicellularity has evolved several times among eukaryotes (see Chapter 27), many species are unicellular.

The first thing that strikes biologists about eukaryotic cells is how much larger they are on average than bacteria and archaea. Most prokaryotic cells measure 1 to 10 µm in diameter, while most eukaryotic cells range from about 5 to 100 µm in diameter. A micrograph of an average eukaryotic cell, at the same scale as the bacterial cell in Figure 7.3, would fill this page. For many species of unicellular eukaryotes, this size difference allows them to make a living by ingesting bacteria and archaea whole.

Large size has a downside, however. As a cell increases in diameter, its volume increases more than its surface area. In other words, the relationship between them—the surface-area-to-volume ratio—changes. (To see how plants and animals are affected by the surface-area-to-volume ratio, see Chapters 34 and 39.) Since the surface is where the cell exchanges substances with its environment, the reduction in this ratio decreases the rate of exchange: Diffusion only allows for rapid movement across very small distances.

Prokaryotic cells tend to be small enough so that ions and small molecules arrive where they are needed via diffusion.

The random movement of diffusion alone, however, is insufficient for this type of transport as the cell's diameter increases.

The Benefits of Organelles

How are the problems associated with a low surface-area-to-volume ratio overcome in eukaryotic cells? The answer lies in their numerous organelles. In effect, the huge volume inside a eukaryotic cell is compartmentalized into many small bins. Because eukaryotic cells are subdivided, the **cytosol**—the fluid portion between the plasma membrane and these organelles—is only a fraction of the total cell volume. This relatively small volume of cytosol offsets the effects of a low cell surface-area-to-volume ratio with respect to the exchange of nutrients and waste products.

Compartmentalization also offers two key advantages:

1. Incompatible chemical reactions can be separated. For example, new fatty acids can be synthesized in one organelle while excess or damaged fatty acids are degraded and recycled in a different organelle.

2. Chemical reactions become more efficient. First, the substrates required for particular reactions can be localized and maintained at high concentrations within organelles. When substrates are used up in a particular part of the organelle, they can be replaced by substrates that have only a short distance to diffuse. Second, groups of enzymes that work together can be clustered within or on the membranes of organelles instead of floating free in the cytosol. When the product of one reaction is the substrate for a second reaction, clustering the two enzymes increases the speed and efficiency of both reactions.

If bacterial and archaeal cells can be compared to specialized machine shops, then eukaryotic cells resemble sprawling industrial complexes. The organelles and other structures found in eukaryotes are like highly specialized buildings that act as administrative centers, factories, transportation corridors, waste and recycling facilities, warehouses, and power stations.

When typical prokaryotic and eukaryotic cells are compared, three key differences stand out:

1. Eukaryotic cells are generally much larger than prokaryotic cells.

2. Prokaryotic chromosomes are in a loosely defined nucleoid region while eukaryotic chromosomes are enclosed within a membrane-bound compartment called the **nucleus.**

3. The cytoplasm of eukaryotic cells is compartmentalized into a larger number of distinct organelles compared to the cytoplasm in prokaryotic cells.

Eukaryotic Cell Structures: A Parts List

Figure 7.6 provides a simplified view of a typical animal cell and a plant cell. The artist has removed most of the cytoskeletal elements to make the organelles and other cellular parts easier to see. As you read about each cell component in the pages that follow, focus on identifying how its structure correlates with its function. Then use Table 7.1 on page 153 as a study guide. As with bacterial cells, let's start from the inside and move to the outside.

(a) Generalized animal cell

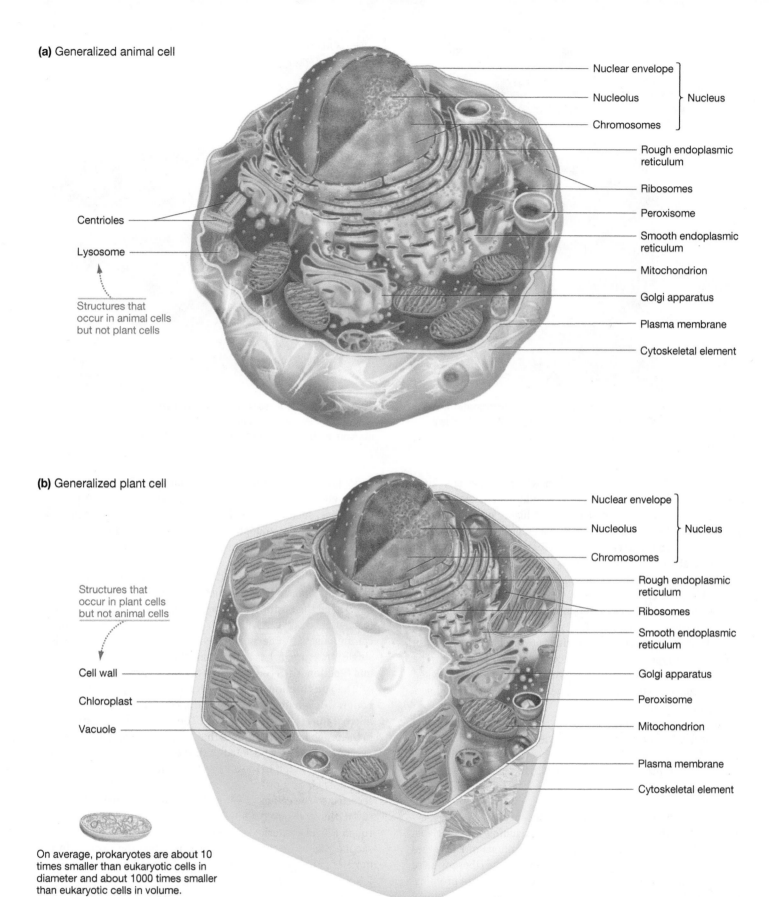

Nuclear envelope ⎤
Nucleolus   ⎬ Nucleus
Chromosomes   ⎦

Rough endoplasmic reticulum

Ribosomes

Peroxisome

Smooth endoplasmic reticulum

Mitochondrion

Golgi apparatus

Plasma membrane

Cytoskeletal element

Centrioles

Lysosome

Structures that occur in animal cells but not plant cells

(b) Generalized plant cell

Nuclear envelope ⎤
Nucleolus   ⎬ Nucleus
Chromosomes   ⎦

Rough endoplasmic reticulum

Ribosomes

Smooth endoplasmic reticulum

Golgi apparatus

Peroxisome

Mitochondrion

Plasma membrane

Cytoskeletal element

Structures that occur in plant cells but not animal cells

Cell wall

Chloroplast

Vacuole

On average, prokaryotes are about 10 times smaller than eukaryotic cells in diameter and about 1000 times smaller than eukaryotic cells in volume.

Figure 7.6 Overview of Eukaryotic Cells. Generalized images of **(a)** an animal and **(b)** a plant cell that illustrate the cellular structures in the "typical" eukaryote. The structures have been color-coded for clarity. Compare with the prokaryotic cell, shown at true relative size at bottom left.

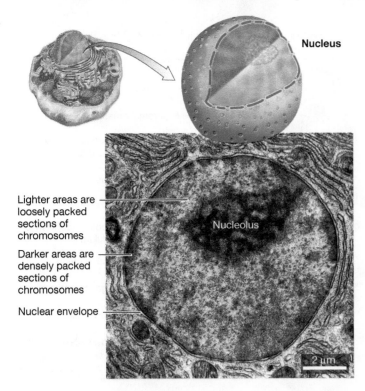

Nucleus

Lighter areas are loosely packed sections of chromosomes

Darker areas are densely packed sections of chromosomes

Nuclear envelope

Nucleolus

2 μm

Figure 7.7 The Nucleus Stores and Transmits Information. The genetic, or hereditary, information is encoded in DNA, which is a component of the chromosomes inside the nucleus.

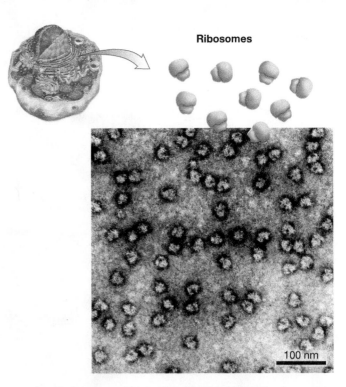

Ribosomes

100 nm

Figure 7.8 Ribosomes Are the Site of Protein Synthesis. Eukaryotic ribosomes are larger than bacterial and archaeal ribosomes, but similar in overall structure and function.

The Nucleus The nucleus contains the chromosomes and functions as an administrative center for information storage and processing. Among the largest and most highly organized of all organelles (Figure 7.7), it is enclosed by a unique structure—a complex double membrane called the **nuclear envelope.** As Section 7.4 will detail, the nuclear envelope is studded with pore-like openings, and the inside surface is linked to fibrous proteins that form a lattice-like sheet called the **nuclear lamina.** The nuclear lamina stiffens the membrane and maintains organelle shape.

Chromosomes do not float freely inside the nucleus—instead, each chromosome occupies a distinct area, which may vary in different cell types and over the course of cell replication. The chromosomes are arranged in the nucleus with densely packed sections concentrated at the periphery and loosely packed sections toward the interior.

The nucleus also contains specific sites where gene products are processed and includes at least one distinctive region called the **nucleolus,** where the RNA molecules found in ribosomes are manufactured and the large and small ribosomal subunits are assembled.

Ribosomes In eukaryotes, the cytoplasm consists of everything inside the plasma membrane excluding the nucleus. Scattered throughout this cytoplasm are millions of ribosomes (Figure 7.8). Like bacterial ribosomes, eukaryotic ribosomes are complex macromolecular machines that manufacture proteins. Note that ribosomes are not surrounded by membranes, so they are not classified as organelles.

Eukaryotic ribosomes are not only scattered free in the cytosol, but are also associated with an organelle called the endoplasmic reticulum. Proteins manufactured by free ribosomes either remain in the cytosol or are imported into other organelles, such as the nucleus (see Section 7.4). Those made at the surface of the endoplasmic reticulum have a different fate. Let's take a closer look at this organelle to learn more.

Endoplasmic Reticulum Portions of the nuclear envelope extend into the cytoplasm to form an extensive membrane-enclosed factory called the **endoplasmic reticulum (ER)** (literally, "inside-formed-network"). As Figure 7.6 shows, the ER membrane is continuous with the nuclear envelope. Although the ER is a single structure, it has two regions that are distinct in structure and function. Let's consider each region in turn.

The **rough endoplasmic reticulum (RER),** or more simply **rough ER,** is named for its appearance in transmission electron micrographs (see Figure 7.9, left). The knobby-looking structures in the rough ER are ribosomes that are attached to the membrane.

The ribosomes associated with the rough ER synthesize proteins that function in the ER or will be shipped to another destination, such as a different organelle, the plasma membrane, or secreted to the cell exterior. As the proteins are being manufactured, they move to the interior of the sac-like component of the rough ER. The interior of the rough ER, like the interior of any sac-like structure in a cell or body, is called the **lumen.** In the lumen of the rough ER, newly manufactured proteins undergo folding and other types of processing.

The proteins produced in the rough ER play a variety of roles for the cell. Some carry messages to other cells; some act as membrane transport proteins or pumps; others catalyze reactions. The common theme is that many of the rough ER products are packaged

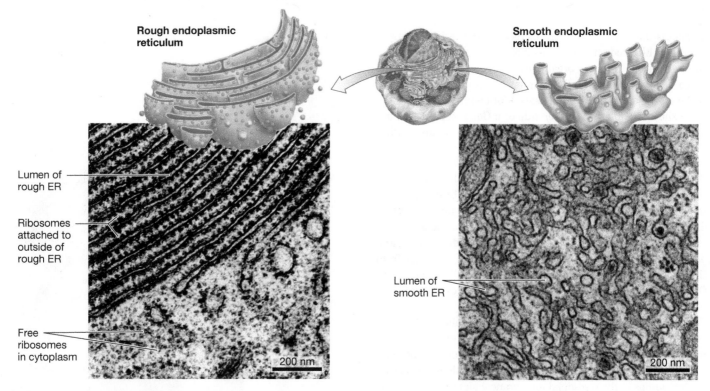

Figure 7.9 **The Endoplasmic Reticulum Is a Site of Synthesis, Processing, and Storage.** The ER is continuous with the nuclear envelope and possesses two distinct regions: on the left, the rough ER is a system of membrane-bound sacs and tubules with ribosomes attached; on the right, the smooth ER is a system of membrane-bound sacs and tubules that lacks ribosomes.

into vesicles and transported to various distant destinations—often to the surface of the cell or beyond (see Section 7.5).

In electron micrographs, parts of the ER that are free of ribosomes appear smooth and even. Appropriately, these parts of the ER are called the **smooth endoplasmic reticulum (SER),** or **smooth ER** (see Figure 7.9, right).

The smooth ER contains enzymes that catalyze reactions involving lipids. Depending on the type of cell, these enzymes may synthesize lipids needed by the organism or break down lipids and other molecules that are poisonous. For example, the smooth ER is the manufacturing site for phospholipids used in membranes. In addition, the smooth ER functions as a reservoir for calcium ions (Ca^{2+}) that can be released to trigger a wide array of activities inside the cell.

The structure of the endoplasmic reticulum correlates closely with its function. The rough ER has ribosomes and functions primarily as a protein-manufacturing center; the smooth ER lacks ribosomes and functions primarily as a lipid-processing center.

Golgi Apparatus   In most cases, the proteins that leave the rough ER must first pass through the **Golgi apparatus** before they reach their final destination. In most eukaryotes, the Golgi apparatus consists of dozens of stacks of discrete flattened, membranous sacs called **cisternae** (singular: **cisterna**), which are stacked on top of each other like pancakes (**Figure 7.10**). When the cisternae are stacked in this way, the Golgi apparatus has a distinct polarity or sidedness. The *cis* ("on this side") surface is closest to the nucleus, and the *trans* ("across") surface is oriented toward the plasma membrane.

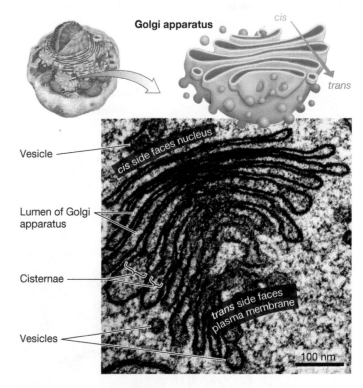

Figure 7.10 **The Golgi Apparatus Is a Site of Protein Processing, Sorting, and Shipping.** The Golgi apparatus is a collection of flattened sacs called cisternae.

The *cis* side of a Golgi apparatus receives the vesicles containing rough ER products, referred to as cargo, and the *trans* side ships them out to other organelles or the cell surface. As the cargo moves through the Golgi apparatus from the *cis* to *trans* surfaces, it is processed and packaged for delivery. Micrographs often show "bubbles" on either side of a Golgi stack. These are membrane-bound transport vesicles that carry proteins or other products to and from the organelle.

Lysosomes   Animal cells contain organelles called **lysosomes** that function as recycling centers (**Figure 7.11**). Lysosomes contain about 40 different enzymes, each specialized for hydrolyzing different types of macromolecules—proteins, nucleic acids, lipids, or carbohydrates. The amino acids, nucleotides, sugars, and other molecules that result from hydrolysis are exported from the lysosome via transport proteins in the organelle's membrane. Once in the cytosol, they can be used as sources of energy or building blocks for new molecules.

The digestive enzymes inside lysosomes are collectively called acid hydrolases because under acidic conditions (pH of 5.0), they use water to break monomers from macromolecules. In the cytosol, where the pH is about 7.2, acid hydrolases would be less active. Proton pumps in the lysosomal membrane maintain an acidic pH in the lumen of the lysosome by importing hydrogen ions.

Even though lysosomes are physically separated from the Golgi apparatus and the endoplasmic reticulum, these various organelles jointly form a key functional grouping referred to as the **endomembrane system.** The endomembrane ("inner-membrane") system is a center for producing, processing, and transporting proteins and lipids in eukaryotic cells. For example,

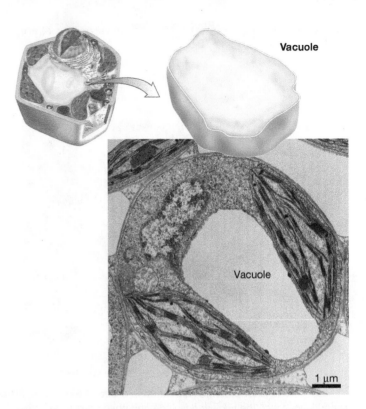

Figure 7.12 Vacuoles Are Generally Storage Centers in Plant and Fungal Cells. Vacuoles vary in size and function. Some contain digestive enzymes and serve as recycling centers; most are large storage containers.

✔ Propose a hypothesis to explain why toxins like nicotine, cocaine, and caffeine are stored in vacuoles instead of the cytosol.

acid hydrolases are synthesized in the ER, processed in the Golgi apparatus, and then shipped to the lysosome. Section 7.5 analyzes the intracellular movement of molecules through the endomembrane system in more detail.

Vacuoles   The cells of plants, fungi, and certain other groups lack lysosomes. Instead, they contain a prominent organelle called a vacuole. Compared with the lysosomes of animal cells, the **vacuoles** of plant and fungal cells are large—in plants, sometimes taking up as much as 80 percent of a cell's volume (**Figure 7.12**).

Although some vacuoles contain hydrolases and play a similar role to the lysosome of animal cells, most of the vacuoles in plant and fungal cells act as storage depots. In many cases, ions such as potassium (K^+) and chloride (Cl^-), among other solutes, are stored at such high concentrations that they draw water in from the environment. As the vacuole expands in volume, the cytoplasm pushes the plasma membrane against the cell wall. The effect of this change in volume is observed when wilted green plants regain their rigid structure after water is added to the soil. In other plant cells, vacuoles include more specialized storage functions:

- In seeds, cells may contain a large vacuole filled with proteins. When the embryonic plant inside the seed begins to grow, enzymes begin digesting these proteins to provide amino acids for the growing individual.

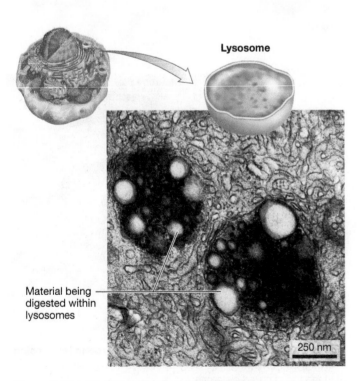

Material being digested within lysosomes

Figure 7.11 Lysosomes Are Recycling Centers. Lysosomes are oval or globular organelles that contain enzymes to digest macromolecules.

- In flower petals or fruits, cells may contain vacuoles that are filled with colorful pigments.

- Elsewhere, vacuoles may be packed with noxious compounds that protect leaves and stems from being eaten by predators. The type of chemical involved varies by species, ranging from bitter-tasting tannins to toxins such as nicotine, morphine, caffeine, or cocaine.

Peroxisomes Virtually all eukaryotic cells contain globular organelles called **peroxisomes** (Figure 7.13). These organelles have a single membrane and originate as vesicles from the ER.

Although different types of cells from the same individual may have distinct types of peroxisomes, these organelles all share a common function: Peroxisomes are centers for reduction–oxidation (redox) reactions. (Chapter 8 explains in detail how redox reactions transfer electrons between atoms and molecules.) For example, the peroxisomes in your liver cells contain enzymes that remove electrons from, or oxidize, the ethanol in alcoholic beverages. In the leaves of plants, specialized peroxisomes called **glyoxysomes** are packed with enzymes that oxidize fats to form a compound that can be used to store energy for the cell.

In animals and plants, the products of these reactions often include hydrogen peroxide (H_2O_2), which is highly reactive. If hydrogen peroxide escaped from the peroxisome, it would quickly react with and damage DNA, proteins, and cellular membranes. This event is rare, however, because inside the peroxisome, the enzyme catalase quickly "detoxifies" hydrogen peroxide by catalyzing its oxidation to form water and oxygen. The enzymes found inside the peroxisome make a specialized set of oxidation reactions possible and safe for the cell.

Mitochondria Most of the work required to keep up the structure and function of a cell depends on the chemical energy stored in adenosine triphosphate (ATP). The organelle primarily responsible for supplying ATP in animals, plants, and virtually all other eukaryotic cells is the **mitochondrion** (plural: **mitochondria**).

As Figure 7.14 shows, each mitochondrion has two membranes. The outer membrane defines the organelle's surface, while the inner membrane forms a series of sac-like **cristae** (singular: **crista**). The solution enclosed within the inner membrane is called the **mitochondrial matrix.** In eukaryotes, the chemical energy in carbohydrates and fats is used to produce ATP. Most of the enzymes and molecular machines responsible for synthesizing ATP are embedded in the inner membrane or suspended in the matrix (see Chapter 9). Depending on the type of cell, the number of mitochondria can range from one to more than a million.

Each mitochondrion has many copies of a small, circular or, in some species, linear chromosome called **mitochondrial DNA (mtDNA)** that is independent of the nuclear chromosomes. The mitochondrial DNA contains only a tiny fraction of the genes responsible for the function of the organelle—the other genes reside in the nuclear DNA.

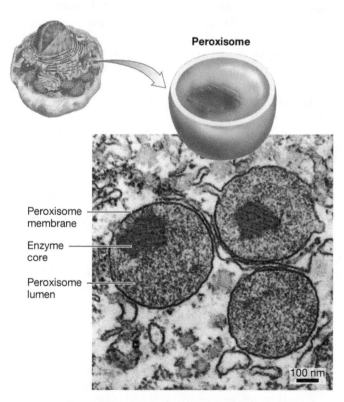

Peroxisome

Peroxisome membrane

Enzyme core

Peroxisome lumen

100 nm

Figure 7.13 Peroxisomes Are the Site of Oxidation Reactions.
Peroxisomes are globular organelles that contain enzymes involved in detoxifying reactive molecules, such as hydrogen peroxide.

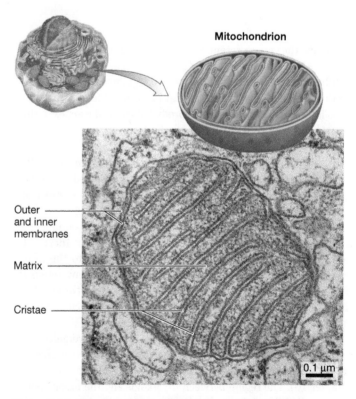

Mitochondrion

Outer and inner membranes

Matrix

Cristae

0.1 μm

Figure 7.14 Mitochondria Are Power-Generating Stations.
Mitochondria vary in size and shape, but all have two membranes with sac-like cristae formed from the inner membrane that are involved in producing ATP.

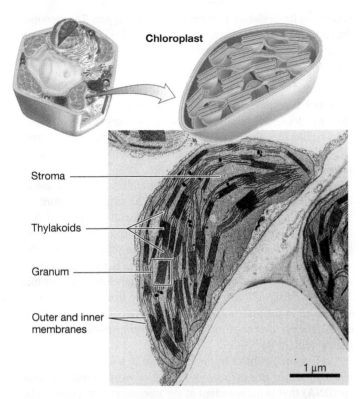

Chloroplast

Stroma

Thylakoids

Granum

Outer and inner
membranes

1 µm

**Figure 7.15 Chloroplasts Are Sugar-Manufacturing Centers
in Plants and Algae.** Many of the enzymes and other molecules
required for photosynthesis are located in membranes inside the
chloroplast. These membranes form thylakoids that consist of discs
stacked into grana.

Among the genes present in mitochondrial DNA are those that
encode RNAs for mitochondrial ribosomes. These ribosomes are
smaller than those found in the cytosol, yet they still function to
produce some of the mitochondrial proteins. (Most of the proteins found in mitochondria are produced from ribosomes in the
cytosol and imported into the organelle.)

Chloroplasts Most algal and plant cells possess an organelle
called the **chloroplast,** in which sunlight is converted to chemical energy during photosynthesis (**Figure 7.15**). The number of
chloroplasts per cell varies from none to several dozen.

Like the mitochondrion, the chloroplast is surrounded by
a double membrane. Unlike mitochondria, however, there are
no cristae extending from the inner membrane into the interior. Instead, a third membrane forms an independent network
of hundreds of flattened, sac-like structures called **thylakoids**
throughout the interior. Most thylakoids are arranged in interconnected stacks called **grana** (singular: **granum**).

Many of the pigments, enzymes, and macromolecular
machines responsible for converting light energy into chemical energy are embedded in the thylakoid membranes (see
Chapter 10). The region between thylakoids and the inner membrane, called the **stroma,** contains enzymes that use this chemical energy to produce sugars.

Like mitochondria, each chloroplast contains copies of its own
circular chromosome and small ribosomes that manufacture some,

but not all, of the organelle's proteins. Both mitochondria and
chloroplasts also grow and divide independently of cell division.

These attributes are odd compared with those of the other
organelles and have led biologists to propose that mitochondria
and chloroplasts were once free-living bacteria. According to
the **endosymbiosis theory,** these bacteria were engulfed by the
ancestors of modern eukaryotes, but were not destroyed—instead,
a mutually beneficial relationship evolved. (In Chapter 27, you
will learn more about the origins of these eukaryotic organelles.)

Cytoskeleton The final major structural feature to discuss is
common to all eukaryotes—the cytoskeleton. This extensive system of protein fibers gives the cell its shape and structural stability. It is also involved in moving the materials within the cell
as well as the cell itself. In essence, the cytoskeleton organizes
all the organelles and other cellular structures into a cohesive
whole. Recall that prokaryotes also have a cytoskeleton, but it
is far less extensive. Section 7.6 will analyze the structure and
functions of the cytoskeleton in detail.

The Eukaryotic Cell Wall In fungi, algae, and plants, cells possess an outer cell wall in addition to their plasma membrane. The
cell wall is located outside the plasma membrane and furnishes
a durable, outer layer that gives structural support to the cell.
The cells of animals, amoebae, and other groups lack a cell wall—
their exterior surface consists of the plasma membrane only.

Although the composition of the eukaryotic cell wall varies
among species and even among types of cells in the same individual, the general plan is similar: Rods or fibers composed of a
carbohydrate run through a stiff matrix made of other polysaccharides and proteins (see Chapter 11 for details).

To summarize: Within a cell, the structure of each component
correlates with its function. As we will see in the next section, the
overall size, shape, and composition of a cell similarly correlate
with its function.

CHECK YOUR UNDERSTANDING

If you understand that ...

• Each structure in a eukaryotic cell performs a function vital
  to the cell.

• In eukaryotes, many of the cellular functions are
  compartmentalized into organelles.

✔ **You should be able to ...**

1. Explain how the structure of lysosomes and peroxisomes
   correlates with their function.

2. In Table 7.1, label each component with one of the
   following analogous roles: administrative/information hub,
   power station, warehouse, large molecule manufacturing
   and shipping facility (with subtitles for lipid factory,
   protein finishing and shipping line, protein synthesis and
   folding center, waste processing and recycling center),
   support beams, perimeter fencing with secured gates,
   protein factory, food-manufacturing facility, and fatty-acid
   processing and detox center.

Answers are available in Appendix A.

Icons Not to Scale		Structure		Function
		Membrane	Components	
	Nucleus	Double ("envelope"); openings called nuclear pores	Chromosomes Nucleolus Nuclear lamina	Information storage and transmission Ribosome subunit assembly Structural support
	Ribosomes	None	Complex of RNA and proteins	Protein synthesis
	Endomembrane system			
	Endoplasmic reticulum: rough	Single; contains receptors for entry of selected proteins	Network of branching sacs Ribosomes associated	Protein synthesis and processing
	Endoplasmic reticulum: smooth	Single; contains enzymes for synthesizing phospholipids	Network of branching sacs Enzymes for synthesizing or breaking down lipids	Lipid synthesis and processing
	Golgi apparatus	Single; contains receptors for products of rough ER	Stack of flattened, distinct cisternae	Protein, lipid, and carbohydrate processing
	Lysosomes	Single; contains proton pumps	Acid hydrolases (catalyze hydrolysis reactions)	Digestion and recycling
	Vacuoles	Single; contains transporters for selected molecules	Varies—carbohydrates, water, pigments, oils, toxins, or hydrolases	Storage, digestion, and recycling
	Peroxisomes	Single; contains transporters for selected macromolecules	Enzymes that catalyze oxidation reactions Catalase (processes peroxide)	Oxidation of fatty acids, ethanol, or other compounds
	Mitochondria	Double; inner contains enzymes for ATP production	Enzymes that harvest energy from molecules to make ATP	ATP production
	Chloroplasts	Double; plus membrane-bound sacs in interior	Pigments Enzymes that use light energy to make sugars	Production of sugars via photosynthesis
	Cytoskeleton	None	Actin filaments Intermediate filaments Microtubules	Structural support; movement of materials; in some species, movement of whole cell
	Plasma membrane	Single; contains transport and receptor proteins	Phospholipid bilayer with transport and receptor proteins	Selective permeability—maintains intracellular environment
	Cell wall	None	Carbohydrate fibers running through carbohydrate or protein matrix	Protection, structural support

7.3 Putting the Parts into a Whole

If the industrial complex serves as an analogy for a eukaryotic cell, then a city that consists of many different industries might represent a multicellular organism. Just as a clothing manufacturing center has a very different layout and composition from an airplane production facility, cells in your muscles differ from nearby fat cells. How does the physical and chemical makeup of a cell correlate with its function?

Structure and Function at the Whole-Cell Level

An individual plant or animal is made up of cells specialized for certain tasks. These different cells have structures that correlate with their functions. For example, the cardiac muscle cells in your heart are long and rectangular. They are filled with protein fibers that slide past one another as the muscle flexes or relaxes to generate the heartbeat. Muscle cells are also packed with mitochondria, which produce the ATP required for the sliding motion to occur.

In contrast, fat cells are rounded, globular structures that store lipids. They consist of little more than a plasma membrane, a nucleus, and a fat droplet. Neither cell bears a close resemblance to the generalized animal cell pictured in Figure 7.6a. To drive home the correlation between the overall structure and function of a cell, examine the transmission electron micrographs in Figure 7.16.

- The animal cell in Figure 7.16a is from the pancreas. It is packed with rough ER that manufactures digestive enzymes.

- The animal cell in Figure 7.16b is from the testis. It is dominated by smooth ER that synthesizes lipids like testosterone—a steroid hormone.

- The plant cell in Figure 7.16c is from the leaf of a potato. It has many chloroplasts that are specialized for absorbing light and manufacturing sugar.

- The animal cells in Figure 7.16d come from cardiac muscle. The cells have numerous mitochondria that use the energy stored in sugars to produce ATP.

In each case, the size and number of different types of organelles in each cell correlate with the cell's specialized function.

The Dynamic Cell

Biologists study the structure and function of organelles and cells with a combination of tools and approaches. For several decades, a technique called **differential centrifugation** was particularly important because it allowed researchers to isolate particular cell components and analyze their chemical composition. Differential centrifugation is based on breaking cells apart to create a complex mixture and separating components in a centrifuge (see BioSkills 7). The individual parts of the cell can then be purified and studied in detail, in isolation from other parts of the cell.

Historically and currently, however, the most important research in cell biology is based on imaging—simply looking at cells. Recent innovations allow biologists to put fluorescing tags or other types of markers on particular cell components and

(a) Animal pancreatic cell: Exports digestive enzymes.

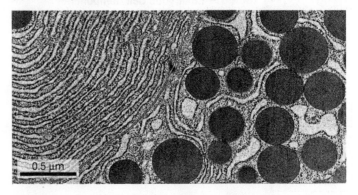

(b) Animal testis cell: Exports lipid-soluble signals.

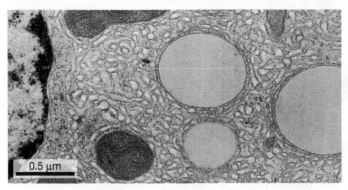

(c) Plant leaf cell: Manufactures ATP and sugar.

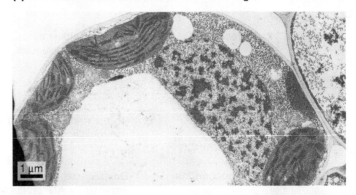

(d) Cardiac muscle: Uses ATP to generate the heartbeat.

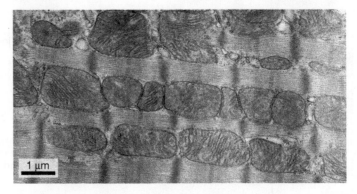

Figure 7.16 Cell Structure Correlates with Function.

✔ In part (a), label the rough ER and the dark, round secretory vesicles. In (b), label the smooth ER. In (c), label the chloroplasts, vacuole, and nucleus. In (d), label the mitochondria.

then look at them with increasingly sophisticated light microscopes and electron microscopes. Advances in microscopy provide increasingly high magnification and better resolution (some of the imaging techniques are featured in BioSkills 9).

It's important to recognize, though, that these techniques have limitations. Differential centrifugation splits cells into parts that are analyzed independently, and electron microscopy gives a fixed "snapshot" of the cell or organisms being observed. Neither technique allows investigators to explore directly how things move from place to place in the cell or how parts interact. The information gleaned from these techniques can make cells seem static. In reality, however, cells are dynamic.

The amount of chemical activity and the speed of molecular movement inside cells are nothing short of fantastic. Here are some remarkable cellular feats:

- In an average second, a typical cell in your body uses an average of 10 million ATP molecules and synthesizes just as many.

- It's not unusual for a cellular enzyme to catalyze 25,000 or more reactions per second; most cells contain hundreds or thousands of different enzymes.

- A minute is more than enough time for each membrane phospholipid in your body to travel the breadth of the organelle or cell where it resides.

- The hundreds of trillions of mitochondria inside you are completely replaced about every 10 days, for as long as you live.

Within a cell, events take nanoseconds, and speeds are measured in micrometers per second. This is the speed of life.

The rest of this chapter focuses on this theme of cellular dynamism and movement. Its goal is to put some of the individual pieces of a cell together and ask how they work as systems to accomplish key tasks.

To begin, let's first look at how molecules move into and out of the cell's control center—the nucleus—and then consider how proteins move from ribosomes into the lumen of the rough ER and then to the Golgi apparatus and beyond. The chapter closes by introducing the cytoskeletal elements and their associated motor proteins and how they are used to transport cargo inside the cell or move the cell itself.

7.4 Cell Systems I: Nuclear Transport

The nucleus is the information center of eukaryotic cells—a corporate headquarters, design center, and library all rolled into one. Appropriately enough, its interior is highly organized. Specific centers exist where the genetic information in DNA is decoded and processed. At these locations, large suites of enzymes interact to produce RNA messages from specific genes at specific times. Meanwhile, the nucleolus functions as the site of ribosome assembly.

Structure and Function of the Nuclear Envelope

The nuclear envelope separates the nucleus from the rest of the cell. Starting in the 1950s, transmission electron micrographs of cross sections through the nuclear envelope showed that the structure is supported by an internal fibrous nuclear lamina and bounded by two membranes. How does this administrative center communicate with the rest of the cell across the double membrane barrier?

Micrographs like the one in **Figure 7.17** show that the nuclear envelope is perforated with openings that are approximately 60 nanometers (nm) in diameter. Follow-up research showed that these openings are formed by an elaborate structure called the **nuclear pore complex.** As shown in the diagram on the right side of Figure 7.17, the nuclear pore complex extends through both the inner and outer nuclear membranes, connecting the inside of the nucleus with the cytosol. Each nuclear pore complex consists of approximately 30 different proteins.

What substances travel through nuclear pore complexes, and how are they transported? Chromosomal DNA clearly does not travel—it remains in the nucleus as long as the nuclear envelope is intact. But most of the RNA that is synthesized from DNA is exported through nuclear pore complexes to the cytosol.

Several types of RNA molecules are produced, each distinguished by size and function. For example, **ribosomal RNAs** are manufactured in the nucleolus, where they bind to proteins to form ribosomes. Molecules called **messenger RNAs (mRNA)** carry the information required to manufacture proteins. Both the newly assembled ribosomes and the mRNAs must be

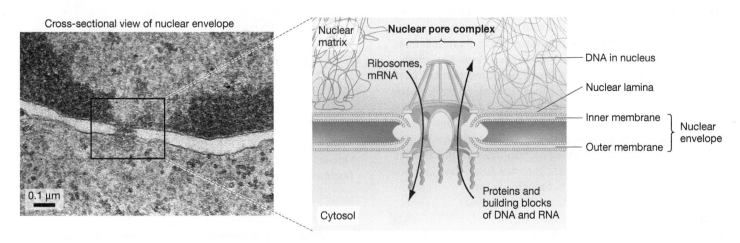

Cross-sectional view of nuclear envelope

0.1 μm

Nuclear matrix

Nuclear pore complex

Ribosomes, mRNA

DNA in nucleus

Nuclear lamina

Inner membrane ⎫
Outer membrane ⎬ Nuclear envelope

Proteins and building blocks of DNA and RNA

Cytosol

Figure 7.17 **Structure of the Nuclear Envelope and Nuclear Pore Complex.**

transported from the nucleus to the cytoplasm, where protein synthesis takes place.

Inbound traffic is also impressive. Nucleoside triphosphates that act as building blocks for DNA and RNA enter the nucleus, as do a variety of proteins responsible for copying DNA, synthesizing RNAs, or assembling ribosomes.

To summarize, a typical cell imports or exports over 500 molecules through each of the 2000–5000 nuclear pores every second. The scale of traffic through the nuclear pore complexes is mind-boggling. How is it regulated and directed?

How Do Molecules Enter the Nucleus?

Through experiments that evaluated the size of molecules allowed to pass through the nuclear pores, it was found that small molecules, like nucleotides, could freely diffuse into the nucleus. However, it was clear from these experiments that size was not the sole factor in selective transport across the nuclear envelope. Certain proteins were concentrated in the nucleus, while others were completely excluded—even if they were similar in size.

Based on these observations, researchers hypothesized that the nuclear pore complex serves as a gate to control passage through the envelope. If this is the case, then what is required to open these gates so that only certain proteins may pass?

A series of experiments on a protein called nucleoplasmin helped researchers understand the nature of nuclear import. Nucleoplasmin is strictly found in the nucleus and plays an important role in the assembly of chromatin. When researchers labeled nucleoplasmin with a radioactive atom and injected it into the cytoplasm of living cells, they found that the radioactive protein was quickly concentrated into the nucleus. Is there a "send-to-nucleus" signal within the nucleoplasmin protein that is responsible for this directed transport?

As shown in **Figure 7.18**, the distinctive quaternary structure (see Chapter 3) of nucleoplasmin was used to further investigate this process. Nucleoplasmin is composed of five identical polypeptide subunits, each with a sequence of amino acid residues at the N-terminus called the "core" (represented by green spheres in the figure) and a sequence of amino acid residues at the C-terminus called the "tail" (green rods). First, researchers used enzymes called proteases to cleave the core sections of nucleoplasmin from the tails. After separating the tails from the core fragments, they labeled each component with radioactive atoms and injected them into the cytoplasm of different cells.

At various times after the injections, researchers examined the nuclei and cytoplasm of the cells to track down the radioactive label. The results were striking. They found that tail fragments were rapidly transported from the cytoplasm into the nucleus. Core fragments, in contrast, were not allowed to pass through the nuclear envelope and remained in the cytoplasm.

These data led to a key hypothesis: Nuclear proteins contain a kind of "zip code"—a molecular address tag—that marks them for transport through the nuclear pore complex. These proteins are synthesized by ribosomes that are free in the cytosol and the zip code allows them to pass into the nucleus.

By analyzing different stretches of the tail, the biologists eventually found a 17-amino-acid-residue-long section of the polypeptide that had to be present to direct nucleoplasmin to the

RESEARCH

QUESTION: Does the nucleoplasmin protein contain a "Send to nucleus" signal?

HYPOTHESIS: Nucleoplasmin contains a discrete "Send to nucleus" signal that resides in either the tail or core region.

NULL HYPOTHESIS: Nucleoplasmin does not require a signal to enter the nucleus, or the entire protein serves as the signal.

EXPERIMENTAL SETUP:

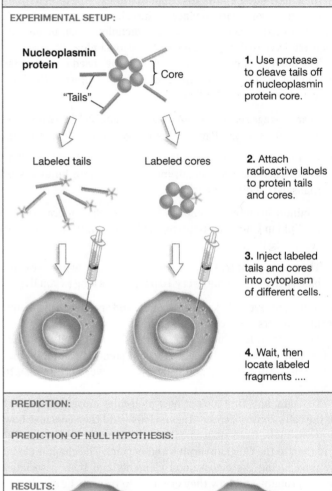

1. Use protease to cleave tails off of nucleoplasmin protein core.

2. Attach radioactive labels to protein tails and cores.

3. Inject labeled tails and cores into cytoplasm of different cells.

4. Wait, then locate labeled fragments ....

PREDICTION:

PREDICTION OF NULL HYPOTHESIS:

RESULTS:

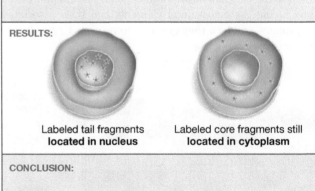

Labeled tail fragments **located in nucleus**

Labeled core fragments still **located in cytoplasm**

CONCLUSION:

Figure 7.18 Does the Nucleoplasmin Protein Contain a "Send to Nucleus" Signal?

SOURCES: Mills, A. D., R. A. Laskey, P. Black, et al. 1980. An acidic protein which assembles nucleosomes in vitro is the most abundant protein in *Xenopus* oocyte nuclei. *Journal of Molecular Biology* 139: 561–568; Dingwall, C., S. V. Sharnick, and R. A. Laskey. 1982. A polypeptide domain that specifies migration of nucleoplasmin into the nucleus. *Cell* 30: 449–458.

✔ **PROCESS OF SCIENCE** Without looking at the text, fill in the predictions and conclusion in this experiment.

nucleus. Follow-up work confirmed that other proteins transported into the nucleus, even those expressed by some viruses, have similar amino acid sequences directing their transport. This common sequence came to be called the **nuclear localization signal (NLS).** Proteins that leave the nucleus have a different signal, required for nuclear export.

More recent research has shown that the movement of proteins and other large molecules into and out of the nucleus is an energy-demanding process that involves special transport proteins. These nuclear transport proteins function like trucks that haul cargo into or out of the nucleus through the nuclear pore complex, depending on whether they have an import or export zip code. Biologists are now trying to unravel how all this traffic in and out of the nucleus is regulated to avoid backups and head-on collisions.

✔ If you understand the process of nuclear transport, you should be able to compare and contrast the movement of (1) nucleotides and (2) large proteins through the nuclear pore complex. Which would you expect to require an input of energy?

7.5 Cell Systems II: The Endomembrane System Manufactures, Ships, and Recycles Cargo

The nuclear membrane is not the only place in cells where cargo moves in a regulated and energy-demanding fashion. Most of the proteins found in peroxisomes, mitochondria, and chloroplasts are also actively imported after being manufactured by ribosomes that are free in the cytosol.

If you think about it for a moment, the need to sort proteins and ship them to specific destinations should be clear. Proteins are produced by ribosomes that are either free in the cytosol or on the surface of the ER. Many of these proteins must be transported to a compartment inside the eukaryotic cell. Acid hydrolases must be shipped to lysosomes and catalase to peroxisomes. To get to the right location, each protein must have a specific zip code and a delivery system.

To get a better understanding of protein sorting and transport in eukaryotic cells, let's consider perhaps the most intricate of all manufacturing and shipping complexes: the endomembrane system. In this system, proteins that are synthesized in the rough ER move to the Golgi apparatus for processing, and from there they travel to the cell surface or other destinations.

Studying the Pathway through the Endomembrane System

The idea that materials move through the endomembrane system in an orderly way was inspired by a simple observation. According to electron micrographs, cells that secrete digestive enzymes or other proteins have particularly large amounts of rough ER and Golgi (the extensive rough ER is shown in Figure 7.16a). This correlation led to the idea that these organelles may participate in a "secretory pathway" that starts in the rough ER and ends with products leaving the cell (**Figure 7.19**). How does this hypothesized pathway work?

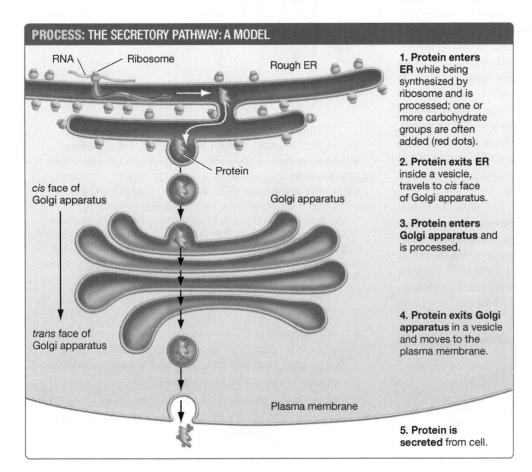

PROCESS: THE SECRETORY PATHWAY: A MODEL

RNA — Ribosome — Rough ER

1. Protein enters ER while being synthesized by ribosome and is processed; one or more carbohydrate groups are often added (red dots).

Protein

cis face of Golgi apparatus

Golgi apparatus

2. Protein exits ER inside a vesicle, travels to *cis* face of Golgi apparatus.

3. Protein enters Golgi apparatus and is processed.

trans face of Golgi apparatus

4. Protein exits Golgi apparatus in a vesicle and moves to the plasma membrane.

Plasma membrane

5. Protein is secreted from cell.

Figure 7.19 The Secretory Pathway Hypothesis. This hypothesis proposes that proteins intended for secretion from the cell are synthesized and processed in a highly prescribed series of steps. Note that proteins are packaged into vesicles when they move from the rough ER to the Golgi and from the Golgi to the cell surface.

Tracking Protein Movement via Pulse–Chase Assay George Palade and colleagues did pioneering research on the secretory pathway using a **pulse–chase experiment** to track protein movement. This strategy is based on two steps:

1. *The "Pulse"* Expose experimental cells to a high concentration of a modified amino acid for a short time. For example, if a cell is briefly exposed to a large amount of radioactively labeled amino acid, virtually all the proteins synthesized during that interval will be radiolabeled.

2. *The "Chase"* The pulse ends by washing away the modified amino acid and replacing it with the normal version of the same molecule. The time following the end of the pulse is referred to as the chase. The proteins synthesized during the chase period will *not* be radiolabeled.

The idea is to mark a population of molecules at a particular interval (the pulse) and then follow their fate over time (the chase). This approach is analogous to adding a small amount of dye to a stream and then following the movement of the dye to track the water flow pattern.

To understand why the chase requires unlabeled amino acids in these experiments, imagine what would happen if you added dye to a stream continuously. Soon the entire stream would be dyed—you could no longer track a specific population of dye molecules.

In testing the secretory pathway hypothesis, Palade's team focused on pancreatic cells that were growing in **culture,** or in vitro.[1] These cells are specialized for secreting digestive enzymes into the small intestine and are packed with rough ER and Golgi.

The basic experimental approach was to pulse the cell culture for 3 minutes with a radiolabeled version of the amino acid leucine, followed by a long chase period with nonradioactive leucine (**Figure 7.20a**). The pulse produced a population of proteins that were related to one another by the timing of their synthesis. At different points during the chase, the researchers tracked the movement of these proteins by preparing samples of the cells for autoradiography and electron microscopy (see **BioSkills 6** and **9**). The drawings in Figure 7.20a illustrate what the researchers observed from micrographs taken at the end of the pulse and at different times during the chase.

Results of the Pulse–Chase Experiment The graph in **Figure 7.20b** was based on the electron microscopy results, which showed that proteins are trafficked through the secretory pathway in a highly organized and directed manner. Track the movement of proteins through the cell during the chase by covering the graph with a piece of paper and then slowly sliding it off from left to right. Notice what is happening to each line at the following three time points:

1. Immediately after the pulse, most of the newly synthesized proteins are inside this cell's rough ER.

---

[1]The term "in vitro" is Latin for "in glass." Experiments that are performed outside living organisms are done in vitro. The term "in vivo," in contrast, is Latin for "in life." Experiments performed within living organisms are done in vivo.

(a) Setup for a pulse-chase experiment

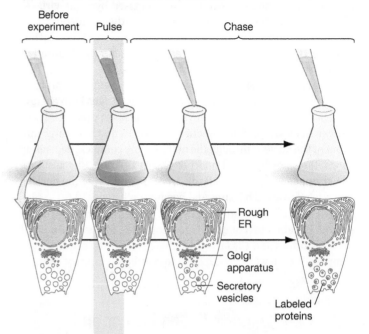

(b) Tracking pulse-labeled proteins during the chase

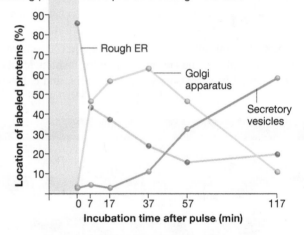

Figure 7.20 Tracking Protein Movement in a Pulse–Chase Experiment. Part **(a)** shows how newly synthesized proteins are labeled during the pulse when exposed to medium containing radioactive amino acids (red). At the start of the chase, this medium is replaced with medium containing non-radioactive amino acids (yellow) so only those proteins labeled in the pulse will be tracked (red dots). Part **(b)** provides the results of a pulse–chase experiment. The graph shows the relative abundance of radiolabeled proteins in three different organelles during the chase.

DATA: Jamieson, J. D., and Palade, G. E. 1967. *Journal of Cell Biology* 34: 597–615.

2. At 37 minutes into the chase, the situation has changed. Most of the labeled proteins have left the rough ER and entered the Golgi apparatus, and some of them have accumulated inside structures called secretory vesicles.

3. By the end of the chase, at 117 minutes, most of the labeled proteins have left the Golgi and are either in secretory vesicles or were secreted from the cells.

Over a period of two hours, the labeled population of proteins moved along a defined trail through the rough ER, Golgi apparatus, and secretory vesicles to reach the exterior of the cell.

✔ QUANTITATIVE If you understand how the pulse–chase experiment is used to track proteins, use the graph in Figure 7.20b to estimate the shortest time it would take for a protein to pass through the Golgi apparatus.

The results support the hypotheses that a secretory pathway exists and that the rough ER and Golgi apparatus function together as parts of an integrated endomembrane system. Next, let's break this secretory pathway down to examine four of the steps in more detail:

1. How do proteins enter the lumen of the rough ER?

2. How do the proteins move from the ER to the Golgi apparatus?

3. Once they're inside the Golgi apparatus, what happens to them?

4. And finally, how does the Golgi apparatus sort out the proteins so each will end up going to the appropriate place?

Entering the Endomembrane System: The Signal Hypothesis

The synthesis of proteins destined to be secreted or embedded in membranes begins in ribosomes free in the cytosol. Günter Blobel and colleagues proposed that at some point these ribosomes become attached to the outside of the ER. But what directs ribosomes to the ER surface? The signal hypothesis predicts that proteins bound for the endomembrane system have a molecular zip code that serves a similar role to the nuclear localization signal in nucleoplasmin. Blobel proposed that the first amino acid

residues of the growing protein act as a signal that marks the ribosome for transport to the ER membrane.

Blobel's group went on to produce convincing data that supported the hypothesis: They identified a "send-to-ER" signal, or **ER signal sequence,** that moves the growing protein and associated ribosome to the rough ER. The ER signal sequence typically is present in the first 20 amino acid residues and is removed when protein synthesis is complete.

More recent work has documented the mechanisms responsible for receiving this send-to-ER signal and inserting the protein into the rough ER. **Figure 7.21** illustrates the key steps involved for a protein that will eventually be shipped to the inside of an organelle or secreted from the cell.

Step 1 Protein synthesis begins on a free ribosome in the cytosol. The ribosome synthesizes the ER signal sequence, using information carried in an mRNA.

Step 2 The signal sequence binds to a **signal recognition particle (SRP)**—a complex of RNA and protein. The attached SRP causes protein synthesis to stop.

Step 3 The ribosome + signal sequence + SRP complex moves to the rough ER membrane, where it attaches to the SRP receptor. Think of the SRP as a key that is activated by an ER signal sequence. The SRP receptor in the ER membrane is the lock.

Step 4 Once the lock (the receptor) and key (the SRP) connect, the SRP is released and protein synthesis continues through a channel called the translocon.

Step 5 The growing protein is fed into the ER lumen, and the ER signal sequence is removed.

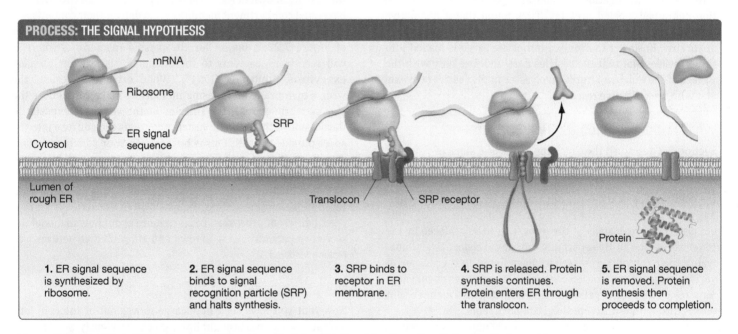

PROCESS: THE SIGNAL HYPOTHESIS

1. ER signal sequence is synthesized by ribosome.

2. ER signal sequence binds to signal recognition particle (SRP) and halts synthesis.

3. SRP binds to receptor in ER membrane.

4. SRP is released. Protein synthesis continues. Protein enters ER through the translocon.

5. ER signal sequence is removed. Protein synthesis then proceeds to completion.

Figure 7.21 The Signal Hypothesis Explains How Proteins Destined for Secretion Enter the Endomembrane System. According to the signal hypothesis, proteins destined for secretion contain a short stretch of amino acids that interact with a signal recognition particle (SRP) in the cytosol. This interaction directs the synthesis of the remaining protein into the rough ER lumen.

After cleavage of the signal sequence, the protein may be completely released into the ER lumen. Some proteins, however, remain associated with the membrane as integral membrane proteins. How do such proteins get inserted into the ER membrane? Current models propose that the translocon has molecular "gates" that divert the transmembrane portions of the growing protein into the phospholipid bilayer, while the rest of the protein enters the ER lumen.

Once proteins are inside the rough ER or inserted into its membrane, they fold into their three-dimensional shape with the help of chaperone proteins (see Chapter 3). In addition, proteins that enter the ER lumen interact with enzymes that catalyze the addition of carbohydrate side chains (see Figure 7.19). Because carbohydrates are polymers of sugar monomers, the addition of one or more carbohydrate groups is called **glycosylation** ("sugar-together"). The resulting molecule is a **glycoprotein** ("sugar-protein"; see Chapter 5). The number and arrangement of these sugars changes as the protein matures, serving as an indicator for shipment to the next destination.

Moving from the ER to the Golgi Apparatus

How do proteins travel from the ER to the Golgi apparatus? In Palade's pulse–chase experiment, labeled proteins found between the rough ER and the Golgi apparatus were encapsulated within small membrane-bound structures. Based on these observations, Palade's group suggested that proteins are transported in vesicles that bud off from the ER, move away, fuse with the membrane on the *cis* face of the Golgi apparatus, and dump their cargo inside.

This hypothesis was supported when other researchers used differential centrifugation to isolate and characterize the vesicles that contained labeled proteins. They found that a distinctive type of vesicle carries proteins from the rough ER to the Golgi apparatus. Ensuring that only appropriate cargo is loaded into these vesicles and that the vesicles dock and fuse only with the *cis* face of the Golgi apparatus involves a complex series of events and is an area of active research.

What Happens Inside the Golgi Apparatus?

Section 7.2 described the Golgi apparatus as a stack of flattened vesicles called cisternae, with cargo entering one side of the organelle and exiting the other. Recent research has shown that the composition of the Golgi apparatus is dynamic. New cisternae constantly form at the *cis* face of the Golgi apparatus, while old cisternae break apart at the *trans* face, to be replaced by the cisternae behind it. By separating individual cisternae and analyzing their contents, researchers have found that cisternae at various stages of maturation contain different suites of enzymes. As a result, the cargo gets modified in a stepwise manner as it moves through the different Golgi compartments.

If the rough ER is like a foundry and stamping plant where rough parts are manufactured, then the Golgi apparatus can be considered a finishing area where products are polished, painted, and readied for shipping.

How Do Proteins Reach Their Destinations?

The rough ER and Golgi apparatus constitute an impressive assembly line. Certain proteins manufactured by this process remain in these organelles, replacing worn-out resident molecules. But those proteins that are simply passing through as cargo must be sorted and sent to their intended destination as the *trans* cisterna breaks up into vesicles. How is cargo put into the right shipping containers, and how are the different containers addressed?

Studies on enzymes that are shipped to lysosomes have provided some answers to both questions. A key finding was that lysosome-bound proteins have a phosphate group attached to a specific sugar on their surface, forming the compound mannose-6-phosphate. If this phosphorylated sugar is removed from these proteins, they are not transported to a lysosome.

The mannose-6-phosphate tag serves as a zip code, like the nuclear localization signal and ER signal sequence discussed earlier. Data indicate that a receptor protein in the membrane of the *trans*-Golgi cisterna binds to this tag. Regions that are enriched with these receptor–cargo complexes will form cargo-filled vesicles that include specific membrane proteins to direct their transport to pre-lysosomal compartments. In this way, the presence of mannose-6-phosphate targets proteins to organelles that eventually become lysosomes.

Figure 7.22 presents a simplified model of how cargo is sorted and loaded into specific vesicles that are shipped to different destinations. Each cargo protein has a molecular tag that directs it to particular vesicle budding sites by interacting with receptors in the *trans* cisterna. These receptors, along with other membrane and cytosolic proteins that are not shown, direct the transport vesicles to the correct destinations. Take a moment to observe how the vesicles shown in the middle of Figure 7.22 fuse with the pre-lysosomal compartment membrane and deliver their contents.

Next, notice that the transport vesicle shown on the right of Figure 7.22 is bound for the plasma membrane, where it will secrete its contents to the outside. This process is called **exocytosis** ("outside-cell-act"). When exocytosis occurs, the vesicle membrane and plasma membrane make contact. As the two membranes fuse, the interior of the vesicle is exposed to the outside of the cell. The vesicle's contents then diffuse into the space outside the cell. This is how cells in your pancreas deliver digestive enzymes to the duct that leads to your small intestine, where food is digested.

When illustrating the process of transporting cargo through the endomembrane system, biologists often use arrows that represent different processes. To learn more about how to model the secretory pathway using arrows and simplified structures, see **Making Models 7.1**.

Recycling Material in the Lysosome

Now that you have seen how cargo moves out of the cell, let's look at how cargo is brought into the cell. Previously, you learned about how cells import small molecules across lipid bilayers (see Chapter 6), but this is not possible for large molecules like proteins and complex carbohydrates. For these molecules to be

Lumen of
Golgi apparatus

"Tags"

Cytosol

Receptors

To **other organelle**

Transport
vesicles

To **pre-lysosomal
compartment**

To **plasma
membrane**
for secretion

1. In the endomembrane system, proteins bound for different destinations carry distinct tags that serve as molecular zip codes.

2. Proteins are sorted in the Golgi apparatus when they bind to different receptors.

3. Transport vesicles bud off the *trans* face of the Golgi apparatus and travel to their destinations.

4. Cytosolic and membrane proteins cause transport vesicles to attach and fuse at destinations.

5. Vesicles deliver contents.

Figure 7.22 In the Golgi Apparatus, Proteins Are Sorted into Vesicles That Are Targeted to a Destination.

recycled and used by the cell, they must first be digested in the lysosome—but how do they get there?

There are three pathways that animal cells commonly use to recycle material in the lysosome (see **Figure 7.23** on page 162). Two of these three pathways involve pinching off the plasma membrane to take up material from outside the cell, by a process called **endocytosis** ("inside-cell-act").

One pathway originating at the plasma membrane is called **receptor-mediated endocytosis.** As its name implies, the sequence of events begins when particles outside the cell bind to receptors on the plasma membrane. More than 25 distinct receptors have now been characterized, each specialized for binding to different cargo.

Once receptor binding occurs, the plasma membrane folds in and pinches off to form an endocytic vesicle. These vesicles then drop off their cargo in an organelle called the **early endosome** ("inside-body"). The activity of proton pumps in the membrane of this organelle acidifies its lumen, which causes the cargo to be released from their receptors. Many of these emptied cargo receptors are then repackaged into vesicles and returned to the plasma membrane.

As proton pumps continue to lower the early endosome's pH, it undergoes a series of processing steps that cause it to mature into a **late endosome.** The late endosome is the pre-lysosomal

---

✏️ **Making Models 7.1 Tips on Drawing Cell Structures and Processes**

In models of a cell, scientists often draw single lines to represent membranes and use different shapes to distinguish structures within the cell. Arrows can indicate a variety of processes, from the transport of cargo to the fusion of a vesicle with another membrane to the maturation of an organelle.

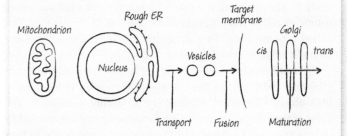

MODEL Draw the path of a secretory protein within a cell from the site of synthesis to exocytosis. Identify all the relevant cell structures and add notes indicating what happens to the protein at each step.

To see this model in action, go to https://goo.gl/2fp5km

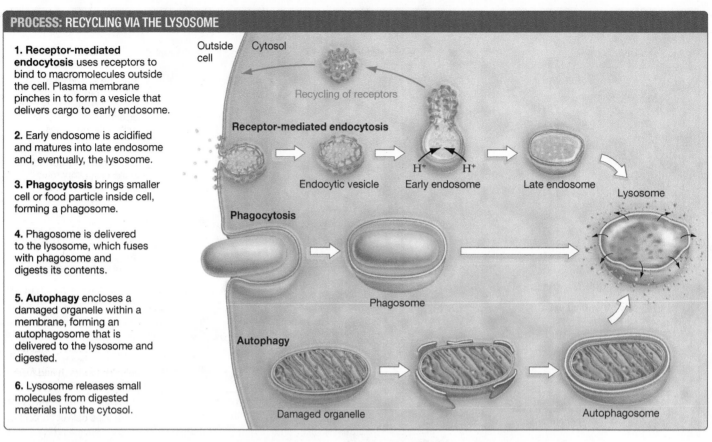

1. Receptor-mediated endocytosis uses receptors to bind to macromolecules outside the cell. Plasma membrane pinches in to form a vesicle that delivers cargo to early endosome.

2. Early endosome is acidified and matures into late endosome and, eventually, the lysosome.

3. Phagocytosis brings smaller cell or food particle inside cell, forming a phagosome.

4. Phagosome is delivered to the lysosome, which fuses with phagosome and digests its contents.

5. Autophagy encloses a damaged organelle within a membrane, forming an autophagosome that is delivered to the lysosome and digested.

6. Lysosome releases small molecules from digested materials into the cytosol.

Outside cell · Cytosol

Recycling of receptors

Receptor-mediated endocytosis

Endocytic vesicle · Early endosome · Late endosome · Lysosome

H^+ · H^+

Phagocytosis

Phagosome

Autophagy

Damaged organelle · Autophagosome

Figure 7.23 Three Pathways Exist to Recycle Material in the Lysosome. Receptor-mediated endocytosis and phagocytosis involve bringing in material from the outside and surrounding it with a lipid bilayer from the plasma membrane. Endosomes mature into lysosomes or, like phagosomes, will fuse with existing lysosomes. In autophagy, material within the cytoplasm is encapsulated with an internal membrane before fusing with the lysosome.

compartment introduced earlier (Figure 7.22), where the acid hydrolases from the Golgi apparatus are dropped off. As before, the emptied cargo receptors transported from the Golgi apparatus are removed from the late endosome as it matures into a fully active lysosome.

A second pathway that involves recycling material brought in from the outside of the cell is called **phagocytosis** ("eat-cell-act"). In phagocytosis, the plasma membrane of a cell surrounds a smaller cell or food particle and engulfs it, forming a structure called a phagosome. This structure is delivered to a lysosome, where it is taken in and digested.

Cells are also involved in recycling large structures and organelles that exist within the cytoplasm through a process called **autophagy** (literally, "same-eating"). During autophagy, portions of the cytoplasm, including damaged organelles marked for destruction, are enclosed within an internal membrane to form an autophagosome. Like the phagosome, this vesicle is also delivered to a lysosome.

Regardless of whether the materials digested by lysosomes originate via autophagy, phagocytosis, or receptor-mediated endocytosis, the result is similar: Molecules are hydrolyzed and the digested products are released back into the cytosol for recycling.

Throughout this section, vesicles have been key to the transport of cargo. If these transport steps depended on the random movement of diffusion alone, however, then the vesicles and their cargo might never reach their intended destinations. Instead, there are defined tracks that direct the movement of these shipping containers. What are these tracks, and what molecule or molecules function to transport the vesicles along them? Let's delve into these questions in the next section.

CHECK YOUR UNDERSTANDING

If you understand that …

- In cells, the transport of proteins and other large molecules is energy demanding and tightly regulated.
- Proteins must have the appropriate molecular zip code to be directed into the nucleus, the lumen of the rough ER, or vesicles destined for different parts of the cell.

✔ **You should be able to …**

1. Compare and contrast the movement of proteins into the nucleus versus the ER lumen.
2. Predict the final location of a protein that includes an ER signal sequence, mannose-6-phosphate tag, and a nuclear localization signal. Justify your answer by addressing the impact of each signal on its transport.

Answers are available in Appendix A.

7.6 Cell Systems III: The Dynamic Cytoskeleton

The endomembrane system may be the best-studied example of how individual organelles work together in a dynamic, highly integrated way. This integration depends in part on the physical relationship of organelles, which is organized by the cytoskeletal system.

The cytoskeleton is a dense and complex network of fibers that helps maintain cell shape by providing structural support. However, the cytoskeleton is not a static structure like the scaffolding used at construction sites. Like the rest of the cell, the cytoskeleton is dynamic. Its fibrous proteins move and change to alter the cell's shape, shift its contents, and even move the cell itself.

As Table 7.2 shows, there are three distinct cytoskeletal elements in eukaryotic cells: actin filaments, intermediate filaments, and microtubules. These three eukaryotic filaments are structurally and functionally related to cytoskeletal elements in bacteria and archaea.

Each of the three cytoskeletal filaments found in eukaryotes has a distinct size, structure, and function. Let's look at each one in turn, starting at the smallest and working up to the largest.

Actin Filaments

Sometimes called **microfilaments** because they are the cytoskeletal element with the smallest diameter, **actin filaments** are fibrous structures made of the globular protein actin (Table 7.2). In animal cells, actin is often the most abundant of all proteins—typically it represents 5–10 percent of the total protein in the cell. Each of your liver cells contains about half a billion of these molecules.

Actin Filament Structure A completed actin filament resembles two long strands that coil around each other. These filaments form when individual actin protein subunits assemble, or polymerize, from head to tail through the formation of noncovalent bonds.

Because actin proteins are not symmetrical, this head-to-tail arrangement of subunits results in filaments that have distinct polarity, or two different ends. The two distinct ends of an actin filament are referred to as plus and minus ends. These names reflect differences between rates of assembly—the plus end grows faster than the minus end.

In animal cells, actin filaments are particularly abundant just under the plasma membrane. They are organized into long, parallel bundles or dense, crisscrossing networks in which actin filaments are linked to one another by other proteins. The reinforced bundles and networks of actin filaments help stiffen the cell and define its shape.

Actin Filament Function In addition to providing structural support, actin filaments are involved in movement. In several cases, actin's role in movement depends on the protein myosin. Myosin is a **motor protein:** a protein that converts the chemical energy in ATP into the kinetic energy of mechanical work, just as a car's motor converts the chemical energy in gasoline into spinning wheels.

The interaction between actin and myosin is frequently presented in the context of how it produces muscle contraction and movement (Chapter 45). For now, it's enough to recognize that when myosin binds and hydrolyzes ATP to ADP, it undergoes a series of shape changes that extends the "head" region, attaches it to actin, and then contracts to pull itself along the actin filament. The shape change of this protein causes the actin and myosin to slide past each other. After repeated rounds of this contraction cycle, the myosin progressively moves toward the

SUMMARY Table 7.2 Cytoskeletal Filaments

Filament	Structure	Subunits	Functions
The three types of filaments that make up the cytoskeleton are distinguished by their size, structure, and type of protein subunit.			
Actin filaments (microfilaments)	Two coiled strands 7 nm – end + end	Actin	• maintain cell shape by resisting tension (pull) • move cells via muscle contraction or cell crawling • divide animal cells in two • move organelles and cytoplasm in plants, fungi, and animals
Intermediate filaments	Fibers wound into thicker cables 10 nm	Keratins, lamins, or others	• maintain cell shape by resisting tension (pull) • anchor nucleus and some other organelles
Microtubules	Hollow tube 25 nm – end + end	α- and β-tubulin dimers	• maintain cell shape by resisting compression (push) • move cells via flagella or cilia • move chromosomes during cell division • assist formation of cell plate during plant cell division • provide tracks for intracellular transport

(a) Actin and myosin interact to cause movement.

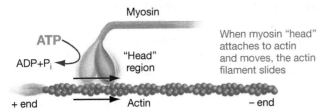

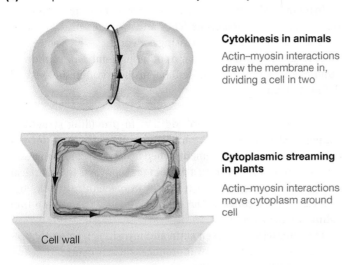

(b) Examples of movement caused by actin–myosin interactions

Cytokinesis in animals

Actin–myosin interactions draw the membrane in, dividing a cell in two

Cytoplasmic streaming in plants

Actin–myosin interactions move cytoplasm around cell

Figure 7.24 Many Cellular Movements Are Based on Actin–Myosin Interactions. (a) ATP hydrolysis in the "head" region of myosin causes the protein to attach to actin and change shape. The movement slides the myosin toward the plus end of actin. **(b)** Actin–myosin interactions can divide cells and move organelles and cytoplasm.

plus end of the actin filament (**Figure 7.24a**). This type of movement resembles the arms of a sailor hauling in a rope.

As **Figure 7.24b** shows, the ATP-powered interaction between actin and myosin is the basis for an array of cell movements:

- **Cytokinesis** ("cell-moving") is the final stage in cell division when the cytoplasm is divided to form two cells. In animals, this occurs by the use of actin filaments that are connected to the plasma membrane and arranged in a ring. Myosin causes the filaments to slide past one another, reducing the diameter of the ring and pulling in the membrane that eventually fuses to produce two cells.

- **Cytoplasmic streaming** is the directed flow of cytosol and organelles that is often seen within plant and fungal cells. The movement occurs along actin filaments and is powered by myosin. It is especially common in large cells, where the circulation of cytoplasm facilitates material transport.

In addition, the movement called **cell crawling** occurs when groups of actin filaments grow, creating bulges in the plasma membrane that extend and move the cell. Cell crawling occurs in a wide range of organisms and cell types, including amoebae, slime molds, and certain animal cells.

Intermediate Filaments

There are many types of **intermediate filament,** each consisting of a different—though similar in size and structure—type of protein (Table 7.2). Humans, for example, have 70 genes that code for different intermediate filament proteins. This is in stark contrast to actin filaments and microtubules, which are made from the same protein subunits in all eukaryotic cells.

Also unlike actin filaments, intermediate filaments do not exhibit filament polarity nor do they serve as tracks for the directed movement of motor proteins. Instead, these filaments have identical ends and appear to only serve a structural role in eukaryotic cells.

The most familiar intermediate filaments belong to a family of molecules called the keratins. The cells that make up your skin and line surfaces inside your body contain about 20 types of keratin. These intermediate filaments provide the mechanical strength required for these cells to resist pressure and abrasion. Certain cells in the skin can also produce secreted forms of keratin. Depending on the location of the cell and keratins involved, the secreted filaments form fingernails, toenails, or hair.

Nuclear lamins, which make up the nuclear lamina layer introduced in Section 7.4, also are intermediate filaments. Nuclear lamins form a dense mesh inside the nuclear envelope that anchors the chromosomes, defines the shape of the nucleus, and stabilizes the envelope. By controlling the interactions between these lamins, the cell is able to break down and reform the nuclear envelope as the nucleus divides during mitosis.

Various types of intermediate filaments are found throughout the cytoplasm of the cell. Some intermediate filaments project from the nucleus to hold it in place. Others run parallel to the cell surface and interact with proteins embedded in the plasma membrane. To summarize, intermediate filaments function like a flexible cargo net to help secure the shape and stability of the cell.

Microtubules

Microtubules are the largest cytoskeletal components in terms of diameter. As Table 7.2 shows, they are assembled from subunits consisting of two polypeptides, α-tubulin and β-tubulin, that exist as stable protein **dimers** ("two-parts").

Tubulin dimers polymerize from head to tail via noncovalent bonds to form filaments that interact with one another to create hollow tubes. Because of these head-to-tail interactions, microtubules exhibit polarity—they have α-tubulin polypeptides at one end (the minus end) and β-tubulins at the other end (the plus end). Similar to actin filaments, microtubules are dynamic and their plus ends grow faster than their minus ends.

Microtubules originate from a structure called the **microtubule-organizing center (MTOC).** Their plus ends grow outward, radiating throughout the cell. Although plant cells typically have hundreds of sites where microtubules start growing, most animal and fungal cells have just one site that is near the nucleus, called the **centrosome.** As **Figure 7.25** shows, animal centrosomes contain two bundles of microtubules called

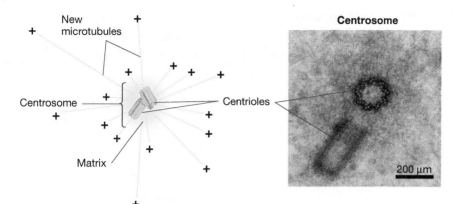

Centrosome

200 μm

Figure 7.25 Centrosomes Are a Type of Microtubule-Organizing Center. Microtubule-organizing centers, such as the centrosomes of animal cells, are the sites where new microtubules are made. Microtubules grow from the matrix surrounding the centrioles, and their positive ends point away from the centrosomes. The two centrioles inside a centrosome consist of microtubules as triplets arranged in a circle.

centrioles. Although additional microtubules emanate from these centrosomes in animals, they do not grow directly from the centrioles.

In function, microtubules are similar to actin filaments: They provide stability and are involved in movement. Like steel girders in a skyscraper, the microtubules that radiate from an organizing center stiffen the cell by resisting compression forces. Microtubules also provide a structural framework for organelles. If microtubules are prevented from forming, the network-like configuration of the ER collapses and the Golgi apparatus breaks up into vesicles.

Microtubules are best known for their role in separating chromosomes during mitosis and meiosis (see Chapters 12 and 13), but they are involved in many other types of cellular movement as well. Let's first consider their role in moving materials inside cells and then explore how microtubules can help cells to swim.

Microtubules Serve as Tracks for Vesicle Transport Recall from Section 7.5 that vesicles are used to transport materials to a wide array of destinations inside cells. To study how this movement happens, Ronald Vale and colleagues focused on an extremely large nerve cell in squid called the giant axon. This cell runs the length of the animal's body. If the squid is disturbed, the cell signals muscles to contract so it can jet away to safety.

The squid giant axon provided a system that could be observed and manipulated efficiently in the lab. The researchers found that if they gently squeezed the cytoplasm out of the cell, vesicle transport still occurred in the extracellular cytoplasmic material. This allowed them to do experiments on vesicle transport without the plasma membrane being in the way. To watch vesicle transport in action, the researchers mounted a video camera to a microscope. As **Figure 7.26** shows, this technique allowed them to document that vesicle transport occurred along filamentous tracks.

To identify the filament involved, the biologists measured the diameter of the tracks and analyzed their chemical composition. Both types of data indicated that the tracks consist of microtubules. Microtubules also appear to be required for movement of materials elsewhere in the cell. For instance, the movement of vesicles from the rough ER to the Golgi apparatus requires microtubule tracks.

The general message of these experiments is that transport vesicles move through the cell along microtubules. How? Do the tracks themselves move, like a conveyer belt, or are vesicles carried along on some sort of molecular vehicle?

Motor Proteins Pull Vesicles Along the Tracks To study the way vesicles move along microtubules, Vale's group took the squid axon's transport system apart and then determined what components were required to put it back together. A simple experiment convinced the group that this movement is an energy-dependent process: If they depleted the amount of ATP in the cytoplasm, vesicle transport stopped.

To examine this process further, they mixed purified microtubules and vesicles with ATP, but no transport occurred. Something had been left out—but what? To find the missing component or components, the researchers purified one subcellular part after another and added it to the microtubule + vesicle + ATP system.

(a) Electron micrograph

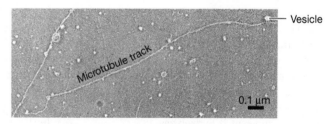

Vesicle

Microtubule track

0.1 μm

(b) Video image

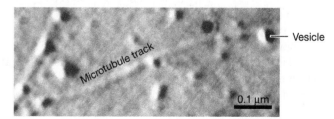

Vesicle

Microtubule track

0.1 μm

Figure 7.26 Transport Vesicles Move along Microtubule Tracks. The images show extruded cytoplasm from a squid giant axon. **(a)** An electron micrograph that allowed researchers to identify the filaments as microtubules. In the upper part of this image, you can see a vesicle on a "track." **(b)** A video microscope image using enhanced contrast that allowed researchers to watch vesicles move in real time.

(a) Structure of kinesin

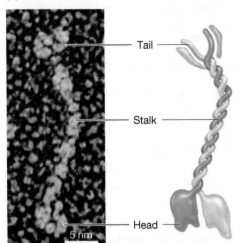

Tail

Stalk

Head

5 nm

(b) Kinesin "walks" along a microtubule track.

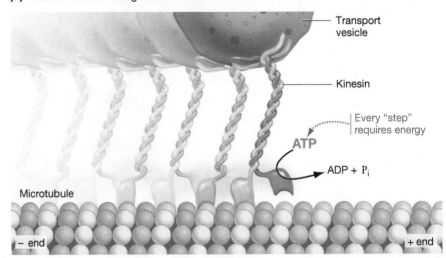

Transport vesicle

Kinesin

Every "step" requires energy

ATP

ADP + P$_i$

Microtubule

– end

+ end

Figure 7.27 Motor Proteins Move Vesicles Along Microtubules. (a) Kinesin has three distinct regions.
(b) The current model depicting how kinesin "walks" along a microtubule track to transport vesicles. The two head segments act like feet that alternately attach, pivot, and release in response to the gain or loss of a phosphate group from ATP.

Through trial and error, and further purification steps, the researchers finally succeeded in isolating a protein that generated vesicle movement. They named the molecule **kinesin,** from the Greek word *kinein* ("to move").

Like myosin, kinesin is a motor protein. Kinesin converts the chemical energy in ATP into mechanical energy in the form of movement. More specifically, when ATP is hydrolyzed by kinesin, the protein moves along microtubules in a directional manner: toward the plus end.

Biologists began to understand how kinesin works by first focusing on its structure. Kinesin consists of multiple subunits, with two large polypeptides that have three major regions: a head section, a tail associated with small polypeptides, and a stalk that connects the head and tail (**Figure 7.27a**). The head region binds to the microtubule while the tail region binds to the transport vesicle. Recent work has shown that kinesin uses these domains to "walk" along the microtubule through a series of conformational changes as it hydrolyzes ATP (**Figure 7.27b**). In this way, kinesin races long at an amazing 375 "steps" per second.

The discovery of kinesin explained how secretory vesicles could be moved toward the plus end of microtubules, during their transport from the *trans*-Golgi cisterna to the plasma membrane. What about transporting vesicles in the opposite direction, toward the minus end of microtubules located at the centrosome? By studying whole-cell locomotion, researchers discovered a motor protein that could fill this role.

Flagella and Cilia: Moving the Entire Cell

Some eukaryotic cells use long, whiplike flagella that project from the cell surface for locomotion. While many prokaryotes also have flagella, the structure is completely different in the two groups.

- A prokaryotic flagellum consists of a single helical rod made of flagellin (in bacteria) or other types of proteins (in archaea); a eukaryotic flagellum consists of several microtubules constructed from tubulin dimers.

- Prokaryotic flagella move the cell by rotating the rod like a ship's propeller; eukaryotic flagella move the cell by undulating—they whip back and forth.

- Eukaryotic flagella are surrounded by the plasma membrane; prokaryotic flagella are not.

Based on these observations, biologists conclude that the prokaryotic and eukaryotic flagella evolved independently, even though their function is similar.

The eukaryotic flagellum is closely related to a structure called the **cilium** (plural: **cilia**), which is a short, hairlike projection that is also found in some eukaryotic cells (**Figure 7.28**). Flagella are generally much longer than cilia, and the two structures differ in their abundance and pattern of movement. But when researchers examined the two structures with an electron microscope, they found that their underlying organization is identical.

How Are Cilia and Flagella Constructed? In the 1950s, anatomical studies established that most cilia and flagella have a characteristic "9 + 2" arrangement of microtubules. As **Figure 7.29a** shows, nine microtubule pairs, or doublets, surround two central microtubules. The doublets are arranged around the periphery of the structure.

The entire 9 + 2 structure is called the **axoneme** ("axle-thread"). The nine doublets of the axoneme originate from a structure called the **basal body.** The basal body is identical in structure with a centriole and plays a central role in the growth of the axoneme.

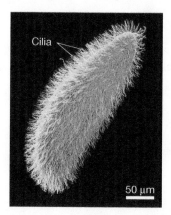
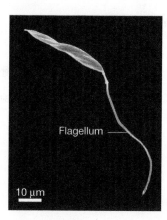

Figure 7.28 Cilia and Flagella Differ in Length and Number.
Cilia range in length from 1 to 10 μm, while flagella are typically longer and can exceed 1 mm. Cells with flagella typically possess only 1–4 flagella. Cilia tend to occur in larger numbers, and certain ciliated cells have up to 14,000 cilia. The cells in these scanning electron micrographs have been colorized.

Through further study, biologists gained a more detailed view of the axoneme's structure. Spoke-like proteins connect each doublet to the central pair of microtubules, and molecular links connect the nine doublets to one another (Figure 7.29b). Each doublet also has a set of arms that project toward an adjacent doublet.

Axonemes are complex. How do their components interact to generate motion?

What Provides the Force Required for Movement? In the 1960s Ian Gibbons began studying the cilia of a common unicellular eukaryote called *Tetrahymena*. He isolated the axonemes from cilia and found that they would beat only if he supplied them with ATP, confirming that the beating of cilia requires energy.

In another experiment, Gibbons treated the isolated axonemes with a molecule that disrupts the arms from the doublets. The resulting axonemes could not beat even after being supplied with ATP. This result suggested that the arms are required for movement. Follow-up work showed that the arms are made of a large protein that Gibbons named **dynein** (from the Greek root *dyne*, meaning "force").

Like myosin and kinesin, dynein is a motor protein that uses ATP to undergo conformational changes. These shape changes move dynein along microtubules toward the minus end. In the cytoplasm, dynein motors are known to play various roles similar to those of other motor proteins, including the transport of vesicles. In the context of the axoneme, however, the outcome of dynein walking in the axoneme is very different.

So what is special about the axoneme? Remember that each of the nine doublets in the axoneme is connected to the central pair of microtubules by a spoke and adjacent doublets by linking proteins (Figure 7.29b). As a result, the sliding motion produced by dynein walking is constrained—if one doublet slides, it transmits force to the rest of the axoneme via the links and spokes (Figure 7.29c). If the dynein arms on just one side of the axoneme are activated, then the localized movement results in bending. The bending of cilia or flagella results in a swimming motion.

(a) Transmission electron micrograph of axoneme

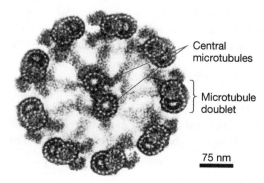

Central microtubules

Microtubule doublet

75 nm

(b) Structure of axoneme

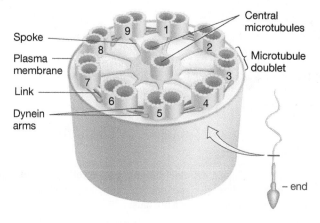

Spoke
Plasma membrane
Link
Dynein arms

Central microtubules
Microtubule doublet

– end

(c) Mechanism of axoneme bending

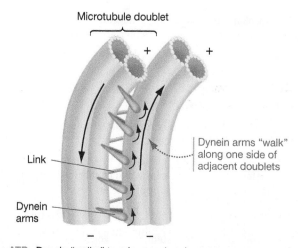

Microtubule doublet

Link
Dynein arms

Dynein arms "walk" along one side of adjacent doublets

+ ATP: Dynein "walks" to minus end and causes linked doublets to bend

Figure 7.29 The Structure and Function of Cilia and Flagella.
(a) Transmission electron micrograph of a cross section through an axoneme. **(b)** The microtubules in cilia and flagella are connected by links and spokes, and the entire structure is surrounded by the plasma membrane. **(c)** When dynein arms "walk" along the microtubule doublets on one side of a flagellum, force is transmitted to these links and spokes, causing the entire axoneme to bend.

✔ **MODEL** If the links were removed from the pair of doublets in part (c), draw how the structure would appear after adding ATP. Would this alteration affect bending or not?

Scaled for size, axoneme-powered swimming can be rapid. In terms of the number of body or cell lengths traveled per second, a sperm cell from a bull moves faster than a human world-record-holder does when swimming freestyle. At the cellular level, life is fast paced.

Taken together, the data reviewed in this chapter can be summed up in six words: Cells are dynamic, highly integrated structures. To maintain the level of organization that is required for life, chemical reactions must take place at mind-boggling speeds. How cells accomplish this feat is taken up elsewhere (see Chapter 8).

CHAPTER 7 REVIEW

For media, go to MasteringBiology

7.1 Bacterial and Archaeal Cell Structures and Their Functions

- There are two basic cellular designs: prokaryotic and eukaryotic. A defining characteristic that differentiates prokaryotes from eukaryotes is the absence of a nucleus.
- Structures common to most, if not all, prokaryotes are ribosomes, a cell wall, a plasma membrane, an interior cytoskeleton, and a nucleoid.
- Many prokaryotes also possess flagella, fimbriae, and internal membrane structures, some of which are considered organelles.

7.2 Eukaryotic Cell Structures and Their Functions

- Eukaryotic cells are usually much larger and more structurally complex than prokaryotic cells.
- Eukaryotic cells contain numerous specialized organelles that compartmentalize the cytoplasm and enable the cells to grow to a large size. Common eukaryotic organelles are as follows:
  1. The nucleus, which contains the cell's chromosomes and serves as its control center.
  2. The endomembrane system, which consists of a diverse group of interrelated organelles, including the endoplasmic reticulum, Golgi apparatus, lysosomes or vacuoles, and endosomes. These organelles work together to synthesize, process, sort, transport, and recycle material.
  3. Peroxisomes are organelles where key reactions take place that often result in the generation of toxic by-products. Specialized enzymes within the peroxisomes safely disarm these by-products soon after they are generated.
  4. Mitochondria and chloroplasts, which have extensive internal membrane systems where the enzymes responsible for ATP generation and photosynthesis reside.

7.3 Putting the Parts into a Whole

- Cells have a tightly organized interior, where the presence and quantity of organelles often reflect the function of the cell.
- The activity in a cell illustrates the dynamic nature of life. Organelles and cytosolic proteins continually bustle about with a seemingly nonstop rush hour.
- Much of what is known about cellular activity has come from advances in cell imaging and techniques for isolating cellular components.

7.4 Cell Systems I: Nuclear Transport

- Traffic across the nuclear envelope occurs through nuclear pore complexes that serve as gatekeepers.
- Small molecules passively diffuse through nuclear pore complexes while larger molecules require a nuclear localization signal to direct them through the nuclear pore complex via nuclear transport proteins.

7.5 Cell Systems II: The Endomembrane System Manufactures, Ships, and Recycles Cargo

- Molecules synthesized in the ER may be transported as cargo to the Golgi apparatus and then to other organelles or outside the cell.
- Before products leave the Golgi apparatus, they are sorted by their molecular "zip codes" that help package them into specific vesicles. Other membrane and cytosolic proteins deliver the vesicles to their target locations.
- Lysosomes consist of enzymes and membranes that are made and processed through the endomembrane system. Lysosomes are involved in recycling products via autophagy, phagocytosis, and receptor-mediated endocytosis.

7.6 Cell Systems III: The Dynamic Cytoskeleton

- The cytoskeleton is an extensive system of fibers that provides (1) structural support for organizing organelles and other cell components; (2) paths for moving intracellular structures and organelles; and (3) cellular locomotion via flagella, cilia, or cell crawling.

- The cytoskeleton is dynamic. Actin filaments and microtubules are polarized, meaning they have different ends designated as plus or minus ends. The plus ends have a higher growth rate than the minus ends.

- Motor proteins move along actin filaments and microtubules using chemical energy stored in ATP. Myosin motor proteins move toward the plus ends of actin filaments. Kinesin and dynein motor proteins move along microtubules toward the plus and minus ends, respectively.

- In the axonemes of eukaryotic cilia and flagella, dynein motors move microtubules to generate forces that bend the structures and enable cells to swim.

Answers are available in Appendix A

✔ TEST YOUR KNOWLEDGE

1. What are three attributes of mitochondria and chloroplasts that suggest they were once free-living bacteria?

2. **PROCESS OF SCIENCE** Which of the following results provided evidence of a discrete nuclear localization signal somewhere on the nucleoplasmin protein?
   a. The nucleoplasmin protein was small and easily slipped through the nuclear pore complex.
   b. After cleavage of the nucleoplasmin protein, only the tail segments appeared in the nucleus.
   c. Removing the tail from the nucleoplasmin protein allowed the core segment to enter the nucleus.
   d. The SRP bound only to the tail of the nucleoplasmin protein, not the core segment.

3. Molecular zip codes direct molecules to particular destinations in the cell. How are these signals read?
   a. They bind to receptor proteins.
   b. They enter transport vesicles.
   c. They bind to motor proteins.
   d. They are glycosylated by enzymes.

4. How does the hydrolysis of ATP result in the movement of a motor protein along a cytoskeletal filament?

✔ TEST YOUR UNDERSTANDING

5. Which of the following cell structures would you expect to be most important in the growth of bacteria on the surface of your teeth?
   a. cell wall
   b. fimbriae
   c. flagella
   d. cilia

6. Cells that line your intestines are known to possess a large number of membrane proteins that transport small molecules and ions across the plasma membrane. Which of the following cell structures would you expect to be required for this function of the cells?
   a. the endoplasmic reticulum
   b. peroxisomes
   c. lysosomes
   d. the cell wall

7. Most of the proteins that enter the nucleus possess a nuclear localization signal (NLS), even if they are small enough to pass through the nuclear pore complex unhindered. Why would a small protein have an NLS, when it naturally diffuses across the nuclear pore complex without one?

8. Compare and contrast the structure of a generalized plant cell, animal cell, and prokaryotic cell. Which features are common to all cells? Which are specific to just prokaryotes, or just plants, or just animals?.

✔ TEST YOUR PROBLEM-SOLVING SKILLS

9. Upon analyzing a sample of cells from a patient, you find the lysosomes to be filled with undigested material. This observation makes you think that the lysosomes are not functioning properly. What are three different defects that could be responsible for malfunctioning lysosomes?

10. George Palade's research group used the pulse–chase assay to dissect the secretory pathway in pancreatic cells. If they had instead performed this assay on muscle cells, which have high energy demands and primarily consist of actin and myosin filaments, where would you expect the labeled proteins to go during the chase?

✔ PUT IT ALL TOGETHER: Case Study

What organelles are required to color your cells?

The color of your eyes, skin, and hair is a product of cellular activity. In some animals, pigmentation is dynamic. Most people are familiar with scenes of an octopus blending in with its environment or chameleons turning bright red to ward off threats. Although less dynamic, human skin color can also change—or tan—when exposed to sunlight. How do cells pull off this remarkable feat?

11. Colorful animal cells are rich in melanosomes, a specialized organelle that contains pigments, like melanin, and the enzymes that produce them. Melanosomes are found only in certain cells and are called lysosome-related organelles based on their origin, but they do not contain hydrolases or have a low pH. How would you expect these melanosomes to form?

12. **MODEL** The distribution of melanosomes in cells is tightly regulated in animals that rapidly change color. Dark-colored cells have melanosomes scattered throughout the cytoplasm while light-colored cells have them aggregated near the nucleus. Draw a model of a cell representing each state, and predict how cells could use microtubules and motor proteins to change the distribution of melanosomes.

13. The color of human skin is determined by the abundance of melanosomes in keratinocytes—the dominant cell type in skin. But keratinocytes do not produce melanosomes. Instead, less abundant melanosome factories called melanocytes make and secrete the organelles. How could keratinocytes take up these organelles? What about this process must be altered to ensure the organelles remain in the keratinocytes?

14. **PROCESS OF SCIENCE** After exposure to the sun, human skin can darken, or tan, in response to the damaging effects of UV radiation. Propose a hypothesis to explain this phenomenon, and describe how you could set up an experiment to test your hypothesis using microscopy.

15. Even without being exposed to sunlight, humans exhibit a wide range of skin colors due to differences in the abundance of melanosomes. A recent hypothesis to address this difference is that autophagy plays a role in these differences. What is autophagy, and how might you expect this process to differ between individuals with darker skin and those with lighter skin?

16. **QUANTITATIVE** One research group investigated the role of autophagy on skin color using drugs that either induce autophagy (rapamycin) or inhibit autophagy (HCQ) in cells. The graph below compares the level of melanin in the treated samples to that of an untreated control. Explain these results, and use the P values provided in the graph to determine if the differences are significant or not (* means $P < 0.05$, ** means $P < 0.01$; see BioSkills 3). What conclusion, if any, can be drawn from this study?

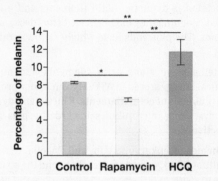

Source: D. Murase et al. 2013. *Journal of Investigative Dermatology* 133: 2416–2424.

MasteringBiology®

Students Go to MasteringBiology for assignments, the eText, and the Study Area with animations, practice tests, and activities.

Professors Go to MasteringBiology for automatically graded tutorials and questions that you can assign to your students, plus Instructor Resources.

8 Energy and Enzymes: An Introduction to Metabolism

When sugar is heated in the presence of oxygen, it undergoes the uncontrolled oxidation reaction known as burning. In this process, the chemical energy in sugar is released as heat and light. Cells do not burn sugar, but the same chemical energy that fuels this type of reaction drives the energy-demanding processes required for life.

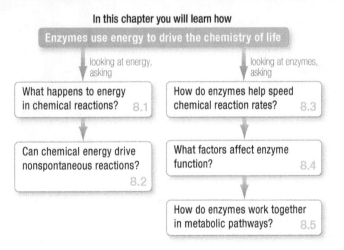

In this chapter you will learn how

Enzymes use energy to drive the chemistry of life

looking at energy, asking

What happens to energy in chemical reactions? 8.1

Can chemical energy drive nonspontaneous reactions? 8.2

looking at enzymes, asking

How do enzymes help speed chemical reaction rates? 8.3

What factors affect enzyme function? 8.4

How do enzymes work together in metabolic pathways? 8.5

This chapter is part of the Big Picture. See how on pages 232–233.

Cells are dynamic. A complex array of macromolecules are continually assembled and disassembled, millions of proteins transport substances across cellular membranes, and vesicles move cargo between organelles and to other destinations. These activities change constantly in response to signals from other cells or the environment.

What is responsible for all this activity? The answer is twofold—energy and enzymes. Because staying alive takes work, there is no life without energy. Life, at its most basic level, consists of chemical reactions catalyzed by enzymes. By using enzymes to direct which reactions occur and when, life possesses the distinguishing feature of creating order from a naturally disordered environment.

This chapter is about how enzymes work to help cells acquire and use energy. It is also your introduction to metabolic pathways—the ordered series of chemical reactions that build up or break down a particular molecule.

Let's begin by reviewing some fundamental concepts about energy and how it is used in cells.

8.1 What Happens to Energy in Chemical Reactions?

When biologists consider the amount of energy in chemical reactions that is available to do work, they evaluate two types of energy: kinetic energy and potential energy (Chapter 2). **Kinetic energy** is energy of motion. All moving objects have kinetic energy. Sound, thermal energy, electricity, and electromagnetic radiation (e.g., light) are other forms of kinetic energy. **Potential energy** is energy that is stored in position or configuration. Different forms of potential energy include gravitational, electrical, or chemical gradients, as well as energy in chemical bonds.

The existence of two types of energy—kinetic and potential—does not mean that energy is locked into either type. Rather, it is often transformed from one type to the other. To drive this point home, consider a drop of water sitting at the top of a waterfall, as in Figure 8.1.

Step 1 The water drop has potential energy (E_p) when it is at the top of the waterfall—this is gravitational potential energy.

Step 2 As the drop passes over the waterfall, some of its potential energy is converted to kinetic energy (E_k), in the form of motion.

Step 3 As the drop approaches the rocks below most of the potential energy has been converted to kinetic energy. When the drop reaches the bottom, some of the kinetic energy generates a force that breaks up rocks (mechanical energy). The rest of the energy is transformed into different forms of kinetic energy, such as thermal energy that raises the temperature of the water and rocks and sound.

Chemical Reactions Involve Energy Transformations

At the molecular level, kinetic energy is typically in the form of thermal energy and potential energy and is stored in chemical bonds. The amount of potential energy in a covalent bond is based on the position of the shared electrons relative to the nuclei of the bonded atoms (see Figure 8.2). This is analogous to the gravitational energy present in the water drop at the top of the waterfall. If the shared electrons are far from the positive charges in both nuclei, the bond has high potential energy. In general, the potential energy of a molecule depends on how its shared electrons are configured or positioned: Weaker bonds with equally shared electrons have high potential energy, and stronger bonds with unequally shared electrons have low potential energy.

In chemical reactions, if the products formed have shorter, stronger covalent bonds than the reactants, the potential energy stored within the bonds decreases. This change in potential energy is transformed into an equal amount of kinetic energy

PROCESS: ENERGY TRANSFORMATION IN A WATERFALL

1. Potential energy
A water drop sitting at the top of a waterfall has a defined amount of potential energy, $E_{p\,(top)}$.

2. Kinetic energy
As the drop of water falls, some of this potential energy is converted to kinetic energy (the energy of motion), E_k.

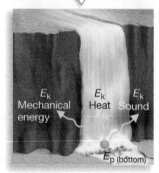

3. Other forms of kinetic energy
When the water drop strikes the rocks below, its potential energy is now much lower. The change in potential energy has been transformed into an equal amount of kinetic energy in the form of motion that exerts a force, thermal energy, and sound.

Result: $E_{p\,(top)} = E_{p\,(bottom)} + E_{k\,(total)}$

Conclusion: Energy is neither created nor destroyed; it simply changes form.

Figure 8.1 **Energy Transformations.** During an energy transformation, the total amount of energy in the system remains constant.

that usually takes the form of thermal energy, but sometimes it takes the form of light.

These examples illustrate the **first law of thermodynamics**, which states that energy is conserved. Energy cannot be created or destroyed, but only transferred and transformed.

The total energy in a molecule is referred to as its **enthalpy** (represented by H). Enthalpy includes the potential energy of the molecule, often referred to as heat content, plus the effect of the molecule on the pressure and volume of its surroundings.

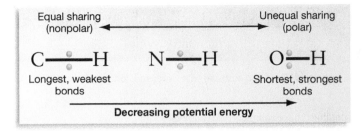

Figure 8.2 Potential Energy in Molecules Is Based on Bonds.
Potential energy stored in the bonds of molecules is directly related to electron position.

The contributions of potential energy, pressure, and volume to the enthalpy of a molecule are best understood by observing the change in enthalpy in a chemical reaction. For example, let's examine the reaction responsible for the explosive bursts of scalding hot liquid a bombardier beetle can produce when provoked, as seen in **Figure 8.3**:

$$2\,H_2O_2(aq) \rightarrow 2\,H_2O(l) + O_2(g)$$

In this reaction, a large change in enthalpy occurs as hydrogen peroxide (H_2O_2) is broken down into water and O_2 gas, which expands to over 500 times the original volume of the H_2O_2. Heat given off from the reaction also increases the temperature of the liquid dramatically. These massive increases in temperature and volume generate the pressure that propels the boiling liquid out of an opening at the tip of the beetle's abdomen.

Changes in enthalpy in chemical reactions can be measured and are represented by ΔH. (The uppercase Greek letter delta, Δ, is often used in chemical and mathematical notation to represent change.) The value of ΔH is primarily based on the difference in potential energy, since—apart from the reaction in the

Figure 8.3 Reactions May Be Explosive Due to Changes in Enthalpy. When provoked, the bombardier beetle mixes reactants with enzymes in a special chamber near the tip of its abdomen. The enzyme-catalyzed reaction releases heat energy and oxygen gas. The result is the projection of boiling hot liquid at a predator.

bombardier beetle—most biological reactions do not result in substantial changes in pressure and volume. When a reaction releases heat (products have less potential energy than the reactants), it is **exothermic** and the ΔH is negative. If heat is taken up during the reaction, generating products that have higher potential energy than the reactants, the reaction is **endothermic** and ΔH is positive.

Another factor that changes during a chemical reaction is the amount of disorder or **entropy** (symbolized by S). When the products of a chemical reaction become less ordered than the reactant molecules were, entropy increases and ΔS is positive. The **second law of thermodynamics**, in fact, states that total entropy always increases in a system that includes the surroundings as well as the products of the reaction (see Chapter 2 for an introduction to the first and second laws of thermodynamics).

To determine whether a chemical reaction is spontaneous, it's necessary to assess the amount of energy in the reaction available to do work—what chemists call **Gibbs free energy** (symbolized by G). This is accomplished by determining the change in Gibbs free energy (ΔG) in the reaction, which is based on changes in enthalpy and entropy as shown in the **standard free-energy change** equation:

$$\Delta G = \Delta H - T\Delta S$$

Here, T stands for temperature measured on the Kelvin scale (see BioSkills 1). To convert Celsius to Kelvin, you add $273.15°$.

In words, the change in Gibbs free energy in a reaction is equal to the change in enthalpy minus the product of the change in entropy and the temperature. Thermal energy increases the amount of disorder in the system, so the $T\Delta S$ term simply means that the faster molecules are moving, the more important entropy becomes in determining the change in Gibbs free energy.

Chemical reactions are spontaneous when ΔG is less than zero. Such reactions are said to be **exergonic**. Reactions are nonspontaneous when ΔG is greater than zero. Such reactions are termed **endergonic**. When ΔG is equal to zero, reactions are at equilibrium. ✔ If you understand these concepts, you should be able to explain (1) why the same reaction can be nonspontaneous at low temperature but spontaneous at high temperature, and (2) why some exothermic reactions are nonspontaneous.

Spontaneous chemical reactions run in the direction that lowers the free energy of the system. Exergonic reactions are spontaneous and release energy; endergonic reactions are nonspontaneous and require an input of energy to proceed. Be careful not to confuse these terms with the exothermic and endothermic reactions introduced earlier, which address only the change in enthalpy and do not include the effect of changes in entropy.

Temperature and Concentration Affect Reaction Rates

Even if a chemical reaction occurs spontaneously, it may not happen quickly. For example, the reactions that convert iron to rust, or sugar molecules to carbon dioxide and water, are spontaneous, but at room temperature they occur very slowly, if at all.

QUESTION: Do chemical reaction rates increase with increased temperature and concentration?

RATE INCREASE HYPOTHESIS: Chemical reaction rates increase with increased temperature. They also increase with increased concentration of reactants.

NULL HYPOTHESIS: Chemical reaction rates are not affected by increases in temperature or concentration of reactants.

EXPERIMENTAL SETUP:

Experimental reaction: $3\ HSO_3^-(aq) + IO_3^-(aq) \rightleftharpoons 3\ HSO_4^-(aq) + I^-(aq)$

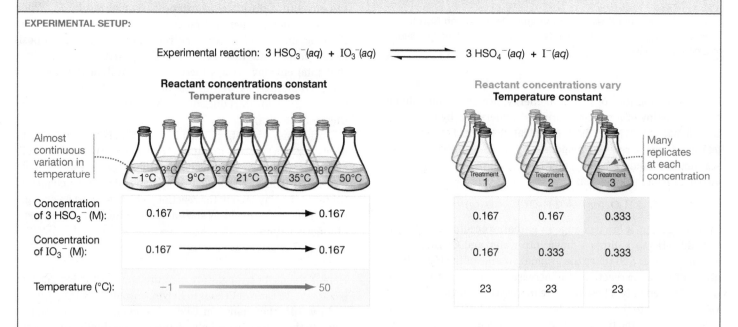

PREDICTION: Reaction rate, measured as 1/(time for reaction to go to completion), will increase with increased concentrations of reactants and increased temperature of reaction mix.

PREDICTION OF NULL HYPOTHESIS: There will be no difference in reaction rates among treatments in each setup.

RESULTS:

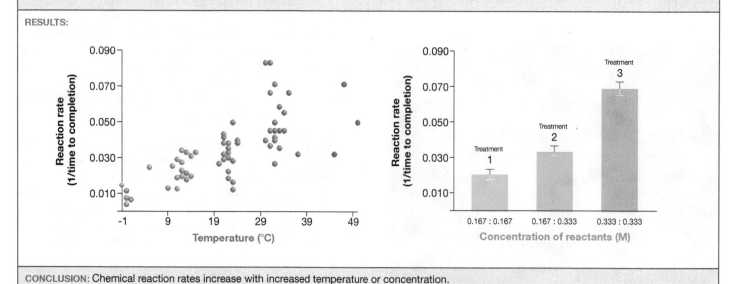

CONCLUSION: Chemical reaction rates increase with increased temperature or concentration.

Figure 8.4 Testing the Hypothesis that Reaction Rates Are Sensitive to Changes in Temperature and Concentration.

✔ Use **BioSkills 3** to explain why no error bars are used for the points shown on the graph on the left side of the "Results" section.

For most reactions to proceed, one or more chemical bonds have to break and others have to form. For this to happen, the substances involved must collide in a specific orientation that brings the electrons involved near each other. (See Chapter 2 to review the forces involved in bond formation.)

The number of collisions occurring between the substances in a mixture depends on their temperature and concentration:

- When the concentration of reactants is high, more collisions will occur and reactions should proceed more quickly.

- When their temperature is high, reactants will move faster and should collide more frequently.

Higher concentrations and higher temperatures should therefore speed up chemical reactions. To test this hypothesis, students at Parkland College in Champaign, Illinois, performed the experiments shown in **Figure 8.4**. Pay special attention to the two graphs in the "Results" section:

- ***Temperature versus reaction rate*** The graph on the left is based on experiments where the concentration of the reactants was the same, but the temperature varied. Each data point represents one experiment. Notice that the points represent a trend that rises from left to right—meaning, in this case, that the reaction rate increased when the temperature of the reaction mixture was higher.

- ***Concentration versus reaction rate*** The graph on the right is based on experiments where the temperature was constant, but the concentration of reactants varied. Each bar represents the average reaction rate over many replicates of each treatment, or set of concentrations. The thin lines at the top of each bar indicate the standard error of the mean—a measure of variability (see BioSkills 3). The take-home message of this graph is that reaction rates are higher when reactant concentrations are higher.

The reactions shown in Figure 8.4 were exergonic, meaning that the products had lower free energy than the reactants, so no input of energy was required. But, what drives nonspontaneous, endergonic reactions? Let's take a closer look.

8.2 Nonspontaneous Reactions May Be Driven Using Chemical Energy

By definition, endergonic reactions require an input of energy to proceed. Recall that radiation from the Sun and electricity from lightning could have driven nonspontaneous reactions during chemical evolution (Chapter 2). What source of energy drives these reactions inside cells?

Figure 8.5 shows how **energetic coupling** between exergonic and endergonic reactions allows free energy released from one reaction to drive another. In cells, this process generally occurs in one of two ways, either through the transfer of electrons or the transfer of a phosphate group.

Redox Reactions Transfer Energy via Electrons

Chemical reactions that involve the loss or gain of one or more electrons are called **reduction–oxidation reactions**, or **redox reactions**. When an atom or molecule loses one or more electrons, it is oxidized. This makes sense if you notice that the term "oxidized" sounds as if oxygen has done something to an atom or molecule. Recall that oxygen is highly electronegative and often pulls shared electrons away from other atoms in covalent bonds (Chapter 2). On the other hand, when an atom or molecule gains one or more electrons, it is reduced. To keep these terms straight, students often use the mnemonic "OIL RIG"—**Oxidation** *Is Loss* of electrons; **Reduction** *Is Gain* of electrons.

Oxidation events are always paired with a reduction; if one atom loses an electron, another has to gain it, and vice versa. Since electron position is related to potential energy, redox reactions represent the energetic coupling of two half-reactions, one exergonic and one endergonic. Oxidation is the exergonic

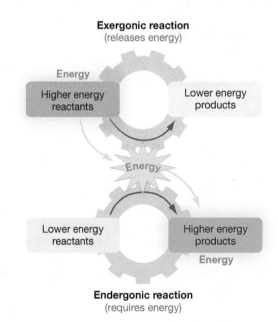

Exergonic reaction
(releases energy)

Energy

Higher energy reactants

Lower energy products

Energy

Lower energy reactants

Higher energy products

Energy

Endergonic reaction
(requires energy)

Figure 8.5 Energetic Coupling Allows Endergonic Reactions to Proceed Using the Free Energy Released from Exergonic Reactions.

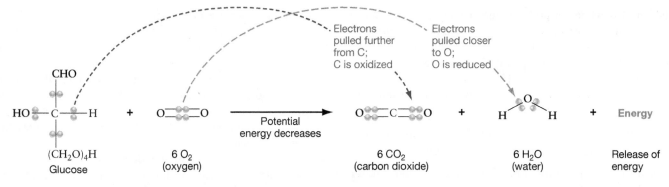

Figure 8.6 Redox Reactions Involve the Gain or Loss of One or More Electrons. This diagram shows how the position of shared electrons changes when glucose reacts with oxygen. The carbons of glucose are oxidized while the oxygen atoms of O_2 are reduced.

half-reaction, and reduction is the endergonic half-reaction. Some of the energy that is lost by the oxidized molecule is used to increase potential energy of the reduced molecule. In cases where more free energy is released by the oxidation step than is necessary for the reduction step, the overall reaction is exergonic.

In redox reactions, electrons may be gained or lost in two different ways. First, transferred electrons may result in a change in the number of electrons in the valence shell of an atom, such as when iron atoms are reduced from Fe^{3+} to Fe^{2+}. In other cases, electrons are transferred as new covalent bonds that are formed with other atoms. In such cases, an atom is reduced or oxidized based on the change in the position of shared electrons relative to the atom's nucleus.

An Example of Redox in Action To see how redox reactions work, consider the spontaneous reaction that occurs when reduced carbons in glucose ($C_6H_{12}O_6$) are oxidized as the sugar is burned in the presence of oxygen (O_2) (**Figure 8.6**). The orange dots in the illustration represent the positions of the electrons involved in covalent bonds.

Now compare the position of the shared electrons in the first reactant, glucose, with their position in the first product, carbon dioxide. Notice that the number of electrons around carbon has not changed, but instead the shared electrons have moved farther from the carbon nucleus in carbon dioxide. This means that carbon has been oxidized: it has "lost" electrons. The change occurred because the carbon and hydrogen atoms in glucose share electrons equally, while the carbon and oxygen atoms in CO_2 don't. In CO_2, the high electronegativity of the oxygen atoms pulled electrons away from the carbon atom.

Now compare the position of the shared electrons in the reactant O_2 molecules with their position in the product water molecules. In water, these electrons have moved closer to the oxygen nuclei than they were in the O_2 molecules, meaning that the oxygen atoms have been reduced. Oxygen has "gained" electrons. Thus, when glucose burns, carbon atoms are oxidized while oxygen atoms are reduced.

These changes in electron position correspond to changes in the amount of chemical energy. When glucose reacts with oxygen, the new bonds formed in the products are stronger and the electrons are held much tighter than in the reactant molecules. This means the potential energy in the products is lower than the reactants. The entropy of the products is also much higher than that of the reactants, as indicated by the increase in the number of molecules. As a result, this reaction is exergonic. It releases energy in the form of heat and light.

Another Approach to Understanding Redox During the redox reactions that occur in cells, electrons (e^-) may also be transferred from an atom in one molecule, called the **electron donor**, to an atom in a different molecule, the **electron acceptor**. When this occurs, the electron may be accompanied by a proton (H^+), which would result in the addition of a neutral hydrogen (H) atom to the electron acceptor.

Most electron acceptors gain potential energy as they are reduced because the new bonds, often formed with hydrogen atoms, are weaker than the original bonds. This observation should sound familiar, from what you have learned about carbohydrates (see Chapter 5). Molecules that have a large number of C—H bonds, such as carbohydrates and fats, store a great deal of potential energy.

Conversely, molecules that are oxidized in cells often lose potential energy. To understand why, review Figure 8.6 and note that the oxidized carbons have an increased number of C—O bonds. Because oxygen atoms have extremely high electronegativity, the electrons involved in bonds with oxygen atoms have low potential energy.

In many redox reactions in biology, understanding where oxidation and reduction have occurred is a matter of following hydrogen atoms—reduction often "adds H's" and oxidation often "removes H's." For example, **flavin adenine dinucleotide (FAD)** is a cellular electron acceptor that is reduced by two electrons accompanied by two protons to form **FADH$_2$** (Figure 8.7a). FADH$_2$ readily donates these electrons to other molecules. As a result, it is called an **electron carrier** and is said to have "reducing power."

Another common electron carrier is **nicotinamide adenine dinucleotide (NAD$^+$)**, which is reduced to form **NADH**. As with FAD, two electrons reduce NAD$^+$. These carriers differ, however, in the number of hydrogen atoms transferred. NAD$^+$ acquires only one of the two hydrogen atoms and releases the second into the environment as H^+ (**Figure 8.7b**).

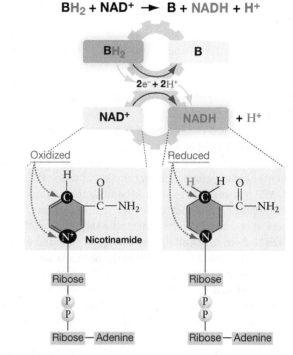

(a) Flavin adenine dinucleotide

$$AH_2 + FAD \longrightarrow A + FADH_2$$

AH$_2$ A

2e$^-$ + 2H$^+$

FAD   FADH$_2$

Oxidized   Reduced

Flavin

(b) Nicotinamide adenine dinucleotide

$$BH_2 + NAD^+ \longrightarrow B + NADH + H^+$$

BH$_2$ B

2e$^-$ + 2H$^+$

NAD$^+$ NADH   + H$^+$

Oxidized   Reduced

Nicotinamide

Figure 8.7 Redox Reactions May Transfer Electrons Alone or as Hydrogen Atoms. FADH$_2$ and NADH are important electron carriers that are formed by transferring electrons (e$^-$) from other molecules (symbolized as AH$_2$ or BH$_2$) to FAD and NAD$^+$. Some of these transferred electrons are accompanied by protons (H$^+$), which result in the formation of new covalent bonds with hydrogen atoms.

✔ If you understand how electrons are transferred in redox reactions, you should be able to identify the electron donors and electron acceptors in the two reactions shown in Figure 8.7.

The two examples in Figure 8.7 illustrate an important point—all redox reactions involve the transfer of electrons, but they do not always involve the transfer of hydrogen atoms. Redox reactions are central in biology—they transfer energy via electrons. The energy released from certain key redox reactions (see Chapters 9 and 10) is used to drive the endergonic formation of the nucleotide ATP from ADP and P$_i$. How is the energy stored in ATP used by the cell?

ATP Transfers Energy via Phosphate Groups

Adenosine triphosphate (ATP) (introduced in Chapter 4) can make things happen in cells because it has a great deal of potential energy. As **Figure 8.8a** shows, four negative charges are confined to a small area in the three phosphate groups of ATP. In part

(a) ATP stores a large amount of potential energy.

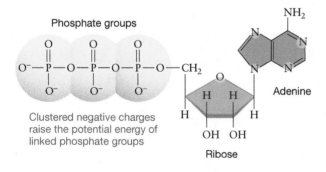

Phosphate groups

Clustered negative charges raise the potential energy of linked phosphate groups

Adenine

Ribose

Figure 8.8 Adenosine Triphosphate (ATP) Has High Potential Energy. (a) ATP's high potential energy results, in part, from the four negative charges clustered in its three phosphate groups. The negative charges repel each other, raising the potential energy of the bonds. **(b)** When ATP is hydrolyzed to ADP and inorganic phosphate, a large free-energy change occurs.

(b) Energy is released when ATP is hydrolyzed.

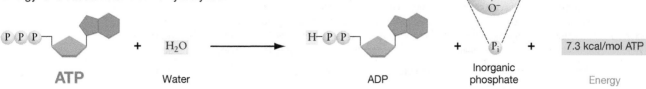

ATP   Water   ADP   Inorganic phosphate   7.3 kcal/mol ATP

Energy

because these negative charges repel each other, the potential energy of the bonds between the phosphate groups is extraordinarily high.

ATP Hydrolysis Releases Free Energy When ATP reacts with water during a hydrolysis reaction, the bond between ATP's outermost phosphate group and its neighbor is broken, resulting in the formation of ADP and inorganic phosphate, P_i, which has the formula HPO_4^{2-} (**Figure 8.8b**). This reaction is highly exergonic. Under standard conditions of temperature and pressure in the laboratory, a total of 7.3 kilocalories of energy per mole of ATP (or 7.3 kcal/mol), is released during the reaction. A **kilocalorie (kcal)** of energy raises 1 kilogram (kg) of water 1°C.

ATP hydrolysis is exergonic because the entropy of the product molecules is higher than that of the reactants, and because there is a large drop in potential energy when ATP is hydrolyzed to form ADP and P_i. The change in potential energy occurs because the new bonds formed in the products are much stronger than those in ATP. The destabilizing effect of the negative charges is also reduced in ADP and P_i because these products interact with the partial positive charges on surrounding water molecules more efficiently than the clustered negative charges on ATP did.

How Does ATP Drive Endergonic Reactions? If the reaction diagrammed in Figure 8.8b occurred in a test tube, the energy released would be lost as heat. But cells don't lose that 7.3 kcal/mole as heat. Instead, they use it to make things happen. Specifically, the energy that is released when ATP is hydrolyzed may be used to transfer the cleaved phosphate to a target molecule, called a **substrate**.

The addition of a phosphate group to a substrate is called **phosphorylation**. When ATP is the phosphate donor, phosphorylation is exergonic because the newly formed bonds in ADP and the phosphorylated substrate have much less potential energy than the bonds that were broken in the reactants.

To see how this process works, consider an endergonic reaction between two reactant molecules—compound A and compound B—that results in a product AB needed by your cells. For this reaction to proceed, an input of energy is required.

When a phosphate group from ATP is added to one of the reactant molecules, the potential energy of the reactant is increased. This phosphorylated intermediate is referred to as an activated substrate. This is the critical point: Activated substrates have high enough potential energy that the reaction between compound A and, for example, the activated form of compound B is now exergonic. The two compounds then go on to react and form the product molecule AB.

Figure 8.9 graphs how phosphorylation can couple exergonic and endergonic reactions. After the exergonic transfer of a phosphate group from ATP to B occurs, the free energy of the reactants A and BP is high enough to make the reaction that forms AB exergonic. When reactant molecules in an endergonic reaction are phosphorylated, the increase in potential energy in the reactants makes the combined overall reaction exergonic.

✔ If you understand the principles of energetic coupling, you should be able to compare and contrast how energy is transferred via redox reactions and ATP hydrolysis.

It is hard to overstate the importance of energetic coupling. In the time it takes to read this sentence, ATP has been used to convert millions of endergonic reactions into exergonic reactions. If the cells in your body could no longer couple these reactions, you would die within minutes.

Now the question is, What role do enzymes play in these reactions?

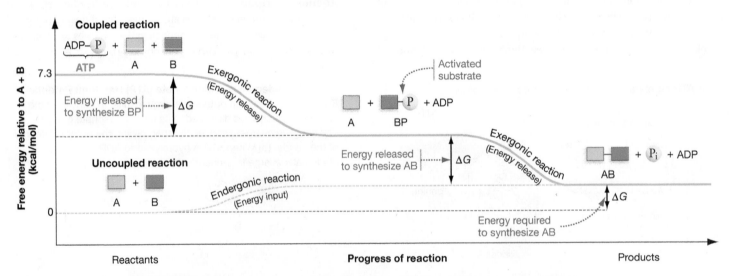

Figure 8.9 Exergonic Phosphorylation Reactions Are Coupled to Endergonic Reactions. In cells, many reactions occur only if one reactant is activated by phosphorylation. The phosphorylated reactant molecule has high enough free energy that the subsequent reaction is exergonic. In this graph, the free energy being tracked on the y-axis represents A, B, and the 7.3 kcal/mol that is released when ATP is hydrolyzed. For simplicity, the free energy in ADP and P_i is not shown. ΔG represents the change in free energy between the reactants and products for each indicated step.

✔ Label the ΔG in the uncoupled reaction and the two steps of the coupled reaction to indicate if the change is representing a positive ($>$ 0) or negative ($<$ 0) value.

8.3 How Enzymes Work

Regardless of whether reactions in cells are spontaneous or not, none would occur at the speed required for life without the support of enzymes. How do they do it?

Recall that the initial hypothesis for how enzymes speed up reactions—the "lock-and-key" model—was first proposed in 1894 by Emil Fischer (introduced in Chapter 3). In this model, the substrates would fit into enzymes and react in a manner analogous to a key being inserted into a lock. In this way, enzymes are **catalysts**—they bring substrates together in a precise orientation that makes reactions more likely. Fischer's model also explained why many enzymes are specific for a single reaction—specificity is a product of the geometry and chemical properties of the sites where substrates bind.

Enzymes Help Reactions Clear Two Hurdles

Recall that two hurdles must be cleared before reactions can take place: Reactants need to **(1)** collide in a precise orientation and **(2)** have enough kinetic energy to overcome repulsion between electrons that come into contact as a bond forms (Chapter 2). To appreciate how enzymes work, let's consider each hurdle in turn.

Enzymes Bring Substrates Together Part of the reason enzymes are such effective catalysts is that they bring substrate molecules together in a substrate binding site known as the enzyme's **active site** (Chapter 3). In this way, enzymes help substrates collide in a precise orientation so that old bonds can break and new bonds can form to generate products.

The vast majority of enzymes are roughly globular proteins much larger than substrates (recall that some enzymes are made of RNA; see Chapters 4 and 17). The active site is in a cleft or cavity within the enzyme structure. A good example can be seen in the enzyme glucokinase, which catalyzes the phosphorylation of the sugar glucose. (Many enzymes have names that hint at the identity of the substrate and end with *–ase*.) As the left side of **Figure 8.10** shows, the active site in glucokinase is a small notch in an otherwise large, crescent-shaped enzyme.

In Fischer's original lock-and-key model, enzymes were conceived of as being rigid—almost literally as rigid as a lock. As research on enzyme action progressed, however, Fischer's model had to be modified. Perhaps the most important realization was that enzymes are not rigid and static, but flexible and dynamic. In fact, many enzymes undergo a significant change in shape, or conformation, when reactant molecules bind to the active site. You can see this conformational change, called an **induced fit**, in the glucokinase molecule on the right side of Figure 8.10. Once glucokinase binds its substrates—ATP and glucose—the enzyme rocks forward over the active site to bring the two substrates together.

In addition, recent research has clarified the nature of Fischer's key. When one or more substrate molecules enter the active site, they are held in place through hydrogen bonding or other weak interactions with amino acid residues in the active site. Once the substrate is bound, one or more R-groups in the active site come into play. The degree of interaction between the substrate and enzyme increases and reaches a maximum when a temporary, unstable, intermediate condition called the **transition state** is formed. When Fischer's key is in its lock, it represents

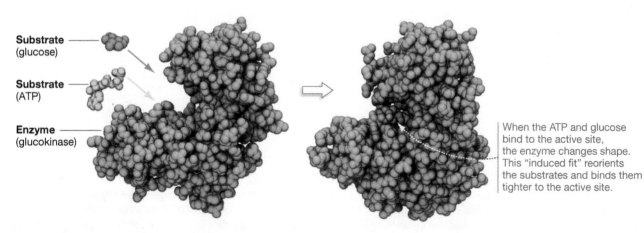

Substrate (glucose)

Substrate (ATP)

Enzyme (glucokinase)

When the ATP and glucose bind to the active site, the enzyme changes shape. This "induced fit" reorients the substrates and binds them tighter to the active site.

Figure 8.10 Substrate Molecules Bind to Specific Locations in an Enzyme. The substrate (reactant) molecules, shown in red and orange, fit into a precise location, called the active site, in the green enzyme. In this enzyme and in many others, the binding event causes the protein to change shape.

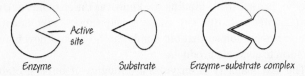

the transition state of the substrate. To practice modeling how enzymes interact with their substrates, see **Making Models 8.1**.

There is more to achieving this transition state than simply an enzyme binding to its substrates, however. Even if the reaction is spontaneous, a certain amount of kinetic energy—called the **activation energy**—is required to strain the chemical bonds in substrates so they can achieve the transition state. How do enzymes help clear the activation energy hurdle?

Enzymes Lower the Activation Energy Reactions happen when reactants have enough kinetic energy to overcome the activation energy barrier. The kinetic energy of molecules, in turn, is a function of their temperature. (This is why reactions tend to proceed faster at higher temperatures.)

Figure 8.11 graphs the changes in free energy that take place during the course of a chemical reaction. As you read along the

x-axis from left to right, note that a dramatic rise in free energy occurs when the reactants combine to form the transition state—followed by a dramatic drop in free energy when products form. The free energy of the transition state is high because the bonds that existed in the substrates are destabilized—it is the transition point between breaking old bonds and forming new ones.

The ΔG label on the graph indicates the overall change in free energy in the reaction—that is, the energy of the products minus the energy of the reactants. In this particular case, the products have lower free energy than the reactants, meaning that the reaction is exergonic. But because the activation energy for this reaction, symbolized by E_a, is high, the reaction would proceed slowly—even at high temperature.

This is an important point: The more unstable the transition state, the higher the activation energy and the less likely a reaction is to proceed quickly.

Reaction rates, then, depend on both the kinetic energy of the reactants and the activation energy of the particular reaction—meaning the free energy of the transition state. If the kinetic energy of the participating molecules is high, such as at high temperatures, then molecular collisions are more likely to overcome the activation energy barrier. At this point, the transition state is formed and the reaction takes place.

Enzymes don't change the temperature of a solution, though. How do they fit in?

Interactions with amino acid residues within the enzyme's active site stabilize the transition state and thus lower the activation energy required for the reaction to proceed. At the atomic level, R-groups that line the active site may form short-lived covalent bonds that assist with the transfer of atoms or groups of atoms from one reactant to another. Commonly, the presence of acidic or basic R-groups allows the reactants to lose or gain a proton more readily.

Figure 8.12 diagrams how enzymes lower the activation energy for a reaction. Note that the presence of an enzyme does not affect the overall energy change, ΔG, or change the energy of

Figure 8.11 Changes in Free Energy during a Chemical Reaction. The energy profile shows changes in free energy that occur over the course of a hypothetical reaction between a molecule A and a molecule containing parts B and C. The overall reaction would be written as $A + BC \rightarrow AB + C$. E_a is the activation energy of the reaction.

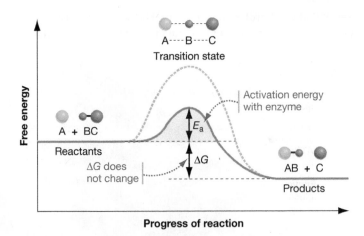

Figure 8.12 An Enzyme Changes the Activation Energy of a Reaction. The energy profile for the same reaction diagrammed in Figure 8.11, but now with a catalyst (enzyme) present. Even though the energy barrier to the reaction, E_a, is much lower, ΔG does not change.

✓ **CAUTION** Can a catalyst alone make a nonspontaneous reaction occur spontaneously? Explain why or why not.

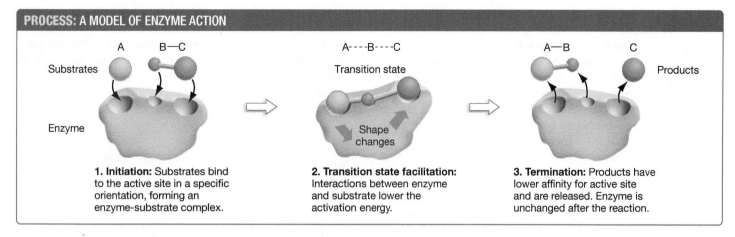

1. Initiation: Substrates bind to the active site in a specific orientation, forming an enzyme-substrate complex.

2. Transition state facilitation: Interactions between enzyme and substrate lower the activation energy.

3. Termination: Products have lower affinity for active site and are released. Enzyme is unchanged after the reaction.

Figure 8.13 A Three-Step Process to Model Enzyme Action.

the reactants or the products. An enzyme only lowers the activation energy required to achieve the transition state.

Most enzymes are specific in their activity—they catalyze just a single reaction by lowering the activation energy that is required—and many are astonishingly efficient. Most of the important reactions in biology would not occur at all, or else proceed at imperceptible rates, without a catalyst. It's not unusual for enzymes to speed up reactions by a factor of a million; some enzymes make reactions go many *trillions* of times faster than they would without a catalyst.

It's also important to note that an enzyme is not consumed in a chemical reaction, even though it participates in the reaction. The composition of an enzyme is exactly the same after the reaction as it was before. **Figure 8.13** summarizes how enzymes catalyze reactions.

1. *Initiation* Instead of substrates occasionally colliding in a random fashion, enzymes precisely orient substrates as they bind at specific locations within the active site.

2. *Transition state facilitation* Inside a catalyst's active site, substrate molecules are more likely to reach their transition state. In some cases the transition state is stabilized by a change in the enzyme's shape. Interactions between the substrate and R-groups in the enzyme's active site lower the activation energy required for the reaction. Thus, the catalyzed reaction proceeds much more rapidly than the uncatalyzed reaction.

3. *Termination* The reaction products have less affinity for the active site than the transition state does. Binding ends, the products are released, and the enzyme returns to its original conformation.

✔ If you understand the basic principles of enzyme catalysis, you should be able to complete the following sentences: (1) Enzymes speed reaction rates by _____ and lowering activation energy. (2) Activation energies drop because enzymes destabilize bonds in the substrates, forming the _____. (3) Enzyme specificity is a function of the active site's shape and the chemical properties of the _____ at the active site. (4) In enzymes, as in many molecules, function follows from _____.

What Limits the Rate of Catalysis?

For several decades after Fischer's model was published, most research on enzymes focused on rates of enzyme action, or what biologists call enzyme kinetics. Researchers observed that, when the amount of product produced per second—indicating the speed of the reaction—is plotted as a function of substrate concentration, a graph like that shown in **Figure 8.14** results.

In this graph, each data point represents an experiment where reaction rate was measured when substrates were present in various concentrations. The two lines represent two series of experiments: one with the reactions catalyzed by an enzyme and the other uncatalyzed. As you read the curve for the catalyzed reaction from left to right, note that it has three basic sections:

1. When substrate concentrations are low, the speed of an enzyme-catalyzed reaction increases in a steep, linear fashion.

2. At intermediate substrate concentrations, the increase in speed begins to slow.

3. At high substrate concentration, the reaction rate plateaus at a maximum speed.

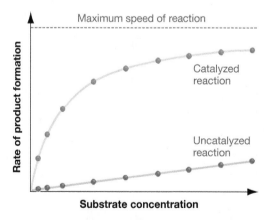

Figure 8.14 Enzyme-Catalyzed Reactions Can Be Saturated. At high substrate concentration, enzyme-catalyzed reactions reach a maximum rate. Uncatalyzed reactions slowly increase as substrate concentration increases.

✔ Predict how you could increase the rate of product formation above the maximum shown in the graph.

This pattern is in striking contrast to the situation for the uncatalyzed reactions, where the reaction speed is far slower, but tends to show a continuing linear increase with substrate concentration. The "saturation kinetics" of enzyme-catalyzed reactions were taken as strong evidence that the enzyme–substrate complex proposed by Fischer actually exists. The idea was that, at some point, active sites cannot accept substrates any faster, no matter how large the concentration of substrates gets. Stated another way, reaction rates level off because all available enzyme molecules are being used.

Do Enzymes Work Alone?

The answer to this question, in many cases, is no. Ions or molecules that are not part of an enzyme's primary structure are often required for an enzyme to function normally. These enzyme "helpers" can be divided into three different types:

1. **Cofactors** are inorganic ions, such as the metal ions Zn^{2+} (zinc), Mg^{2+} (magnesium), and Fe^{2+} (iron), that reversibly interact with enzymes. Cofactors that participate in key reactions in virtually all living cells are thought to have been involved in catalysis early on in chemical evolution (see Chapter 2).

2. **Coenzymes** are organic molecules that reversibly interact with enzymes, such as the electron carriers NADH or $FADH_2$.

3. **Prosthetic groups** are non–amino acid atoms or molecules that are permanently attached to proteins, such as the molecule retinal. Retinal is involved in converting light energy into chemical energy (see Chapter 44).

In many cases, these enzyme helpers are part of the active site and play a key role in stabilizing the transition state. Their presence is therefore essential for the catalytic activity of many enzymes.

To appreciate why this is important, consider that many of the vitamins in your diet are required for the production of coenzymes. Vitamin deficiencies result in coenzyme deficiencies.

Lack of coenzymes, in turn, disrupts normal enzyme function and causes disease. For example, thiamine (vitamin B_1) is required for the production of a coenzyme called thiamine pyrophosphate, which is required by three different enzymes. Lack of thiamine in the diet dramatically reduces the activity of these enzymes and causes an array of nervous system and heart disorders collectively known as beriberi.

8.4 What Factors Affect Enzyme Function?

Given that an enzyme's structure is critical to its function, it's not surprising that an enzyme's activity is sensitive to conditions that alter protein shape. Recall that protein structure is dependent on the chemical bonds and interactions that fold the polypeptide into its functional form (Chapter 3).

In particular, the activity of an enzyme often changes drastically as a function of temperature, pH, interactions with other molecules, and modifications of its primary structure. Let's take a look at how enzyme function is affected by, and sometimes even regulated by, each of these factors.

Enzymes Are Optimized for Particular Environments

Temperature affects the folding and movement of an enzyme as well as the kinetic energy of its substrates. The concentration of protons in a solution, as measured by pH, also affects enzyme structure and function. The pH affects the charge on carboxyl and amino groups in residue side chains, and also the active site's ability to participate in reactions that involve the transfer of protons or electrons.

Do data support these assertions? **Figure 8.15a** shows how the activity of an enzyme, plotted on the y-axis, changes as a

(a) Enzymes from different organisms may function best at different temperatures.

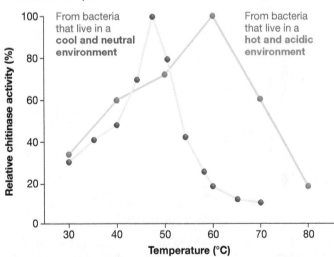

(b) Enzymes from different organisms may function best at different pHs.

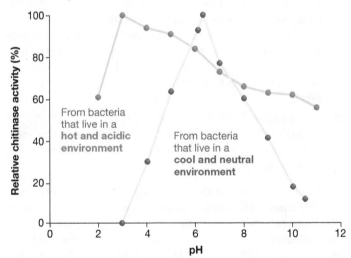

Figure 8.15 Enzymes Have an Optimal Temperature and pH. The activity of enzymes is sensitive to changes in temperature **(a)** and pH **(b)**.

DATA: Nawani, N., B. P. Kapadnis, A. D. Das, et al. 2002. *Journal of Applied Microbiology* 93: 865–975. Also Nawani, N., and B. P. Kapadnis. 2001. *Journal of Applied Microbiology* 90: 803–808.

function of temperature, plotted on the x-axis. These data were collected for an enzyme called chitinase, which is used by bacteria to digest cell walls of fungi. In this graph, each data point represents the enzyme's relative activity—meaning the rate of the enzyme-catalyzed reaction, scaled relative to the highest rate observed—in experiments conducted under conditions that differed only in temperature. Results are shown for two types of bacteria.

Note that, in both bacterial species, the enzyme has a distinct optimum or peak—a temperature at which it functions best. One of the bacterial species lives in the cool soil under palm trees, where the temperature is about 25°C, while the other lives in hot springs, where temperatures can be close to 100°C. The temperature optimum for the enzyme reflects these environments.

The two types of bacteria have different versions of the enzyme that differ in primary structure. Natural selection (introduced in Chapter 1) has resulted in each species having a structure that is best suited for its distinct environment. The two versions are adaptations that allow each species to thrive at different temperatures.

Figure 8.15b makes the same point for pH. The effect of pH on enzyme activity was tested on the same chitinases used in Figure 8.15a, but this time using conditions that varied only in pH. The soil-dwelling bacteria described earlier grow in a neutral pH environment, but the species that lives in hot springs is also exposed to acidic conditions.

Note that the organism that thrives in a hot, acidic environment has a version of the enzyme that performs best at high temperatures and low pH; the organism that lives in the cool soil has a version of the enzyme that functions best at cooler temperatures and nearly neutral pH. Each enzyme is sensitive to changes in temperature and pH, but each species' version of the enzyme has a structure that allows it to function best in its particular environment.

To summarize, the rate of an enzyme-catalyzed reaction depends not only on substrate concentration and the enzyme's intrinsic affinity for the substrate but also on temperature and pH (among other factors). Temperature affects the kinetic energy; both temperature and pH affect enzyme shape and reactivity.

Most Enzymes Are Regulated

Controlling when and where enzymes will function is vital to the work of a cell. While temperature and pH affect the activity of enzymes, they are not often used as a means of regulating enzyme function. Instead, other molecules, in some cases other enzymes, regulate most of the cell's enzymatic activity. These regulatory molecules often change the enzyme's structure or its ability to bind the substrate in some way to either activate or inactivate the function of the enzyme.

Regulating Enzymes via Noncovalent Interactions Many molecules that regulate enzyme activity bind noncovalently to the enzyme to alter the reaction rate. Since the interaction does not permanently affect the enzyme's primary structure, it is often referred to as being "reversible."

Reversible interactions affect enzyme function in one of two ways:

1. The regulatory molecule is similar in size and shape to the enzyme's natural substrate and inhibits catalysis by binding to the enzyme's active site. This event is called **competitive inhibition** because the molecule involved competes with the substrate for access to the enzyme's active site (Figure 8.16a).

2. The regulatory molecule binds at a location other than the active site and changes the shape of the enzyme. This type of interaction is called **allosteric** ("different-structure") **regulation** because the binding event changes the shape of the enzyme in a way that makes the active site available or unavailable (Figure 8.16b and 8.16c).

(a) Competitive inhibition

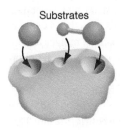
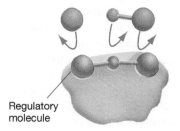

Substrates

Regulatory molecule

Enzyme in absence of regulation

The substrates cannot bind when a regulatory molecule binds to the enzyme's active site.

(b) Allosteric regulation (activation)

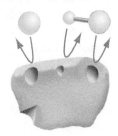
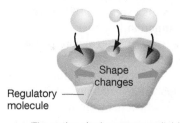

Regulatory molecule

Shape changes

Enzyme in absence of regulation

The active site becomes available to the substrates when a regulatory molecule binds to a different site on the enzyme.

(c) Allosteric regulation (inhibition)

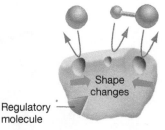

Shape changes

Regulatory molecule

Enzyme in absence of regulation

The active site becomes unavailable to the substrates when a regulatory molecule binds to a different site on the enzyme.

Figure 8.16 An Enzyme's Activity Is Precisely Regulated. Enzymes are turned on or off when specific regulatory molecules bind to them.

Both strategies depend on the concentration of the regulatory molecule—the more regulatory molecule present, the more likely it will be to bind to the enzyme and affect its activity. The amount of regulatory molecule is often tightly controlled and, as you'll see in Section 8.5, the regulatory molecules themselves often manage the enzymes that produce them.

Regulating Enzymes via Covalent Modifications In some cases, the function of an enzyme is altered by a chemical change in its primary structure. This change may be reversible or irreversible, depending on the type of modification.

Irreversible changes often result from the cleavage of peptide bonds that make up the primary structure of the enzyme. The enzyme trypsin, for example, is not functional until a small section of the protein is removed by a specific protease.

The most common modification of enzymes is the addition of one or more phosphate groups, similar to what was described for activated substrates in Section 8.2. In this case, however, the enzyme is phosphorylated instead of the substrate molecule. The transfer of a phosphate from ATP to the enzyme may be catalyzed by the enzyme itself or by a different enzyme.

When phosphorylation adds a negative charge to one or more amino acid residues in a protein, the chemical bonds that are responsible for the enzyme structure change configuration. This change in conformation may activate or inactivate the function of the active site.

Note that the term "activated" is used differently to describe the effect of phosphorylating substrates versus enzymes. When a substrate is activated, its potential energy has increased, and this energy is used to convert an endergonic reaction to one that is exergonic. When an enzyme is activated, its catalytic function has been turned on—any change in the potential energy of the enzyme is not directly used in driving the reaction.

To see how phosphorylation can affect the shape of an enzyme, let's look at an example called mitogen-activated protein (MAP) kinase, which is involved in cell signaling (see Chapter 11). As shown in **Figure 8.17**, phosphorylation of key amino acid residues in a particular loop of the primary sequence causes a shape change, which functions like a switch to activate the enzyme.

Phosphorylation of an enzyme is a reversible modification to the protein's structure. Dephosphorylation—removal of phosphates—can quickly return the protein to its previous shape. The relative abundance of enzymes that catalyze phosphorylation and dephosphorylation, then, regulates the function of the protein.

8.5 Enzymes Can Work Together in Metabolic Pathways

The eukaryotic cell has been compared to an industrial complex, where distinct organelles are functionally integrated into a cooperative network with a common goal—life (see Chapter 7). Similarly, enzymes often work together in a manner resembling an assembly line in a factory. Each of the molecules of life presented in this book is built by a series of reactions, each catalyzed by a different enzyme. These multistep processes are referred to as **metabolic pathways**.

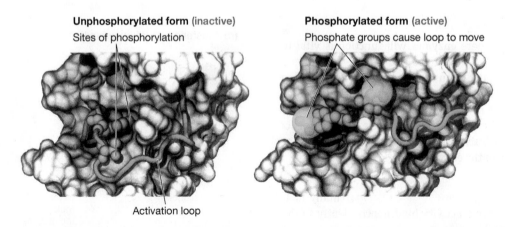

Unphosphorylated form (inactive)
Sites of phosphorylation

Phosphorylated form (active)
Phosphate groups cause loop to move

Activation loop

Figure 8.17 Phosphorylation Changes the Shape and Activity of Proteins. When proteins are phosphorylated, they often change shape in a way that alters their activity. The figure shows the structural change that occurs when the activation loop of MAP kinase is phosphorylated.

The following is an example of this type of teamwork, where an initial substrate A is sequentially modified by enzymes 1–3 to produce product D:

$$A \xrightarrow{\text{enzyme 1}} B \xrightarrow{\text{enzyme 2}} C \xrightarrow{\text{enzyme 3}} D$$

The B and C molecules are referred to as intermediates in the pathway—they serve as both a product and a reactant. For example, molecule B is the product of reaction 1 and the reactant for reaction 2.

Although these reactions have been written in a single direction, from left to right, the directionality often depends on the relative concentrations of the reactants and products, and the change in free energy (ΔG) for each reaction. For each step in the pathway, however, the concentration of the product will generally be higher than the concentration of its respective reactant at equilibrium. Since D is the overall product for this pathway, it would be expected to have the highest concentration relative to A, B, and C.

Metabolic Pathways Are Regulated

Since enzymes catalyze the reactions in metabolic pathways, the mechanisms that regulate enzyme function introduced in Section 8.4 also apply to the individual steps in a pathway. For example, to understand how blocking an individual reaction can affect an entire pathway, go back to the pathway model that produces product D and inactivate enzyme 2 by crossing it out.

✔ **MODEL** If you understand the assembly-line behavior of enzymes in a metabolic pathway, you should be able to predict how inactivating enzyme 2 would affect the concentration of molecules A, B, C, and D relative to what they would be if the pathway were fully functional.

A convenient way to regulate metabolic pathways is to use the final product of the reaction sequence to inactivate one of the enzymes. This type of regulation is called **feedback inhibition**. As the concentration of the product molecule becomes abundant, it "feeds back" to stop the reaction sequence (**Figure 8.18**). By inhibiting a step early in the pathway, the amount of the initial substrate is not depleted unnecessarily, allowing it to be stored or used for other reactions.

Metabolic Pathways Evolve

While many enzymes are extraordinarily specific, some can catalyze a range of reactions and are able to interact with a family of related substrates. Research suggests that this flexibility allowed new enzymes to evolve and that enzymes specialized for catalyzing key reactions provided cells with a selective advantage. Could the same flexibility also help explain the evolution of the stepwise series of reactions seen in metabolic pathways?

In 1945, Norman Horowitz proposed a simple, stepwise process that could have directed pathway evolution. In Horowitz's model, enzymes first would have evolved to make the building blocks of life from readily available substrates, such as small organic compounds (see Chapter 2).

If an original substrate were depleted, natural selection would favor the evolution of a new enzyme to make more of it from

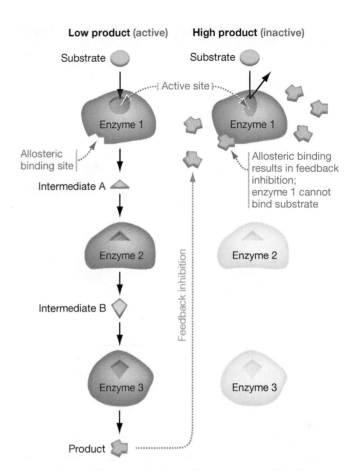

Figure 8.18 Feedback Inhibition Regulates Some Metabolic Pathways. Feedback inhibition occurs when the product of a metabolic pathway inhibits an enzyme that functions early in the pathway.

other existing molecules. By evolving a new reaction step to produce the original substrate—now serving as an intermediate in a two-step pathway—the original enzyme would have been able to continue its work. **Figure 8.19** on page 186 illustrates this model—referred to as retro-evolution—in which repetition of this backward process produces a multistep metabolic pathway.

Researchers also speculate that as early pathways emerged, these enzymes may have been recruited to new pathways, where they evolved new catalytic activities that performed new tasks. This hypothesis is called patchwork evolution, since the new reaction series would consist of enzymes brought together from different pathways.

Evidence of patchwork evolution has been observed in modern organisms, where new metabolic activities have emerged in response to human-made chemicals. For example, a novel pathway has recently evolved in one bacterial species to use the pesticide pentachlorophenol as a source of energy and carbon building blocks. Pentachlorophenol was first introduced into the environment in the 1930s as a timber preservative. The new pathway evolved by using enzymes from two preexisting pathways in a novel series of reactions. The metabolic activity of microbes is now being scrutinized and engineered to clean up a variety of human-made pollutants—giving rise to a new technology called **bioremediation** (see Chapter 26).

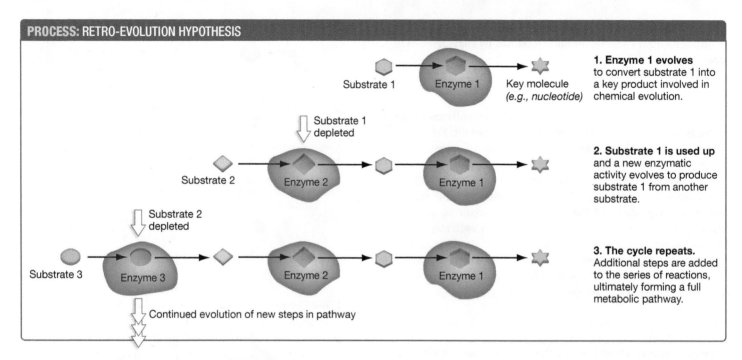

1. Enzyme 1 evolves to convert substrate 1 into a key product involved in chemical evolution.

2. Substrate 1 is used up and a new enzymatic activity evolves to produce substrate 1 from another substrate.

3. The cycle repeats. Additional steps are added to the series of reactions, ultimately forming a full metabolic pathway.

Figure 8.19 A Hypothetical Model for Metabolic Pathway Evolution.

Regardless of how they evolved, metabolic pathways are now vital to the function of all cells. Those that break down molecules for sources of energy and carbon building blocks are called **catabolic pathways**; those that use energy and carbon building blocks to synthesize molecules are called **anabolic pathways.**

You are being kept alive by key catabolic and anabolic pathways. The catabolic pathways of cellular respiration (introduced in Chapter 9) harvest electrons from reduced carbons (from sugars like glucose) and pass them through redox reactions to generate ATP. These reduced carbons are in turn produced by the anabolic pathways of photosynthesis that are driven by light energy (introduced in Chapter 10). The reactions involved in cellular respiration and photosynthesis perform the most important energy transformations to life on Earth.

CHAPTER 8   REVIEW

For media, go to MasteringBiology

8.1 What Happens to Energy in Chemical Reactions?

- The standard free-energy change for a chemical reaction is an equation used to measure the overall change in Gibbs free energy (ΔG)—that is, to calculate the combined effects of changes in enthalpy (ΔH) and entropy (ΔS).

- Reactions with a negative ΔG are exergonic and will occur spontaneously

- Reactions with a positive ΔG are endergonic and will not occur without an input of energy.

8.2 Nonspontaneous Reactions May Be Driven Using Chemical Energy

- Redox reactions transfer energy by coupling exergonic oxidation reactions to endergonic reduction reactions.

- High-energy bonds may be formed during the reduction step of a redox reaction. Many of these bonds form when an electron is transferred along with a proton (H^+).

- The hydrolysis of ATP is an exergonic reaction and is used to drive a variety of cellular processes.

- When a phosphate group from ATP is added to a substrate, it increases the potential energy of the substrate and may be used to convert endergonic reactions into exergonic reactions.

8.3 How Enzymes Work

- Enzymes are catalysts. They speed reaction rates but do not affect the change in free energy of the reaction.
- Enzymes have active sites that bring substrates together and may change shape to stabilize the transition state.
- Activation energy is the amount of kinetic energy required to reach the transition state of a reaction.
- Enzymes speed up a reaction by lowering the activation energy, often with the help of cofactors, coenzymes, or prosthetic groups.

8.4 What Factors Affect Enzyme Function?

- Most enzymes are proteins, and thus their activity can be directly influenced by modifications or environmental factors, such as temperature and pH, that alter their three-dimensional structure.
- Enzyme activity may be regulated by molecules that compete with substrates to occupy the active site or alter enzyme shape.
- Protein cleavage and phosphorylation may regulate enzyme activity by modifying the primary structure of the enzyme.

8.5 Enzymes Can Work Together in Metabolic Pathways

- In cells, enzymes often work together in metabolic pathways that sequentially modify a substrate to make a product.
- A pathway may be regulated by controlling the activity of one enzyme by feedback inhibition, often the first in the series of reactions.
- Metabolic pathways were vital to the evolution of life, and new pathways continue to evolve in cells.

Answers are available in Appendix A

✔ TEST YOUR KNOWLEDGE

1. If a reaction is exergonic, then which of these statements is true?
   a. The products have lower Gibbs free energy than the reactants.
   b. Energy must be added for the reaction to proceed.
   c. The products have lower entropy (are more ordered) than the reactants.
   d. The reaction always occurs quickly.

2. What is a transition state?
   a. the shape adopted by an enzyme that has an inhibitory molecule bound at its active site
   b. the amount of kinetic energy required for a reaction to proceed
   c. the intermediate complex formed as covalent bonds in the reactants are being broken and re-formed during a reaction
   d. the structure of an enzyme when an allosteric regulatory molecule binds to it

3. How does pH affect enzyme-catalyzed reactions?
   a. Protons serve as substrates for most reactions.
   b. Energy stored in protons is used to drive endergonic reactions.
   c. Proton concentration increases the kinetic energy of the reactants, enabling them to reach their transition state.
   d. The concentration of protons affects an enzyme's folded structure and reactivity.

4. Explain how feedback inhibition regulates metabolic pathways.

✔ TEST YOUR UNDERSTANDING

5. Explain the lock-and-key model of enzyme activity. What is incorrect about this model?

6. If you were to expose glucose to oxygen on your lab bench, why would you not expect to see it burn as shown in Figure 8.6?
   a. The reaction is endergonic and requires an input of energy.
   b. The reaction is not spontaneous unless an enzyme is added to the substrates.
   c. The sugar must first be phosphorylated to increase its potential energy.
   d. Activation energy is required for the sugar and oxygen to reach their transition state.

7. QUANTITATIVE In Figure 8.9, the energetic coupling of ATP hydrolysis and an endergonic reaction are shown. If the hydrolysis of ATP releases 7.3 kcal of free energy, use the graph in this figure to estimate what you would expect the ΔG values to be for the uncoupled reaction and the two steps in the coupled reaction.

8. Using what you have learned about changes in Gibbs free energy, would you predict the ΔG value of catabolic reactions to be positive or negative? What about anabolic reactions? Justify your answers using the terms "enthalpy" and "entropy."

✔ TEST YOUR PROBLEM-SOLVING SKILLS

9. MODEL Draw a chemical equation to represent the redox reaction that occurs when methane (CH_4) burns in the presence of oxygen (O_2). Identify the reactant that is being reduced and the reactant that is being oxidized. Of the four molecules that should be in your equation, point out the one that has the highest energy bonds.

10. You have discovered an enzyme that appears to function only when a particular sugar accumulates. Which of the following scenarios would you predict to be responsible for activating this enzyme?
    a. The sugar cleaves the enzyme to form the active conformation.
    b. The sugar is an allosteric regulatory molecule for the enzyme.
    c. The sugar is a competitive inhibitor for the enzyme.
    d. The sugar phosphorylates the enzyme to form the active conformation

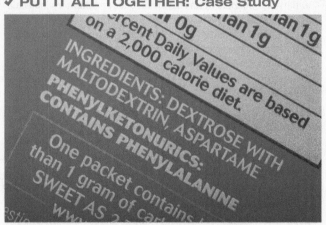

How can an essential nutrient—the amino acid phenylalanine—be toxic?

The amino acid phenylalanine is present in many foods and commonly used in artificial sweeteners, but it is toxic to those born with a metabolic disorder called phenylketonuria (PKU). These people may have severe and permanent mental disability if they ingest high levels of phenylalanine. What type of metabolic defect causes this problem, and how might this knowledge lead to a cure?

11. Phenylalanine is required for the production of many of your proteins, but none of your cells are capable of synthesizing this amino acid. What type of metabolic pathway must be responsible for providing this essential amino acid to your cells? How would your diet affect the amount of phenylalanine that is available?

12. **MODEL** The first reaction in the catabolism of phenylalanine uses the enzyme phenylalanine hydroxylase (PAH) to convert phenylalanine into tyrosine, a different amino acid. PKU results from defects in this enzyme. It has been hypothesized that phenylalanine is both the substrate and an allosteric regulatory molecule for PAH. If this is true, draw two models to show how PAH would appear if the phenylalanine concentration is low (inactive enzyme) vs. high (active enzyme). Label phenylalanine, the allosteric binding site, and the active site.

13. **PROCESS OF SCIENCE** Protein structure is often evaluated using enzymes like trypsin that cut the protein at specific amino acid residues exposed on the surface. The results from this type of experiment using PAH in the presence (+) or absence (−) of phenylalanine is shown below (see BioSkills 6 to review gel electrophoresis). Interpret the results in terms of the effect phenylalanine has on the structure of PAH. Do the results support the hypothesis that phenylalanine is an allosteric regulator?

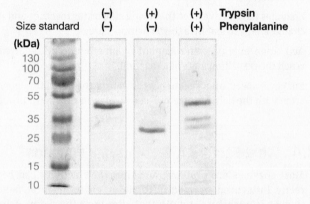

Source: Jaffe, E. K., et al. 2013. *Archives of Biochemistry and Biophysics* 530: 73–82.

14. The catalytic activity of PAH also requires a coenzyme that is oxidized in the reaction. This coenzyme is then subsequently reduced by NADH to regenerate it for additional PAH reactions. If a person were diagnosed with a novel form of PKU, in which the PAH enzyme was fully functional, what defects would you look for to explain the accumulation of phenylalanine?

15. The functional form of PAH contains four identical active sites, but based on the amino acid sequence of the protein, only one active site can be formed. What does this imply concerning the structure of the functional enzyme?

16. **SOCIETY** Starting in the 1960s, newborns that were identified as having PKU were placed on a strict low-protein diet that reduced the effects of PKU on mental impairment. What are other avenues of research that may lead to a cure beyond this restrictive diet?

MasteringBiology®

Students Go to MasteringBiology for assignments, the eText, and the Study Area with animations, practice tests, and activities.

Professors Go to MasteringBiology for automatically graded tutorials and questions that you can assign to your students, plus Instructor Resources.

9 Cellular Respiration and Fermentation

This hydroelectric dam on the Duero, a river between Spain and Portugal, uses pumps to move water from the lower reservoir to the upper reservoir. During periods of high energy demand, the potential energy stored as a result of this activity is used to generate electricity. Cells use a similar process to produce ATP during cellular respiration.

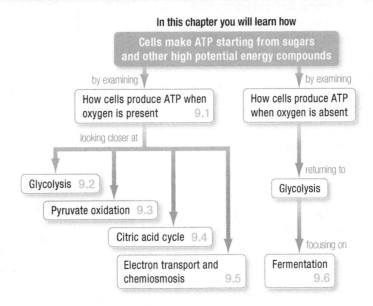

In this chapter you will learn how

Cells make ATP starting from sugars and other high potential energy compounds

by examining

How cells produce ATP when oxygen is present   9.1

by examining

How cells produce ATP when oxygen is absent

looking closer at

Glycolysis   9.2

Pyruvate oxidation   9.3

Citric acid cycle   9.4

Electron transport and chemiosmosis   9.5

returning to

Glycolysis

focusing on

Fermentation   9.6

This chapter is part of the Big Picture. See how on pages 232–233.

ife requires energy. From the very start, chemical evolution was driven by energy from chemicals, radiation, heat, or other sources (see Chapter 2). Harnessing energy and controlling its flow has been the single most important step in the evolution of life.

What fuels life in cells? The answer is the nucleotide adenosine triphosphate (ATP). ATP has high potential energy and allows cells to overcome life's energy barriers (see Chapter 8).

This chapter investigates how cells make ATP, starting with an introduction to the metabolic pathways that harvest energy from high-energy molecules like the sugar **glucose**—the most common source of chemical energy used by organisms. As cells process sugar, the energy that is released is used to transfer a phosphate group to adenosine diphosphate (ADP), generating ATP. (You can see the Big Picture of how the production of glucose in photosynthesis is related to its catabolism in cellular respiration on pages 232–233.)

9.1 An Overview of Cellular Respiration

In general, a cell contains only enough ATP to sustain from 30 seconds to a few minutes of normal activity. Because it has such high potential energy, ATP is unstable and is not stored. As a result, most cells are making ATP all the time.

Much of the ATP your cells produce is made using the chemical energy from glucose. How do cells obtain glucose? Photosynthetic organisms can produce glucose from the products of photosynthesis, where the energy in sunlight is used to reduce carbon dioxide (CO_2). These organisms will either use the glucose to make ATP or store it in other energy-rich molecules like starch. When photosynthetic organisms are eaten or decompose, their glucose molecules are obtained by animals, fungi, and many bacteria and archaea.

Storage carbohydrates, such as starch and glycogen, act like savings accounts for chemical energy (see Chapter 5). ATP, in contrast, is like cash. To withdraw chemical energy from the accounts to get cash, storage carbohydrates are first hydrolyzed into their glucose monomers. The glucose is then used to produce ATP through one of two general processes: cellular respiration or fermentation (Figure 9.1). The primary difference between these two processes lies in the degree to which glucose is oxidized.

What Happens When Glucose Is Oxidized?

When glucose undergoes the uncontrolled oxidation reaction called burning, some of the potential energy stored in its chemical bonds is converted to kinetic energy in the form of heat and light:

$$C_6H_{12}O_6 + 6\,O_2 \longrightarrow 6\,CO_2 + 6\,H_2O + \text{Heat and light}$$
$$\text{glucose} \quad \text{oxygen} \qquad \text{carbon dioxide} \quad \text{water} \qquad \text{energy}$$

More specifically, a total of about 685 kilocalories (kcal) of heat is released when one mole of glucose is oxidized. To put this in perspective, if you burned one mole of glucose (~180 grams), it would give off enough heat to bring almost 2.5 gallons of room-temperature water to a boil.

Glucose does not burn in cells, however. Instead, it is oxidized through a long series of carefully controlled redox reactions (see Chapter 8). These reactions are occurring, millions of times per minute, in your cells right now. Instead of releasing all of this energy as heat, the released free energy is used to synthesize ATP from ADP and P_i. You use this ATP to read, think, move, and stay alive.

Fermentation is another process that oxidizes glucose. So how does fermentation differ from cellular respiration? Cellular respiration, like burning, results in the complete oxidation of glucose into CO_2 and water. Fermentation, on the other hand,

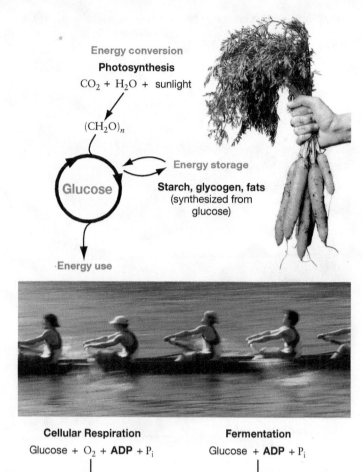

Cellular Respiration
$$\text{Glucose} + O_2 + \textbf{ADP} + P_i$$
$$\downarrow$$
$$CO_2 + H_2O + \textbf{ATP}$$

Fermentation
$$\text{Glucose} + \textbf{ADP} + P_i$$
$$\downarrow$$
$$\text{Small organic molecules} + \textbf{ATP}$$

Figure 9.1 Glucose Is the Hub of Energy Processing in Cells. Glucose is a product of photosynthesis. Both plants and animals store glucose and oxidize it to provide chemical energy in the form of ATP.

does not fully oxidize glucose. Instead, small, reduced organic molecules are produced as waste. As a result, cellular respiration releases more energy from glucose than fermentation.

You can think of the complete oxidation of glucose via cellular respiration as a set of four interconnected processes that together convert the chemical energy in glucose to chemical energy in ATP. Each of the four processes consists of a distinctive starting molecule, a series of chemical reactions, and a characteristic set of products.

1. *Glycolysis* During **glycolysis,** one six-carbon molecule of glucose is broken into two molecules of the three-carbon compound pyruvate. During this process, ATP is produced from ADP and P_i, and nicotinamide adenine dinucleotide (NAD^+) is reduced to form NADH.

2. *Pyruvate processing* Each pyruvate is processed to release one molecule of CO_2, and the remaining two carbons are used to form the compound acetyl CoA. The oxidation of pyruvate results in more NAD^+ being reduced to NADH.

3. **Citric acid cycle** Each acetyl CoA is oxidized to two molecules of CO_2. During this sequence of reactions, more ATP and NADH are produced, and flavin adenine dinucleotide (FAD) is reduced to form $FADH_2$.

4. **Electron transport and oxidative phosphorylation** Electrons from NADH and $FADH_2$ move through a series of proteins that together are called an electron transport chain (ETC). The energy released in this chain of redox reactions is used to create a proton gradient across a membrane; the ensuing flow of protons back across the membrane is used to make ATP. Because this mode of ATP production links the phosphorylation of ADP with the oxidation of NADH and $FADH_2$, it is called **oxidative phosphorylation.**

Figure 9.2 summarizes the four processes in cellular respiration. Formally, **cellular respiration** is defined as any set of reactions that uses electrons harvested from high-energy molecules to produce ATP via an electron transport chain. **Making Models 9.1** provides some tips for how you can use models like the one shown in Figure 9.2 as references to draw your own models of cellular respiration. Such models are essential in biology to distill complex topics into understandable narratives.

The enzymes, products, and intermediates involved in cellular respiration do not exist in isolation. Instead, they are part of a huge and dynamic inventory of chemicals inside the cell.

✎ Making Models 9.1 Tips on Drawing Flow Charts

Cellular respiration is complex. By drawing your own simple models, you can practice keeping track of the main events. The details you choose to include depend on the focus of your model. For example, the flow chart in Figure 9.2 summarizes the main In's and Out's of the four processes of cellular respiration. The flow chart below uses "balls" to represent carbons to track the fate of carbon during cellular respiration.

Glucose   2 Pyruvate $2\ CO_2$ + 2 Acetyl CoA $4\ CO_2$

MODEL Where do all the carbons of glucose end up when glucose is completely oxidized? Add detail to the model by labeling the processes represented by the arrows.

To see this model in action, go to https://goo.gl/8T54kd

This complexity can be boiled down to a simple essence, however. Two of the most fundamental requirements of a cell are energy and carbon. They need a source of energy for generating ATP and a source of carbon that can be used as raw material to synthesize DNA, RNA, proteins, fatty acids, and other

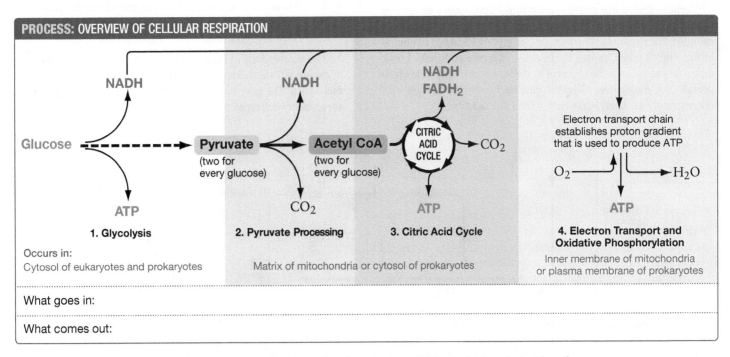

PROCESS: OVERVIEW OF CELLULAR RESPIRATION

1. Glycolysis	**2. Pyruvate Processing**	**3. Citric Acid Cycle**	**4. Electron Transport and Oxidative Phosphorylation**
Occurs in: Cytosol of eukaryotes and prokaryotes	Matrix of mitochondria or cytosol of prokaryotes		Inner membrane of mitochondria or plasma membrane of prokaryotes

What goes in:

What comes out:

Figure 9.2 Cellular Respiration Oxidizes Glucose to Make ATP. Cells produce ATP from glucose via a series of processes: (1) glycolysis, (2) pyruvate processing, (3) the citric acid cycle, and (4) electron transport and oxidative phosphorylation. Each process produces high-energy molecules in the form of nucleotides (ATP) and/or electron carriers (NADH or $FADH_2$). Because the four processes are connected, cellular respiration is an integrated metabolic pathway. The first three processes oxidize glucose to produce NADH and $FADH_2$, which then feed the electron transport chain.

✔ Use what you have learned in the text to fill in the chart along the bottom of the figure.

molecules. With these requirements in mind, let's take a closer look at the central role cellular respiration plays in cellular metabolism.

Cellular Respiration Plays a Central Role in Metabolism

Recall that sets of reactions that break down molecules are called catabolic pathways (Chapter 8). These reactions often harvest stored chemical energy to produce ATP. Anabolic pathways, on the other hand, are sets of reactions that synthesize larger molecules from smaller components. Anabolic reactions often use energy in the form of ATP.

Does the process of cellular respiration interact with other catabolic and anabolic pathways? The answer is most definitely yes! Let's first consider how other catabolic pathways feed into cellular respiration, then examine how the intermediates and products of glycolysis, pyruvate processing, and the citric acid cycle feed into anabolic pathways.

Catabolic Pathways Break Down a Variety of Molecules Most organisms ingest, absorb, or synthesize many different carbohydrates—not just glucose. These molecules range from sucrose, maltose, and other simple sugars to large polymers such as glycogen and starch (see Chapter 5). Using enzyme-catalyzed reactions, cells can break down and transform these other carbohydrates to produce glucose or intermediates in cellular respiration.

Carbohydrates are not the only important source of carbon compounds used in catabolic pathways, however. Fats are highly reduced macromolecules consisting of glycerol bonded to chains of fatty acids (see Chapter 6). In cells, enzymes routinely break down fats to release the glycerol and convert the fatty acids into acetyl CoA molecules. Glycerol can be further processed and enter glycolysis. Acetyl CoA enters the citric acid cycle.

Proteins can also be catabolized, meaning that they can be broken down and used to produce ATP. Once they are hydrolyzed to their constituent amino acids, enzyme-catalyzed reactions remove the amino ($-NH_2$) groups. The amino groups are excreted in urine as waste, and the remaining carbon compounds are converted to pyruvate, acetyl CoA, or other intermediates in glycolysis and the citric acid cycle.

The top half of **Figure 9.3** summarizes the catabolic pathways of carbohydrates, fats, and proteins and shows how their breakdown products feed an array of steps in cellular respiration. When all three types of molecules are available in the cell to generate ATP, carbohydrates are used up first, then fats, and finally proteins.

Catabolic Intermediates Are Used in Anabolic Pathways Where do cells get the precursor molecules required to synthesize amino acids, RNA, DNA, phospholipids, and other cell components? Not surprisingly, the answer often involves intermediates in cellular respiration. For example,

- In humans, about half the required amino acids can be synthesized from molecules siphoned from the citric acid cycle.

- Acetyl CoA is the starting point for anabolic pathways that result in the synthesis of fatty acids. Fatty acids can then be used to build phospholipids and fats.

- Intermediates in glycolysis can be used in the synthesis of ribonucleotides and deoxyribonucleotides. Nucleotides, in turn, are building blocks used in RNA and DNA synthesis.

- If ATP is abundant, pyruvate and lactate (from fermentation) can be used in the synthesis of glucose. Excess glucose may be converted to glycogen or starch and stored.

The bottom half of Figure 9.3 summarizes how intermediates in carbohydrate metabolism are drawn off to synthesize macromolecules. The take-home message is that the same molecule can serve many different functions in the cell. As a result, catabolic

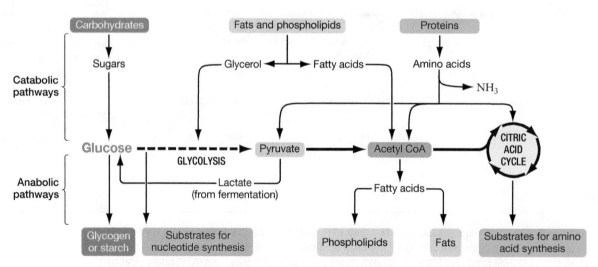

Figure 9.3 Cellular Respiration Interacts with Other Catabolic and Anabolic Pathways. A variety of high-energy compounds from carbohydrates, fats, or proteins can be broken down in catabolic reactions and used by cellular respiration for ATP production. Several of the intermediates in cellular respiration serve as precursor molecules in anabolic reactions leading to the synthesis of carbohydrates, nucleotides, lipids, and amino acids.

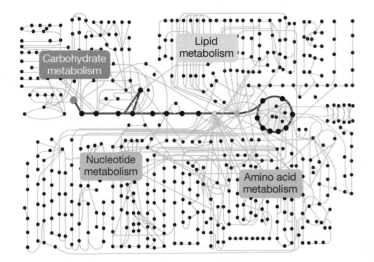

Figure 9.4 Cellular Respiration Plays a Central Role in the Metabolic Activity of Cells. Cellular respiration is connected to a multitude of different chemical reactions. In this schematic diagram, dots represent a few of the many thousands of molecules involved in metabolism, and green lines represent enzyme-catalyzed reactions. At the center of all this, the first three metabolic pathways involved in cellular respiration (see Figure 9.3) are emphasized by bold dots along a thick black line. For reference, the bold dots representing glucose, pyruvate, and acetyl CoA are identified by the same distinctive colors used in Figure 9.3.

and anabolic pathways are closely intertwined. ✔ **CAUTION** If you understand this relationship, you should be able to explain why many different molecules—including lipids, amino acids, and CO_2—end up as radiolabeled when cells are fed glucose with radioactive carbons (^{14}C).

Metabolism comprises thousands of different chemical reactions, yet the amounts and identities of molecules inside cells are relatively constant. By regulating key reactions involved in catabolic and anabolic pathways, the cell is able to maintain its internal environment even under different environmental conditions—a condition referred to as **homeostasis.** While the ATP generated by cellular respiration and fermentation are crucial for survival, the intermediates in these pathways also are central parts of a highly integrated metabolism (**Figure 9.4**).

Once you've filled in the chart at the bottom of Figure 9.2, you'll be ready to analyze each of the four steps of cellular respiration in detail. As you delve in, keep asking yourself the same key questions: What goes in and what comes out? What happens to the energy that is released? Where does each step occur, and how is it regulated? Then take a look in the mirror. All these processes are occurring right now, in virtually all your cells.

9.2 Glycolysis: Oxidizing Glucose to Pyruvate

Because the enzymes responsible for glycolysis have been observed in nearly every prokaryote and eukaryote, it is logical to infer that the ancestor of all organisms living today made ATP by glycolysis. It's ironic, then, that the process was discovered by accident.

In the 1890s Hans and Edward Buchner were working out techniques for breaking open baker's yeast cells and extracting the contents for commercial and medicinal use. (Yeast extracts are still added to some foods as a flavor enhancer or nutritional supplement.) In one set of experiments, the Buchners added sucrose to their extracts. At the time, sucrose was commonly used as a preservative—a substance used to prevent food from decaying.

Instead of preserving the yeast extracts, though, the sucrose was quickly broken down and alcohol appeared as a by-product. This was a key finding: It showed that metabolic pathways could be studied in vitro—outside the organism. Until then, researchers thought that metabolism could take place only in intact organisms.

When researchers studied how the sugar was being processed, they found that the reactions could go on much longer than normal if inorganic phosphate were added to the mixture. This result implied that some of the compounds involved were being phosphorylated. Soon after, a molecule called fructose bisphosphate was isolated. (The prefix *bis*– means that the phosphate groups are attached to the fructose molecule at two different locations.) Subsequent work showed that all but the starting and ending molecules in glycolysis—glucose and pyruvate—are phosphorylated.

In 1905 researchers found that the processing of sugar by yeast extracts stopped if they boiled the reaction mix. Because it was known that enzymes could be inactivated by heat, this discovery suggested that enzymes were involved in at least some of the processing steps. Years later, investigators realized that each step in glycolysis is catalyzed by a different enzyme. Eventually, each of the 10 reactions and enzymes involved was worked out.

Glycolysis Is a Sequence of 10 Reactions

In both eukaryotes and prokaryotes, all 10 reactions of glycolysis occur in the cytosol (see **Figure 9.5** on page 194). Note three key points about this reaction sequence:

1. Glycolysis starts by *using* ATP, not producing it. In the initial step, glucose is phosphorylated to form glucose-6-phosphate. After the second reaction rearranges the sugar to form fructose-6-phosphate, the third reaction adds a second phosphate group, forming the compound fructose-1,6-bisphosphate observed by early researchers. Thus, in reactions 1–5, two ATP molecules are used up before any ATP is produced. This part of glycolysis is referred to as the energy-investment phase.

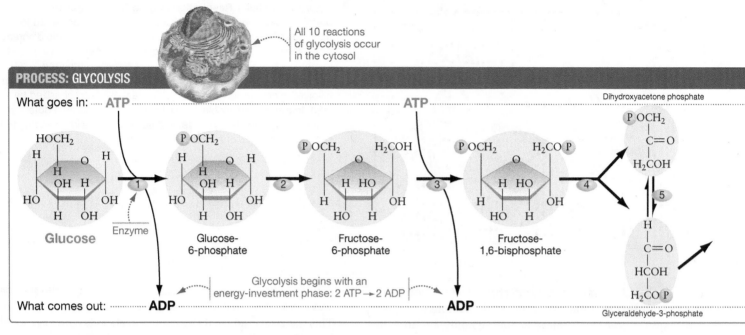

All 10 reactions of glycolysis occur in the cytosol

PROCESS: GLYCOLYSIS

What goes in: ···· **ATP** ·· **ATP** ············

Dihydroxyacetone phosphate

Glucose

Enzyme

Glucose-6-phosphate

Fructose-6-phosphate

Fructose-1,6-bisphosphate

Glyceraldehyde-3-phosphate

Glycolysis begins with an energy-investment phase: 2 ATP → 2 ADP

What comes out: ·············· **ADP** ··· **ADP** ············

Figure 9.5 Glycolysis Pathway. This sequence of 10 reactions oxidizes glucose to pyruvate. Each reaction is catalyzed by a different enzyme to produce two net ATP (4 ATP are produced, but 2 are invested), two molecules of NADH, and two molecules of pyruvate. In step 4, fructose-1,6-bisphosphate is divided into two products that both proceed through steps 6–10. The amounts for "What goes in" and "What goes out" are the combined totals for both molecules.

2. The energy-payoff phase of glycolysis occurs in reactions 6–10 of Figure 9.5. The first high-energy molecules are produced in the sixth reaction, where two molecules of NAD^+ are reduced to form two NADH. In reactions 7 and 10, enzymes catalyze the transfer of a phosphate group from a phosphorylated substrate to ADP, forming ATP. Enzyme-catalyzed reactions that result in ATP production are termed **substrate-level phosphorylation** (Figure 9.6).

3. For each molecule of glucose processed by glycolysis, the net yield is two molecules of NADH, two of ATP, and two of pyruvate.

The discovery and elucidation of the glycolytic pathway ranks as one of the great achievements in the history of biochemistry. For more detail about the enzymes that catalyze each step, see

Table 9.1. While the catabolism of glucose can occur via other pathways, this set of reactions is among the most ancient and fundamental of all life processes.

How Is Glycolysis Regulated?

An important advance in understanding how glycolysis is regulated occurred when biologists observed that high levels of ATP inhibit a key glycolytic enzyme called phosphofructokinase. **Phosphofructokinase** catalyzes reaction 3 in Figure 9.5—the synthesis of fructose-1,6-bisphosphate from fructose-6-phosphate. This is a key step in the sequence.

The products of reactions 1 and 2 can be easily converted back to glucose by an array of enzymes. Before reaction 3, then, the sequence is not committed to glycolysis and glucose can be used in other pathways. But once fructose-1,6-bisphosphate is synthesized, it will not be converted back to glucose. Based on these observations, it makes sense that the pathway is regulated at the first committed step—reaction 3. How do cells do it?

As shown in Figure 9.5, ATP serves as a substrate for the addition of a phosphate to fructose-6-phosphate. In the vast majority of cases, increasing the concentration of a substrate would *speed* the rate of a chemical reaction, but in this case, it inhibits it. Why would ATP—a substrate that is required for the reaction—also serve as an inhibitor of the reaction? The answer lies in knowing that ATP is also the end product of the overall catabolic pathway.

Recall that when an enzyme in a pathway is inhibited by the product of the reaction sequence, feedback inhibition occurs (see Chapter 8). When the product molecule is abundant, it can inhibit its own production by interfering with one of the reactions used to create it. Cells that are able to stop glycolytic

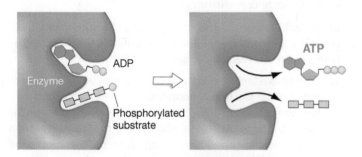

Enzyme

ADP

Phosphorylated substrate

ATP

Figure 9.6 Substrate-Level Phosphorylation Involves an Enzyme and a Phosphorylated Substrate. Substrate-level phosphorylation occurs when an enzyme catalyzes the transfer of a phosphate group from a phosphorylated substrate to ADP, forming ATP.

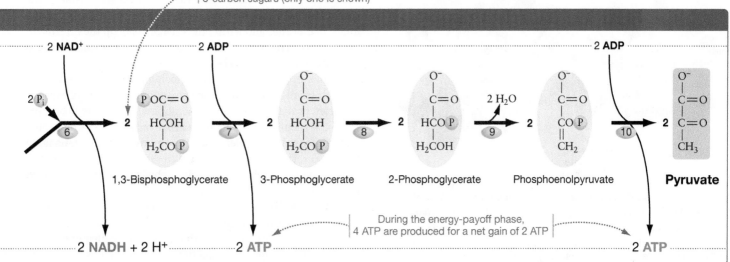

The "2" indicates that fructose-1,6-bisphosphate has been split into two 3-carbon sugars (only one is shown)

1,3-Bisphosphoglycerate

3-Phosphoglycerate

2-Phosphoglycerate

Phosphoenolpyruvate

Pyruvate

During the energy-payoff phase, 4 ATP are produced for a net gain of 2 ATP

2 NADH + 2 H$^+$

2 ATP

2 ATP

reactions when ATP is abundant can conserve their stores of glucose for times when ATP is scarce. As a result, homeostasis is maintained via feedback inhibition.

How do high levels of the substrate inhibit the enzyme? As **Figure 9.7** on page 196 shows, phosphofructokinase has two distinct binding sites for ATP. ATP can bind at the enzyme's active site, where it is used to phosphorylate fructose-6-phosphate, or at a regulatory site, where it turns off the enzyme's activity.

The key to feedback inhibition lies in the ability of the two sites to bind to ATP. When concentrations are low, ATP binds only to the active site, which has a greater affinity for ATP than does the regulatory site. As ATP concentrations increase, however, it also binds at the regulatory site on phosphofructokinase. When ATP binds at this second location, the enzyme's conformation changes in a way that dramatically lowers the reaction rate at the active site. In phosphofructokinase, ATP acts as an allosteric regulator (see Chapter 8). ✔ **QUANTITATIVE** If you understand how ATP regulates glycolysis, you should be able to draw a graph showing the rate of ATP production as a function of ATP concentration. Predict how the rate would change if the regulatory site in phosphofructokinase had higher affinity for ATP than the active site did.

Table 9.1 **The Reactions of Glycolysis**

Step	Enzyme	Reaction
1	Hexokinase	Uses **ATP** to phosphorylate glucose, increasing its potential energy.
2	Phosphoglucose isomerase	Converts glucose-6-phosphate to fructose-6-phosphate; referred to as an isomer of glucose-6-phosphate.
3	Phosphofructokinase	Uses **ATP** to phosphorylate the opposite end of fructose-6-phosphate, increasing its potential energy.
4	Fructose-bis-phosphate aldolase	Cleaves fructose-1,6-bisphosphate into two different three-carbon sugars.
5	Triose phosphate isomerase	Converts dihydroxyacetone phosphate (DAP) to glyceraldehyde-3-phosphate (G3P). Although the reaction is fully reversible, the DAP-to-G3P reaction is favored because G3P is immediately used as a substrate for step 6.
6	Glyceraldehyde-3-phosphate dehydrogenase	A two-step reaction that first oxidizes G3P using the **NAD$^+$** coenzyme to produce **NADH**. Energy from this reaction is used to attach a P$_i$ to the oxidized product to form 1,3-bisphosphoglycerate.
7	Phosphoglycerate kinase	Transfers a phosphate from 1,3-bisphosphoglycerate to **ADP** to make 3-phosphoglycerate and **ATP**.
8	Phosphoglycerate mutase	Rearranges the phosphate in 3-phosphoglycerate to make 2-phosphoglycerate.
9	Enolase	Removes a water molecule from 2-phosphoglycerate to form a C=C double bond and produce phosphoenolpyruvate.
10	Pyruvate kinase	Transfers a phosphate from phosphoenolpyruvate to **ADP** to make pyruvate and **ATP**.

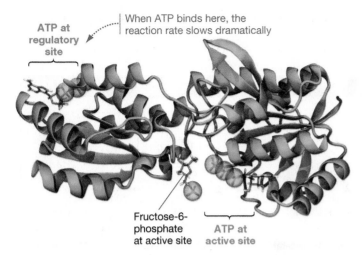

ATP at regulatory site

When ATP binds here, the reaction rate slows dramatically

Fructose-6-phosphate at active site

ATP at active site

Figure 9.7 Phosphofructokinase Has Two Binding Sites for ATP.
A model of one of the four identical subunits of phosphofructokinase. In the active site, ATP is used as a substrate to transfer one of its phosphate groups to fructose-6-phosphate. In the regulatory site, ATP binding inhibits the reaction by changing the shape of the enzyme.

To summarize, glycolysis starts with one 6-carbon glucose molecule and ends with two 3-carbon pyruvate molecules. The reactions occur in the cytosol, and the energy that is released is used to produce a net total of two ATP and two NADH. Now the question is, what happens to the pyruvate?

9.3 Processing Pyruvate to Acetyl CoA

In eukaryotes, the pyruvate produced by glycolysis is transported from the cytosol to mitochondria. Mitochondria are organelles found in virtually all eukaryotes (see Chapter 7).

As shown in **Figure 9.8**, mitochondria have two membranes, called the outer membrane and inner membrane. Portions of the inner membrane fill the interior of the organelle with sac-like structures called **cristae.** Short tubes connect the cristae to the rest of the inner membrane. The regions between the outer and inner membranes and within the cristae make up the intermembrane space. The region enclosed within the inner membrane is the **mitochondrial matrix.**

Pyruvate moves across the mitochondrial outer membrane through small pores and is transported into the matrix through a carrier protein in the inner membrane. Once it is inside the matrix, a sequence of reactions occurs inside an enormous and intricate enzyme complex called **pyruvate dehydrogenase.** In eukaryotes, this complex is located in the mitochondrial matrix. In bacteria and archaea, pyruvate dehydrogenase is located in the cytosol.

As pyruvate is being processed, one of its carbons is oxidized to CO_2 and NAD^+ is reduced to NADH. The remaining two-carbon acetyl unit ($-COCH_3$) reacts with a compound called **coenzyme A (CoA).** Coenzyme A is sometimes abbreviated as CoA-SH to call attention to its key sulfhydryl functional group. The acetyl is transferred to CoA to produce acetyl CoA (**Figure 9.9**). In this and many other reactions, CoA acts as a coenzyme by accepting and then later transferring an acetyl group to another substrate ("A" stands for acetylation).

Acetyl CoA is the final product of the pyruvate-processing step in glucose oxidation. Pyruvate, NAD^+, and CoA go in; CO_2, NADH, and acetyl CoA come out.

Like glycolysis, pyruvate processing is regulated by feedback inhibition. When the products of glycolysis and pyruvate processing are in abundant supply, the process shuts down. Pyruvate processing stops when the pyruvate dehydrogenase complex becomes phosphorylated and changes shape. The rate

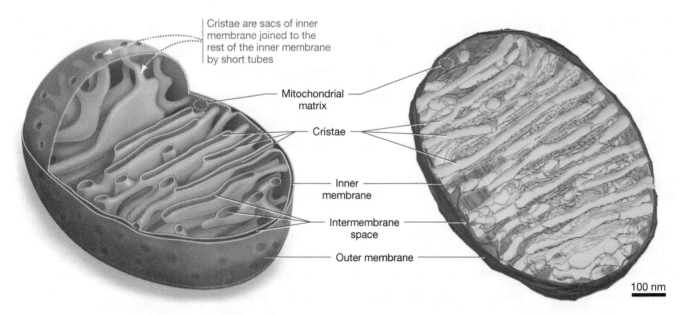

Cristae are sacs of inner membrane joined to the rest of the inner membrane by short tubes

Mitochondrial matrix

Cristae

Inner membrane

Intermembrane space

Outer membrane

100 nm

Figure 9.8 The Structure of the Mitochondrion. Mitochondria have outer and inner membranes that define the intermembrane space and matrix. Pyruvate processing occurs within the mitochondrial matrix. Recent research using cryo-electron tomography (the colorized image on the right) shows that the sac-like cristae are expansions of short tubes formed from the inner membrane.

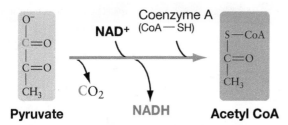

Figure 9.9 Pyruvate Is Oxidized to Acetyl CoA. The reaction shown here is catalyzed by pyruvate dehydrogenase. In the process, one carbon (red in the diagram) is fully oxidized to CO_2 and released.

of phosphorylation increases when one or more of the products are at high concentration.

In contrast, a high concentration of reaction substrates—which indicates low ATP supplies—results in more dephosphorylated and active forms of the pyruvate dehydrogenase complex.

Pyruvate processing is thus under both positive and negative regulation. Large supplies of products inhibit the enzyme complex; large supplies of reactants and low supplies of products stimulate it. ✔ If you understand positive and negative regulation, you should be able to list three molecules whose presence speeds up the reaction shown in Figure 9.9. Label them "Positive regulation." Then list three molecules whose presence slows down the reaction. Label them "Negative regulation by feedback inhibition."

To summarize, pyruvate processing starts with a three-carbon pyruvate molecule and ends with one carbon released as CO_2 and the remaining two carbons in the form of acetyl CoA. The reactions occur in the mitochondrial matrix, and the released free energy is used to produce one NADH for each pyruvate that is processed. Now the question is, what happens to the acetyl CoA?

9.4 The Citric Acid Cycle: Oxidizing Acetyl CoA to CO_2

While researchers were working out the sequence of reactions in glycolysis, biologists in other laboratories were focusing on redox reactions that oxidize small organic acids called **carboxylic acids.** Note that carboxylic acids all have carboxyl functional groups (R-COOH), hence the name.

Early researchers identified eight small carboxylic acids that are rapidly oxidized in sequence, from most reduced to most oxidized. Redox reactions that involve carboxylic acids often produce carbon dioxide, which is the endpoint of glucose oxidation via cellular respiration. When they added one of the eight carboxylic acids to cells, the rate of glucose oxidation increased, suggesting that the reactions are somehow connected to pathways involved in glucose catabolism. What they found next was puzzling. Whichever carboxylic acid they added, it did not appear to be used up. Instead, virtually all the acids could be recovered later. How is this possible?

Hans Krebs solved the mystery when he proposed that the reaction sequence occurs in a cycle instead of a linear pathway. Krebs had another crucial insight when he suggested that the reaction sequence was directly tied to the processing of pyruvate.

To test these hypotheses, Krebs and a colleague set out to determine if adding pyruvate could link the two ends of the sequence of eight carboxylic acids. If pyruvate is the key link in forming a cycle, it would need to be involved in the conversion of oxaloacetate, the most oxidized of the eight carboxylic acids, to citrate, the most reduced carboxylic acid. When Krebs added pyruvate, the series of redox reactions occurred. The conclusion? The sequence of eight carboxylic acids is indeed arranged in a cycle (see **Figure 9.10** on page 198).

Many biologists now refer to the cycle as the **citric acid cycle** because it starts with citrate, which is the salt of citric acid after the protons are released. The citric acid cycle is also known as the tricarboxylic acid (TCA) cycle, because citrate has three carboxyl groups, or as the Krebs cycle, after its discoverer.

In each cycle, the energy released by the oxidation of one molecule of acetyl CoA is used to produce three molecules of NADH, one of $FADH_2$, and one of ATP or guanosine triphosphate (GTP), through substrate-level phosphorylation. Whether ATP or GTP is produced depends on the version of the enzyme used in the fifth reaction.[1] For example, the enzyme used in muscle cells of mammals produces ATP, while the enzyme used in liver cells produces GTP. For simplicity, ATP has been used as the product of the citric acid cycle throughout this chapter.

In prokaryotes (bacteria and archaea), the enzymes responsible for the citric acid cycle are located in the cytosol. In eukaryotes, most of the enzymes responsible for the citric acid cycle are located in the mitochondrial matrix. Because glycolysis produces two molecules of pyruvate, the cycle turns twice for each molecule of glucose processed in cellular respiration.

How Is the Citric Acid Cycle Regulated?

By now, it shouldn't surprise you to learn that the citric acid cycle is also carefully regulated. The citric acid cycle can be turned off at multiple points, via several different mechanisms of feedback inhibition. Reaction rates are high when ATP and NADH are scarce; the rates are low when ATP or NADH is abundant.

Figure 9.11 on page 198 highlights the major control points. In step 1, the enzyme that combines acetyl CoA and oxaloacetate to form citrate is shut down when ATP binds at an allosteric regulatory site. In step 3, NADH interferes with the reaction by binding to the enzyme's active site. This is an example of competitive inhibition (see Chapter 8). In step 4, ATP again functions as an allosteric regulator.

To summarize, the citric acid cycle starts with the two-carbon acetyl molecule in the form of acetyl CoA and ends with the release of two CO_2. For more detail concerning the enzymes that

---

[1] Traditionally it was thought that the citric acid cycle produced GTP, which was later converted to ATP in the same cell. Recent work suggests that ATP is produced directly in some cell types, while GTP is produced in other cells. See J. D. Johnson et al., Genetic evidence for the expression of ATP- and GTP-specific succinyl-CoA synthetases in multicellular eukaryotes. *Journal of Biological Chemistry* 42 (1998): 27580–27586.

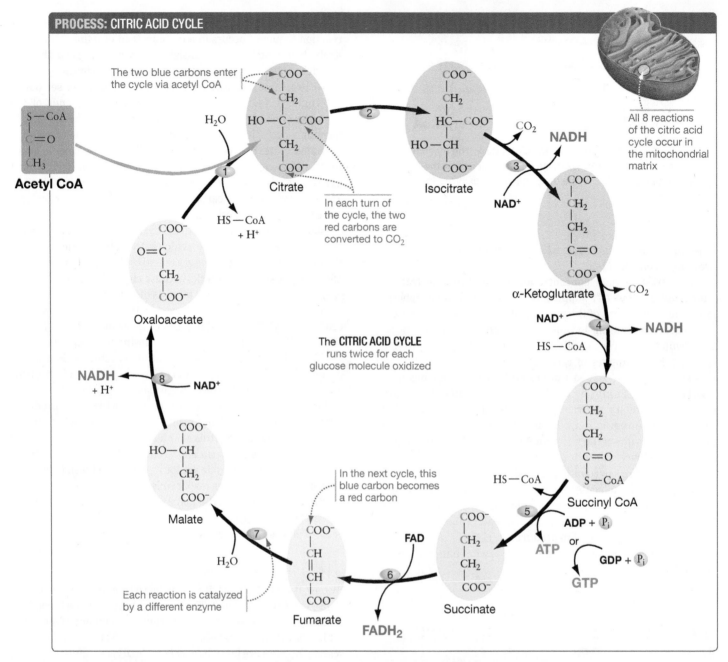

The two blue carbons enter the cycle via acetyl CoA

In each turn of the cycle, the two red carbons are converted to CO_2

Acetyl CoA

Citrate

Isocitrate

All 8 reactions of the citric acid cycle occur in the mitochondrial matrix

H_2O

$HS—CoA$ $+ H^+$

NADH

NAD^+

CO_2

Oxaloacetate

α-Ketoglutarate

NAD^+

$HS—CoA$

NADH

CO_2

The **CITRIC ACID CYCLE** runs twice for each glucose molecule oxidized

NADH $+ H^+$

NAD^+

Malate

Succinyl CoA

$HS—CoA$

$ADP + P_i$

ATP

or

$GDP + P_i$

GTP

In the next cycle, this blue carbon becomes a red carbon

FAD

H_2O

Each reaction is catalyzed by a different enzyme

Fumarate

FADH₂

Succinate

Figure 9.10 The Citric Acid Cycle Completes the Oxidation of Glucose. Acetyl CoA goes into the citric acid cycle, and carbon dioxide, NADH, FADH₂, and ATP or GTP come out. ATP or GTP is produced by substrate-level phosphorylation. If you follow individual carbon atoms around the cycle several times, you'll come to an important conclusion: Each of the carbons in the cycle is eventually a "red carbon" that is released as CO_2.

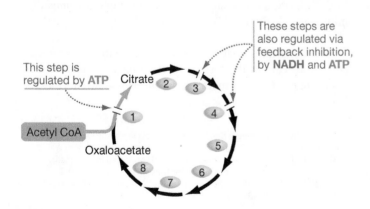

This step is regulated by **ATP**

Citrate

Acetyl CoA

Oxaloacetate

These steps are also regulated via feedback inhibition, by **NADH** and **ATP**

Figure 9.11 The Citric Acid Cycle Is Regulated by Feedback Inhibition. The citric acid cycle slows down when ATP and NADH are plentiful. ATP acts as an allosteric regulator, while NADH acts as a competitive inhibitor.

Step	Enzyme	Reaction
1	Citrate synthase	Transfers the 2-carbon acetyl group from acetyl CoA to the 4-carbon oxaloacetate to produce the 6-carbon citrate.
2	Aconitase	Converts citrate to isocitrate by the removal of one water molecule and the addition of another water molecule.
3	Isocitrate dehydrogenase	Oxidizes isocitrate using the **NAD^+** coenzyme to produce **NADH** and release one CO_2, resulting in the formation of the five-carbon molecule α-ketoglutarate.
4	α-Ketoglutarate dehydrogenase	Oxidizes α-ketoglutarate using the **NAD^+** coenzyme to produce **NADH** and release one CO_2. The remaining four-carbon molecule is added to coenzyme A (CoA) to form succinyl CoA.
5	Succinyl-CoA synthetase	CoA is removed, converting succinyl CoA to succinate. The energy released is used to transfer P_i to ADP to form **ATP**, or to GDP to form **GTP**, depending on the enzyme used.
6	Succinate dehydrogenase	Oxidizes succinate by transferring two hydrogens to the coenzyme **FAD** to produce **$FADH_2$**, resulting in the formation of fumarate.
7	Fumarase	Converts fumarate to malate by the addition of one water molecule.
8	Malate dehydrogenase	Oxidizes malate by using the **NAD^+** coenzyme to produce **NADH**, resulting in the regeneration of the oxaloacetate that will be used in step 1 of the cycle.

catalyze each step, see Table 9.2. All of these reactions occur in the mitochondrial matrix, and the released free energy is used to produce three NADH, one $FADH_2$, and one ATP for each acetyl oxidized. But a major question remains.

What Happens to the NADH and $FADH_2$?

Figure 9.12 reviews the relationships of glycolysis, pyruvate processing, and the citric acid cycle and identifies where each process takes place in eukaryotic cells. As you study this figure, note that for each molecule of glucose that is fully oxidized to 6 carbon dioxide molecules, the cell produces 10 molecules of NADH,

2 of $FADH_2$, and 4 of ATP. The ATP molecules are produced by substrate-level phosphorylation and can be used to drive endergonic reactions. The CO_2 molecules are a gas that is disposed of as you exhale.

What happens to the NADH and $FADH_2$ produced by glycolysis, pyruvate processing, and the citric acid cycle? Recall that the overall reaction for glucose oxidation is

$$C_6H_{12}O_6 + 6\,O_2 \longrightarrow 6\,CO_2 + 6\,H_2O + Energy$$

These three steps account for the glucose, the CO_2, and—because ATP is produced—some of the chemical energy that results from the overall reaction. But the O_2 and the H_2O are

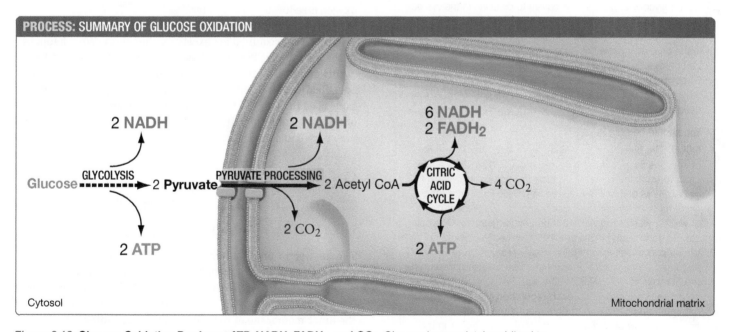

PROCESS: SUMMARY OF GLUCOSE OXIDATION

Figure 9.12 **Glucose Oxidation Produces ATP, NADH, $FADH_2$, and CO_2.** Glucose is completely oxidized to carbon dioxide via glycolysis, pyruvate processing, and the citric acid cycle. In eukaryotes, glycolysis occurs in the cytosol; pyruvate oxidation and the citric acid cycle take place in the mitochondrial matrix.

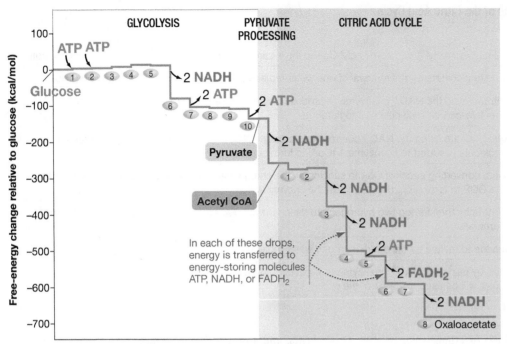

Figure 9.13 Free Energy Changes as Glucose Is Oxidized. If you read the vertical axis of this graph carefully, it should convince you that about 685 kcal/mol of free energy is released from the oxidation of glucose. Much of the energy is harnessed in the form of ATP, NADH, and FADH$_2$. The numbered green ovals identify the reaction steps in glycolysis and the citric acid cycle (see Tables 9.1 and 9.2).

DATA: Li, X., R. K. Dash, R. K. Pradhan, et al. 2010. *Journal of Physical Chemistry B.* 114: 16068–16082.

✔ **QUANTITATIVE** Based on the data in this graph, which one of the three high-energy molecules produced during glucose oxidation would you expect to carry the highest amount of chemical energy? Justify your answer.

still unaccounted for. As it turns out, so is much of the chemical energy. The relative changes in free energy that occur as the carbons in glucose are oxidized are shown in **Figure 9.13**.

In glycolysis, pyruvate processing, and the citric acid cycle, redox reactions transfer electrons to NAD$^+$ and FAD to form NADH and FADH$_2$. At this point, the reaction that has yet to occur is

$$10\,\text{NADH} + 2\,\text{FADH}_2 + 6\,\text{O}_2 + 10\,\text{H}^+ \longrightarrow$$
$$10\,\text{NAD}^+ + 2\,\text{FAD} + 12\,\text{H}_2\text{O} + \text{Energy}$$

In the above reaction, those electrons are transferred from NADH and FADH$_2$ to oxygen. Recall that when NADH is formed, it takes on two electrons, but only one proton (Chapter 8). The second proton for each NADH is represented by the 10 H$^+$ in the equation. As NADH and FADH$_2$ are oxidized to NAD$^+$ and FAD, oxygen is reduced to form water.

Now, all the components of the overall reaction for glucose oxidation are accounted for, except for the energy. What happens to the energy that is released as electrons are transferred from NADH and FADH$_2$ to the highly electronegative oxygen atoms? Specifically, how is the energy that is released from these reactions used to make ATP? In the 1960s—decades after the details of glycolysis and the citric acid cycle had been worked out—an unexpected answer to this question emerged.

9.5 Electron Transport and Chemiosmosis: Building a Proton Gradient to Produce ATP

The answer to one fundamental question about the oxidation of NADH and FADH$_2$ turned out to be relatively straightforward. By isolating different parts of mitochondria, researchers determined that NADH is oxidized when combined with the inner membrane of the mitochondria, including the cristae. In prokaryotes, the oxidation of NADH occurs in the plasma membrane. These membranes were then hypothesized to contain components responsible for oxidizing NADH and FADH$_2$.

CHECK YOUR UNDERSTANDING

If you understand that ...

• During glycolysis, glucose is oxidized to pyruvate in the cytosol.
• During pyruvate processing, pyruvate is oxidized to acetyl CoA in the mitochondrial matrix.
• In the citric acid cycle, the acetyl from acetyl CoA is oxidized to carbon dioxide (CO$_2$) in the mitochondrial matrix.
• Glycolysis, pyruvate processing, and the citric acid cycle are all regulated processes. The cell produces ATP only when ATP is needed.

✔ **You should be able to ...**

1. **MODEL** The flow chart in Making Models 9.1 tracks the fate of carbons as glucose is oxidized to CO$_2$. Now draw a flow chart to track the flow of electrons from glucose to NADH or FADH$_2$ as glucose is oxidized to CO$_2$. (Hint: Rather than showing balls for carbons, use triangles to represent pairs of electrons, starting with 12 triangles for glucose. One pair should go to each NADH or FADH$_2$ formed.)
2. Which processes involved in cellular respiration are *negatively* regulated? For each glucose oxidized, determine the number of CO$_2$, ATP, NADH, and FADH$_2$ molecules that could be produced up to each regulation point. (If a process has multiple points of negative regulation, assume you are calculating based on the first that would occur in the pathway.)

Answers are available in Appendix A.

Biologists made a key discovery when they isolated the membrane components after exposing them to NADH and FADH$_2$—the components were found to cycle between oxidized and reduced states. What are these molecules, and how do they work?

The Electron Transport Chain

Collectively, the molecules responsible for the oxidation of NADH and FADH$_2$ are designated the **electron transport chain (ETC).** Several points are fundamental to understanding how the ETC works:

- Most of the molecules are proteins that contain distinctive cofactors and prosthetic groups where the redox events take place (see Chapter 8). They include iron–sulfur complexes, ring-containing structures called flavins, or iron-containing heme groups called cytochromes. Each of these groups is readily reduced or oxidized.

- The inner membrane of the mitochondrion also contains a molecule called **ubiquinone,** which is not a protein. Ubiquinone got its name because it is nearly ubiquitous in organisms and belongs to a family of compounds called quinones. Also called **coenzyme Q,** or simply Q, ubiquinone is lipid soluble and moves efficiently throughout the hydrophobic interior of the inner mitochondrial membrane.

- The molecules involved in processing NADH and FADH$_2$ differ in their ability to accept electrons in a redox reaction, referred to as the **redox potential** of the electron acceptors. In addition, some of the molecules pick up a proton with each electron, forming hydrogen atoms, while others obtain only electrons.

Because Q and the ETC proteins differ in redox potential, investigators realized that it should be possible to arrange them into a logical sequence. The idea was that electrons would pass from a molecule with a lower redox potential to one with a higher redox potential, via a redox reaction.

As electrons moved through the chain, they would be held more and more tightly. As a result, a small amount of energy would be released in each reaction, and the potential energy in each successive bond would lessen.

Organization of the Electron Transport Chain Researchers worked out the sequence of the redox reactions in the ETC by experimenting with poisons that inhibit particular proteins in the inner membrane. It was expected that if part of the chain were inhibited, then the components upstream of the block would become reduced and those downstream would remain oxidized.

Experiments with various poisons showed that NADH donates an electron to a flavin-containing protein (FMN) at the top of the chain, while FADH$_2$ donates electrons to an iron- and sulfur-containing protein (Fe·S) that then passes them directly to Q. After passing through each of the remaining components in the chain, the electrons are finally accepted by oxygen.

Figure 9.14 shows how the potential energy in shared electrons steps down from the electron carriers NADH and FADH$_2$ to O$_2$. The x-axis plots the sequence of redox reactions in the ETC; the y-axis plots the free-energy changes that occur. ✔ If you understand how electrons are transferred in the electron transport chain, you should be able to use Figure 9.14 to

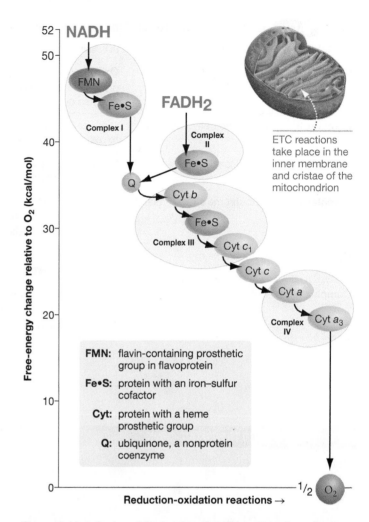

Figure 9.14 A Series of Reduction–Oxidation Reactions Occur in an Electron Transport Chain. The potential energy in shared electrons steps down from the electron carriers NADH and FADH$_2$ through an electron transport chain to a final electron acceptor. In this electron transport chain, oxygen is the final electron acceptor and it forms water as a by-product. The overall free-energy change of 52 kcal/mol (from NADH to oxygen) is broken into small steps.

DATA: Wilson, D. F., M. Erecinska, and P. L. Dutton. 1974. *Annual Review of Biophysics and Bioengineering* 3: 203–230. Also Sled, V. D., N. I. Rudnitzky, Y. Hatefi, et al. 1994. *Biochemistry* 33: 10069–10075.

identify the ETC electron acceptor with the highest redox potential and the acceptor with the lowest redox potential.

The components of the electron transport chain are organized into four large complexes of proteins, often referred to as simply complexes I–IV. Q and the protein **cytochrome c** act as shuttles that transfer electrons between these complexes. Once the electrons at the bottom of the ETC are accepted by oxygen to form water, the oxidation of glucose is complete. Details on the names of the complexes and their role in the electron transport chain are provided in Table 9.3 on page 202.

Under controlled conditions in the laboratory, the total potential energy difference from NADH to oxygen is a whopping 52 kilocalories/mole (kcal/mol). Oxidation of the 10 molecules of NADH produced from each glucose therefore accounts for almost 80 percent of the total energy released from the sugar. What does the ETC do with all this energy?

Table 9.3 **The Reactions of the Electron Transport Chain**

ETC Component	Descriptive Name	Reaction
Complex I	NADH dehydrogenase	Oxidizes **NADH** and transfers the two electrons through proteins containing FMN prosthetic groups and Fe·S cofactors to reduce an oxidized form of ubiquinone (Q). Four **H$^+$** are pumped out of the matrix to the intermembrane space.
Complex II	Succinate dehydrogenase	Oxidizes **FADH$_2$** and transfers the two electrons through proteins containing Fe·S cofactors to reduce an oxidized form of Q. This complex is also used in step 6 of the citric acid cycle.
Q	Ubiquinone	Reduced by complexes I and II and moves throughout the hydrophobic interior of the ETC membrane, where it is oxidized by complex III.
Complex III	Cytochrome *c* reductase	Oxidizes Q and transfers one electron at a time through proteins containing heme prosthetic groups and Fe·S cofactors to reduce an oxidized form of cytochrome *c* (cyt *c*). A total of four **H$^+$** for each pair of electrons is transported from the matrix to the intermembrane space.
Cyt *c*	Cytochrome *c*	Reduced by accepting a single electron from complex III and moves along the surface of ETC membrane, where it is oxidized by complex IV.
Complex IV	Cytochrome *c* oxidase	Oxidizes cyt *c* and transfers each electron through proteins containing heme prosthetic groups to reduce oxygen gas (O$_2$), which picks up two **H$^+$** from the matrix to produce water. Two additional **H$^+$** are pumped out of the matrix to the intermembrane space.

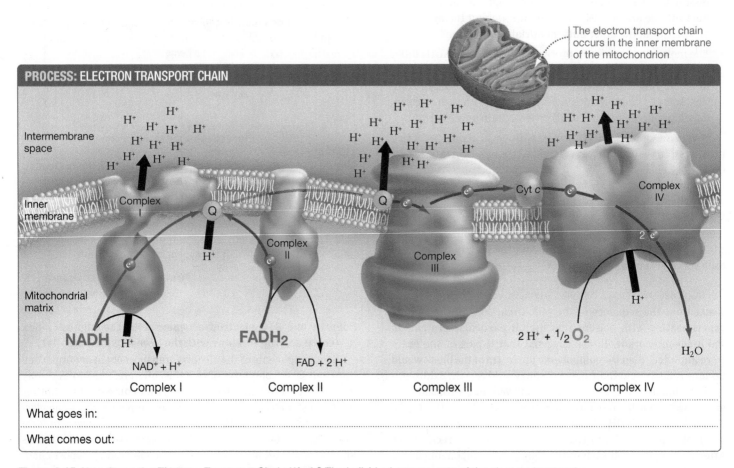

Figure 9.15 How Does the Electron Transport Chain Work? The individual components of the electron transport chain diagrammed in Figure 9.14 are found in the inner membrane of mitochondria. Electrons are carried from one complex to another by Q and by cytochrome *c*; Q also shuttles protons across the membrane. The orange arrow indicates Q moving back and forth. Complexes I and IV use the energy released by the redox reactions to pump protons from the mitochondrial matrix to the intermembrane space.

✔ Draw an arrow across the membrane from low to high proton concentration and label it "Proton gradient." In the boxes at the bottom, list "What goes in" and "What comes out" for each complex.

Role of the Electron Transport Chain Throughout the 1950s most biologists working on cellular respiration assumed that electron transport chains include enzymes that catalyze substrate-level phosphorylation. Recall that when substrate-level phosphorylation occurs, a phosphate group is transferred from a phosphorylated substrate to ADP, forming ATP. Despite intense efforts, however, no one was able to find an enzyme among the components of the ETC that would catalyze the phosphorylation of ADP to produce ATP.

But researchers did find that the energy released from the redox reactions is used to actively transport protons across the inner membrane from the matrix into the intermembrane space (see **Figure 9.15**). The exact route and mechanism used to pump protons is still being worked out. In some cases, it is not clear how the complex uses redox reactions to transport protons.

The best-understood interaction between electron transport and proton transport takes place in complex III. Research has shown that when Q accepts electrons from complex I or complex II, it picks up protons from the matrix side of the inner membrane. The reduced form of Q then diffuses through the inner membrane, where its electrons are used to reduce a component of complex III near the intermembrane space. The protons held by Q are then released to the intermembrane space.

In this way, through redox reactions alone, Q shuttles electrons and protons from one side of the membrane to the other. The electrons proceed down the transport chain, and the transported protons contribute to an electrochemical gradient.

Once the nature of the electron transport chain became clear, biologists understood the fate of the electrons and the energy carried by NADH and $FADH_2$. Much of the chemical energy that was originally present in glucose is now accounted for in the proton electrochemical gradient. This is satisfying, except for a key question: If electron transport doesn't make ATP, what does?

The Discovery of ATP Synthase

In 1960 Efraim Racker made several key observations about how ATP is synthesized in mitochondria. When he used mitochondrial membranes to make vesicles, Racker noticed that some vesicles formed with their membrane inside out. Electron microscopy revealed that the inside-out membranes had many large proteins studded along their surfaces. Each protein appeared to have a base in the membrane, from which a lollipop-shaped stalk and a knob projected (**Figure 9.16**). If the solution was vibrated or treated with a compound called urea, the stalks and knobs fell off.

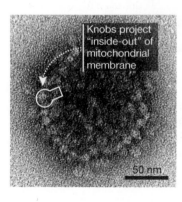

Figure 9.16 The Discovery of ATP Synthase. When patches of mitochondrial membrane turn inside out and form vesicles, the lollipop-shaped stalk-and-knob structures of ATP synthase proteins face outward. Normally, the stalk and knob face inward, toward the mitochondrial matrix.

Racker seized on this technique to isolate the stalks and knobs and do experiments with them. For example, he found that these isolated structures could hydrolyze ATP, forming ADP and inorganic phosphate. The vesicles that contained just the base component, without the stalks and knobs, could not process ATP. The base components were, however, capable of transporting protons across the membrane.

Based on these observations, Racker proposed that the stalk-and-knob component of the protein was an enzyme that both hydrolyzes and synthesizes ATP. To test his idea, Racker added the stalk-and-knob components back to vesicles that had been stripped of them and confirmed that the vesicles regained the ability to synthesize ATP. The entire complex is known as **ATP synthase.** Follow-up work also confirmed his hypothesis that the membrane-bound base component of ATP synthase is a proton channel. Is there a connection between proton transport and ATP synthesis?

The Chemiosmosis Hypothesis

In 1961 Peter Mitchell broke with the prevailing ideas that electron transport produces ATP via substrate phosphorylation. Instead, he proposed something completely new—an indirect connection between electron transport and ATP production. Mitchell proposed that the real job of the electron transport chain is to pump protons across the inner membrane of mitochondria from the matrix to the intermembrane space. After a proton gradient is established, an enzyme in the inner membrane, like Racker's ATP synthase, would synthesize ATP from ADP and P_i.

Mitchell introduced the term **chemiosmosis** to describe the use of a proton gradient to drive energy-requiring processes, like the production of ATP. Similar to osmosis, chemiosmosis involves diffusion across a membrane, but in this case, protons are diffusing along its gradient rather than water. Although proponents of a direct link between electron transport and substrate-level phosphorylation objected vigorously to Mitchell's idea, several key experiments supported it.

Figure 9.17 on page 204 illustrates how the existence of a key element in Mitchell's hypothesis was confirmed: A proton gradient alone can be used to synthesize ATP via ATP synthase. The researchers made vesicles from artificial membranes that contained Racker's ATP synthase from mitochondria along with ADP and P_i. To generate a proton gradient across the membrane, they also included bacteriorhodopsin, a well-studied membrane protein that acts as a light-activated proton pump.

When light strikes bacteriorhodopsin, it absorbs some of the light energy and changes conformation in a way that pumps protons from the interior of a membrane to the exterior. As a result, the experimental vesicles established a strong electrochemical gradient favoring proton movement to the interior. When the vesicles were illuminated to initiate proton pumping, ATP began to be produced from ADP and P_i inside the vesicles.

Mitchell's prediction was correct: In this situation, ATP production depended solely on the existence of a **proton-motive force,** which is based on a proton electrochemical gradient. It could occur in the *absence* of an electron transport chain. This result, along with many others, has provided strong support for the hypothesis of chemiosmosis. Most of the ATP produced by cellular respiration is made by a flow of protons.

QUESTION: How are the electron transport chain and ATP production linked?

CHEMIOSMOTIC HYPOTHESIS: The linkage is indirect. The ETC creates a proton gradient and ATP synthase uses the gradient to synthesize ATP.

ALTERNATIVE HYPOTHESIS: The linkage is direct. Specific ETC proteins are required for ATP synthesis by ATP synthase.

EXPERIMENTAL SETUP:

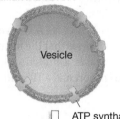

Vesicle

ATP synthase

Bacterio-rhodopsin

1. **Produce vesicles from artificial membranes**; add ATP synthase, an enzyme found in mitochondria.

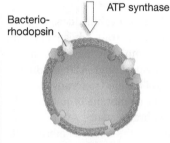

2. **Add bacteriorhodopsin**, a protein that acts as a light-activated proton pump.

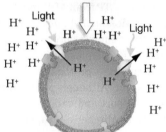

Light

H^+ H^+ H^+ H^+ H^+ H^+ H^+ H^+ Light H^+ H^+ H^+ H^+ H^+ H^+ H^+ H^+ H^+

3. **Illuminate vesicle** so that bacteriorhodopsin pumps protons out of vesicle, creating a proton gradient.

PREDICTION OF CHEMIOSMOTIC HYPOTHESIS: ATP will be produced within the vesicle.

PREDICTION OF ALTERNATIVE HYPOTHESIS: No ATP will be produced without the ETC.

RESULTS:

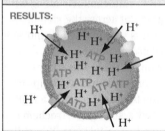

H^+ H^+ H^+ H^+ ATP H^+ H^+ H^+ ATP H^+ H^+ H^+ H^+ ATP ATP H^+ H^+ H^+ H^+ ATP H^+ H^+ H^+ H^+

ATP is produced within the vesicle, in the absence of the electron transport chain.

CONCLUSION: The linkage between electron transport and ATP production by ATP synthase is indirect; the synthesis of ATP only requires a proton gradient.

Figure 9.17 Evidence for the Chemiosmotic Hypothesis.

SOURCE: Racker, E., and W. Stoeckenius. 1974. Reconstitution of purple membrane vesicles catalyzing light-driven proton uptake and adenosine triphosphate formation. *Journal of Biological Chemistry* 249: 662–663.

✔ **PROCESS OF SCIENCE** If bacteriorhodopsin were not available, how else could the researchers have generated a proton gradient?

✔ If you understand chemiosmosis, you should be able to explain the relationships among glucose oxidation, the proton gradient, and ATP synthase.

Organisms throughout the tree of life use electron transport chains and ATP synthases. These processes are humming away in your cells now and produce most of the ATP that keeps you alive. Let's look in more detail at how they function.

The Proton-Motive Force Couples Electron Transport to ATP Synthesis As **Figure 9.18** shows, the structure of ATP synthase is now well understood. The ATP synthase "knob" component is called the F_1 unit; the membrane-bound, proton-transporting base component is the F_0 unit. The F_1 and F_0 units are connected by a shaft, as well as by a stator, which holds the two units in place.

The F_0 unit serves as a rotor, whose turning is conveyed to the F_1 unit via the shaft. A flow of protons through the F_0 unit causes the rotor and shaft to spin. By attaching long actin filaments to the shaft and examining them with a videomicroscope, researchers have been able to see the rotation, which can reach speeds of 350 revolutions per second. As the shaft spins within the F_1 unit, it is thought to change the conformation of the F_1 subunits in a way that catalyzes the phosphorylation of ADP to ATP.

Chemiosmosis resembles the process of generating electricity in a hydroelectric dam like the one pictured on the first page of this chapter. The ETC pumps protons across the inner membrane, similar to the way a series of gigantic pumps force

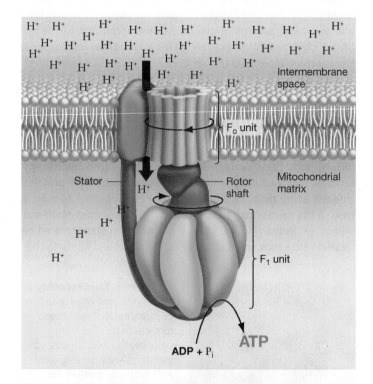

Intermembrane space

F_0 unit

Stator

H^+

Rotor shaft

Mitochondrial matrix

F_1 unit

ADP + P_i

ATP

Figure 9.18 Oxidative Phosphorylation Involves the ATP Synthase Motor and a Proton Gradient. ATP synthase has two major components, designated F_0 and F_1, connected by a shaft. The F_0 unit spins as protons pass through. The shaft transmits the rotation to the F_1 unit, causing it to make ATP from ADP and P_i.

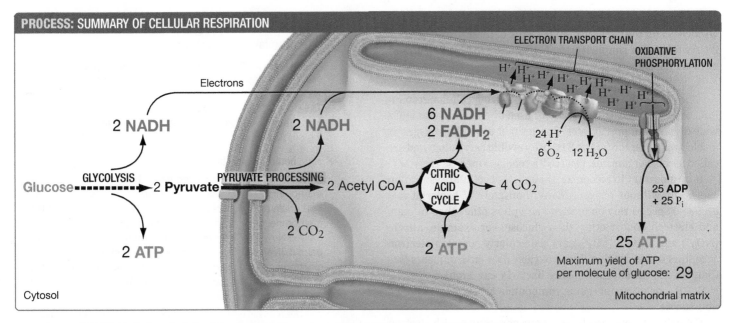

PROCESS: SUMMARY OF CELLULAR RESPIRATION

ELECTRON TRANSPORT CHAIN

OXIDATIVE PHOSPHORYLATION

Electrons

2 NADH

2 NADH

6 NADH
2 FADH$_2$

24 H$^+$
+
6 O$_2$ 12 H$_2$O

GLYCOLYSIS

PYRUVATE PROCESSING

CITRIC ACID CYCLE

Glucose - - - - - - - → 2 **Pyruvate** ⟶ 2 Acetyl CoA → 4 CO$_2$

25 **ADP**
+ 25 P$_i$

2 CO$_2$

2 ATP

2 ATP

25 **ATP**

Maximum yield of ATP per molecule of glucose: 29

Cytosol

Mitochondrial matrix

Figure 9.19 ATP Yield during Cellular Respiration. The actual yield of ATP per glucose (29 ATP) is lower than the theoretical calculation (38 ATP) because the proton motive force is used to drive other mitochondrial activities, such as the active transport of P$_i$ into the mitochondrial matrix.

water up and behind a dam. When protons pass through the ATP synthase, it spins and releases energy used to synthesize ATP. This is analogous to how water passing through the turbines of hydroelectric dams causes them to spin and generate electricity.

The key idea to note here is that the energy to produce ATP in oxidative phosphorylation comes from an established proton gradient, not phosphorylated substrates as used in substrate-level phosphorylation.

It has been determined that the ETC transports enough protons to produce approximately three ATP for each NADH and two for each FADH$_2$, depending on the type of ATP synthase used. These yields, however, are not observed in cells, since the proton-motive force is also used to drive other processes, such as the import of phosphates into the mitochondrial matrix.

ATP synthase also can hydrolyze ATP and reverse the direction of its spin. If the proton gradient dissipates, this ATP-powered reversal is used to pump protons from the matrix to the intermembrane space. Understanding how these reactions occur is currently the focus of intense research.

The Proton-Motive Force and Chemical Evolution Since chemiosmosis is responsible for most of the ATP produced by cells throughout the tree of life, it likely arose early in evolution. But how could a complex electron transport chain evolve to produce the proton-motive force without a proton-motive force to supply the energy?

This apparent conundrum left many of the chemical evolution theorists perplexed until a key discovery was made deep in the ocean along the Mid-Atlantic Ridge—the Lost City hydrothermal vents (see Chapter 2). Researchers propose that the alkaline fluid (low proton concentration) released from these vents in the acidic oceans (high proton concentration) of early Earth may have provided such a gradient.

While the debate continues over the role hydrothermal vents may have played in chemical evolution, their discovery has generated much excitement. By harnessing the natural electrochemical gradient deep in the early oceans, oxidative phosphorylation may have evolved before an electron transport chain existed. If this were the case, the subsequent evolution of a proton-pumping electron transport chain would have been necessary to establish an environment that would mimic the natural gradients present in the vent environment.

Organisms Use a Diversity of Electron Acceptors

Figure 9.19 summarizes glucose oxidation and cellular respiration by tracing the fate of the carbon atoms and electrons in glucose. Notice that electrons from glucose are transferred to NADH and FADH$_2$, passed through the electron transport chain, and accepted by oxygen. Proton pumping during electron transport creates the proton-motive force that drives ATP synthesis.

The diagram also indicates the approximate yield of ATP from each component of the process. Recent research shows that about 29 ATP molecules are produced from each molecule of glucose.[2] Of these, 25 ATP molecules are produced by ATP synthase. What is the fundamental message here? The vast majority of the "payoff" from the oxidation of glucose occurs via oxidative phosphorylation.

The chemical equation that represents the overall process involved in cellular respiration is

$$C_6H_{12}O_6 + 6 H_2O + 6 O_2 + 29 ADP + 29 P_i \longrightarrow$$
$$6 CO_2 + 12 H_2O + 29 ATP$$

---

[2] Traditionally, biologists thought that up to 38 ATP would be synthesized for every molecule of glucose oxidized in cells. More recent work has shown that actual yield is only about 29 ATP [see P. R. Rich, The molecular machinery of Keilin's respiratory chain. *Biochemical Society Transactions* 6 (2003): 1095–1105]. Also, it's important to note that yield varies with conditions in the cell.

The reactants include six water molecules that are used in glycolysis and the citric acid cycle (some of these are depicted in Figure 9.10). For simplicity, the NADH and $FADH_2$ electron carriers are not shown.

Aerobic versus Anaerobic Respiration   During cellular respiration, oxygen is the electron acceptor used by all eukaryotes and a wide diversity of prokaryotes. Species that depend on oxygen as an electron acceptor for the ETC use **aerobic** respiration and are called aerobic organisms. (The Latin root *aero* means "air.")

It is important to recognize, though, that cellular respiration can occur without oxygen. Many thousands of bacterial and archaeal species rely on electron acceptors other than oxygen, and electron donors other than glucose. For example, nitrate (NO_3^-) and sulfate (SO_4^{2-}) are particularly common electron acceptors in species that live in oxygen-poor environments (see Chapter 26). In addition, many bacteria and archaea use H_2, H_2S, CH_4, or other inorganic compounds as electron donors—not glucose.

Cells that depend on electron transport chains with electron acceptors other than oxygen are said to use **anaerobic** ("no air") respiration. Even though the starting and ending points of cellular respiration differ, aerobic and anaerobic respiring cells still use an ETC to create a proton-motive force that drives the synthesis of ATP. In bacteria and archaea, the ETC and ATP synthase are located in the plasma membrane.

Aerobic Respiration Is Most Efficient   Even though an array of compounds can serve as the final electron acceptor in cellular respiration, oxygen provides the greatest energy yield. Because oxygen is so highly electronegative, the potential energy in bonds between an oxygen atom and a non-oxygenic atom, such as hydrogen, is low. As a result, there is a large difference between the potential energy of reduced electron donors, like NADH, and reduced forms of oxygen, like water (see Figure 9.14). This large differential in potential energy means that the electron transport chain can generate a large proton-motive force.

Cells that do not use oxygen as an electron acceptor cannot generate such a large potential energy difference. As a result, they make less ATP per electron donor, such as glucose, than cells that use aerobic respiration. This finding is important: If cells that use anaerobic respiration compete with cells using aerobic respiration, those that use oxygen as an electron acceptor almost always grow faster and reproduce more.

What happens when the electron acceptors in an ETC get used up? When there is no terminal electron acceptor, the electrons in each of the complexes of the electron transport chain have no place to go and the electron transport chain stops. Without an oxidized complex I, NADH remains reduced. The concentration of NAD^+ drops rapidly as cells continue to convert NAD^+ to NADH.

This situation is life threatening. When there is no longer any NAD^+ to drive glycolysis, pyruvate processing, and the citric acid cycle, then no ATP can be produced. If NAD^+ cannot be regenerated somehow, the cell will die.

How do cells cope?

9.6 Fermentation

Fermentation is a metabolic pathway that regenerates NAD^+ by oxidizing stockpiles of NADH. The electrons removed from NADH are transferred to pyruvate, or a molecule derived from pyruvate, instead of an electron transport chain (**Figure 9.20**).

In respiring cells, fermentation serves as an emergency back-up to produce ATP even when the ETC and oxidative phosphorylation is shut down. If the ETC is not available to oxidize NADH, then the concentration of NAD^+ rapidly drops and glycolysis, pyruvate processing, and the citric acid cycle will halt. Fermentation may allow the cell to survive in the absence of an active electron transport chain by regenerating NAD^+ in the cytosol, where glycolysis can continue to produce ATP. How does fermentation regenerate NAD^+, and what is being reduced in this redox reaction?

Many Different Fermentation Pathways Exist

When you run up a long flight of stairs, your muscles begin metabolizing glucose so fast that the supply of oxygen is rapidly used up by their mitochondria. When oxygen runs out, the electron transport chains shut down and NADH cannot donate its electrons there. When fermentation takes place in your cells, the pyruvate produced by glycolysis then begins to accept electrons from NADH. This process, called **lactic acid fermentation,** regenerates NAD^+ by forming lactate: a deprotonated form of lactic acid (**Figure 9.21a**).

When your muscles are deprived of oxygen, your body reacts by making you breathe faster and increasing your heart rate. By getting more oxygen to your muscle cells, the electron transport chain is revived. The lactic acid produced by fermentation can be converted back to pyruvate and used as a source of energy to drive cellular respiration when oxygen is present.

In many cases, however, the cell cannot use the molecule that is formed when pyruvate (or another electron acceptor) accepts electrons from NADH. This by-product may even be toxic and excreted from the cell as waste even though it has not been fully oxidized.

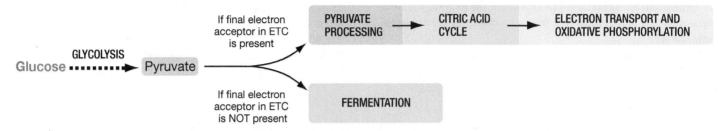

Figure 9.20 Cellular Respiration and Fermentation Are Alternative Pathways for Producing ATP. When oxygen or another final electron acceptor used by the ETC is present in a cell, the pyruvate produced by glycolysis enters the citric acid cycle and the electron transport system is active. But if no electron acceptor is available to keep the ETC running, then pyruvate undergoes reactions known as fermentation.

Figure 9.21b illustrates **alcohol fermentation,** which occurs in the eukaryote *Saccharomyces cerevisiae*, strains of which are used to make baker's and brewer's yeast. When yeast cells grow in bread dough or a bottle of grape juice, they quickly use up all the available oxygen. Instead of using NADH to reduce pyruvate, yeast first convert pyruvate to the two-carbon compound acetaldehyde.

This reaction gives off carbon dioxide, which causes bread to rise and produces the bubbles in champagne and beer.

Acetaldehyde then accepts electrons from NADH, forming the NAD^+ required to keep glycolysis going. The addition of electrons to acetaldehyde forms ethanol as a waste product. The yeast cells excrete ethanol as waste. In essence, the active ingredient in alcoholic beverages is like yeast urine.

Cells that employ other types of fermentation are used commercially in the production of soy sauce, tofu, yogurt, cheese, vinegar, and other products. The products of these reactions are responsible for many of the complex flavors in these foods.

Bacteria and archaea that rely exclusively on fermentation are called obligate anaerobes. These organisms are present in phenomenal numbers in your intestines and in the first compartment of a cow's stomach, called the rumen. The rumen is a specialized digestive organ that contains over 10^{10} (10 billion) bacterial and archaeal cells per *milliliter* of fluid. The fermentations that occur in these cells produce an array of high-energy products, like fatty acids. Cattle don't actually live off grass directly—they eat it to feed their bacteria and archaea and then use the fermentation by-products for energy.

Fermentation as an Alternative to Cellular Respiration

Even though fermentation is a widespread type of metabolism, it is extremely inefficient compared with cellular respiration. Fermentation produces just 2 molecules of ATP per molecule of glucose metabolized, while aerobic cellular respiration produces about 29—almost 15 times more ATP per glucose

(a) Lactic acid fermentation occurs in humans.

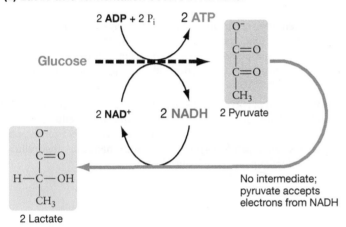

2 Lactate

No intermediate; pyruvate accepts electrons from NADH

(b) Alcohol fermentation occurs in yeast.

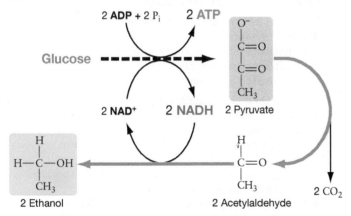

2 Ethanol   2 Acetylaldehyde   2 CO_2

Figure 9.21 Fermentation Regenerates NAD^+ So That Glycolysis Can Continue. These are just two examples of the many types of fermentation that occur in prokaryotes and eukaryotes.

molecule than fermentation. The reason for the disparity is that the fermentation reactions that follow glycolysis are not used to generate ATP.

Organisms that can switch between fermentation and aerobic cellular respiration are called **facultative anaerobes.** The adjective "facultative" reflects the ability to use aerobic cellular respiration when oxygen is present and anaerobic fermentation when it is absent. Many of your cells can function as facultative anaerobes to a certain extent; however, you cannot survive for long without oxygen. To make this point clear, try holding your breath—it should take only a minute for you to realize how important electron transport is to your cells.

9.1 An Overview of Cellular Respiration

- Cellular respiration is based on redox reactions that oxidize a compound with high potential energy, such as glucose, and produce molecules with low potential energy, such as CO_2 and water.

- In eukaryotes, cellular respiration consists of four steps: glycolysis, pyruvate processing, the citric acid cycle, and electron transport coupled to oxidative phosphorylation.

- Glycolysis, pyruvate processing, and the citric acid cycle are central to the metabolism of most cells. Other catabolic pathways feed into them, and the intermediates of the central pathways are used in the synthesis of many key molecules.

9.2 Glycolysis: Oxidizing Glucose to Pyruvate

- The glycolytic pathway is a 10-step reaction sequence in which glucose is broken down into two molecules of pyruvate. It takes place in the cytosol and produces ATP and NADH.

- Glycolysis slows when ATP binds to a regulatory site in phosphofructokinase.

9.3 Processing Pyruvate to Acetyl CoA

- Pyruvate processing is a series of reactions that convert pyruvate to acetyl CoA in the mitochondrial matrix in eukaryotes and the cytosol of prokaryotes. NADH and CO_2 are produced.

- The pyruvate dehydrogenase complex is inhibited when it is phosphorylated by ATP. It speeds up in the presence of reactants and slows down in the presence of products.

9.4 The Citric Acid Cycle: Oxidizing Acetyl CoA to CO_2

- The citric acid cycle is an eight-step reaction cycle in the matrix of mitochondria or cytosol of prokaryotes. It begins with acetyl CoA and produces $FADH_2$, NADH, and ATP or GTP. By the end of the citric acid cycle, all of the carbons from glucose are completely oxidized to CO_2.

- Certain enzymes in the citric acid cycle are inhibited when NADH or ATP binds to them.

9.5 Electron Transport and Chemiosmosis: Building a Proton Gradient to Produce ATP

- The electron transport chain resides in the inner membrane of mitochondria and consists of a series of electron acceptors that vary in their redox potential. It begins with the oxidation of NADH and $FADH_2$ and ends with the reduction of a terminal electron acceptor, like O_2.

- The energy released from redox reactions in the electron transport chain is used to transport protons across the inner mitochondrial membrane, creating an electrochemical gradient.

- ATP production is coupled to the ETC by oxidative phosphorylation. The potential energy stored in the proton gradient is used to spin components of the ATP synthase to produce ATP. This process is responsible for most of the ATP made by cellular respiration.

9.6 Fermentation

- Fermentation occurs in the cytosol of many cells when an electron transport chain is not present or it is inactive due to an insufficient amount of the final electron acceptor. It begins by reducing pyruvate, or a molecule derived from pyruvate, to regenerate NAD^+ from NADH.

- Production of NAD^+ enables glycolysis to continue producing ATP, albeit significantly less ATP than produced by cellular respiration. Depending on the molecule that acts as an electron acceptor, fermentation pathways produce lactate, ethanol, or other reduced organic compounds as a by-product.

Answers are available in Appendix A

✓ TEST YOUR KNOWLEDGE

1. Where does the citric acid cycle occur in eukaryotes?
   a. in the cytosol of cells
   b. in the intermembrane space of mitochondria
   c. in the inner membrane of mitochondria
   d. in the matrix of mitochondria

2. What does the chemiosmotic hypothesis claim?
   a. ATP is generated using phosphates taken from intermediates in the electron transport chain.
   b. ATP is generated using a phosphate gradient produced by glycolysis and the citric acid cycle.
   c. ATP is generated using a proton-motive force that is produced by the electron transport chain.
   d. Water is generated using electrons taken from NADH and $FADH_2$ and transported through the electron transport chain.

3. After glucose is fully oxidized by glycolysis, pyruvate processing, and the citric acid cycle, where is most of its energy stored?

4. What is the primary function of the reactions that follow glycolysis in a fermentation pathway?
   a. to regenerate NAD^+ from NADH, so glycolysis can continue
   b. to synthesize pyruvate from lactate
   c. to regenerate NADH from NAD^+, so electrons can be donated to the electron transport chain
   d. to synthesize electron acceptors, so that cellular respiration can continue

✔ TEST YOUR UNDERSTANDING

5. Compare and contrast substrate-level phosphorylation and oxidative phosphorylation.

6. If you were to expose cells that are undergoing aerobic cellular respiration to a radioactive oxygen isotope in the form of O_2, which of the following molecules would you expect to be radiolabeled?
   a. pyruvate   b. water   c. NADH   d. CO_2

7. In step 3 of the citric acid cycle, the enzyme isocitrate dehydrogenase is regulated by NADH. Compare and contrast the regulation of this enzyme with the regulation of phosphofructokinase in glycolysis.

8. Explain the relationship between electron transport and oxidative phosphorylation. What does ATP synthase look like, and how does it work?

✔ TEST YOUR PROBLEM-SOLVING SKILLS

9. Cyanide ($C \equiv N^-$) blocks complex IV of the electron transport chain. Suggest a hypothesis for what happens to the ETC when complex IV stops working. Your hypothesis should explain why cyanide poisoning in humans is fatal.

10. QUANTITATIVE Early estimates suggested that the oxidation of glucose via aerobic respiration would produce 38 ATP. Based on what you know of the theoretical yields of ATP from each step, show how this total was determined. Why do biologists now think this amount of ATP/glucose is not achieved in cells?

✔ PUT IT ALL TOGETHER: Case Study

Does the Fountain of Youth spring from the mitochondrial proton gradient?

For thousands of years, explorers have sought mythical waters that promote a long life. In modern times, the quest for extending the human life span continues. Current research points to changes in the mitochondrial electron transport chain and the proton gradient

as a cause of aging. How is the ETC involved in aging? Can it be manipulated to increase longevity?

11. Research has shown that cellular damage associated with aging occurs via the formation of oxygen radicals called reactive oxygen species (ROS). These radicals are produced when an excessive proton gradient across the inner mitochondrial membrane slows down the rate of electron transport in the ETC. Propose a hypothesis to explain how a proton gradient can reduce the rate of electron transport.

12. QUANTITATIVE The production of ROS can be reduced using drugs that allow protons to freely pass through the inner membrane. The effect of a drug called DNP on the life span of mice is shown in the graph below. Each point represents the death of a single mouse. At what age is the difference in survival between the DNP-treated and the untreated control the greatest?

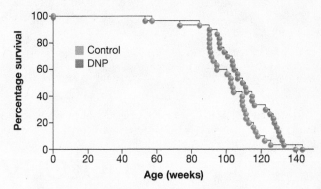

Source: C. C. Caldeira da Silva et al. 2008. *Aging Cell* 7: 552–560.

13. QUANTITATIVE In the above study, the investigators determined that a *low* concentration of DNP increased the average life span from 719 days (Control) to 770 days (DNP). If the U.S. population has an average life span of 79 years, then how many years would be added if the same percentage increase were observed?

14. PROCESS OF SCIENCE How could you determine if the mitochondrial ETC is affected in DNP-treated mice? Propose an experiment to determine if there is a correlation between life span and ETC activity in mitochondria isolated from mice used in the experiment above.

15. In addition to an increased life span, mice treated with *low* concentrations of DNP also showed a significantly lower weight gain compared to the control group despite no difference in the amount or type of food ingested. Propose an explanation for why DNP would have this effect.

16. SOCIETY In the 1930s, DNP was introduced as a diet drug until it was banned from human use because of adverse side effects when *high* concentrations of the drug were used. These included increased respiration and even death. Propose an explanation for the side effects based on the effect DNP has on the proton gradient.

MasteringBiology®

Students Go to MasteringBiology for assignments, the eText, and the Study Area with animations, practice tests, and activities.
Professors Go to MasteringBiology for automatically graded tutorials and questions that you can assign to your students, plus Instructor Resources.

10 Photosynthesis

A close-up of moss cells filled with chloroplasts, where photosynthesis converts the energy in sunlight to chemical energy in the bonds of sugar. Directly or indirectly, most organisms on Earth get their energy from photosynthesis.

In this chapter you will learn how

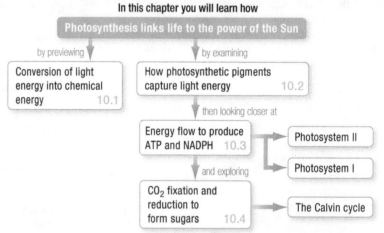

Photosynthesis links life to the power of the Sun

by previewing → Conversion of light energy into chemical energy   10.1

by examining → How photosynthetic pigments capture light energy   10.2

then looking closer at

Energy flow to produce ATP and NADPH   10.3 → Photosystem II / Photosystem I

and exploring

CO_2 fixation and reduction to form sugars   10.4 → The Calvin cycle

BIG PICTURE

This chapter is part of the Big Picture. See how on pages 232–233.

Some 3 billion years ago, a novel combination of light-absorbing molecules and enzymes gave a bacterial cell the capacity to capture light and then convert it to chemical energy in C–C and C–H bonds. The origin of **photosynthesis**—the use of sunlight to manufacture carbohydrate—ranks as one of the great events in the history of life.

The vast majority of organisms alive today rely on photosynthesis, either directly or indirectly, to stay alive. Maples, mosses, and other photosynthetic organisms are termed **autotrophs** (literally, "self-feeders") because they make all their own food from ions and simple molecules. Humans, houseflies, and other non-photosynthetic organisms are called **heterotrophs** ("different-feeders") because they have to obtain the sugars and many of the other macromolecules they need from other organisms.

Because heterotrophs depend on the molecules produced by autotrophs, photosynthesis is fundamental to almost all life. From an ecological viewpoint—meaning, in terms of how organisms interact with one another—photosynthesis is easily the most important energy-related pathway.

How does photosynthesis work? Let's begin with an overview and then delve into a step-by-step analysis of some of the most remarkable chemistry on Earth.

10.1 Photosynthesis Harnesses Sunlight to Make Carbohydrate

Photosynthetic organisms cannot store the electromagnetic energy of light unless it is first converted into another form. In photosynthesis, energy in sunlight is transformed to chemical energy in the C–C and C–H bonds of carbohydrate. The overall reaction—the sum of many independent reactions—can be simplified and written as

$$CO_2 + H_2O + \text{light energy} \longrightarrow (CH_2O)_n + O_2$$

In this reaction, the product of photosynthesis is represented as a ratio of C, H, and O that is typical in carbohydrates, and n represents a number of three or more (see Chapter 5). As you will see in Section 10.4, the actual carbohydrate produced by photosynthesis is a phosphorylated three-carbon sugar.

Now read the reaction again, and note the contrast with cellular respiration (see Chapter 9). Photosynthesis is an energy-demanding series of redox reactions that produce sugar and oxygen (O_2) from carbon dioxide (CO_2) and water (H_2O). Cellular respiration is an energy-releasing series of redox reactions that produces CO_2 and water from sugar and O_2.

Figure 10.1 provides an incomplete electron-sharing diagram that illustrates the formation of a three-carbon sugar from CO_2 and H_2O. ✔ If you understand the fundamental principles of reduction–oxidation (see Chapter 8), you should be able to complete Figure 10.1 (following the instructions in the caption exercise) and then explain why the reaction requires the input of energy.

So how does photosynthesis produce O_2 and carbohydrate? Research on this process began early in the history of biological science. In the 1770s, Joseph Priestley performed a series of experiments showing that the green parts of plants would "restore air" that had been consumed by animals or fire. This work led to the discovery of the element oxygen and the finding that plants produce O_2 in the presence of sunlight, CO_2, and water.

Early investigators assumed that CO_2 and H_2O molecules react directly to produce the $(CH_2O)_n$ found in carbohydrates and release O_2 as a by-product. This idea, however, turned out to be incorrect. Instead, CO_2 and H_2O participate in entirely different reactions, and the oxygen atoms in O_2 come from water. How was this discovered?

Photosynthesis: Two Linked Sets of Reactions

Starting in the 1930s, two independent lines of research on photosynthesis converged, leading to a major advance in biologists' understanding of how oxygen gas (O_2) and carbohydrate are produced.

The first research program, led by Cornelius van Niel, focused on photosynthesis in organisms called purple sulfur bacteria. Van Niel and his group found that these bacteria are autotrophs that manufacture their own carbohydrates from CO_2, sunlight, and hydrogen sulfide (H_2S, the equivalent of H_2O in plant reactions).

Van Niel also showed that these bacteria did not produce oxygen as a by-product of photosynthesis. Instead, they released elemental sulfur (S). In these organisms, a simplified version of the overall reaction for photosynthesis is

$$CO_2 + 2\,H_2S + \text{light energy} \longrightarrow (CH_2O)_n + H_2O + 2\,S$$

Van Niel's work was crucial for two reasons:

1. It showed that in these bacteria, H_2S and CO_2 do *not* combine directly during photosynthesis.

2. It showed that the oxygen atoms in CO_2 are *not* released as O_2. The purple sulfur bacteria produced no oxygen, even though carbon dioxide participated in the reaction—just as it did in plants.

Based on these findings, biologists hypothesized that the oxygen atoms released during plant photosynthesis must come from H_2O. The hypothesis was confirmed when heavy isotopes of oxygen—^{18}O in contrast to the normal isotope, ^{16}O—became available to researchers. They observed the ^{18}O in oxygen gas only when algae or plants were exposed to ^{18}O-labeled H_2O, not the ^{18}O-labeled CO_2.

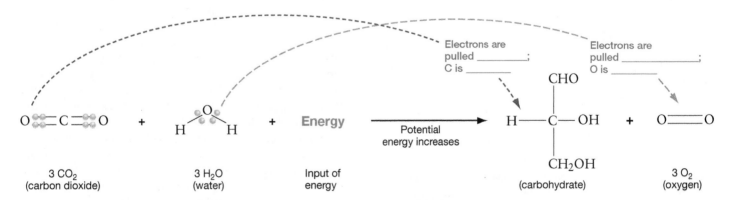

Figure 10.1 Electron Transfer during Photosynthesis.

✔ Fill in the electron positions for each bond in the reaction products, and complete the labels explaining which product is reduced and which is oxidized.

In addition, the reactions responsible for producing O_2 occurred only in the presence of sunlight, but did not require the presence of CO_2. These data suggested that there were two distinct sets of reactions: one that uses light to produce O_2 from H_2O and one that converts CO_2 into sugars.

A second major line of research supported the idea of two sets of reactions. Between 1945 and 1955, a team led by Melvin Calvin began introducing radioactively labeled carbon dioxide ($^{14}CO_2$) to algae and identifying the molecules that subsequently became labeled with the radioisotope. These experiments allowed researchers to identify the sequence of reactions involved in reducing CO_2 to sugars.

Because Calvin played an important role in this research, the reactions that reduce carbon dioxide and produce sugar came to be known as the **Calvin cycle.** Later research showed that the Calvin cycle functions only if the light-capturing reactions that produce O_2 are also occurring.

To summarize: Early research showed that photosynthesis consists of two linked sets of reactions. One set is triggered by light; the other set—the Calvin cycle—requires the products of the light-capturing reactions. The light-capturing reactions produce oxygen from water; the Calvin cycle produces sugar from carbon dioxide. (See **Making Models 10.1** to learn how to track the In's and Out's of photosynthesis using flow charts.)

The two reactions are linked by a series of redox reactions that starts when water is split, or oxidized, to form O_2. During the light-capturing reactions, electrons are promoted to a high-energy state by light and then transferred through a series of reactions to reduce a phosphorylated version of NAD^+, called **$NADP^+$ (nicotinamide adenine dinucleotide phosphate).** This reaction forms **NADPH,** which functions as a reducing agent similar to the NADH produced in cellular respiration. Some of the energy released from these redox reactions is also used to produce ATP (**Figure 10.2**). During the Calvin cycle, the electrons in NADPH and the potential energy in ATP are used to reduce CO_2 to carbohydrate.

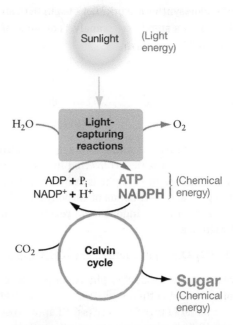

Figure 10.2 **Photosynthesis Has Two Linked Components.** In the light-capturing reactions of photosynthesis, light energy is transformed to chemical energy in the form of ATP and NADPH. During the Calvin cycle, the ATP and NADPH produced in the light-capturing reactions are used to reduce carbon dioxide to sugar.

Photosynthesis Occurs in Chloroplasts

Once later experiments established that photosynthesis takes place only in the green portions of plants, biologists focused on the bright green organelles called **chloroplasts** ("green-formed elements"). One leaf cell typically contains 40 to 50 chloroplasts, and a square millimeter of leaf averages about 500,000 (**Figure 10.3**).

When membranes derived from chloroplasts were found to release oxygen after exposure to sunlight, the hypothesis that chloroplasts are the site of photosynthesis became widely accepted.

As Figure 10.3 shows, a chloroplast is enclosed by an outer membrane and an inner membrane (see Chapter 7). The interior is dominated by flattened, sac-like structures called **thylakoids,** which often occur in interconnected stacks called **grana** (singular: granum). The space inside a thylakoid is its **lumen.** (Lumen is a general term for the interior of any sac-like structure. Your stomach and intestines have a lumen.) The fluid-filled space between the thylakoids and the inner membrane is the **stroma.**

When researchers analyzed the chemical composition of thylakoid membranes, they found huge quantities of pigments. **Pigments** are molecules that absorb only certain wavelengths of light—other wavelengths are either reflected or transmitted (pass through). Pigments appear colored because people see the reflected wavelengths that are *not* absorbed.

The most abundant pigment in the thylakoid membranes of green plants is chlorophyll ("green-leaf"), which reflects or transmits green light. As a result, chlorophyll is responsible for the green color of plants, some algae, and many photosynthetic bacteria.

Before plunging into the details of how photosynthesis occurs, take a moment to consider just how astonishing the process is. Using some CO_2 gas, water, and sunlight, photosynthesis produces

---

✎ Making Models 10.1 Tips on Drawing Flow Charts

Photosynthesis is a complex process. By drawing your own flow charts, you can practice keeping track of the main events. Use boxes or ovals to represent processes, enzymes, or molecules. Use arrows to represent the movement of molecules and/or energy. Be sure to label your flow chart clearly. Remember, models are flexible, so there are many correct ways to show the same idea.

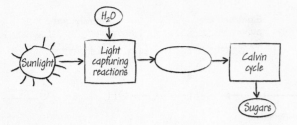

MODEL Add detail to the model by showing what links the light-capturing reactions and the Calvin cycle. Also, add ovals and arrows to show where O_2 and CO_2 fit in.

To see this model in action, go to https://goo.gl/9TeyBC

the raw materials for every organic molecule in the organism. The energy stored in the bonds of these molecules may also be extracted via cellular respiration. Plants oxidize sugars in their mitochondria and consume O_2 in the process of producing ATP, just as animals and other eukaryotes do. If photosynthesis is not *the* most sophisticated biochemistry on Earth, it is certainly a contender.

✔ If you understand the role of photosynthesis in autotrophs, you should be able to predict which of a plant's macromolecules would be radiolabeled if the plant were grown in the presence of $^{14}CO_2$. Explain your answer.

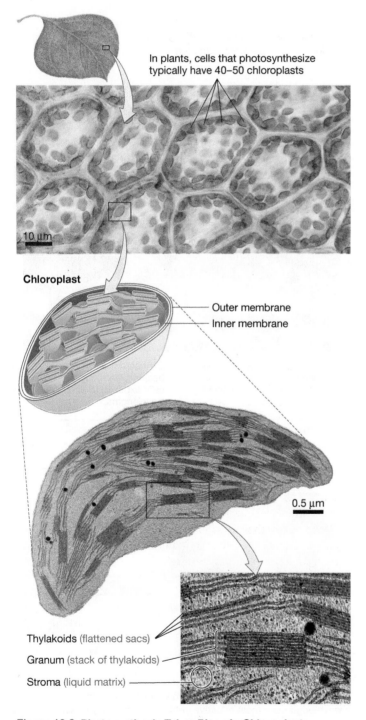

In plants, cells that photosynthesize typically have 40–50 chloroplasts

10 µm

Chloroplast

Outer membrane
Inner membrane

0.5 µm

Thylakoids (flattened sacs)
Granum (stack of thylakoids)
Stroma (liquid matrix)

Figure 10.3 Photosynthesis Takes Place in Chloroplasts.

10.2 How Do Pigments Capture Light Energy?

The light-capturing reactions of photosynthesis begin with the simple act of sunlight striking chlorophyll. To understand the consequences of this event, it's helpful to review the nature of light.

Light is a type of electromagnetic radiation, a form of energy. Physicists describe light's behavior as both wavelike and particlelike. Like water waves or airwaves, electromagnetic radiation is characterized by its **wavelength**—the distance between two successive wave crests (or wave troughs). The wavelength determines the type of electromagnetic radiation.

Figure 10.4 illustrates the range of wavelengths of electromagnetic radiation—the **electromagnetic spectrum.** The electromagnetic radiation that humans can see, **visible light,** ranges in wavelength from about 400 to about 710 nanometers (nm, or 10^{-9} m). Shorter wavelengths of electromagnetic radiation contain more energy than longer wavelengths do. Thus, there is more energy in blue light than in red light.

To emphasize the particle-like nature of light, physicists point out that it exists in discrete packets called **photons.** Each photon of light has a characteristic wavelength and energy level. Pigment molecules absorb the energy of some of these photons. How?

Photosynthetic Pigments Absorb Light

Sunlight includes white light, which consists of all wavelengths in the visible portion of the electromagnetic spectrum at once. When a photon strikes an object, the photon may be absorbed, transmitted, or reflected. A pigment molecule absorbs photons of particular wavelengths.

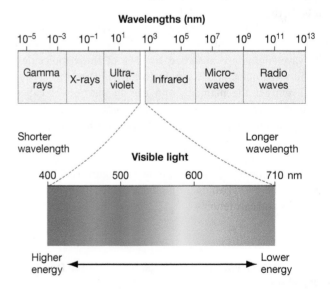

Figure 10.4 The Electromagnetic Spectrum. Electromagnetic energy radiates through space in the form of waves. The shorter the wavelength of electromagnetic radiation, the higher its energy. Humans can see radiation at wavelengths between about 400 nanometers (nm) to 710 nm.

(a) PROCESS: ISOLATING PIGMENTS VIA THIN LAYER CHROMATOGRAPHY

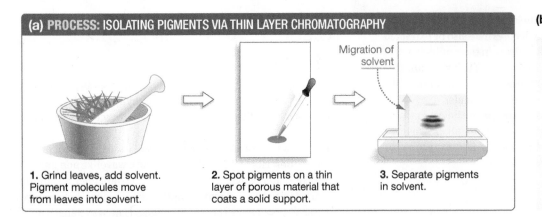

1. Grind leaves, add solvent. Pigment molecules move from leaves into solvent.

2. Spot pigments on a thin layer of porous material that coats a solid support.

3. Separate pigments in solvent.

Migration of solvent

(b) A finished chromatograph

- Carotene
- Pheophytin
- Chlorophyll *a*
- Chlorophyll *b*
- Xanthophyll

Figure 10.5 Chromatography Is a Technique for Separating Molecules. Different species of photosynthetic organisms may contain different types and quantities of pigments. The pigments in this example were extracted from grass leaves.

If a pigment absorbs all the visible wavelengths, the pigment appears black because no visible wavelength of light is reflected back to your eye. If a pigment absorbs many or most of the wavelengths in the blue and green parts of the spectrum but transmits or reflects longer wavelengths, it appears red.

What wavelengths do various plant pigments absorb? In one approach to answering this question, researchers grind up leaves in a liquid that acts as a solvent to extract pigment molecules from the leaf mixture. A technique called thin layer chromatography (see BioSkills 6) separates the pigments in the extract **(Figure 10.5a)**.

To begin, spots of raw leaf extract are placed near the bottom of a stiff support that is coated with a thin layer of silica gel, cellulose, or similar porous material. The coated support is then placed in a solvent solution. As the solvent wicks upward through the coating, it carries the pigment molecules in the mixture with it. Because the pigment molecules vary in size, solubility, or both, they are carried at different rates.

Figure 10.5b shows a chromatograph from a grass-leaf extract. Notice that this leaf contains an array of pigments. To find out which wavelengths are absorbed by each of these molecules, researchers cut out a single region (color band) of the porous material, extract the pigment, and use an instrument called a spectrophotometer to record the wavelengths absorbed. (For more information on spectrophotometry, see BioSkills 8).

Different Pigments Absorb Different Wavelengths of Light
Research based on the techniques shown in Figure 10.5 has confirmed that there are two major pigment classes in plant leaves: chlorophylls and carotenoids.

Figure 10.6 Certain Wavelengths of Light Are Used to Drive Photosynthesis.

SOURCE: Engelmann, T. W. 1882. Oxygen excretion from plant cells in a microspectrum. *Botanische Zeitung* 40: 419–426.

✔ Draw what you expect the results of this experiment would look like if the pigments that drive photosynthesis in the algae were to absorb most strongly at 500 nm and 560 nm.

RESEARCH

QUESTION: Which of the wavelengths found in white light are responsible for driving photosynthesis?

HYPOTHESIS: No specific hypothesis.

EXPERIMENTAL SETUP:

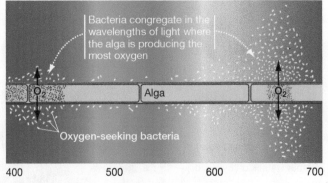

Alga (*Cladophora* sp.)

1. Expose algal cells to all the wavelengths of visible light in the presence of oxygen-seeking bacteria.

2. Record the number of bacteria swarming near algal cells exposed to different wavelengths.

PREDICTION: No specific prediction.

RESULTS:

Swarming bacteria, observed and sketched by Engelmann (1882)

Bacteria congregate in the wavelengths of light where the alga is producing the most oxygen

O₂   Alga   O₂

Oxygen-seeking bacteria

400   500   600   700

CONCLUSION: Pigments that absorb violet-to-blue and red wavelengths are most effective at triggering photosynthesis.

1. **Chlorophylls,** designated chlorophyll *a* and chlorophyll *b*, absorb strongly in the blue and red regions of the visible spectrum. The presence of chlorophylls makes plants look green because they reflect green light, which they do not absorb.

2. **Carotenoids** absorb in the blue and green parts of the visible spectrum. Thus, carotenoids appear yellow, orange, or red. The carotenoids found in plants belong to two classes, called carotenes and xanthophylls.

Which of these wavelengths drive photosynthesis?

In 1882, T. W. Engelmann answered this question by studying the photosynthetic activity of a filamentous alga that was spread across a microscope slide and illuminated with a spectrum of colors (**Figure 10.6**). The idea was that the algal cells would begin performing photosynthesis in response to the various wavelengths of light and produce oxygen as a by-product. To determine exactly where oxygen was being produced, Engelmann added bacterial cells from a species that is attracted to oxygen.

As the drawing in the "Results" section of Figure 10.6 shows, most of the bacteria congregated in the violet-to-blue and red regions of the slide. Because wavelengths in these parts of the spectrum were associated with high oxygen concentrations, Engelmann concluded that they defined the **action spectrum** for photosynthesis—the wavelengths that drive the light-capturing reactions. Engelmann's data indicate that violet-to-blue and red photons are the most effective at driving photosynthesis. Because the chlorophylls absorb these wavelengths, this early experiment showed that chlorophylls are the main photosynthetic pigments.

Using thin layer chromatography, and more advanced techniques to evaluate photosynthetic activity, biologists have produced data like those shown in **Figure 10.7**. This graph shows the action spectrum (production of O_2) of photosynthesis and the absorption spectra for three different pigments found in chloroplasts. An **absorption spectrum** measures how the wavelength of photons influences the amount of light absorbed by a pigment. In the combined graph, peaks indicate wavelengths where absorbance or photosynthetic activity is high; troughs indicate wavelengths where absorbance or photosynthetic activity is low.

Chlorophylls
ABSORB: violet-to-blue and red light
TRANSMIT: green light

Action spectrum of photosynthesis

Carotenoids
ABSORB: blue and green light
TRANSMIT: yellow, orange, or red light

Figure 10.7 There Is a Strong Correlation between the Absorption Spectra of Pigments and the Action Spectrum for Photosynthesis.

DATA: Singhal, G. S., et al. 1999. *Concepts in Photobiology: Photosynthesis and Photomorphogenesis*. Dordrecht: Kluwer Academic; co-published with Narosa Publishing House (New Delhi), 11–51.

Which Part of a Pigment Absorbs Light? As **Figure 10.8a** shows, chlorophyll *a* and chlorophyll *b* are similar in structure. Both have two fundamental parts: a long isoprenoid "tail" (introduced in Chapter 6) and a "head" consisting of a large ring structure with a magnesium atom in the middle. The tail interacts with proteins embedded in the thylakoid membrane; the head is where light is absorbed.

The structure of β-carotene, shown in **Figure 10.8b**, has an isoprenoid chain connecting two rings that are responsible for absorbing light. This pigment is what gives carrots their orange color. A xanthophyll called zeaxanthin, which gives corn kernels their bright yellow color, is nearly identical to β-carotene, except that the ring structures on either end of the molecule contain a hydroxyl (−OH) group.

Researchers had shown that chlorophylls are the main photosynthetic pigments, but carotenoids also absorb light. What do they do? Before analyzing what happens when chlorophyll pigments absorb light, let's first look at the function of the carotenoids.

(a) Chlorophylls *a* and *b*

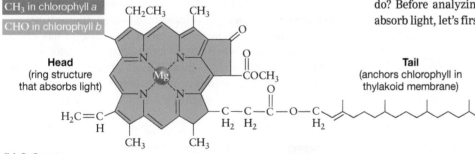

Head
(ring structure that absorbs light)

Tail
(anchors chlorophyll in thylakoid membrane)

(b) β-Carotene

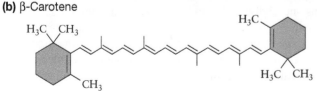

Figure 10.8 Photosynthetic Pigments Contain Ring Structures.
(a) Although chlorophylls *a* and *b* are very similar structurally, they have the distinct absorption spectra shown in Figure 10.7.
(b) β-Carotene is an orange carotenoid found in carrot roots and other plant tissues.

What Is the Role of Carotenoids and Other Accessory Pigments?

Carotenoids are called accessory pigments because they absorb light and pass the energy on to chlorophyll. Both xanthophylls and carotenes are found in chloroplasts. In late summer, the leaves of deciduous trees increase synthesis of carotenoids and other accessory pigments. In the autumn, when leaves start to die, their chlorophyll degrades first, leaving the carotenoids and other pigments that turn forests into spectacular displays of yellow, orange, and red.

Carotenoids absorb some of the wavelengths of light that are not absorbed by chlorophyll. As a result, they extend the range of wavelengths that can drive photosynthesis.

Researchers discovered an even more important function for carotenoids, though, by analyzing what happens to leaves when these pigments are destroyed. Many herbicides, for example, work by inhibiting enzymes that are involved in carotenoid synthesis. Plants lacking carotenoids rapidly lose their chlorophyll, turn white, and die. Based on these results, researchers have concluded that the primary function of carotenoids is to protect the plant.

To understand why carotenoids are protective, recall that photons—especially the high-energy, short-wavelength photons in the ultraviolet part of the electromagnetic spectrum—contain enough energy to knock electrons out of atoms and create free radicals (see Chapter 2). Free radicals, in turn, trigger reactions that can disrupt and degrade molecules.

Carotenoids "quench" free radicals by accepting or stabilizing unpaired electrons. As a result, they protect chlorophyll molecules from harm. When carotenoids are absent, chlorophyll molecules are destroyed by free radicals and photosynthesis stops. Starvation and death follow.

When Light Is Absorbed, Electrons Enter an Excited State

Just what is absorption? What happens when a photon of a particular wavelength—say, red light with a wavelength of 680 nm—strikes a chlorophyll molecule? When a chlorophyll molecule absorbs a photon, the photon's energy is transferred to bonds in the chlorophyll molecule's head region. In response, an electron becomes "excited," or bumped up to a higher energy state.

The excited electron states that are possible in a particular pigment are discrete—meaning, incremental rather than continuous—and can be represented as lines on an energy scale. These discrete energy levels are a property of the electron configurations in a particular pigment.

Figure 10.9 shows the ground state, or unexcited state, as 0 and the higher energy states as 1 and 2. If the difference between the possible energy states is the same as the energy in the photon, the photon can be absorbed and an electron excited to a higher energy state.

In chlorophyll, for example, the energy difference between the ground state and state 1 is equal to the energy in a red photon, while the energy difference between state 0 and state 2 is equal to the energy in a blue photon. Thus, chlorophyll can readily absorb red photons and blue photons.

Chlorophyll does not absorb green light well, because there is no discrete step—no difference in possible energy states for

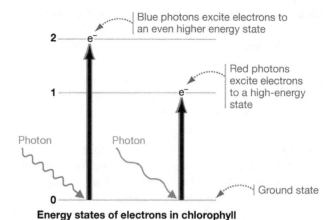

Energy states of electrons in chlorophyll

Figure 10.9 Electrons Are Promoted to High-Energy States When Photons are Absorbed by Chlorophyll. The unexcited, or ground state of the electron, is labeled 0, and the discrete energy states are labeled 1 and 2. The absorption of particular wavelengths of light that excite electrons to these higher energy states is a property of chlorophyll's structure.

✔ Where you would predict the energy states to be on this diagram for a carotenoid pigment that absorbs blue and green photons? (Hint: Review Figure 10.4.)

its electrons—that corresponds to the amount of energy in a green photon.

Wavelengths in the ultraviolet part of the spectrum have so much energy that they may actually eject electrons from a pigment molecule and create a free radical. In contrast, wavelengths in the infrared regions have so little energy that in most cases they merely increase the movement of atoms in the pigment, generating heat rather than exciting electrons.

But if a pigment absorbs a photon with the right amount of energy in the form of electromagnetic radiation, an electron is excited. The electron now has high potential energy, but this excited state is unstable and it will last for only a short time—on the order of picoseconds (1×10^{-12} seconds). What happens next?

If the excited electron simply falls back to its ground state, the absorbed energy is released as heat or a combination of heat and electromagnetic radiation (light). When the electron energy produces light, it is called **fluorescence.** Because some of the original photon's energy is transformed to heat, the electromagnetic radiation that is given off during fluorescence has lower energy and a longer wavelength than the original photon did.

When pigments in chloroplasts absorb photons, about 2 percent of the excited electrons produce fluorescence. The other 98 percent of the energized pigments use their excited electrons to drive photosynthesis.

To understand what happens to these excited electrons, it's important to recognize that chlorophyll molecules work in groups—not individually. In the thylakoid membrane, 200–300 chlorophyll molecules and accessory pigments are organized by an array of proteins to form structures called the **antenna complex** and the reaction center. These complexes, along with the molecules that capture and process excited electrons, form a **photosystem.**

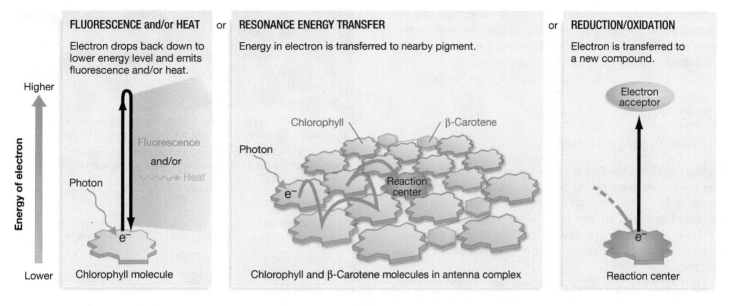

Figure 10.10 Four Fates for Excited Electrons in Photosynthetic Pigments. When sunlight promotes electrons in pigments to a high-energy state, four things can happen: They can fluoresce, release heat, pass energy to a nearby pigment via resonance, or transfer the electron to an electron acceptor.

The Antenna Complex When pigments in the antenna complex absorb photons, the energy—but not the electron itself—is passed to a nearby chlorophyll molecule, where another electron is excited in response. This phenomenon is known as **resonance energy transfer.**

Resonance energy transfer is possible only between pigments that are able to absorb different wavelengths of photons—from those absorbing higher-energy photons to those absorbing lower-energy photons. The organization of the antenna complex makes it possible for this resonance energy to be efficiently moved between pigments, as the potential energy drops at each step.

Once the energy is transferred, the original excited electron falls back to its ground state. In this way, energy is transferred inside the antenna complex in a manner that may be likened to the transfer of sound between tuning forks, or excitement between fans at a sports event during the "wave." But unlike the stadium wave, most of this resonance energy is directed to a particular location in a photosystem, called the reaction center.

The Reaction Center When a photon or resonance energy from the antenna complex reaches the **reaction center,** the energy is absorbed by one of two specialized chlorophyll molecules. When this pigment is energized, an excited electron is transferred from the pigment to an electron acceptor. As the acceptor becomes reduced, its potential energy increases. This is a key step in the transformation of light energy: Electromagnetic energy from sunlight has now been transformed to chemical energy.

Note that in the absence of light, the electron acceptor does not accept electrons. It remains in an oxidized state because the redox reaction that transfers an electron to the electron acceptor is endergonic. But when light excites electrons in chlorophyll to a high-energy state, the reaction becomes exergonic. In this way, the energy in light transforms an endergonic reaction to an exergonic one.

Figure 10.10 summarizes the four possible fates of electrons in chlorophyll that are excited by photons. The energy released from these electrons can

1. be emitted in the form of light via fluorescence, or
2. be given off as heat alone, or
3. excite an electron in a nearby pigment and induce resonance, or
4. be transferred to an electron acceptor in a redox reaction.

Fluorescence is typical of isolated pigments and is less frequent in chloroplasts, resonance energy transfer occurs in antenna complex pigments, and redox occurs in reaction center pigments.

■ CHECK YOUR UNDERSTANDING

If you understand that ...

- Pigments absorb specific wavelengths of light.
- When a chlorophyll molecule in the antenna complex of a chloroplast membrane absorbs red or blue light, one of its electrons is promoted to a high-energy state.
- In the antenna complex, excited electrons transmit energy between chlorophyll molecules by resonance energy transfer from higher to lower levels toward the reaction center.
- When energy is transferred to a chlorophyll molecule in the reaction center, the excited electron is transferred to an electron acceptor. In this way, light energy is transformed to chemical energy.

✔ **You should be able to ...**

Predict how the pigments of the antenna complex would be organized, with regard to the wavelength of photons absorbed, to allow directional transport of energy from the outer pigments to the reaction center.

Answers are available in Appendix A.

Now the question is, what happens to the electrons that are transferred to the electron acceptor in the reaction center? Specifically, how are these reduced molecules used to manufacture sugar?

10.3 The Discovery of Photosystems I and II

During the 1950s, the fate of excited electrons in photosystems was the central issue facing biologists interested in photosynthesis. A key breakthrough began with simple experiments by Robert Emerson on how green algae responded to various wavelengths of light. The algal cells being studied responded to wavelengths in the red and far-red regions of the visible spectrum.

Emerson found that if the algal cells were illuminated with either red or far-red wavelengths of light, the photosynthetic response was moderate. But if cells were exposed to a combination of both wavelengths, the rate of photosynthesis increased more than the sum of the rates produced by each wavelength independently. This phenomenon was called the enhancement effect, and is not limited to algal cells. In follow-up work by other researchers, it was also observed in isolated chloroplasts from plants (**Figure 10.11**). Why the enhancement effect occurred was a complete mystery at the time.

Robin Hill and Faye Bendall proposed a solution to this puzzle. They hypothesized that this enhancement effect resulted from two distinct types of reaction centers, each absorbing different wavelengths of light. According to the two-photosystem hypothesis, the enhancement effect occurs because photosynthesis is much more efficient when both photosystems operate together.

Subsequent work has shown that the two-photosystem hypothesis is correct for cyanobacteria ("blue-green bacteria") and the chloroplasts of eukaryotes, such as algae and plants. These two photosystems differ in structure and function, but work together in the light-capturing reactions.

To figure out how the two photosystems work, investigators focused on species of photosynthetic bacteria that possess one or the other of the two photosystems, but not both. Once each type of photosystem was understood in isolation, researchers explored how they work in combination. Let's do the same—by analyzing first **photosystem II,** then **photosystem I** (so named because it was discovered first), and then how the two interact.

How Does Photosystem II Work?

To study photosystem II, researchers first focused on the single photosystem of purple photosynthetic bacteria, including the purple sulfur bacteria that were studied by van Niel (see Section 10.1). The bacteria's photosystem shares many components with the photosystem II of cyanobacteria and eukaryotic chloroplasts of algae and plants, but was easier to study in the lab. For simplicity, the eukaryotic chloroplast—and its now well-characterized photosystems—will serve as the model system for the remainder of the chapter.

RESEARCH

QUESTION: Red and far-red light each stimulate a moderate rate of photosynthesis. How does a combination of both wavelengths affect the rate of photosynthesis?

HYPOTHESIS: When red and far-red light are combined, the rate of photosynthesis will be the sum of the single wavelength rates.

NULL HYPOTHESIS: When red and far-red light are combined, the rate of photosynthesis will be no more than the highest single wavelength rate.

EXPERIMENTAL SETUP:

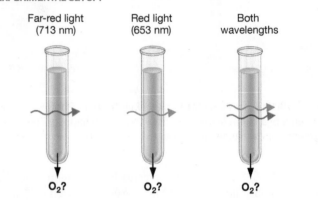

1. Expose algal cells to far-red light and then red light. Record oxygen produced as a measure of rate of photosynthesis.

2. Expose same cells to a combination of both lights.

PREDICTION: When the two wavelengths are combined, the amount of oxygen produced will be the sum of the single wavelength tests.

PREDICTION OF NULL HYPOTHESIS: When the two wavelengths are combined, the amount of oxygen produced will be no more than the single wavelength test that yielded the highest amount of oxygen.

RESULTS:

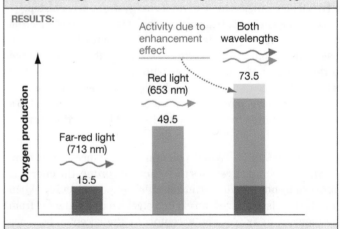

CONCLUSION: Neither hypothesis is correct. The combination of both wavelengths yielded more oxygen than the sum of the single tests. A new hypothesis is required to explain this enhancement effect.

Figure 10.11 The "Enhancement Effect" of Two Different Wavelengths in Isolated Chloroplasts.

SOURCE: Govindjee, R., Govindjee, and G. Hoch. 1964. Emerson enhancement effect in chloroplast reactions. *Plant Physiology* 39: 10–14.

✔ **PROCESS OF SCIENCE** Was it important for the researchers to keep the density of chloroplasts constant in each treatment? Explain why or why not.

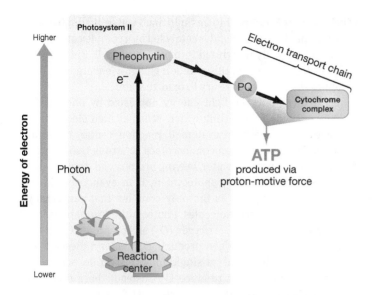

Figure 10.12 **Photosystem II Feeds Excited Electrons to an Electron Transport Chain.** When an excited electron leaves the chlorophyll in the reaction center of photosystem II, the electron is accepted by pheophytin, transferred to plastoquinone (PQ), and then stepped down in energy along an electron transport chain.

Converting Light Energy into Chemical Energy In photosystem II, the action begins when the antenna complex transmits resonance energy to the reaction center, where the electron acceptor pheophytin comes into play (**Figure 10.12**). Structurally,

pheophytin is identical to chlorophyll except that pheophytin lacks a magnesium atom in its head region. Functionally, the two molecules are extremely different.

Unlike other pigments, pheophytin does not become excited by photons or resonance energy—it accepts excited electrons from the reaction center chlorophylls. The redox reaction between pheophytin and the reaction center chlorophyll pigment is a key step in transforming light energy into chemical energy.

Immediately after the excited electron is transferred to pheophytin, however, the reaction center pigment becomes an incredibly strong oxidizing agent. What prevents the electron from being pulled back to the oxidized pigment? The answer is that the electron is quickly shuttled away from the reaction center to an electron transport chain (ETC) in the thylakoid membrane.

In both structure and function, the thylakoid ETC is similar to components in the mitochondrial ETC (see Chapter 9).

- Structurally, the photosystem II and mitochondrial ETCs both contain quinones and cytochromes.

- Functionally, the redox reactions that occur in both ETCs result in protons being actively transported from one side of an internal membrane to the other. The resulting proton-motive force drives ATP production via ATP synthase.

Figure 10.13 explains how the electron transport chain associated with photosystem II works in more detail. Start by focusing on the molecule called **plastoquinone (PQ)**—a quinone similar to ubiquinone in the ETC of cellular respiration. Recall that

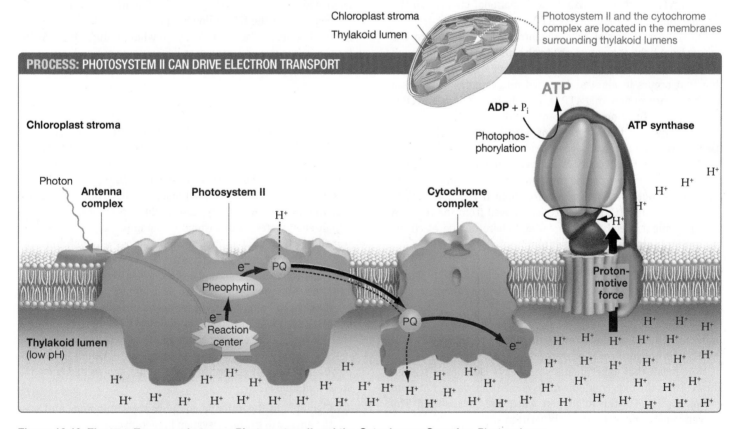

Figure 10.13 **Electron Transport between Photosystem II and the Cytochrome Complex.** Plastoquinone (PQ) carries electrons from photosystem II along with protons from the stroma. The cytochrome complex oxidizes plastoquinone, releasing the protons in the thylakoid lumen that drive ATP synthesis.

ubiquinone is a small hydrophobic molecule that can transport electrons between molecules (see Chapter 9). Because plastoquinone is lipid soluble and not anchored to the thylakoid membrane, it is free to move within the thylakoid membrane.

When plastoquinone receives electrons from photosystem II, it carries them across the membrane to the lumen side of the thylakoid and delivers them to molecules with a higher redox potential in the cytochrome complex. In this way, plastoquinone shuttles electrons from photosystem II to the cytochrome complex much like ubiquinone shuttled electrons between complexes I or II and complex III in mitochondria. The potential energy released by these reactions allows plastiquinone to pick up protons from the chloroplast stroma and drop them off in the thylakoid lumen.

The protons transported by plastoquinone result in a high concentration of protons in the thylakoid lumen. The pH in the thylakoid reaches 5 while the pH of the stroma hovers around 8. Because the pH scale is logarithmic (see BioSkills 5), the difference of 3 units means that the concentration of H^+ is $10 \times 10 \times 10 = 1000$ times higher in the lumen than in the stroma. In addition, the stroma becomes negatively charged relative to the thylakoid lumen.

The net effect of electron transport, then, is a large proton electrochemical gradient. This gradient results in a proton-motive force that, in turn, drives H^+ out of the thylakoid lumen and into the stroma. Proton flow down the electrochemical gradient is an exergonic process that is coupled to the endergonic synthesis of ATP from ADP and P_i. The stream of protons flows through ATP synthase, causing conformational changes in the enzyme that drive production of ATP.

Since the synthesis of ATP in chloroplasts is initiated by the energy from light, it is called **photophosphorylation.** Although photophosphorylation is similar to the oxidative phosphorylation that occurs in plant and animal mitochondria, there is a key difference in how this ATP is used. In mitochondria, ATP is exported and fuels many different cellular processes. In chloroplasts, however, the ATP remains within the organelle and is used for the production of carbohydrate.

The photosystem II story is not yet complete, however. The electrons from PQ are passed through the cytochrome complex, but what about the oxidized photosystem II reaction center? To continue this ETC, the electrons removed from the reaction center pigments need to be replaced. Where do the electrons required by photosystem II come from?

Photosystem II Obtains Electrons by Oxidizing Water Think back to the simplified overall reaction for photosynthesis:

$$CO_2 + H_2O + \text{light energy} \longrightarrow (CH_2O)_n + O_2$$

In the presence of sunlight, carbon dioxide and water are used to produce carbohydrate and oxygen gas.

Now recall that experiments with heavy isotopes of oxygen showed that the oxygen atoms in O_2 come from water, not from carbon dioxide. For this to happen, water must be oxidized. The oxygen-generating reaction can be written as

$$2\,H_2O \longrightarrow 4\,H^+ + 4\,e^- + O_2$$

This reaction is referred to as "splitting" water. It supplies electrons for photosystem II and is catalyzed by a complex of enzymes that are physically integrated into photosystem II. Since oxygen is very electronegative, this reaction is highly endergonic. What supplies the energy necessary to oxidize water?

As it turns out, the light energy harvested by photosystem II is responsible for splitting water. When excited electrons are removed from the photosystem II reaction center, the redox potential of oxidized pigments becomes so strong that enzymes can pull electrons from water, leaving protons and oxygen.

Among all life-forms, photosystem II in cyanobacteria and eukaryotic chloroplasts is the only complex that can catalyze the oxidation of water molecules. Photosynthetic organisms that oxidize water will generate oxygen (O_2) as a by-product, and thus perform **oxygenic** ("oxygen-producing") photosynthesis. Other organisms that have only a single photosystem do not oxidize water, and thus do not produce O_2. Instead, these organisms use different electron donors, such as H_2S in the purple sulfur bacteria, to perform **anoxygenic** ("no oxygen-producing") photosynthesis.

✔ **MODEL** If you understand photosystem II, you should be able to make a flowchart that tracks the flow of energy through photosystem II and the ETC, including the antenna complex, ATP synthase, pheophytin, light, the proton gradient, and a reaction center. Be sure to show where the splitting of water fits in.

Recall that carbohydrates contain reduced carbons in the form of C–C and C–H bonds (see Chapter 5). To manufacture sugar from oxidized carbons in CO_2, strong reducing agents like NADPH are required. If the ETC following photosystem II is responsible for driving the synthesis of ATP, then what produces the NADPH for the Calvin cycle? The answer lies in photosystem I. Let's take a closer look.

How Does Photosystem I Work?

Recall that researchers dissected photosystem II by studying similar, but simpler, photosystems in purple photosynthetic bacteria. To understand the structure and function of photosystem I, they turned to heliobacteria ("sun-bacteria").

Like the purple bacteria, heliobacteria have only one photosystem that uses the energy in sunlight to promote electrons to a high-energy state. But instead of being passed to an electron transport chain that pumps protons across a membrane, the excited electrons in heliobacteria are used to reduce NAD^+. When NAD^+ gains two electrons and a proton, NADH is produced.

In the chloroplasts of cyanobacteria and eukaryotes, a similar set of light-capturing reactions reduces a phosphorylated version of NAD^+, symbolized $NADP^+$, to yield NADPH. Both NADH and NADPH function as electron carriers.

Figure 10.14 explains how photosystem I works in chloroplasts—put your finger on the "2 Photons" arrows and trace the steps that follow.

1. Pigments in the antenna complex absorb photons and pass the energy to the photosystem I reaction center.

2. Electrons are excited in reaction center chlorophyll molecules.

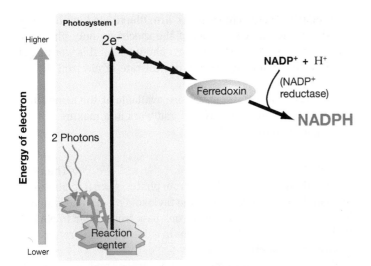

Figure 10.14 **Photosystem I Produces NADPH.** When excited electrons leave the chlorophyll molecule in the reaction center of photosystem I, they pass through a series of iron- and sulfur-containing proteins until they are accepted by ferredoxin. In an enzyme-catalyzed reaction, the reduced form of ferredoxin reacts with $NADP^+$ to produce NADPH.

3. The reaction center pigments are oxidized, and the excited electrons are passed through a series of carriers inside the photosystem, then to a molecule called **ferredoxin,** and then to the enzyme called $NADP^+$ reductase.

4. $NADP^+$ reductase transfers two electrons and a proton to reduce $NADP^+$ and form NADPH.

To summarize: Electrons from photosystem I are used to produce NADPH, which is a reducing agent similar in function to the NADH and $FADH_2$ produced by the citric acid cycle (see Chapter 9). Electrons from photosystem II, in contrast, are used to produce a proton-motive force that drives the synthesis of ATP.

In combination, then, photosystems II and I produce chemical energy stored in ATP and NADPH. But there are still gaps in the flow of electrons through these two photosystems. Where do the electrons from photosystem II end up? How does the oxidized reaction center of photosystem I obtain electrons so NADPH will continue to be made?

The Z Scheme: Photosystems II and I Work Together

Figure 10.15 illustrates the **Z-scheme** model for how photosystems II and I interact. The name was inspired by the changes occurring in electron potential energy as plotted on a vertical axis, which takes on the shape of a Z that has fallen over.

To drive home how energy flows through the light-capturing reactions, trace the route of electrons through Figure 10.15 with your finger. Start on the lower left. The process starts when photons excite electrons in the chlorophyll molecules of photosystem II's antenna complex. When the energy in the excited electrons is transferred to the reaction center, a specialized pair of chlorophyll molecules, each called P680, passes excited electrons to pheophytin. These are the same reaction center pigments described previously, and the name represents the optimal wavelength absorbed by the pigments (680 nm).

When pheophytin is reduced, it transfers an electron from the high-energy bond to an electron transport chain. There the electron is gradually stepped down in potential energy through redox reactions among a series of quinones and cytochromes. Using the energy released by the redox reactions, plastoquinone (PQ) carries protons across the thylakoid membrane, from the stroma to the lumen. ATP synthase uses the resulting proton-motive force to phosphorylate ADP, creating ATP.

When electrons reach the end of the cytochrome complex, they are passed to a small diffusible protein called **plastocyanin (PC).** The reduced plastocyanin diffuses through the lumen of the thylakoid, and donates the electron to an oxidized reaction center pigment in photosystem I.

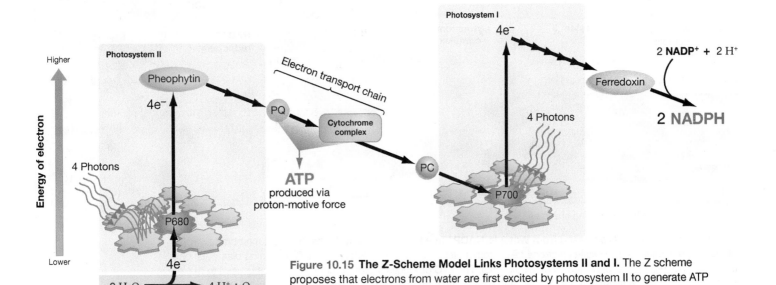

Figure 10.15 **The Z-Scheme Model Links Photosystems II and I.** The Z scheme proposes that electrons from water are first excited by photosystem II to generate ATP and then excited again by photosystem I to reduce $NADP^+$ to NADPH.

Stop tracing for a moment, and consider the following:

- Plastocyanin is critical—it forms a physical link between photosystem II and photosystem I.

- A single plastocyanin molecule can shuttle over 1000 electrons per second between the cytochrome complex and photosystem I.

- The flow of electrons between photosystems, by means of plastocyanin, is important because it replaces electrons that are carried away from the pair of pigments in the photosystem I reaction center. This pair of specialized chlorophyll molecules is called P700 (optimal absorption of 700-nm wavelength).

Now keep going. The electrons that flow from photosystem II to P700, via plastocyanin, are eventually transferred to the protein ferredoxin, which passes electrons to an enzyme that catalyzes the reduction of $NADP^+$ to NADPH.

Finally, direct your attention back to the lower-left portion of the figure. Note that the electrons that initially left photosystem II are replaced by electrons that are stripped away from water, producing O_2 as a by-product and H^+ ions that contribute to the electrochemical gradient.

Understanding the Enhancement Effect The Z-scheme model helps explain the enhancement effect documented in Figure 10.11. When chloroplasts are illuminated with wavelengths in the red portion of the spectrum, only photosystem II can run at a maximum rate. The overall rate of electron flow through the Z scheme is moderate because photosystem I's efficiency is reduced.

Similarly, when chloroplasts are illuminated with wavelengths in the far-red portion of the spectrum, only photosystem I is capable of peak efficiency; photosystem II is working at a below-maximum rate, so the overall rate of electron flow is reduced.

But when both wavelengths are available at the same time, both photosystems are activated and work at a maximum rate, leading to enhanced efficiency.

Noncyclic Electron Flow between Water and $NADP^+$ The complete path that electrons follow from photosystem II to photosystem I and how it is oriented in the thylakoid membrane is shown in **Figure 10.16**. Note that electrons pass from water to $NADP^+$ through a chain of redox reactions in a linear fashion, referred to as **noncyclic electron flow.**

Compare the movement of electrons and protons in Figure 10.16 with what you have learned about electron transport chains in mitochondria (see Figure 9.15). In both these organelles, the energy released from redox reactions is used to build a proton gradient for ATP production. At the end of the chains, electrons are donated to terminal electron acceptors.

Chloroplasts and mitochondria differ, however, in how electron potential energy changes between the primary electron donor and the terminal electron acceptor. In the mitochondrial ETC, electron potential energy starts high and then steadily drops as the electrons are transferred to the terminal electron acceptor, which has the lowest potential energy. In chloroplasts, the electron donor (H_2O) has lower potential energy than the reduced terminal electron acceptor (NADPH) (see Figure 10.15).

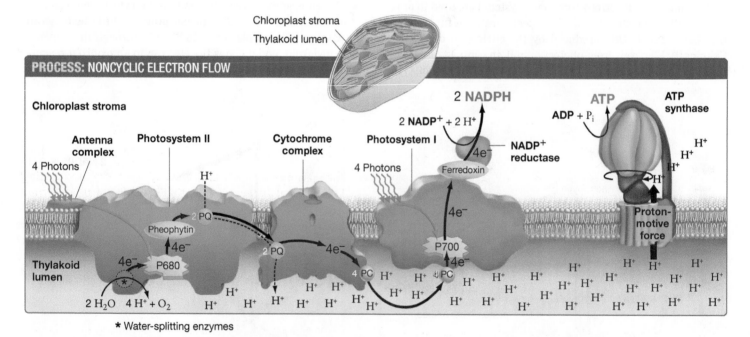

* Water-splitting enzymes

Figure 10.16 Electrons Are Passed from Water to $NADP^+$ in a Linear Pathway. In the thylakoid membrane, photosystem II uses light to excite electrons taken from water and pass them through an ETC including plastoquinone (PQ), the cytochrome complex, and plastocyanin (PC). The ETC produces a proton-motive force that is used to make ATP. Photosystem I excites electrons from PC and passes them on to ferredoxin to reduce $NADP^+$ to NADPH.

✔ MODEL If you understand how the photosystems work, you should be able to draw a model of a section of thylakoid membrane showing how the following elements are related: the two photosystems, the cytochrome complex, ATP synthase, photons, electrons, and protons.

Cyclic Electron Flow Recycles Electrons and Drives Photophosphorylation

Recent evidence indicates that an alternative electron path, called **cyclic electron flow,** also occurs in green algae and land plants (**Figure 10.17**). In these organisms, ATP is produced via cyclic as well as noncyclic photophosphorylation.

During cyclic electron flow, electrons excited in photosystem I are transferred back to the electron transport chain, generating ATP through photophosphorylation instead of reducing $NADP^+$. Cyclic electron flow coexists with noncyclic electron flow and produces additional ATP to meet the energy demand for manufacturing sugars from carbon dioxide (CO_2).

Oxygenic Photosynthesis and the Evolution of Earth

Although oxygen is a by-product of oxygenic photosynthesis, the impact of producing this molecule on the environment of early Earth cannot be overstated. Photosynthesis produces the oxygen that is keeping you alive right now. Biologists rank the evolution of Earth's oxygen-rich atmosphere as one of the most important events in the history of life. Why?

According to the geologic record, oxygen levels in the atmosphere and oceans began to rise only about 2 billion years ago, as organisms that performed oxygenic photosynthesis increased in abundance. O_2 was, in fact, almost nonexistent on Earth before enzymes evolved that could catalyze the oxidation of water. Since ozone is formed from O_2 gas, this protective layer would have arisen in our atmosphere only after the evolution of oxygenic photosynthesis. Without the ozone layer, Earth's surface would have been bombarded continually by the searing intensity of ultraviolet radiation—making the evolution of life on land nearly impossible.

As oxygen became more abundant, bacterial cells that evolved the ability to use it as an electron acceptor via cellular respiration flourished. O_2 is so electronegative that it creates a huge potential energy drop for the electron transport chains involved in cellular respiration. As a result, organisms that use O_2 as an electron acceptor in cellular respiration can produce much more ATP than can organisms that use other electron acceptors (see Chapter 9).

Despite the importance of oxygen in the evolution and maintenance of life, in terms of photosynthesis, it is simply waste. The useful products of the light-capturing reactions are ATP and NADPH, which are required to reduce carbon dioxide to sugar. Your life, and the life of most organisms, depends on the production of sugar from CO_2. How does it happen?

CHECK YOUR UNDERSTANDING

If you understand that ...

- Photosystem II contributes excited electrons to an electron transport chain that pumps protons, creating a proton-motive force that drives ATP synthase.
- Photosystem I uses excited electrons to make NADPH and can produce additional ATP by building a proton-motive force via cyclic electron flow.

✔ You should be able to ...

Compare and contrast the flow of electrons in mitochondria (see Chapter 9) and chloroplasts. What are the primary electron donors and terminal electron acceptors, and how do they differ in terms of initial and final energy states?

Answers are available in Appendix A.

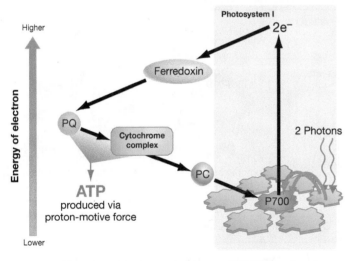

Figure 10.17 Cyclic Electron Flow Leads to ATP Production. Cyclic electron flow is an alternative to the Z scheme. Instead of being donated to $NADP^+$, electrons are returned to plastoquinone (PQ) and cycle between photosystem I and the ETC, resulting in the production of additional ATP via photophosphorylation.

10.4 How Is Carbon Dioxide Reduced to Produce Sugars?

The reactions analyzed in Section 10.3 are triggered by light. This is logical, because their entire function is focused on transforming electromagnetic energy in the form of sunlight into chemical energy in the bonds of ATP and NADPH. The reactions that produce sugar from carbon dioxide, in contrast, are not triggered directly by light. Instead, they depend on the ATP and NADPH produced by the light-capturing reactions.

The Calvin Cycle Fixes Carbon

Carbon fixation is the addition of carbon dioxide to an organic compound. The word "fix" is appropriate because the process converts—or fixes—CO_2 gas to a biologically useful form. Once carbon atoms are fixed, they can be used as sources of energy and as building blocks to construct the molecules found in cells.

Carbon fixation is a redox reaction—the carbon atom in CO_2 is reduced by attaching it to another carbon. Research on how this happens in chloroplasts gained momentum just after World War II, when radioactive isotopes of carbon became available for research purposes.

Melvin Calvin's group made great strides early in this effort by tracking the incorporation of $^{14}CO_2$ into molecules during photosynthesis (Figure 10.18). After injecting $^{14}CO_2$ into a culture of algae that were undergoing photosynthesis, they stopped the reaction at different periods of time by killing the cells in hot alcohol. This treatment immediately denatured the enzymes involved in the reactions, effectively halting any further change in the radiolabeled intermediates.

The molecules labeled with the ^{14}C in this extract were separated by chromatography and detected using X-ray film. If radioactively labeled molecules were present in the chromatograph, the energy they emitted would expose the film and create a dark spot. The labeled compounds could then be isolated and identified.

By varying the amount of time the algae were exposed to labeled $^{14}CO_2$, Calvin and co-workers pieced together the sequence in which various intermediates formed. For example, when the team analyzed cells almost immediately after adding the $^{14}CO_2$, they found that the ^{14}C was predominantly in a three-carbon organic acid called 3-phosphoglycerate (3PGA). This result suggested that 3PGA was the initial product of carbon reduction. Stated another way, it appeared that carbon dioxide reacted with some unknown molecule to produce 3PGA.

This was an intriguing result, because 3-phosphoglycerate is also one of the 10 intermediates in glycolysis. The Calvin cycle manufactures carbohydrate; glycolysis breaks it down. Because the two processes are related in this way, it was logical that at least some intermediates in glycolysis and the Calvin cycle are the same.

RuBP Is the Initial Reactant with CO_2 Which compound reacts with CO_2 to produce 3PGA? This was the key, initial step. Since 3PGA has three carbons, Calvin's group searched for a two-carbon compound that might serve as the initial carbon dioxide acceptor. They were unsuccessful.

Then, while Calvin was running errands one day, it occurred to him that the molecule reacting with carbon dioxide might contain five carbons, not two. Adding CO_2 to a five-carbon molecule would produce a six-carbon compound, which could then split in half to form 2 three-carbon molecules.

Experiments to test this hypothesis confirmed that the five-carbon compound **ribulose bisphosphate (RuBP)** is the initial reactant.

The Calvin Cycle Is a Three-Step Process The complete Calvin cycle, as it came to be called, has three phases (Figure 10.19):

1. **Fixation phase** The Calvin cycle begins when CO_2 reacts with RuBP. This phase fixes carbon and produces two molecules of 3PGA, which is a three-carbon organic acid.

2. **Reduction phase** The 3PGA is phosphorylated by ATP and then reduced by electrons from NADPH. The product

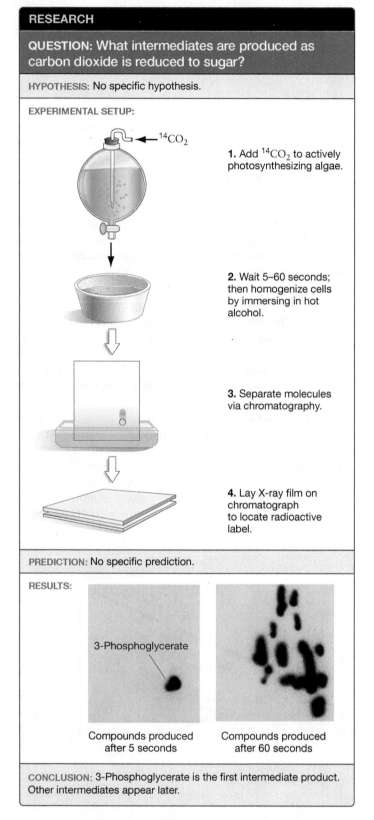

Figure 10.18 **Experiments Revealed the Reaction Pathway Leading to Reduction of CO_2.**

SOURCE: Benson, A. A., J. A. Bassham, M. Calvin, et al. 1950. The path of carbon in photosynthesis. V. Paper chromatography and radioautography of the products. *Journal of the American Chemistry Society* 72: 1710–1718.

✔ **PROCESS OF SCIENCE** Why wasn't this experiment based on a specific hypothesis and set of predictions?

(a) The Calvin cycle has three phases.

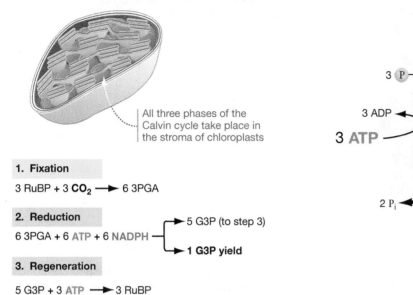

All three phases of the Calvin cycle take place in the stroma of chloroplasts

1. Fixation

3 RuBP + 3 CO_2 ⟶ 6 3PGA

2. Reduction

6 3PGA + 6 ATP + 6 NADPH ⟶ 5 G3P (to step 3) / 1 G3P yield

3. Regeneration

5 G3P + 3 ATP ⟶ 3 RuBP

(b) The reaction occurs in a cycle.

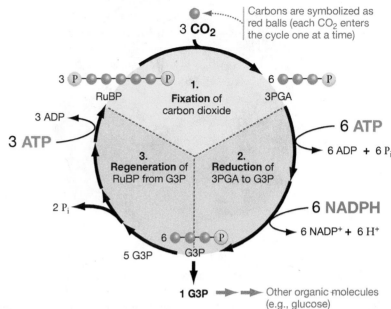

Figure 10.19 Carbon Dioxide Is Reduced in the Calvin Cycle. The number of reactants and products resulting from three turns of the cycle are shown. Of the six G3Ps that are generated during the reduction phase, one is used in the synthesis of other molecules, such as glucose, and the other five are used to regenerate RuBP. The three RuBPs that are regenerated participate in fixation reactions for additional turns of the cycle.

is the phosphorylated three-carbon sugar **glyceraldehyde-3-phosphate (G3P).** Some of the G3P that is synthesized is drawn off to produce other organic molecules, like the six-carbon sugar glucose.

3. *Regeneration phase* The rest of the G3P keeps the cycle going by serving as the substrate for the third phase in the cycle: reactions that use additional ATP in the regeneration of RuBP.

All three phases take place in the stroma of chloroplasts. One turn of the Calvin cycle fixes one molecule of CO_2. Three turns of the cycle fix three molecules of CO_2, yielding one molecule of G3P and three fully regenerated RuBP (Figure 10.19).

The discovery of the Calvin cycle clarified how the ATP and NADPH produced by light-capturing reactions allow cells to fix and reduce CO_2 gas to carbohydrate $(CH_2O)_n$. Because sugars store a great deal of potential energy, producing them takes a great deal of chemical energy. In the Calvin cycle, each mole of CO_2 requires the energy from 3 moles of ATP and 2 moles of NADPH to fix it and reduce it to sugar.

✔ **QUANTITATIVE** If you understand the Calvin cycle, you should be able to provide the *minimum number* of RuBP, ATP, and NADPH molecules that would be required to run through six complete cycles. Explain why you would not need six RuBP molecules to fix and reduce six CO_2.

The conversion of CO_2 gas into carbohydrate is, without doubt, worthy of this energy investment. Plants use sugars to fuel cellular respiration and build all of the organic molecules in leaves and other structures. Millions of non-photosynthetic

organisms also depend on this reaction to provide the sugars they need for cellular respiration and raw material for synthesis of their own organic molecules (see Chapter 9).

Ecologically, the addition of CO_2 to RuBP is the most important chemical reaction on Earth. The enzyme that catalyzes it is fundamental to life. How does this protein work?

The Discovery of Rubisco

In the Calvin cycle, most of the reactions involved in reducing CO_2 also occur in glycolysis or other metabolic pathways. The reaction responsible for fixing CO_2 gas to RuBP, however, is entirely unique.

To find the enzyme that fixes CO_2 to RuBP, Arthur Weissbach and colleagues ground up spinach leaves, purified a large series of proteins from the resulting cell extracts, and tested each protein to see if it could catalyze this step. Eventually they isolated the catalyst, which happens to be the most abundant enzyme in leaf tissue. The researchers' data suggested that it constituted almost 50 percent of the total protein in spinach leaves.

All photosynthetic organisms that use the Calvin cycle to fix carbon require the CO_2-fixing enzyme ribulose-1,5-bisphosphate carboxylase/oxygenase (commonly referred to as **rubisco**). As shown in **Figure 10.20** on page 226, the rubisco enzyme is roughly cube-shaped and consists of 16 polypeptides that form eight active sites where CO_2 is fixed. Some of these polypeptide subunits are made in the chloroplast while others are made in the cytoplasm and then imported into the organelle.

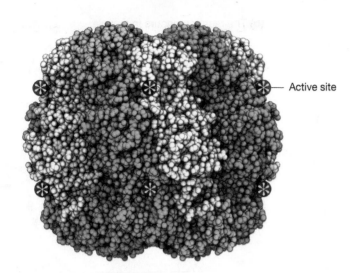

Active site

Figure 10.20 **Rubisco Is a Large Enzyme Complex.** The cube shape of rubisco consists of 16 polypeptides that form into 8 catalytic active sites.

Despite its large number of active sites, rubisco is a slow enzyme. Each active site catalyzes just three reactions per second; other enzymes typically catalyze thousands of reactions per second. Plants synthesize huge amounts of rubisco, possibly as an adaptation compensating for its lack of speed. As a result, rubisco is thought to be the most abundant enzyme on Earth.

Besides being slow, rubisco is also inefficient because it will catalyze the addition of either O_2 or CO_2 to RuBP. This is a key point: Oxygen and carbon dioxide compete at the enzyme's active sites, which slows the rate of CO_2 reduction.

The reaction of O_2 with RuBP actually does more than just compete with the reaction of CO_2 at the same active site. One of the molecules produced from the addition of oxygen to RuBP (2-phosphoglycolate) is processed in reactions that require ATP and release CO_2, regenerating 3PGA. Part of this pathway occurs in chloroplasts, and part occurs in peroxisomes and mitochondria. The reaction sequence resembles respiration, because it consumes oxygen and produces carbon dioxide. As a result, it is called **photorespiration** (Figure 10.21).

Because photorespiration requires energy and releases fixed CO_2, it "undoes" photosynthesis. When photorespiration occurs, the overall rate of CO_2 fixation declines. This does not mean that the plant does not benefit, however. Some of the products from photorespiration are known to be involved in plant signaling and development. In addition, a protective role for photorespiration has been proposed when plants are in conditions with high light and low CO_2.

How Is Photosynthesis Regulated?

Like cellular respiration, photosynthesis regulation is based on the presence of inputs and outputs. Although the mechanisms responsible for turning photosynthesis on or off are still under investigation, several patterns have emerged:

- The presence of light triggers the production of proteins required for photosynthesis.

- When sugar supplies are high, the production of proteins required for photosynthesis is inhibited, but the production of proteins required to process and store sugars is stimulated.

- Rubisco is activated by regulatory molecules that are produced when light is available, but inhibited in conditions of low CO_2 availability—when photorespiration is favored.

The central message here is that the rate of photosynthesis is finely tuned to use resources efficiently in response to changes in environmental conditions.

To maximize carbon fixation in photosynthetic tissues, concentrations of CO_2 must be higher than the O_2 produced by the light reactions. How does a plant manage the amount of these two gases?

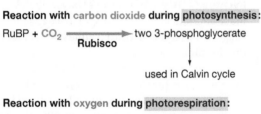

Reaction with carbon dioxide during photosynthesis:

$$\text{RuBP} + CO_2 \xrightarrow{\text{Rubisco}} \text{two 3-phosphoglycerate}$$

used in Calvin cycle

Reaction with oxygen during photorespiration:

$$\text{RuBP} + O_2 \xrightarrow{\text{Rubisco}} \text{3-phosphoglycerate} + \text{2-phosphoglycolate}$$

used in Calvin cycle — when processed, CO_2 is released and ATP is used

Figure 10.21 **Rubisco Can React with CO_2 or O_2.** In addition to fixing CO_2 in photosynthesis, rubisco catalyzes a competing reaction with O_2 with a very different outcome.

(a) Leaf surfaces contain stomata.

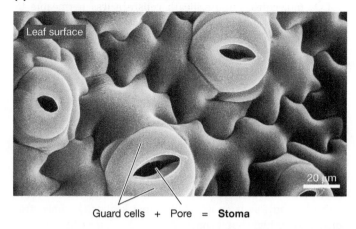

Guard cells + Pore = **Stoma**

(b) Carbon dioxide diffuses into leaves through stomata.

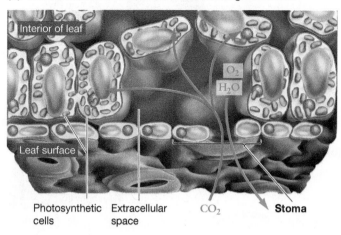

Photosynthetic cells | Extracellular space | CO_2 | **Stoma**

Figure 10.22 Leaf Cells Obtain Carbon Dioxide through Stomata.

Oxygen and Carbon Dioxide Pass through Stomata

Atmospheric carbon dioxide is a key reactant in photosynthesizing cells. It would seem straightforward, then, for CO_2 to diffuse directly into plants along a concentration gradient. But the situation is not this simple, because plants are covered with a waxy coating called a cuticle. This lipid layer prevents water from evaporating out of tissues, but it also prevents the transport of gases like CO_2 and O_2.

Instead, CO_2 gets into photosynthesizing tissues through specialized pores. The surface of a leaf is dotted with openings bordered by two distinctively shaped cells called **guard cells** (Figure 10.22a). The opening between these paired cells is called a pore, and the entire structure is a **stoma** (plural: **stomata**).

An open stoma allows CO_2 from the atmosphere to diffuse into air-filled spaces inside the leaf and excess O_2 to diffuse out (Figure 10.22b). Eventually the CO_2 diffuses along a concentration gradient into the chloroplasts of photosynthesizing cells. A strong concentration gradient favoring entry of CO_2 is maintained by the Calvin cycle, which constantly uses up the CO_2 in chloroplasts.

Stomata are normally open during the day, when photosynthesis is occurring, and closed at night. But if the daytime is extremely hot and dry, leaf cells may lose a great deal of water to evaporation through their stomata. When this occurs, they must either close the openings and halt photosynthesis or risk death from dehydration.

When conditions are hot and dry, then, stomata must close and CO_2 and O_2 transport stops—meaning that photosynthesis slows and photorespiration increases. How do plants that live in hot, dry environments prevent dehydration while keeping CO_2 supplies high enough to avoid increased photorespiration?

Mechanisms for Increasing CO_2 Concentration

The oxygenation reaction that triggers photorespiration is favored when oxygen concentrations are high and CO_2 concentrations are low. But even with the stomata open, the atmosphere is 21 percent oxygen and only 0.04 percent carbon dioxide. How can photosynthesizing cells raise CO_2 concentrations to make photosynthesis more efficient? An answer emerged in a surprising experimental result.

The C_4 Pathway After the Calvin cycle had been worked out in algae, researchers in a variety of labs used the same radioactive carbon dioxide tracking approach to investigate how carbon fixation occurs in other species. Researchers in the labs of Hugo Kortschak and Y. S. Karpilov exposed leaves of sugarcane and maize (corn) to $^{14}CO_2$ and sunlight; then they isolated and identified the intermediates.

Both research teams expected to find the first of the radioactive carbon atoms in 3-phosphoglycerate—the normal product of carbon fixation by rubisco. Instead, they found that in their species, the radioactive carbon atom ended up in four-carbon compounds such as malate and aspartate.

Instead of creating a three-carbon molecule as in the Calvin cycle, it appeared that these species were able to fix CO_2 to produce four-carbon molecules. This newly identified set of reactions became known as the **C_4 pathway** to distinguish it from Calvin's CO_2 fixation via what is now termed the **C_3 pathway** (Figure 10.23).

C_4 plants:

$$\text{3-carbon compound} + \textbf{CO}_2 \xrightarrow{\textbf{PEP carboxylase}} \text{4-carbon organic acid}$$

C_3 plants:

$$\text{RuBP} + \textbf{CO}_2 \xrightarrow{\textbf{Rubisco}} \text{two 3-phosphoglycerate (3-carbon organic acid)}$$

Figure 10.23 Initial Carbon Fixation in C_4 Plants Is Different from That in C_3 Plants.

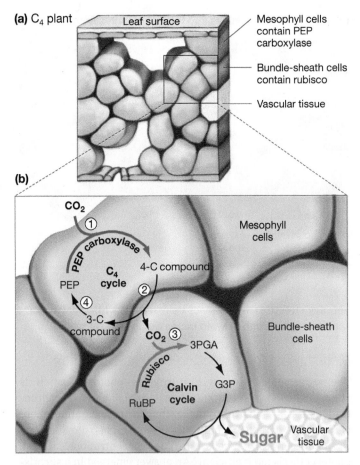

(a) C$_4$ plant

Leaf surface

Mesophyll cells contain PEP carboxylase

Bundle-sheath cells contain rubisco

Vascular tissue

(b)

CO$_2$

① PEP carboxylase

PEP

C$_4$ cycle

4-C compound

②

④

3-C compound

CO$_2$ ③

3PGA

Rubisco

RuBP

Calvin cycle

G3P

Sugar

Mesophyll cells

Bundle-sheath cells

Vascular tissue

Figure 10.24 In C$_4$ Plants, Carbon Fixation and the Calvin Cycle Occur in Different Cell Types. (a) The carbon-fixing enzyme PEP carboxylase is located in mesophyll cells, while rubisco is in bundle-sheath cells. **(b)** CO$_2$ is fixed to the three-carbon compound PEP by PEP carboxylase, forming a four-carbon organic acid. A CO$_2$ molecule can be released from the organic acid to feed the Calvin cycle.

Researchers who followed up on the initial reports found that the C$_4$ pathway does not replace the Calvin cycle, but serves as an additional fixation step. C$_4$ plants can actually fix carbon dioxide using both pathways—to a three-carbon compound by an enzyme called **PEP carboxylase** (C$_4$) and to RuBP by rubisco (C$_3$). They also showed that the two pathways are found in distinct cell types within the same leaf. PEP carboxylase is common in **mesophyll cells** near the surface of leaves, while rubisco is found in **bundle-sheath cells** that surround the vascular tissue in the interior of the leaf (**Figure 10.24a**). Vascular tissue conducts water and nutrients in plants (see Chapter 35).

Based on the observations about C$_4$ plants, Hal Hatch and Roger Slack proposed a four-step model to explain how the CO$_2$ that is fixed to form a four-carbon molecule can be released to feed the Calvin cycle (**Figure 10.24b**):

Step 1 PEP carboxylase fixes CO$_2$ to a three-carbon molecule (phosphoenolpyruvate, or PEP) in mesophyll cells.

Step 2 The four-carbon molecules that result are transported to bundle-sheath cells via channels called plasmodesmata (see Chapter 11).

Step 3 The four-carbon molecules are broken down to release CO$_2$ molecules. Bundle-sheath cells are less permeable to gases, so CO$_2$ concentrations rise and promote carbon fixation by rubisco to form 3PGA. This step initiates the Calvin cycle.

Step 4 The three-carbon compound remaining after CO$_2$ is released is returned to the mesophyll cell to regenerate PEP.

In effect, then, the C$_4$ pathway acts as a CO$_2$ concentrator. The reactions that take place in mesophyll cells require energy in the form of ATP, but they increase CO$_2$ concentrations in cells where rubisco is active. Because it increases the ratio of carbon dioxide to oxygen in photosynthesizing cells, less O$_2$ binds to rubisco's active sites. As a result, the C$_4$ pathway improves the efficiency of the Calvin cycle.

The C$_4$ pathway is an adaptation that keeps CO$_2$ concentrations in leaves high, but it comes at a cost. For each G3P molecule generated via photosynthesis, C$_4$ plants expend 15 ATP molecules compared to the 9 ATP molecules required by C$_3$ plants (see Fig. 10.19). This energy expenditure, however, is justified by the increased efficiency of photosynthesis in conditions where stomata are mostly closed to prevent dehydration. The affinity for CO$_2$ by PEP carboxylase is also much higher than that of rubisco, which means that stomata can be open for shorter periods in C$_4$ plants.

This strategy is not the only mechanism that plants use to continue growth in hot, dry climates, however. Some environments are so arid that even C$_4$ plants are unable to avoid dehydration. Nevertheless, certain plants use the C$_4$ pathway in a unique way that allows them to thrive in these deserts. How do they do it?

CAM Plants Researchers studying a group of flowering plants called the Crassulaceae discovered a second mechanism for limiting the effects of dehydration and photorespiration. This photosynthetic pathway, **crassulacean acid metabolism,** or **CAM,** resembles the C$_4$ pathway in a number of ways. It is a CO$_2$ concentrator that acts as an additional, preparatory step to the Calvin cycle. It also generates a four-carbon organic acid in its first CO$_2$ fixation step. But unlike the C$_4$ pathway, CAM occurs at a different time than the Calvin cycle does—not in a different place.

CAM occurs in cacti and other species that routinely keep their stomata closed on hot, dry days. At night, when conditions are cooler and more humid, CAM plants open their stomata and take in huge quantities of CO$_2$. The CO$_2$ is temporarily fixed to organic acids and stored in the central vacuoles of photosynthetic cells. During the day, when stomata are closed, these acids are processed in reactions that release the CO$_2$ and feed the Calvin cycle (**Figure 10.25**).

The C$_4$ and CAM pathways function as CO$_2$ pumps. They minimize photorespiration when stomata are closed and CO$_2$ cannot diffuse in directly from the atmosphere. Both are found in species that live in hot, dry environments.

But while C$_4$ plants stockpile CO$_2$ by fixing and storing organic acids in cells *where* rubisco is not active, CAM plants store CO$_2$ *when* rubisco is inactive. In C$_4$ plants, the reactions catalyzed by PEP carboxylase and rubisco are separated in space; in CAM plants, the reactions are separated in time.

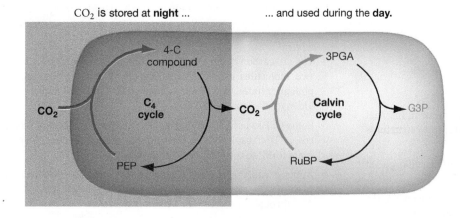

CO₂ is stored at **night** ... ... and used during the **day**.

4-C compound

CO₂

C₄ cycle

PEP

CO₂

3PGA

Calvin cycle

G3P

RuBP

Figure 10.25 In CAM Plants, Carbon Fixation Occurs at Night and the Calvin Cycle Occurs during the Day.

✔ At what part of the day would there be the highest concentration of four-carbon acids in the vacuoles of CAM plants?

What Happens to the Sugar That Is Produced by Photosynthesis?

The products of the Calvin cycle enter one of several reaction pathways. The most important of these reaction sequences uses G3P to produce the monosaccharide glucose, a process called **gluconeogenesis.** This glucose is often combined with fructose, which is also made from G3P, to form the disaccharide ("two-sugar") **sucrose.**

When photosynthesis is taking place slowly, almost all the G3P that is produced is used to make sucrose. Sucrose is water soluble and readily transported to other parts of the plant. If sucrose is delivered to rapidly growing parts of the plant, it is broken down to fuel cellular respiration and growth.

An alternative pathway occurs when photosynthesis is proceeding rapidly and sucrose is abundant. Under these conditions, the glucose molecules are polymerized to form **starch,** which is stored in the cells of leaves and roots. Starch production occurs inside the chloroplast; sucrose synthesis takes place in the cytosol.

In photosynthesizing cells, starch acts as a temporary sugar-storage product. At night, the starch that is stored in leaf cells is broken down to glucose molecules. The glucose is then fed into cellular respiration or used to manufacture sucrose for transport to other parts of the plant. In this way, chloroplasts provide sugars for cells throughout the plant by day and by night.

If a mouse eats the starch that is stored in the leaves or roots of a plant, however, the chemical energy in the reduced carbons of starch fuels the mouse's growth and reproduction. If an owl eats the mouse, the chemical energy in the mouse's tissues fuels the predator's growth and reproduction. (You can see how energy is processed via photosynthesis and cellular respiration in the Big Picture on pages 232–233.)

In this way, virtually all cell activity can be traced back to the sun's energy that was originally captured by photosynthesis. Photosynthesis is the staff of life.

CHECK YOUR UNDERSTANDING

If you understand that ...

- The Calvin cycle is a three-phase process: CO_2 fixation (synthesis of 3PGA), carbon reduction (synthesis of G3P), and regeneration of RuBP.
- The C_4 and CAM pathways are mechanisms for increasing CO_2 concentrations in photosynthesizing cells. They limit the effect of photorespiration and allow photosynthesis to continue after stomata close.
- In photosynthesizing cells, G3P is used to make glucose that is stored as starch or used to make sucrose. Sucrose is transported to all plant cells and used to drive cellular respiration.

✔ You should be able to ...

1. Describe how CO_2 is delivered to rubisco in (a) C_3 plants, (b) C_4 plants, and (c) CAM plants.
2. Predict the relative concentration of starch in leaves at the start of the day versus the end of the day.

Answers are available in Appendix A.

10.1 Photosynthesis Harnesses Sunlight to Make Carbohydrate

- The light-capturing reactions of photosynthesis occur in internal membranes of the chloroplast that are organized into structures called thylakoids that stack to form grana.

- The Calvin cycle takes place in a fluid portion of the chloroplast called the stroma.

- The CO_2-reduction reactions of photosynthesis depend on the products of the light-capturing reactions: ATP and NADPH.

10.2 How Do Pigments Capture Light Energy?

- Pigment molecules capture light energy by exciting electrons after a photon is absorbed. Each pigment absorbs photons of particular wavelengths.

- After a pigment molecule absorbs a photon, the excitation energy is quickly released as fluorescence and heat, heat alone, resonance energy that excites another pigment, or it is transferred as an excited electron to reduce an electron acceptor.

- Pigments organized into antenna complexes transfer absorbed light energy via resonance to the reaction center, where an excited electron is transferred to an electron acceptor.

10.3 The Discovery of Photosystems I and II

- In photosystem II, excited electrons are transferred to plastoquinone at the start of an electron transport chain. The redox reactions in the ETC are used to generate a proton-motive force that drives the synthesis of ATP. Electrons taken from photosystem II are replaced by splitting water, releasing oxygen and protons.

- In photosystem I, excited electrons are passed to ferredoxin. In an enzyme-catalyzed reaction, the reduced form of ferredoxin passes electrons to $NADP^+$, forming NADPH.

- The Z scheme connects photosystems II and I. Electrons excited by light in photosystem II are passed through the ETC, picked up by plastocyanin, and transferred to oxidized pigments in the photosystem I reaction center. These electrons are again excited by light in photosystem I and subsequently used to reduce $NADP^+$.

- Electrons from photosystem I may occasionally be passed back to plastoquinone instead of $NADP^+$. This cyclic flow of electrons between the photosystem I and the ETC boosts ATP supplies.

10.4 How Is Carbon Dioxide Reduced to Produce Sugars?

- The Calvin cycle starts when rubisco catalyzes the fixation of CO_2 to a five-carbon compound called ribulose bisphosphate (RuBP).

- The six-carbon compound that results immediately splits to form two molecules of 3-phosphoglycerate (3PGA), which are then phosphorylated by ATP and reduced by NADPH to produce glyceraldehyde-3-phosphate (G3P).

- Some G3P is used to synthesize other organic molecules, like glucose; ATP phosphorylates the rest in a series of reactions to regenerate RuBP so the cycle can continue.

- Rubisco catalyzes the addition of oxygen as well as carbon dioxide to RuBP. The reaction with oxygen leads to a loss of fixed CO_2 and ATP through a process called photorespiration.

- In C_4 plants and CAM plants, CO_2 is initially fixed to four-carbon compounds, then released to fuel the Calvin cycle. This increases CO_2 levels in plant tissues and reduces the effect of photorespiration when stomata are closed.

Answers are available in Appendix A

✓ TEST YOUR KNOWLEDGE

1. In antenna complexes, how is energy transferred among the pigment molecules?
   a. by heat
   b. by redox reactions
   c. by fluorescence
   d. by resonance

2. Why is chlorophyll green?
   a. It absorbs all wavelengths in the visible spectrum.
   b. It absorbs wavelengths only in the red portions of the spectrum (680–700 nm).
   c. It absorbs wavelengths only in the blue part of the visible spectrum (450–480 nm).
   d. It absorbs wavelengths in only the blue and red parts of the visible spectrum.

3. What do the light-capturing reactions of photosynthesis produce?
   a. ATP and NADPH
   b. RuBP
   c. G3P
   d. glucose

4. At what point in photosynthesis is the electromagnetic energy of light first converted into chemical energy?

✓ TEST YOUR UNDERSTANDING

5. Why is the chlorophyll in chloroplasts less likely to produce fluorescence compared to extracted chlorophyll molecules?

6. Describe the three phases of the Calvin cycle and how the products of the light-capturing reactions participate in this process.

7. QUANTITATIVE Use what you know of the relationship between the light-capturing reactions and Calvin cycle to calculate the number of photons used to produce a new G3P and regenerate the RuBP. (Assume 1 ATP is produced for each pair of electrons used to form NADPH.)

8. CAUTION Which process in plants generates the most ATP for driving cellular activities, photosynthesis or cellular respiration? Explain your answer.

9. Predict how the following conditions would affect the production of O_2, ATP, and NADPH and state whether noncyclic or cyclic electron flow would occur in each: (1) Only blue photons hit a chloroplast; (2) blue and red photons hit a chloroplast, but no $NADP^+$ is available; (3) blue and red photons hit a chloroplast, but a proton channel has been introduced into the thylakoid membrane, so it is fully permeable to protons.

10. An investigator exposes chloroplasts to 700-nm photons and observes low O_2 production, but high ATP production. Which of the following best explains this observation?
    a. The electrons from water are directly transferred to $NADP^+$, which is used to generate ATP.
    b. Photosystem II is not splitting water, and the ATP is being produced by cycling electrons via photosystem I.
    c. The O_2 is being converted to water as a terminal electron acceptor in the production of ATP.
    d. Electron transport has stopped and ATP is being produced by the Calvin cycle.

✔ PUT IT ALL TOGETHER: Case Study

Can green algae replace "black gold"?

Over the past decade, there has been great interest in developing a sustainable and renewable energy source that would displace our dependence on fossil fuels. Photosynthetic organisms, like the microalgae being cultured in the image above, are currently being used to produce bioethanol, biodiesel, and bio-H_2. How are photosynthetic organisms being engineered to promote the production of these biofuels?

11. Aquatic plants and algae carry out photosynthesis using the same light reactions and Calvin cycle as in land plants. Would you expect any of these organisms to also require the C_4 pathway? Describe the problem that is solved by the C_4 pathway in land plants and if this could ever be an issue in an aquatic environment.

12. Fossil fuel consists of coal, oil, and natural gas that have been formed from the remains of plants and animals that died millions of years ago. What was the source of the energy used to produce the high-energy molecules in these fossil fuels?

13. One of the contributing factors to environmental pollution and climate change is the production of CO_2 via the combustion of fossil fuels. What is a benefit of using biofuels, produced by living organisms, if they will release similar amounts of CO_2 when used to meet our energy demand?

14. A promising group of organisms for biofuel production are microalgae like *Chlamydomonas reinhardtii*. When grown in full sunlight, however, they have a reduced yield of chemical energy per photon absorbed. What is likely happening to the absorbed light energy that is not being used to drive photosynthesis?

15. **PROCESS OF SCIENCE** To overcome the reduced photosynthetic efficiency of *C. reinhardtii*, researchers engineered the organism by decreasing the size of antenna complexes used in the two photosystems. Comparisons of the photosynthetic activity and growth rate between this engineered strain and a control under high-light conditions are shown below. What can you conclude based on these results?

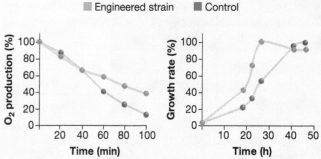

Source: J. H. Mussgnug et al. 2007. *Plant Biotechnology Journal* 5: 802–814.

16. Cultures of microalgae are often grown in large pools of water or clear tanks, like those shown in the photograph. Consider such a three-dimensional habitat, then speculate as to why reducing the size of the antenna complexes would benefit the entire culture when grown in full sunlight.

MasteringBiology®

Students Go to MasteringBiology for assignments, the eText, and the Study Area with animations, practice tests, and activities.
Professors Go to MasteringBiology for automatically graded tutorials and questions that you can assign to your students, plus Instructor Resources.

THE BIG PICTURE

It takes energy to stay alive. Use this concept map to review how energy is harvested and used by cells to drive the reactions required to sustain life.

As you read the map, remember that chemical energy is a form of potential energy. Potential energy is based on the position of matter in space, and chemical energy is all about the position of electrons in covalent bonds. When hydrogen gas reacts explosively with oxygen, all that's happening is that electrons are moving from high-energy positions to lower-energy positions.

In essence, organisms transform energy from the Sun into chemical energy in the C–C and C–H bonds of sugars, such as glucose, and then into chemical energy in the bonds between phosphates in ATP.

The potential energy in ATP allows cells to do work: pump ions, synthesize molecules, move cargo, and transfer information.

ENERGY FOR LIFE

begins as

Electromagnetic energy in SUNLIGHT   10.2

Text section where you can find more information

drives

PHOTOSYNTHESIS (in chloroplasts)   10.1

begins with

Antenna complex
- Light excites electrons in pigment molecules   10.2

H_2O

enters

donates energy from excited electrons to

donates energy from excited electrons to

Photosystem II
- "Splits" water to yield electrons
- Electron transport chain pumps H^+ 10.3

donates electrons to

Photosystem I
- Electron transport ends with ferredoxin   10.3

Chemiosmosis
- H^+ gradient drives ATP synthase   9.5, 10.3

releases

yields

O_2

ATP 8.2

NADPH 10.1

used in

CO_2

fixed by rubisco to start

Calvin cycle
- Series of enzyme-catalyzed reactions   10.4

yields substrate for synthesis of

stored as

broken down to yield

Starch 5.2

GLUCOSE 5.1

CHECK YOUR UNDERSTANDING

If you understand the big picture …

✔ You should be able to …

1. Explain how H_2O and O_2 are cycled between photosynthesis and cellular respiration.
2. Explain how CO_2 is cycled between photosynthesis and cellular respiration.
3. Describe what might happen to life on Earth if rubisco were suddenly unable to fix CO_2.
4. Fill in the blue ovals with appropriate linking verbs or phrases.

Answers are available in Appendix A.

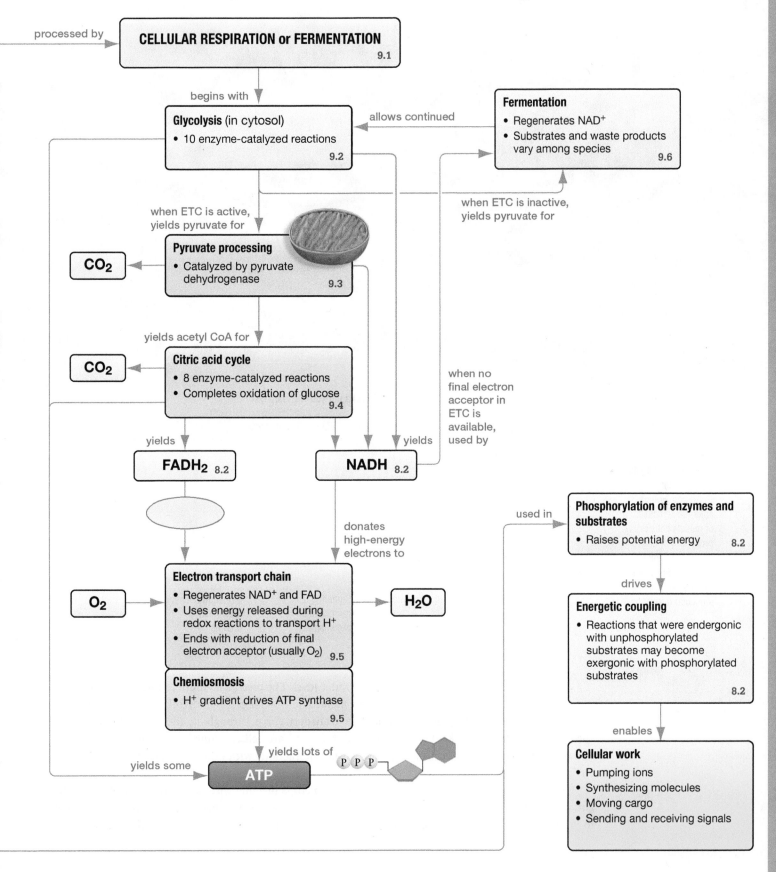

processed by →

CELLULAR RESPIRATION or FERMENTATION
9.1

begins with ↓

Glycolysis (in cytosol)
• 10 enzyme-catalyzed reactions
9.2

← allows continued

Fermentation
• Regenerates NAD^+
• Substrates and waste products vary among species
9.6

when ETC is active, yields pyruvate for ↓

when ETC is inactive, yields pyruvate for

Pyruvate processing
• Catalyzed by pyruvate dehydrogenase
9.3

CO_2 ←

yields acetyl CoA for ↓

Citric acid cycle
• 8 enzyme-catalyzed reactions
• Completes oxidation of glucose
9.4

CO_2 ←

when no final electron acceptor in ETC is available, used by

yields ↓

FADH$_2$ 8.2

yields ↓

NADH 8.2

yields →

donates high-energy electrons to

used in →

Phosphorylation of enzymes and substrates
• Raises potential energy
8.2

drives ↓

Electron transport chain
• Regenerates NAD^+ and FAD
• Uses energy released during redox reactions to transport H^+
• Ends with reduction of final electron acceptor (usually O_2)
9.5

O_2 →

→ H_2O

Energetic coupling
• Reactions that were endergonic with unphosphorylated substrates may become exergonic with phosphorylated substrates
8.2

enables ↓

Chemiosmosis
• H^+ gradient drives ATP synthase
9.5

yields lots of ↓

yields some →

ATP

P P P

Cellular work
• Pumping ions
• Synthesizing molecules
• Moving cargo
• Sending and receiving signals

11 Cell–Cell Interactions

In this micrograph of cardiac tissue, muscle cells are stained red and their nuclei are stained blue. The green dye highlights a protein called dystrophin, which links the cytoskeleton of muscle cells to proteins that attach to the extracellular matrix. Deficiency in dystrophin leads to muscular dystrophy.

In this chapter you will learn how

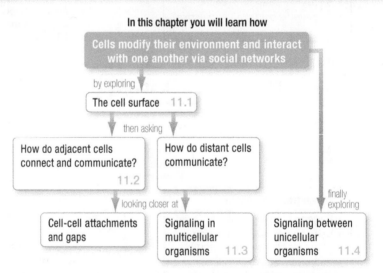

Cells modify their environment and interact with one another via social networks

by exploring

The cell surface   11.1

then asking

How do adjacent cells connect and communicate? 11.2

How do distant cells communicate?

looking closer at

Cell-cell attachments and gaps

Signaling in multicellular organisms   11.3

finally exploring

Signaling between unicellular organisms   11.4

A diversity of events take place at the cellular level. The plasma membrane surrounds a bustling enterprise consisting of organelles, molecular machines, and cytoskeletal elements (see Chapters 6 and 7). Molecular motors transport cargo throughout the cell at breathtaking speed. It would be a mistake, however, to think that cells are self-contained—that they are worlds in and of themselves. Instead, cells are dependent on interactions with other cells and the surrounding environment.

For most unicellular species, the outside environment is teeming with other organisms. Inside your gut, for example, hundreds of billions of bacterial cells are jostling for space and resources. In addition to interacting with these individuals, every unicellular organism must contend with constant shifts in environmental conditions, such as heat, light, ion concentrations, and food supplies. If unicellular organisms cannot sense these conditions and respond appropriately, they die.

In multicellular species, the environment outside the cell is made up of other cells, both neighboring and distant. The cells that make up a redwood tree, a mushroom, or your body are intensely social. Although biologists often study cells in isolation, an individual tree, fungus, or person is actually an interdependent community of cells. If those cells do not communicate and cooperate, the whole will break into dysfunctional parts and die.

To understand the life of a cell, then, it is critical to analyze how the cell interacts with the world outside its membrane. How do cells obtain information about the world and respond to that information? In particular, how do cells interact with other cells? To answer these questions, let's begin at the cell surface—with the molecules that separate the cell from its environment.

Figure 11.1 **Fiber Composites Resist Tension and Compression.** Reinforced concrete is an example of a fiber composite consisting of a ground substance (concrete) that fills spaces between cross-linked fibers (steel rods).

11.1 The Cell Surface

The line between life and nonlife is drawn by the plasma membrane that surrounds every cell. Recall that the structure of this membrane consists of a phospholipid bilayer studded with membrane proteins. These proteins are integral, meaning embedded in the bilayer, or peripheral, meaning attached to one surface. Some membrane proteins participate in the primary function of the plasma membrane: to create an environment inside the cell that is different from conditions outside by regulating the transport of substances (see Chapter 6).

The plasma membrane does not exist in isolation, however. Many membrane proteins attach to cytoskeletal elements on the interior surface of the bilayer (see Chapter 7) or to a complex array of extracellular structures, including those attached to the membranes of neighboring cells. Let's consider the nature of the material outside the cell and then analyze how the cell interacts with it and other cells.

The Structure and Function of an Extracellular Layer

It is extremely rare for cells to be bounded simply by a plasma membrane. Most cells secrete products that are assembled into a layer or wall just beyond the membrane. This extracellular material helps define the cell's shape and either attaches it to another cell or acts as a first line of defense against the outside world.

Virtually all types of extracellular structures—from the cell walls of bacteria, archaea, algae, fungi, and plants to the extracellular material that surrounds most animal cells—have the same fundamental design. Like reinforced concrete, they are fiber composites: They consist of a cross-linked network of long filaments embedded in a stiff surrounding material called the ground substance (**Figure 11.1**). The molecules that make up the

filaments and ground substance vary among organisms, but the engineering principle is the same. Why?

- The rods or filaments in a fiber composite are extremely effective at withstanding stretching and straining forces, or tension. The filaments in the extracellular material of most cells are functionally similar to the steel rods in reinforced concrete—they resist being pulled or pushed lengthwise.

- The stiff ground substance is effective at withstanding pressing forces, called compression. Concrete performs this function in highways, and a gel-forming mixture of polysaccharides plays the same role in extracellular material.

Thanks to the combination of tension- and compression-resisting elements, fiber composites are particularly rugged. In many living cells, fiber composites are flexible as well as strong.

What molecules make up the filaments and ground substance found on the surface of plant and animal cells? How are these extracellular materials synthesized, and what do they do?

The Extracellular Matrix in Animals

Most animal cells secrete a fiber composite called the **ECM,** that is, the **extracellular matrix.** Like the extracellular materials found in other organisms, the ECM provides structural support.

ECM design follows the same principles observed in the cell walls of bacteria, archaea, algae, fungi, and plants. There is a key difference, however: The animal ECM contains much more protein relative to carbohydrate than does a cell wall (see **Figure 11.2** on page 236).

- The fibrous component of animal ECM is dominated by a cable-like protein named collagen (Figure 11.2a).

- The ground substance that surrounds **collagen** and other fibrous components of the ECM contains gel-forming **proteoglycans** (Figure 11.2b).

(a) Each collagen protein consists of three polypeptide chains that wind around one another to form the fibrous component of the animal ECM.

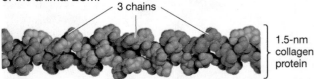

3 chains

1.5-nm collagen protein

Figure 11.2 The Extracellular Matrix of Animals Is a Fiber Composite. (a) Although several types of fibrous proteins are found in the ECM, the most abundant is collagen. **(b)** The spaces between the collagen fibers are filled with a ground substance consisting of proteoglycans. Each proteoglycan consists of a core protein attached to many polysaccharides. In some tissues, the proteoglycans are assembled into large complexes.

(b) Complexes of gelatinous proteoglycans form the ground substance of the animal ECM.

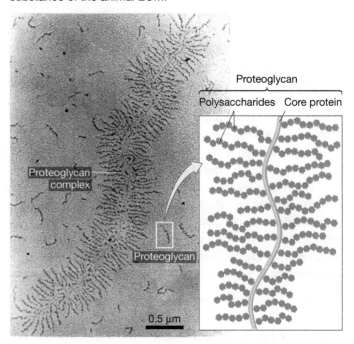

Proteoglycan complex

Proteoglycan

Proteoglycan

Polysaccharides   Core protein

0.5 μm

Most ECM proteins are synthesized in the rough ER, processed in the Golgi apparatus, and secreted from the cell via exocytosis. After secretion, however, these proteins may assemble into larger structures. For example, groups of collagen proteins may coalesce to form collagen fibrils, and bundles of fibrils may link to form even larger collagen fibers. In addition, secreted proteoglycans may be attached to long polysaccharides synthesized by cellular enzymes in the extracellular space. The resulting huge complexes, such as the one shown in Figure 11.2b, are responsible for the rubber-like consistency of cartilage.

Even in the same organism, the amount of ECM varies among different types of **tissues,** which consist of similar cells that function as a unit. Bone and cartilage, for example, have relatively few cells surrounded by a large amount of ECM. Skin cells, in contrast, are packed together with a minimal amount of ECM.

The composition of the ECM also varies among tissue types. For example, the ECM surrounding cells in lung tissue contains large amounts of a rubber-like protein called elastin, which allows the ECM to expand and contract during breathing. The structure of a tissue's ECM correlates with the function of the tissue.

Although collagen and the other common ECM proteins are much more elastic and bendable than the stiff cell walls of plants, they support cell structure via their attachments to the cell surface. As Figure 11.3 shows, membrane proteins called **integrins** bind to extracellular crosslinking proteins, including **laminins,** which in turn bind to other components of the ECM. (Don't confuse laminins with lamins, which are intermediate filaments found in the nucleus; see Chapter 7.)

The intracellular portions of the integrins bind to proteins that are connected to the cytoskeleton, effectively linking the cytoskeleton and ECM. This linkage is critical. Besides keeping individual cells in place, it helps adjacent cells adhere to each other via their common connection to the ECM.

Cells monitor the cytoskeleton–ECM linkage via signaling pathways that will be introduced in Section 11.3. When integrins bind to the ECM, they transmit signals that inform the cell it is in the right place and properly anchored. If this linkage breaks down, the signals are not transmitted and cells normally die as a result. For most of the cells in your body, anchorage to the ECM is a matter of life and death.

The Cell Wall in Plants

Virtually all plant cells are surrounded by a cell wall—a fiber composite that is the basis of major industries. The paper in this book, the threads in your cotton clothing, and the wood in your neighborhood's houses are made up primarily of plant cell walls.

Primary Cell Walls   When plant cells first form, they secrete an initial fiber composite called a **primary cell wall.**

- The fibrous component of the primary cell wall consists of long strands of cellulose. These strands are bundled into stout, cable-like structures termed **microfibrils,** which are cross-linked via hydrogen bonds to other polysaccharide filaments. The microfibrils are synthesized as a crisscrossed network by a complex of enzymes in the plasma membrane (Figure 11.4).

- The spaces between microfibrils are filled with gelatinous polysaccharides such as **pectins**—the molecules that are used to thicken jams and jellies. Because these polysaccharides are hydrophilic, they attract and hold large amounts of water,

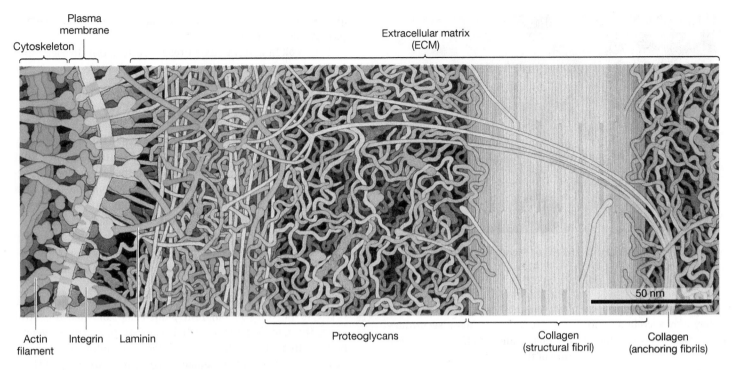

Figure 11.3 **Integrins Connect the Extracellular Matrix to the Cytoskeleton.**

keeping the cell wall moist. The gelatinous components of the cell wall are synthesized in the rough endoplasmic reticulum (ER) and Golgi apparatus and secreted into the extracellular space (see Chapter 7).

The primary cell wall defines the shape of a plant cell. Under normal conditions, the concentration of solutes is higher inside the cell than outside, causing water to enter the cell via osmosis. The incoming water increases the cell's volume, pushing the plasma membrane up against the wall. The force exerted by the cell against the wall is known as **turgor pressure.**

Although plant cells experience turgor pressure throughout their lives, it is particularly important in young cells that are actively growing. Young plant cells secrete proteins named expansins into their cell wall. **Expansins** disrupt the hydrogen bonds that cross-link the microfibrils in the wall, allowing the microfibrils to slide past one another. Turgor pressure then forces the wall to elongate and expand, resulting in cell growth (see Chapter 37).

✔ If you understand the structure and function of the primary cell wall, you should be able to predict what would happen to a plant cell if it were treated with an enzyme that digests the cellulose microfibrils.

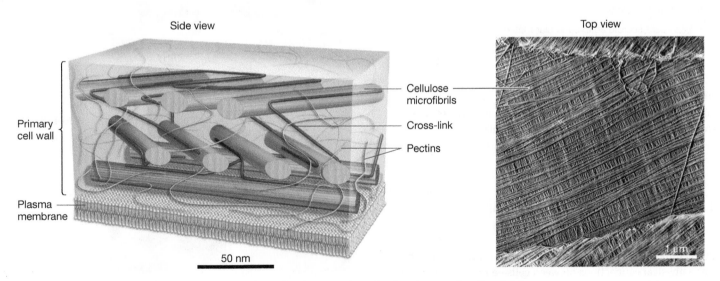

Figure 11.4 **Primary Cell Walls of Plants Are Fiber Composites.** In a plant's primary cell wall, cellulose microfibrils are connected by polysaccharide cross-links. The spaces between the microfibrils and cross-links are filled with pectin molecules, which form a gelatinous solid.

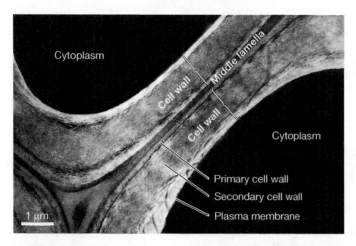

Figure 11.5 **Secondary Cell Walls of Plants Vary in Composition and Function.**

Secondary Cell Walls As plant cells mature and stop growing, they may secrete an additional layer of material—a **secondary cell wall**—between the plasma membrane and the primary cell wall (**Figure 11.5**). The structure of the secondary cell wall varies from cell to cell in the plant and correlates with each cell's function. Cells on the surface of a leaf have secondary cell walls containing waxes that form a waterproof coating; cells that support a plant's stem have stiff secondary cell walls that contain a great deal of cellulose.

In cells that form wood, the secondary cell wall also contains **lignin,** a complex polymer that forms an exceptionally rigid network. Thick secondary cell walls of cellulose and lignin help plants withstand the forces of gravity and wind.

Much like the ECM of animal cells, plant cell walls can be used to connect adjacent cells. Let's now turn to intercellular connections and learn more about their structure and function.

CHECK YOUR UNDERSTANDING

If you understand that ...

• Most cells secrete an extracellular material that supports the cell and helps define its shape. This material is usually a fiber composite—a combination of cross-linked filaments surrounded by a ground substance.

✔ You should be able to ...

Compare and contrast the molecular composition of the animal cell ECM and cell walls of plant cells.

Answers are available in Appendix A.

11.2 How Do Adjacent Cells Connect and Communicate?

Intercellular connections are the basis of **multicellularity.** These physical connections between cells—either direct, or indirect via the ECM—maintain the structure and function of tissues. The muscle tissue in your heart, for example, depends on such connections to support the structure of the cells as they contract and relax with each beat (see the micrograph on the opening page of this chapter).

Let's look first at the structures that attach cells to each other and then examine how they allow adjacent cells to exchange materials and information.

Cell–Cell Attachments in Multicellular Eukaryotes

Materials and structures that bind cells together are particularly important in **epithelia** (singular: **epithelium**)—tissues that form external and internal surfaces. Epithelia function as barriers between the external and internal environments of plants and animals. In animals, epithelia also separate organs, preventing mixing of solutions between adjacent organs or structures.

The adhesive structures that hold cells together vary among multicellular organisms. Let's examine this variation by considering the intercellular connections in plants and animals.

Indirect Intercellular Attachments The extracellular space between the walls of adjacent plant cells sandwich a central layer, the middle lamella, which consists primarily of gelatinous pectins. Because the middle lamella is continuous with the primary cell walls of the adjacent cells, it serves to glue them together (**Figure 11.6**). The two cell walls are like slices of bread, and the middle lamella is like a layer of peanut butter. If enzymes degrade the middle lamella, as they do when flower petals and leaves detach and fall, the adjacent cells separate.

In many animal tissues, integrins connect the cytoskeleton of each cell to the extracellular matrix (see Figure 11.3). A middle lamella–like layer of gelatinous polysaccharides and proteoglycans lies between adjacent animal cells. Along with the cytoskeleton–ECM connections, this layer helps glue cells together in tissues. In addition, in certain animal tissues the glue is reinforced by collagen fibrils that span the ECM and connect adjacent cells.

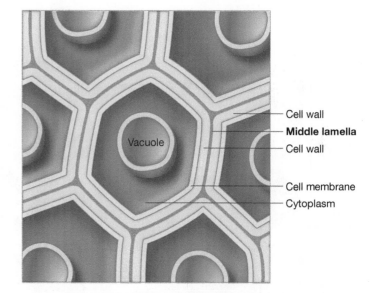

Figure 11.6 **The Middle Lamella Connects Adjacent Plant Cells.** The middle lamella contains gelatinous polysaccharides, called pectins, that help glue together the walls of adjacent cells.

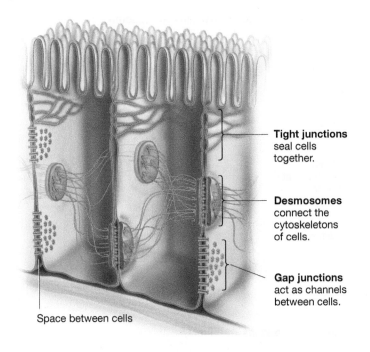

Tight junctions
seal cells
together.

Desmosomes
connect the
cytoskeletons
of cells.

Gap junctions
act as channels
between cells.

Space between cells

Figure 11.7 An Array of Structures Are Involved in Cell–Cell Adhesion and Communication between Animal Cells.

In animals, where cell walls do not exist, a variety of membrane proteins allow for direct cell–cell attachments in epithelia and other tissues (**Figure 11.7**). Let's start by looking at tight junctions and desmosomes, which hold cells together, and then examine the role of gap junctions and plasmodesmata in intercellular communication.

Tight Junctions Form a Seal between Cells A **tight junction** is a cell–cell attachment composed of specialized proteins in the plasma membranes of adjacent animal cells (**Figure 11.8a**). As the drawing in **Figure 11.8b** indicates, a long chain of these proteins forms on the surface of a cell that attaches to the same proteins on adjacent cells. The tight interactions between these proteins will pull the membranes of the two cells very close together. The resulting structure resembles a quilt, where the proteins "stitch" the membranes of two cells together to form a watertight seal. In this way, tight junctions prevent solutions from flowing through the space between the two cells.

Because tight junctions form a watertight seal, this type of attachment is commonly found between cells that form a barrier, such as the epithelial cells lining your stomach and intestines. There, tight junctions restrict the passive movement of substances between the inside of your gut and the rest of your body. Selected nutrients may cross the epithelia via specialized transport proteins and channels in the plasma membrane (Chapter 6).

Although all tight junctions stitch together adjacent cells, their ability to restrict the movement of substances will vary in different tissues. For example, the tight junctions between the cells lining your bladder draw the cells closer together than those between the cells lining your small intestine, because they consist of different proteins. As a result, small ions can pass between the cells lining the surface of the small intestine more easily than between those lining the bladder—helping you absorb ions in your food and eliminate them in your urine.

Tight junctions are also dynamic. For example, they loosen to permit more transport between epithelial cells lining the small intestine after a meal and then retighten later. In this way, tight junctions can open and close in response to changes in environmental conditions.

(a) Electron micrograph of a tight junction in longitudinal section

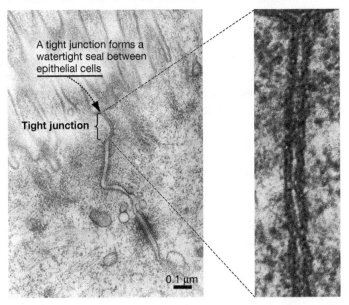

A tight junction forms a watertight seal between epithelial cells

Tight junction

0.1 µm

(b) Three-dimensional view of a tight junction

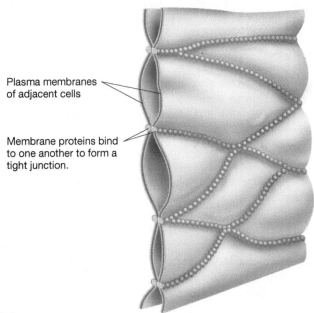

Plasma membranes of adjacent cells

Membrane proteins bind to one another to form a tight junction.

Figure 11.8 In Animals, Tight Junctions Form a Seal between Adjacent Cells.

(a) Micrograph of a desmosome in longitudinal section

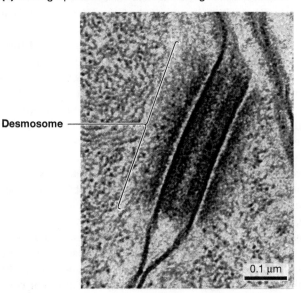

Desmosome

0.1 μm

(b) Three-dimensional view of a desmosome

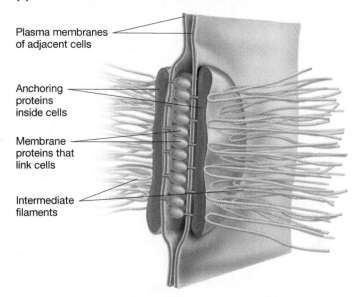

Plasma membranes of adjacent cells

Anchoring proteins inside cells

Membrane proteins that link cells

Intermediate filaments

Figure 11.9 Adjacent Animal Cells Are Linked by Desmosomes, Which Bind Cytoskeletons Together.

Although tight junctions are very good at holding cells close together, they are weak adhesions that can be easily broken. Since epithelial cells often experience pulling and shearing forces, other intercellular adhesions are required to help hold cells together in a tissue. What are these other adhesions, and how do they resist being pulled apart?

Desmosomes Form Secure Adhesions **Figure 11.9a** illustrates a **desmosome,** a cell–cell attachment particularly common in animal epithelial cells and certain muscle cells. In their structure and function, desmosomes are analogous to the rivets that hold pieces of sheet metal together.

As **Figure 11.9b** indicates, desmosomes consist of integral membrane attachment proteins that form bridges between anchoring proteins inside adjacent cells. Intermediate filaments help reinforce desmosomes by attaching to the anchoring proteins in the cytoplasm. In this way, desmosomes help form a continuous structural support system between all the cells in the tissue (see Figure 11.7).

What are the membrane proteins that serve this cell attachment function in desmosomes? The answer to this question traces back to some of the first experiments conducted on cell–cell interactions.

Intercellular Adhesions Are Selective Long before electron micrographs revealed the presence of desmosomes, biologists realized that some sort of molecule must bind animal cells to one another. This insight grew out of experiments conducted by H. V. Wilson on sponges in the early 1900s.

Sponges are aquatic animals, and the sponge species used in these experiments consists of just two basic types of tissues. When Wilson treated adult sponges with chemicals that made the cells separate from one another, the result was a jumbled mass of individual, unconnected cells. But when normal chemical conditions were restored, the cells gradually began to move and stick together.

As the experiment continued, cells began to aggregate based on their origin—adhering to other cells of the same tissue type. This phenomenon is now called **selective adhesion.** Eventually, the cells re-formed functional adult sponges with two distinct tissues. How could this happen?

The Discovery of Cell–Cell Adhesion Proteins What is the molecular basis of selective adhesion? The initial hypothesis, proposed in the 1970s, was that specialized membrane proteins were involved. The idea was that different types of cells have different types of adhesion proteins in their membranes, and only cells with the same or complementary adhesion proteins can attach to one another.

This hypothesis was tested through experiments that relied on molecules called antibodies. An **antibody** is a protein produced by an immune response that binds specifically to a unique type of molecule, often another protein (see Chapter 48). When an antibody binds to a protein, it can change that protein's structure or interfere with its ability to interact with other molecules. This property of antibodies was crucial to these experiments.

Figure 11.10 shows how researchers tested the hypothesis that cell–cell adhesion takes place via interactions between membrane proteins:

Step 1 Isolate the membrane proteins from cells that adhere to one another in a certain tissue. Produce pure preparations of each protein.

Step 2 Inject one of the purified membrane proteins into a rabbit. The rabbit's immune system cells recognize the protein as foreign and respond by producing antibodies to it. Purify those antibodies, and then repeat this procedure for the other

QUESTION: Do animal cells have adhesion proteins on their surfaces?

HYPOTHESIS: Selective adhesion is due to specific membrane proteins.

NULL HYPOTHESIS: Selective adhesion is not due to specific membrane proteins.

EXPERIMENTAL SETUP:

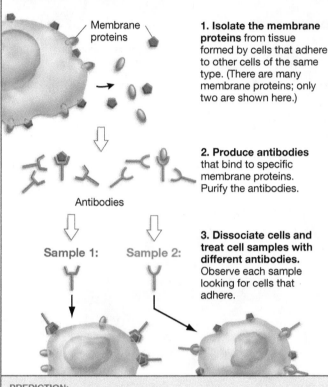

Membrane proteins

1. Isolate the membrane proteins from tissue formed by cells that adhere to other cells of the same type. (There are many membrane proteins; only two are shown here.)

2. Produce antibodies that bind to specific membrane proteins. Purify the antibodies.

Antibodies

Sample 1:   Sample 2:

3. Dissociate cells and treat cell samples with different antibodies. Observe each sample looking for cells that adhere.

PREDICTION:

PREDICTION OF NULL HYPOTHESIS:

RESULTS:

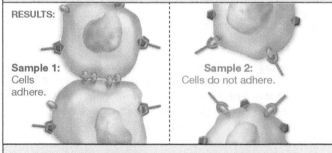

Sample 1:
Cells adhere.

Sample 2:
Cells do not adhere.

CONCLUSION: The protein that was blocked in sample 2 (called a cadherin) is involved in cell–cell adhesion.

Figure 11.10 Evidence for Adhesion Proteins on Animal Cells.

SOURCES: Hatta, K., and M. Takeichi. 1986. Expression of N-cadherin adhesion molecules associated with early morphogenetic events in chick development. *Nature* 320: 447–449. Takeichi, M. 1988. The cadherins: Cell–cell adhesion molecules controlling animal morphogenesis. *Development* 102: 639–655.

✔ **PROCESS OF SCIENCE** Fill in the prediction made by each hypothesis.

membrane proteins that were isolated. In this way, obtain a large collection of different antibodies—each of which binds specifically to only one of the membrane proteins.

Step 3 Dissociate cells from the original tissue. Take identical samples of the cells and add antibodies directed against a different membrane protein to each sample.

Step 4 Observe whether the cells in each sample adhere to one another.

If treatment with a particular antibody prevents the cells from adhering to one another, the antibody is probably bound to an adhesion protein. The logic is that if the antibody binds to the adhesion protein, the adhesion protein can't bind to other adhesion proteins and attach the cells to one another.

This approach allowed biologists to identify several major classes of cell adhesion proteins, including **cadherins**—the proteins that link cells in desmosomes (Figure 11.8). There are various types of cadherins, and cells from different tissues have different types of cadherins in their plasma membranes. Each cadherin can bind only to cadherins of the same type. In this way, cells of the same tissue type attach specifically to one another.

To summarize: Animal cells attach to one another in a selective manner because different types of cell adhesion proteins can bind and rivet certain cells together. Cadherins provide the physical basis for selective adhesion in cells that form tissues and are a critical component of desmosomes.

✔ If you understand cell–cell attachments, you should be able to predict what would happen if all of the cells in a developing frog embryo expressed the same type of cadherin on their surfaces.

Besides giving structural support to tissues, intercellular connections can direct cell–cell communication. But how can cellular connections pass information between cells?

Cells Communicate via Cell–Cell Gaps

In both plants and animals, direct connections between cells in the same tissue help the cells to work in a coordinated fashion. One way of accomplishing this is to have channels in the membranes of adjacent cells, allowing the cells to communicate via the diffusion of cytosolic ions and small molecules from cell to cell.

Ions and small molecules are just two of many different forms of signals that convey information between cells in a tissue. How cells respond to this exchange of information depends on the type of cell and the type of signal, but there are two general mechanisms:

1. Signals may regulate gene expression, altering which proteins are produced and which are not; or

2. Signals may activate or inactivate particular proteins that already exist in the cell—often those involved in metabolism, membrane transport, secretion, and the cytoskeleton.

Whatever the mechanism, the cell's activity often changes dramatically after the signal arrives. Let's take a look at how signals travel between adjacent cells connected by gap junctions and plasmodesmata.

(a) Gap junctions create gaps that connect animal cells.

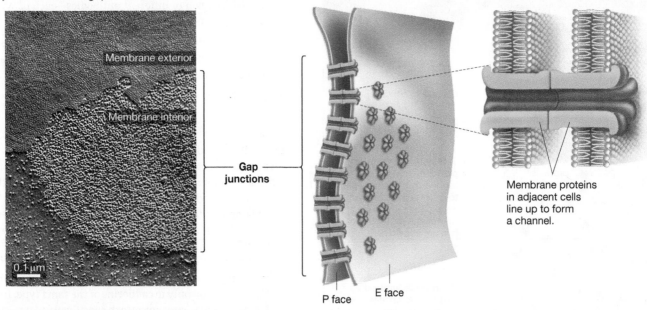

(b) Plasmodesmata create gaps that connect plant cells.

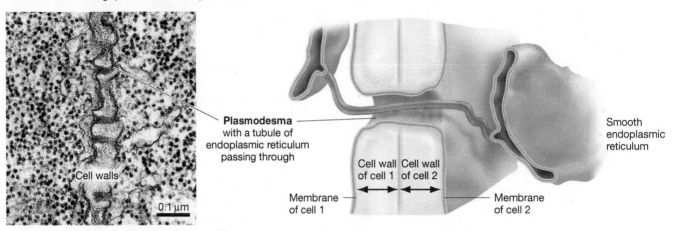

Figure 11.11 Adjacent Animal Cells and Adjacent Plant Cells Communicate Directly. (a) In certain animal tissues, gap junction proteins form channels between adjacent cells. In freeze fracture electron micrographs like the one shown here (see Chapter 6), they appear as clusters of small dots. **(b)** In plant cells, plasmodesmata connect the cytoplasm of adjacent cells by forming membrane-lined channels through the cell walls.

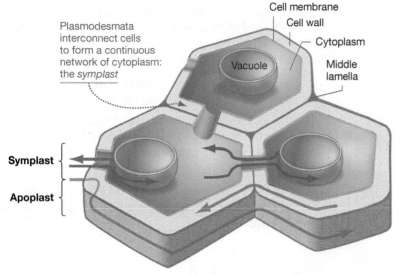

Figure 11.12 Most Plant Tissues Are Divided into Two Corridors: Symplast and Apoplast. Small molecules may travel through plant tissues either within the shared cytoplasm (symplast, shown in blue) or through the extracellular space (apoplast, shown in gray).

Gap Junctions Connect Cells via Protein Channels In many animal tissues, structures called **gap junctions** connect adjacent cells. In a gap junction, specialized proteins assemble in the membranes of adjacent cells, creating interconnected channels that allow water, ions, and small molecules such as amino acids, sugars, and nucleotides to move between the cells (Figure 11.11a).

Gap junctions are communication portals. They can help adjacent cells coordinate their activities by allowing the rapid passage of regulatory ions or small molecules. In the muscle cells of your heart, for example, a flow of ions through gap junctions acts as a signal that coordinates contractions. Without this cell–cell communication, a normal heartbeat would be impossible.

In plants, direct interactions between membrane proteins are impossible due to the presence of cell walls. How do adjacent plant cells communicate?

Plasmodesmata Connect Cells via Membrane-Lined Channels In plants, gaps in cell walls allow direct connections between the cytoplasm of adjacent cells. At these connections, named **plasmodesmata** (singular: **plasmodesma**), the plasma membrane and cytoplasm of the two cells are continuous. Tubular extensions from the smooth ER run through these membrane-lined channels (Figure 11.11b).

Like gap junctions, plasmodesmata are communication portals through the plasma membrane. In plants, the plasma membrane separates most tissues into two independent corridors: **(1)** the **symplast,** which is a continuous network of cytoplasm connected by plasmodesmata, and **(2)** the **apoplast,** which is the region outside the plasma membrane (Figure 11.12). The apoplast consists of cell walls, the middle lamella, and air spaces. Small molecules can move through plant tissues in either of these compartments without ever crossing a membrane (see Chapter 35).

Gap junctions and plasmodesmata allow adjacent cells to transmit information, like a conversation between neighbors. But how do multicellular organisms send messages between different tissues, where in most cases there is no direct contact? For example, suppose that you become dehydrated while exercising or that you are startled by a loud noise. How do cells that sense dehydration or loud noises signal tissues or organs elsewhere in your body to release materials that are needed to promote rehydration or prepare your muscles for fleeing from danger? Distant cell communication is the subject of Section 11.3.

11.3 How Do Distant Cells Communicate?

Cells that are not in physical contact communicate with one another. This is true for unicellular organisms, where hundreds or thousands of cells may live in close proximity, as well as for multicellular organisms like humans and maple trees, which typically contain trillions of cells and dozens of tissue types.

Cell–cell communication is one of the most dynamic research areas in biology. Let's begin by analyzing how distant cells in humans and other multicellular eukaryotes exchange information, and then in Section 11.4 explore how unicellular organisms communicate.

Cell–Cell Signaling in Multicellular Organisms

Suppose that cells in your brain sense that you are becoming dehydrated. Brain cells can't do much about the water you lose during urination, but kidney cells can. In response to dehydration, certain brain cells release a signaling molecule that travels to the kidneys and activates the expression of water channels called aquaporins (see Chapter 6). As a result, water moves out of the urine and back into the blood, preventing further dehydration.

Biologists have classified many types of signaling molecules that keep distant tissues in touch. One type, neurotransmitters, may open or close ion channels in the plasma membrane of distant cells, changing the electrical properties of the membrane. This type of signal is responsible for the transmission of information through the nervous system, allowing your brain to control the movements of the rest of your body (see Chapters 43 and 45).

The best-studied means of distant signaling, however, may be via **hormones**—information-carrying molecules that are secreted by plant and animal cells into bodily fluids and act on distant target cells. Hormones are usually small molecules and include certain peptides, steroids, and even gases. Although hormones are typically present in minute concentrations, they have a large impact on the activity of target cells.

The most important point about a hormone or other signaling molecule is how a cell interprets the information it conveys. How do cells receive and process signals from distant cells? The basic steps are common to all cell signaling systems. Let's consider each step in turn.

Signal Reception

Hormones and other types of cell–cell signaling molecules deliver their message by binding to receptor molecules. The key characteristic of this interaction is that it changes the shape, or conformation, of the receptor. A **signal receptor,** then, is a protein that changes its shape and activity after binding to a signaling molecule. This change in shape is how a signal is passed from the signaling molecule to its receptor.

CHECK YOUR UNDERSTANDING

If you understand that ...

- In plants and animals, adjacent cells are connected, either directly or, via the ECM, indirectly.
- Adjacent cells may communicate with each other through openings in their plasma membranes.

✔ **You should be able to ...**

1. Compare and contrast the structure and function of the middle lamella of plants and the tight junctions and desmosomes of animals.
2. Describe the structure and function of plasmodesmata and gap junctions.

Answers are available in Appendix A.

The presence of an appropriate signal receptor dictates which cells will respond to a particular signaling molecule. For example, even though the molecule that carries the message "We're getting dehydrated—conserve water" is broadcast throughout the body, only certain kidney cells respond because only they have the receptor that binds to that molecule.

Cells in a wide array of tissues may respond to the same signaling molecule, though, if they have the appropriate receptor. If you are startled by a loud noise, cells in your adrenal glands secrete the hormone adrenaline (also called epinephrine), which carries the message "Get ready to fight or run." In response, your heart rate increases, your breathing rate increases, and cells in your liver release glucose, which your muscles can use to power rapid movement. This response is the basis of an "adrenaline rush." Cells in your heart, lung, and liver respond to adrenaline because they all have the receptor that binds to it. Identical receptors in diverse cells and tissues allow long-distance signals to coordinate the activities of cells throughout a multicellular organism.

Where does the interaction between a signaling molecule and its receptor occur—inside the target cell or outside? The answer depends on the signaling molecule's ability to pass through plasma membranes.

- Most lipid-soluble signaling molecules can diffuse across the hydrophobic region of the membrane and enter the cytosol of their target cells. The receptors for these molecules exist inside the cell.

- Large or hydrophilic signaling molecules are lipid insoluble, and most cannot cross the plasma membrane. To affect a target cell, they have to be recognized at the cell surface. Their receptors are usually located in the plasma membrane.

It's critical to note two additional points about signal receptors, no matter where they're located:

1. **Receptors are dynamic.** The number of receptors in a particular cell may decline if hormonal stimulation occurs at high levels over a long time. The ability of a receptor to bind tightly to a signaling molecule may also decline in response to intensive stimulation. As a result, the sensitivity of a cell to a particular hormone may change over time.

2. **Receptors can be blocked.** The drugs called beta-blockers, for example, bind to certain adrenaline receptors. When adrenaline binds to receptors in heart cells, it stimulates more rapid and forceful contractions. So if a physician wants to reduce the strength of a patient's heart cell contractions as a way to lower blood pressure, she is likely to prescribe a beta-blocker.

The change in receptor structure that occurs after a signaling molecule binds means that the signal has been received. It's like throwing an "on" switch. What happens next?

Signal Processing

Once a cell receives a signal, it has to process the signal to initiate a response. This step happens in one of two ways, depending on whether the receptors are located in the cytosol or at the membrane surface.

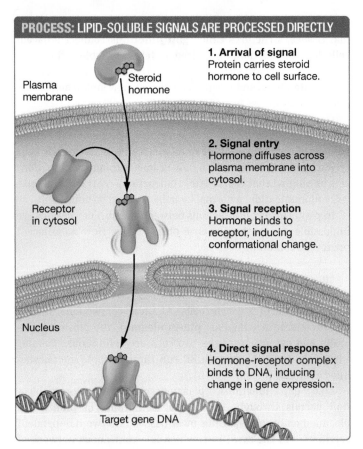

PROCESS: LIPID-SOLUBLE SIGNALS ARE PROCESSED DIRECTLY

Plasma membrane
Steroid hormone

1. Arrival of signal
Protein carries steroid hormone to cell surface.

Receptor in cytosol

2. Signal entry
Hormone diffuses across plasma membrane into cytosol.

3. Signal reception
Hormone binds to receptor, inducing conformational change.

Nucleus

4. Direct signal response
Hormone–receptor complex binds to DNA, inducing change in gene expression.

Target gene DNA

Figure 11.13 Some Cell–Cell Signaling Molecules Enter the Cell and Bind to Receptors in the Cytosol. Because they are lipids, steroid hormones can diffuse across cell membranes and bind to signal receptors located in the cytosol. The hormone–receptor complex may then be transported to the nucleus, where it changes the activity of genes.

✔ Based on what you have learned about nuclear transport (see Chapter 7), what type of signal would you expect to be exposed on the cytosolic receptor after the steroid hormone changes the receptor's conformation?

Processing Lipid-Soluble Signaling Molecules Steroid hormones such as estrogens and cortisol are examples of lipid-soluble signaling molecules. Because they are hydrophobic, most lipid-soluble signaling molecules are carried through the bloodstream via hydrophilic proteins. After reaching their target cells, these signaling molecules are released from the carrier proteins and enter the cytosol. Often, a hormone–receptor complex is formed in the cytosol and then transported to the nucleus, where it triggers changes in gene expression (**Figure 11.13**). By altering the expression of genes (see Chapter 17), the cell produces different proteins that will directly affect the function or shape of the cell.

Processing Lipid-Insoluble Signaling Molecules Hormones that *cannot* diffuse across the plasma membrane and enter the cytosol do not *directly* participate in intracellular activities, like

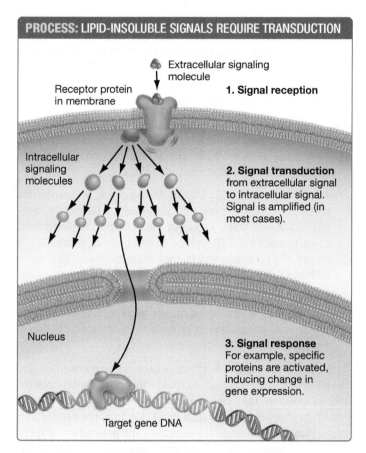

PROCESS: LIPID-INSOLUBLE SIGNALS REQUIRE TRANSDUCTION

Extracellular signaling molecule

Receptor protein in membrane

1. Signal reception

Intracellular signaling molecules

2. Signal transduction from extracellular signal to intracellular signal. Signal is amplified (in most cases).

Nucleus

3. Signal response For example, specific proteins are activated, inducing change in gene expression.

Target gene DNA

Figure 11.14 Signal Transduction Converts an Extracellular Signal to an Intracellular Signal. A lipid-insoluble signaling molecule will not pass through the membrane to direct a cellular response. Instead, the molecule activates a surface receptor that directs a multistep process to generate intracellular signals. One or more of these intracellular signaling molecules may then be transported to the nucleus to change the activity of genes.

changing gene expression. Instead, the signal that arrives at the surface of the cell has to produce an intracellular signal—the processing step is indirect.

When a signaling molecule binds at the cell surface, it triggers **signal transduction**—the conversion of a signal from one form to another. A long and often complex series of events ensues, collectively called a signal transduction pathway.

Signal transduction is a common occurrence in everyday life. For example, the text messages you receive are sent from one phone to another as radio wave transmissions. These electronic signals can be transmitted efficiently over long distances but would be meaningless to you. Software in your phone has to transduce, or convert, the signals into a form that you can understand and respond to, such as words in a text message.

Signal transduction pathways in cells work in a similar way **(Figure 11.14)**. In a cell, signal transduction converts an extracellular signal to an intracellular signal. As in a text message, a signal that is easy to transmit is converted to a signal that is easily understood and that triggers a response.

Intracellular Signals May Be Amplified and Diversified Recall that hormones are present in minuscule concentrations but trigger a large response from cells. Signal amplification is one reason this is possible. When a hormone arrives at the cell surface, the message it transmits may be amplified as it changes form. An increased number of intracellular signals makes it possible for hormones to affect different molecules in the cell. Your portable music player performs an analogous function: By amplifying a tiny sound signal, it enables the sound to affect a whole roomful of people—some may dance while others may plug their ears.

In cells, signal transduction begins at the plasma membrane; amplification takes place inside. Amplification may occur in a variety of ways, depending on the mechanism of signal transduction. In general, the arrival of a single signaling molecule results in a secondary signal that involves many ions or molecules.

For example, one major type of signal transduction system involves signal receptors that are also ion channels. Signal transduction opens the channels, allowing ions to diffuse into the cytosol. In muscle cells, this type of amplification occurs when calcium ions flood into the cytosol, causing the entire cell to contract as a whole (see Chapter 45).

Here let's focus on two other major types of signal transduction and amplification systems that are distinguished based on how they are initiated:

1. G-protein-coupled receptors initiate the production of intracellular "second messengers," which then amplify the signal.

2. Enzyme-linked receptors amplify the signal by triggering the activation of a series of proteins inside the cell, through the addition of phosphate groups.

Although there are many variations in the signaling pathways that fall within these two categories, the common features are emphasized here.

Signal Transduction via G-Protein-Coupled Receptors Many signal receptors span the plasma membrane and are closely associated with membrane-anchored proteins inside the cell called **G proteins.** When G proteins are activated by a signal receptor, they trigger a key step in signal transduction: the production of a **second messenger**—a small, nonprotein signaling molecule or ion that elicits an intracellular response to the first messenger (the signaling molecule that arrived at the cell surface). G proteins link the receipt of an extracellular signal to the production of an intracellular signal.

G proteins got their name because their activity is regulated by the type of guanine nucleotide they are bound to: either **guanosine triphosphate (GTP)** or guanosine diphosphate (GDP). GTP is a nucleoside triphosphate that is similar in structure to adenosine triphosphate (ATP; introduced in Chapter 4). Recall that nucleoside triphosphates have high potential energy because their three phosphate groups have four negative charges close together.

When GTP binds to a G protein, the addition of the negative charges alters the protein's shape. Changes in shape produce changes in activity. G proteins are activated when they bind

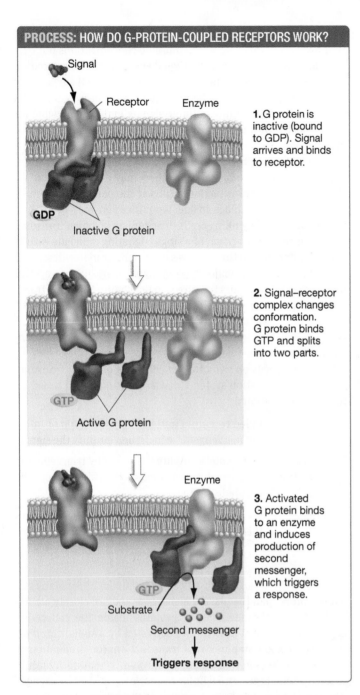

PROCESS: HOW DO G-PROTEIN-COUPLED RECEPTORS WORK?

Signal

Receptor   Enzyme

GDP

Inactive G protein

1. G protein is inactive (bound to GDP). Signal arrives and binds to receptor.

GTP

Active G protein

2. Signal–receptor complex changes conformation. G protein binds GTP and splits into two parts.

Enzyme

GTP

Substrate

Second messenger

Triggers response

3. Activated G protein binds to an enzyme and induces production of second messenger, which triggers a response.

Figure 11.15 G-Protein-Coupled Receptors Trigger the Production of a Second Messenger.

GTP; they are inactivated when a phosphate group, and thus a negative charge, is removed from GTP to form GDP. The G protein will remain inactive until the GDP is replaced with a new GTP.

To understand how G proteins fit into an overall signal transduction pathway, follow the events in **Figure 11.15.**

Step 1 A signaling molecule arrives and binds to a receptor in the plasma membrane. Notice that the receptor is a transmembrane protein whose intracellular portion is coupled to a G protein composed of multiple subunits.

Step 2 In response to binding of the signaling molecule, the receptor changes shape and activates its G protein. Specifically, the receptor kicks out the GDP from the inactive G protein, allowing GTP to bind to the protein. When GTP is bound, the G protein will change shape radically: The active GTP-binding subunit splits off.

Step 3 The active G protein subunit interacts with a nearby enzyme that is embedded in the plasma membrane. This interaction stimulates the enzyme to catalyze production of a second messenger.

Second messengers are effective because they are small and therefore can diffuse rapidly to spread the signal throughout the cell. In addition, they can be produced quickly in large quantities. This characteristic is important. Because the arrival of a single signaling molecule can stimulate the production of many second messengers, the signal transduction event amplifies the original signal.

Several types of small molecules and ions act as second messengers in cells. **Table 11.1** lists some of the best-studied second messengers and provides an example of how cells respond to each of them. Note that several second messengers activate **protein kinases**—enzymes that activate or inactivate other proteins by adding a phosphate group to them.

It's also important to note two things:

1. Second messengers aren't restricted to a single role—the same second messenger can initiate dramatically different events in the same cell or in different cell types receiving the same signaling molecule.

2. More than one type of second messenger may be involved in triggering a cell's response to the same extracellular signaling molecule.

Table 11.1 Examples of Second Messengers

Name	Type of Response
Cyclic guanosine monophosphate (cGMP)	Opens ion channels; activates certain protein kinases
Diacylglycerol (DAG)	Activates certain protein kinases
Inositol trisphosphate (IP_3)	Opens calcium channels, allowing stored calcium ions to enter cytosol
Cyclic adenosine monophosphate (cAMP)	Activates certain protein kinases
Calcium ion (Ca^{2+})	Binds to a receptor called calmodulin; Ca^{2+}/calmodulin complex then activates proteins

To make sure that you understand how G proteins and second messengers work, imagine the following movie scene: A spy arrives at a castle gate. The castle guard receives a note from the spy, but he cannot read the coded message on the note. Instead, the guard gives the note to the queen. She reads the message and summons the commander of the guard, who sends soldiers throughout the castle to warn everyone of approaching danger.

✔ **MODEL** You should be able to identify which characters in the scene correspond to the second messenger, G protein, signaling molecule, receptor, and enzyme activated by the G protein.

It's difficult to overstate the importance of signal transduction by G-protein-coupled receptors. Biomedical researchers estimate that a third of all human drugs target these signal receptors. These drugs include the beta-blockers that regulate heart rate. In 2012, Brian Kobilka and Robert Lefkowitz won the Nobel Prize in Chemistry for their work on the structure and function of G-protein-coupled receptors.

Signal Transduction via Enzyme-Linked Receptors Enzyme-linked receptors transduce hormonal signals by directly catalyzing a reaction inside the cell. **Figure 11.16** focuses on the best-studied group of enzyme-linked receptors: the **receptor tyrosine kinases (RTKs).**

Step 1 A hormone binds to two subunits of an RTK and causes them to form a dimer.

Step 2 The conformational change in the RTK turns on its catalytic activity, allowing the RTK to phosphorylate itself at tyrosine residues using ATP inside the cell.

Step 3 Proteins inside the cell bind to the phosphorylated RTK, forming a bridge between the receptor and a peripheral membrane protein called **Ras,** which is a single subunit G protein. The formation of the RTK bridge activates Ras by causing it to exchange its bound GDP for a GTP.

Step 4 When Ras is activated, it triggers the phosphorylation and activation of a protein kinase.

Step 5 The Ras-activated kinase catalyzes the phosphorylation and activation of a second kinase, which then phosphorylates and activates a third kinase. The third kinase triggers the cell response by phosphorylating additional proteins.

This sequence of protein modifications that culminates in a cell response is termed a **phosphorylation cascade.** Since these cascades are often initiated by mitogens—signaling molecules that activate cell division—the numbered kinases in Figure 11.15 are called **mitogen-activated protein kinases (MAPKs).** (The *mito—* in mitogen stands for mitosis, a process involved in eukaryotic cell division.)

In some cases, each copy of an enzyme in the cascade catalyzes the phosphorylation of many copies of the next "downstream" enzyme, and so on. When this occurs, there are more activated enzymes at each stage in the cascade than in the preceding stages, and the original signal is amplified many times over.

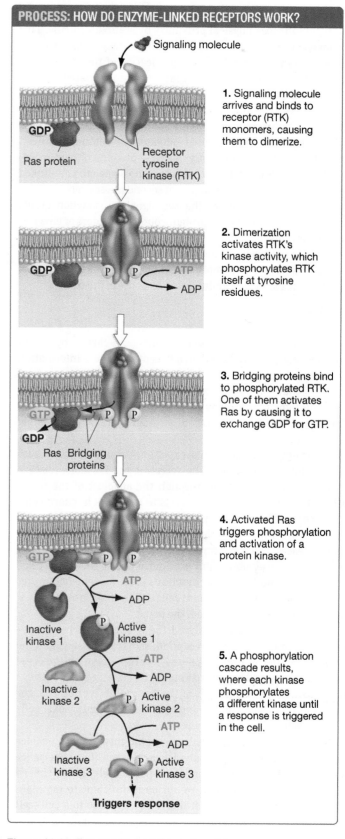

PROCESS: HOW DO ENZYME-LINKED RECEPTORS WORK?

1. Signaling molecule arrives and binds to receptor (RTK) monomers, causing them to dimerize.

2. Dimerization activates RTK's kinase activity, which phosphorylates RTK itself at tyrosine residues.

3. Bridging proteins bind to phosphorylated RTK. One of them activates Ras by causing it to exchange GDP for GTP.

4. Activated Ras triggers phosphorylation and activation of a protein kinase.

5. A phosphorylation cascade results, where each kinase phosphorylates a different kinase until a response is triggered in the cell.

Figure 11.16 Enzyme-Linked Receptors Trigger a Phosphorylation Cascade.

The proteins that take part in a phosphorylation cascade are often held in close physical proximity by scaffold proteins. This arrangement increases the speed and efficiency of the reaction sequence, but it decreases the amplification of the response by limiting the number of proteins that are phosphorylated.

In general, intracellular signals initiated by G-protein-coupled receptors result in the production of second messengers, while enzyme-linked receptors drive phosphorylation cascades. These pathways are not entirely independent of one another, however, and often overlap significantly. Some G-protein-coupled receptors trigger phosphorylation cascades, and some enzyme-linked receptors result in the production of second messengers.

To summarize: Many of the key signal transduction events observed in cells occur via G-protein-coupled receptors or enzyme-linked receptors. A signal transduction event has two results: **(1)** It converts an extracellular message into an intracellular message, and **(2)** in some cases it amplifies and diversifies the original message to elicit a large and multifaceted response in the cell.

Signal Response

What is the ultimate response to the messages carried by signaling molecules? Recall that when adjacent cells share information through cell–cell gaps, two general categories of response may occur: a change in gene expression or a change in the activity of proteins that already exist in the cell (see Section 11.2). The same holds for responses to messages carried by signaling molecules.

For example, when plants experience drought, the tissues in the root system respond by secreting the hormone abscisic acid. This hormone travels through the apoplast of the plant. When it reaches the leaves, it binds to receptors in guard cells, which control the stomatal pores that allow for gas exchange (see Chapter 10). Binding initiates a signal transduction pathway that increases the concentration of calcium ions inside the guard cells. In response, potassium ions move out of the guard cells, creating an osmotic gradient that leads to the movement of water out of the guard cells. The guard cells deflate and close the pores, which prevents water loss from the plant.

At this point, you've analyzed the first three steps of cell–cell communication: signal reception, signal processing, and the response. ✔ If you understand how cells receive and process signals, you should be able to explain how adrenaline can bind to the same receptor in cells of the heart and liver but trigger different responses (increasing contraction rate in heart cells and releasing glucose by liver cells).

Now the question is, how is the signal turned off? Consider the response plants have to abscisic acid when they experience drought. If this response continued indefinitely, gas exchange through the closed stomata would be insufficient to maintain photosynthetic activity. What limits the response to a cell–cell signal?

Signal Deactivation

Cells have built-in systems for turning off intracellular signals. Although many different mechanisms may be used, most signal transduction systems are exquisitely sensitive to small changes in the concentration of signaling molecules or the number and activity of signal receptors. As a result, they trigger a rapid response and can be shut down quickly.

For example, once an activated G protein turns on a downstream enzyme, the bound GTP is hydrolyzed by the G protein to GDP and P_i. This reaction changes the G protein's conformation and returns the protein to its inactive state. Activation of its downstream target stops, and production of the second messenger ceases. To continue the response from a G-protein-coupled receptor, the G protein must be reactivated by the signal receptor to start the process again. Otherwise, the signal transduction system quickly shuts down.

Phosphorylation cascades are also sensitive to the continuing presence of external signaling molecules. If stimulation of a receptor tyrosine kinase ends, enzymes called **phosphatases** will remove phosphate groups from components of the phosphorylation cascade, causing the response to cease.

The presence of second messengers in the cytosol is also short lived. For example, pumps in the membrane of the smooth ER return calcium ions to storage, and enzymes called phosphodiesterases convert active cAMP and cGMP (see Table 11.1) to inactive AMP and GMP, respectively. When second messengers have been cleared from the cytosol, the response stops.

To appreciate what happens when a signal transduction system does not shut down properly, let's return to the phosphorylation cascade illustrated in Figure 11.16. Recall that Ras is active when it binds to GTP, but it is deactivated when it hydrolyzes GTP to GDP and P_i. If this hydrolysis activity were defective, however, Ras would remain active and continue stimulating the cascade even when the external signal is no longer present.

Why is continuously active Ras a problem? Many of the mitogen-activated protein kinases that are activated by Ras induce cells to divide. Cells expressing this defective Ras would receive a never-ending "divide now" signal that could lead to the development of cancer. In fact, an estimated 25–30 percent of all human cancers involve cells that express this type of defective Ras. (To learn more about the family of diseases called cancer, see Chapters 12 and 19.)

Crosstalk: Synthesizing Input from Many Signals

Although this section has focused on how cells respond to individual signals, it's crucial to realize that cells receive and process an almost constant stream of different signals. Just as you receive information about your environment via text messages, e-mails, phone calls, and talking to friends, cells process an array of chemical signals about changes in their environment.

The signal transduction pathways that are triggered by different signals and receptors often intersect. In reality, they are not strictly linear like the pathways illustrated in Figures 11.13 through 11.16. Instead, signal transduction pathways form a network. This complexity is important: It allows cells to respond to many different signals in an integrated way.

The diverse signals that a cell receives are integrated by **crosstalk**—interactions among different signaling pathways that modify the cell response (**Figure 11.17**). Crosstalk is like getting advice from multiple people before making a decision.

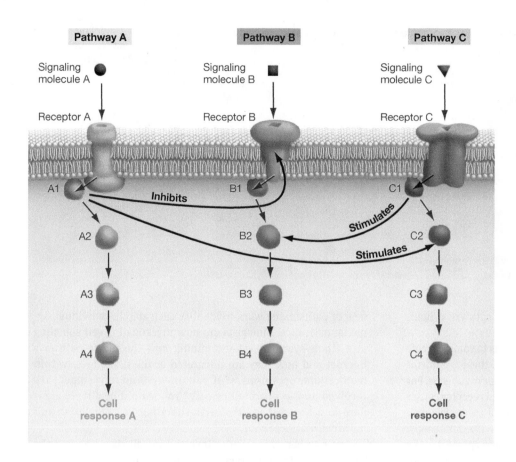

Pathway A

Signaling molecule A

Receptor A

A1

Inhibits

A2

A3

A4

Cell response A

Pathway B

Signaling molecule B

Receptor B

B1

B2

B3

B4

Cell response B

Pathway C

Signaling molecule C

Receptor C

C1

Stimulates

C2

Stimulates

C3

C4

Cell response C

Figure 11.17 Signaling Pathways Interact via Crosstalk.

✔ Predict which responses would occur in cells exposed to the following signaling molecules: (1) A + B; (2) A + C; (3) C alone.

Here are three key things to note:

1. One pathway may inhibit steps in a second pathway, reducing the cell's response to the second pathway even though the appropriate signal is present.

2. One pathway may stimulate steps in a second pathway, leading to the production of two different responses to a single signaling molecule.

3. The presence of multiple steps in a signaling pathway provides a series of points where crosstalk can regulate the flow of information. This regulation is vital because it allows the cell to respond appropriately to many signals at the same time.

CHECK YOUR UNDERSTANDING

If you understand that …

*   Intercellular signals coordinate the activities of cells throughout the body of a multicellular organism in response to changes in internal or external conditions.
*   If intercellular signaling molecules do not enter the cell, they bind to a receptor on the plasma membrane. The signal they carry is then transduced to an intracellular signal that the cell responds to.

✔ **You should be able to …**

1. Explain why only certain cells respond to particular signaling molecules that are sent throughout the body.
2. Explain how some signals are amplified by cells.

Answers are available in Appendix A.

11.4 Signaling between Unicellular Organisms

Surprisingly, much of what we know about signal transduction in multicellular organisms has come from the study of unicellular organisms. While the signal reception and processing events in signal transduction pathways are similar in unicellular and multicellular organisms, the topic of conversation often differs. Rather than involving calls for help, as when a dehydrated brain asks the kidney to conserve water, the conversations between unicellular microbes are often about changes in the environment.

One environmental factor that is closely monitored by populations of unicellular organisms is the density of the population. The use of signaling pathways that respond to population density in prokaryotic and eukaryotic microbes is referred to as **quorum sensing.** The name was inspired by the observation that cells of the same species may undergo dramatic changes in activity when their numbers reach a threshold, or quorum.

Quorum sensing is based on signaling molecules that are secreted by cells and diffuse through the environment. The response to these molecules depends on the species. In bacteria, quorum sensing is often used to help glue a community of microbes to a surface in a biofilm (see Chapter 26), such as the plaque that forms on your teeth. Quorum sensing is also involved in light emission (bioluminescence) by certain bacteria. For example, bacterial species including *Vibrio fischeri* are actively cultured in the light organs of the bobtail squid; after reaching

(a) Slime mold amoebae aggregate in response to sensing a quorum.

(b) Aggregated amoebae form a sluglike body that crawls across a surface.

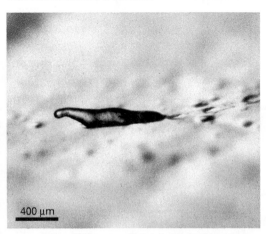

100 µm

Cells migrate toward a central point

400 µm

a certain density, they express enzymes that catalyze a light-producing reaction (see the Chapter 18 Case Study).

Quorum sensing allows unicellular organisms to communicate and coordinate their activities. When it occurs, these organisms take on some of the characteristics of multicellular organisms. For example, quorum sensing via a G-protein-coupled receptor causes the free-living cells (amoebae) of the slime mold *Dictyostelium* to aggregate into multicellular mounds (**Figure 11.18**). Amazingly, the slug-like body that is formed from one of these aggregates can crawl across a surface and eventually organize itself into a fruiting body that releases spores into the air (see BioSkills 11).

Cell signaling has been one of the hottest research areas in biological science over the past two decades. It has taken a great deal of painstaking work to identify each step in individual signaling pathways. Biologists are now investigating cell signaling at a whole-system level—examining how the major pathways interact and how they are integrated at the tissue level within multicellular organisms. ✔ If you understand how signals are received and interpreted by cells, you should be able to compare and contrast intercellular signaling in unicellular and multicellular organisms.

The number of molecules involved in cell signaling and the complexity of their interactions can seem overwhelming, but the punch line is simple: Cell signaling helps organisms ranging from bacteria to blue whales receive information about their environment and respond appropriately to changing conditions.

CHAPTER 11 **REVIEW**

For media, go to MasteringBiology

11.1 The Cell Surface

- The vast majority of cells produce material that forms a layer outside the plasma membrane.

- In bacteria, archaea, algae, fungi, and plants, the extracellular material is stiff and forms a cell wall. In animals, the material is flexible and is called the extracellular matrix (ECM).

- Extracellular layers are fiber composites. They consist of cross-linked filaments that provide tensile strength and a ground substance that fills space and resists compression.

- In plants, the extracellular filaments are cellulose microfibrils; in animals, the most abundant filaments are made of the protein collagen. In both plants and animals, the ground substance is composed primarily of gel-forming polysaccharides.

11.2 How Do Adjacent Cells Connect and Communicate?

- In multicellular organisms, molecules in the extracellular layer and plasma membrane mediate interactions between adjacent cells.

- Adjacent cells may be physically bound to one another by a glue-like middle lamella in plants or by tight junctions and desmosomes in animals.

- The cytoplasm of adjacent cells may be in direct contact through openings called plasmodesmata in plants and gap junctions in animals. These openings allow adjacent cells to communicate via cytosolic signals.

- Cells may respond to signals by altering the expression of their genes or by changing the activity of existing proteins. These responses enable cells within tissues to coordinate their activities.

11.3 How Do Distant Cells Communicate?

- Distant cells in multicellular organisms communicate by secreting signaling molecules that bind to receptors located in the cytosol or on the surface of specific target cells.

- Lipid-soluble signaling molecules often pass through the plasma membrane and bind to cytosolic signal receptors. Signaling molecules that are not lipid soluble often bind to signal receptors in the plasma membrane.

- Signal receptors in the plasma membrane change their conformation on binding to the signal, which triggers production of a second messenger or activates a phosphorylation cascade.

- The cell's response to signals is tightly regulated. Intracellular signals are quickly deactivated without constant signaling from the receptors, and signaling pathways often interact.

11.4 Signaling between Unicellular Organisms

- Unicellular organisms use chemical signals to sense aspects of their environment, such as their population density. Quorum sensing allows populations and communities of cells to coordinate changes in their activities when population density is high.

Answers are available in Appendix A

✓ TEST YOUR KNOWLEDGE

1. What is a fiber composite? How do cellular fiber composites resemble reinforced concrete?

2. Where are protein components of the extracellular matrix synthesized?
   a. in the rough ER
   b. in the Golgi apparatus
   c. in the plasma membrane
   d. in the extracellular layer itself

3. What characteristics do desmosomes bestow on tissues that use these adhesions to connect adjacent cells?
   a. They allow communication between adjacent cells.
   b. They form a watertight barrier between the cells.
   c. They use the extracellular matrix to indirectly connect adjacent cells.
   d. They provide strong connections to resist pulling forces.

4. What does it mean to say that a signal is transduced?
   a. The signaling molecule enters the cell directly and elicits a cellular response.
   b. The signal is generated by the production of proteins.
   c. The physical form of the signal changes between the outside of the cell and the inside.
   d. The signal is amplified.

✓ TEST YOUR UNDERSTANDING

5. How do the extracellular fibers in plants differ from those in animals?
   a. Plant fibers resist compression forces; animal fibers resist pulling forces.
   b. Animal fibers consist of proteins; plant fibers consist of polysaccharides.

c. Plant extracellular fibers never move; animal fibers can slide past one another.
   d. Plant fibers run parallel to one another; animal fibers crisscross.

6. Summarize the experimental evidence in sponges showing that animal cells adhere to each other selectively. Explain the molecular basis of selective adhesion.

7. QUANTITATIVE Suppose you were to model amplification by the phosphorylation cascade in Figure 11.16, using a penny for each kinase 1, a nickel for each kinase 2, and a dime for each kinase 3. Also suppose that Ras and each of the kinases can activate 10 proteins. How much money would you need to construct your model?

8. What is the significance of the observation that many signal transduction pathways create a network, where they intersect or overlap?

✓ TEST YOUR PROBLEM-SOLVING SKILLS

9. Steroid hormones, like most lipid-soluble signaling molecules, are processed directly. How does the absence of a signal transduction cascade in the processing of steroid hormones affect (a) signal amplification, (b) signal regulation, and (c) the cellular response that is possible?

10. Suppose you have an antibody that binds to the receptor tyrosine kinase illustrated in Figure 11.16. When you add this antibody to the cell, you find that it activates the cell response, even when no signaling molecule is present. Explain this result.

✓ PUT IT ALL TOGETHER: Case Study

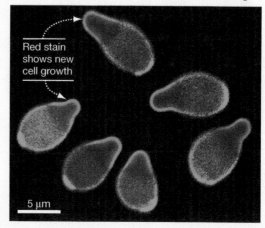

Red stain shows new cell growth

5 µm

What type of foreplay is required for sexual reproduction in yeast?

Some unicellular eukaryotes, including the yeast *Saccharomyces cerevisiae*, can reproduce sexually (see Chapter 13). At the most basic level, sexual reproduction involves the fusion of two cells and the combining of genetic material from each cell into one nucleus. Yeast cells are not motile, so the opposite mating types, referred to as "**a**" cells and "alpha **(α)**" cells, must alter their growth (indicated by red staining in the photograph above) in order to attach and fuse. How does a yeast cell arouse this cellular reponse in the opposite mating type?

11. Yeast cells secrete signaling molecules called pheromones that are specific for their mating type. Type α cells produce the pheromone α factor, which binds to a G-protein-coupled receptor on type **a** cells, and vice versa. Explain what happens to the G protein when one of these receptors binds to a pheromone.

12. Instead of involving the production of second messengers, the pheromone-activated response in yeast involves a peripheral membrane protein related to Ras. Based on what you've learned about signal processing in multicellular organisms, predict how the pheromone signal in yeast is further processed in the cell to trigger the cell response.

13. Some of the intracellular proteins involved in the pheromone-activated response in yeast are organized by a scaffold protein called Ste5. When pheromone binding occurs, one of these proteins, called Fus3, is released from Ste5 and triggers the response. Explain how this organization affects the speed of the response and amplification of the signal.

14. **QUANTITATIVE** Ste5 can be phosphorylated by Fus3 or dephosphorylated by a phosphatase named Ptc1. To examine the role of Ste5 phosphorylation on the release of Fus3, researchers created a yeast strain with the *ptc1* gene deleted (*ptc1Δ*). They then measured the amount of binding between Fus3 and Ste5 in cells of this strain and in wild-type cells as they added increasing concentrations of α factor. Their results are shown in the graph that follows. Use the graph to evaluate how the phosphorylation status of Ste5 affects its ability to release Fus3.

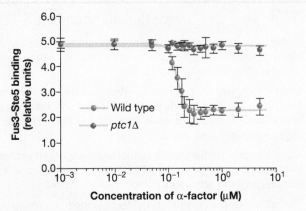

Source: M. Malleshaiah et al. 2010. *Nature* 456: 101–105.

15. **PROCESS OF SCIENCE** The cellular response to pheromone signaling includes assembly of microfilaments that direct growth toward the signal source. Propose a hypothesis that explains how growth might be limited to the region where signal receptors are activated.

16. **PROCESS OF SCIENCE** Sex is dangerous in yeast—when cells are exposed to the pheromone of the opposite mating type, 10–15 percent of them die. For two yeast cells to fuse, portions of their cell walls must be broken down. How could you test the hypothesis that cell-wall destruction is responsible for pheromone-induced cell death in yeast?

12 The Cell Cycle

This cell, from a hyacinth plant, is undergoing a type of nuclear division called mitosis. Understanding how mitosis occurs is a major focus of this chapter.

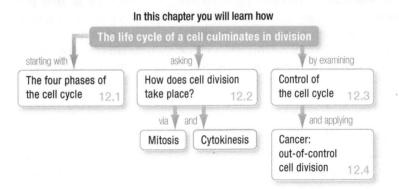

In this chapter you will learn how

The life cycle of a cell culminates in division

starting with ➔ The four phases of the cell cycle 12.1

asking ➔ How does cell division take place? 12.2

via ➔ Mitosis and ➔ Cytokinesis

by examining ➔ Control of the cell cycle 12.3

and applying ➔ Cancer: out-of-control cell division 12.4

This chapter is part of the Big Picture. See how on pages 396–397.

The cell theory maintains that all organisms are made of cells and that all cells arise from preexisting cells (Chapter 1). Although the cell theory was widely accepted among biologists by the 1860s, most thought that new cells arose within preexisting cells by a process that resembled the growth of mineral crystals. But Rudolf Virchow proposed that new cells are formed by the splitting of preexisting cells—that is, by **cell division.**

In the late 1800s, microscopic observations of newly developing organisms, or **embryos,** confirmed Virchow's hypothesis. Plants and animals start life as single-celled embryos and grow through a series of cell divisions.

Early studies revealed two fundamentally different ways that nuclei divide before cell division: meiosis and mitosis. In animals, **meiosis** leads to the production of sperm and eggs, which are the male and female reproductive cells termed **gametes. Mitosis** leads to the production of all other cell types, referred to as **somatic** (literally, "body-belonging") **cells.** (You can see how meiosis and mitosis are related to each other and to the transmission of genetic information in the Big Picture on pages 396–397.)

Mitosis and meiosis are usually accompanied by **cytokinesis**—the division of the cytoplasm into two distinct cells. When cytokinesis is complete, a so-called parent cell has given rise to two daughter cells.

Mitotic and meiotic cell divisions are responsible for one of the five fundamental attributes of life: reproduction (see Chapter 1). But even though mitosis and meiosis share many characteristics, they are fundamentally different. During mitotic division, the genetic material is copied and then divided equally between two cells. This is referred to as cellular *replication*, since the daughter cells are genetically identical to the parent cell. In contrast, meiosis results in daughter cells that are genetically different from each other and that have half the amount of hereditary material as the parent cell.

This chapter focuses on mitotic cell division; meiotic cell division is the subject of another chapter (Chapter 13). Let's begin with a look at the key events in a cell's life cycle, continue with an in-depth analysis of mitosis and the regulation of the cell cycle, and end by examining how uncontrolled cell division can lead to cancer.

12.1 How Do Cells Replicate?

For life on Earth to exist, cells must replicate. The basic steps in cellular replication are **(1)** copying the DNA (deoxyribonucleic acid), **(2)** separating the copies, and **(3)** dividing the cytoplasm to create two complete cells. This chapter focuses on a process that has been studied for well over a century: how eukaryotic cells replicate. Like much work in biology, the research on eukaryotic cell replication began with simple observations of the process.

What Is a Chromosome?

As studies of cell division in eukaryotes began, biologists found that certain chemical dyes made threadlike structures visible within nuclei. In 1879, Walther Flemming used a dye made from a coal tar to observe these structures and watch them change in the dividing cells of salamander embryos. The threads first appeared in pairs just before cell division and then split to produce single, unpaired threads in the daughter cells. Flemming introduced the term "mitosis," from the Greek *mitos* ("thread"), to describe this process.

Others studied the roundworm *Ascaris* and noted that the number of threads in a cell was the same before and after mitotic division. All of these cells had the same number of threads.

In 1888, Wilhelm Waldeyer coined the term **chromosome** ("colored-body") to refer to these threadlike structures (visible in the chapter-opening photo). Research carried out since then has shown that a chromosome consists of a single long DNA double helix that is wrapped around proteins, called **histones,** in a highly organized manner (see Chapter 19). DNA encodes the cell's hereditary information, or genetic material. A **gene** is a region of DNA in a chromosome that codes for a particular protein or ribonucleic acid (RNA).

Before mitosis, each chromosome is replicated. As mitosis starts, the chromosomes condense into compact structures that can be moved around the cell efficiently. Then one copy of each chromosome is distributed to each of two daughter cells.

Figure 12.1 illustrates an unreplicated chromosome, the same chromosome after it has been replicated, and the replicated chromosome that has condensed at the start of mitosis. Each of the double-stranded DNA copies in a replicated chromosome is called a **chromatid.** Before mitosis, the two chromatids are joined along their entire length by proteins called cohesins. Once mitosis begins, however, these connections are removed except

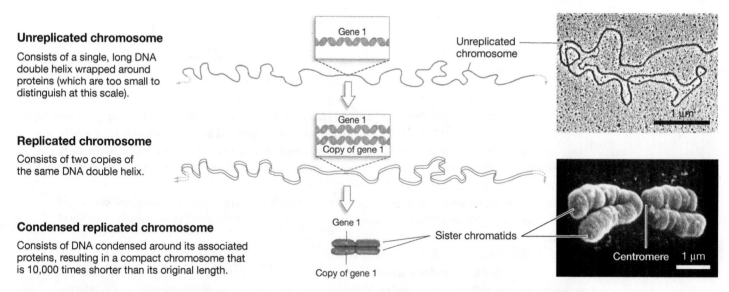

Unreplicated chromosome

Consists of a single, long DNA double helix wrapped around proteins (which are too small to distinguish at this scale).

Replicated chromosome

Consists of two copies of the same DNA double helix.

Condensed replicated chromosome

Consists of DNA condensed around its associated proteins, resulting in a compact chromosome that is 10,000 times shorter than its original length.

Gene 1

Gene 1
Copy of gene 1

Gene 1
Copy of gene 1

Unreplicated chromosome

1 µm

Sister chromatids

Centromere   1 µm

Figure 12.1 Changes in Chromosome Morphology. After chromosomes replicate, the two identical copies of the double-stranded DNA are attached to each other along their entire length. Early in mitosis, replicated chromosomes condense and sister chromatids remain attached at a region called the centromere.

for those at a specialized region of the chromosome called the **centromere.** Chromatid copies that remain attached at their centromere are referred to as **sister chromatids.** Even though a replicated chromosome consists of two chromatids, it is still considered a single chromosome. In **Making Models 12.1,** you will practice drawing chromosomes to represent the difference between unreplicated and replicated versions.

Cells Alternate between M Phase and Interphase

The division of eukaryotic cells is like a well-choreographed stage performance. The most visually stimulating part of the show occurs when cells are in the process of separating their chromosomes, called **M** (*mitotic* or *meiotic*) **phase.** Stained chromosomes can be observed with a light microscope when they condense into compact structures during M phase.

The rest of the time, the cell is in **interphase** ("between-phase"). No dramatic changes in the nucleus are visible by light microscopy during interphase. The chromosomes uncoil into the extremely long, thin structures shown in Figure 12.1 and no longer appear as individual threads. However, this does not mean that the cell is idle. Interphase is an active time: The cell is either growing and preparing to divide or fulfilling its specialized function in a multicellular individual. Cells actually spend most of their time in interphase.

The Discovery of S Phase

Once M phase and interphase were identified by microscopy, researchers could start assigning roles to these distinct phases. They could see that the separation of chromosomes and cytokinesis take place during M phase, but when are the chromosomes replicated?

To answer this question, researchers needed to distinguish cells that were making copies of their DNA from those that were not. They were able to do this by adding radioactive phosphorus, in the form of phosphates, to cells. Those cells that were

synthesizing DNA would incorporate the radioactive isotope into nucleotides. (See Chapter 4 to review where phosphates are in DNA.) There were three steps in this procedure:

1. Label DNA as chromosomes were being replicated.

2. Wash away any radioactive phosphorus that hadn't been incorporated and remove RNA, which would also incorporate phosphorus.

3. Visualize the labeled, newly synthesized DNA by exposing the treated cells to X-ray film. Emissions from radioactive phosphorus create black dots in the film. This technique is called autoradiography (see BioSkills 6).

In 1951, Alma Howard and Stephen Pelc performed this procedure and found black dots—indicating active DNA synthesis—in *some* interphase cells, but not in M-phase cells. This result showed that DNA replication occurs during a period in interphase. Several years later, this result was verified using radioactive thymidine, which is incorporated into DNA but not RNA.

Thus, biologists had identified a new stage in the life of a cell. They called it **S** (or **synthesis**) **phase.** S phase is part of interphase. The process of copying the genetic material is separated, in time, from the partitioning of replicated chromosomes during M phase.

Howard and Pelc coined the term **cell cycle** to describe the orderly sequence of events that leads a eukaryotic cell through the duplication of its chromosomes to the time it divides.

The Discovery of the Gap Phases

In addition to discovering S phase, Howard and Pelc made another key observation—not all interphase cells were labeled. This meant that there was at least one "gap" in interphase when DNA was not being replicated.

Howard and Pelc, along with researchers in other labs, followed up on these early results by asking where S phase was positioned in interphase. There were three possible scenarios:

1. The S phase is immediately before M phase, with a single gap between the end of M phase and the start of S phase.

2. The S phase is immediately after M phase, with a single gap between the end of S phase and the start of M phase.

3. Two gaps exist, one before and one after S phase.

To address which of these scenarios, if any, was correct, many experiments were done on cells in culture. Cultured cells are powerful experimental tools because they can be manipulated much more easily than cells in an intact organism (see BioSkills 11). In most of these experiments, researchers used cultures that were *asynchronous*, meaning that the cells were randomly distributed in various stages of the cell cycle.

To understand the value of asynchronous cultures, imagine the cell cycle as a clock. Every complete rotation of the second hand around the clock would represent one cell division, and each tick would represent a different point in the cycle. At any given time, an asynchronous culture would have at least one cell at each of the ticks on the clock. As time passed, these cells would move around this cell-cycle clock at the same rate and in the same direction.

Figure 12.2 A Pulse–Chase Experiment Reveals a Gap Phase. Cells labeled with radioactive thymidine during the pulse were tracked during the chase. The period between the end of the pulse and the appearance of the first labeled mitotic cells represents a gap between the end of S phase and start of M phase.

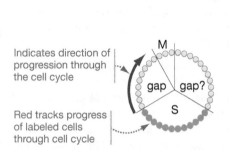

Indicates direction of progression through the cell cycle

Red tracks progress of labeled cells through cell cycle

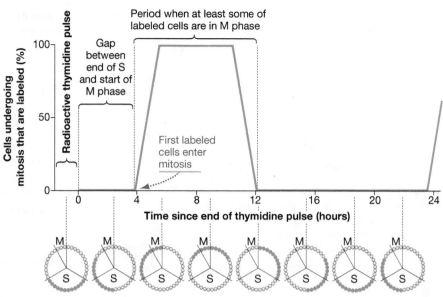

Period when at least some of labeled cells are in M phase

Gap between end of S and start of M phase

First labeled cells enter mitosis

Time since end of thymidine pulse (hours)

In one experiment, researchers added radioactively labeled thymidine to the cells in a human cell culture. A short time later, they stopped the labeling by flooding the solution surrounding the cultured cells with nonradioactive thymidine, which washed away any labeled thymidine that had not already been incorporated into DNA. This pulse–chase approach (introduced in Chapter 7) labeled only those cells that were in S phase during the radioactive pulse. Imagine these labeled cells moving together through the cell cycle like the second hand moving around a clock.

Once the pulse ended, the researchers took samples of cells from the culture at different times during the chase. In each sample, they recorded how many labeled cells were undergoing mitosis, meaning how many cells that were in S phase during the pulse had entered M phase. **Figure 12.2** summarizes the results of this experiment.

One striking result emerged early on: None of the labeled cells started mitosis immediately. Because the cultures were asynchronous, at least some of the cells must have been at the very end of their S phase when they were exposed to the pulse. If S phase were immediately followed by M phase, then some of these labeled cells would have entered M phase just as the chase began. Instead, it took several hours before any of the labeled cells began mitosis.

The time between the end of the pulse and the appearance of the first labeled mitotic nuclei corresponds to a gap between the end of S phase and the beginning of M phase. This gap is a period when chromosome replication is complete but mitosis has not yet begun. The graph in Figure 12.2 shows how cells labeled with radioactive thymidine can be tracked as they progress through M phase.

✔ If you understand how the pulse–chase approach was used in Figure 12.2, you should be able to predict how the graph would appear if the *y*-axis represented the percentage of all cells that were labeled, not just the labeled cells undergoing mitosis.

This result narrowed the possible scenarios for the organization of the cell cycle: There could be either one gap between the end of S phase and the start of M phase, or two gaps flanking S phase. Which scenario represents the eukaryotic cell cycle? Once researchers determined the lengths of the S and M phases, they

found that the combined time, including the gap between them, was shorter than the length of the cell cycle. This discrepancy indicated that there must be an additional gap between the end of M phase and the start of S phase.

The cell cycle was thus finally mapped out. The gap between the end of M phase and the start of S phase is called **G₁ phase.** The second gap, between the end of S phase and the start of M phase, is called **G₂ phase.**

The Cell Cycle

Figure 12.3 pulls these results together into a comprehensive view of the cell cycle. The cell cycle involves four phases: M phase and an interphase consisting of the G₁, S, and G₂ phases. In the

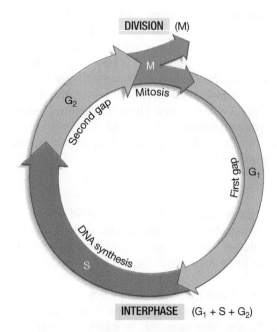

DIVISION (M)

M

Mitosis

G₂

Second gap

First gap

G₁

DNA synthesis

S

INTERPHASE (G₁ + S + G₂)

Figure 12.3 The Cell Cycle Has Four Phases. The duration of the G₁ and G₂ phases varies dramatically among cells and organisms.

cycle diagrammed here, G_1 phase is about twice as long as G_2 phase, but their actual durations vary depending on the cell type and growth conditions.

Why do the gap phases exist? In multicellular organisms, cells perform their functional roles mostly during G_1 phase. G_1 is also the period when the cell "decides" to begin replication and transitions to S phase (as will be explained in Section 12.4). Before mitosis can take place, a cell uses G_2 phase to prepare for M phase. The time spent in both G_1 and G_2 allows the cell to grow and replicate organelles so it will be able to divide into two cells that can function normally.

Now let's turn to M phase. Once the genetic material has been copied in S phase, how is it divided between daughter cells?

12.2 What Happens during M Phase?

M phase typically consists of two distinct events: the division of the nucleus and the division of the cytoplasm. Mitosis divides the replicated chromosomes to form two daughter nuclei with identical chromosomes and genes. Cytokinesis usually follows mitosis and divides the cytoplasm of the parent cell to form two daughter cells.

Figure 12.4 provides an overview of how chromosomes change before, during, and after mitosis and cytokinesis, beginning with a hypothetical plant cell or animal cell in G_1 phase. The first drawing shows a total of four chromosomes in the cell, but chromosome number varies widely among species—potato plants have 48 chromosomes in each cell, dogs have 78, fruit flies have 8, and you have 46.

Eukaryotic chromosomes consist of DNA wrapped around globular histone proteins. This DNA–histone complex is called **chromatin.** During interphase, the chromatin of each chromosome is in a "relaxed" or less condensed state, forming long, thin strands (see Figure 12.1, top).

The second drawing in Figure 12.4 shows G_2 phase, where the cell contains replicated chromosomes before mitosis. Each chromosome now consists of two sister chromatids. Each chromatid contains one long DNA double helix, and sister chromatids represent exact copies of the same genetic information.

At the start of mitosis, then, each chromosome consists of two sister chromatids that are attached to each other at the centromere.

✔ You should be able to explain the relationship between chromosomes and (1) DNA, (2) chromatin, and (3) sister chromatids.

Events in Mitosis

As the third drawing in Figure 12.4 indicates, mitosis begins when chromatin condenses to form a much more compact structure. Replicated, condensed chromosomes correspond to the paired threads observed by early biologists.

During mitosis, the two sister chromatids separate to form independent daughter chromosomes. One copy of each chromosome goes to each of the two daughter cells. (See the final drawing in Figure 12.4.) As a result, each cell receives the same complement of chromosomes (identical copies of each chromosome) as the parent cell had.

Biologists have identified five subphases within M phase based on distinctive events that occur: prophase, prometaphase, metaphase, anaphase, and telophase.

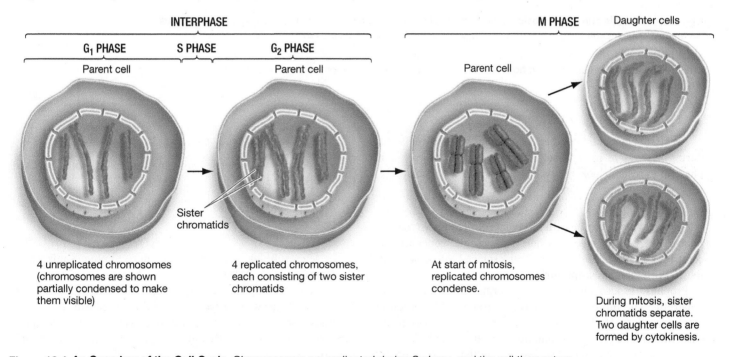

INTERPHASE

G_1 PHASE   S PHASE G_2 PHASE

Parent cell   Parent cell

Sister chromatids

M PHASE   Daughter cells

Parent cell

4 unreplicated chromosomes (chromosomes are shown partially condensed to make them visible)

4 replicated chromosomes, each consisting of two sister chromatids

At start of mitosis, replicated chromosomes condense.

During mitosis, sister chromatids separate. Two daughter cells are formed by cytokinesis.

Figure 12.4 An Overview of the Cell Cycle. Chromosomes are replicated during S phase, and the cell then enters G_2 phase. During M phase, the replicated chromosomes are partitioned to the two daughter cells. Each daughter cell contains the same complement of chromosomes that the parent cell had.

Sister chromatids separate; one chromosome copy goes to each daughter nucleus.

Centrioles
Centrosomes   Chromosomes   Early spindle apparatus   Polar microtubules   Kinetochore microtubules   Astral microtubules

Sister chromatids   Kinetochore

1. Interphase: After chromosome replication, each chromosome is composed of two sister chromatids. Centrosomes have replicated.

2. Prophase: Chromosomes condense, and spindle apparatus begins to form.

3. Prometaphase: Nuclear envelope breaks down. Microtubules contact chromosomes at kinetochores.

4. Metaphase: Chromosomes complete migration to middle of cell.

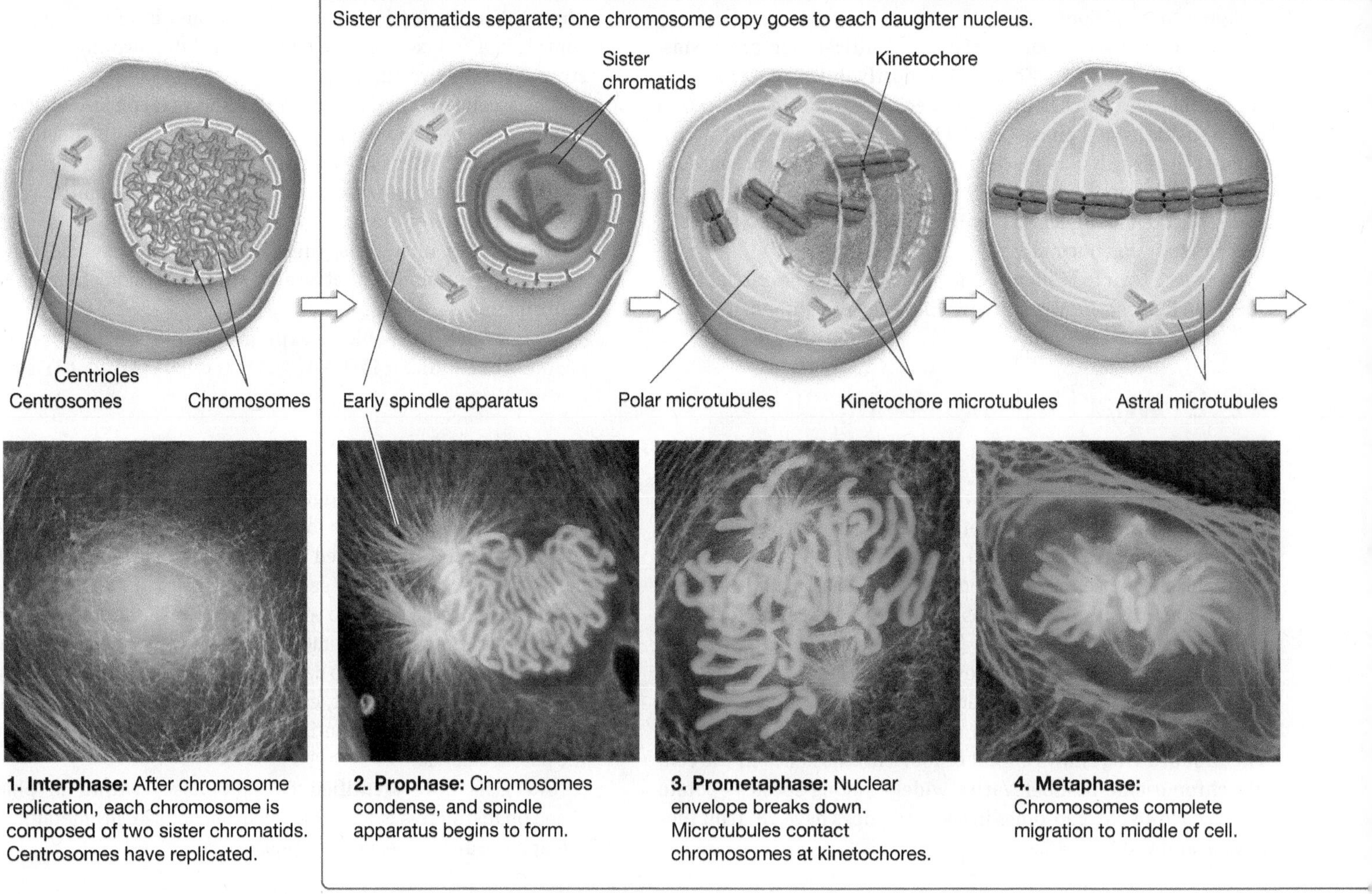

Figure 12.5 Mitosis and Cytokinesis. In the micrographs of newt lung cells under the drawings, chromosomes are stained blue, microtubules are yellow/green, and intermediate filaments are red.

✔ **CAUTION** If the cell shown in the micrographs has 60 picograms of DNA (6×10^{-11}g) and 22 chromosomes in its G_1 phase, how much DNA and how many chromosomes are in **(1)** the prophase cell; **(2)** the anaphase cell; and **(3)** each daughter cell?

Recall that before mitosis begins, chromosomes are replicated during S phase of interphase. Now let's investigate each subphase of mitosis to look at how cells separate the chromatids of these replicated chromosomes (**Figure 12.5**).

Prophase   Mitosis begins with the events of **prophase** ("before-phase," Figure 12.5, step 2), when chromosomes condense into compact structures. Individual chromosomes first become visible in the light microscope during prophase.

Prophase is also marked by the formation of the spindle apparatus. The **spindle apparatus** is a structure that produces mechanical forces that **(1)** move replicated chromosomes during early mitosis and **(2)** pull chromatids apart in late mitosis.

The spindle apparatus consists of microtubules—components of the cytoskeleton. Microtubules have the following characteristics (see Chapter 7):

- They are composed of α-tubulin and β-tubulin dimers.
- They are asymmetric—meaning they have a plus end and a minus end.
- The plus end is the site where microtubule growth normally occurs. Microtubule disassembly is more frequent at the minus end.

Microtubules originate from microtubule-organizing centers (MTOCs). MTOCs define the two poles of the spindle apparatus and produce large numbers of microtubules, whose plus ends grow outward through the cytoplasm. During prophase, some of these microtubules extend from each spindle pole and overlap with one another—these are called **polar microtubules.**

Although the nature of the MTOC varies among plants, animals, fungi, and other eukaryotic groups, the spindle apparatus

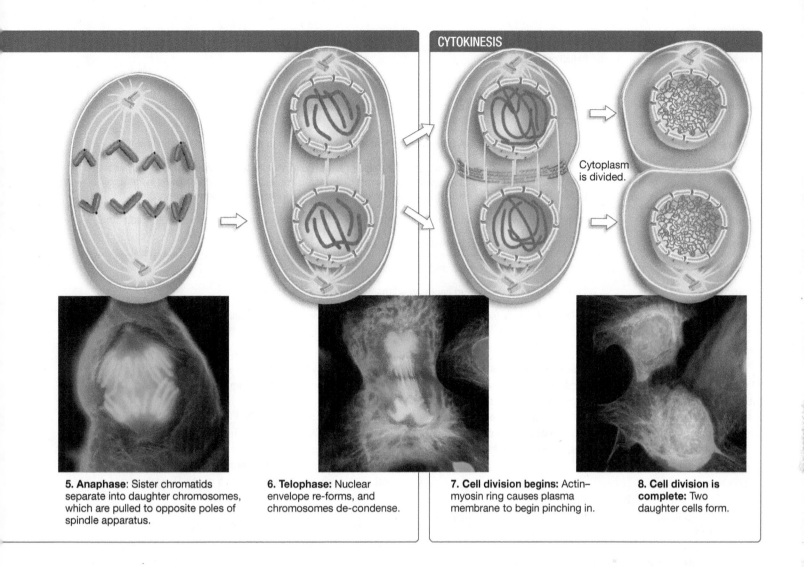

Cytoplasm is divided.

5. Anaphase: Sister chromatids separate into daughter chromosomes, which are pulled to opposite poles of spindle apparatus.

6. Telophase: Nuclear envelope re-forms, and chromosomes de-condense.

7. Cell division begins: Actin–myosin ring causes plasma membrane to begin pinching in.

8. Cell division is complete: Two daughter cells form.

has the same function. Figure 12.5 illustrates mitosis in newt lung cells, where the MTOC is a **centrosome**—a structure that contains a pair of **centrioles** (see Chapter 7). During prophase in animal cells, the spindle apparatus begins to form around the chromosomes by moving centrosomes to opposite sides of the nucleus.

Prometaphase   In many eukaryotes, once chromosomes have condensed, the nuclear envelope disintegrates. Removal of the envelope allows the cytoplasmic microtubules to attach to chromosomes at specialized structures called **kinetochores.** These events define the start of **prometaphase** ("before middle-phase"; see Figure 12.5, step 3).

Each sister chromatid has its own kinetochore, which is assembled at the centromere. Since the centromere is also the attachment site for chromatids, the result is two kinetochores on opposite sides of each replicated chromosome. The microtubules that are attached to these structures are called **kinetochore microtubules.**

Early in prometaphase, kinesin and dynein motors attached to the kinetochores "walk" the chromosomes up and down microtubules. This process is similar to the way the same motors

transport vesicles and organelles along microtubules (see Chapter 7). When the chromosomes reach the plus ends of the microtubules, the kinetochore proteins secure their attachment.

Eventually, the kinetochore on each chromatid of a chromosome is attached to microtubules that originate from one of the two spindle poles. The chromosomes are pushed and pulled by microtubules and motor proteins until they reach the middle of the spindle.

Metaphase   Once all the chromosomes have migrated to the middle of the spindle (Figure 12.5, step 4), the mitotic cells enter **metaphase** ("middle-phase"). At this point, the chromosomes are lined up on an imaginary plane between the two spindle poles called the **metaphase plate.**

The formation of the spindle apparatus is now complete. The polar microtubules that extend from each spindle pole overlap in the middle of the cell, thereby forming a pole-to-pole connection. Each chromosome is held by kinetochore microtubules reaching out from opposite poles and exerting the same amount of tension, or pull. The spindle poles are held in place partly because of **astral microtubules** that extend from the MTOCs and interact with proteins on the plasma membrane.

Structure	Definition
Chromosome	A structure containing genetic information in the form of genes.
Chromatin	The material that makes up eukaryotic chromosomes; consists of a DNA molecule complexed with histone proteins (see Chapter 19)
Chromatid	One double-stranded DNA copy of a replicated chromosome with its associated proteins
Sister chromatids	The two attached, double-stranded DNA copies of a replicated chromosome. When chromosomes are replicated, they consist of two sister chromatids. The genetic material in sister chromatids is identical. When sister chromatids separate during mitosis, they become independent chromosomes.
Centromere	A specialized region of a chromosome where sister chromatids are most closely joined to each other
Kinetochores	The structures on sister chromatids where microtubules attach
Microtubule-organizing center	Any structure that organizes microtubules (see Chapter 7)
Centrosome	The microtubule-organizing center in animals and certain plants and fungi
Centrioles	Cylindrical structures consisting of microtubule triplets, located inside animal centrosomes

The polarized growth and disassembly of the kinetochore microtubules contributes to the alignment of the chromosomes at the metaphase plate. The slow disassembly of the minus ends at the MTOCs is balanced by the slow growth of the plus ends at the kinetochores. Since the sister chromatids of each chromosome are connected to opposite poles, a tug of war between the poles begins during metaphase.

Anaphase   At the start of **anaphase** ("against-phase"), the cohesins that hold sister chromatids together at the centromeres split (Figure 12.5, step 5). Because the chromatids are under tension, each replicated chromosome is pulled apart, creating two independent daughter chromosomes. By definition, this separation of chromatids instantly doubles the number of chromosomes in the cell.

Two types of movement occur during anaphase. First, the daughter chromosomes move to opposite poles via the attachment of kinetochore proteins to the shrinking kinetochore microtubules. Second, the two poles of the spindle are pushed and pulled farther apart. The push comes from motor proteins in overlapping polar microtubules, which force the poles away from each other. The pull comes from different motors on the plasma membrane, which walk along on the astral microtubules and drag the poles to opposite sides of the cell.

The separation of replicated chromosomes to opposite poles is a critical step in mitosis because it ensures that each daughter cell receives the same complement of chromosomes. When anaphase is complete, two complete sets of chromosomes are fully separated, each set being identical to that of the parent cell before chromosome replication.

Telophase   During **telophase** ("end-phase"), the nuclear envelope re-forms around each set of chromosomes, and the chromosomes begin to de-condense (Figure 12.5, step 6). Once two independent nuclei have formed, mitosis is complete. At this point,

most cells go on to divide their cytoplasm via cytokinesis, which begins at the center of the spindle apparatus and forms two daughter cells.

Table 12.1 summarizes the key structures involved in mitosis.

✔After you've studied Table 12.1 and reviewed Figure 12.5, you should be able to make a new table that summarizes what happens to (1) the spindle apparatus, (2) the nuclear envelope, and (3) the chromosomes in each of the five phases of mitosis.

How Do Chromosomes Move during Anaphase?

The exact and equal partitioning of genetic material to the two daughter nuclei is the most fundamental aspect of mitosis. To understand how sister chromatids separate and move to opposite sides of the spindle, biologists have focused on the role of kinetochore microtubules. How do these microtubules pull chromatids apart?

Mitotic Spindle Forces   During mitosis, the microtubules originating from the spindle poles are highly dynamic. Rapid growth and disassembly ensures that some of the microtubules will be able to attach to kinetochores with their plus ends. Others will be stabilized by different proteins in the cytoplasm and become polar or astral microtubules.

These observations suggest two hypotheses for the movement of chromosomes during anaphase. The simpler hypothesis is that kinetochore microtubules stop growing at their plus ends but remain attached to the kinetochores. As the minus ends disassemble at the spindle poles, the chromosomes would be reeled in like hooked fish. An alternative hypothesis is that the chromosomes move along microtubules that are being disassembled at their plus ends at the kinetochores. In this case, each chromosome would be like a yo-yo running up a string into your hand.

To test these hypotheses, biologists introduced fluorescently labeled tubulin subunits into prophase or metaphase

QUESTION: How do kinetochore microtubules shorten to pull daughter chromosomes apart during anaphase?

HYPOTHESIS: Microtubules shorten at the spindle pole.

ALTERNATIVE HYPOTHESIS: Microtubules shorten at the kinetochore.

EXPERIMENTAL SETUP:

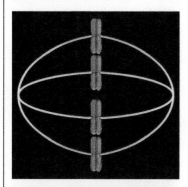

1. Label targets:
Use fluorescent labels to make the metaphase chromosomes fluoresce blue and the microtubules fluoresce yellow.

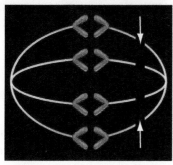

2. Mark microtubules:
At the start of anaphase, darken sections of microtubules to mark them without changing their function.

PREDICTION:

PREDICTION OF ALTERNATIVE HYPOTHESIS: Daughter chromosomes will move toward the pole faster than the darkened sections.

RESULTS:

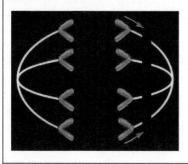

The darkened sections of the microtubules remained stationary as the chromosomes moved through them toward the pole.

CONCLUSION: Kinetochore microtubules shorten at the kinetochore to pull daughter chromosomes apart during anaphase.

Figure 12.6 During Anaphase, Microtubules Shorten at the Kinetochore.

SOURCE: Gorbsky, G. J., P. J. Sammak, and G. G. Borisy. 1987. Chromosomes move poleward in anaphase along stationary microtubules that coordinately disassemble from their kinetochore ends. *The Journal of Cell Biology* 104: 9–18.

✔ Complete the prediction for the hypothesis that microtubules shorten at the spindle pole.

cells. This treatment made the kinetochore microtubules visible (**Figure 12.6**, step 1). Once anaphase began, the researchers marked a bar-shaped region of these microtubules with a beam of laser light. The laser permanently bleached sections of the fluorescently labeled microtubules, darkening them—although they were still functional (Figure 12.6, step 2).

As anaphase progressed, two things happened: **(1)** The darkened sections of the microtubules appeared to remain stationary, and **(2)** the chromosomes moved closer to the darkened sections, eventually overtaking them.

This result suggested that the kinetochore microtubules remain stationary during anaphase, but shorten because tubulin subunits are lost from their plus ends. As the microtubule ends shrink back to the spindle poles, the chromosomes are pulled along. But if the microtubule is disassembling at the kinetochore, how does the chromosome remain attached?

Kinetochores Are Linked to Retreating Microtubule Ends The kinetochore is a complex of many proteins that attaches the centromere region of the chromosome to one or more microtubules. **Figure 12.7** shows a current model of kinetochore structure and function during chromosome movement in anaphase. For simplicity, a yeast kinetochore is shown, which attaches to only one microtubule. (Other eukaryotes can have as many as 30 microtubules attached to each kinetochore.)

Fibers that extend from the yeast kinetochore are tethered to a ring that surrounds the kinetochore microtubule (Figure 12.7, top). Biologists have found that as anaphase gets under way,

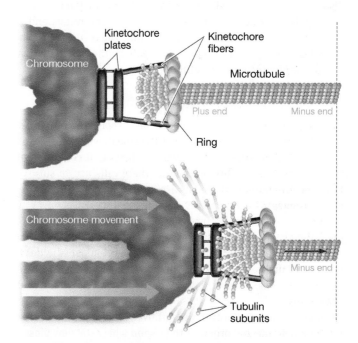

Figure 12.7 How Do Microtubules Move Chromosomes during Anaphase? Microtubules are disassembled at the kinetochore during anaphase. In yeast, kinetochore plates and fibers tether the chromosome to a ring that is pushed toward the spindle pole by the fraying plus end of the microtubule.

(a) Cytokinesis in plants

Microtubules direct vesicles to center of spindle, where they fuse to divide the cell in two

Microtubule   Cell plate

5 µm

(b) Cytokinesis in animals

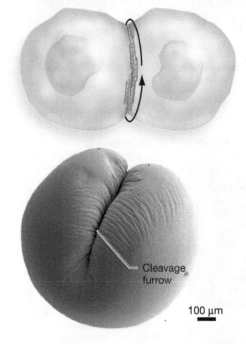

Actin–myosin interactions pinch the plasma membrane in two

Cleavage furrow

100 µm

Figure 12.8 **The Mechanism of Cytokinesis Varies among Eukaryotes. (a)** In plants, the cytoplasm is divided by a cell plate that forms in the middle of the parent cell. **(b)** In animals, the cytoplasm is divided by a cleavage furrow. (The cells in both micrographs have been stained or colorized.)

the plus end of the kinetochore microtubule begins to fray and disassemble. As the fraying end widens, its expansion forces the ring, and the attached chromosome, toward the minus end of the microtubule (see Figure 12.7, bottom). The result is that the chromosome is pulled to the spindle pole by the depolymerization of the kinetochore microtubule.

Cytokinesis Results in Two Daughter Cells

At this point, the chromosomes have been replicated in S phase and distributed to opposite sides of the spindle via mitosis. Now it's time to divide the cell into two daughters that contain identical copies of each chromosome. If these cells are to survive, however, the parent cell must also ensure that more than just chromosomes make it into each daughter cell.

While the cell was in interphase, the cytoplasmic contents, including the organelles, increased in number or volume. During cytokinesis (Figure 12.5, steps 7 and 8), the cytoplasm divides to form two daughter cells, each with its own nucleus and complete set of organelles. In most types of cells, cytokinesis directly follows mitosis.

In plants, polar microtubules left over from the spindle apparatus help define and organize the region where the new plasma membranes and cell walls will form. Vesicles from the Golgi apparatus carry components for a new cell wall to the middle of the dividing cell. These vesicles are moved along the polar microtubules via motor proteins. In the middle of what was the spindle, the vesicles start to fuse and form a flattened, sac-like structure called the **cell plate** (Figure 12.8a). The cell plate

continues to grow as new vesicles fuse with it. Eventually, the cell plate contacts and fuses with the existing plasma membrane, dividing the cell into two daughter cells.

In animals and many other eukaryotes, cytokinesis begins with the formation of a **cleavage furrow** (Figure 12.8b). The furrow appears when a ring of overlapping actin filaments starts to contract just inside the plasma membrane, in the middle of what used to be the spindle. This contraction is caused by myosin motor proteins that bind to the actin filaments and use adenosine triphosphate (ATP) to slide the filaments past one another (see Chapter 7).

As myosin moves the actin filaments, the ring shrinks and tightens. Because the ring is attached to the inside of the plasma membrane, the contracting ring pulls the membrane with it. As a result, the plasma membrane is drawn inward. Myosin continues to slide the actin filaments past each other, tightening the ring further, until the plasma membrane fuses and cell division is complete.

Chromosome separation and cytoplasmic division are common requirements for all organisms, not just eukaryotes. What is known about cell division in prokaryotes? Is the process of cell division in your cells similar to that in bacteria?

Bacterial Cell Replication

Many bacteria divide using a process called **binary fission.** Although binary fission does not involve mitosis, recent research has shown that chromosome segregation and cytokinesis in bacteria are strikingly similar to what occurs in the

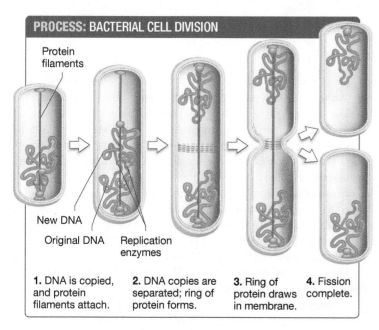

PROCESS: BACTERIAL CELL DIVISION

Protein filaments

New DNA

Original DNA   Replication enzymes

1. DNA is copied, and protein filaments attach.

2. DNA copies are separated; ring of protein forms.

3. Ring of protein draws in membrane.

4. Fission complete.

Figure 12.9 Bacterial Cells Divide but Do Not Undergo Mitosis.

eukaryotic M phase (**Figure 12.9**). As the bacterial chromosome is being replicated, protein filaments attach to the copies and separate them.

Once the chromosome copies have been moved to opposite sides of the cell, other filaments, made of proteins similar to eukaryotic tubulin, divide the cytoplasm. These filaments attach to the plasma membrane and form a ring between the chromosome copies. A signal from the cell causes the filaments to draw in the membrane, eventually cleaving the parent cell into two genetically identical cells.

Having explored what occurs during cell division, let's focus on how it is controlled in eukaryotes. When does a eukaryotic cell divide, and when does it stop dividing?

CHECK YOUR UNDERSTANDING

If you understand that ...

- At the start of mitosis, microtubules form a spindle that moves replicated chromosomes to the metaphase plate.
- During anaphase, chromatids are separated to form daughter chromosomes, which move to opposite poles of the spindle.
- Cytokinesis partitions the nuclei and cytoplasmic components into two daughter cells that are genetically identical to each other and the parent cell.

✔ **You should be able to ...**

1. Draw the mitotic spindle for an animal cell that has two chromosomes in metaphase. Label the sister chromatids, kinetochores, centrosomes, and three types of microtubules.
2. Use your drawing to explain the two types of movement that are responsible for separating daughter chromosomes during anaphase.
3. Compare and contrast cytokinesis in plant and animal cells.

Answers are available in Appendix A.

12.3 Control of the Cell Cycle

Although the events of mitosis are similar in all eukaryotes, control of the cell cycle often varies—even among cells in the same organism. In humans, for example, intestinal cells routinely divide twice a day to replace tissue that is lost during digestion, whereas mature nerve and muscle cells do not divide at all.

Most of these differences are due to variation in the length of G_1 phase. In rapidly dividing cells, G_1 is essentially eliminated. Most nondividing cells, in contrast, are permanently stuck in G_1. Researchers refer to this arrested state as the G_0 state, or simply "G zero." Nerve cells, muscle cells, and many other cell types enter G_0 once they have matured.

A cell's division rate can also vary in response to changing conditions. For example, human liver cells normally divide about once per year. But if part of the liver is damaged or lost, the remaining cells divide every one or two days until repair is accomplished. Cells of unicellular eukaryotes, such as yeasts and some protists, divide rapidly only if the environment is rich in nutrients; otherwise, they enter G_0.

To explain these differences, biologists hypothesized that the cell cycle must be regulated in some way. Cell-cycle control is now the most prominent issue in research on cell division—partly because defects in control can lead to uncontrolled cell growth and cancer.

The Discovery of Cell-Cycle Regulatory Molecules

The first solid evidence for cell-cycle control molecules came to light in 1970. Researchers found that when they fused cells that were in different stages of the cell cycle, forming a single cell with two nuclei, one of the nuclei changed phases. For example, when a cell in M phase was fused with one in interphase, the nucleus of the interphase cell immediately initiated mitosis, even if its chromosomes had not been replicated.

To explain these results, the researchers hypothesized that the cytoplasm of M-phase cells contains a regulatory molecule that induces interphase cells to enter M phase. But cell-fusion experiments were difficult to control and didn't explain whether the nucleus or the cytoplasm was responsible for the induction. To address this issue, they turned to the South African clawed frog, *Xenopus laevis*.

As an egg of these frogs matures, it changes from a cell called an immature oocyte, which is arrested in G_2, to a mature egg that is arrested in M phase. The large size of these cells—more than 1 mm in diameter—makes them relatively easy to manipulate. Using extremely fine pipets, researchers could specifically examine the effects of the cytoplasm by removing a sample from an immature oocyte or mature egg and injecting it into an oocyte arrested in G_2.

When biologists purified cytoplasm from M-phase frog eggs and injected it into the cytoplasm of frog oocytes arrested in G_2, the oocytes immediately entered M phase (see **Figure 12.10** on page 264). But when the same experiment was done using the cytoplasm from immature oocytes, the cells remained in the G_2 phase. The researchers concluded that the cytoplasm of M-phase cells—but not the cytoplasm of interphase cells—contains a factor that drives immature oocytes into M phase to complete their maturation.

The factor that initiates M-phase in oocytes was purified and is now called **M phase–promoting factor,** or **MPF.** Subsequent experiments showed that MPF induces M phase in all eukaryotes. For example, injecting M-phase cytoplasm from mammalian cells into immature frog oocytes results in egg maturation, and human MPF can trigger M phase in yeast cells.

RESEARCH

QUESTION: Is M phase controlled by regulatory molecules in the cytoplasm?

HYPOTHESIS: Cytoplasmic regulatory molecules control entry into M phase.

NULL HYPOTHESIS: M-phase regulatory molecules are not in the cytoplasm or do not exist.

EXPERIMENTAL SETUP:

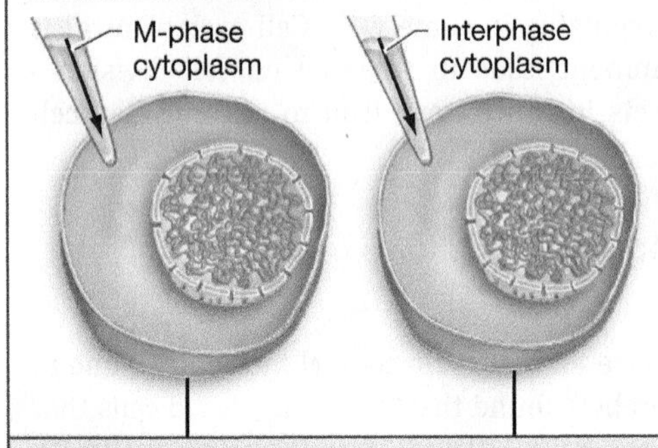

M-phase cytoplasm

Interphase cytoplasm

Microinject cytoplasm from M-phase cell into one frog oocyte and cytoplasm from interphase cell into another frog oocyte.

PREDICTION: Only the oocyte injected with M-phase cytoplasm will begin M phase.

PREDICTION OF NULL HYPOTHESIS: Neither oocyte will begin M phase.

RESULTS:

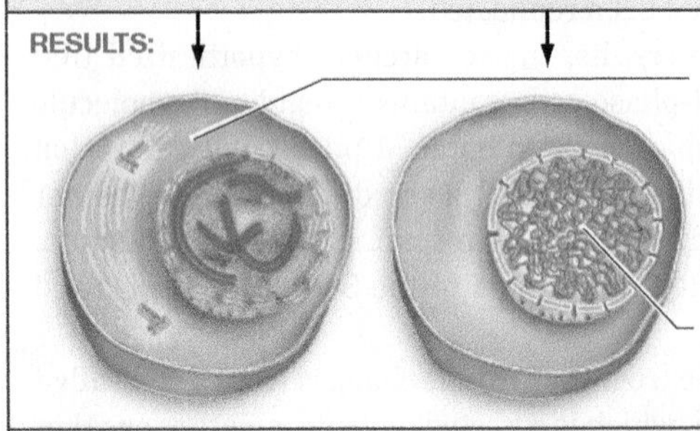

Oocyte is driven into M phase (nuclear envelope begins to break down, spindle apparatus forms).

Oocyte remains in G_2 phase.

CONCLUSION: M-phase cytoplasm contains a regulatory molecule that induces M phase in interphase cells.

Figure 12.10 Experimental Evidence for Cell-Cycle Control Molecules. When the cytoplasm from M-phase cells is microinjected into cells in interphase, the interphase chromosomes condense, and the cells begin M phase.

SOURCE: Masui, Y., and C. L. Markert. 1971. Cytoplasmic control of nuclear behavior during meiotic maturation of frog oocytes. *Journal of Experimental Zoology* 177: 129–145.

✔ **PROCESS OF SCIENCE** This experiment was done using samples taken from the cytoplasm of cells. What could the investigators do to determine whether the regulatory molecule was present in the cytosol or in a cytoplasmic organelle (see **BioSkills 7**)?

MPF appears to be a general signal that says "Start M phase." How does it work?

MPF Contains a Protein Kinase and a Cyclin MPF is made up of two distinct polypeptide subunits. One subunit is a protein kinase—an enzyme that catalyzes the transfer of a phosphate group from ATP to a target protein. Recall that phosphorylation may activate or inactivate the function of proteins by changing their shape (Chapter 8). As a result, kinases frequently act as regulatory proteins in the cell.

These observations suggested that MPF phosphorylates proteins that trigger the onset of M phase. But research showed that the concentration of the protein kinase is more or less constant throughout the cell cycle. How can MPF trigger M phase if the protein kinase subunit is always present?

The answer lies in the second MPF subunit, which belongs to a family of proteins called **cyclins.** Cyclins got their name because their concentrations fluctuate throughout the cell cycle.

As **Figure 12.11** shows, the concentration of the cyclin associated with MPF builds during interphase and peaks in M phase. The timing of this increase is important because the protein kinase subunit in MPF is functional only when it is bound to the cyclin subunit. As a result, the protein kinase subunit of MPF is called a **cyclin-dependent kinase,** or **Cdk.**

To summarize, MPF is a dimer consisting of a cyclin and a cyclin-dependent kinase. The cyclin subunit regulates the formation of the MPF dimer; the kinase subunit catalyzes the phosphorylation of other proteins to start M phase.

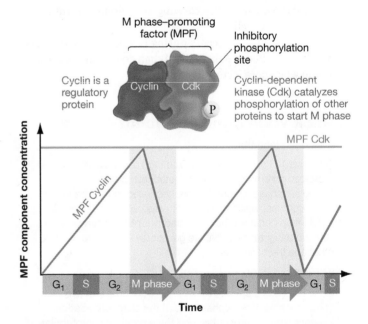

Figure 12.11 Cyclin Concentration Regulates the Concentration of the MPF Dimer. Cyclin concentrations fluctuate in dividing cells, reaching a peak in M phase. The activity of MPF, shown in the blue shaded areas, requires both cyclin and Cdk components.

✔ In this figure, the concentration of cyclin declines rapidly during M phase. Why do you think this decline is important?

How Is MPF Turned On? According to Figure 12.11, the concentration of cyclin builds up steadily during interphase. Why doesn't the resulting increase in the concentration of MPF trigger the onset of M phase earlier in the cell cycle?

The answer is that the activity of MPF's Cdk subunit is further regulated by two phosphorylation sites on the subunit. Phosphorylation of one site activates the kinase, but phosphorylation of the second site inhibits the kinase. Both sites are phosphorylated after cyclin binds to the Cdk subunit. This allows the concentration of the dimer to increase without prematurely starting M phase. Late in G_2 phase, however, an enzyme removes the inhibitory phosphate. This dephosphorylation reaction, coupled with the addition of the activating phosphate, changes the Cdk's shape in a way that turns on its kinase activity.

Once MPF is active, it triggers a chain of events. Although the exact mechanisms involved are still under investigation, the result is that chromosomes begin to condense and the spindle apparatus starts to form. In this way, MPF triggers the onset of M phase.

How Is MPF Turned Off? During anaphase, an enzyme complex begins degrading MPF's cyclin subunit, triggering a chain of events that leads to the deactivation of MPF.

MPF deactivation illustrates two key concepts about regulatory systems in cells:

- **Negative feedback** occurs when a process is slowed or shut down by one of its products. Thermostats shut down furnaces when temperatures are high; enzymes in glycolysis are inhibited by ATP (see Chapter 9); MPF is turned off by an enzyme complex that is activated by events in mitosis.

- Destroying specific proteins is a common way to control cell processes. In the case of MPF, the enzyme complex that is activated in anaphase attaches small proteins called ubiquitins to MPF's cyclin subunit. This marks the subunit for destruction by a protein complex known as the proteasome.

In response to MPF activity, then, the concentration of cyclin declines rapidly. It slowly builds up again during interphase.

✔ If you understand this aspect of cell-cycle regulation, you should be able to explain the relationship between MPF and cyclin, Cdk, and the enzymes that phosphorylate MPF, dephosphorylate MPF, and degrade cyclin.

Cell-Cycle Checkpoints Can Arrest the Cell Cycle

The dramatic changes in cyclin concentration and Cdk activity drive the ordered events of the cell cycle. These events are occurring in your body right now. Over a 24-hour period, you swallow millions of cheek cells and lose millions of cells from your intestinal lining as waste. To replace them, other cells in your cheek and intestinal tissue are making and degrading cyclin and pushing themselves through the cell cycle.

MPF is only one of many protein complexes involved in regulating the cell cycle, however. A different cyclin complex triggers the passage from G_1 phase into S phase, and several regulatory molecules hold cells in particular stages.

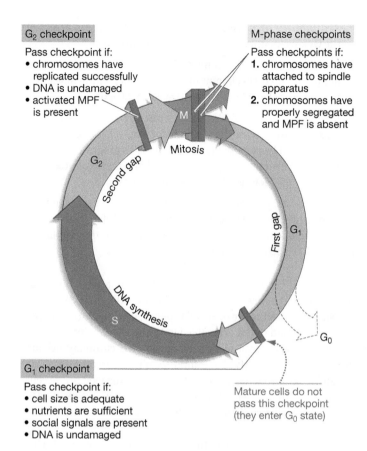

Figure 12.12 **The Four Cell-Cycle Checkpoints.**

To make sense of these observations, Leland Hartwell and Ted Weinert introduced the concept of **cell-cycle checkpoints.** A cell-cycle checkpoint is a critical point in the cell cycle that is regulated.

Hartwell and Weinert identified checkpoints by analyzing yeast cells with defects in the cell cycle. The defective cells kept dividing under culture conditions that caused normal cells to stop dividing, because the defective cells lacked a specific checkpoint. In multicellular organisms, cells that keep dividing in this way may form a mass of cells called a **tumor.**

There are distinct checkpoints in three of the four phases of the cell cycle (**Figure 12.12**). In effect, interactions among regulatory molecules at each checkpoint allow a cell to "decide" whether to proceed with division or not. If these regulatory molecules are defective, the checkpoint may fail and cells may start dividing in an uncontrolled fashion.

G_1 Checkpoint The first cell-cycle checkpoint occurs late in G_1 phase. For most cells, this checkpoint is the most important in establishing whether the cell will continue through the cycle and divide, or exit the cycle and enter G_0. What factors are important in determining whether a cell passes the G_1 checkpoint?

- **Size** Because a cell must reach a certain size before its daughter cells will be large enough to function normally, biologists hypothesize that some mechanism exists to arrest the cell cycle if the cell is too small.

- **Availability of nutrients** Unicellular organisms arrest at the G_1 checkpoint if nutrient conditions are poor.

- **Social signals** Cells in multicellular organisms pass (or do not pass) the G_1 checkpoint in response to signaling molecules from other cells, which are termed social signals.

- **Damage to DNA** If DNA is physically damaged, the protein **p53** activates genes that either stop the cell cycle until the damage can be repaired or cause the cell's programmed, controlled destruction—a phenomenon known as **apoptosis.** In this way, p53 acts as a brake on the cell cycle.

If "brake" molecules such as p53 are defective, damaged DNA remains unrepaired. Damage in genes that regulate cell growth can lead to uncontrolled cell division. Consequently, regulatory proteins like p53 are called **tumor suppressors.**

G_2 Checkpoint The second checkpoint occurs after S phase, at the boundary between the G_2 and M phases. Because MPF is the key signal triggering the onset of M phase, investigators were not surprised to find that it is involved in the G_2 checkpoint.

Data suggest that if DNA is damaged or if chromosomes are not replicated correctly, the inhibitory phosphate on MPF's Cdk subunit is not removed. As a result, MPF is not turned on, and cells remain in G_2 phase. Cells at the G_2 checkpoint may also respond to signals from other cells and to internal signals relating to cell size.

M-Phase Checkpoints The final two checkpoints occur during mitosis. The first regulates the transition from metaphase to anaphase. This checkpoint ensures that the sister chromatids do not split until all kinetochores are attached properly to the spindle apparatus. If the metaphase checkpoint did not exist, some chromosomes might not separate correctly, and daughter cells would receive either too many or too few chromosomes.

The second checkpoint regulates the transition from anaphase to telophase. To exit M phase and progress into G_1 phase, cells must degrade all of their cyclins and thus turn off MPF activity. The enzymes responsible for degrading cyclins are activated only when all the chromosomes have been properly separated. If chromosomes do not fully separate during anaphase, the remaining MPF activity will prevent the cell from entering telophase and undergoing cytokinesis. If cells are arrested by either of these two checkpoints, they will remain in M phase.

To summarize, the four cell-cycle checkpoints have the same purpose: They prevent the division of cells that are damaged or that have other problems. The G_1 checkpoint also prevents mature cells that are in the G_0 state from dividing.

Understanding cell-cycle regulation is fundamental. If one of the checkpoints fails, the affected cells may begin dividing in an uncontrolled fashion. For a multicellular organism as a whole, the consequences of uncontrolled cell division may be dire: cancer.

12.4 Cancer: Out-of-Control Cell Division

Forty percent of American men and women will develop cancer during their lifetime. In the United States, one in four of all deaths is from cancer. It is the second leading cause of death, exceeded only by heart disease.

Cancer is a general term for disease caused by cells that divide in an uncontrolled fashion, invade nearby tissues, and spread to other sites in the body. Cancerous cells cause disease because they use nutrients and space needed by normal cells and disrupt the function of normal tissues.

Humans suffer from at least 200 types of cancer. Stated another way, cancer is not a single illness but a complex family of diseases that affect an array of organs, including the breast, colon, brain, lung, and skin (**Figure 12.13**). In addition, several types of cancer can affect the same organ. Skin cancers, for example, come in multiple forms.

Although cancers vary in time of onset, growth rate, lethality, and cause, they have a unifying feature: Cancers arise from cells in which cell-cycle checkpoints have failed.

Cancerous cells have two types of defects related to cell division: **(1)** defects that activate the proteins required for cell growth when they shouldn't be active, and **(2)** defects that prevent tumor suppressor genes from shutting down the cell cycle.

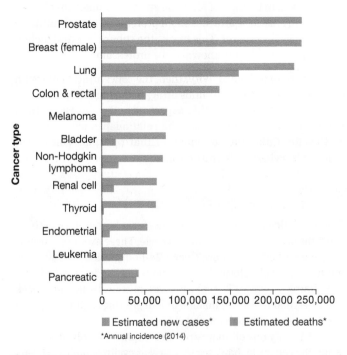

Figure 12.13 Cancers Vary in Type and Lethality.

DATA: The website of the National Cancer Institute (http://www.cancer.gov), Common Cancer Statistics, December 2014.

For example, the protein Ras is a key component in signal transduction systems—including phosphorylation cascades that trigger cell growth (see Chapter 11). Many cancers have defective forms of Ras that do not become inactivated. Instead, the defective Ras constantly sends signals that trigger mitosis and cell division.

Likewise, a large percentage of cancers have defective forms of the tumor suppressor protein p53. Instead of being arrested or destroyed, cells with damaged DNA are allowed to continue dividing.

Let's review the general characteristics of cancer and then explore how regulatory mechanisms become defective.

Properties of Cancer Cells

When even a single cell in a multicellular organism begins to divide in an uncontrolled fashion, a mass of cells called a tumor may result. Some tumors can be surgically removed without damage to the affected organ. Often, though, tumor removal doesn't cure cancer. Why?

In addition to uncontrolled replication, cancer cells are invasive—meaning that they are able to spread to adjacent tissues and throughout the body via the bloodstream or the lymphatic vessels (introduced in Chapter 42), which collect excess fluid from tissues and return it to the bloodstream.

Invasiveness is a defining feature of a **malignant tumor**—one that is cancerous. Masses of noninvasive cells are non-cancerous and form **benign tumors.** Some benign tumors are largely harmless. Others grow quickly and can cause problems if they are located in the brain or other sensitive parts of the body.

Cells in a tumor become cancerous if they gain the ability to detach from the tumor and invade other tissues. By spreading from the primary tumor site, cancer cells can establish secondary tumors elsewhere in the body (**Figure 12.14**). This process is called **metastasis.**

If metastasis has occurred by the time the original tumor is detected, secondary tumors may have already formed and surgical removal of the primary tumor will not lead to a cure. This is why early detection is the key to treating cancer most effectively.

Cancer Involves Loss of Cell-Cycle Control

What causes cancer at the molecular level? Recall that when many cells mature, they enter the G_0 state—meaning their cell cycle is arrested at the G_1 checkpoint. In contrast, cells that do pass through the G_1 checkpoint are irreversibly committed to replicating their DNA and entering G_2.

Based on this observation, biologists hypothesize that many types of cancer involve defects in the G_1 checkpoint. To understand the molecular nature of the disease, then, researchers have focused on understanding the normal mechanisms that operate at that checkpoint. Cancer research and research on the normal cell cycle have become two sides of the same coin.

Social Control   In unicellular eukaryotes, passage through the G_1 checkpoint is thought to depend primarily on cell size and the availability of nutrients. If nutrients are plentiful, cells grow, pass through the checkpoint, and divide rapidly.

(a) Benign tumor

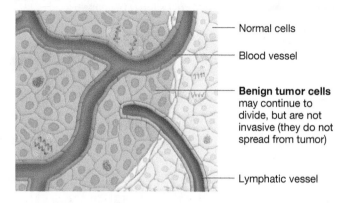

- Normal cells
- Blood vessel
- **Benign tumor cells** may continue to divide, but are not invasive (they do not spread from tumor)
- Lymphatic vessel

(b) Malignant tumor

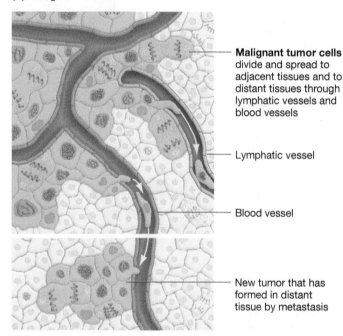

- **Malignant tumor cells** divide and spread to adjacent tissues and to distant tissues through lymphatic vessels and blood vessels
- Lymphatic vessel
- Blood vessel
- New tumor that has formed in distant tissue by metastasis

Figure 12.14 **Cancers Spread to New Locations in the Body.** **(a)** Benign tumors grow in a single location. **(b)** Malignant tumors are invasive and may be metastatic—meaning that their cells can spread to distant parts of the body and initiate new tumors. Malignant tumors cause cancer.

In multicellular organisms, however, cells divide in response to signals from other cells. Biologists refer to this as *social control* over cell division. The general idea is that individual cells are allowed to divide only when it is in the best interests of the organism as a whole.

Social control of the cell cycle is based on **growth factors**—polypeptides or small proteins that stimulate cell division. Many growth factors were discovered by researchers who were trying to grow cells in culture. When isolated mammalian cells were placed in a culture flask and provided with adequate nutrients, they arrested in G_1 phase. The cells began to grow again only when biologists added **serum**—the liquid portion of blood that remains after blood cells and cell fragments have been removed. Researchers identified growth factors as the components in the

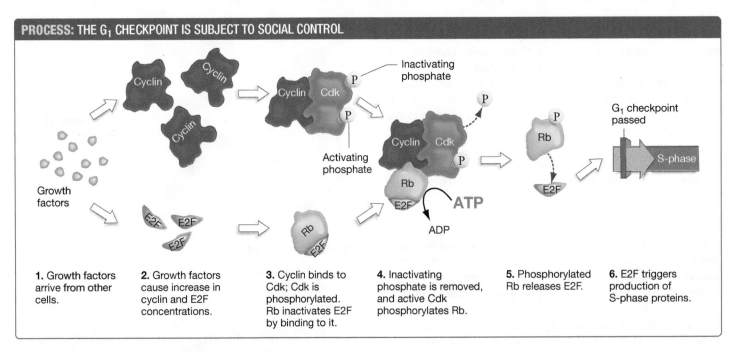

Figure 12.15 Growth Factors Move Cells through the G₁ Checkpoint.

serum that were responsible for allowing cells to pass through the G₁ checkpoint.

Cancer cells are an exception. They can often be grown successfully in culture without externally supplied growth factors. This observation suggests that the normal social controls on the G₁ checkpoint have broken down in cancer cells.

How Does the G₁ Checkpoint Work?

In G₀ cells, the arrival of growth factors stimulates the production of a key regulatory protein called E2F. When E2F is activated, it triggers the expression of genes required for S phase.

When E2F is first produced, however, its activity is blocked by a tumor suppressor protein called Rb. **Rb protein** is one of the key molecules that enforces the G₁ checkpoint. It is called Rb because a nonfunctional version was first discovered in children with **retinoblastoma**, a cancer in the light-sensing tissue, or retina, of the eye.

When E2F is bound to Rb, E2F is in the "off" position—it can't activate the genes required for S phase. As long as Rb stays bound to E2F, the cell remains in G₀. But as **Figure 12.15** shows, the situation changes dramatically if growth factors continue to arrive. To understand how growth factors affect E2F activity, think back to how cells progress from G₂ to M phase. As in passage from G₂ to M phase, phosphorylation of proteins catalyzed by an activated cyclin–Cdk dimer permits passage from G₁ to S.

Step 1 Growth factors arrive from other cells.

Step 2 The growth factors stimulate the production of E2F and of G₁ cyclins, which are different from those used in MPF.

Step 3 Rb binds to E2F, inactivating it. The G₁ cyclins begin forming cyclin–Cdk dimers, which are initially phosphorylated and inactive similar to the MPF in M phase.

Step 4 When dephosphorylation turns on the G₁ cyclin–Cdk complexes, they catalyze the phosphorylation of Rb.

Step 5 The phosphorylated Rb changes shape and releases E2F.

Step 6 The unbound E2F is free to activate its target genes. Production of S-phase proteins gets S phase under way.

In this way, growth factors function as a social signal that says, "It's OK to override Rb. Go ahead and pass the G₁ checkpoint and divide."

How Do Social Controls and Cell-Cycle Checkpoints Fail?

Cells can become cancerous when social controls fail—meaning, when cells begin dividing in the absence of the go-ahead signal from growth factors. One of two things can go wrong: The G₁ cyclin is overproduced, or Rb is defective.

When G₁ cyclins are overproduced and stay at high concentrations, they bind to the Cdk and help activate it so that Rb is continuously phosphorylated and unable to bind to E2F. The pool of free E2F sends the cell into S phase.

What happens if Rb is defective? When Rb is missing or mutated so it does not bind normally to E2F, any E2F that is present will activate the genes that push the cell into S phase. The loss of Rb activity, either by mutation or keeping it phosphorylated by overproduction of G₁ cyclins, leads to uncontrolled cell division.

Because cancer is a family of diseases with a complex and highly variable molecular basis, there will be no "magic bullet," or single therapy, that cures all forms of the illness. Still, recent progress in understanding the cell cycle and the molecular basis of cancer has been dramatic, and cancer prevention and early detection programs are increasingly effective. The prognosis for many cancer patients is remarkably better now than it was even a few years ago. Thanks to research, almost all of us know someone who is a cancer survivor.

12.1 How Do Cells Replicate?

- For a cell to replicate, it must copy its chromosomes, separate the copies, and divide the cytoplasm to generate daughter cells that have the same chromosomal complement as the parent cell.

- Eukaryotic cells divide by cycling between interphase and M phase.

- Interphase consists of S phase, when chromosomes replicate, and the G_1 and G_2 phases, when cells grow and prepare for division.

- M phase consists of mitosis or meiosis, when chromosomes separate, and cytokinesis, when the parent cell divides into two daughter cells.

12.2 What Happens during M Phase?

- Mitosis can be described as a sequence of five phases:

  1. **Prophase** Chromosomes condense. The spindle apparatus begins to form, and polar microtubules overlap each other.

  2. **Prometaphase** In cells of many organisms, the nuclear envelope disintegrates. Microtubules attach to the kinetochores of chromosomes, which begin moving to the middle of the spindle.

  3. **Metaphase** All the chromosomes are positioned in the middle of the spindle. The spindle is anchored to the plasma membrane by astral microtubules.

  4. **Anaphase** Sister chromatids are pulled apart by the disassembly of kinetochore microtubules at the kinetochore. The separated chromatids are now daughter chromosomes. The spindle poles are moved farther apart to fully separate the replicated chromosomes.

  5. **Telophase** Daughter chromosomes are fully separated and are clustered at opposite poles of the spindle. A nuclear envelope forms around each set, and the chromosomes de-condense.

- In most cells, mitosis is followed by cytokinesis—division of the cytoplasm to form two daughter cells.

12.3 Control of the Cell Cycle

- The onset of the S and M phases is primarily determined by the activity of protein complexes consisting of a cyclin and a cyclin-dependent kinase (Cdk).

- Cyclin concentrations oscillate during the cell cycle, regulating the formation of the complexes. The activity of the Cdk is further regulated by addition of a phosphate in its activating site and removal of one from its inhibitory site.

- Progression through the cell cycle is controlled by checkpoints in three phases.

  1. The G_1 checkpoint regulates progress based on nutrient availability, cell size, DNA damage, and social signals.

  2. The G_2 checkpoint delays progress until chromosome replication is complete and any damaged DNA present is repaired.

  3. The two M-phase checkpoints **(1)** delay anaphase until all chromosomes are correctly attached to the spindle apparatus and **(2)** delay the onset of cytokinesis and G_1 until all chromosomes have been properly partitioned.

12.4 Cancer: Out-of-Control Cell Division

- Cancer is characterized by **(1)** loss of control at the G_1 checkpoint, resulting in cells that divide in an uncontrolled fashion; and **(2)** metastasis, or the ability of tumor cells to spread throughout the body.

- The G_1 checkpoint depends in part on Rb protein, which prevents progression to S phase, and G_1 cyclin–Cdk complexes, which trigger progression to S phase. Defects in Rb and G_1 cyclin are common in cancer.

Answers are available in Appendix A

✔ TEST YOUR KNOWLEDGE

1. Which statement about the daughter cells following mitosis and cytokinesis is correct?
   a. They are genetically different from each other and from the parent cell.
   b. They are genetically identical to each other and to the parent cell.
   c. They are genetically identical to each other but different from the parent cell.
   d. Only one of the two daughter cells is genetically identical to the parent cell.

2. After S phase, what comprises a single chromosome?
   a. two daughter chromosomes
   b. a double-stranded DNA molecule
   c. two single-stranded DNA molecules
   d. two sister chromatids

3. Progression through the cell cycle is regulated by oscillations in the concentration of which type of molecule?
   a. p53, Rb, and other tumor suppressors
   b. receptor tyrosine kinases
   c. cyclins
   d. cyclin-dependent kinases

4. What major events occur during anaphase of mitosis?

✔ TEST YOUR UNDERSTANDING

5. Identify at least two events in the cell cycle that must be completed successfully for daughter cells to share an identical complement of chromosomes.

6. What evidence suggests that during anaphase, kinetochore microtubules shorten at the kinetochore?

7. Evaluate each of the following defects. Which could lead to uncontrolled growth in cancer?

   True/False: The overexpression of MPF activity.
   True/False: A nonfunctional Rb protein.
   True/False: The overexpression of G1 cyclin.
   True/False: A nonfunctional E2F protein.

8. Compare and contrast the effects of removing growth factors from asynchronous cultures of human cells that are normal and those that are cancerous.

✔ TEST YOUR PROBLEM-SOLVING SKILLS

9. QUANTITATIVE A particular cell type spends 4 hours in G_1 phase, 2 hours in S phase, 2 hours in G_2 phase, and 30 minutes in M phase. If a pulse–chase experiment were performed with radioactive thymidine on an asynchronous culture of such cells, what percentage of mitotic cells would be radiolabeled 9 hours after the pulse?

a. 0 percent   **c.** 75 percent
b. 50 percent   **d.** 100 percent

10. When a fruit fly embryo first begins to develop, a large cell is generated that contains over 8000 genetically identical nuclei. What is most likely responsible for this result?

✔ PUT IT ALL TOGETHER: Case Study

What are the molecular targets of anticancer drugs?

The bark of the Pacific yew tree (*Taxus brevifolia*) was the original source of one of the most effective drugs for treating tumors of the breast, lung, and other sites. Taxol, a chemical extracted from this bark, kills actively replicating cells by inhibiting the depolymerization of microtubules. Why are microtubules good targets for killing cancerous cells?

11. During what phases in the cell cycle would you expect there to be large changes in the polymerization or depolymerization of microtubules? Why are these changes necessary?

12. When actively growing cells are treated with Taxol, they often are unable to complete the cell cycle. Based on what you have learned about cell-cycle checkpoints, which checkpoint likely causes these cells to arrest? Explain your reasoning.

13. QUANTITATIVE Suppose you performed the pulse–chase experiment illustrated in Figure 12.2 but included Taxol in

the medium during the chase. Draw a new line on the graph to show the results you would expect, and explain why you would expect them.

14. PROCESS OF SCIENCE Aggressive forms of breast cancer are resistant to Taxol chemotherapy. In these cancers, the gene encoding a protein called stathmin is overexpressed. To investigate the mechanism of action of stathmin, investigators measured tumor volume over time in mice with aggressive cancers under three conditions: no treatment (control), Taxol treatment, and Taxol treatment with stathmin gene expression turned off (Taxol + Δ stathmin). Their results are shown below. Use these results to hypothesize how the stathmin protein affects microtubule stability.

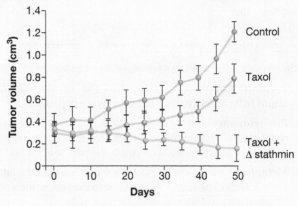

Source: C. Miceli et al. 2013. *Cancer Gene Therapy* 20: 298–307.

15. In normal cells, stathmin is inactivated by phosphorylation at the start of M phase. Phosphatases remove these phosphates as the cell transitions from M phase to G_1. What enzyme is likely to be responsible for phosphorylating stathmin during M phase?

16. Inhibiting expression of the stathmin gene arrests cells in M phase and is being investigated as an alternative therapy for treating cancer. What additional genes could be therapeutic targets that, when inactivated, would arrest cancerous cells in G_1 phase?

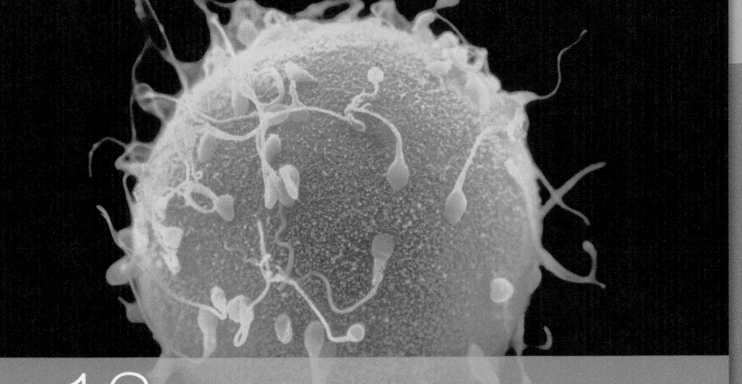

13 Meiosis

Scanning electron micrograph (with color added) showing human sperm attempting to enter a human egg. This chapter introduces the type of nuclear division called meiosis, which in animals occurs before sperm and eggs are formed.

In this chapter you will learn how

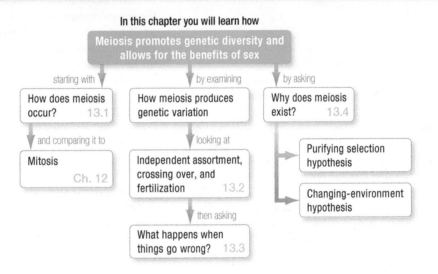

Meiosis promotes genetic diversity and allows for the benefits of sex

starting with → How does meiosis occur?   13.1

and comparing it to → Mitosis   Ch. 12

by examining → How meiosis produces genetic variation

looking at → Independent assortment, crossing over, and fertilization   13.2

then asking → What happens when things go wrong?   13.3

by asking → Why does meiosis exist?   13.4

→ Purifying selection hypothesis

→ Changing-environment hypothesis

This chapter is part of the Big Picture. See how on pages 396–397.

Why sex?

Simple questions—such as why sexual reproduction exists—are sometimes the best for getting to the heart of things. This chapter asks what sexual reproduction is and why some organisms employ it. The focus here is on how organisms reproduce, or replicate—one of the five fundamental attributes of life introduced in Chapter 1.

For centuries people have known that during sexual reproduction, a male reproductive cell—a **sperm**—and a female reproductive cell—an **egg**—unite in a process called **fertilization** to form a new individual. The first biologists to observe fertilization studied the large, translucent eggs of sea urchins. Thanks to the semitransparency of these eggs, researchers were able to see the nuclei of a sperm and an egg fuse.

When these observations were published in 1876, they raised an important question, because biologists had already established that the number of chromosomes is constant from cell to cell within a multicellular organism. How could the chromosomes from a sperm cell and an egg cell combine, but form an offspring that has the same chromosome number as in its mother and its father individually? A hint at the answer came in 1883 with the observation that cells in the body of roundworms of the genus *Ascaris* have four chromosomes, while their sperm and egg nuclei each have only two chromosomes.

Four years later, German biologist August Weismann formally proposed a hypothesis to explain the riddle: During the formation of **gametes**—reproductive cells such as sperm and eggs—some type of cell division must take place that leads to a reduction in chromosome number. Specifically, if the sperm and egg contribute an equal number of chromosomes to the fertilized egg, Weismann reasoned that they must each contain half of the usual number of chromosomes. In this way, when sperm and egg combine, the resulting cell has the same chromosome number as its mother's cells and its father's cells have.

In the decades that followed, biologists confirmed this hypothesis by observing gamete formation in a wide variety of plant and animal species. Eventually this form of cell division came to be called meiosis (literally, "lessening-act"). **Meiosis** is nuclear division that leads to a halving of chromosome number and ultimately to the production of sperm and egg. (Meiosis is an important part of The Big Picture of Genetic Information on pages 396–397.) To a biologist, asking "Why sex?" is equivalent to asking "Why meiosis?" Let's delve in by first looking at how meiosis happens.

13.1 How Does Meiosis Occur?

To understand meiosis, it is critical to grasp some key ideas about chromosomes. For example, when cell biologists began to study the cell divisions that lead to gamete formation, they made an important observation: Each organism has a characteristic number of chromosomes.

Consider the drawings in **Figure 13.1**, based on research begun by the American cell biologist Nettie Maria Stevens in 1906. Stevens was the first person to study chromosomes during the cell divisions leading up to the formation of egg and sperm. Using the fruit fly *Drosophila melanogaster,* a major model organism (see BioSkills 13), she identified a total of eight chromosomes in *Drosophila* cells. Chromosome number varies widely between species—your cells have 46 chromosomes, whereas some ferns have over 1000.

Chromosomes Come in Distinct Sizes and Shapes

Stevens found that each *Drosophila* cell has eight chromosomes, but just five distinct types, distinguished by their size and shape. Three of these chromosome types always occurred in pairs and are labeled chromosomes 2–4 in Figure 13.1. In males, Stevens observed that two chromosomes, known as the X and the Y chromosomes, were unpaired. In females, Stevens found that there was a pair of X chromosomes and no Y chromosome. This is the same situation as in mammals. The X and Y chromosomes are called **sex chromosomes** and are associated with an individual's sex. Any chromosomes other than sex chromosomes, such as chromosomes 2–4 in *Drosophila*, are **autosomes.**

The terminology for chromosomes and chromosome number is some of the trickiest in all of biology. You'll need to pay careful attention. Chromosomes that are the same size and shape are called **homologous chromosomes,** or **homologs** ("same proportion"), and the pair is called a **homologous pair.** Homologous pairs also contain the same genes in the same positions along the chromosomes. Typically, however, the two chromosomes are *not* identical. To understand how this could be, you need to know the difference between a gene and an allele.

A **gene** is a segment of DNA, found at a specific place on a chromosome, that influences a hereditary trait. For example, each copy of chromosome 2 in *Drosophila* carries many different genes, including one that influences eye color. However, this gene comes in two different forms—one that contributes to normal-colored red eyes and another that can result in purple eyes. Biologists use the term **allele** to denote different forms of a gene. In the case of the eye-color gene on chromosome 2, one homolog may carry the allele associated with red eyes whereas the other homolog may carry the allele associated with purple eyes (**Figure 13.2**). To sum up, homologous chromosomes are not identical, even though they carry the same genes in the same positions, because each homolog may contain different alleles of any particular gene.

Another thing to watch for as you develop the vocabulary of meiosis and genetics is the sometimes imprecise use of terms by both biologists and the media. This is especially true of the words "gene" and "allele." For instance, you might read about the discovery of a new breast cancer gene. What's really meant is that a particular allele of a gene has been discovered. The normal function of the gene isn't to cause breast cancer. For this reason, you'll often need to pay attention to know whether the discussion really is about an allele or a gene.

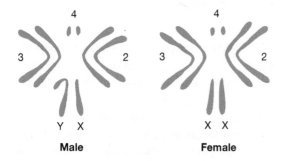

Male   **Female**

Figure 13.1 Cells Contain Different Types of Chromosomes That Often Come in Pairs. Numbers and letters designate the types of *Drosophila* chromosomes.

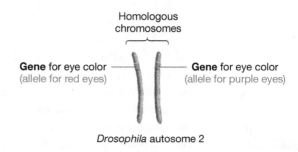

Drosophila autosome 2

Figure 13.2 Homologous Chromosomes May Contain Different Alleles of the Same Gene. The homologs of *Drosophila* chromosome 2 are shown; the location of only one of many genes is indicated.

The Concept of Ploidy

By identifying the number and types of chromosomes present in a *Drosophila* cell, Stevens had determined the *Drosophila* **karyotype.** As more karyotypes were determined, cell biologists realized that, like *Drosophila*, the vast majority of plants and animals have more than one of each type of chromosome.

Insects, humans, oak trees, and other organisms that have two versions (homologs) of each type of chromosome are called **diploid** ("double-form"). Diploid organisms have two alleles of each gene. One allele is carried on each of the homologs. Recall that these alleles may be identical or they may be different, depending on the individual. Although a diploid individual can carry only two different alleles of a gene, there can be many different alleles in a population.

Bacteria, archaea, and many algae and fungi have cells that contain just one of each type of chromosome. These cells and organisms are called **haploid** ("single-form"). Because haploid organisms have only one copy of each chromosome, an individual has just one allele of each gene.

Biologists use a compact notation to indicate the number of chromosomes and chromosome sets in a particular organism or type of cell:

- The letter *n* stands for the number of *distinct types* of chromosomes in a given cell and is called the **haploid number.** If sex chromosomes are present, they are counted as a single type in the haploid number. In humans, *n* is 23.

- To indicate the number of complete chromosome sets when it is greater than one, a number is placed before the *n*: 2*n*, or 3*n*, and so on.

The number of chromosome sets is termed the cell's **ploidy.** Diploid cells or species are designated 2*n*, because two chromosomes of each type are present—one from each parent. A **maternal chromosome** comes from the mother, and a **paternal chromosome** comes from the father. Humans are diploid, so for us 2*n* = 46. Haploid cells or species are labeled simply *n*, because they have just one set of chromosomes—no homologs are present. In haploid cells, the number 1 in front of *n* is implied and is not written out.

To summarize, the haploid number *n* indicates the number of distinct types of chromosomes present. In contrast, a cell's ploidy (*n*, 2*n*, 3*n*, etc.) indicates the number of each type of chromosome present. Stating a cell's ploidy is the same as stating the number of haploid chromosome sets present. ✔ If you understand how these terms relate, you should be able to state the haploid number, ploidy, and total number of chromosomes present in a male *Drosophila*.

Later work revealed that it is common for species—particularly certain plants, such as ferns—to contain more than two of each type of chromosome. Instead of having two homologous chromosomes per cell, these species are **polyploid** ("many-form"), meaning that they have three or more of each type of chromosome in each cell. Depending on the number of homologs present, polyploid species are called triploid (3*n*), tetraploid (4*n*), hexaploid (6*n*), octoploid (8*n*), and so on.

Making Models 13.1 shows you how drawing chromosomes can help you understand the meaning of ploidy and chromosome number.

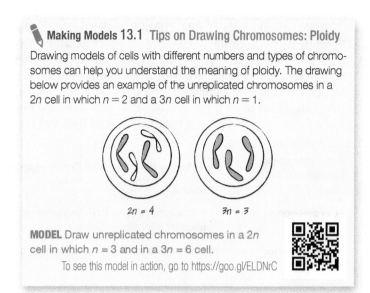

Making Models 13.1 Tips on Drawing Chromosomes: Ploidy

Drawing models of cells with different numbers and types of chromosomes can help you understand the meaning of ploidy. The drawing below provides an example of the unreplicated chromosomes in a 2*n* cell in which *n* = 2 and a 3*n* cell in which *n* = 1.

2*n* = 4   3*n* = 3

MODEL Draw unreplicated chromosomes in a 2*n* cell in which *n* = 3 and in a 3*n* = 6 cell.

To see this model in action, go to https://goo.gl/ELDNrC

Stevens and other early cell biologists who tracked how chromosome numbers change during meiosis confirmed Weismann's idea that a special type of cell division occurs during gamete formation.

An Overview of Meiosis

Cells replicate each of their chromosomes before starting meiosis. At the beginning of meiosis, chromosomes are in the same state they are in at the start of mitosis.

Recall that an unreplicated eukaryotic chromosome consists of a single, long DNA double helix organized around proteins called histones (Chapter 12). During S phase of the cell cycle the DNA is replicated, and therefore each chromosome is also replicated. A replicated chromosome consists of two **sister chromatids** (Figure 13.3). Each sister chromatid contains an identical copy of the DNA double helix that was present in the unreplicated chromosome before S phase. Therefore, each sister chromatid contains the same genetic information. Sister chromatids remain physically joined along their entire length during much of meiosis.

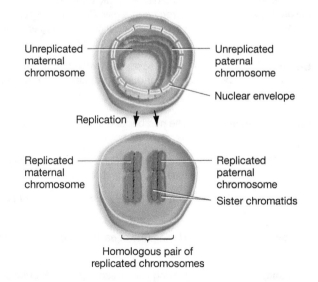

Unreplicated maternal chromosome

Unreplicated paternal chromosome

Nuclear envelope

Replication

Replicated maternal chromosome

Replicated paternal chromosome

Sister chromatids

Homologous pair of replicated chromosomes

Figure 13.3 Each Chromosome Replicates before Undergoing Meiosis. Unreplicated chromosomes (top) are shown as visible structures, but they are not actually condensed at this stage.

To understand meiosis, it is critical to understand the relationship between chromosomes and sister chromatids. The trick is to recognize that an unreplicated chromosome and a replicated chromosome are both *single* chromosomes, even though the replicated chromosome contains *two* sister chromatids. This makes sense if you consider that a chromosome carries a particular set of genetic information in its DNA and that the amount of *unique* information is the same whether there is one copy of it present or two. It's similar to thinking about the amount of information present in one copy of a book or two copies—the two copies may have more pages, but there's no more new information. Don't fall into the mistake of thinking that every time DNA replicates, the number of chromosomes doubles.

SUMMARY Table 13.1 **Terms for Describing Chromosomes**

Term	Definition	Example or Comment
Chromosome	Structure made up of DNA and proteins; carries the cell's hereditary information (genes)	Eukaryotes have linear chromosomes; most bacteria and archaea have just one circular chromosome
• **Sex chromosome**	Chromosome associated with an individual's sex	X and Y chromosomes of humans (males are XY, females XX); Z and W chromosomes of birds and butterflies (males are ZZ, females ZW)
• **Autosome**	Any chromosome other than a sex chromosome	Chromosomes 1–22 in humans
Unreplicated chromosome	A chromosome that consists of one double-helical molecule of DNA packaged with proteins (not shown) for compactness.	
Replicated chromosome	A chromosome after DNA replication. Consists of two identical chromatids, each containing one double-helical DNA molecule packaged with proteins (not shown) for compactness	
Sister chromatids	The two identical chromatid copies in a replicated chromosome	Sister chromatids
Homologous chromosomes (homologs)	Chromosomes that have the same genes in the same position and are the same size and shape. (Because the alleles of particular genes are often different between the homologs, homologs are not called identical chromosomes.)	Homologous chromosomes
Non-sister chromatids	Chromatids on different members of a homologous chromosome pair. (To be non-sister chromatids, one of the chromatids is on one homolog and the other chromatid is on the other homolog.)	Non-sister chromatids
Bivalent	Homologous replicated chromosomes that are joined together during prophase I and metaphase I of meiosis	Bivalent
Haploid number	The number of different types of chromosomes in a cell; symbolized n	Humans have 23 different types of chromosomes ($n = 23$)
Diploid number	The number of chromosomes present in a diploid cell (see below); symbolized $2n$	All human cells except gametes are diploid and contain 46 chromosomes ($2n = 46$)
Ploidy	The number of each type of chromosome present	The number of haploid chromosome sets present; shown by the number in front of n (for example, $2n$)
• **Haploid**	Having one of each type of chromosome (n)	Bacteria and archaea are haploid, as are many algae; most plant and animal gametes are haploid
• **Diploid**	Having two of each type of chromosome ($2n$)	Most familiar plants and animals are diploid
• **Polyploid**	Having more than two of each type of chromosome; may be triploid ($3n$), tetraploid ($4n$), hexaploid ($6n$), and so on	Seedless bananas are triploid; many ferns are tetraploid; bread wheat is hexaploid

By convention, an unreplicated chromosome is never called a chromatid; the term "chromatid" is used only to describe the structures in a replicated chromosome. Table 13.1 summarizes the terms that biologists use to describe chromosomes and illustrates the relationship between chromosomes and chromatids.

✔ CAUTION If you understand the relationship between chromosomes and chromatids, you should be able to draw one chromosome in both an unreplicated and replicated state, label the sister chromatids, indicate the number of double-helical molecules of DNA present in each drawing, and explain why both of your drawings represent single chromosomes.

Meiosis Consists of Two Cell Divisions Two back-to-back cell divisions occur in meiosis, **meiosis I** and **meiosis II**. As Figure 13.4 shows, these divisions differ sharply.

Meiosis I causes the homologs of each chromosome pair to separate so that one homolog goes to one daughter cell and the other homolog goes to the other daughter cell. At the end of meiosis I, each of the two daughter cells has one of each type of chromosome instead of two, and thus half as many chromosomes as the parent cell had. Put another way: During meiosis I, the diploid ($2n$) parent cell produces two haploid (n) daughter cells. Notice, however, that each chromosome still consists of *two sister chromatids*—chromosomes are in their replicated form at the end of meiosis I.

During meiosis II, the sister chromatids of each chromosome separate. One sister chromatid goes to one daughter cell; the other sister chromatid goes to the other daughter cell. Each separated sister chromatid is called a daughter chromosome. Remember that each haploid cell that started meiosis II had only one of each type of chromosome, but each chromosome was still in its replicated form consisting of two sister chromatids. The cells produced by meiosis II also have one of each type of chromosome and are haploid, but now the daughter chromosomes each consist of a single double-helical molecule of DNA and so are said to be unreplicated.

To reiterate, sister chromatids separate into daughter chromosomes during meiosis II. This is just what happens during mitosis. Meiosis II is actually equivalent to mitosis in a haploid cell. In meiosis I, on the other hand, sister chromatids stay together. This sets meiosis I apart from both mitosis and meiosis II.

As in mitosis, chromosome movement during meiosis I and II is coordinated by microtubules of the **spindle apparatus** that attach to **kinetochores** located at the **centromere** of each chromosome. Recall that the centromere is a region on the chromosome; kinetochores are protein-based structures that form on that region (see Chapter 12). Chromosome movement is driven by fraying of the ends of microtubules at each kinetochore, just as it is in mitosis (see Figure 12.7).

Meiosis I Is a Reduction Division A host of early cell biologists worked out the sequence of events in meiosis I and II by carefully observing cells with the light microscope. They came to a key realization: Meiosis I reduces chromosome number. For this reason, meiosis I is known as a reduction division. Reduction is another important way in which meiosis I differs from meiosis II and mitosis.

In most plants and animals, the original cell entering meiosis is diploid and the four final daughter cells are haploid. In animals, the haploid daughter cells, each containing one of each homologous chromosome, may eventually go on to form egg cells or sperm cells to complete the process of **gametogenesis** ("gamete-origin"; see Chapter 47). In some organisms, the haploid cells may divide by mitosis and even go on to produce a haploid multicellular organism.

When two haploid gametes fuse during fertilization, the full diploid complement of chromosomes is restored (Figure 13.5). The diploid cell that results from fertilization is called a **zygote,** and it is the first cell of a new individual. In this way, each diploid individual receives a haploid chromosome set from its mother and a haploid set from its father.

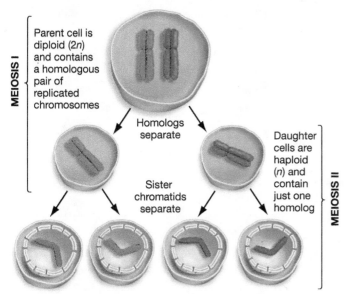

Four daughter cells contain one unreplicated chromosome each (n). In animals, these cells can develop into gametes.

Figure 13.4 Meiosis First Separates Homologs and Then Separates Sister Chromatids. Before undergoing meiosis, DNA and chromosomes are replicated, so there are two chromatids per chromosome. Meiosis reduces chromosome number by half by separating the homologous pairs. In diploid organisms, the cells produced by meiosis are haploid. Maternal chromosomes are shown in red; paternal chromosomes, blue. This color scheme is used throughout the chapter.

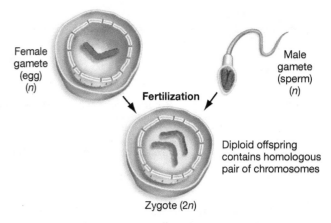

Figure 13.5 Fertilization Restores a Diploid Set of Chromosomes.

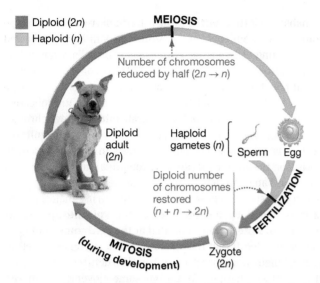

Diploid (2n)
Haploid (n)

MEIOSIS

Number of chromosomes
reduced by half (2n → n)

Diploid adult
(2n)

Haploid gametes (n) { Sperm Egg

Diploid number
of chromosomes
restored
(n + n → 2n)

FERTILIZATION

MITOSIS
(during development)

Zygote
(2n)

Figure 13.6 Ploidy Changes during the Life Cycle of an Animal.
The dog life cycle is typical of most familiar animals, because most
of it involves diploid cells.

Figure 13.6 puts these events into the context of a **life cycle**—the sequence of events that occurs over the life of an individual, from fertilization to the production of offspring. As you study the figure, note how ploidy changes as the result of meiosis and fertilization. In the case of the dog illustrated here, meiosis in a diploid adult results in the formation of haploid gametes, which combine to form a diploid zygote. The zygote marks the start of a new generation, and through mitotic divisions during development, the zygote goes on to form the adult. The dog life cycle is typical of familiar animals. However, life cycles of other types of organisms can be very different (see, for example, Chapters 29 and 30).

✔ **CAUTION** If you understand the events of meiosis, you should be able to predict how many double-helical molecules of DNA will be present in the gametes of the fruit fly *Drosophila*, a diploid organism that has eight replicated chromosomes in each cell that enters meiosis.

Once early research had filled in the details of meiosis and the accompanying changes in ploidy, the mystery of fertilization was solved. To appreciate the consequences of meiosis fully, let's analyze the events in more detail.

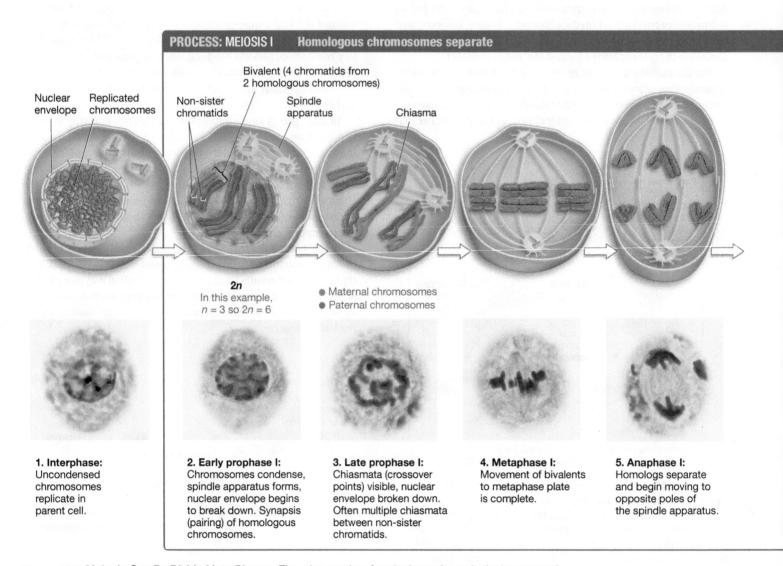

PROCESS: MEIOSIS I **Homologous chromosomes separate**

Nuclear envelope   Replicated chromosomes

Non-sister chromatids

Bivalent (4 chromatids from 2 homologous chromosomes)

Spindle apparatus

Chiasma

2n
In this example,
n = 3 so 2n = 6

● Maternal chromosomes
● Paternal chromosomes

1. Interphase:
Uncondensed chromosomes replicate in parent cell.

2. Early prophase I:
Chromosomes condense, spindle apparatus forms, nuclear envelope begins to break down. Synapsis (pairing) of homologous chromosomes.

3. Late prophase I:
Chiasmata (crossover points) visible, nuclear envelope broken down. Often multiple chiasmata between non-sister chromatids.

4. Metaphase I:
Movement of bivalents to metaphase plate is complete.

5. Anaphase I:
Homologs separate and begin moving to opposite poles of the spindle apparatus.

Figure 13.7 Meiosis Can Be Divided into Phases. The micrographs of each phase shown in the lower panel are from a species of salamander. See pages 277–279 for a full discussion of all the phases.

The Phases of Meiosis I

Meiosis begins after chromosomes are replicated during S phase and the cell moves through G_2 phase (see Chapter 12). Just as for mitosis, before the start of meiosis, chromosomes are extended and not visible under a light microscope. The major steps that occur during meiosis are shown in **Figure 13.7**.

Early Prophase I During early prophase I, the nuclear envelope begins to break down, chromosomes condense, and the spindle apparatus begins to form. Then a crucial event occurs: Homologous chromosome pairs come together. This pairing is unique to meiosis I. The end result is **synapsis,** a tight side-by-side pairing of homologous chromosomes along their corresponding regions. This is illustrated in step 2 of Figure 13.7. In most organisms, synapsis requires breaking and then connecting together DNA of the two homologs at many spots along their length.

The structure that results from synapsis is called a **bivalent** (*bi* means "two" in Latin). A bivalent consists of paired homologous replicated chromosomes, where each homolog consists of two sister chromatids. Chromatids from different homologs are referred to as **non-sister chromatids.** In Figure 13.7, the red-colored chromatids are non-sister chromatids with respect to the blue-colored chromatids.

Late Prophase I During late prophase I, the nuclear envelope breaks down, and the two homologs within each bivalent become attached to microtubule fibers coming from opposing poles of the spindle apparatus—that is, each homolog in the bivalent is attached to a different pole. This form of attachment is unique to meiosis I, and it is essential for separating the homologous pairs.

The homologs that were so closely paired in synapsis now begin to separate at many points along their length. They stay joined, however, by X-shaped structures called **chiasmata** (singular: **chiasma**). (In the Greek alphabet, the letter "X" is called chi.) Normally, at least one chiasma forms in every pair of homologous chromosomes, and there are often several chiasmata. The chiasmata mark particular sites of DNA breakage and rejoining between homologs early in prophase I.

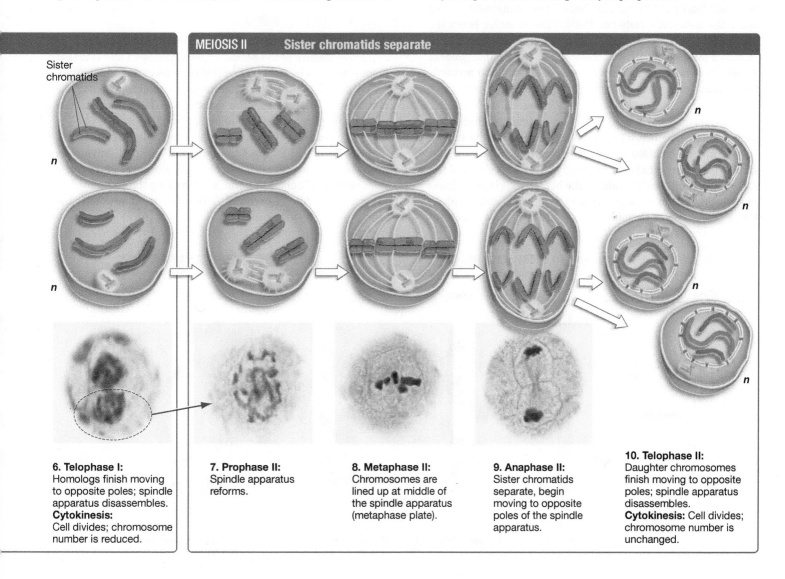

MEIOSIS II   **Sister chromatids separate**

Sister chromatids

n

6. Telophase I: Homologs finish moving to opposite poles; spindle apparatus disassembles. **Cytokinesis:** Cell divides; chromosome number is reduced.

7. Prophase II: Spindle apparatus reforms.

8. Metaphase II: Chromosomes are lined up at middle of the spindle apparatus (metaphase plate).

9. Anaphase II: Sister chromatids separate, begin moving to opposite poles of the spindle apparatus.

10. Telophase II: Daughter chromosomes finish moving to opposite poles; spindle apparatus disassembles. **Cytokinesis:** Cell divides; chromosome number is unchanged.

As step 3 of Figure 13.7 shows, the chromatids that meet to form a chiasma are non-sister chromatids. At each chiasma there is an exchange of parts of chromosomes between paternal and maternal homologs. These reciprocal exchanges between different homologs create chromatids that have both paternal and maternal segments. This process of chromosome exchange is called **crossing over.** Step 4 of Figure 13.7 illustrates that crossing over produces chromosomes with a combination of maternal (red) and paternal (blue) segments. Consequently, these chromosomes have a mixture of maternal and paternal alleles.

Metaphase I In metaphase I, the kinetochore microtubules move the pairs of homologous chromosomes (bivalents) to a region called the **metaphase plate** (step 4). The metaphase plate is not a physical structure but an imaginary plane midway between the poles of the spindle apparatus.

Here are two key points about chromosome movement: **(1)** In metaphase I, each bivalent straddles the metaphase plate with one homolog on one side and the other homolog on the other; and **(2)** the alignment of each bivalent is independent of any other bivalent. This means that if one bivalent has a maternal homolog above the metaphase plate and the paternal homolog below the metaphase plate, the alignment of this pair of homologs has no influence on how any other bivalent will align. The independent alignment of bivalents may seem a trivial detail, but it accounts for the most fundamental principles of genetics (see Chapter 14).

Anaphase I and Telophase I Sister chromatids of each chromosome remain together. The unique attachment of the kinetochores of each homolog to spindle fibers that come from one spindle pole means that each homolog in the pair is attached to a different spindle pole. This allows the homologous chromosomes in each bivalent to separate from each other during anaphase I as they are moved to opposite poles of the spindle apparatus

(step 5). Meiosis I concludes with telophase I, when the homologs finish moving to opposite sides of the spindle (step 6). When meiosis I is complete, **cytokinesis** (division of cytoplasm) occurs and two haploid daughter cells form.

Meiosis I: A Recap Meiosis I results in daughter cells that have only one chromosome of each homologous pair. A reduction in chromosome number has occurred: The daughter cells produced by meiosis I are haploid, having only one copy of each type of chromosome. The sister chromatids remain attached in each chromosome, however, meaning that the haploid daughter cells at the end of meiosis I still contain replicated chromosomes.

It is important to note that the chromosomes in each cell are a random assortment of maternal and paternal chromosomes as a result of **(1)** crossing over and **(2)** the random distribution of maternal and paternal homologs to daughter cells.

Chromosome movement occurs through the dynamic assembly and disassembly of the microtubules attached to the kinetochore. When meiosis I is complete, the cell divides and two haploid daughter cells are produced.

The Phases of Meiosis II

Recall that chromosome replication occurred before meiosis I. An important feature of the period between meiosis I and II is that there is no DNA replication and therefore no chromosome replication. Meiosis II works to separate the sister chromatids of the replicated chromosomes into separate cells. Each of these cells will contain unreplicated daughter chromosomes.

During prophase II, a spindle apparatus forms in both daughter cells (step 7 of Figure 13.7). Microtubules that polymerize from the two spindle poles attach to kinetochores on opposite sides of every chromosome and begin moving the chromosomes toward the middle of each cell. This attachment is exactly the same as observed in mitosis.

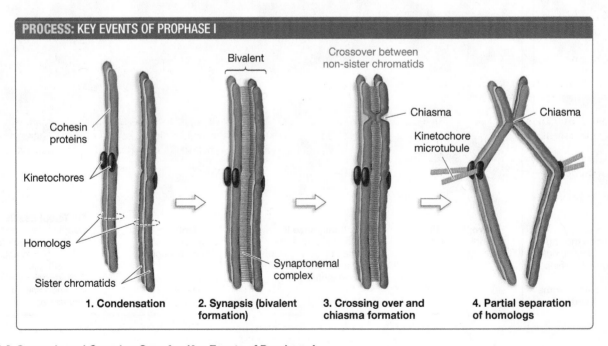

PROCESS: KEY EVENTS OF PROPHASE I

Bivalent

Crossover between non-sister chromatids

Cohesin proteins

Kinetochores

Homologs

Sister chromatids

Synaptonemal complex

Chiasma

Kinetochore microtubule

Chiasma

1. Condensation
2. Synapsis (bivalent formation)
3. Crossing over and chiasma formation
4. Partial separation of homologs

Figure 13.8 **Synapsis and Crossing Over Are Key Events of Prophase I.**

In metaphase II, the chromosomes are lined up at the metaphase plate (step 8). In contrast to metaphase I, each chromosome is attached by spindle fibers to both of the spindle poles. The sister chromatids of each chromosome are separated during anaphase II (step 9) and move to different daughter cells during telophase II (step 10). Once they are separated, each chromatid is considered an independent daughter chromosome. At the end of meiosis II, there are four haploid cells, each with one daughter chromosome of each type in the chromosome set.

Because meiosis II occurs in both daughter cells produced by meiosis I, the overall process results in four daughter cells from each parent cell. To summarize meiosis, one diploid cell with replicated chromosomes gives rise to four haploid cells with unreplicated chromosomes.

A Closer Look at Synapsis and Crossing Over

The pairing of homologs and crossing over in prophase I are both important events unique to meiosis. **Figure 13.8** provides a closer look at how chromosomes come together and exchange parts during meiosis I.

Step 1 At the entry to prophase I, chromosomes begin to condense. Sister chromatids are held together along their full length by proteins known as cohesins.

Step 2 Homologs pair in a process called synapsis and are held together by a network of proteins called the **synaptonemal complex.**

Step 3 In most organisms, one or more breaks are made in the DNA. At least one of these breaks eventually leads to a crossover between non-sister chromatids. Crossover points are visible as chiasmata.

Step 4 The synaptonemal complex disassembles in late prophase I. The two homologs are held together only at chiasmata. Chiasmata are eventually broken to restore individual, unconnected chromosomes.

At a chiasma, the non-sister chromatids from each homolog are *attached to each other at corresponding points*. When chiasmata are broken, corresponding segments of maternal and paternal chromosomes are exchanged. In humans, an average of 1.5 chiasmata form on each chromosome.

Crossing over can occur at many locations along the length of paired homologs, and it routinely occurs at least once between each pair of non-sister chromatids.

Mitosis versus Meiosis

How do mitosis and meiosis compare? **Table 13.2** summarizes some important similarities and differences. A key difference between the two processes is that homologous chromosomes pair early in meiosis but do not pair at all during mitosis. Because homologs in prophase of meiosis I are connected by chiasmata, they can migrate to the metaphase plate together. In meiotic prophase I, the unique attachment of each homolog to spindle fibers coming from only one spindle pole allows for the separation of homologs during anaphase of meiosis I. This results in a reduction division. ✔ If you understand key differences between meiosis and mitosis, you should be able to explain why mitosis in a triploid (3n) cell can occur easily but meiosis is difficult.

See **Figure 13.9** on page 280 for a visual summary of these two processes. Given that mitosis works perfectly well for cell division, why does meiosis exist at all? What are its consequences?

SUMMARY Table 13.2 **Key Differences between Mitosis and Meiosis**

Feature	Mitosis	Meiosis
Number of cell divisions	One	Two
Number of chromosomes in daughter cells compared with parent cell	Same	Half
DNA content of daughter cells compared with parent cell	Reduced to 1/2 as chromosomes go from replicated → unreplicated	Reduced to 1/4 as chromosomes go from replicated diploid sets → replicated haploid sets (meiosis I) → unreplicated haploid sets (meiosis II)
Synapsis of homologs	No	Yes
Spindle fiber attachment	Individual chromatids in each chromosome attach to spindle fibers from different spindle poles.	Both chromatids in each chromosome attach to spindle fibers from the same spindle pole.
Number of crossing-over events	None	One or more per pair of homologous chromosomes
Makeup of chromosomes in daughter cells	Identical	Different—various combinations of maternal and paternal chromosomes, paternal and maternal segments mixed within chromosomes
Role in organism life cycle	Asexual reproduction in some eukaryotes; cell division for growth and wound healing	Halving of chromosome number in cells that will produce gametes

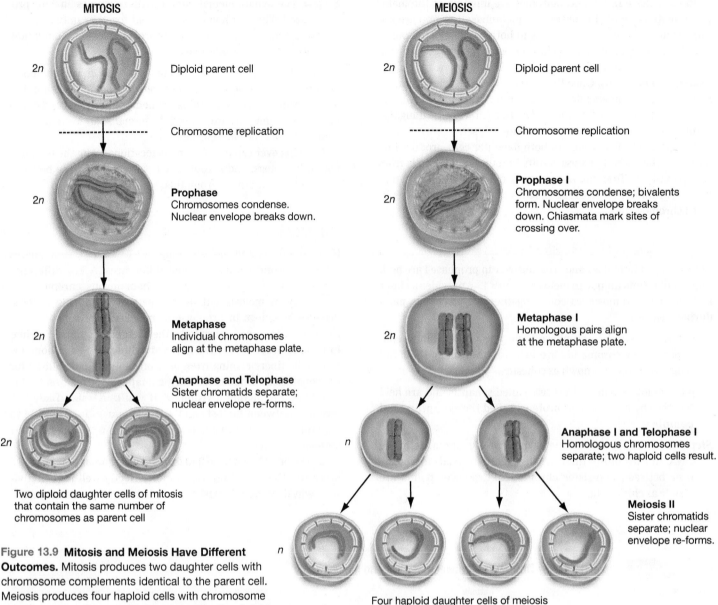

MITOSIS

2n — Diploid parent cell

- - - - - - - - - - - Chromosome replication

2n — **Prophase**
Chromosomes condense.
Nuclear envelope breaks down.

2n — **Metaphase**
Individual chromosomes
align at the metaphase plate.

Anaphase and Telophase
Sister chromatids separate;
nuclear envelope re-forms.

2n — Two diploid daughter cells of mitosis
that contain the same number of
chromosomes as parent cell

MEIOSIS

2n — Diploid parent cell

- - - - - - - - - - - Chromosome replication

2n — **Prophase I**
Chromosomes condense; bivalents
form. Nuclear envelope breaks
down. Chiasmata mark sites of
crossing over.

2n — **Metaphase I**
Homologous pairs align
at the metaphase plate.

n — **Anaphase I and Telophase I**
Homologous chromosomes
separate; two haploid cells result.

Meiosis II
Sister chromatids
separate; nuclear
envelope re-forms.

n — Four haploid daughter cells of meiosis
that contain half the number of
chromosomes as parent cell

Figure 13.9 Mitosis and Meiosis Have Different Outcomes. Mitosis produces two daughter cells with chromosome complements identical to the parent cell. Meiosis produces four haploid cells with chromosome complements unlike one another and unlike the diploid parent cell.

CHECK YOUR UNDERSTANDING

If you understand that ...

- Meiosis is called a reduction division because the total number of chromosomes present is cut in half.
- During meiosis, a single diploid parent cell with replicated chromosomes gives rise to four haploid daughter cells with unreplicated chromosomes.

✔ **You should be able to ...**

1. Identify the event that makes meiosis a reduction division and explain how it reduces chromosome number.
2. **CAUTION** Explain how DNA content is reduced by half in both meiosis I and meiosis II, yet chromosome number is reduced only in meiosis I.

Answers are available in Appendix A.

13.2 Meiosis Promotes Genetic Variation

Given the complexity of meiosis, it is logical to hypothesize that meiosis must do something important—and it does. Thanks to crossing over during meiosis I and the shuffling of maternal and paternal chromosomes into haploid cells, the chromosomes in one gamete are different from the chromosomes in every other gamete and different from the chromosomes in the parent cell. Multiplying this variation in chromosomes and the alleles they carry, fertilization brings together haploid sets of chromosomes from a mother and father to form a diploid offspring. The chromosome complement of this offspring is unlike that of either parent. Instead, it is a random combination of genetic material from each parent.

This change in chromosomal complement is crucial. The critical factor here is that changes in chromosome sets occur only during sexual reproduction—*not* during asexual reproduction.

- **Asexual reproduction** is any mechanism of producing offspring that does not involve the production and fusion of gametes. Asexual reproduction in eukaryotes is based on mitosis. The chromosomes in cells produced by mitosis are identical to the chromosomes in the parental cell.

- **Sexual reproduction** is the production of offspring through the production and fusion of gametes. Sexual reproduction results in offspring that have chromosome complements unlike those of their siblings or their parents.

Why is this difference important?

Chromosomes and Heredity

The changes in chromosome sets that result from meiosis and fertilization are significant because chromosomes contain the cell's hereditary material needed to specify particular traits. These inherited traits range from eye color and height in humans to the number or shape of the bristles on a fruit fly's leg to the color or shape of the seeds found in pea plants.

In the early 1900s, biologists began using the term "gene" to refer to the inherited instructions for a particular trait. Recall that the term "allele" refers to a particular form of a gene and that homologous chromosomes may carry different alleles.

Chromosomes are the repositories of genes, and identical copies of chromosomes are distributed to daughter cells during mitosis. Thus, cells that are produced by mitosis are genetically identical to the parent cell and to each other. Because mitosis is the only cell division involved in asexual reproduction, asexually produced offspring are **clones**—or exact genetic copies—of their parent. A familiar example of asexual reproduction is growing a new plant from a cutting.

In contrast, offspring produced by sexual reproduction are genetically different from one another and unlike either their mother or their father. To understand this, let's begin by analyzing two aspects of meiosis that create variation: **(1)** separation and distribution of homologous chromosomes and **(2)** crossing over.

The Role of Independent Assortment

Each somatic cell in your body contains 23 homologous pairs of chromosomes, or 46 chromosomes in total. Half of these chromosomes came from your mother, and half from your father. Each chromosome contains genes, and genes influence particular traits. For example, one gene that affects the type of hemoglobin in your red blood cells is located on chromosome 11 while a gene that affects the form of an ion channel protein is located on chromosome 7 (**Figure 13.10a**). Why are the type of hemoglobin and the specific form of ion channel important? It's because abnormal forms of these two proteins can lead to sickle cell disease and cystic fibrosis, respectively. These are relatively common and very serious genetic diseases.

Suppose that the chromosomes you inherited from your mother contain alleles associated with normal hemoglobin and an abnormal channel protein that causes cystic fibrosis. In contrast, suppose the chromosomes you inherited from your father include the

(a) Example: An individual has different alleles of two genes implicated in two genetically transmitted diseases.

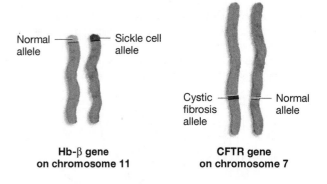

Normal allele — Sickle cell allele

Cystic fibrosis allele — Normal allele

Hb-β gene on chromosome 11

CFTR gene on chromosome 7

(b) During meoisis I, bivalents can line up in two different ways before the homologs separate.

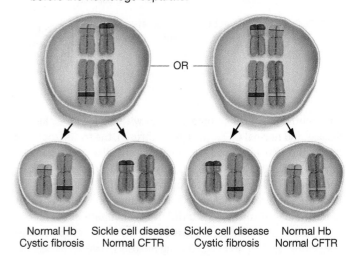

OR

Normal Hb Cystic fibrosis | Sickle cell disease Normal CFTR | Sickle cell disease Cystic fibrosis | Normal Hb Normal CFTR

Figure 13.10 Independent Assortment of Homologous Chromosomes Results in Varied Combinations of Maternal and Paternal Alleles. Maternal chromosomes are shown in red; paternal in blue. CFTR stands for the ion channel protein that causes cystic fibrosis when cells possess two copies of the defective allele; Hb-β is an abbreviation for a gene that determines the type of hemoglobin. Sickle cell disease occurs when there are two copies of the defective Hb-β allele.

alleles for the abnormal hemoglobin that causes sickle cell disease and a normal channel protein that does not cause cystic fibrosis. For a person to have either sickle cell disease or cystic fibrosis, they must possess two copies of the disease-associated allele.

Will some gametes that you produce contain the instructions you inherited from your mother while others contain the instructions you inherited from your father? **Figure 13.10b** shows that when pairs of homologous chromosomes line up during meiosis I and the homologs separate, different combinations of maternal and paternal chromosomes can result. Each daughter cell gets a random assortment of maternal and paternal chromosomes (which will be reduced from 2n to n during meiosis II).

This phenomenon is known as the **principle of independent assortment.** In the example shown in Figure 13.10, meiosis will result in some gametes with alleles for normal hemoglobin (no sickle cell disease) and for cystic fibrosis, the traits from

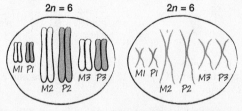

your mother, as well as some gametes with alleles for sickle cell disease and normal CFTR (no cystic fibrosis), the traits from your father. But two additional combinations will also occur: gametes having alleles for no sickle cell disease and no cystic fibrosis, and gametes having alleles for both sickle cell disease and cystic fibrosis. The creation of new combinations of alleles is called **genetic recombination.** Four different combinations of paternal and maternal chromosomes are possible for two chromosomes distributed to daughter cells during meiosis I. (**Making Models 13.2** suggests one strategy for predicting the possible outcomes of independent assortment.)

✔ If you understand how independent assortment produces genetic variation in the daughter cells produced by meiosis, you should be able to explain how genetic variation would be affected if maternal chromosomes always lined up on one side of the metaphase plate during meiosis I and paternal chromosomes always lined up on the other side.

How many different combinations of maternal and paternal homologs are possible when more chromosomes are involved? With each additional pair of chromosomes, the number of combinations doubles. In general, a diploid organism can produce 2^n combinations, where n is the haploid chromosome number. This means that you ($n = 23$) can produce 2^{23}, or about 8.4 million, gametes that differ in their combination of maternal and paternal chromosome sets—an impressive amount of genetic variation.

The Role of Crossing Over

Recall from Section 13.1 that segments of paternal and maternal chromatids exchange when crossing over occurs during meiosis I (for example, see the mixed blue and red segments of chromosomes shown in Figures 13.7 and 13.8). Thus, crossing over produces new combinations of alleles *within* a chromosome—combinations that did not exist in either parent.

Genetic recombination from crossing over and from independent assortment during meiosis is important because it creates genetically diverse gametes. Independent assortment of homologous chromosomes generates varied combinations of chromosomes in gametes; crossing over produces new combinations of alleles along each chromosome. With crossing over, the number of genetically different gametes that you can produce is much more than the 8.4 million—it is virtually limitless.

How Does Fertilization Affect Genetic Variation?

As long as some alleles vary in a diploid individual, crossing over and the independent assortment of maternal and paternal chromosomes ensure that each gamete is genetically unique. These differences between gametes lead to another important source of genetic variation—the random union of gametes at fertilization. Even if two gametes produced by the same individual fuse to form a diploid offspring—in which case **self-fertilization,** or "selfing," is taking place—the offspring still will be genetically different from the parent. Selfing is common in many plant species, and it also occurs in animal species in which single individuals—hermaphrodites—contain both male and female sex organs.

Self-fertilization, however, is rare or nonexistent in many sexually reproducing species. Instead, gametes from different individuals combine to form offspring. This process is called **outcrossing.** Outcrossing increases the genetic diversity of offspring even further because it combines chromosomes from different individuals. These chromosomes are likely to contain different alleles.

How many genetically distinct offspring can be produced when outcrossing occurs? Let's answer this question using humans as an example. Recall that a single human can produce about 8.4 million different gametes by independent assortment alone. When a sperm and egg come together at fertilization, the number of possible genetic combinations that can result is equal to the product of the numbers of different gametes produced by each parent. (To understand this logic, see BioSkills 4.) In humans this means that two parents can potentially produce 8.4 million $\times$ 8.4 million = 70.6×10^{12} genetically distinct offspring, even without crossing over. This number is far greater than the total number of people who have ever lived.

In any complicated process such as meiosis, things can and do go wrong. What happens if there is a mistake, and the chromosomes are not properly distributed?

CHECK YOUR UNDERSTANDING

If you understand that ...

• The daughter cells produced by meiosis are genetically different from the parent cell because (1) maternal and paternal homologs align independently at metaphase of meiosis I and (2) crossing over produces new combinations of alleles within chromosomes.

✔ **You should be able to ...**

1. Discuss how crossing over influences the genetic diversity of the daughter cells produced by meiosis.
2. Using the information from your answer to Making Models 13.2, predict how many genetically different offspring could be produced by outcrossing two 2n = 4 individuals.

Answers are available in Appendix A.

13.3 What Happens When Things Go Wrong in Meiosis?

Errors in meiosis are surprisingly common. If this were like a spelling mistake, it might be only an annoyance. But in humans, a conservative estimate is that a third of conceptions are spontaneously terminated because of problems in meiosis. What are the consequences for offspring if gametes contain an abnormal set of chromosomes?

In 1866 the physician Langdon Down described a distinctive set of conditions that included mental retardation, a high risk for heart problems and leukemia, and a degenerative brain disorder similar to Alzheimer's disease. **Down syndrome,** as the disorder came to be called, is observed in about one infant in every 691 live births in the United States.

For over 80 years the cause of the syndrome was unknown. Then, in the late 1950s, a study of the chromosome sets of nine children with Down syndrome suggested that the condition is associated with an extra copy of chromosome 21. This situation is called **trisomy** ("three-bodies")—in this case, trisomy-21—because each cell has three copies of the chromosome (see Figure 13.11). The explanation proposed for the trisomy was that a mistake had occurred during meiosis in either the mother or the father.

How Do Mistakes Occur?

For a gamete to get one complete set of chromosomes, two steps in meiosis must be perfectly executed.

1. The chromosomes in each homologous pair must separate from each other during the first meiotic division, so that only one homolog ends up in each daughter cell.

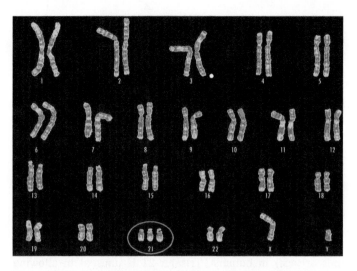

Figure 13.11 **Karyotype of an Individual with Down Syndrome.** The three copies of chromosome 21 are circled.

2. Sister chromatids must separate from each other and move to opposite poles of the dividing cell during meiosis II.

If both homologs in meiosis I or both sister chromatids in meiosis II move to the same daughter cell, the products of meiosis will be abnormal. This sort of meiotic error is referred to as **nondisjunction,** because the homologs or sister chromatids fail to separate, or disjoin.

Figure 13.12 shows what happens when homologs do not separate correctly during meiosis I. Note that at the end of meiosis, two daughter cells have two copies of the same chromosome, while the other two lack that chromosome entirely. Gametes that contain an extra chromosome are symbolized as $n + 1$; gametes that lack one chromosome are symbolized as $n - 1$.

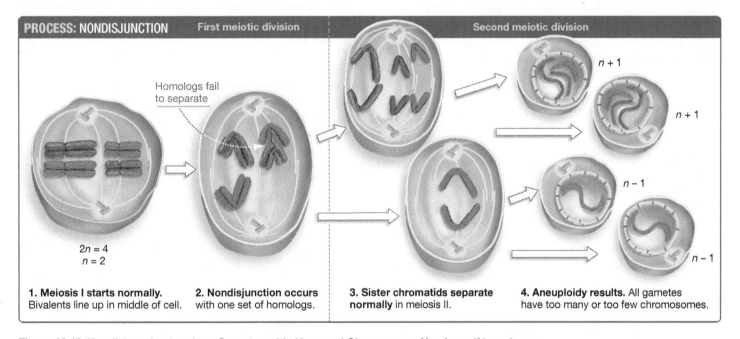

PROCESS: NONDISJUNCTION | First meiotic division | Second meiotic division

$n + 1$

$n + 1$

$n - 1$

$2n = 4$
$n = 2$

$n - 1$

1. Meiosis I starts normally. Bivalents line up in middle of cell.

2. Nondisjunction occurs with one set of homologs.

3. Sister chromatids separate normally in meiosis II.

4. Aneuploidy results. All gametes have too many or too few chromosomes.

Figure 13.12 **Nondisjunction Leads to Gametes with Abnormal Chromosome Numbers.** If homologous chromosomes fail to separate during meiosis I, the gametes that result will have an extra chromosome or will lack a chromosome. Nondisjunction can also occur during meiosis II if sister chromatids fail to separate.

If an $n + 1$ gamete is fertilized by a normal n gamete, the resulting zygote will be $2n + 1$. This situation is trisomy because there are three copies of one type of chromosome. If the $n - 1$ gamete is fertilized by a normal n gamete, the resulting zygote will be $2n - 1$. This situation is called **monosomy** because there is only one copy of one of the chromosomes. Cells that have too many or too few chromosomes of a particular type are said to be **aneuploid** ("without-form").

Meiotic mistakes occur often. Researchers estimate that 35 percent of all human conceptions produce a zygote that is aneuploid. Most of these errors result from the failure of a homologous pair to separate in anaphase of meiosis I; less often, sister chromatids stay together during anaphase of meiosis II.

Mistakes in meiosis are common and are almost always severe. They are the leading cause of spontaneous abortion (miscarriage) in humans. Trisomy-21 is unusual in allowing development to proceed. Even for chromosome 21, live births are not seen when there is only one copy.

Why Do Mistakes Occur?

Trisomy and other meiotic mistakes occur as a result of random errors. Errors like these are especially common in microtubule attachment to kinetochores early in meiosis I, in separation of chromosomes that have a single chiasma near their ends, and in the premature separation of sister chromatids.

A striking pattern that is important for human health is the steep increase in trisomic offspring born to older mothers. For example, in the case of Down syndrome, as **Figure 13.13** shows, the incidence increases dramatically in babies born to mothers over 35 years old. A father's age has a much weaker influence on mistakes in meiosis.

Why are there more errors in women than men? Why is there such a strong correlation between maternal age and frequency of trisomy-21? In part, the answers involve an unusual feature of egg development, or **oogenesis,** in humans. **Primary oocytes,** which are diploid precursors to eggs, enter meiosis I during female embryonic development and arrest in prophase I until the female reaches sexual maturity. After this point, once each month, a small group of primary oocytes reenter meiosis, and only one of them typically produces an egg. For some oocytes, this means a wait as long as 50 years between the start and completion of meiosis. Spindle apparatus function and the proper separation of chromosomes decline after this long period. Much remains to be discovered, but one thing is clear: Successful meiosis is critical to the health of offspring.

13.4 Why Does Meiosis Exist?

Why sex? Although it seems obvious that sex and therefore meiosis are needed universally for reproduction, that's not the case. Meiosis and sexual reproduction occur in only a small fraction of the lineages on the tree of life. Bacteria and archaea normally undergo only asexual reproduction; most algae, all fungi, and some animals and land plants reproduce both sexually and asexually. Asexual reproduction is even observed in some vertebrates. Several species of guppy in the genus *Poeciliopsis,* for example, reproduce exclusively by mitosis.

Although sexual reproduction plays a central role in the life of most familiar organisms—including us—until recently scientists had no clear idea of why it occurs. In fact, on the basis of theory, biologists had good reason to think that sexual reproduction should *not* exist.

The Paradox of Sex

In 1978 evolutionary biologist John Maynard Smith pointed out that the existence of sexual reproduction presents a paradox. Maynard Smith developed a mathematical model showing that because asexually reproducing individuals do not have to produce male offspring, their progeny on average can produce twice as many offspring as individuals that reproduce sexually. **Figure 13.14** diagrams this model by showing the number of females (♀), males (♂), and asexually reproducing organisms (○) produced over several generations by asexual versus sexual reproduction.

In this example, each asexually reproducing individual and each sexually reproducing couple produces four offspring over the course of their lifetimes. Note that in the sexual population, it takes two individuals—one male and one female—to produce four offspring. Two out of every four children that each female produces are males, who cannot themselves give birth to children. As a result, after one generation (generation 2 in Figure 13.14) the sexual population has just half as many child-producing individuals as the asexual population. Maynard Smith referred to this result as the "two-fold cost of males." Asexual reproduction is much more efficient than sexual reproduction because no males are produced.

Based on this analysis, what will happen when asexual and sexual individuals exist in the same population? If all other things are equal, individuals that reproduce asexually should increase in frequency in the population while individuals that reproduce sexually should decline in frequency. In fact, Maynard Smith's model predicts that sexual reproduction is so inefficient that it should be eliminated.

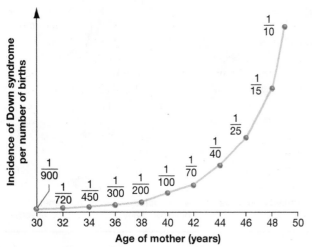

Figure 13.13 The Frequency of Down Syndrome Increases as a Function of a Mother's Age.

DATA: www.ndss.org, National Down Syndrome Society (2012).

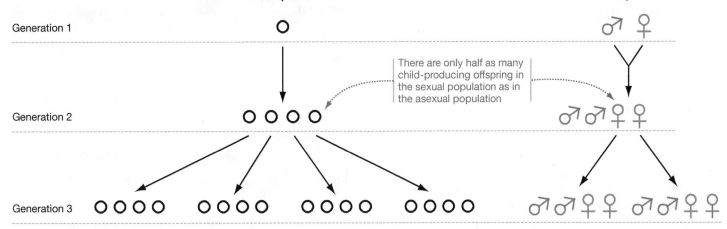

Figure 13.14 Asexual Reproduction Produces More Offspring. Each female (♀), male (♂), and asexual (○) symbol represents an individual. This example assumes that (1) every asexual individual or sexually reproducing couple produces four offspring over the course of a lifetime, (2) sexually reproducing individuals produce half males and half females, and (3) all offspring survive to breed.

✔ **QUANTITATIVE** In generation 2, there are only two more child-producing individuals in the asexual population than in the sexual population. If the same two-fold difference in reproductive rates were continued, how many more child-producing individuals would there be in the asexual compared to the sexual population of generation 5?

To resolve this paradox, biologists began examining the assumption "If all other things are equal." Were there ways that meiosis and outcrossing could lead to the production of offspring that reproduce more than asexually produced individuals do? After decades of debate and analysis, two solid hypotheses to explain the paradox of sex have emerged.

The Purifying Selection Hypothesis

The first clue to unraveling the paradox of sex is a simple observation: If a gene is altered in a way that causes it to function poorly, the alteration will be inherited by *all* of the individual's offspring when asexual reproduction occurs. Suppose the altered gene arose in generation 1 of Figure 13.14. If this gene is important, its alteration might cause the four asexual individuals present in generation 2 to produce fewer than four offspring apiece—perhaps because the members of generation 2 are more likely to die young. If so, then generation 3 will not have twice as many individuals in the asexual lineage compared with the sexual lineage.

An allele that functions poorly and lowers the fitness of an individual is said to be deleterious. Natural selection (see Chapter 22) against deleterious alleles is called purifying selection. Because asexual individuals are doomed to transmit all their deleterious alleles to all of their offspring, purifying selection should reduce the numerical advantage of asexual reproduction.

In contrast, suppose that the same deleterious allele arose in the sexually reproducing female in generation 1 of Figure 13.14. If the female also has a normal copy of the gene and she mates with a male that has two normal copies of the gene, then on average half her offspring will lack the deleterious allele. Importantly, once a deleterious allele appears in a sexually reproducing individual, not all of the offspring from that point forward are doomed to carry it.

These ideas predict that there will be more deleterious alleles in asexually reproducing species. To test this notion, researchers compared the same genes in two closely related species of *Daphnia*, a tiny crustacean that is a common inhabitant of ponds and lakes (see Chapter 47). One species reproduces asexually and the other reproduces sexually. As predicted, the scientists found that individuals in the asexual species contained many more deleterious alleles than individuals in the sexual species. Results like these have convinced biologists that purifying selection is an important factor promoting sexual reproduction.

The Changing-Environment Hypothesis

The second hypothesis to explain sexual reproduction focuses on the benefits of producing genetically diverse offspring. Here's the key idea: Offspring that are genetic clones of their parents are unlikely to thrive if the environment changes.

What type of environmental change might favor genetically diverse offspring? One ever-present change is the rapid evolution of pathogens and parasites—bacteria, viruses, fungi, and other entities that cause disease. These disease agents exert tremendous selective pressure on the organisms they infect. In your own lifetime, for example, several new disease-causing agents have emerged that afflict humans. These include the SARS virus and new strains of the tuberculosis bacterium. Hundreds of genes help defend you against these types of invaders, with some alleles being much more effective than others. In what amounts to an evolutionary arms race, pathogens and parasites constantly evolve new ways to infect the most common types of host, and in turn, host populations are driven to evolve resistance to the new forms of infectious agents.

What happens if all the offspring produced by an individual are genetically identical? If a new strain of pathogen evolves that is more dangerous for that individual, then all the asexually produced offspring will be equally susceptible to that new strain. But if the offspring are genetically varied, then it is likely that at least some will have combinations of alleles that enable them to resist the new strain of pathogen and produce offspring of their own.

Recall from Section 13.2 that over multiple generations, out-crossing—mating between two genetically different individuals—increases the amount of genetic diversity relative to the amount produced by self-fertilization. A logical question is, does exposure to evolving pathogens favor outcrossing in sexually reproducing organisms? To address this question, Levi Morran, Curtis Lively, and colleagues carried out a pivotal study on a tiny 1-mm-long roundworm named *Caenorhabditis elegans*.

C. elegans is an important model organism (see BioSkills 11) that was chosen for this study because it leads an unusual sex life. There are no females, only males and hermaphrodites. Because hermaphrodites have both male and female sex organs, *C. elegans* can reproduce either by self-fertilization or by outcrossing with males. The proportion of worms that reproduce by self-fertilization versus outcrossing can vary between strains or between different environments. This fact allowed the research team to test whether the rate of outcrossing increased in response to intense selection by a pathogen.

The setup of Morran, Lively, and colleagues' experiment is shown in Figure 13.15. The team began with a population of worms that had not been exposed to the pathogen and that reproduced predominantly by self-fertilization. The researchers then split the starting population into different groups. Half the groups were grown in the presence of a pathogen—a deadly bacterium—and the other half were grown without it. Once ingested by a worm, the bacterial pathogen could kill a susceptible individual within 24 hours.

At each generation, bacteria were collected from the carcasses of killed worms. Companion experiments showed that the pathogen evolved to become even more infectious over the course of the study.

The results are shown at the bottom of Figure 13.15. The rate of outcrossing stayed low over 32 generations in populations that did not encounter the pathogen. In contrast, populations that were exposed to the evolving pathogen showed a rapid increase in the rate of outcrossing. The interpretation was that genetic variation promoted by sexual reproduction was favored in the changing environment created by the evolving pathogen.

At the end of the experiment, the worms in the pathogen-exposed population were significantly more resistant to the evolved pathogen than their ancestors. This means that the worms in the predominantly outcrossing population had evolved along with the pathogen. In striking contrast, when a parallel experiment was done with a strain of worms that could reproduce only by self-fertilization, those populations were unable to evolve resistance to the pathogen. In fact, they became extinct.

These results and many others support the changing-environment hypothesis. Although the advantages of sexual reproduction remain an active area of research, more biologists are becoming convinced that sexual reproduction is helpful for two reasons: **(1)** Offspring are not doomed to inherit harmful alleles, and **(2)** the production of genetically varied offspring means that at least some may be able to resist rapidly evolving pathogens and parasites.

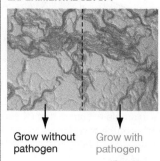
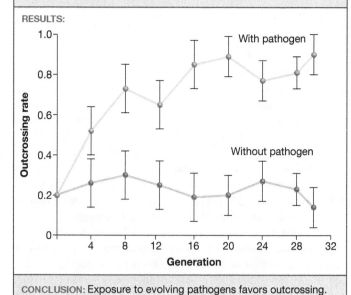
Figure 13.15 Does Exposure to Pathogens Favor Sexual Reproduction through Outcrossing? Each point in the graph shows the average percentage of reproduction by outcrossing for five populations. The bars indicate the degree of variation in the data (see BioSkills 3 for a description of error bars).

SOURCE: Morran, L. T., et al. 2011. Running with the Red Queen: Host–parasite coevolution selects for biparental sex. *Science* 333: 216–218.

✔ **PROCESS OF SCIENCE** What would you predict if a non-evolving pathogen were used?

13.1 How Does Meiosis Occur?

- Meiosis is a nuclear division resulting in cells that have only one of each type of chromosome and half as many chromosomes as the parent cell. In animals it leads to the formation of eggs and sperm.

- In diploid ($2n$) organisms, individuals have two versions of each type of chromosome. The two versions are called homologs. One homolog is inherited from the mother and one from the father. Haploid organisms (n) have just one of each type of chromosome.

- Each chromosome is replicated well before meiosis begins. This occurs as DNA is replicated during the S phase of the cell cycle. At the start of meiosis I, each chromosome consists of a pair of sister chromatids, each with a double-helical DNA molecule identical to that of the other sister chromatid.

- Homologous pairs of chromosomes synapse early in meiosis I, forming a bivalent—two closely paired homologous chromosomes. Non-sister chromatids undergo crossing over.

- The pair of homologous chromosomes, connected by at least one chiasma, is moved to the metaphase plate.

- At the end of meiosis I, the homologous chromosomes are separated and distributed to two daughter cells. The daughter cells are haploid, because each receives one of each type of chromosome.

- During meiosis II, sister chromatids of the replicated chromosomes separate and are distributed to two daughter cells.

- From one diploid cell with replicated chromosomes, meiosis produces four haploid daughter cells with unreplicated chromosomes.

13.2 Meiosis Promotes Genetic Variation

- Each cell produced by meiosis receives a different combination of chromosomes. Because genes are located on chromosomes, and often come in different forms (alleles), each cell produced by meiosis receives a different complement of alleles for its genes. The resulting offspring are genetically distinct from one another and from their parents.

- When meiosis and outcrossing occur, the chromosome complements of offspring differ from one another and from their parents for three reasons:

  1. Gametes receive a random assortment of maternal and paternal chromosomes when homologs separate in meiosis I. This is independent assortment.
  2. Because of crossing over, each chromosome contains a random assortment of paternal and maternal alleles.
  3. Outcrossing results in a combination of chromosome sets from different individuals.

13.3 What Happens When Things Go Wrong in Meiosis?

- If mistakes occur during meiosis, the resulting egg and sperm cells may contain the wrong number of chromosomes. Most often embryos with an incorrect number of chromosomes do not complete development. Children with Down syndrome, who have an extra copy of chromosome 21, are an exception.

- Most of the mistakes in meiosis are failures of either homologous chromosomes or sister chromatids to separate.

13.4 Why Does Meiosis Exist?

- In asexual reproduction, all individuals are capable of bearing offspring. From this standpoint, it is more efficient than sexual reproduction, in which on average half the offspring (males) are unable to bear offspring.

- The leading hypotheses to explain the existence of meiosis and sexual reproduction are that

  1. a parent with a harmful allele can produce offspring without the allele; and
  2. genetically diverse offspring are likely to include some that are better able to resist evolving pathogens and parasites.

Answers are available in Appendix A

✔ TEST YOUR KNOWLEDGE

1. **CAUTION** What are homologous chromosomes?
   a. chromosomes that are similar in their size, shape, and gene content
   b. similar chromosomes that are found in different individuals of the same species
   c. the two chromatids in a replicated chromosome
   d. any chromosome in a diploid cell

2. What is an outcome of genetic recombination?
   a. the synapsing of homologs during prophase of meiosis I
   b. the new combination of maternal and paternal chromosome segments that results when homologs cross over
   c. the new combinations of chromosome segments that result when self-fertilization occurs
   d. the combination of a haploid phase *and* a diploid phase in a life cycle

3. What proportion of chromosomes in a man's skin cell are maternal chromosomes?

4. Nondisjunction that leads to problems in offspring can occur in:
   a. mitosis
   b. meiosis I only
   c. meiosis I and II
   d. mitosis, meiosis I, and meiosis II

✔ TEST YOUR UNDERSTANDING

5. Explain the relationship between homologous chromosomes and the relationship between sister chromatids. How are these relationships different from one another?

6. If you followed a woman's cells through meiosis, at what stage of meiosis would the amount of DNA in one of these cells be equal to the amount of DNA in one of her G_1 phase (before DNA replication) kidney cells?

7. **CAUTION** Dogs have 78 chromosomes in their diploid cells. If a diploid dog cell enters meiosis, how many chromosomes and double-helical molecules of DNA will be present in each daughter cell at the end of meiosis I?
   a. 39 chromosomes and 39 double-helical DNA molecules
   b. 39 chromosomes and 78 double-helical DNA molecules
   c. 78 chromosomes and 78 double-helical DNA molecules
   d. 78 chromosomes and 156 double-helical DNA molecules

8. Triploid (3*n*) watermelons are produced by crossing a tetraploid (4*n*) strain with a diploid (2*n*) plant. Explain why this mating produces a triploid individual.

✔ TEST YOUR PROBLEM-SOLVING SKILLS

9. **QUANTITATIVE** Meiosis results in independent assortment of maternal and paternal chromosomes. If $n = 3$ for a given organism, and there is no crossing over, what is the chance that a gamete will receive *only* paternal chromosomes?
   a. 0; **b.** 1/16; **c.** 1/8; **d.** 1/3

10. **PROCESS OF SCIENCE** A species of rotifer, a small freshwater invertebrate, abandoned sexual reproduction millions of years ago. A remarkable feature of the rotifer's life cycle is its ability to withstand extreme drying. When the rotifer's watery environment dries out, so does the rotifer, and it can be blown in the wind to a new environment. Rotifers that are blown to water will rehydrate and resume an active life. A major pathogen of these rotifers is a species of fungus. Some scientists hypothesize that fungus-infected rotifers rid themselves of the pathogen when they dry.
   a. Design an experimental study to test this hypothesis.
   b. Why might the ability to withstand extreme drying reduce any potential advantage of sexual reproduction in this rotifer species?

✔ PUT IT ALL TOGETHER: Case Study

Why do old eggs go bad?

In analyzing the events of meiosis for answers to why older women produce more aneuploid eggs, biologists have hypothesized that binding between sister chromatids becomes weaker in oocytes of older women. If so, does it lead to problems in chromosome segregation that cause aneuploid conditions such as Down syndrome?

11. **QUANTITATIVE** Researchers used female mice of different ages as a model for aging in women. They measured the percentage of aneuploid eggs, analyzed chromosomes in meiosis for the amount of cohesin connecting the sister chromatids, and measured the distance between sister kinetochores. Does the evidence shown in the graphs support the hypothesis that weakened binding between sister chromatids leads to aneuploidy? Explain.

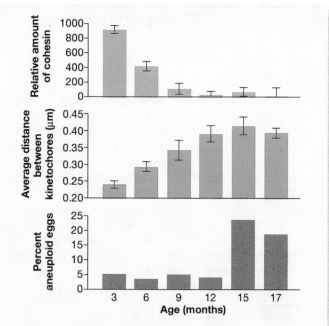

Source: Chiang, T., F. E. Duncan, K. Schindler, et al. 2010. *Current Biology* 20: 1522 28.

12. The data show that there is an inverse relationship between the amount of cohesin on each chromosome and the average distance between kinetochores. Why is this relationship logical?

13. A unique feature of meiosis I is the attachment of both kinetochores of a duplicated chromosome to spindle fibers that come from a single spindle pole. Why is this unusual attachment important?

14. In meiosis I in older females, chromosomes often incorrectly attach to spindle fibers coming from both spindle poles. Based on the data, what is a possible explanation for this increase in attachment error?

15. If the results showing increased aneuploidy in older mice can be related to humans, roughly what age in women would correspond to 15-month-old female mice (see Figure 13.13)?

16. **SOCIETY** Imagine that you are a genetic counselor and are consulting with a 42-year-old woman who has just learned she's pregnant. She knows that Down syndrome births increase with a mother's age and is very worried about her child. You want to comfort her by explaining her chances of *not* having a child with Down syndrome. What will you say?

MasteringBiology®

Students Go to MasteringBiology for assignments, the eText, and the Study Area with animations, practice tests, and activities.
Professors Go to MasteringBiology for automatically graded tutorials and questions that you can assign to your students, plus Instructor Resources.

34 Plant Form and Function

All plants are able to harvest diffuse resources and concentrate them in cells and tissues, but their forms and strategies are diverse. These baobab trees in Madagascar may live to be hundreds of years old despite drought conditions, in part by storing water in their enormous trunks.

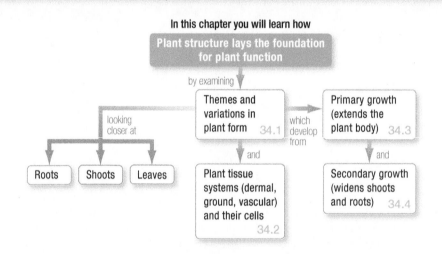

In this chapter you will learn how

Plant structure lays the foundation for plant function

by examining

Themes and variations in plant form 34.1

looking closer at

Roots → Shoots → Leaves

which develop from

Primary growth (extends the plant body) 34.3

and

Plant tissue systems (dermal, ground, vascular) and their cells 34.2

and

Secondary growth (widens shoots and roots) 34.4

This chapter is part of the Big Picture. See how on pages 816–817.

Plants carry out photosynthesis, the most remarkable biochemistry of any terrestrial organisms. Using the energy in sunlight and the simplest of starting materials—carbon dioxide, water, and ions containing nitrogen, phosphorus, potassium, and other key atoms—plants synthesize thousands of different carbohydrates, proteins, nucleic acids, and lipids. They use these compounds to build bodies that may live for thousands of years.

This feat is even more impressive when you consider that the simple starting materials that plants need to grow are tiny and diffuse—carbon dioxide molecules, water molecules, nitrate ions, and other resources are usually found at low concentrations over a large area. To gather the raw materials required for their sophisticated biosynthetic machinery, a plant's roots and shoots grow outward, extending the individual into the soil and atmosphere.

In essence, a plant's body harvests diffuse resources and concentrates them in cells and tissues. The structure of its body is dynamic, because most plants exhibit **indeterminate growth;** that is, unlike animals, plants continue to grow throughout their lives. A bristlecone pine over 5000 years old has roots and shoots that are still growing. In response to favorable conditions, a plant sends shoots and roots in the most promising directions, seeking light and the simple compounds it requires.

The contrast between the plant and animal way of life is striking. Most animals move around, eat concentrated sources of food, and avoid stressful conditions. But plants stay in one place, extend their roots and shoots to harvest diffuse resources, make their own food, and cope with stress where they stand.

This chapter focuses on three fundamental questions:

1. How is the plant body organized?

2. Why are plants so diverse in size and shape?

3. How do plants grow throughout their lives?

Instead of surveying the entire catalog of land plants, though, the focus here is on the flowering plants, or angiosperms. Recall that angiosperms are the most recent major group of plants to appear in the fossil record (see Chapter 28). With about 300,000 species described, they are by far the most abundant, species rich, and geographically widespread plant group today. Also, their economic and medical importance to humans is difficult to overstate. Most of the food we eat and many of the medicines we use are derived from angiosperms.

If you look outside or down the produce aisle of a grocery store, you will see a wide diversity of plants and plant products. By the time you finish this chapter, you'll understand how plants are put together and how they grow. Exploring questions about the anatomy of flowering plants is vital to understanding the world at large as well as the other chapters in this unit. (You can review the importance of plant form and function in the Big Picture of plant and animal physiology on pages 816–817.)

34.1 Plant Form: Themes with Many Variations

Plants—along with algae, cyanobacteria, and a variety of protists—are photosynthetic and able to produce their own food (see Chapter 10). Plants use light energy to synthesize carbohydrates from carbon dioxide in the air and water from the soil. For photosynthesis to occur efficiently, plants need large amounts of light, carbon dioxide, and water.

To synthesize nucleic acids, enzymes, phospholipids, and the other molecules needed to build and maintain cells, plants must obtain nitrogen (N), phosphorus (P), potassium (K), magnesium (Mg), and a host of other nutrients. Most of these key elements exist in nature as ions dissolved in water found in soil.

Figure 34.1 identifies the major structures in the two basic systems that plants use to acquire the resources they need for photosynthesis. A belowground portion called the **root system** anchors the plant and takes in water and nutrients from the soil; an aboveground portion called the **shoot system** harvests light and carbon dioxide from the atmosphere to produce

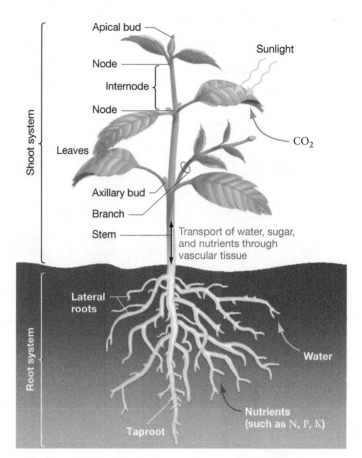

Figure 34.1 Typical Root and Shoot Systems Acquire and Transport Resources. Shoot systems are specialized for harvesting light and CO_2. Root systems absorb water and key nutrients such as nitrogen (N), phosphorus (P), and potassium (K).

✔ Suppose that this plant's growth was limited by access to light and nutrients, and that the plant had a new deposit of nutrient-rich soil to the left and much more sunlight suddenly available to the right. What would you expect this plant to look like in one month?

sugars. Both systems grow throughout the life of the individual, allowing the plant to increase in size, acquire resources, and reproduce. Collectively, the root and shoot systems make up the **plant body.**

Plant bodies can be quite diverse. Some flowering plants, such as duckweed, are small, typically just a few millimeters in length. Others are giants of the natural world. The Centurion tree, for example, has a height of nearly 100 m and represents the tallest angiosperm in the world. Duckweed and the Centurion tree clearly have different challenges to growth and survival. The Centurion tree, for example, requires an extensive root system to support and sustain the shoot system while duckweed does not.

In most plants, vascular tissue connects the root and shoot systems. Through vascular tissue, water and nutrients are transported from roots to shoots; sugars can be transported in both directions. As you learn about how plant form has evolved and serves necessary functions, compare and contrast what you learn with how animals have adapted to new environmental challenges. In many ways the two groups are remarkably similar.

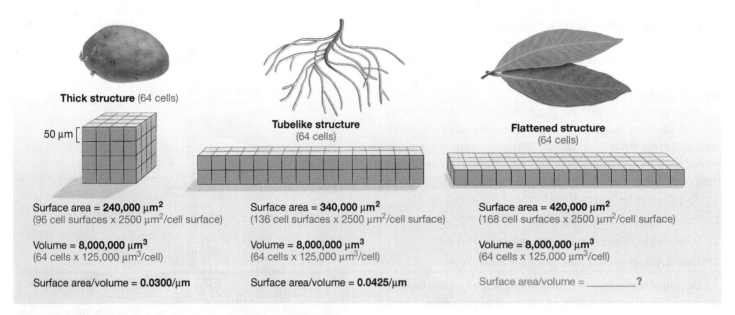

Thick structure (64 cells)

50 μm

Surface area = **240,000 μm²**
(96 cell surfaces x 2500 μm²/cell surface)

Volume = **8,000,000 μm³**
(64 cells x 125,000 μm³/cell)

Surface area/volume = **0.0300/μm**

Tubelike structure
(64 cells)

Surface area = **340,000 μm²**
(136 cell surfaces x 2500 μm²/cell surface)

Volume = **8,000,000 μm³**
(64 cells x 125,000 μm³/cell)

Surface area/volume = **0.0425/μm**

Flattened structure
(64 cells)

Surface area = **420,000 μm²**
(168 cell surfaces x 2500 μm²/cell surface)

Volume = **8,000,000 μm³**
(64 cells x 125,000 μm³/cell)

Surface area/volume = _____ ?

Figure 34.2 The Morphology of Roots and Leaves Gives Them a High Surface Area/Volume Ratio. In this example, the "thick structure" represents a potato-like storage organ; the "tubelike structure" represents a root; the "flattened structure" represents a leaf. Note that each schematic structure has the same number of cells (each represented as a small cube) and the same total volume—but a very different surface area.

✔ **QUANTITATIVE** What is the surface area/volume ratio for the flattened structure?

The Importance of Surface Area/Volume Relationships

Before exploring the nature of root and shoot systems in more detail, it's important to recognize a key structural relationship that is critical to their function.

Root and shoot systems both function in absorption—roots absorb water and key nutrients, and shoots absorb light. Absorption takes place across a surface. But the cells that use the absorbed molecules and light occupy a volume. Thus, a plant body is more efficient as an absorption-and-synthesis machine when it has a large surface area relative to its volume.

Figure 34.2 illustrates this point. In this example, the cells in a plant are represented by cubes; the side of each cell is 50 μm long. Thus, each face of a cell has a surface area of

$$50 \times 50 \text{ (length} \times \text{width)} = 2500 \text{ μm}^2$$

and each cell has a volume of

$$50 \times 50 \times 50 \text{ (length} \times \text{width} \times \text{height)} = 125,000 \text{ μm}^3.$$

Follow the calculations in the figure and note that the surface area/volume ratio of the entire structure changes depending on its shape. For example:

- If 64 cells are arranged in a cube, the surface area/volume ratio is 0.0300/μm.

- If 64 cells are arranged in a long tube, the surface area/volume ratio is 0.0425/μm.

This simple exercise has an important punch line: Tubes have a greater surface area/volume ratio than cubes with the same number and size of cells. If you calculate the ratio for the pictured

flattened structure, you should see that this structure has even more surface area relative to volume than tubes. (To bring this point home, draw it out for yourself in **Making Models 34.1**.)

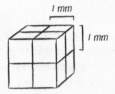

Making Models 34.1 Tips on Modeling Surface Area to Volume Ratios

Surface area/volume relationships depend not only on structure size but also structure shape. For example, the structure below is cubic in shape and is made up of eight smaller cubes. If each smaller cube has a length, width, and height of 1 mm, the surface area of the large cube would be 24 mm² (length × width × 6 sides) while its volume would be 8 mm³ (length × width × height).

1 mm

1 mm

MODEL Redraw the eight small cubes lined up end to end to model a long tube. Determine whether this structure's surface area and volume are any different from that of the large cube.

To see this model in action, go to https://goo.gl/swbhH8

It's no surprise, then, that the absorptive regions of a root system are tubelike, and the absorptive regions of a shoot system are flattened structures called leaves. Storage tissues such as tubers and seeds have a low surface area/volume ratio because they are not involved in absorption.

The Root System

Many root systems have a central **taproot,** as well as numerous **lateral roots** (see Figure 34.1). The root system anchors the plant in soil, absorbs water and ions from the soil, conducts water and selected ions to the shoot, obtains energy in the form of sugar from the shoot, and stores material produced in the shoot for later use.

Root systems can be impressive in extent. For example, in 1937 botanist Howard Dittmer grew a winter rye plant in a container full of soil for four months. He then unearthed the plant and meticulously measured its roots. The root system of this single individual contained more than 14 billion identifiable structures with a combined length of over 11,000 km—over one-fourth of Earth's circumference. The total surface area of the root system was almost 640 m^2, or about the size of 1.5 basketball courts. A root system like this is clearly adapted to absorbing diffuse resources located underground.

Other studies have shown that **(1)** the roots of trees routinely extend beyond the width of their aboveground canopy, and **(2)** it is not unusual for a plant's root system to represent over 80 percent of its total mass. Many plants devote a great deal of energy and resources to the growth of their root systems.

Although most root systems contain the same general structures, the root systems are diverse. This diversity can be analyzed on three levels:

1. morphological diversity among species;

2. phenotypic plasticity, or changes in the structure of an individual's root system in response to the environment; and

3. modified roots that are specialized for unusual functions.

Let's consider each level in turn.

Morphological Diversity in Root Systems

As an example of the range of morphological diversity observed in the root systems of angiosperms, consider prairie plants.

Prairies are grassland ecosystems found in areas of the world such as central North America, the Serengeti Plain of East Africa, the Pampas region of Argentina, and the steppes of central Asia (see Chapter 49). Rain is abundant enough in these areas to support a lush growth of **herbaceous** plants—seed plants that lack woody tissue—yet scarce enough to exclude trees and most shrubs. The growth of woody species is also discouraged by fires that regularly sweep through these ecosystems.

Although the aboveground portions of prairie plants burn during fires and die back during the winter or dry season, their root systems are **perennial,** meaning that they live for many years. The root system sends up a new shoot system each spring and also after a fire. **Figure 34.3** shows that the root systems of prairie plants can be very different, even if they live next to each other. For example, the dense, fibrous root systems of junegrass and switchgrass do not have a taproot, whereas the taproot of a compass plant can reach depths of over 4.5 m. As a result, competition for water and nutrients is minimized between these species.

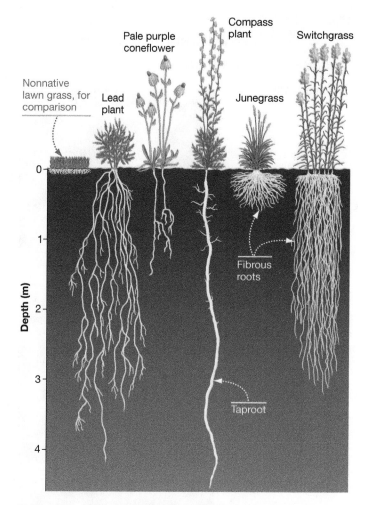

Figure 34.3 Plants Have Diverse Root Systems. The roots of prairie plants that live side by side can be very different.

✔ Which prairie plants would be more likely to absorb rain when it first enters soil? Which would be most likely to absorb water and continue growing during periods of drought?

Phenotypic Plasticity in Root Systems

Morphological diversity in roots occurs within species as well as among species. Some of the within-species variation is due to genetic diversity among individuals, but some is due to how roots respond to the environment.

Roots show a great deal of **phenotypic plasticity**—meaning that their form is changeable, depending on environmental conditions. For example, spruce trees in waterlogged soils tend to have root systems less than a meter deep. Their roots are shallow because wet soil lacks oxygen, and root cells, like animal cells, suffocate in anoxic conditions. The same tree growing in drier soil would develop a root system several meters deep. The key point is that even genetically identical individuals may have very different root systems if they grow in different environments.

Phenotypic plasticity is particularly important in plants because they grow throughout their lives, and sometimes their environment changes. Roots actively grow into areas of soil where resources are abundant, such as nutrient-rich septic fields or sewer pipes that leak human waste. Roots stop growing or die back in areas where resources are used up or lacking.

Form and Function of Modified Roots

Modified Root	Example
Anchor roots	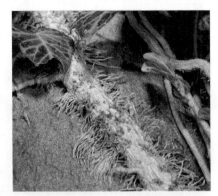
These adventitious roots anchor stems to walls and to other plants	
Prop roots	
These adventitious roots stabilize the stem	
Pneumatophores	
Pneumatophores allow gas exchange between roots and atmosphere	
Storage roots	
Sugar beets store carbohydrates and other nutrients in their taproot for future use	

✔ Why do root cells need oxygen?

Modified Roots The taproots and fibrous roots illustrated earlier do not begin to exhaust the types of roots found among plants (Table 34.1). For example, some roots are **adventitious**—meaning they develop from an unusual source, the shoot system instead of the root system.

- In ivy, anchor roots—adventitious roots that grow from nodes in the shoot system (see Figure 34.1)—help anchor individuals to brick walls or other structures.

- The prop roots of corn are adventitious roots that help brace individuals in windy weather.

Even roots that are part of the root system can have specialized functions—meaning that they do things other than absorb water and nutrients and anchor the shoot system.

The pneumatophores of mangroves in the genus *Avicennia* are specialized lateral roots that function in gas exchange. These mangroves grow in submerged habitats where fine silt is deposited, cutting off the oxygen supply to their roots. Their root cells do not suffocate, however, because oxygen from the atmosphere can diffuse into the root system through the pneumatophores. These roots grow upward—not downward—in response to gravity.

The thick taproot of some biennial plants, such as carrots and beets, stores carbohydrates during the first of the plants' two growing seasons. Carrot roots—the "carrots" you might have eaten for lunch—are typically harvested at this point. Sugar beets are harvested to produce much of the sugar commonly found in grocery stores. If the roots were not harvested, the plants would resume growth after the winter and use that stored energy during a second summer to "go to seed," producing a large flowering shoot. Carbohydrates in the taproot make the energy-intensive reproductive process possible.

The Shoot System

As Figure 34.1 indicates, the shoot system has an array of important anatomical features.

- The shoot system consists of one or more **stems,** which are vertical aboveground structures.

- A stem consists of **nodes,** where leaves are attached, and **internodes,** or segments between nodes.

- A **leaf** is an appendage that projects from a stem laterally. Leaves usually function as photosynthetic organs.

- The nodes where leaves attach to the stem are also the site of **axillary** (or **lateral**) **buds,** which form just above the site of leaf attachment.

- If conditions are appropriate, an axillary bud may grow into a **branch**—a lateral extension of the shoot system.

- The tip of each stem and branch contains an **apical bud,** where growth occurs that extends the length of the stem or branch.

- If conditions are appropriate, apical or axillary buds may develop into flowers or other reproductive structures.

As with root systems, diversity in shoots can be analyzed on three levels: morphological diversity among species, phenotypic plasticity within individuals, and modified shoots with specialized functions.

Morphological Diversity in Shoot Systems The shoot systems of plants, essentially the visible part of the plant, range in size from species like the tiny (< 5 mm diameter) duckweed that you may have seen growing on the surface of stagnant ponds to redwood trees that reach heights of over 100 m (300 ft) and giant sequoias with trunks that weigh 2.6 million kg (over 5.7 million lb)—about the same as 10 diesel locomotives.

Variation in the size and shape of the shoot system is important: It allows plants of different species to harvest light at different locations and thus minimize competition. It also allows plants to thrive in a wide array of habitats.

As an example of how the shape of a shoot system varies among species in different environments, consider the silversword plants native to Hawaii. You might recall that all silverswords are believed to be descended from the same ancestor—a species of tarweed that arrived in Hawaii from North America about 5 million years ago (see Chapter 25).

Silverswords represent an adaptive radiation: a lineage that rapidly split into many species occupying a wide array of habitats. Their shoot systems are particularly diverse in size, shape, and growth habit. Some silverswords grow low to the ground in dense mats; some form bunched rosettes of leaves; some are vines; others are woody shrubs or even small- to medium-sized trees.

Biologists interpret this diversity of shoot systems as a suite of adaptations for harvesting light and carbon dioxide in different environments.

- In lush habitats, where competition for light is intense, woody individuals that grow tall are favored by natural selection.

- In dry, windblown habitats, individuals with short stems or rosettes thrive because they require less water than taller individuals, and they don't blow over.

The adaptive radiation of silverswords has been based in part on diversification in their shoot systems.

Phenotypic Plasticity in Shoot Systems The size and shape of an individual's shoot system can vary dramatically based on variation in growing conditions: temperature, exposure to wind, and availability of water, nutrients, and light.

This conclusion was driven home in an experiment conducted by Jens Clausen and colleagues in the late 1930s. They transplanted several species of herbaceous plants between sites along an elevational gradient: from sea level to alpine habitats. In each case, the transplanted individuals were propagated from cuttings—meaning that they were genetically identical to individuals growing at the other locations. As the "Results" section in **Figure 34.4** shows, the overall size and shape of the shoot system varied markedly among locations. These results indicate that genetics *and* environment affect overall plant form.

Because a plant's shoot system continues to grow over the course of its lifetime, it can respond to changes in environmental conditions just like the root system can. Experiments on phototropism, for example, established that shoot systems can bend toward light if an individual is shaded on one side (see Chapter 37). Plants also undergo differential growth, producing more branches and leaves in regions of the body that are exposed to the highest light levels. A plant's shoot system grows in directions that maximize its chances of capturing light.

RESEARCH

QUESTION: How much does a plant's growth form depend on its environment?

HYPOTHESIS: (No explicit hypothesis—the goal of this experiment was to explore the interaction between genetic makeup versus environmental influence on size and shape.)

EXPERIMENTAL SETUP:

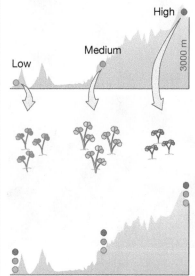

1. **Take cuttings** from individuals of *Potentilla glandulosa* growing in low-, medium-, and high-elevation habitats in the Sierra Nevada mountains.

2. **Propagate** genetically identical individuals.

3. **Transplant** individuals from each source population into each habitat (low, medium, and high elevation). Allow to grow and observe mature plants.

PREDICTION: (No explicit predictions.)

RESULTS:

Examples of mature plants observed:

"High" plant **grown at** low elevation

"High" plant **grown at** medium elevation

"High" plant **grown at** high elevation

CONCLUSION: Environmental conditions have a profound influence on body size and shape (genetically identical plants look different at each site). BUT, genetic makeup also has a large influence on plant morphology. (Though not pictured here, plants from the different source populations looked different, even when all were grown in the same habitat.)

Figure 34.4 Experimental Evidence Supports Phenotypic Plasticity in Shoot Systems.

SOURCE: Clausen, J., D. D. Keck, and W. M. Hiesey. 1940. *Experimental studies on the nature of species. I. Effect of varied environments on western North American plants.* Publication 520. Washington, DC: Carnegie Institution.

✔ **PROCESS OF SCIENCE** Why was it important for the researchers to propagate the individuals from cuttings before transplanting them?

Form and Function of Modified Stems

Modified Stem	Example
Water-storage structures Cactus stems store water; the spines are modified leaves (the example shown is a longitudinal section)	
Stolons Strawberry stolons produce new individuals at nodes aboveground	
Rhizomes Rhizomes produce new individuals at nodes belowground, and store carbohydrates	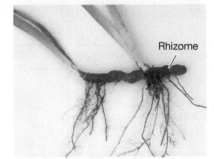
Tubers Tubers such as potatoes store carbohydrates such as starch	
Thorns Thorns provide protection from herbivores	

Modified Stems As in root systems, the stems of many plants have modified structures to serve various functions (Table 34.2).

- Many desert cacti have highly modified stems. Instead of functioning primarily to support leaves, cactus stems often enlarge into water-storage organs. Water accounts for up to 98 percent of the weight of a cactus stem. Cactus stems also contain the plant's photosynthetic tissue.

- **Stolons** are modified stems that grow horizontally along the soil surface, producing adventitious roots and leaves at each node. Because new plants form at these nodes, stolons function in asexual reproduction (see Chapter 38).

- Like stolons, **rhizomes** are stems that grow horizontally instead of vertically. They produce new plants at nodes and thus participate in asexual reproduction. But while stolons grow aboveground, rhizomes spread belowground. One quaking aspen plant in Utah was found to have 47,000 stems rising from a network of rhizomes, making it one of the largest organisms known. What we see as individual aspen trees are actually stems that are connected underground.

- **Tubers** are underground, swollen rhizomes that function as carbohydrate-storage organs. The eyes of a potato—a typical tuber—are nodes in the stem where new branches may arise.

- **Thorns** are modified stems that help protect the plant from attacks by large **herbivores,** or plant eaters, such as deer, giraffe, or cattle.

The Leaf

In most plant species, the vast majority of photosynthesis occurs in the part of the shoot system called the leaf. The total area of leaf produced by a single plant can be enormous—a single tree can have hundreds of thousands of leaves with a total surface area equivalent to that of a football field. All of this area is available for absorbing photons and supporting photosynthesis.

A **simple leaf** (Figure 34.5a) is composed of just two major structures: an expanded portion called the **blade** and a stalk called the **petiole.** But leaves exhibit many variations on the central theme of a flattened structure specialized for performing photosynthesis. Chapter 38 explores leaf development more fully.

Morphological Diversity in Leaves Glance outside or stroll through a garden, and you'll find many types of simple leaves with an easily recognizable blade and petiole. (Grass leaves will stump you, though, because they lack petioles entirely.) You will also find **compound leaves** that have blades divided into a series of leaflets (Figure 34.5b). You may even encounter doubly compound leaves, which have leaflets that are again divided (Figure 34.5c). Although a compound leaf easily can be mistaken for several individual leaves, the defining feature of an individual leaf (whether simple or compound) is the presence of an axillary bud where the petiole joins the stem (see Figure 34.1).

Not all leaf blades are thin with a large surface area, however. For example, plants that thrive in deserts and in cold, dry habitats tend to have needlelike leaves (Figure 34.5d). The leading hypothesis to explain this pattern is based on two observations: **(1)** Water

(a) A simple leaf has a petiole and a single blade.

(b) A compound leaf has a blade divided into leaflets.

(c) A doubly compound leaf is large yet rarely damaged by wind or rain.

(d) Needlelike leaves are characteristic of species adapted to very cold or hot climates.

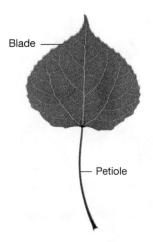

Blade

Petiole

Figure 34.5 **Leaves Vary in Size and Shape.** The structure in **(a)** represents a simple leaf, while **(b)** and **(c)** represent compound leaves. Part **(d)** shows two leaves.

✔ **CAUTION** How many leaves are shown in **(b)** and **(c)**?

is often in short supply in these environments because it is scarce in deserts, or frozen and thus unavailable in cold habitats; and **(2)** leaves with large surface areas lose large amounts of water through an evaporative process called **transpiration** (discussed in Chapter 35). Thus, needlelike leaves are interpreted as adaptations that minimize transpiration in water-scarce habitats. Small, narrow leaves are also much less susceptible to wind damage than are large, broad leaves.

The arrangement of leaves on a stem can vary as much as leaf shape. For example, leaves can be

- arranged to alternate on either side of the stem (**Figure 34.6a**);
- paired opposite each other on the stem (**Figure 34.6b**);
- arranged in a whorl (**Figure 34.6c**);

- found in a compact arrangement where internodes are extremely short—leading to a rosette growth form (**Figure 34.6d**).

Clearly, there is tremendous variation in the ways in which leaves are arranged on stems. Despite this variation, the development and arrangement of leaves follow well-defined patterns that tend to be species specific. Leaf shape and the arrangement of leaves on a stem are usually determined genetically, so these characters are often used for plant identification.

Phenotypic Plasticity in Leaves Even though leaves do not grow continuously, they exhibit phenotypic plasticity just like root systems and stems do. Leaves from the same individual that grow in sun versus shade serve as a prominent example of phenotypic plasticity in leaf morphology. As the oak tree leaves in

(a) Alternate leaves

(b) Opposite leaves

(c) Whorled leaves

(d) Rosette

Figure 34.6 **The Arrangement of Leaves on Stems Varies.**

Figure 34.7 Leaves Exhibit Phenotypic Plasticity. These leaves came from the same tree.

Figure 34.7 show, the leaf grown in the sun is much smaller than the leaf grown in the shade:

- *Sun leaves* typically are thicker and have a relatively small surface area, which reduces water loss in areas of the body where light is abundant.
- *Shade leaves* are relatively thin and broad, providing a high surface area that maximizes absorption of rare photons.

Water loss is less of a problem for shade leaves because temperatures are cooler in shade than in bright sun.

✔ If you understand the concept of phenotypic plasticity, you should be able to explain why phenotypic plasticity in roots and shoots is expected to be more important (1) in environments where conditions are variable versus stable, and (2) in long-lived versus short-lived species.

Modified Leaves   Not all leaves function primarily in photosynthesis; some perform other roles (Table 34.3).

- Onion bulbs consist of thickened leaf bases that store nutrients, separated by highly condensed internodes.
- The thick leaves of plants called succulents, such as aloe vera, store water.
- The tendrils that enable plants, such as a grapevine, to climb are modified leaflets or leaves.
- The bright red leaves of poinsettias attract pollinators to the tiny yellow flowers that they surround.
- The tubelike leaves of the pitcher plant trap insects. When insects enter, they feed on the plant's nectar and appear to become dizzy. Eventually they fall into the bottom of the tube and drown in water that has accumulated. The insects are then digested by bacteria or enzymes secreted by the plant, and the plant absorbs the nutrients released.
- Cactus spines are modified leaves that protect the stem (see top image in Table 34.2).

The variability of plant roots, stems, and leaves is impressive. Diversity, plasticity, and dynamism are recurring themes in the study of plant anatomy. The next section will explore the diversity of cells and tissues found within plants.

SUMMARY Table 34.3
Form and Function of Modified Leaves

Modified Leaves	Example
Bulbs Onion leaves store food	 Stem Leaves
Succulent leaves Aloe vera leaves store water	
Tendrils Pea tendrils aid in climbing	
Floral mimics Red poinsettia leaves attract pollinators	 Flowers Leaves
Traps Pitcher plant leaves trap entering insects, use their hood to discourage insects from flying out, and then digest them	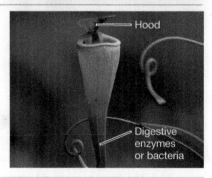 Hood Digestive enzymes or bacteria

34.2 Plant Cells and Tissue Systems

Recall that all eukaryotic cells, including those of plants and animals, share most of their key characteristics: chromosomes enclosed in a nuclear envelope, a plasma membrane studded with proteins that regulate the passage of materials in and out, mitochondria that produce ATP by oxidizing sugars, and an array of other organelles that synthesize or degrade key molecules.

In addition, plant cells have several features that are absent in animal cells (**Figure 34.8**):

1. All plant cells are surrounded by a cellulose-rich **primary cell wall** that supports the cell and defines its shape. In addition, some plant cells go on to form a **secondary cell wall,** which is often hard and rigid.

2. The cytoplasm of adjacent plant cells is often connected via **plasmodesmata** (singular: **plasmodesma**) (see Chapter 11). Plasmodesmata consist of cytoplasm and segments of smooth endoplasmic reticulum (smooth ER) that run through tiny, membrane-lined gaps in the cell wall (Figure 34.8b).

3. Plant cells often contain several types of organelles that are not found in animals—specifically chloroplasts and a large, membrane-bound organelle called a vacuole, which fills most of the cell's volume.

Chloroplasts are the site of photosynthesis (see Chapter 10). Non-photosynthetic cells found in roots, seeds, flower petals, and other locations may have organelles that are similar to chloroplasts but are specialized for storing pigments, starch, oils, or proteins.

Vacuoles, which contain an aqueous solution called **cell sap,** store wastes and in some cases also digest wastes, as do animal lysosomes. In addition, plant vacuoles store water and nutrients. They may also hold pigments that provide color, or poisons that deter herbivores.

Another important distinction between plant cells and animal cells is that plant cells do not change position once they form. Some animal cells migrate within the body either early in the development of an individual or as mature (differentiated) cells.

Like animal cells, plant cells with similar structure are often associated and form distinct tissues. A **tissue** is a group of cells that functions as a unit. Plant tissues that consist of a single cell

(a) Plant cells have cell walls, vacuoles, and chloroplasts.

(b) Adjacent plant cells are connected by plasmodesmata.

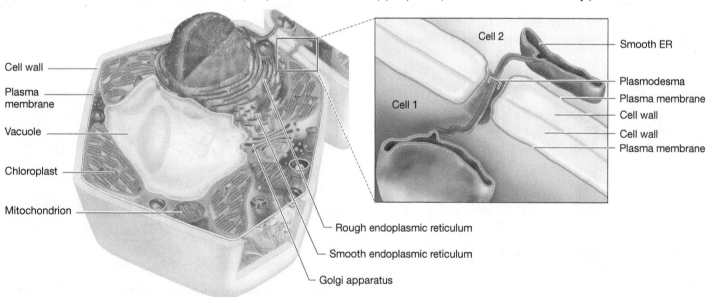

Figure 34.8 A Plant Cell Is Both Similar to and Different from an Animal Cell. Plant vacuoles are similar to animal lysosomes; however, the cell wall, chloroplasts, and plasmodesmata are unique to plants.

type are called **simple tissues;** tissues that contain several types of cells are termed **complex tissues.** Moreover, plant tissues are grouped together into broader categories, referred to as **tissue systems,** based on their structural features and location within the plant. The three tissue systems found in plants are **(1)** the dermal tissue system, **(2)** the ground tissue system, and **(3)** the vascular tissue system. Let's examine each of these in turn.

The Dermal Tissue System

The **dermal tissue system** consists of dermal tissue (literally, "skin" tissue). This tissue, also called the **epidermis,** is the outermost layer of cells and represents the interface between the organism and the external environment. Its primary function in shoots is to protect the plant—from water loss, disease-causing agents, and herbivores. In roots the epidermis includes root hairs, and it functions primarily in absorbing water and nutrients.

The epidermis is made up of several different cell types, and therefore represents a complex tissue. Let's consider the functional significance of cell types found in dermal tissue.

Epidermal Cells Protect the Surface   Most shoot epidermal cells are flattened and usually lack chloroplasts. Epidermal cells in the shoot system fulfill their protective role in part by secreting the **cuticle**—a waxy layer that forms a continuous sheet on the surface of leaves and stems (see Chapter 28). Waxes are lipids and are hydrophobic. As a result, the cuticle reduces the amount of water that stems and leaves lose by evaporation.

From a human perspective, the water-repellent properties of cuticle make it a valuable ingredient in polishes and lipsticks. A wax used in car and floor polishes, for example, is secreted by epidermal cells in the leaves of carnauba palms native to Brazil.

Besides minimizing water loss, the cuticle forms a barrier to protect the plant from viruses, bacteria, and the spores or growing hyphae of parasitic fungi. In this way, the plant epidermis forms the first line of defense against disease-causing agents, or **pathogens.**

Waxes found in the cuticle can also be detrimental to the plant, however, by reducing gas exchange. This can be a serious problem because photosynthesis depends on the free flow of carbon dioxide to photosynthetic cells. The problem is solved by specialized structures in dermal tissue, called stomata.

Stomata Regulate Gas Exchange and Water Loss   Most plants have structures called **stomata** (singular: **stoma**), typically found on leaves, which are pores that allow CO_2 to enter and O_2 to exit photosynthetically active tissues. A stoma is surrounded by two specialized **guard cells,** which change shape to open or close the stoma (**Figure 34.9**).

When stomata are open, CO_2, O_2, water vapor, and other gases can move between the atmosphere and the interior of the plant by diffusion. Stomata open when adequate water is available and CO_2 is needed for photosynthesis. When stomata are open, water diffuses from the moist interior of the leaf to the surrounding atmosphere. Stomata close when conditions are dry. This prevents large amounts of water from being lost by transpiration.

Trichomes Perform an Array of Functions   In addition to minimizing water loss and regulating gas exchange in shoots, cells in dermal tissue protect the individual from the damaging effects of intense sunlight and attacks by herbivores.

Trichomes are hairlike appendages made up of specialized epidermal cells. They are found in shoot systems and come in a wide variety of shapes, sizes, and abundances. Depending on the species, trichomes may **(1)** keep the leaf surface cool by reflecting sunlight; **(2)** reduce water loss by forming a dense mat that limits transpiration; **(3)** provide barbs or store toxic compounds that thwart herbivores (**Figure 34.10**); or **(4)** trap and digest insects.

The Ground Tissue System

Most photosynthesis, as well as most carbohydrate storage, takes place in the **ground tissue system.** Cells in ground tissue are also responsible for most of the synthesis and storage of specialized products such as colorful pigments, hormones, and toxins required for defense. Some ground tissue cells also play a large role in structural support of the shoot system.

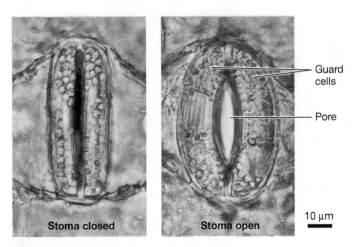

Stoma closed   Stoma open

Guard cells

Pore

10 µm

Figure 34.9 **A Stoma's Guard Cells Regulate the Opening of a Pore.**

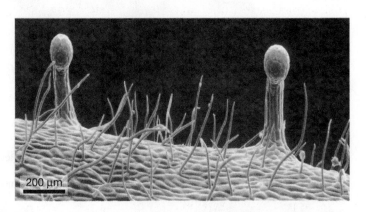

200 µm

Figure 34.10 **Epidermal Cells Produce Trichomes That Provide Protection.** Some trichomes on this leaf are hairlike extensions of a single cell, while others are multicellular structures. The structures that are colored orange here hold toxins.

(a) In leaves: photosynthesis and gas exchange

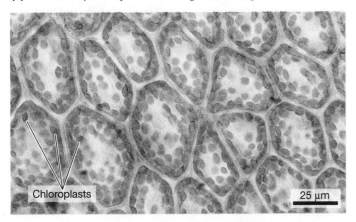

Chloroplasts

25 µm

(b) In roots: carbohydrate storage

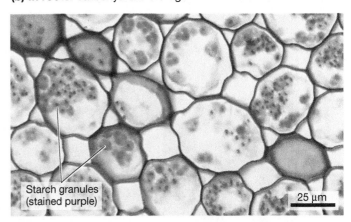

Starch granules
(stained purple)

25 µm

Figure 34.11 Parenchyma Cells Perform a Wide Array of Tasks.

✔ Give three possible examples of genes encoding proteins that are likely to be expressed in leaf cells, but not in root cells.

The ground tissue system consists of three distinct tissues: parenchyma (pronounced *pa-REN-ki-ma*), collenchyma (*ko-LEN-ki-ma*), and sclerenchyma (*skle-REN-ki-ma*).

Parenchyma Consists of "Workhorse" Cells Parenchyma tissue is composed of parenchyma cells, which have relatively thin primary cell walls and are the most common and versatile ground tissue cells. Parenchyma represents a simple tissue.

The parenchyma tissue in leaves consists of parenchyma cells filled with chloroplasts, and it is the primary site of photosynthesis (**Figure 34.11a**). But in other organs, parenchyma cells store starch granules (**Figure 34.11b**). When you eat a potato or an apple, you are ingesting primarily parenchyma cells.

Many parenchyma cells are **totipotent,** meaning they retain the capacity to divide and develop into a complete, mature plant. The totipotency of parenchyma cells is important in healing wounds and in reproducing asexually via stolons or rhizomes. In each case, parenchyma cells may begin to divide, grow, and differentiate to form new roots and shoots.

The totipotency of parenchyma cells also allows gardeners to clone plants by making cuttings. For example, if you cut a piece of stem from a coleus plant and place it in water, parenchyma cells will divide to produce a mass of undifferentiated cells called a **callus.** Roots then develop from the callus, and the new individual can be planted in soil (see BioSkills 11).

Collenchyma Functions Primarily in Shoot Support The cells of **collenchyma** tissue are similar to parenchyma cells but are characterized by an unevenly thickened primary cell wall and are longer and thinner than parenchyma cells. Collenchyma represents another example of a simple tissue.

Collenchyma tissue is often found just under the epidermis of stems, especially outside vascular bundles. Collenchyma cells are not rigid, and their ability to stretch allows stems to flex in the wind without tearing or breaking. These cells provide flexible structural support for shoots. The "strings" you may have peeled from a stalk of celery or rhubarb include many strands of collenchyma cells (**Figure 34.12**).

Sclerenchyma: Two Types of Specialized Support Cells The cells of **sclerenchyma** tissue are characterized by the presence of the thick, rigid secondary cell wall in addition to the relatively thin primary cell wall. Unlike the primary cell wall, the secondary cell wall contains the tough, rigid compound **lignin** in addition to **cellulose** (see Chapter 28).

(a) Cross section of celery stalk

(b) Close-up of "string," in cross section

(c) Collenchyma cells, in cross section

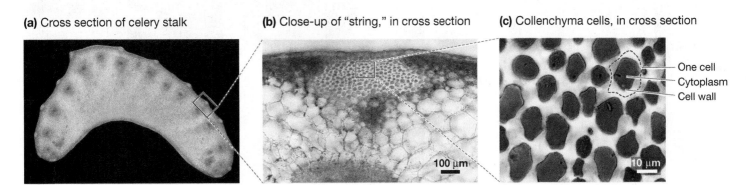

100 µm

One cell
Cytoplasm
Cell wall

10 µm

Figure 34.12 Collenchyma Cells Support Growing Tissues. A celery stalk is actually a petiole; the strands you can peel from it are columns of collenchyma cells.

(a) Fibers

(b) Sclereids

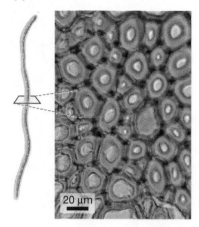

Figure 34.13 Sclerenchyma Cells Support Mature Tissues.
(a) Fibers from *Tilia* (linden tree) and **(b)** sclereids from a pear (stained pink) have thickened secondary cell walls. These cells provide support and protection.

Collenchyma cells can support actively growing parts of the plant because the primary cell wall is expandable. In contrast, the nonexpandable secondary cell wall of sclerenchyma cells specializes them for supporting stems and other structures after growth has ceased. Another key difference between collenchyma and sclerenchyma is that sclerenchyma cells are usually dead at maturity—meaning they contain no cytoplasm.

Two types of sclerenchyma cells are recognized: fibers and sclereids.

- **Fibers** are extremely elongated. The fiber cells from ramie plants, a species of Asian nettle, can be over half a meter long. Fiber cells are important in the manufacture of paper, hemp or jute ropes, and linen and other fabrics (**Figure 34.13a**).

- **Sclereids** are relatively short, have variable shapes, and often function in protection. The tough coats of seeds and the thick shells of nuts are composed of sclereids; these cells are also responsible for the gritty texture of pears (**Figure 34.13b**).

The Vascular Tissue System

The **vascular tissue system** functions in support and in long-distance transport of water and dissolved nutrients in vascular plants (see Chapter 28). It also moves the products of photosynthesis that are made and stored in ground tissue.

The vascular tissue system consists of two complex tissues: xylem and phloem.

- **Xylem** (pronounced *ZYE-lem*) conducts water and dissolved nutrients in one direction: from the root system to the shoot system.

- **Phloem** (*FLO-em*) conducts sugar, amino acids, hormones, and other substances in two directions: from roots to shoots and from shoots to roots.

Xylem Structure The xylem of many plants includes water-conducting cells as well as parenchyma cells and fibers. The two types of water-conducting cells in xylem are tracheids and vessel elements.

- The xylem of all vascular plants contains **tracheids** (*TRAY-kee-ids*).

- In angiosperms, as well as members of the Gnetophyta and a few other groups of vascular plants, xylem also contains **vessel elements** (see Chapter 28).

Although most plant cells perform their function while alive, tracheids and vessel elements—like sclerenchyma cells—are dead at maturity and contain no cytoplasm. The xylem cells have thick, lignin-containing secondary cell walls; in essence, the cell walls form pipelines for the movement of water and nutrients from roots to shoots.

(a) Tracheids are long, tapered, and have pits.

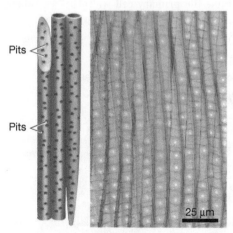

Pits

Pits

(b) Vessel elements are short and wide and have perforations as well as pits.

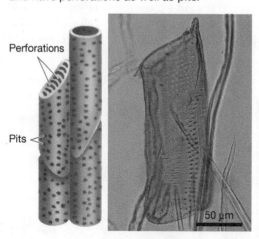

Perforations

Pits

(c) Tracheids and vessel elements are found together in vascular tissue.

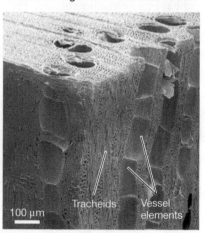

Tracheids

Vessel elements

Figure 34.14 Xylem May Contain Two Types of Water-Conducting Cells. (a) Tracheids are long and thin compared to **(b)** vessel elements, which are much shorter and wider. **(c)** Both types of water-conducting cells are found in the vascular tissue of angiosperms.

Tracheids are long, slender cells with tapered ends (Figure 34.14a). The sides and ends of tracheids have **pits,** which are gaps in the secondary cell wall where only the primary cell wall is present. When water is moving up a plant through tracheids, it moves from cell to cell both vertically and laterally through pits, because that is where resistance to flow is lowest.

Vessel elements, in contrast, are shorter and wider than tracheids (Figure 34.14b). In addition to having pits, vessel elements have **perforations**—openings in the end walls that lack both primary and secondary cell walls. In some species, the ends of vessel elements lack any cell wall at all, and stacked cells form open pipes called vessels. Vessel elements conduct water more efficiently than do tracheids, because their width and perforations offer less resistance to flow. Tracheids and vessel elements are often formed adjacent to each other (Figure 34.14c). ✔ **CAUTION** A poison is injected directly into tracheids. This poison kills living cells by preventing the formation of ATP. What impact will this poison have on transport of water through the tracheids injected with poison?

Phloem Structure In most vascular plants, phloem is made up primarily of two specialized types of cells: sieve-tube elements and companion cells (Figure 34.15). Both are alive at maturity and lack secondary cell walls. The phloem of many plants also includes fibers that aid in structural support.

- **Sieve-tube elements** are long, thin cells that have perforated ends called **sieve plates.** They are responsible for transporting sugars and other nutrients.

- **Companion cells** are not conducting cells, but instead provide materials to maintain the cytoplasm and plasma membrane of sieve-tube elements.

Interestingly, sieve-tube elements lack nuclei and most other organelles, but they are directly connected to adjacent companion cells by means of numerous plasmodesmata (see Figure 34.8b). Companion cells contain most of the organelles normally found in plant cells and support the metabolic activity of sieve-tube elements.

Table 34.4 on page 718 summarizes the major tissues and cell types found in the dermal, ground, and vascular tissue systems. Once you're familiar with the structure and function of plant tissues, you're ready to consider how these cells and tissues arise during primary and secondary growth.

CHECK YOUR UNDERSTANDING

If you understand that ...

- Plant cells are structurally different from animal cells.
- The dermal tissue system protects the plant and controls the exchange of gases and nutrients with the environment.
- The ground tissue system produces and stores the carbohydrates that make life possible.
- The vascular tissue system moves those carbohydrates and water from place to place.

✔ You should be able to ...

1. Explain the structural differences between plant and animal cells.
2. Describe the structure and function of epidermal cells, parenchyma cells, collenchyma cells, tracheids, vessel elements, and sieve-tube elements.

Answers are available in Appendix A.

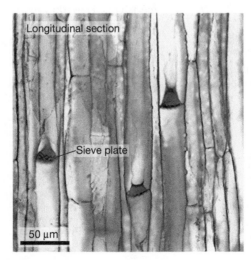
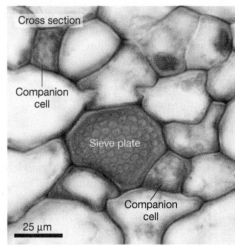

Sieve-tube element (few organelles) Companion cell (many organelles)

Sieve plate

Longitudinal section

Sieve plate

50 µm

Cross section

Companion cell

Sieve plate

Companion cell

25 µm

Figure 34.15 Phloem Consists of Sieve-Tube Elements and Companion Cells. Sieve-tube elements conduct sucrose throughout the body; companion cells support the metabolic activity of sieve-tube elements.

Tissues Present	Description of Tissue	Function
Dermal Tissue System		
Epidermis	Complex tissue consisting of epidermal cells, guard cells, trichomes, and root hairs	Shoots: Protection, gas exchange Roots: Protection, water and nutrient absorption
Ground Tissue System		
Parenchyma	Simple tissue consisting of parenchyma cells (primary cell wall only)	Synthesis and storage of sugars and other compounds
Collenchyma	Simple tissue consisting of collenchyma cells (primary cell wall only; flexible cell walls)	Support (mostly in stems and leaves)
Sclerenchyma	Simple tissue consisting of sclerenchyma cells: sclereids or fibers (primary and secondary cell walls; dead at maturity)	Sclereids: protection (mostly in hard outer surfaces of seeds and fruits) Fibers: support (mostly in stems and leaves)
Vascular Tissue System		
Xylem	Complex tissue consisting of tracheids, vessel elements, and frequently parenchyma cells and fibers (tracheids, vessel elements, and fibers are dead at maturity; primary and secondary cell walls)	Transport of water and nutrients; structural support
Phloem	Complex tissue consisting of sieve-tube elements, companion cells, and frequently fibers (fibers are dead at maturity)	Transport of sugars, amino acids, hormones, etc.; support

34.3 Primary Growth Extends the Plant Body

Plants grow throughout their lives because they have many **meristems**—populations of undifferentiated cells that retain the ability to undergo mitosis. When meristematic cells divide, some of the daughter cells remain in the meristem, allowing the meristem to persist. Other cells, though, differentiate into distinct cell types with specific functions.

Apical meristems are located at the tip of each root and shoot. As cells in apical meristems divide, enlarge, and differentiate, root and shoot tips extend the plant body outward, allowing it to explore new space.

The division of apical meristem cells, and differentiation of those cells, is responsible for **primary growth,** which is common to all plants. The major consequence of primary growth is to increase the length of the root and shoot systems. All of the cells and tissues that are derived directly from apical meristems constitute the **primary plant body.** In general, most plants that do not produce woody tissues consist entirely of primary growth.

How Do Apical Meristems Produce the Primary Plant Body?

Whether located in the tips of roots or shoots, apical meristems give rise to three distinct **primary meristems:** protoderm, ground meristem, and procambium. These regions are partially differentiated but retain the character of meristematic cells because they keep dividing. The three types of primary meristems are important because they give rise to the dermal, ground, and vascular tissue systems (see Section 34.2).

Figure 34.16 indicates where the apical meristems and the three primary meristems—protoderm, ground meristem, and procambium—are found in shoots and roots.

- **Protoderm** gives rise to the dermal tissue system.
- **Ground meristem** gives rise to the ground tissue system, which makes up the bulk of the primary plant body.
- **Procambium** gives rise to the vascular tissue system.

Vascular tissue runs through ground tissue, so the cells that make up ground tissue are usually close to cells that conduct the water and nutrients they need. **Figure 34.17** shows how the dermal, ground, and vascular tissue systems are organized in different parts of the primary plant body. The key point to remember is that the dermal, ground, and vascular tissue systems are derived from cells in primary meristems, which originated from apical meristems. Thus, they represent primary growth and the primary plant body. Table 34.5 summarizes the meristems and the components of primary growth that arise from them.

SUMMARY Table 34.5 Components of Primary Growth

Meristem	Primary Meristem	Primary Tissue System	Primary Tissues
Apical Meristem	**Protoderm**	Dermal tissue system	Epidermis
	Ground meristem	Ground tissue system	Parenchyma Collenchyma Sclerenchyma
	Procambium	Vascular tissue system	Xylem Phloem

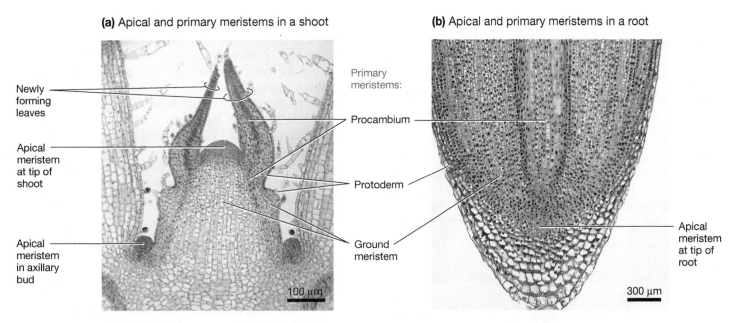

(a) Apical and primary meristems in a shoot

Newly forming leaves

Apical meristem at tip of shoot

Apical meristem in axillary bud

Primary meristems:

Procambium

Protoderm

Ground meristem

100 μm

(b) Apical and primary meristems in a root

Apical meristem at tip of root

300 μm

Figure 34.16 The Apical and Primary Meristems in the Shoot and Root Give Rise to Plant Tissues. Apical meristems consist of small, similar-looking cells that divide when conditions are favorable. Three types of primary meristems—protoderm, ground meristem, and procambium—are derived from the apical meristem and consist of partially differentiated cells that can still divide.

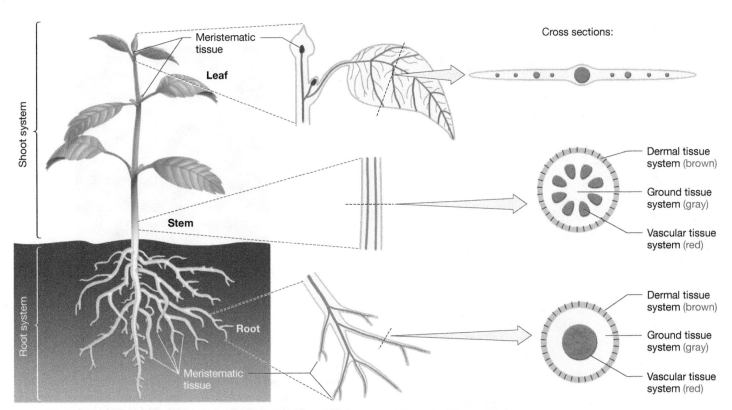

Shoot system

Root system

Meristematic tissue

Leaf

Stem

Root

Meristematic tissue

Cross sections:

Dermal tissue system (brown)

Ground tissue system (gray)

Vascular tissue system (red)

Dermal tissue system (brown)

Ground tissue system (gray)

Vascular tissue system (red)

Figure 34.17 The Primary Plant Body Comprises the Dermal, Ground, and Vascular Tissue Systems.

✔ Are the youngest tissues found at the tip of the shoot or at the base? Explain.

How Is the Primary Root System Organized?

Roots have several features that allow them to grow into new regions of the soil, so they can furnish cells throughout the plant body with water and key nutrients.

As Figure 34.18a shows, a group of cells called the **root cap** protects the root apical meristem. Cells produced by the meristem constantly replenish the cap, which regularly loses cells.

In addition to protecting the root tip, root cap cells are important in sensing gravity and determining the direction of growth. They also synthesize and secrete a slimy, polysaccharide-rich substance that helps lubricate the root tip, reducing friction and protecting the apical meristem as it is pushed through soil.

Three distinct populations of cells exist behind the root cap:

1. The **zone of cellular division** contains the apical meristem, where cells actively divide, along with the protoderm, ground meristem, and procambium, where additional cell division occurs.

2. The **zone of cellular elongation** is made up of cells that are recently derived from the primary meristems and that increase in length.

3. The **zone of cellular maturation** is where older cells complete their differentiation into dermal, vascular, and ground tissues.

The zone of cellular elongation is the region most responsible for the growth of roots through the soil. The cells in this region increase in length by taking up water. Their expansion provides the force that pushes the root cap and apical meristem through the soil. When environmental conditions are good, roots can extend by as much as 4 centimeters per day.

The zone of cellular maturation is the most important root segment in terms of water and nutrient absorption. In this region, epidermal cells produce outgrowths called **root hairs,** which greatly increase the surface area of the dermal tissue.

Root hairs furnish the actual sites of water and nutrient absorption (Figure 34.18b). The rest of the root system provides structural support for the root hairs, conducts water and nutrients to the shoot, stores the products of photosynthesis, and anchors the plant in the soil. Uptake of water and nutrients by root hairs is vital to plants (portions of Chapters 35 and 36 focus on these processes).

The zone of cellular maturation is also where lateral roots begin to grow. In contrast to lateral branches in the shoot, which arise from meristems in axillary buds (see Figure 34.1), lateral roots arise within a ring of cells around the vascular tissue and then erupt through the surrounding ground tissue.

✔ If you understand the organization of the primary root system, you should be able to explain which parts of roots are actively pushed through soil.

How Is the Primary Shoot System Organized?

If you visit a garden regularly, you can imagine how the growing root tips push through the soil and expand to form complex networks underground. But even a casual observer can watch the growth of shoot systems over time, as the tips of stems extend and branch and as new leaves form and expand.

(a) Longitudinal section of a root

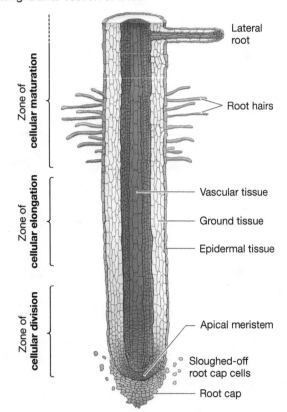

Zone of cellular maturation

Zone of cellular elongation

Zone of cellular division

Lateral root

Root hairs

Vascular tissue

Ground tissue

Epidermal tissue

Apical meristem

Sloughed-off root cap cells

Root cap

(b) Root of germinating radish seed

Figure 34.18 **Roots Extend into the Soil via Growth of Apical Meristems and Cell Elongation. (a)** A summary of the organization of the primary root system. The zone of cellular maturation is actually much larger than can be shown here. **(b)** The root of a germinating radish seed shows extensive growth of root hairs. Most absorption of water and nutrients occurs at root hairs.

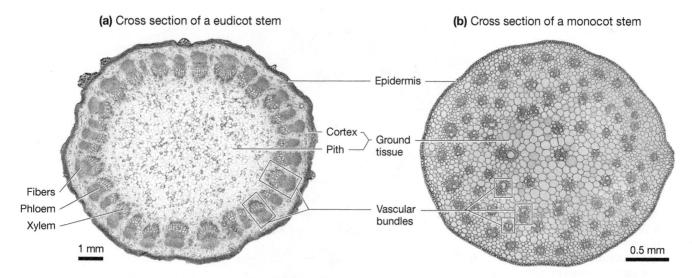

(a) Cross section of a eudicot stem

(b) Cross section of a monocot stem

Epidermis

Cortex
Pith

Ground
tissue

Fibers
Phloem
Xylem

Vascular
bundles

1 mm

0.5 mm

Figure 34.19 Tissue Systems in Stems Have Distinct Arrangements. Vascular bundles are **(a)** arranged in a ring near the perimeter of eudicot stems but **(b)** scattered throughout the ground tissue in monocots.

Just behind each shoot apical meristem, the primary meristems give rise to dermal, ground, and vascular tissues. **Figure 34.19a** shows how these tissues are arranged in the stem of a mature sunflower. Note that vascular tissues are grouped into **vascular bundles,** which form strands running the length of the stem.

In sunflowers and other eudicots, the vascular bundles are arranged in a ring near the stem's perimeter (see Chapter 28). The ground tissue that the vascular tissue runs through is divided into two major regions: **pith,** the ground tissue that is toward the center of the stem, and **cortex,** the ground tissue that is between the vascular bundles and the epidermis. The roots of some plants also have distinct pith and cortex regions.

The arrangement of the vascular bundles and ground tissue is dramatically different in the stems of monocots such as grasses, lilies, and orchids, however. As **Figure 34.19b** shows, vascular bundles in monocot stems are normally scattered throughout the ground tissue. (Review other comparisons of monocots and eudicots in Chapter 28.)

The arrangement of vascular tissue in eudicots is significant and is associated with the ability to produce secondary growth.

The next section explores how secondary growth develops in trees and other woody plants.

34.4 Secondary Growth Widens Shoots and Roots

Primary growth increases the length of roots and shoots; its major function is to extend the reach of the root and shoot system and thus increase a plant's ability to absorb light and acquire carbon dioxide, water, and nutrients.

In trees and other woody plants, **secondary growth** increases the width of roots and shoots. Its major function is to increase the amount of conducting tissue available and provide the structural support required for extensive growth. Recall that the evolution of conducting tissues allowed the vascular plants to grow taller to compete for light (see Chapter 28). Without the support provided by secondary growth, however, roots would not be massive enough to anchor large shoot systems, and long stems would fall over or break. Only with the origin of secondary growth could vascular plants become the giants seen today.

What Is a Cambium?

Secondary growth produces **wood** and occurs only in species that have a cambium in addition to apical meristems. A **cambium** (plural: cambia) is a special type of meristem (also called a lateral meristem) that differs from an apical meristem in two ways:

1. A cambium forms a cylinder that runs the length of a root, tree trunk, or branch and is made up of a single layer of meristematic cells. In contrast, apical meristems are clusters of cells localized at root tips and shoot tips.

2. In a cambium, and only there, cells divide in a way that increases the *width* of roots, trunks, and branches. Cells in an apical meristem, in contrast, divide in a way that extends the *length* of roots and shoots.

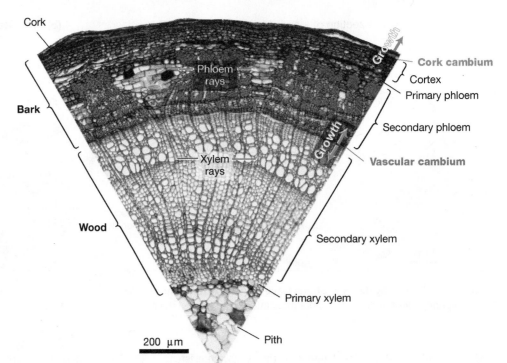

Cork

Phloem rays

Bark

Xylem rays

Wood

200 μm

Growth

Cork cambium

Cortex

Primary phloem

Secondary phloem

Vascular cambium

Growth

Secondary xylem

Primary xylem

Pith

Figure 34.20 Cambia Are Responsible for Secondary Growth. A linden tree (*Tilia* spp.) stem contains two types of cylindrical cambia: vascular cambium and cork cambium. The vascular cambium produces xylem toward the interior of the stem and phloem toward the exterior. Wood consists of xylem and other cells produced by the vascular cambium. The cork cambium produces cells associated with bark.

As Figure 34.20 shows, there are two distinct types of cambia in plants that undergo secondary growth.

- A cylinder of meristematic cells called the **vascular cambium** is located between the secondary xylem and secondary phloem, in roots, trunks, and branches.

- Another cylinder of meristematic cells called the **cork cambium** is located near the outer perimeter of roots, trunks, and branches.

One other observation is critical to understanding how cambia work: The cork cambium produces new cells primarily toward the exterior. The vascular cambium, in contrast, generates new layers of cells toward both the interior and exterior—more to the inside than the outside. The new cells formed to the inside push all of the other cells toward the outside, causing an increase in girth. Tree trunks and branches grow wider each year as a result

of cell divisions that occur exclusively in cambia located just underneath the bark.

Table 34.6 summarizes the major types of cells that arise from each type of lateral meristem. Now let's explore how secondary growth is initiated in trees.

How Does a Cambium Initiate Secondary Growth?

Imagine a very young tree seedling. Initially, all of the seedling's tissues represent primary growth because they were derived from apical meristems. However, at some point the seedling will start to produce woody, secondary growth. As the tree matures, the woody shoot system is commonly referred to as the trunk and branches. It's important to note that although a tree can get taller with each passing year, the position of any existing region of the

SUMMARY TABLE 34.6 **Components of Secondary Growth**

Meristematic Tissue	Mature Tissue	Direction of Growth	Mature Cell Composition	Mature Tissue Function
Cork Cambium	Cork	Produced to the outside	Cork cells	Protection
Vascular Cambium	Secondary phloem	Produced to the outside	Sieve-tube elements, companion cells, and sclerenchyma cells (fibers)	Transport of sugars, amino acids, hormones, etc.
	Secondary xylem*	Produced to the inside	Tracheids, vessels, parenchyma cells (arranged in rays) and sclerenchyma cells (fibers)	Transport of water and ions; structural support

*Secondary xylem is also called wood.

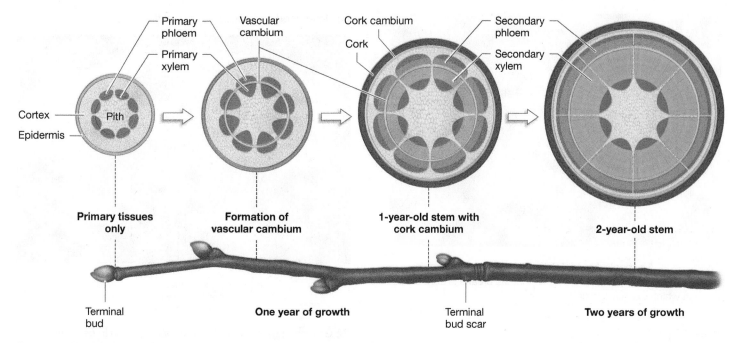

Figure 34.21 Initiation of Secondary Growth in Trees. Growth at the tips of tree trunks and branches begins as primary growth. Secondary growth is initiated when the vascular cambium and cork cambium become meristematic, thereby increasing the width, or girth, of the trunk or branch.

✔ **CAUTION** You attached a birdfeeder to a tree 5 years ago at a position 6 feet aboveground. The tree grew taller at a rate of 1 foot per year since you attached the birdfeeder. What is the current height of the birdfeeder?

trunk will stay at that same height, because new growth is initiated in the apical meristem. What occurs during the initiation of secondary growth?

Recall that the stems of eudicots contain vascular bundles arranged in a ring toward the periphery (see Figure 34.19a). Within each vascular bundle, xylem cells are located toward the interior while phloem cells are located toward the exterior. A single layer of cells located between the xylem and phloem becomes meristematic. This layer of cells represents the beginning of the vascular cambium (**Figure 34.21**).

Likewise, a ring of cells located just beneath the epidermis becomes meristematic. This represents the beginning of the cork cambium. The cork cambium and vascular cambium cells divide throughout the plant's life, producing secondary growth each year.

Secondary growth in roots occurs similarly to that in shoots. A vascular cambium forms between the xylem and phloem, and a cork cambium forms interior to the epidermis. These lateral meristems increase the overall girth of roots.

What Do Vascular Cambia Produce?

Vascular cambia in roots and stems produce both phloem and xylem (see Figure 34.20). These vascular tissues are referred to as *secondary* xylem and phloem, because they are formed as a result of secondary growth. In contrast, the procambium derived from the apical meristem produces *primary* xylem and phloem.

Secondary phloem and secondary xylem cells are not always produced simultaneously. In most cases, the vascular cambium produces many more secondary xylem cells than secondary phloem cells.

Structurally, primary and secondary phloem and primary and secondary xylem are complex tissues, made up of more than one cell type. Functionally, primary and secondary phloem are similar, as are primary and secondary xylem.

- Primary and secondary phloem function in sugar transport.
- Primary and secondary xylem function in water transport and structural support.

Secondary xylem makes up the structural material called wood, while secondary phloem makes up the inner part of a tree's bark, which is described later.

Besides producing conducting cells such as sieve-tube elements, tracheids, and vessel elements, the vascular cambium also produces sclerenchyma cells (fibers) for additional strength, along with some parenchyma cells. The parenchyma cells are formed in rows that radiate laterally across the xylem and phloem. These rows of cells are called **rays** (see Figure 34.20), and they form a living conduit through which water and nutrients are transported laterally across the trunk.

It's important to realize, though, that the results of cell division in a vascular cambium are highly asymmetrical. As the vascular cambium grows, all of the secondary xylem is retained and accumulates as wood, but the primary xylem eventually clogs and may rot away. In addition, the outermost secondary phloem becomes fragmented and compressed as the root or shoot increases in diameter. As a result, mature woody roots, trunks, and branches are dominated by secondary xylem.

Figure 34.22 Lenticels Are Visible in the Bark of Paperbark Cherry (Prunus serrula). Lenticels are natural breaks in cork tissue through which oxygen can enter a trunk.

What Do Cork Cambia Produce?

The main role of cork cambia is to produce **cork cells** toward the exterior (Figure 34.20). Together with the secondary phloem, the cork cambium and cork cells make up the **bark** of a tree trunk.

Bark provides a particularly tough barrier in species whose cork cells secrete a strong secondary cell wall containing lignin. Bark also helps prevent water loss because cork cells produce a layer of wax and other molecules inside their cell walls, making them impermeable to water and gases. Gas exchange can still occur between the atmosphere and living tissues inside the trunk, though—through small, spongy openings in the bark called **lenticels** (Figure 34.22). Cork cells die when they mature. As a trunk continues to widen, the cork layer often cracks and flakes, and the outer layers might even slough off the tree.

Bark is important because it protects the woody trunk from damage and pathogens as it increases in girth. As a trunk matures, the epidermal tissue produced by the apical meristem during primary growth is replaced by the bark, which takes over the role of preventing water loss and protecting from pathogens and herbivores. In some species, exceptionally thick bark can even protect the shoot system from fire damage. Redwood trees, for example, are adapted to fire-prone habitats and can have bark that is 20 cm (12 in.) thick.

The Structure of Tree Trunks

Trees are perennial plants that live for many years. As a tree matures and grows in width, the innermost xylem layers stop transporting water—only the xylem from the most recent years actually transports fluid.

Heartwood and Sapwood

Xylem that no longer transports water begins accumulating protective compounds secreted by other tissues. These compounds form resins, gums, and other complex mixtures. The deposition of these molecules causes the oldest portions of secondary xylem to become darker than the younger portions. The darker-colored, inner xylem region is called **heartwood,** while the lighter-colored, outer xylem is called **sapwood** (Figure 34.23a). Such variations are often visible in wood floors and furniture.

(a) Heartwood and sapwood have different functions.

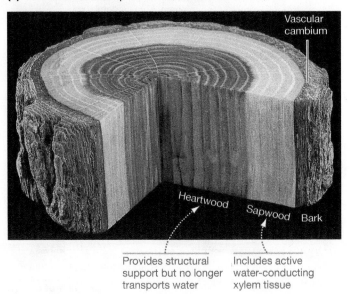

Vascular cambium

Heartwood   Sapwood   Bark

Provides structural support but no longer transports water

Includes active water-conducting xylem tissue

(b) Growth rings result from seasonal variation in cell size.

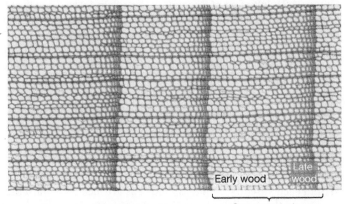

Early wood   Late wood

One growth ring

(c) Patterns in growth rings can tell a tree's history.

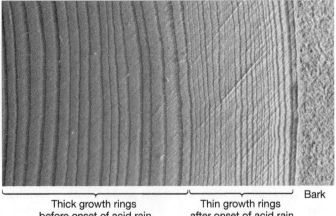

Bark

Thick growth rings before onset of acid rain

Thin growth rings after onset of acid rain

Figure 34.23 Anatomy of a Tree Trunk. (a) Transverse section of a tree trunk. **(b)** Section of wood, stained to show individual cells under a light microscope. **(c)** Unstained section through a fir tree from Germany's Black Forest.

✔ In part **(c)**, pick a thick growth ring and label the early wood and late wood.

Annual Growth Rings Another important phenomenon occurs in environments where the vascular cambium stops growing for a portion of each year. This period of **dormancy** takes place during the winter in cold climates and during the dry season in tropical habitats.

When the vascular cambium resumes growth in the spring or at the start of the rainy season, it produces large, relatively thin-walled cells, called early wood. As the growing season nears its end, conditions tend to dry out or become cooler; the secondary xylem cells that are produced at this time tend to be smaller, thicker walled, and darker and are called late wood. Thus, when growth is seasonal, regions of large, thin-walled cells alternate with layers of small, thick-walled cells, resulting in annual growth rings in the secondary xylem (**Figure 34.23b**).

Analyzing patterns in tree growth rings is an important field of study in biology. Because trees grow faster when moisture and nutrients are plentiful, wide tree rings are reliable indicators of wet years. In contrast, narrow rings signal drought years—or in the case of the tree shown in **Figure 34.23c**, years when abundant acid rain, due to air pollution, reduced growth. Years with generally less than optimal growth conditions could also be related to temperature or disease

Dendrochronology is the science of dating and studying tree growth rings. By studying growth rings in fossil trees, dead trees, and extremely old living trees, biologists can often assemble a continuous record of growth dating back thousands of years. In doing so, they gain a better understanding of climate changes, fires, and other environmental events that occurred in the past. With continued research, scientists also hope to predict how forests might respond to the fluctuating temperatures associated with global climate change.

CHECK YOUR UNDERSTANDING

If you understand that ...

- Secondary growth occurs in species with a vascular cambium and cork cambium and results in a broadening of the shoot and root systems.
- Vascular cambium gives rise to secondary xylem and secondary phloem tissues. Cork cambium gives rise to the protective tissue called bark.

✓ **You should be able to ...**

MODEL Draw a three-year-old woody trunk in cross section, labeling secondary xylem and phloem, vascular and cork cambia, and cork. Add arrows showing the direction of growth in each meristem.

Answers are available in Appendix A.

For media, go to MasteringBiology (MB)

34.1 Plant Form: Themes with Many Variations

- The root and shoot systems of plants are specialized for harvesting the light, water, and nutrients required for performing photosynthesis. Structures involved in absorption have a high surface area/volume ratio.
- Roots extract water and nutrients such as nitrogen, phosphorus, and potassium from the soil.
- The shoot system consists of all aboveground portions of the plant, including stems and leaves.
- Leaves carry out photosynthesis by capturing light and carbon dioxide from the atmosphere and usually consist of a flattened blade that extends from a petiole.
- The morphology of root and shoot systems varies widely among species, allowing individuals to reduce competition for resources.
- Roots and shoots may be modified to perform a variety of other functions, however, including nutrient storage, water storage, protection, and asexual reproduction.
- Because roots and shoots grow throughout life, a plant is able to respond appropriately to changes in environmental conditions.

34.2 Plant Cells and Tissue Systems

- The dermal tissue system is usually one cell layer thick and plays a role in protection and water absorption by roots. In shoots the epidermis synthesizes the cuticle, which aids in water conservation.
- Stomata are formed by pairs of epidermal guard cells that open and close to control CO_2 uptake and water loss by leaves.
- The ground tissue system performs photosynthesis and stores carbohydrates and other compounds.

- The vascular tissue system transports materials throughout the plant. Within the vascular system, xylem tissue transports water and dissolved ions up the plant; phloem tissue transports sugars up and down.
- Ground tissue contains **(1)** parenchyma cells, which function in material synthesis, transport and storage; **(2)** collenchyma cells, which provide structural support for growing regions; and **(3)** sclerenchyma cells—fibers and sclereid cells—that strengthen regions of the body that have stopped growing.

34.3 Primary Growth Extends the Plant Body

- Each apical meristem gives rise to three primary meristems: protoderm, ground meristem, and procambium.
- The primary meristems give rise to the dermal, ground, and vascular tissue systems, which extend throughout the plant body.
- Behind the zone of cellular division in roots, cells become longer in the zone of cellular elongation and acquire specialized functions in the zone of cellular maturation.

34.4 Secondary Growth Widens Shoots and Roots

- In some plants, shoots and roots are widened by cylindrical meristems called vascular cambia that produce secondary xylem and secondary phloem, and cork cambia that produce cork.
- Cork cells produce waxes that protect stems from water loss.
- Wood consists of secondary xylem, while bark consists of all tissue outside of the vascular cambium.

✔ TEST YOUR KNOWLEDGE

1. What is a sieve-tube element?
   a. the sugar-conducting cell found in phloem
   b. the widened, perforation-containing, water-conducting cell found only in angiosperms
   c. the nutrient- and water-absorbing cell found in root hairs
   d. the nucleated and organelle-rich support cell found in phloem

2. How do tracheids differ from vessel elements, in addition to their different overall shapes?
   a. Tracheids are stacked end to end to form continuous, open columns.
   b. In tracheids, water flows from cell to cell primarily through gaps in the secondary cell wall called pits.
   c. Tracheids are dead at maturity.
   d. In tracheids, secondary cell walls are reinforced with lignin.

3. Which statement best characterizes primary growth?
   a. It does not occur in roots, only in shoots.
   b. It leads to the development of cork.
   c. It produces the dermal, ground, and vascular tissues.
   d. It produces rings of xylem and phloem tissue as well as rings of cork tissue.

4. Which statement best characterizes secondary growth?
   a. It results from cell divisions in the vascular and cork cambia.
   b. It increases the length of the plant stem.
   c. It results from divisions in the apical meristem cells.
   d. It often produces phloem cells to the inside and xylem cells to the outside of the vascular cambium.

✔ TEST YOUR UNDERSTANDING

5. Describe the general function of the shoot and the general function of the root system. Which tissues are continuous throughout these two systems? Suggest a hypothesis to explain why the shoot and root systems of different species are so variable in size and shape.

6. Explain why continuous growth enhances the phenomenon known as phenotypic plasticity.

7. What does the cuticle do? What do stomata do? Predict how the thickness of cuticle and the number of stomata differ in plants from wet habitats versus dry habitats.

8. CAUTION The current diameter of a tree trunk is 10 inches. The trunk diameter increases at a rate of 2 inches per year. An insect burrows into the trunk and lays its eggs in the secondary xylem, 1 inch out from the center of the tree. How far from the center will the dormant eggs be located in two years?

✔ TEST YOUR PROBLEM-SOLVING SKILLS

9. Identify the structure you are consuming when you eat each of the following: asparagus, Brussels sprouts, celery, spinach, carrot, potato.

10. Trees can be killed by girdling—the removal of bark and vascular cambium in a ring all the way around the tree. Explain why.

MasteringBiology®

Students Go to MasteringBiology for assignments, the eText, and the Study Area with animations, practice tests, and activities.

Professors Go to MasteringBiology for automatically graded tutorials and questions that you can assign to your students, plus Instructor Resources.

✔ PUT IT ALL TOGETHER: Case Study

How is plant growth affected by acid rain?

Plants experience a vast array of conditions that can alter their growth and development, including temperature and availability of water, nutrients, and light. They are also exposed to pollutants such as acid rain formed largely as a result of burning fossil fuels and volcanic eruptions. Acid rain is still a major environmental problem in certain regions. How does acid rain affect plant growth?

11. Develop a hypothesis on the likely effects of acid rain on primary growth in trees. Based on your hypothesis, make some predictions about the impact of acid rain on the height of tree trunks.

12. QUANTITATIVE Researchers tested the effects of acid rain on seedlings of two different species, camphor tree (*Cinnamomum camphora*) and chinaberry tree (*Melia azedarach*). Results of the experiments are shown here. Note that acid rain caused a significant reduction of growth in chinaberry trees (*** means $P < 0.001$, see BioSkills 3), but not in camphor trees. What was the approximate percentage of growth reduction observed in the chinaberry trees treated with acid rain?

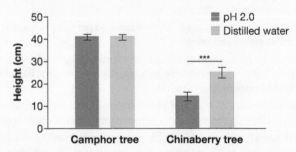

Source: Fan, H. B., and Y. H. Wang. 2000. *Forest Ecology and Management* 126: 321–329.

13. Which meristem was likely affected in the chinaberry tree?

14. Give a plausible explanation for the differential effect of acid rain on height in camphor and chinaberry trees (i.e., what structural features might offer more protection from acid rain in one species versus another?).

15. Based on the results presented here, predict the impact of acid rain on the vascular cambium in the two species. How would that effect be apparent in the amount of wood produced in the tree trunks?

16. Beyond primary and secondary growth, what other aspects of plant growth might be negatively affected when plants are exposed to environmental stress?

38 Plant Reproduction and Development

This chapter focuses on the function of plant reproductive structures like this flower, and the developmental processes involved in transforming a seed into a mature flowering plant.

In this chapter you will learn that

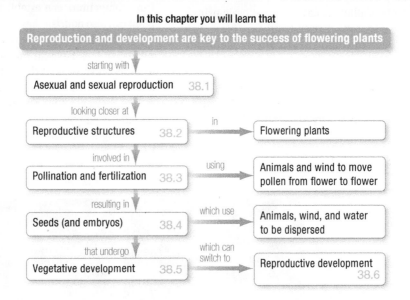

Reproduction and development are key to the success of flowering plants

starting with ↓

Asexual and sexual reproduction   38.1

looking closer at ↓

Reproductive structures   38.2   — in →   Flowering plants

involved in ↓

Pollination and fertilization   38.3   — using →   Animals and wind to move pollen from flower to flower

resulting in ↓

Seeds (and embryos)   38.4   — which use →   Animals, wind, and water to be dispersed

that undergo ↓

Vegetative development   38.5   — which can switch to →   Reproductive development   38.6

This chapter is part of the Big Picture. See how on pages 816–817.

t would be difficult to overemphasize the importance of the plant reproductive organs and developmental processes that are analyzed in this chapter—for plants, for biologists, and for you.

- For plants, every structure in the body and every physiological process—from water transport to photosynthesis—exist for one reason: to maximize the chances that the individual will produce offspring. Reproduction is the unconscious goal of everything that an organism does (see Chapter 1).

- For biologists, plant reproduction and development are not only fundamental to understanding how plants work but also the basis for major industries. Agriculture, horticulture, forestry, biotechnology, and ecological restoration draw extensively on what biologists know about plant reproduction and development.

- For you, plant reproduction and development for the most part means food. Human diets are based on consuming plant reproductive structures—primarily the seeds and fruits derived from flowers. A **flower** is a reproductive structure in angiosperms that produces gametes, attracts pollinators, receives gametes from other individuals, nourishes embryos, and develops seeds and fruits. **Seeds** consist of an embryo and nutrient stores surrounded by a protective coat. **Fruits** develop from the flower's seed-producing organ and contain seeds.

This chapter focuses on angiosperms, for three reasons: (**1**) Angiosperms represent over 85 percent of the land plants described to date; (**2**) virtually every important domesticated plant is an angiosperm; and (**3**) aspects of reproduction in other land plant lineages were described previously (see Chapter 28). Before delving into how a seed can ultimately develop into a mature flowering plant, let's examine some of the general principles that underlie plant reproduction.

38.1 An Introduction to Plant Reproduction

Plant reproductive structures and processes vary among species. Consider just one aspect of reproductive organs—size. Flowers vary from microscopic to the size of a small child; seeds and fruits range from dustlike particles to coconuts.

Fortunately for students of plant biology, several basic principles unify this diversity of reproductive systems. Let's begin by exploring how plants can reproduce either asexually or sexually.

Asexual Reproduction

Asexual reproduction does not involve fertilization and results in the production of **clones**—genetically identical copies of the parent plant.

Some plants extend their life indefinitely by asexual reproduction. The oldest of all known plants is a ring of creosote bushes in the Mojave Desert of California. The bushes comprise a clone that originated from a parent plant that started growing some 12,000 years ago.

Although all asexual reproduction is based on mitotic cell division, it includes a wide array of structures and mechanisms.

- **Figure 38.1a** shows shoots and roots emerging from a horizontal stem called a **rhizome,** which grows underground. If the emerging individuals become separated from the parent plant, they represent asexually produced offspring.

- The gladiolus plant in **Figure 38.1b** has propagated itself via modified stems called **corms,** which grow under the surface of the soil.

- The kalanchoe in **Figure 38.1c** produces "plantlets" (small plants) from meristematic tissue located along the margins of its leaves. When the plantlets mature, they drop off the parent plant and grow into independent individuals.

- In some species, including the dandelion in **Figure 38.1d,** mature seeds can form without fertilization occurring. This phenomenon, known as **apomixis,** results in seeds that are genetically identical to the parent.

The key characteristic of asexual reproduction is efficiency. If an herbivore or a disease wipes out other plants that surround a grass plant, the grass can quickly send out rhizomes. Its asexually produced offspring are likely to fill the unoccupied space before seeds from competitors can establish themselves and grow. The parent plant can also nourish these progeny as they become established.

Although asexual reproduction is extremely common in plants, it does have an important downside: A fungus or other disease-causing agent that infects an individual plant will probably succeed in infecting the plant's cloned offspring as well, even if they are no longer physically connected.

This predicted outcome is based on the observation that plants fight disease with a wide variety of molecules (see

(a) Rhizome

(b) Corm

Parent corm

New corms

(c) Plantlets

(d) Asexual seeds

Figure 38.1 The Mechanisms of Asexual Reproduction Are Diverse. These are just a few mechanisms of asexual reproduction in plants.

Chapter 37). Populations of asexually produced individuals can lack the genetic diversity needed to generate an arsenal of effective disease-fighting compounds.

Evidence supporting this disadvantage of asexual reproduction comes from agriculture and horticulture. Asexually propagated apples, bananas, and other crops are known to be more susceptible to epidemics than are sexually propagated species. What are the fundamental events involved in sexual reproduction?

Sexual Reproduction and the Plant Life Cycle

Most plants reproduce sexually. **Sexual reproduction** is based on meiosis and fertilization. Recall that **meiosis** is a type of nuclear division that results in four daughter cells, each made up of half the number of chromosomes present in the original parent cell, and **fertilization** is the fusion of haploid cells termed **gametes** (see Chapter 13). Meiosis results in offspring that are genetically different from each other and different from their parents.

The advantages of sexual reproduction are common to all eukaryotes that undergo meiosis. When and where meiosis occurs, however, is highly variable. In most animals, meiosis leads directly to the formation of gametes. In land plants, the situation is much different—meiosis and fertilization occur in alternate phases of a life cycle.

Land plants are characterized by a life cycle with two distinct multicellular forms—one diploid and one haploid. An individual in the diploid phase of the life cycle is called a **sporophyte,** while an individual in the haploid phase of the life cycle is called a **gametophyte.** A good way to keep these terms straight is to remember that "sporophyte" means spore-plant, while

"gametophyte" means gamete-plant. Sporophytes produce spores by meiosis. Gametophytes produce gametes by mitosis.

You may recall that this type of life cycle, called **alternation of generations,** has evolved independently in various protists and land plants. (For more information on alternation of generations, see Chapters 27 and 28.)

Figure 38.2 diagrams the life cycle of an angiosperm, highlighting five key processes that are common to all land plant life cycles:

1. Meiosis occurs in sporophytes and results in the production of haploid **spores.** Meiosis and spore production occur inside structures called **sporangia.**

2. Spores undergo mitosis and develop into multicellular, haploid gametophytes.

3. Gametophytes produce **sperm** (male gametes) and **eggs** (female gametes) by mitosis.

4. Fertilization occurs when two gametes fuse to form a diploid **zygote.**

5. The zygote undergoes mitosis and grows into a multicellular, diploid embryo (sporophyte).

Details on the development of male and female gametophytes and the unique process of fertilization in angiosperms will be explored more fully in Sections 38.2 and 38.3.

✔ If you understand the angiosperm life cycle, you should be able to (1) identify the male spore and female spore in Figure 38.2, and (2) provide evidence to support the statement that in angiosperms, female gametophytes don't leave their parent plant.

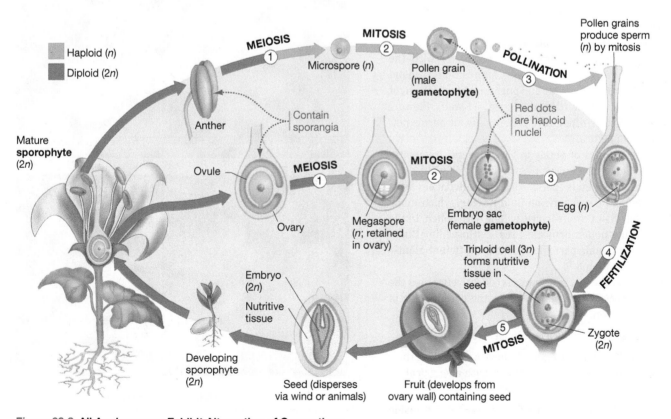

Figure 38.2 All Angiosperms Exhibit Alternation of Generations.

38.2 Reproductive Structures

Each major group of plants, from mosses to angiosperms, has a characteristic variation on the theme of alternation of generations, as well as characteristic male and female reproductive structures (see Chapter 28). Here, though, the focus is on the flower, found only in angiosperms.

The General Structure of the Flower

Structurally, all flowers are variations on a theme. They are made up of four basic organs that are essentially modified leaves: **(1)** sepals, **(2)** petals, **(3)** stamens, and **(4)** one or more carpels. These organs are attached to a compressed portion of stem called the receptacle (Figure 38.3a).

Not all four organs are present in all flowers, however, and as Figure 38.3b shows, the colors, sizes, and shapes of these four components are fabulously diverse. Let's consider each of the four parts, in turn.

Sepals Form an Outer, Protective Whorl **Sepals** are leaflike structures that make up the outermost parts of a flower. Sepals are usually green and photosynthetic, and they are relatively thick compared with other parts of the flower.

Because they are attached to the receptacle in a circle or whorled arrangement, sepals enclose the flower bud as it develops and grows—protecting young buds from damage by desiccation, insects, or disease-causing agents. The entire group of sepals in the flower is collectively called the **calyx.**

Petals Furnish a Visual Advertisement Like sepals, **petals** are arranged around the receptacle in a whorl. Often brightly colored and scented, petals function to advertise the flower to bees, flies, hummingbirds, and other pollinators.

In some cases, the color of the petals correlates with the visual abilities of particular animals. Bees, for example, respond strongly to wavelengths in the blue and purple regions of the light spectrum, as well as yellow (they don't see red well). Flowers that attract bees, in turn, often have yellow, blue, or purple petals with ultraviolet patches.

The ultraviolet regions of petals in "bee flowers" frequently highlight the center of the flower (Figure 38.4). Why? In these flowers, the base of the petals contains a gland called a **nectary.** The nectary produces the sugar-rich fluid **nectar,** which many of the animals that visit flowers harvest along with pollen. In the process of collecting pollen or nectar, the visiting animal usually deposits on the female parts pollen from a different plant—accomplishing pollination.

The entire group of petals in a flower is collectively called the **corolla.** In some species, the petals within the corolla vary in size, shape, and function:

- Flattened petals may provide a landing pad for flying insects.
- Elongated, tubelike petals frequently have a nectary at their base that can be reached only by animals with a long beak or tongue-like proboscis.
- Some petals protect the reproductive organs located inside the corolla.

(a) Basic parts of a flower

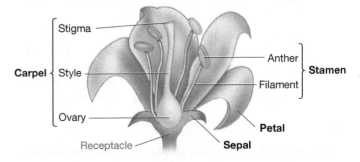

(b) Examples of flower diversity

Figure 38.3 The Basic Structures in Flowers Are Highly Variable. (a) Flowers comprise sepals, petals, stamens, and carpels. **(b)** The four parts vary greatly among species.

(a) What you and a bee see

(b) What a bee sees in addition

Figure 38.4 Insects See in the Ultraviolet Range. (a) The inflorescence (flower cluster) of a black-eyed Susan, seen by the unaided human eye. **(b)** The same structure, photographed with a camera that records ultraviolet wavelengths that are visible to bees but invisible to humans.

- Specialized cells in some petals synthesize and release molecules that provide a scent attractive to certain species of pollinating animals.

In contrast, wind-pollinated angiosperms such as oaks, birches, pecans, and grasses have flowers that have small petals or no petals at all, and they lack nectaries. These species do not invest in structures that aren't required for pollination.

Stamens Produce Pollen **Stamens** are reproductive structures that produce male gametophytes—also known as pollen grains. The male gametophytes, in turn, produce sperm (see Figure 38.2).

Each stamen consists of two components:

1. a slender stalk termed the **filament,** and
2. the pollen-producing organs called **anthers** (see Figure 38.3a).

The anther is the business end of the stamen—where meiosis and pollen formation take place. The filament holds the stamen in a place where wind, insects, hummingbirds, bats, or other agents can make contact with the pollen grains produced in the anther.

Carpels Produce Ovules The fourth reproductive structure in flowers is the **carpel,** which produces female gametophytes. A carpel consists of three regions:

1. The **stigma** is a sticky tip that receives pollen.
2. The **style** is a slender stalk.
3. The **ovary** is an enlarged structure at the base of the carpel (see Figure 38.3a).

Inside the ovary, female gametophytes are produced in structures called **ovules.** An ovary may contain more than one ovule. When the female gametophytes that are produced inside ovules mature, they produce eggs (see Figure 38.2).

The "Sex" of Flowers Varies In most angiosperm species, stamens and carpels are produced on the same individual. Flowers that contain both stamens and carpels are referred to as **perfect.**

Flowers can also be **imperfect,** however, meaning they contain either stamens *or* carpels, but not both. Imperfect flowers

(a) Corn is monoecious.

(b) *Cannabis* is dioecious.

Figure 38.5 "Male" and "Female" Flowers Can Occur on the Same Individual or on Different Individuals. (a) The tassels of corn contain male flowers; ears contain female flowers. **(b)** In *Cannabis sativa*, male and female flowers are found on different individuals.

that contain only stamens can be considered "male" flowers. Similarly, imperfect flowers that contain only carpels can be considered "female" flowers.[1]

In some cases, separate stamen- or carpel-producing flowers occur on the same individual. Species like these, including the corn plants illustrated in **Figure 38.5a**, are **monoecious** (literally, "one-house"). In corn, the tassel is a collection of stamen-producing "male" flowers, and the ear contains a group of carpel-producing "female" flowers.

In contrast, some species with imperfect flowers are **dioecious** ("two-houses")—meaning that each individual plant produces either stamen-bearing flowers only or carpel-bearing flowers only. *Cannabis sativa* is a dioecious species (**Figure 38.5b**).

How Are Female Gametophytes Produced?

What purposes do the three parts of the carpel serve? The function of the stigma and style will become clear in Section 38.3; for now, let's concentrate on what happens inside the ovary.

---

[1] Technically, flowers are not referred to as male and female. Instead, they are staminate or carpellate. Staminate flowers produce stamens, which produce pollen grains, which produce male gametes (sperm). Carpellate flowers produce carpels, which contain ovaries. Female gametophytes develop inside ovaries and produce female gametes (eggs). For convenience, though, the text will sometimes refer to male and female flowers and reproductive structures.

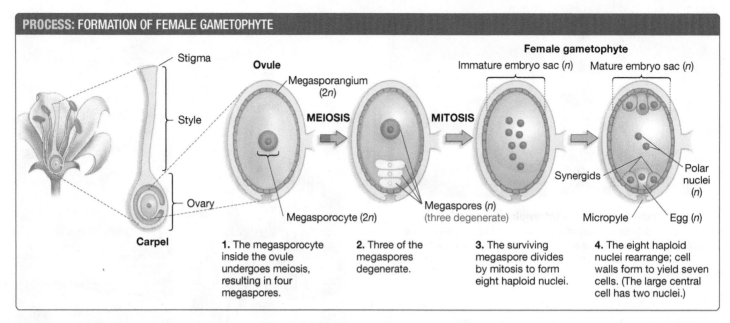

Figure 38.6 In Angiosperms, Megaspores Produce Female Gametophytes.

Figure 38.6 illustrates a longitudinal section showing the inside of a typical angiosperm ovary. Notice that it contains one or more ovules. Each ovule contains a structure called the megasporangium, inside which there is a diploid cell called the megasporocyte. (The use of "mega" is appropriate, because these structures are much larger than their counterparts in the stamen.) The megasporangium is comparable to spore-producing structures found in other plants, such as those on the back of fern leaves (see Chapter 28).

When you study Figure 38.6, note four important points:

1. The megasporocyte divides by meiosis.

2. Four haploid **megaspores** result from meiosis, but three degenerate.

3. The surviving megaspore divides by mitosis to produce a structure with haploid nuclei. This is the female gametophyte—usually known as the **embryo sac.**

4. The haploid nuclei segregate to different positions in the embryo sac, and cell walls form around some of them. One of these cells becomes the haploid egg.

In the carpel, then, a diploid megasporocyte divides by meiosis to form a megaspore, which then divides by mitosis to form the female gametophyte. Female gametophytes are encased in an ovary, are retained in the flower, and produce an egg.

In many angiosperms, the embryo sac contains eight haploid nuclei and seven cells. Typically, two **polar nuclei** stay together within one central cell—the largest cell in the ovule. The number of polar nuclei varies among species, however. As you'll see later, the polar nuclei play an important role in seed development after pollination and fertilization take place.

The egg cell is located at one end of the female gametophyte, near an opening in the ovule called the **micropyle** ("little-gate"). The micropyle is where sperm will enter the ovule before fertilization. Two haploid cells called **synergids** lie close to the egg.

You will soon learn more about the importance of synergids during the fertilization process.

How Are Male Gametophytes Produced?

Figure 38.7 provides a detailed look at the stamen and the steps that occur in the production of male gametophytes (that is, pollen). Recall that a stamen consists of two major parts: an anther and a filament. Inside the anther, structures known as microsporangia contain diploid cells called microsporocytes.

When you study Figure 38.7, note three important points:

1. Microsporocytes undergo meiosis.

2. Each haploid cell that results is a **microspore.** Normally, all of the microspores survive. Microspores then divide by mitosis.

3. The two nuclei that result from mitotic division in a microspore form a haploid, immature male gametophyte, also known as a **pollen grain.**

In the anther, then, diploid microsporocytes divide by meiosis to form microspores, which then divide by mitosis to form male gametophytes (pollen grains). Each diploid microsporocyte ultimately yields four haploid pollen grains. Male gametophytes are dispersed from the flower and eventually produce sperm.

At the immature stage—before it has produced sperm—the male gametophyte consists of two cells: a small generative cell enclosed within a larger tube cell. The male gametophyte is considered mature when the haploid generative cell undergoes mitosis and produces two sperm cells.

In some species, this maturation step occurs while pollen is still in the anther. In other species, maturation and sperm production don't occur until after the pollen grain lands on a stigma and begins to grow. The reasons for this difference are not understood.

The wall of a pollen grain develops a tough outer coat that includes the watertight compound called **sporopollenin**

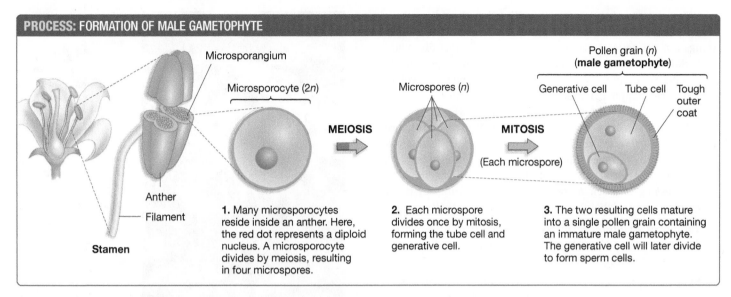

1. Many microsporocytes reside inside an anther. Here, the red dot represents a diploid nucleus. A microsporocyte divides by meiosis, resulting in four microspores.

2. Each microspore divides once by mitosis, forming the tube cell and generative cell.

3. The two resulting cells mature into a single pollen grain containing an immature male gametophyte. The generative cell will later divide to form sperm cells.

Figure 38.7 In Angiosperms, Microspores Produce Male Gametophytes.

✔ Define a gametophyte. Why do pollen grains conform to the definition of a gametophyte?

(introduced in Chapter 28). This coat protects the male gametophyte when the pollen is released from the parent plant into the environment. Depending on the species, pollen grains may be dispersed by an animal, the wind, or water currents.

But, how does a pollen grain get to the mature carpel of the same species, where an egg cell is waiting?

38.3 Pollination and Fertilization

Pollination is the transfer of pollen grains from an anther to a stigma; fertilization occurs when a sperm and an egg actually unite to form a diploid zygote. The two events are separated in space and time.

Pollination is not restricted to angiosperms. Gymnosperms (introduced in Chapter 28) also package their male gametes in pollen grains. This section focuses on pollination and fertilization in flowering plants. Managing pollination and fertilization in angiosperms is a critical challenge for fruit growers and plant breeders.

In addition, angiosperms' pollination and fertilization systems are thought to be key to their evolutionary success. What aspects of pollination and fertilization allowed flowering plants to become so successful in terms of their numbers of species?

Pollination

Pollen can fall on the stigma of the same individual or the stigma of a different individual. **Self-fertilization,** or selfing, occurs when a sperm and an egg from the same individual combine to produce an offspring. In most cases, though, plants **outcross**—meaning that a sperm and an egg from different individuals combine to form an offspring. Outcrossing is the result of **cross-pollination**—when pollen is carried from the anther of one individual to the stigma of a different individual.

Selfing versus Outcrossing: Costs and Benefits Selfing and outcrossing each have advantages and disadvantages. The primary advantage of selfing is that successful pollination is virtually assured—it doesn't depend on agents other than the plant itself.

Biologists have documented the benefit of pollination assurance by hand-pollinating plants that normally outcross. In most cases, the hand-pollinated individuals produce far more seed than do individuals that are pollinated naturally.

Other things being equal, self-fertilization should result in the production of many more seeds than outcrossing. Other things are not equal, however. Selfing has a distinct disadvantage: Selfed offspring are usually much less diverse genetically than outcrossed offspring are, even though selfing still involves meiosis (see Chapter 13). In some cases, selfed offspring may also suffer from inbreeding depression (see Chapter 23).

Although outcrossing is riskier in terms of the reduced chance that pollination will occur, it results in genetically diverse offspring that may be much more successful at warding off attacks from viruses, bacteria, and other pathogens.

Outcrossing is much more common than selfing. In many cases, plants have elaborate mechanisms to prevent selfing:

- *Temporal avoidance* In some species that have perfect flowers, male and female gametophytes mature at different times. Thus, selfing does not occur.

- *Spatial avoidance* Selfing isn't possible in dioecious species and may be rare in monoecious species, unless pollinators transfer pollen between "different-sexed" flowers on the same individual. And in some species with perfect flowers, the anthers and stigma are so far apart that self-pollination is extremely unlikely—if pollen falls inside the flower, it has almost no chance of landing on the stigma.

- *Molecular matching* In many species that produce both pollen and ovules on the same plant, molecular interactions occur that prevent pollen grains from delivering sperm to the female gametophytes produced on the same plant. Such species are said to be **self-incompatible.** Many plants, just like animals, have the ability to recognize self and non-self cells and tissues.

Pollination Syndromes Cross-pollination can be accomplished in various ways: Pollen can be carried from flower to flower by physical agents such as wind or water, or by organisms such as insects, birds, or bats.

Recall that animals visit flowers to eat pollen grains, harvest nectar, or both. As an animal feeds from a flower, pollen grains adhere to its body incidentally. When the same individual visits another flower of the same species to feed, some of these grains are deposited on a stigma of the second flower.

In most cases, animal pollination is an example of **mutualism:** a mutually beneficial relationship between two species. Pollinators usually benefit by receiving food; flowering plants gain by having their male gametophytes transferred to a different individual so that outcrossing takes place. How did these pollinator–plant relationships evolve?

Pollination syndromes are suites of flower characters that are associated with certain types of pollinators. For example, many bird-pollinated flowers tend to be red and unscented, and they open during the day when birds are active. In contrast, moths and bats are usually active at night. If they feed on nectar or pollen, the flowers they visit tend to be white—and thus more visible in low light, have a strong scent, and open at night. Observations such as these have led to the directed-pollination hypothesis, which proposes that natural selection has favored flower colors, shapes, and scents to attract specific pollinators (see Chapter 28).

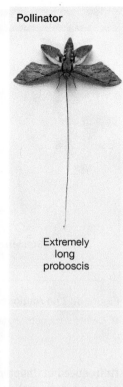

Flower

Extremely long spur with nectary at the base

Pollinator

Extremely long proboscis

Figure 38.8 **Pollinators Can Sometimes Be Inferred from Flower Structure and Color.** Charles Darwin predicted the existence of a moth that would be able to pollinate the orchid sometimes referred to as Darwin's orchid (left). Just such a pollinator (right) was discovered some 40 years after Darwin made his prediction.

Structures associated with pollination syndromes are thought to be adaptations: traits that increase the fitness of individuals in a particular environment. In this case, flowers and pollinators have adaptations that increase pollination frequency and feeding efficiency, respectively. To capture this point, biologists say that **coevolution** has occurred (see Chapters 28 and 52).

One of the most famous examples of coevolution in pollination involves a species called Darwin's orchid (**Figure 38.8**), which is native to Madagascar. When first discovered by Western scientists, the orchid attracted a great deal of attention because it has a "spur" that can be as much as 28 cm (11 in) long, and there is a nectary at its base. Charles Darwin hypothesized that it must be pollinated by a moth with a tongue-like proboscis as long as the spur. The idea seemed preposterous at the time, but 40 years later, a hawk moth species with a proboscis that averages 38 cm in length was discovered pollinating the orchid in the wild.

Why Did Pollination Evolve? In mosses, ferns, and other groups that do not form pollen, sperm have flagella and swim to the egg through droplets of water, or are transferred on water droplets that cling to the legs of tiny soil arthropods, such as springtails and mites (see Chapter 28). In conifers and most other gymnosperms, wind transmits pollen from male cones to female cones. In some of the other groups that produce pollen, such as the cycads, gnetophytes, and angiosperms, many species are pollinated by animals—particularly by insects.

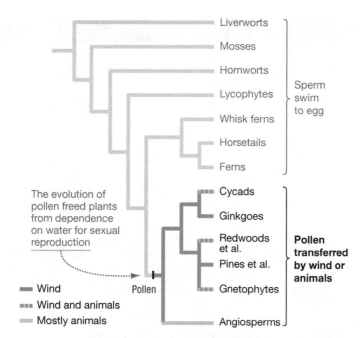

Figure 38.9 Pollen Is a Relatively Recent Innovation in Land Plant Evolution. Evolutionary relationships are evident among the major groups of plants. In the lineages colored gray, sperm have flagella and swim to the egg. In the lineages colored blue or orange, sperm are produced by pollen grains.[2]

When these observations are mapped onto the phylogenetic tree shown in **Figure 38.9**, two important patterns emerge.

1. Pollination evolved late in land plant evolution. Mosses and other groups that do not form pollen appear first in the fossil record of land plants. Conifers and other groups that are strictly or primarily wind pollinated evolved later but before angiosperms.

2. Seed plants do not need external water for sexual reproduction to occur. As a result, the evolution of pollen allowed these species to be much less dependent on wet habitats. Along with the evolution of the seed—highlighted in Section 38.4—pollen paved the way for the colonization of drier environments.

In addition, it's critical to realize that pollination became a much more precise process when plants began to recruit animals to act as pollinators. Wind-borne pollen grains have a low probability of landing successfully on a flower stigma. Animal-borne pollen, in contrast, is much more likely to be successfully transferred to flowers of the same species.

Wind-pollinated species invest in making large numbers of pollen grains; animal-pollinated species make fewer pollen grains but invest in structures that attract and reward animals.

In effect, plants "pay" nectar- and pollen-eating animals to work for them. Wind is free, but may not result in pollen arriving at its desired location. Animals are more precise at delivering pollen to other flowers. Animal pollination is an important adaptation because it increases the efficiency of sexual reproduction.

Does Pollination by Animals Encourage Speciation?

In addition to affecting the fitness of individual plants, does pollination by animals make the formation of entirely new species more likely?

To answer this question, consider the following situation. A biologist has documented that two populations of a mountain-dwelling species called the alpine skypilot have flowers with different characteristics.

- Alpine skypilots that grow in forested habitats at or below timberline have small flowers with short stalks and an aroma described as "skunky."
- Individuals that grow in the tundra habitats above timberline have large flowers with long stalks and a sweet smell.

These differences are interesting, because different insects pollinate the two populations. Small flies are abundant at slightly lower elevations, are attracted to skunky odors, and pollinate the timberline individuals; large bumblebees are abundant at higher elevations, are attracted to sweet odors, and pollinate the tundra flowers.

Experiments have shown that bumblebees prefer to pollinate big flowers—probably because larger flowers can support their larger mass. Because flies and bumblebees prefer to visit different types of flowers, gene flow between the two skypilot populations is low and they are evolving distinct characteristics. The two populations may be on their way to becoming different species.

The message here is that evolutionary changes in the size or food-finding habits of a pollinator affect the angiosperm populations they pollinate. In return, changes in flower size and shape affect the insects pollinating that population. If a small population of Darwin's orchids evolved longer spurs, for example, the hawk moth pollinators living in that area would be under intense selection that favored the evolution of a longer proboscis.

Because mutation continuously introduces variations in traits, insect and angiosperm populations frequently change, diverge, and form new species. Changes in pollination can trigger the evolution of new species. It is no surprise that insects and angiosperms are exceptionally species-rich groups.

It is clear that pollination was a crucial innovation during plant evolution. Now let's get down to specifics. What happens once a pollen grain is deposited on a stigma?

---

[2] Cycads and ginkgoes also produce motile sperm that swim a short distance to the egg. However, as with other seed plants, the sperm are produced within pollen grains and therefore do not rely on an external source of water for sexual reproduction.

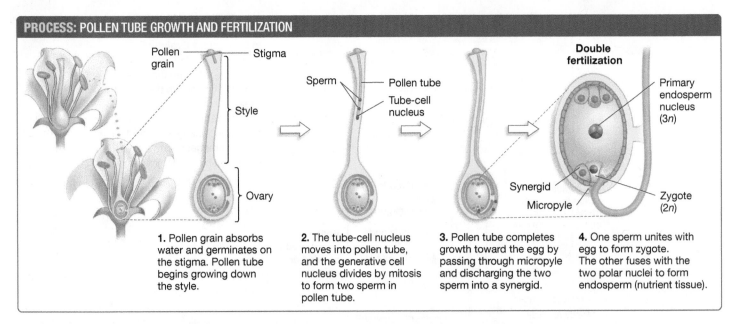

1. Pollen grain absorbs water and germinates on the stigma. Pollen tube begins growing down the style.

2. The tube-cell nucleus moves into pollen tube, and the generative cell nucleus divides by mitosis to form two sperm in pollen tube.

3. Pollen tube completes growth toward the egg by passing through micropyle and discharging the two sperm into a synergid.

4. One sperm unites with egg to form zygote. The other fuses with the two polar nuclei to form endosperm (nutrient tissue).

Figure 38.10 Double Fertilization Produces a Zygote and an Endosperm Nucleus. When the pollen tube reaches the female gametophyte, one sperm nucleus fertilizes the egg while the second fuses with the polar nuclei.

Fertilization

A pollen grain landing on the stigma of a mature flower of the same species initiates a series of events that lead to fertilization. **Figure 38.10** walks you through the steps.

Step 1 After landing on the stigma of a mature flower from the same species, a pollen grain absorbs water and germinates. **Germination** is a resumption of growth and development. This step is blocked in many self-incompatible species if the pollen came from the same plant.

Step 2 When the male gametophyte germinates, a long tubular cell called a **pollen tube** grows through the stigma and down the length of the style. The direction of growth is affected by chemical attractants, called LUREs, which are small proteins released by the synergids. In most species, like the one illustrated in the figure, the tube-cell nucleus and the generative cell travel down the length of the tube, and the generative cell divides to form two sperm. In other species, the generative cell forms sperm before the pollen is shed.

Step 3 When the pollen tube reaches the micropyle of the ovule, it grows through it and enters a synergid within the female gametophyte. The synergid degenerates and two sperm are released—each with a different fate, as described in Step 4.

Step 4 In most plant groups, fertilization is straightforward—sperm and egg simply combine, and a diploid zygote is formed. In angiosperms, however, an unusual event called **double fertilization** takes place. One sperm unites with the egg to form the zygote. The other sperm moves through the female gametophyte and fuses with the polar nuclei in the central cell. In most cases, two polar nuclei are present and a large triploid ($3n$) cell forms.

The triploid nucleus resulting from this second fertilization undergoes mitosis and cytokinesis to form the **endosperm** ("inside-seed") tissue. In most species, endosperm is triploid and stores nutrients for the embryo, including starch or oils (lipids) plus proteins and other nutrients. As one example, most of the cells in corn kernels are endosperm.

After fertilization, embryogenesis ensues (see Section 38.5 for details) and seeds develop into mature, dormant structures that are adapted for dispersal by wind, water, or animals. How do seeds become dormant, and how are they dispersed?

✔ If you understand double fertilization, you should be able to identify in a female gametophyte, immediately after fertilization occurs, which cells are haploid, diploid, and triploid.

CHECK YOUR UNDERSTANDING

If you understand that ...

- Wind, water, or animals carry pollen grains from one plant to another.
- When a pollen grain lands on a stigma, the grain germinates. A pollen tube forms and grows until it reaches the ovule.
- Sperm cells produced by the male gametophyte fertilize the egg and combine with the polar nuclei, forming a diploid zygote and in most cases a triploid endosperm, respectively.

✔ **You should be able to ...**

1. Explain why insects increase their fitness by visiting flowers and why flowers increase their fitness by rewarding insects.
2. Describe the functional roles of the two products of double fertilization in angiosperms.

Answers are available in Appendix A.

38.4 Seeds and Fruits

Fertilization triggers the development of a young, diploid sporophyte. In angiosperms, the first stage in the sporophyte's life is seed development.

As a seed matures, the embryo and endosperm develop inside the ovule and become surrounded by a covering called a **seed coat.** At the same time, the ovary around the ovule develops into a fruit, which encloses and protects the seed (or seeds, if a single ovary contains multiple ovules). Besides protecting the seeds, fruits often aid in dispersing seeds away from the parent plant. The mature seed consists of an embryo, a food supply—originating with endosperm—and a seed coat. In most cases, mature seeds leave the parent plant encased in a fruit (see Chapter 28).

Along with pollen, the evolution of the seed was a crucial innovation as land plants diversified. Because seeds contain stored nutrients that the embryo will use for growth and development once the seed germinates, they allow offspring to be much more successful in colonizing habitats that are crowded with competitors than are offspring produced from spores, which are single cells. As a young plant emerges from the seed, it can subsist on stored nutrients until it is well enough established to absorb water from the soil and feed itself via photosynthesis. This also makes sense since many seeds germinate underground where light is not available and seedlings are unable to produce organic compounds through photosynthesis.

Recall that one prominent lineage of angiosperms—the monocots—have just one **cotyledon** ("seed-leaf"), whereas eudicots have two (see Chapter 28). In most eudicots, the cotyledons take up the nutrients that were initially stored in the endosperm and store them again. In these species, there is no endosperm left by the time the seed matures—instead, the cotyledons function as the nutrient storage organ in mature seeds. **Figure 38.11** compares the seed structure in beans and corn—a representative eudicot and monocot, respectively.

By the time a seed matures, the precursors of the root and shoot systems, along with the seed leaves, have formed. Once these events are accomplished, the seed tissues dry and the embryo becomes dormant—meaning it stops growing and waits.

The Role of Drying in Seed Maturation

The seeds of many species dry out, or desiccate, as they mature. Water makes up 90 percent of normal plant cells, but dried seeds contain just 5–20 percent water.

Loss of water is an adaptation that prevents seeds from germinating until after they are dispersed. The dry condition of seeds ensures that they will not germinate until water is available. This is adaptive in temperate species because water is crucial to the survival of germinated seedlings. Dry seeds are also less susceptible than wet seeds to damage from freezing.

How do the cellular structures in the embryo and endosperm survive the drying process? When researchers reduce the amount of water surrounding isolated membranes or isolated proteins to the levels observed in extremely dry seeds, the membranes disintegrate and the proteins denature. Clearly, something is happening at the molecular level in seeds to keep these cell components intact.

Researchers established that one of these "somethings" involves sugars. As water leaves the seed during drying, sugars become concentrated and maintain the integrity of plasma membranes and proteins. If drying is extreme, the sugars form an extremely viscous liquid that contains little if any water. Substances such as this are considered vitrified, or glass-like. Biologists propose that this glassy state helps maintain the integrity of plasma membranes and proteins in seeds that experience extremely dry conditions. When seeds imbibe water, the sugars dissolve and germination proceeds.

Drying is only one part of the seed maturation process, however. Equally important is the development of tissues surrounding the seed itself. In many cases, these tissues are required for the seed to be dispersed from the parent plant.

Fruit Development and Seed Dispersal

Fertilization in angiosperms initiates the development of the fruit as well as the seed and embryo (see Figure 38.2). After pollination and fertilization occur, the ovary begins to develop into the fruit while the ovules develop into seeds. As a fruit matures, the walls of the ovary thicken to form the **pericarp,** the part of the fruit that surrounds and protects the seed or seeds (**Figure 38.12**). Fruits can be dry when they are mature, as in nuts, or fleshy, as in cherries and tomatoes. Note that fruits are formed from tissues derived from the mother—not the embryo. Let's look at fruit structure and function in turn.

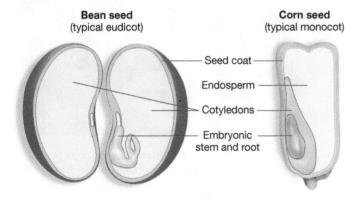

Figure 38.11 Seeds Contain an Embryo and a Food Supply Surrounded by a Tough Coat. In beans (left), the nutrients in the endosperm have been absorbed by the cotyledons and stored. In corn (right), the endosperm is intact.

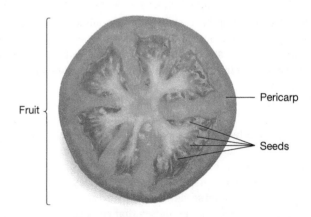

Figure 38.12 In Maturing Fruits, the Ovary Wall Develops into a Pericarp That Surrounds the Seeds. The seeds develop from ovules. A fruit consists of a pericarp and the enclosed seeds.

Fruit Structure   Fruits come in three basic types (**Figure 38.13**).

- **Simple fruits** like the cherry develop from a single flower that contains a single carpel or several carpels that are fused together. This is the most common type of fruit.

- **Aggregate fruits** like the blackberry also develop from a single flower, but one that contains many separate carpels.

- **Multiple fruits** like the pineapple develop from many flowers and thus many carpels.

In addition to the structures just mentioned, **accessory fruits** develop not from ovaries, but from other modified floral tissues. For example, the tiny seeds on the outside of strawberries are individual fruits, while the enlarged portion of the strawberry develops from a region of the stem called the receptacle (see Figure 38.3).

Fruit Function   Fruits have two functions: They frequently aid in seed dispersal, and they protect seeds from physical damage and seed predators. Dispersal is important to the fitness of the young sporophyte. This is especially true in long-lived species, in which the offspring would compete with the parent plant for light, water, and nutrients if there were no dispersal. Fruits sometimes split open and release seeds to be dispersed directly. In many cases, however, seeds are dispersed to new locations while they are still enclosed in the fruit.

Dry fruits may simply fall to the ground or be dispersed by wind, propulsion, or animals. Some dry fruits have hooks or barbs that adhere to passing animals, while nuts are dispersed by seed predators. Fruits that are dispersed by wind often have external structures to catch the breeze and extend the distance they travel; the fruits of dandelions and maple trees are familiar examples. Fruits that float, such as coconuts, can disperse seeds in water.

Some plants actually disperse dry fruits via propulsion. The sandbox tree, for example, produces a seed pod that shrinks as it dries. Eventually the pod splits apart violently, spraying seeds in all directions with so much force that the plant is sometimes called the dynamite tree. The bursting seed pod sounds like a pistol shot, and seeds can be scattered as much as 40 m away from the parent plant. Similarly, the dwarf mistletoe fruit fills with sugars as it matures. Enough water follows via osmosis to make the fruit explode and shoot seeds as far as 5 m.

Animals are the most common dispersal agent for fleshy fruits. Just as plants have evolved to use animals for pollination, they have also evolved to use specific types of animals for seed dispersal. In cases like this, seed dispersal is an example of mutualism. The plant provides a fruit rich in sugars and other nutrients; in return, the animal carries the fruit to a new location and excretes the seeds along with a supply of fertilizer.

Mammals and birds are the most common seed dispersers. Mammals are often active at night and use their well-developed sense of smell to locate fruits. As you might imagine, fruits of mammal-dispersed seeds are usually dull colored and fragrant. In contrast, birds are usually active in the day and see well. Fruits of bird-dispersed seeds are usually brightly colored.

Some animals are seed predators that compete with dispersers. For example, birds usually swallow fruit whole and disperse seeds over long distances. Fruit-eating mice, on the other hand,

(a) Simple fruit (e.g., cherry):
Develops from a single flower with one carpel or fused carpels

(b) Aggregate fruit (e.g., blackberry):
Develops from a single flower with many separate carpels

(c) Multiple fruit (e.g., pineapple):
Develops from many flowers with many carpels

Figure 38.13 Three Major Types of Fruits. The structure of a fruit depends on the number of carpels found in each flower and whether the carpels are fused.

✔ **PROCESS OF SCIENCE** When fruits ripen, their color changes in a way that makes them more conspicuous to fruit eaters. State a hypothesis to explain why this color change might increase the fitness of an individual.

chew their food, often killing the seeds inside. How can plants discourage seed predators such as mice from eating their fruits? The answer is one that might be familiar to you. Some plants such as chili peppers lace their fruits with a spicy-hot repellent called capsaicin. But does it work?

An experiment by ecologists Joshua Tewksbury and Gary Nabhan tested the hypothesis that capsaicin promoted dispersal by the curve-billed thrasher and deterred predation by cactus mice (Figure 38.14). Each animal was offered three kinds of fruit: hackberries, fruits from a strain of chilies that can't synthesize capsaicin (non-pungent chilies), and pungent chilies that have lots of capsaicin. All three fruits looked similar and had equivalent nutritional value. For each animal tested, the researchers recorded the percentage of each fruit eaten during a specific time interval. They then calculated the average amount of fruit that was eaten by five test individuals from each species.

Curve-billed thrashers ate all three fruits equally, but the cactus mice ate fewer non-pungent chilies and avoided the capsaicin-laced fruits entirely. In a follow-up experiment, the researchers fed non-pungent chilies to each kind of animal. When the seeds had passed through the animal's digestive tract and were excreted, the researchers collected and planted the seeds. About 60 percent of the seeds that passed through the birds germinated, but none of those eaten by the mice germinated. Capsaicin appears to be an effective deterrent to seed predation.

Seed Dormancy

Once they have dispersed from the parent plant, seeds may not germinate for a period of time. This condition is known as **dormancy.** Dormancy is usually a feature of seeds from species that inhabit seasonal environments, where for extended periods conditions may be too cold or dry for seedlings to thrive. Based on this observation, dormancy is interpreted as an adaptation that allows seeds to remain viable until conditions improve.

Consistent with this hypothesis, dormancy is rare or nonexistent in seeds produced by plants that inhabit tropical wet forests or other areas where conditions are suitable for germination year-round.

What molecular mechanisms are responsible for dormancy?

How Do Hormones Regulate Dormancy? The answer to this question is not well understood, but the hormone abscisic acid (ABA) plays important roles in seed development and dormancy (see Chapter 37). Mutants of some plants that cannot either make or respond to ABA exhibit a property called viviparity, in which the seeds germinate on the parent plant as soon as they are mature. In many species, ABA triggers the accumulation of storage compounds, desiccation tolerance, and the prevention of germination.

After a seed has been dispersed from the parent plant, it may remain dormant in the soil for years or even centuries before it will germinate. An ongoing, long-term experiment on seed dormancy began over 130 years ago when botanist William Beal initiated an experiment to address the question of just how long dormant seeds can remain viable. He collected seeds from soil in

RESEARCH

QUESTION: Does the presence of capsaicin in chilies deter some predators but not others?

HYPOTHESIS: Capsaicin deters cactus mice (seed predators) but not birds (seed dispersers).

NULL HYPOTHESIS: Cactus mice and birds respond to capsaicin in the same way.

EXPERIMENTAL SETUP:

PREDICTION: Both will eat hackberry, but only thrashers will eat pungent chilies.

PREDICTION OF NULL HYPOTHESIS: No difference between thrashers and mice in fruit consumed.

RESULTS:

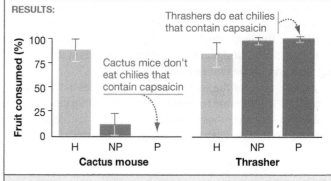

CONCLUSION: The presence of capsaicin deters cactus mice but not thrashers.

Figure 38.14 Experimental Evidence Supports the Hypothesis that Capsaicin Deters Seed Predators but Not Seed Dispersers.
SOURCE: Tewksbury, J. J., and G. P. Nabhan. 2001. Directed deterrence by capsaicin in chilies. *Nature* 382: 403–404.

✔ **PROCESS OF SCIENCE** Why were hackberries used in this experiment?

Michigan and filled 20 glass bottles with 50 seeds from each of 20 different plant species. The bottles were buried, and every 20 years one of the bottles is dug up and its seeds are planted. The most recent bottle excavation was in the year 2000, and most of the seeds were indeed still viable. The current record for longest seed dormancy is a lotus seed that germinated after being submerged in an ancient lakebed in China for 1450 years.

What finally causes dormant seeds to germinate? Thanks to the broad range of habitats in which plants are adapted, germination depends on a wide variety of internal and external factors.

How Is Dormancy Broken? The coats of some seeds are thick enough to prevent water and oxygen from physically reaching the embryo. For germination to occur, these seed coats must be disrupted, or **scarified.**

Crop seeds that require scarification are placed in large, revolving drums with pieces of sandpaper that abrade and scarify the seeds. When planted, these scarified seeds germinate quickly and uniformly. In nature, impermeable seed coats protect nutritious seeds from being killed by soil bacteria and fungi, and they often prevent seeds from germinating for many years.

To germinate, most seeds must experience particular environmental conditions. Species native to high latitudes or high elevations often produce seeds that must undergo cool, wet conditions before they will germinate. Without this level of control, germination before the ensuing winter would likely result in death of the seedling. Studies reveal that germination is regulated by two hormones, gibberellin and ABA, and that the levels of these hormones in seeds are affected by temperature (see Chapter 37). After the seed goes through a winter, its gibberellin levels increase and germination begins.

Because small seeds have few nutrient reserves in their cotyledons or endosperm, many small-seeded species need to germinate near the soil surface, where individuals are exposed to light and can feed themselves via photosynthesis. Lettuce seeds and other small seeds must be exposed to red light before they will break dormancy and germinate (see Chapter 37). Red light is an important environmental cue, because wavelengths in the red portion of the light spectrum are used for photosynthesis. Red light and blue light signal that sunlight is abundant and that the seedling will not be shaded by other plants.

Finally, many of the seeds produced by species native to habitats where wildfires are frequent, such as the California chaparral and South African fynbos, have an unusual chemical requirement to break dormancy: They must be exposed to fire or smoke before they will germinate. In fact, the commercial food product "liquid smoke" induces germination in these seeds as well as actual smoke does. In fire-prone habitats, it is advantageous for seeds to germinate after fire has cleared away existing vegetation.

The message here is that dormancy can be broken in response to a wide variety of habitat-specific environmental cues. In general, the cue that triggers germination is a reliable signal that conditions for seedling growth are favorable for a particular species in a particular environment.

Seed Germination

The formation of a mature embryo is just one requirement to ensure the development of viable seeds. Even if specific environmental signals, such as light or heat, are required to break dormancy, seeds do not germinate without water. Water uptake is the first event in germination. Once the seed coat allows water penetration, water enters by moving along a steep water-potential gradient, because the seed is so dry.

Water uptake in a typical angiosperm seed has three distinct phases:

Phase 1 Germination begins with a rapid influx of water. Oxygen consumption and protein synthesis in the seed increase dramatically, but no new messenger RNAs are transcribed (see Chapter 16). Based on these observations, biologists have concluded that some of the key early events in germination are driven by mRNAs that are stored in the seed before maturation.

Phase 2 This phase is an extended period when water uptake slows or stops. New mRNAs are transcribed and translated into protein products. Mitochondria also begin to multiply. In effect, seeds take up enough water in phase 1 to hydrate their existing proteins and membranes and then begin to manufacture the proteins and mitochondria needed to support growth.

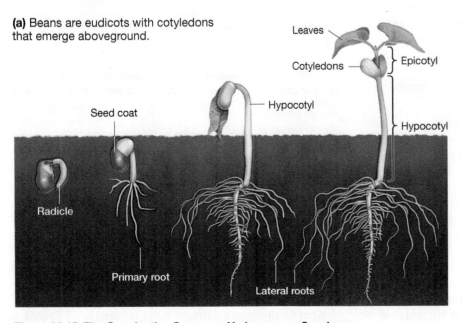

(a) Beans are eudicots with cotyledons that emerge aboveground.

Leaves
Cotyledons — Epicotyl
Hypocotyl
Seed coat
Hypocotyl
Radicle
Primary root
Lateral roots

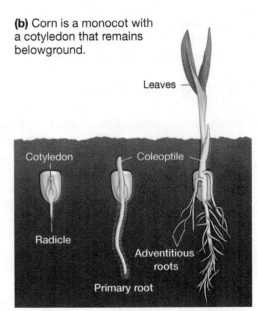

(b) Corn is a monocot with a cotyledon that remains belowground.

Leaves
Cotyledon — Coleoptile
Radicle
Adventitious roots
Primary root

Figure 38.15 The Germination Sequence Varies among Species.

✔ In which of these species are cotyledons photosynthetic?

Phase 3 Water uptake resumes as growth begins. This renewed phase of water uptake enables cells to develop enough turgor pressure to enlarge. Eventually, the seedling bursts from the seed coat.

Figure 38.15 shows what happens as eudicot and monocot embryos emerge from the seed. The **radicle,** or embryonic root, emerges first, and it then develops into the mature root system. This is important because the seedling must have a source of water in order to grow. Initially, leaves are less important because of the nutrients stored in the seed.

In eudicots, the shoot system with its cotyledons usually emerges shortly after the radicle appears. In monocots such as corn, the emerging shoot is covered by the protective coleoptile (see Chapter 37). Note that in eudicots, the emerging stem has a hook shape. As with the coleoptile of monocots, this trait is thought to protect the apical meristem from damage as the shoot works its way upward through rough soil particles. Recall that **meristems** are regions of active cell division that represent the ultimate source of all cells within plants (see Chapter 34). The role of meristems in plant development is described more fully in Section 38.5.

The next major event in the seedling's life occurs when either the cotyledons or the earliest leaves produced by the growing seedling commence photosynthesis. The seedling is said to be established when the young plant no longer relies on food reserves in its endosperm or cotyledons. Instead, it receives all of its nourishment on its own, from the compounds produced by photosynthesis.

Once established, the seedling embarks on a series of developmental events that ultimately leads to the formation of an adult plant with mature roots, stems, leaves, and eventually flowers. How does this transformation take place? What developmental events occur as a plant progresses from an immature embryo to a mature plant?

38.5 Embryogenesis and Vegetative Development

Plant development occurs as vegetative or reproductive development. **Vegetative development** produces the nonreproductive portions of the plant body—the roots, leaves, and stems. As a plant matures, some shoot meristems will produce reproductive structures, a process known as **reproductive development** (see Section 38.6).

Plants have to contend with varied environmental conditions throughout their developmental phases. Unlike most animals, they don't move around to find a place that suits their requirements. Instead, they adjust to their immediate surroundings, largely by continuously growing and developing roots, stems, and leaves. If an oak tree is heavily shaded on one side, it stops growing in that direction and extends branches on the other side. If it is heavily shaded on all sides, it directs its growth upward. This constant adjustment to changing environmental conditions is possible thanks to the meristems that are located at the tips of shoots and roots—meristems that are first initiated while the plant is developing as an embryo within a seed.

Let's begin our discussion of vegetative development by examining the earliest stages of development that occur during embryogenesis, including some of the key events involved in differentiation of the major parts of the embryo.

Embryogenesis

Embryogenesis is the developmental process by which a single-celled zygote becomes a multicellular embryo. Although the details vary among species, the fundamental sequence of events during embryogenesis in all flowering plants is the same. The events illustrated in **Figure 38.16** represent what occurs in the model plant *Arabidopsis* (see BioSkills 11).

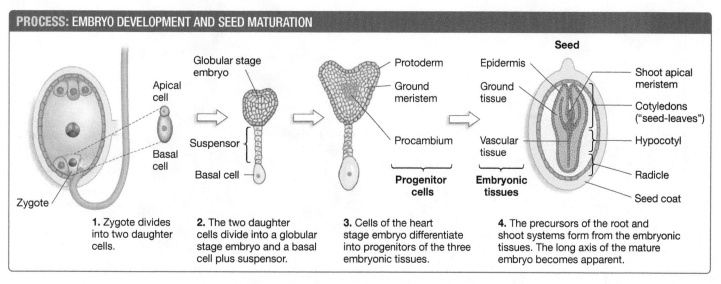

PROCESS: EMBRYO DEVELOPMENT AND SEED MATURATION

1. Zygote divides into two daughter cells.

2. The two daughter cells divide into a globular stage embryo and a basal cell plus suspensor.

3. Cells of the heart stage embryo differentiate into progenitors of the three embryonic tissues.

4. The precursors of the root and shoot systems form from the embryonic tissues. The long axis of the mature embryo becomes apparent.

Figure 38.16 Embryonic Tissues and Structures Develop Inside Seeds. The embryo inside a seed has cotyledons and the beginnings of root and shoot systems. The embryonic epidermis and the ground and vascular tissues are organized in distinct layers.

✔ Label the apical–basal and radial axes on the globular stage embryo.

After fertilization, the zygote divides (see Figure 38.16 step 1), and it produces daughter cells that are different in size, content, and fate. This type of cell division is called an asymmetric division. The bottom, or basal, cell is large and gives rise to a column of cells called the **suspensor.** The suspensor provides a route for nutrient transfer from the parent plant to the developing embryo. The small cell above the basal cell, the apical cell, gives rise to almost the entire embryo.

Apical refers to the tip; **basal** refers to the base. The asymmetry between the basal and apical cells helps establish one of the primary axes (directions) of the plant body: the **apical–basal axis.** As step 2 in Figure 38.16 shows, the basal cell divides parallel to the future apical–basal axis to produce the suspensor. The apical cell produces daughter cells that divide both perpendicularly to the apical–basal axis and parallel to it to produce a group of cells called the globular stage embryo (Figure 38.16, step 2). As you learned in an earlier chapter, the regulation of cleavage plane orientation and the direction of cell expansion are critical for creating structures in the plant (Chapter 21).

Another asymmetry arises as cells of the globular stage embryo continue to divide. Cells in the interior of the structure are completely surrounded by other cells of the embryo. In contrast, cells in the outermost layer contact surrounding tissues in the seed in addition to underlying embryo cells. Interior and exterior cells become visibly different. This creates the second major body axis, the **radial axis.** The radial axis extends from the interior of the plant body out to the exterior.

The initial events in embryogenesis illustrate a general point: The fate of a plant cell can be summed up in the old quip about the three keys to success in real estate—"location, location, location." Starting with the initial division that creates the apical and basal cells, plant cells differentiate based on where they are in the body.

As the embryo continues to develop, the long axis of the plant begins to emerge and several important structures take shape (see Figure 38.16, step 4): **(1)** cotyledons, which in many species absorb nutrients from the endosperm and supply them to the rest of the embryo, **(2)** the **hypocotyl** ("under-cotyledon"), which is the embryonic stem, and **(3)** the radicle, the embryonic root. Some embryos also have an **epicotyl** ("above-cotyledon"), which is a portion of the embryonic stem that extends above the cotyledons (see Figure 38.15). ✔ If you understand the basic steps in embryonic development, you should be able to compare and contrast a cotyledon with a radicle in terms of their tissue composition and the progenitor cells they originated from.

Meristem Formation

The apical–basal and radial axes that are established during early embryogenesis are retained at later stages of development (**Figure 38.17a**). As the cotyledons, hypocotyl, and root begin to take shape, groups of cells called the **shoot apical meristem (SAM)** and **root apical meristem (RAM)** are specified. **Figure 38.17b** provides a close-up view of a shoot apical meristem.

The cells within the meristem are small and undifferentiated. Within each meristem, the rate of cell division is dictated by cell–cell signals produced in response to environmental cues, such as the arrival of spring, the presence of abundant water, or the amount of light striking the plant.

(a) Meristems are located at the tips of shoots and roots.

(b) Longitudinal section of a shoot apical meristem

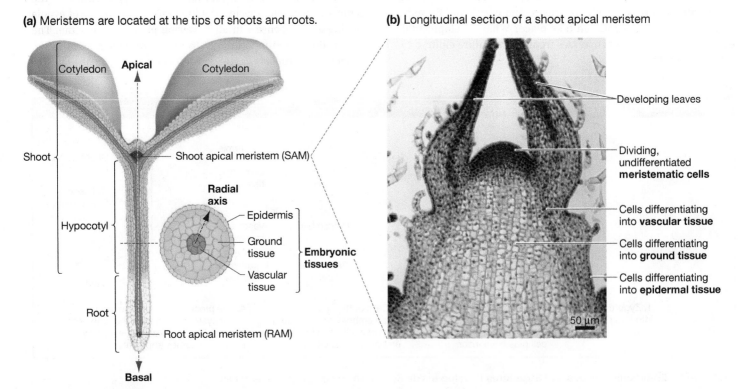

Figure 38.17 Embryogenesis Establishes the Apical–Basal and Radial Axes as Well as Apical Meristems. When cells in a meristem divide, the daughter cells either remain undifferentiated and continue to divide, or they differentiate into new epidermal, ground, or vascular cells.

Just below and at the periphery of the meristem, daughter cells produced by mitosis and cytokinesis in the meristem grow in specific directions and initially differentiate into epidermal, ground, or vascular tissue. During embryogenesis, these tissues are produced and arranged along the radial axis (see Figures 38.16 and 38.17):

1. The **epidermis** ("over-skin") is an outer covering of specialized cells that protects the individual.

2. Inside the epidermal layer of cells is **ground tissue,** a mass of cells that may later differentiate into cells that are specialized for photosynthesis, food storage, or other functions.

3. The **vascular tissue** in the center of the plant will eventually differentiate into specialized cells that transport food and water between root and shoot.

Careful microscopy allowed biologists to tease out the sequence of events that occur as meristems grow, and intense research continues to explore how interactions between cell–cell signals such as auxin influence the fate of cells produced by meristems. The root meristem can form all the underground portions of the plant, and the shoot meristem can form all the aerial portions, including reproductive structures. Throughout a plant's life, meristematic tissues continue to produce cells that can differentiate into adult tissues and structures (see Chapter 34).

For the cotyledons and other embryonic structures to take shape, cell divisions need to occur in precise orientations. What's more, the resulting cells must exhibit differential growth. Some cells grow larger than others, and the direction of cell expansion along the apical–basal or radial axes is tightly controlled and often radically different.

Let's now examine the genetic control of axis determination in plants, which is initiated during embryogenesis.

Which Genes Determine Body Axes in the Plant Embryo?

The genetic approach to exploring development that began with research on *Drosophila melanogaster* has also proven to be a powerful tool for studying plant embryogenesis. Although the specific genes involved are different in plants than in animals, the basic mechanism by which genes direct the earliest events in development is similar.

Research on the genetics of early development in plants was pioneered by Gerd Jürgens and colleagues in the 1990s. This research group set out to identify genes that are transcribed in the zygote or embryo of *Arabidopsis* and that are responsible for establishing the apical–basal axis of the plant body. It's no coincidence that this effort was similar to the work on anterior–posterior pattern formation in *Drosophila* (see Chapter 21) since Jürgens had participated in the work with flies.

The biologists' initial goal was to identify individuals with developmental defects at the seedling stage. More specifically, they were looking for patterning mutants that lacked particular regions along the apical–basal axis of the body. The team succeeded in finding several bizarre-looking mutants (Figure 38.18). Apical mutants lacked the first leaves, or cotyledons. Some mutants, called central mutants, lacked the embryonic stem,

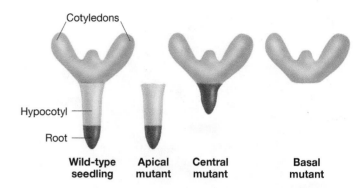

Figure 38.18 *Arabidopsis* **Developmental Mutations Can Result in Misshapen Embryos.** Researchers have identified *Arabidopsis* patterning mutants that are missing specific sections of the body along the apical–basal axis.

or hypocotyl. Other plants, dubbed basal mutants, lacked both hypocotyls and roots.

To interpret these results, the researchers suggested that each type of *Arabidopsis* mutant had a defect in a different gene and that each gene played a role in specifying the position of cells along the apical–basal axis of the body. They hypothesized that these genes are analogous to the segmentation genes of fruit flies, which specify the fate of cells within well-defined regions along the anterior–posterior axis of insects.

What are these *Arabidopsis* genes, and how do they exert their effects? To answer these questions, consider the gene responsible for the basal mutants, which lack hypocotyls and roots. This gene has been cloned and sequenced and named *MONOPTEROS*. Because its DNA sequence indicated that its protein product has a DNA-binding domain, *MONOPTEROS* was hypothesized to encode a transcription factor that regulates the activity of target genes. This hypothesis was later shown to be correct.

The *MONOPTEROS* gene is activated in response to signals from auxin—a cell-to-cell signal molecule. Auxin is produced in the shoot apical meristem and transported toward the basal parts of the individual. This results in an auxin concentration gradient along the apical–basal axis of a plant. Much like the Bicoid concentration gradient in fruit fly embryos (see Chapter 21), the auxin concentration gradient provides positional information.

Together these observations indicate that auxin acts as a morphogen to trigger the production of the regulatory transcription factor MONOPTEROS. In turn, MONOPTEROS unleashes a regulatory cascade that determines which cells in the basal portion of the embryo will form hypocotyl and roots.

The take-home message? Although the specific genes and proteins differ in animals and plants, independent evolution in the two groups has either converged or been constrained to adopt solutions for development that involve common principles. Cell-to-cell signals and regulatory cascades result in the step-by-step specification of a cell's position and fate.

Researchers have also taken up the question of which genes respond to these signals to direct the development of specific structures. Let's consider one example—the genetic control of leaf shape.

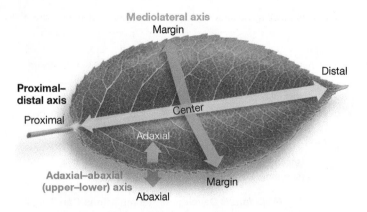

Figure 38.19 **Leaves Have Three Axes.** Overall, the plant body has just two axes: apical–basal and radial. Individually, however, every leaf has the three axes shown here. (To remember the difference between adaxial and abaxial, imagine that the *b* in *a*baxial stands for "below.")

Which Genes Determine Leaf Structure and Shape?

Once a leaf begins to grow, its structure develops along three different axes: the proximal–distal, mediolateral ("middle-to-side"), and adaxial–abaxial ("upper–lower"; **Figure 38.19**). Proximal is toward the main body; distal is away from the main body. The mediolateral axis runs from the middle of a leaf toward its margin.

Researchers have begun to identify the genes responsible for specifying the three leaf axes. For example, analyses of mutant snapdragons and other species have shown that a gene called *PHANTASTICA* (abbreviated *PHAN*) may play a critical role in setting up the adaxial–abaxial axis of leaves.

The protein product of *PHAN* is a regulatory transcription factor. PHAN controls the expression of genes that cause cells to form the upper surface of leaves. It is part of a regulatory cascade that begins with auxin and other cell–cell signals and ends with the growth of a normal-shaped leaf.

All leaves are built along three axes, but the shape of leaves varies within an individual and between species (see Chapter 34). What controls these differences between species?

Experimentally altering regulatory genes involved in leaf development can lead to striking changes in leaf shape.

Figure 38.20 shows how mutations in two different regulatory genes can alter leaf shape in tomato plants. Studies like these are beginning to reveal the genes that control the development of particular leaf shapes and how changes in these genes may have led to the evolution of different types of leaves.

CHECK YOUR UNDERSTANDING

If you understand that ...

- Early embryonic development results in the formation of the apical–basal and radial axes of the plant body, apical meristems, and three embryonic tissues.
- Vegetative growth and development occur in ways that increase an individual's ability to survive and produce offspring in the face of changing environmental conditions.
- Continuous development is possible in plants because meristematic tissue is present at the tips of roots and shoots.
- Master regulatory genes activated by cell–cell signals turn on genetic programs that create plant structures and cell types.

✔ **You should be able to ...**

1. Explain the statement, "Meristems are perpetually embryonic."
2. Describe an experimental approach for potentially changing a plant that produces simple leaves into one that produces compound leaves.

Answers are available in Appendix A.

38.6 Reproductive Development

Reproductive development is a distinguishing feature of plants. In animals, determination of cells that have the potential to form sperm or egg—the germ line—is one of the earliest events in development. In plants, there is no predetermined germ line. Instead, shoot meristems have the potential to switch from vegetative to reproductive development in response to environmental conditions. Plants form reproductive structures—flowers—when environmental conditions trigger a shoot apical

Mutant 1 (*LANCEOLATE*)	Wild type	Mutant 2 (*CLAUSA*)

Figure 38.20 **Regulatory Genes Control the Development of Leaf Shape.** A wild-type tomato leaf is shown in the middle panel surrounded by tomato leaves produced by two different regulatory gene mutations, *LANCEOLATE* and *CLAUSA*.

(a) Whorls of cells in floral meristem

(b) Whorls of organs in flower

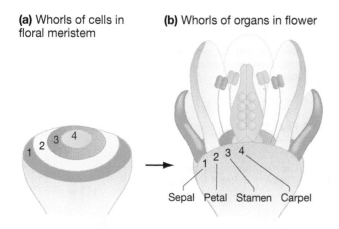

Sepal Petal Stamen Carpel

Figure 38.21 Whorls of Floral Meristem Cells Produce Circularly Arranged Flower Organs.

meristem to switch from vegetative to reproductive development (Chapter 37). In some plants, the transition from vegetative to reproductive development occurs just once while in others reproductive development can occur on a yearly basis.

The Floral Meristem and the Flower

Through a series of genetically controlled steps, a shoot apical meristem (SAM) transitions to a **floral meristem;** instead of vegetative structures, such as roots, stems, or leaves, the floral meristem produces flowers. The genes that take part in the regulatory cascade responsible for the maturation of a floral meristem are now well known.

Recall that a flower contains four kinds of organs: **(1)** sepals, **(2)** petals, **(3)** stamens, and **(4)** carpels. As **Figure 38.21** shows, each of these organs is arranged in a characteristic pattern of whorls within whorls (a whorl is a circular arrangement). How does the floral meristem produce these four organs in their characteristic arrangement?

The first hint of an answer came over 100 years ago, when researchers discovered several types of **homeotic mutations** in flowers of popular garden plants. (Recall from Chapter 21 that homeotic genes regulate the development of various body parts in plants and animals.) In the mutants, one kind of floral organ was replaced by another. For example, one homeotic mutant had flowers with sepals, petals, another ring of petals, and carpels instead of having sepals, petals, stamens, and carpels. These mutants are similar to *Drosophila* homeotic mutants (Chapter 21), where individuals have legs or antennae growing in the wrong location in place of the appropriate structure.

Just as an analysis of homeotic mutants in fruit flies led to understanding the genetic control of the body plan in animals, an analysis of homeotic flower mutants in *Arabidopsis* triggered a breakthrough in understanding the genetic control of flower structure.

The Genetic Control of Flower Structures

Over 100 years after floral homeotic mutants were first described, Elliot Meyerowitz and colleagues assembled a large collection of *Arabidopsis* homeotic flower-structure mutants. The researchers' goal was to identify and characterize the genes responsible for specifying the four floral organs.

The group found three general classes of mutants that are shown in **Figure 38.22**. Some mutants had only carpels and stamens; others had only sepals and carpels; still others had only petals and sepals. The key observation was that each type of mutant lacked the elements found in *two* of the four whorls.

What was going on? The biologists hypothesized that each class of homeotic mutant was caused by a defect in a single gene. They reasoned that if three genes set up the pattern of a flower, the mutant phenotypes suggested a hypothesis for how the three gene products interact. Because they referred to the three hypothetical genes as *A*, *B*, and *C*, the hypothesis is called the ABC model.

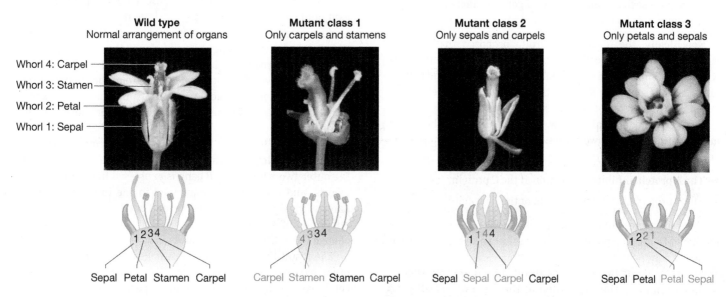

Figure 38.22 Homeotic Mutants of *Arabidopsis* Can Have Flower Organs in the Wrong Locations. Red labels in the mutants indicate a homeotic transformation (misplaced structure).

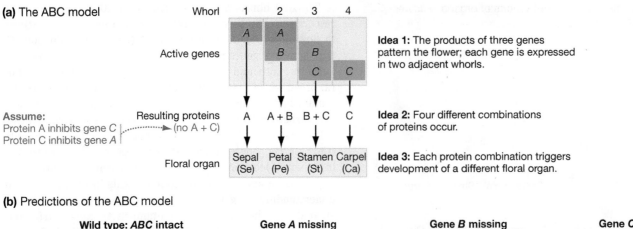

(a) The ABC model

Idea 1: The products of three genes pattern the flower; each gene is expressed in two adjacent whorls.

Assume:
Protein A inhibits gene *C* ········► (no A + C)
Protein C inhibits gene *A*

Idea 2: Four different combinations of proteins occur.

Idea 3: Each protein combination triggers development of a different floral organ.

(b) Predictions of the ABC model

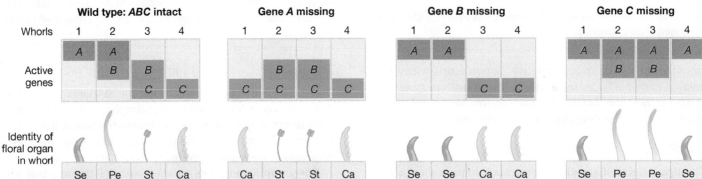

Figure 38.23 The ABC Model Illustrates Genetic Control of Flower Development. The ABC model is a hypothesis to explain the existence of three types of homeotic mutants in *Arabidopsis* flowers. The regions of gene expression were determined by in situ hybridization.

The ABC Model Three basic ideas underlie the ABC model (**Figure 38.23a**):

- Each of the three genes is expressed in two adjacent whorls.

- Because each gene is expressed in two adjacent whorls, a total of four **different combinations of gene products** can occur.

- Each of these four combinations of gene products triggers the development of a different floral organ.

Specifically, the Meyerowitz group proposed that **(1)** the A protein alone causes cells to form sepals, **(2)** a combination of A and B proteins sets up the formation of petals, **(3)** B and C combined specify stamens, and **(4)** the C protein alone designates cells as the precursors of carpels.

Does this model explain how the three classes of homeotic mutants occur? The answer is yes, if two additional elements are added to the model:

- The A protein inhibits production of the C protein.

- The C protein inhibits production of the A protein.

With these ideas in mind, patterns of gene expression can be predicted that correspond to the mutant phenotypes. These are shown in **Figure 38.23b**.

For example, if the A gene is disabled by mutation, then it no longer inhibits the expression of the *C* gene, and all cells produce the C protein. As a result, cells in the outermost whorl express only C protein and develop into carpels, while cells

in the whorl just to the inside produce B and C proteins and develop into stamens.

✔ If you understand the ABC model, you should be able to explain why in mutants that lack *C* gene expression, *A* genes become expressed across all whorls.

Testing the Model Although the ABC model is plausible, elegant, and capable of explaining the data, it needed to be tested. To do so, Meyerowitz and co-workers mapped the genes responsible for the mutant phenotypes and cloned the genes using techniques you learned about earlier (Chapter 20). Once they had isolated the genes, they were able to obtain probes to perform in situ hybridizations. The goal was to learn the pattern of expression of the A, B, and C genes and see if that pattern corresponded to the model's predictions.

The mRNAs for the A, B, and C genes showed up in the sets of whorls predicted by the model. The A gene is expressed in the outer two whorls, the B gene is expressed in the middle two whorls, and the C gene is expressed in the inner two whorls. Later work showed that there weren't single A, B, and C genes, but groups of A, B, and C class genes. However, this finding didn't change the outline of the ABC model.

The result that A, B, and C class genes were expressed in the predicted regions supported the ABC model. Just as different combinations of *Hox* gene products specify the identity of fly segments (Chapter 21), different combinations of floral identity genes specify the parts of a flower.

Plant Tool-kit Genes Like animals, plants have a genetic tool kit for development, although the tools have turned out to be different from those of animals. The differences, however, are not in the types of tools—hammer versus saw—but in their particular forms: nail hammer versus finishing hammer; circular saw versus band saw. For example, plants use a group of proteins called MADS-box transcription factors to specify structures, and animals use Hox transcription factors; plants use graded concentrations of auxin to specify position within the embryo, and animals use graded concentrations of other molecules, such as Bicoid. The details are different, but the broad mechanisms are the same.

Why should this be? There's likely a limit to the number of ways to build a multicellular organism. The different evolutionary paths taken in plants and animals to achieve this end have converged on these similar mechanisms, but each has used a different set of tools.

CHECK YOUR UNDERSTANDING

If you understand that . . .

- Reproductive development in plants begins when SAMs are converted to floral meristems.
- In *Arabidopsis*, development of the four floral organs depends on the expression of regulatory transcription factors encoded by the *A, B,* and *C* genes.

✔ **You should be able to . . .**

1. Describe fundamental differences in the generation of plant and animal reproductive cells and structures.
2. Explain how homeotic mutations in plants are similar to those in animals.

Answers are available in Appendix A.

38.1 An Introduction to Plant Reproduction

- Most plants are capable of asexual reproduction, which results in offspring that are genetically identical to the parent plant.

- Plants undergo alternation of generations, in which a diploid sporophyte phase alternates with a haploid gametophyte phase. Sporophytes produce spores by meiosis. Gametophytes produce gametes by mitosis.

- The relative size and life span of the gametophyte and sporophyte phases vary a great deal among plant groups.

- In angiosperms, or flowering plants, sporophytes are the large and long-lived phase where photosynthesis takes place; gametophytes consist of just a few cells.

38.2 Reproductive Structures

- In angiosperms, male and female gametophytes are microscopic and are produced inside flowers. Flowers are made up of sepals, petals, stamens, and one or more carpels.

- The lower part of the carpel, the ovary, contains one to many ovules. Within the ovule, a megasporocyte undergoes meiosis, producing a megaspore that develops into the female gametophyte.

- In the anthers of stamens, microsporocytes undergo meiosis. The resulting microspores develop into male gametophytes, which are enclosed in pollen grains.

38.3 Pollination and Fertilization

- Pollination occurs when pollen grains are transported to the stigma of the carpel. In most cases, the structure of a flower correlates with the morphology and behavior of its pollinator.

- If allowed to germinate on the stigma, a pollen grain sends a long pollen tube down the style. Two sperm travel down the pollen tube and enter the female gametophyte.

- In double fertilization, one sperm fuses with the egg to form a zygote, while the other fuses with polar nuclei within the female gametophyte. The fusion of sperm and polar nuclei produces endosperm—nutritive tissue that in most species is triploid.

38.4 Seeds and Fruits

- Seeds contain an embryo and a food supply surrounded by a coat.

- As an embryo develops, endosperm cells divide to form a nutrient-rich tissue. In addition, cells along the outside of the ovules form a protective seed coat, and the ovary develops into a fruit.

- In many cases, the mature fruit contains structures that help disperse the mature seed via wind, water, propulsion, or animals.

- Many seeds do not germinate immediately but instead experience a period of dormancy.

- A wide variety of conditions, ranging from scarification to exposure to red light, may break seed dormancy. In many cases, the event that triggers germination ensures that the seed germinates when environmental conditions are favorable.

38.5 Embryogenesis and Vegetative Development

- Vegetative development is the development and growth of all plant structures except flowers.

- Vegetative development begins with embryogenesis and occurs throughout the plant's life.

- Apical–basal and radial axes and apical meristems are established during early embryogenesis and retained in subsequent developmental stages.

- The development of an angiosperm embryo includes the formation of dermal tissue (epidermis), ground tissue, and vascular tissue layers and the development of the radicle, hypocotyl, and cotyledons.

- Vegetative development depends on meristems present at the tips of roots and shoots.
- The growth that occurs in vegetative development is finely tuned to the environment, allowing plants to adopt forms that maximize their survival and reproduction.
- Regulatory genes that control vegetative development are being discovered.

38.6 Reproductive Development

- Reproductive development is initiated when a shoot meristem switches from producing cells that will form shoots and leaves to producing cells that will form flowers, the plant's reproductive structure.
- The switch from vegetative to reproductive development in shoot meristems occurs in response to environmental conditions in many plants.
- Once a floral meristem is established, combinations of regulatory transcription factors encoded by A, B, and C classes of genes interact to specify the flower's sepals, petals, stamens, and carpels.

Answers are available in Appendix A

✔ TEST YOUR KNOWLEDGE

1. What happens when double fertilization occurs?
   a. Two zygotes are formed, but only one survives.
   b. Two sperm fertilize the egg, forming a triploid zygote.
   c. One sperm fertilizes the egg, while another sperm fuses with the polar nuclei.
   d. One sperm fertilizes the egg, while two other sperm fuse with a polar nucleus.

2. **CAUTION** In angiosperms, are sperm and eggs produced by mitosis or meiosis? Which cells are spores? Which structures are gametophytes?

3. Which of the following does *not* occur during embryogenesis?
   a. formation of the radial axis
   b. production of the suspensor
   c. formation of the cotyledons and hypocotyl
   d. formation of the leaf lateral and proximal–distal axes

4. When does the apical–basal axis first become apparent?
   a. when the epidermal, ground, and vascular tissues form
   b. when the cotyledons, hypocotyl, and root form
   c. when the first cell division produces the apical cell and basal cell
   d. during the globular stage, when the suspensor is complete

✔ TEST YOUR UNDERSTANDING

5. Why is the emergence of the radicle an important first step in germination?
   a. Its hook helps protect the shoot that emerges later.
   b. It carries out photosynthesis to supply the embryo with food.
   c. It is important for establishing a supply of water to the growing embryo.
   d. It is necessary to break the seed coat.

6. What are the advantages and disadvantages of self-fertilization versus those of outcrossing?

7. In what sense are the tissues produced in the SAMs and RAMs of a 300-year-old oak tree "embryonic"?

8. Human embryonic stem cells are capable of forming all types of cells in the human body. How are these cells similar to meristem cells in plants?

✔ TEST YOUR PROBLEM-SOLVING SKILLS

9. **PROCESS OF SCIENCE** Consider the following fruits: an acorn, a cherry, a burr, and a dandelion seed. Based on the structure of each of these fruits, predict how the seed is dispersed. Design a study that would estimate the average distance that each type of seed is dispersed from the parent plant.

10. **MODEL** Make a sketch of a simplified flower with all four organs, and indicate how the pattern of expression for just two genes (e.g., "D" and "E") could, hypothetically, regulate the development of each organ. Consider that what's important is whether a gene is on or off and that a structure can be specified when neither gene is expressed.

✔ PUT IT ALL TOGETHER: Case Study

How important are bees to pollination?

Most flowering plants can achieve pollination in several different ways. Those that produce pollen and carpels on the same plant may be self-pollinated, but they may also be cross-pollinated by insects or other pollinators. The cape gooseberry (*Physalis peruviana*) shown above is able to produce seed whether it is self- or cross-pollinated. Is one type of pollination better than the other?

11. Considering the gooseberry flower shown above, what types of cues might attract bees to the plant? What type of rewards do bees seek?

12. **QUANTITATIVE** Researchers conducted controlled experiments to test for effects of different types of pollination on cape gooseberry fruit size and seed production. The types of pollination included self-pollination, manual cross-pollination (transferring pollen from one plant to another by hand),

and cross-pollination by bees. Results are shown in the graphs below. Compared to self-pollination, do bees have a significant impact on fruit mass? How about on seed formation? (* means $P < 0.05$; see BioSkills 3.)

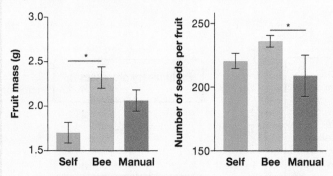

Source: Chautá-Mellizo, A., S. Campbell, M. Argenis Bonilla et al. 2012. *Basic and Applied Ecology* 13: 524–532.

13. Why might it be advantageous for plants to promote cross-pollination? What are the advantages of self-pollination?

14. **QUANTITATIVE** In general, larger fruits tend to earn higher profits for farmers who grow cape gooseberries as a crop. Compared to self-pollinated flowers, what is the approximate percentage of difference in fruit size of bee-pollinated flowers?

15. Based on the data in the graphs provided, approximately how many ovules are found in each gooseberry carpel?

16. **SOCIETY** Global bee populations have been declining over the past decade. What impact might this have on the world's human population?

THE BIG PICTURE

Plants and animals are diverse lineages of multicellular eukaryotes. They are different in important ways. Each lineage evolved independently from a different single-celled protist—plants with the ability to make their own food by photosynthesis, and animals reliant on obtaining energy from other organisms. Furthermore, plants are sessile, while most animals are capable of complex movements and locomotion.

Yet despite these differences, plants and animals face many of the same challenges to survive and reproduce in water and on land. Use this concept map to explore some of their similarities and differences in form and function.

Note that most boxes in the concept map indicate the chapters where you can go for more information. Also, be sure to do the blue exercises in the Check Your Understanding box below.

CHECK YOUR UNDERSTANDING

If you understand the big picture …

✔ You should be able to …

1. Propose one mechanism that both plants and animals use on land to limit the evaporative loss of water.
2. Describe one difference between plants and animals regarding the haploid stage of their life cycles.
3. Give an example of an adaptation that enables large plants and animals to survive the physical constraints imposed by large body size.
4. Explain where cellular respiration fits into this map.

Answers are available in Appendix A.

Plant and Animal FORM AND FUNCTION

are the product of

Evolutionary processes
22, 23

including

occurring in

Changing ecological contexts Unit 9

because plants and animals have

Abiotic environment
- Temperature
- Light
- Water availability
- pH, salinity, dissolved gases, nutrients
- Habitat structure
49

create

Biotic environment
- Parental care
- Competitors
- Predators, prey
- Parasites, hosts
- Mutualists
51, 52

Key FUNCTIONS to survive and reproduce

correlate with

including

PLANTS

REGULATION OF WATER AND IONS
- Water moves along a water potential gradient
- Turgor pressure provides structural support
- Terrestrial plants lose water evaporatively by transpiration, regulated by stomata and waxy surfaces
35

NUTRITION
- Autotrophic; make their own food by photosynthesis

- Take in sunlight, CO_2, and minerals
- Obtain ions from soil, symbiotic fungi, or bacteria
36

ANIMALS

- Osmotic stress varies in marine, freshwater, and terrestrial habitats
- Urinary system maintains homeostasis of water and electrolytes while managing excretion of nitrogenous wastes
- Terrestrial animals limit evaporative loss
39

- Heterotrophic; must eat food to acquire energy
- Take in carbohydrates, fats, proteins, vitamins, and minerals
- Obtain nutrients by ingestion, digestion, and absorption
40

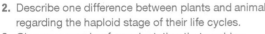

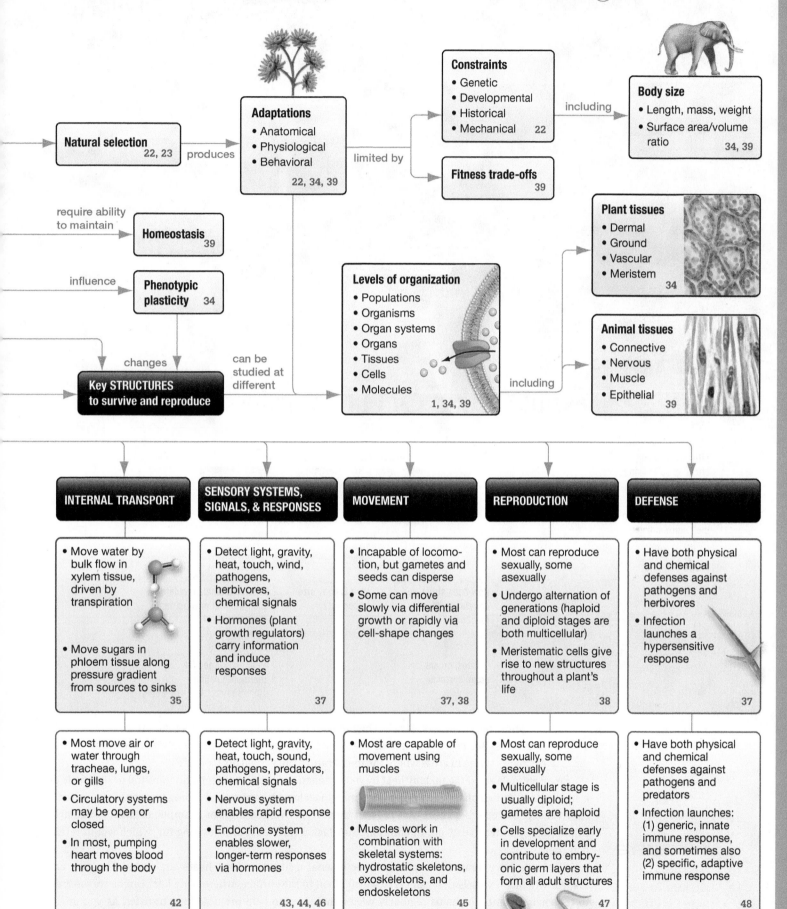

Natural selection
22, 23

— produces →

Adaptations
• Anatomical
• Physiological
• Behavioral
22, 34, 39

— limited by →

Constraints
• Genetic
• Developmental
• Historical
• Mechanical   22

Fitness trade-offs
39

— including →

Body size
• Length, mass, weight
• Surface area/volume ratio
34, 39

require ability to maintain →

Homeostasis
39

influence →

Phenotypic plasticity   34

— changes →

Key STRUCTURES to survive and reproduce

— can be studied at different →

Levels of organization
• Populations
• Organisms
• Organ systems
• Organs
• Tissues
• Cells
• Molecules
1, 34, 39

Plant tissues
• Dermal
• Ground
• Vascular
• Meristem
34

— including →

Animal tissues
• Connective
• Nervous
• Muscle
• Epithelial
39

INTERNAL TRANSPORT

• Move water by bulk flow in xylem tissue, driven by transpiration

• Move sugars in phloem tissue along pressure gradient from sources to sinks
35

• Most move air or water through tracheae, lungs, or gills

• Circulatory systems may be open or closed

• In most, pumping heart moves blood through the body
42

SENSORY SYSTEMS, SIGNALS, & RESPONSES

• Detect light, gravity, heat, touch, wind, pathogens, herbivores, chemical signals

• Hormones (plant growth regulators) carry information and induce responses
37

• Detect light, gravity, heat, touch, sound, pathogens, predators, chemical signals

• Nervous system enables rapid response

• Endocrine system enables slower, longer-term responses via hormones
43, 44, 46

MOVEMENT

• Incapable of locomotion, but gametes and seeds can disperse

• Some can move slowly via differential growth or rapidly via cell-shape changes
37, 38

• Most are capable of movement using muscles

• Muscles work in combination with skeletal systems: hydrostatic skeletons, exoskeletons, and endoskeletons
45

REPRODUCTION

• Most can reproduce sexually, some asexually

• Undergo alternation of generations (haploid and diploid stages are both multicellular)

• Meristematic cells give rise to new structures throughout a plant's life
38

• Most can reproduce sexually, some asexually

• Multicellular stage is usually diploid; gametes are haploid

• Cells specialize early in development and contribute to embryonic germ layers that form all adult structures
47

DEFENSE

• Have both physical and chemical defenses against pathogens and herbivores

• Infection launches a hypersensitive response
37

• Have both physical and chemical defenses against pathogens and predators

• Infection launches: (1) generic, innate immune response, and sometimes also (2) specific, adaptive immune response
48

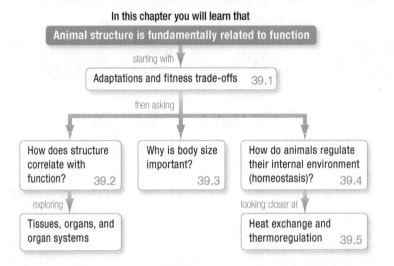

39 Animal Form and Function

African elephants are adapted to living in hot environments. Their large ears facilitate heat loss to their surroundings.

In this chapter you will learn that

Animal structure is fundamentally related to function

starting with

Adaptations and fitness trade-offs   39.1

then asking

How does structure correlate with function?   39.2

Why is body size important?   39.3

How do animals regulate their internal environment (homeostasis)?   39.4

exploring

Tissues, organs, and organ systems

looking closer at

Heat exchange and thermoregulation   39.5

This chapter is part of the Big Picture. See how on pages 816–817.

lephants are symbolic of Africa. They inhabit a wide range of habitats there, from dense forests to deserts. But one thing that all these habitats have in common is high temperature. African elephants thrive in areas where the temperature can exceed 50°C (122°F).

Small animals avoid the midday heat by retreating to a cool burrow deep underground or the shade of a small shrub. But elephants and other large mammals have a harder time hiding from sunlight, so their survival depends on other traits that prevent them from overheating. For example, elephants regularly roll in muddy water to cool off. In addition, they lack a thick coat of insulating fur, which would retain body heat.

Elephants have another weapon in their arsenal against extreme heat—large ears. The ears are loaded with blood vessels that can carry warm blood to the surface, where body heat can be transferred to the environment. Elephants regularly wiggle their ears to help promote heat transfer. As you might predict, African elephants have ears that are two to three times as large as those of closely related Asian elephants, which generally inhabit cooler environments.

In elephants, regulating heat exchange with the environment thus involves both structure (sparse fur and large ears) and function (shunting blood to the surface of the ears).

Anatomy refers to an organism's physical structure, or form. **Physiology** is how the physical structures in an organism function. You can review the importance of form and function in plants and animals in the Big Picture on pages 816–817. Unit 7 focuses on the relationship between anatomy and physiology in animals.

39.1 Form, Function, and Adaptation

Biologists who study animal anatomy and physiology are studying **adaptations**—heritable traits that make individuals more likely to survive and reproduce in a certain environment than individuals that lack those traits (see Chapter 22).

Recall that adaptation results from evolution by natural selection. Natural selection, in turn, occurs whenever individuals with certain alleles leave more offspring that survive to reproductive age than do individuals with different alleles. Because of this difference in reproductive success, the frequency of the selected alleles increases from one generation to the next.

Elephants with alleles for larger ears have a better chance of surviving to produce more offspring than do elephants with alleles for smaller ears. The ability to use their ears to regulate body temperature is an adaptation that helps elephants thrive in hot environments.

The Role of Fitness Trade-Offs

Adaptations increase fitness—the ability to produce viable offspring. But no adaptation is "perfect." Instead, adaptations are limited by which alleles are present in a population and by the nature of the traits that already exist—because all adaptations derive from preexisting traits.

The human spine, for example, is a highly modified form of the vertebral column in ancestors that walked on all fours (see Chapter 32). The modifications in the human spine can be considered adaptations that support our upright posture, but they are far from perfect—most adults experience back pain at some point during their lives. The evolution of the human spine has been constrained by the nature of the ancestral trait and by a lack of alleles that would improve its structure and function.

The most important constraint on adaptation, though, may be **trade-offs**—inescapable compromises between traits. For example, it takes a lot of energy to produce offspring through the process of reproduction and also to mount an immune response during an infection. Animals sometimes do not have enough energy to satisfy both needs. In these cases, a trade-off emerges: The animal may devote more energy to reproduction at the expense of strong immune function, or vice versa, or both traits might be negatively affected.

How do biologists study trade-offs in animal physiology? Let's consider experimental work on trade-offs in crickets. During mating, a male cricket produces a **spermatophore,** a packet of sperm surrounded by a large, gelatinous mass. The male deposits the spermatophore on the female's genital opening (**Figure 39.1a**). After mating, the female begins to eat the gelatinous mass (**Figure 39.1b**). The sperm packet remains behind, and the sperm slowly begin to enter her reproductive tract.

The longer it takes for the female to eat the mass, the more sperm are transferred to her, increasing the number of eggs fertilized by the male. Therefore, it might seem advantageous for the male to make as large a spermatophore as possible. However, there is a cost involved. Spermatophores comprise up to 6 percent of a male cricket's body mass, and it takes a male more than three hours to make a new one.

During the time males spend making new spermatophores, they lose other mating opportunities. Are there other costs? For example, is there a trade-off in male crickets between producing spermatophores and mounting an immune response against a pathogen?

(a) Decorated crickets mating

(b) The female eats the gelatinous mass.

Figure 39.1 Mating in Crickets Involves Transfer of a Spermatophore from the Male to the Female.
The spermatophore contains a gelatinous mass and a sperm packet. The female eats the gelatinous mass as the sperm from the packet enter her reproductive tract to fertilize her eggs.

QUESTION: Is there a trade-off between reproductive and immune function in male crickets?

HYPOTHESIS: Male crickets need to make an energy trade-off between reproductive function and immune function.

NULL HYPOTHESIS: No energy trade-off between reproductive function and immune function is required.

EXPERIMENTAL SETUP:

1. Remove spermatophores from male crickets for 5 days:

Spermatophores removed daily

No removal (control)

2. Draw hemolymph samples from both sets of crickets.

3. Add bacteria to samples; measure lysis of bacteria.

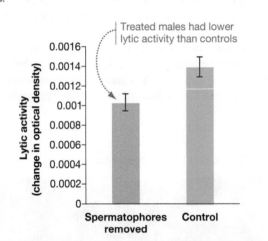

Spectrophotometer

EXPERIMENTAL SETUP:

1. Inject male crickets:

With lipopolysaccharide (LPS) to simulate bacterial infection

With placebo (control)

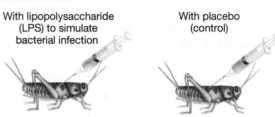

2. Remove spermatophores and measure size of gelatinous mass.

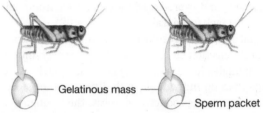

Gelatinous mass

Sperm packet

PREDICTION: Hemolymph from males forced to produce more spermatophores will exhibit lower lytic activity than controls.

PREDICTION OF NULL HYPOTHESIS: There will be no difference in lytic activity between treated males and control males.

PREDICTION: Spermatophores from LPS-injected males will have smaller gelatinous masses than those from control males.

PREDICTION OF NULL HYPOTHESIS: There will be no difference in gelatinous mass size between treated males and control males.

RESULTS:

Treated males had lower lytic activity than controls

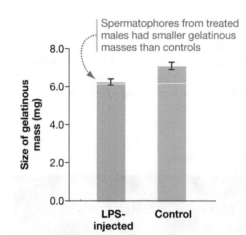

RESULTS:

Spermatophores from treated males had smaller gelatinous masses than controls

CONCLUSION: Male crickets must make an energy trade-off to support increased reproductive effort.

Figure 39.2 Trade-offs Between Reproduction and Immune Function in Male Crickets. This study showed that males with experimentally increased investment in reproduction had a lower ability to kill bacteria than control males, and that males with experimentally stimulated immune function had lower reproductive function than control males.

SOURCE: Kerr, A. M., S. N. Gershman, and S. K. Sakaluk. 2010. Experimentally induced spermatophore production and immune responses reveal a trade-off in crickets. *Behavioral Ecology* 21: 647–654.

✔ **PROCESS OF SCIENCE** If the null hypothesis were supported by the results, what would each graph look like?

To answer this question, biologists carried out an experiment using a powerful method—a reciprocal design. They altered the energetic investment crickets made into each trait—reproduction and immune function—and observed the effect on the other trait (Figure 39.2).

First, the biologists removed spermatophores from male crickets daily, causing the crickets to spend more energy to make new ones. The biologists then took a sample of the crickets' hemolymph (a circulating fluid similar to blood) and added bacteria to find out whether the hemolymph could lyse, or rupture, the bacteria. As bacteria are lysed, the opaque hemolymph becomes clear. Lytic activity was measured using a spectrophotometer (see BioSkills 8), which displayed the change in opacity, or optical density, of the hemolymph over time.

Compared to control crickets, which did not have their spermatophores removed, the experimental crickets had lower lytic activity (fewer bacteria lysed). This suggested that increased investment into making spermatophores was traded off against investment into immune function.

Next, the biologists injected male crickets with a component of the cell walls of bacteria called lipopolysaccharide (LPS), which caused the crickets to mount an immune response. The effect on spermatophore size was dramatic: Injected crickets produced smaller spermatophores than control crickets.

When the researchers looked more closely, they realized that the size of the sperm packet remained largely unchanged, but the size of the gelatinous mass decreased in injected crickets. Smaller gelatinous masses are eaten more quickly by females, allowing less time for sperm transfer and decreasing male crickets' reproductive success. Taken together, these two sets of reciprocal experiments provide very strong evidence that there is a trade-off between reproductive and immune function in crickets.

Trade-offs are common in nature. Desert animals that sweat to cool off are threatened with dehydration. An eagle's beak is superbly adapted for tearing meat but not for weaving nesting materials together. In studying animal form and function, biologists study compromise and constraint as well as adaptation.

Adaptation and Acclimatization

In biology, adaptation refers to a genetic change in a population in response to natural selection exerted by the environment. Short-term, phenotypic change in an individual in response to environmental fluctuations is referred to as **acclimatization.** Acclimatization is reversible. It is similar to acclimation, which refers to changes that occur in an organism in a laboratory setting.

If you moved to Tibet, your body would acclimatize to the high elevation by making more of the oxygen-carrying pigment hemoglobin and more hemoglobin-carrying red blood cells. But human populations that have lived at high elevations in Tibet for many generations have adapted to this environment through genetic changes. For example, these populations have a high frequency of an allele that increases the ability of hemoglobin to hold oxygen. In populations of Tibetans that do not live at high elevations, this allele is rare or nonexistent.

The ability to acclimatize is itself an adaptation. Light-skinned humans, for example, vary in the ability to tan in response to

sunlight. Some individuals tan easily—they have alleles that allow them to acclimatize efficiently to environments with intense sunlight—while others do not. In this and many other cases, the ability to acclimatize is a genetically variable trait that can respond to natural selection.

39.2 Tissues, Organs, and Systems: How Does Structure Correlate with Function?

If a structure found in an animal is adaptive—meaning that it helps the individual survive and produce viable offspring—it is common to observe that the structure's size, shape, or composition correlates closely with its function.

For example, recall that biologists have documented extensive changes in beak size and shape in the medium ground finch (*Geospiza fortis*) on the Galápagos Islands (see Chapter 22). Such changes are due to natural selection. Individuals with deep beaks are better able to crack the large seeds that predominate during drought years, while individuals with small beaks are better able to harvest the small seeds that predominate during wet years.

As Figure 39.3 shows, a strong correlation between diet and beak structure is also found among different species of Galápagos finches. Species with small, cone-shaped beaks eat small seeds; species with large, cone-shaped beaks eat large seeds; and species with long, tweezer-like beaks pick insects off tree trunks or other surfaces.

The mechanism responsible for these structure–function correlations is straightforward: If a mutant allele alters the size or shape of a structure in a way that makes it function more efficiently, individuals with that allele will produce more offspring than will other individuals. As a result, the allele will increase in frequency in the population over time.

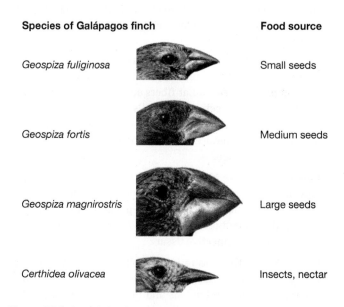

Species of Galápagos finch		Food source
Geospiza fuliginosa		Small seeds
Geospiza fortis		Medium seeds
Geospiza magnirostris		Large seeds
Certhidea olivacea		Insects, nectar

Figure 39.3 **In Animal Anatomy and Physiology, Form Often Correlates with Function.**

Structure–Function Relationships at the Molecular and Cellular Levels

Correlations between form and function start at the molecular level. For example, earlier chapters emphasized that the shape of proteins correlates with their role as enzymes, structural components of the cell, or transporters. The membrane proteins called channels form pores that allow specific ions or molecules to pass in or out of cells (see Chapter 6). The ends and interior of a channel are hydrophilic, which allows the protein to interact with the surrounding solution or the interior of the cell, while the perimeter is hydrophobic—allowing the protein to interact with the lipid bilayer. The protein's structure fits its function.

Similar correlations between structure and function occur at the level of the cell. In fact, it is possible to predict a cell's specialized function by examining its internal structure. Cells that manufacture and secrete large amounts of protein are packed with rough endoplasmic reticulum (ER) and Golgi apparatuses; cells that store energy are dominated by large fat droplets; and cells that ingest and destroy invading bacteria have many lysosomes.

The overall shape of a cell can also correlate with its function. For example, cells that are responsible for transporting materials into or out of the body often have extremely large areas of plasma membrane. As a result, they have room to accommodate the thousands of membrane channels, carrier proteins, and pumps required for extensive transport.

Tissues Are Groups of Cells That Function as a Unit

Animals are multicellular—their bodies contain distinct types of cells that are specialized for different functions. Frequently, groups of animal cells work together to perform the same function. A **tissue** is a group of cells that function as a unit.

Most adult animals have four tissue types: **(1)** connective tissue, **(2)** nervous tissue, **(3)** muscle tissue, and **(4)** epithelial tissue. In each case, the structure of the tissue correlates closely with its function. Let's consider each type in turn.

Connective Tissue **Connective tissue** consists of cells that are loosely arranged in a liquid, jellylike, or solid matrix. The matrix comprises extracellular fibers and other materials, and it is secreted by the connective tissue cells themselves (Table 39.1). Each type of connective tissue secretes a distinct type of extracellular matrix. The nature of the matrix determines the nature of the connective tissue.

- **Loose connective tissue** contains an array of fibrous proteins in a soft matrix; it serves as a packing material holding organs and tissues together and as padding under the skin. Cells called **fibroblasts** make the fibers and extracellular matrix in loose connective tissue.

- **Dense connective tissue** is found in the tendons and ligaments that connect muscles, bones, and organs. As Table 39.1 shows, the matrix in tendons and ligaments is dominated by tough collagen fibers (introduced in Chapter 11), also secreted by fibroblasts.

SUMMARY	Table 39.1 **Connective Tissues**
Type	**Example**

Loose
soft extracellular matrix; holds tissue together loosely

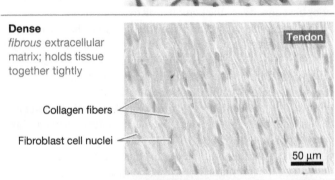

Fibroblast cell nuclei

Elastin fibers

Matrix

Collagen fiber

10 µm

Dense
fibrous extracellular matrix; holds tissue together tightly

Tendon

Collagen fibers

Fibroblast cell nuclei

50 µm

Supporting
firm extracellular matrix; functions in structural support and protection

Bone

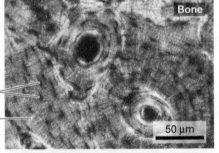

Bone cells

Matrix

50 µm

Cartilage

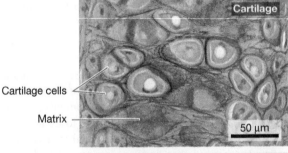

Cartilage cells

Matrix

50 µm

Fluid
liquid extracellular matrix; functions in transport

Blood

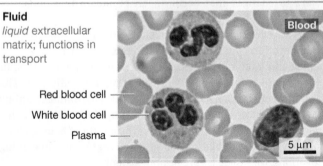

Red blood cell

White blood cell

Plasma

5 µm

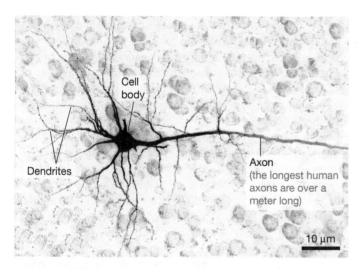

Figure 39.4 **Neurons Transmit Electrical Signals.** In a neuron, information is transmitted from dendrites to the cell body to the axon.

✔ Given a neuron's structure, is a neuron more likely to provide signals to specific cells and tissues or to broadcast signals widely throughout the body?

- **Supporting connective tissue** has a firm extracellular matrix. **Bone** and **cartilage** are connective tissues that provide structural support for the vertebrate body as well as protective enclosures for the brain and other components of the nervous system.

- **Fluid connective tissue** consists of cells surrounded by a liquid extracellular matrix. **Blood,** which transports materials throughout the vertebrate body, contains a variety of cell types and has a specialized extracellular matrix called plasma (see Chapter 42).

Nervous Tissue   **Nervous tissue** consists of nerve cells, which are also called **neurons,** and several types of supporting cells. Neurons transmit electrical signals, which are produced by changes in the permeability of the cell's plasma membrane to ions (see Chapter 43). Supporting cells have many functions,

including regulating ion concentrations in the space surrounding neurons, supplying neurons with nutrients, or serving as scaffolding or support for neurons.

Although they vary widely in shape, all neurons have projections that approach other cells. As **Figure 39.4** shows, most neurons have two distinct types of projections from the cell body, where the nucleus is located: **(1)** highly branched, relatively short processes called **dendrites,** and **(2)** a relatively long structure called an **axon.** Dendrites facilitate transmission of signals from adjacent cells to the neuronal cell body; the axon carries electrical signals from the cell body to other cells. Neuron structure is an excellent example of the relationship between structure and function: The long dendrites and axons permit rapid signaling of information throughout an animal's body.

Muscle Tissue   **Muscle tissue** was a key innovation in the evolution of animals—like nervous tissue, it appears in no other lineage on the tree of life (see Chapter 30). Some of the functions of muscle include movement of the body, pumping of the heart, and mixing of food in the gastrointestinal tract. There are three types of muscle tissue (**Figure 39.5**); you, along with other vertebrates, have all three.

1. **Skeletal muscle** attaches to bones and exerts a force on them when it contracts. Skeletal muscle is responsible for most body movements. It has long cells with a striated, or striped, appearance produced by an overlapping arrangement of proteins.

2. **Cardiac muscle** makes up the walls of the heart and is responsible for pumping blood throughout the body. The branching pattern of cardiac muscle allows electrical signals to spread throughout all cells of the heart, resulting in their coordinated contraction and relaxation.

3. **Smooth muscle** cells, which are tapered at each end, form a muscle tissue that lines the walls of the digestive tract and the blood vessels. Contraction and relaxation of smooth muscle help move food through the digestive tract and regulate blood pressure.

(Muscle tissue and movement are explored in detail in Chapter 45.)

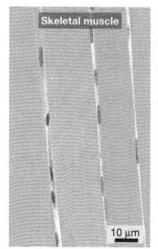
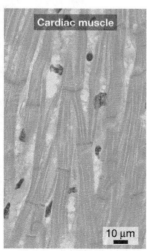
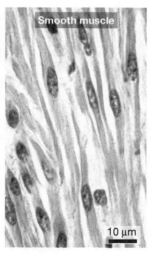

Long cells,
voluntary movement

Branched cells,
involuntary movement

Tapered cells,
involuntary movement

Figure 39.5 **Muscle Tissue Comprises Cells That Contract.** The three types of muscle tissue have distinctive structures and functions.

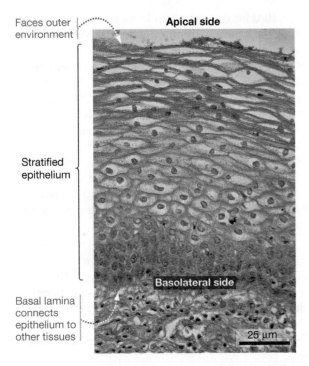

Faces outer environment

Apical side

Stratified epithelium

Basal lamina connects epithelium to other tissues

Basolateral side

25 μm

Figure 39.6 Epithelial Cells Provide Protection and Regulate which Materials Pass across Body Surfaces. Stratified epithelium is found in organs such as the vagina (shown here) and the skin, which are subjected to a lot of wear and tear.

Epithelial Tissues **Epithelial tissues** are also called **epithelia** (singular: **epithelium**). Epithelia cover the outside of the body, line the inner surface of many organs, and form glands. An **organ** is a structure that serves a specialized function and consists of two or more tissues; a **gland** is an organ that secretes specific molecules or solutions such as hormones or digestive enzymes.

Epithelia form the interface between the interior of an organ or body and the exterior. In addition to providing protection, epithelial tissues are gatekeepers. Water, nutrients, and other substances are transported, often selectively, across epithelia. For example, the epithelial tissue in your skin prevents water from being absorbed when you swim. Gaining water requires drinking, where the epithelial cells in your small intestine will absorb water.

Because the primary function of epithelia is to act as barriers and protective layers, it's not surprising to observe that epithelial cells typically form layers of closely packed cells (**Figure 39.6**). Adjacent epithelial cells are joined by structures that hold them tightly together, such as tight junctions and desmosomes (introduced in Chapter 11). Epithelia can be divided into two major types: *simple epithelium* (a single cell layer thick) and *stratified epithelium* (multiple cell layers thick).

✔ If you understand the functions of epithelia, you should be able to predict which of the following is more likely to contain stratified epithelium: the inside surface of the mouth or the gas exchange surface of the lungs.

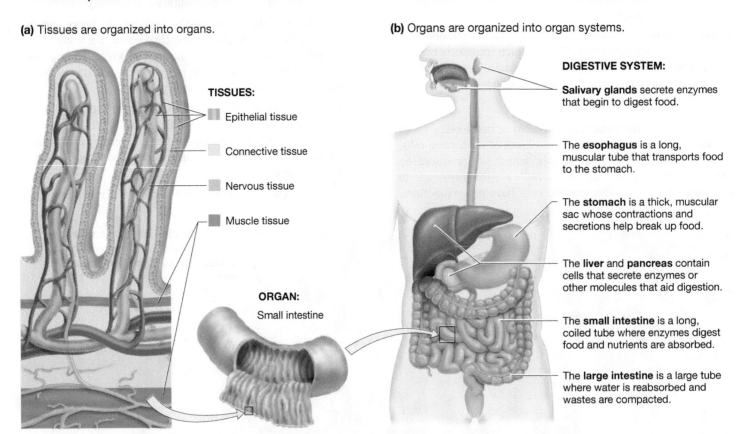

(a) Tissues are organized into organs.

TISSUES:

☐ Epithelial tissue

☐ Connective tissue

☐ Nervous tissue

☐ Muscle tissue

ORGAN:

Small intestine

(b) Organs are organized into organ systems.

DIGESTIVE SYSTEM:

Salivary glands secrete enzymes that begin to digest food.

The **esophagus** is a long, muscular tube that transports food to the stomach.

The **stomach** is a thick, muscular sac whose contractions and secretions help break up food.

The **liver** and **pancreas** contain cells that secrete enzymes or other molecules that aid digestion.

The **small intestine** is a long, coiled tube where enzymes digest food and nutrients are absorbed.

The **large intestine** is a large tube where water is reabsorbed and wastes are compacted.

Figure 39.7 Organs Are Composed of Tissues; Organ Systems Are Made Up of Organs. (a) The human small intestine is an organ composed of all four major tissue types. **(b)** The human digestive system is essentially one long tube divided into chambers where food is processed and nutrients are absorbed. The salivary glands, liver, and pancreas are organs that secrete specific enzymes or other compounds into the tube.

Epithelial tissue has polarity, or sidedness. An epithelium has an **apical** side, which faces away from other tissues and toward the environment, and a **basolateral** side, which faces the interior of the animal and connects to connective tissues. This connection is made by a layer of fibers called the **basal lamina.**

The apical and basolateral sides of an epithelium have distinct structures and functions. Epithelial cells, for example, line the surface of your trachea, or windpipe. The apical side of these cells secretes mucus and is covered with cilia that help sweep away dust, bacteria, and viruses. The basolateral side lacks these features and is cemented to the basal lamina.

Epithelial cells have short life spans. The cells that line your esophagus—the tube connecting your mouth and stomach—live for 2 to 3 days, while the cells that line your large intestine live for a maximum of 6 days. Muscle cells and neurons, in contrast, normally live as long as you do. Epithelial cells are short lived because they are exposed to harsh environments, where they are likely to be killed or scraped away.

Epithelial tissue as a whole does not wear away, however, because it includes cells that actively undergo mitosis and cytokinesis—producing new epithelial cells to replace those lost on the apical side.

Organs and Organ Systems

Cells with similar functions are organized into tissues, and tissues are organized into specialized structures called organs. Recall that an organ is a structure that serves a specialized function and consists of at least two types of tissues. The small intestine, for example, consists of muscle, nervous, connective, and epithelial tissues (**Figure 39.7a**).

An **organ system** consists of groups of tissues and organs that work together to perform one or more functions. Using the digestive system as an example, **Figure 39.7b** illustrates how the structure of organs correlates with their function and how the components of an organ system work together in an integrated fashion.

Because an animal's body contains molecules, cells, tissues, organs, and organ systems, biologists who study animal anatomy and physiology must work at various levels of organization to understand how that body operates.

Figure 39.8 illustrates these levels of organization, using the human nervous system as an example. Because the structure and function of each component in the body are integrated with those of other components, and because each level of organization is integrated with other levels of organization, the organism as a whole is greater than the sum of its parts. In other words, an organism is more than just a collection of individual systems, and each system is more than just a collection of individual cells, tissues, or even organs.

Each subsequent chapter in this unit focuses on a different organ system found in animals, beginning with the excretory system and ending with the immune system. Each of these systems can be interpreted as a suite of adaptations and trade-offs. Each system accomplishes a specific task required for survival and reproduction, and each works in conjunction with other systems.

Before delving into the various systems, however, it's essential to examine general phenomena that affect all systems in animals. Let's start by looking at how body size affects animal physiology.

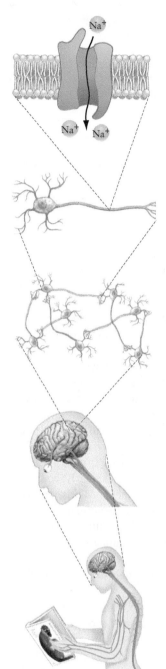

Atomic and molecular levels:
Membrane protein in neurons regulates flow of ions.

Cellular level:
Electrical signal travels down length of neuron.

Tissue level:
Signals travel from cell to cell in nervous tissue.

Organ level:
Nervous tissue and connective tissue in brain aid in sight, smell, memory, and thought.

Organ system level:
Brain and nerves send signals throughout the body to control breathing, digestion, movement, and other functions.

Organism level:
Nervous system coordinates the functions of other systems to support life.

Figure 39.8 Biologists Study Anatomy and Physiology at Many Levels. The levels of organization within an organism are not independent of each other. Instead, they are tightly integrated.

39.3 How Does Body Size Affect Animal Physiology?

Animals are living machines, made up of molecules, cells, tissues, organs, and organ systems that have changed over time in response to natural selection.

The laws of physics affect the anatomy and physiology of a living machine. The force of gravity, for example, limits how large an animal can be and still move efficiently. Or consider the forces exerted by the medium in which animals live. Because water is much denser than air, it is harder for animals to move through water. As a result, fish and aquatic mammals have much more streamlined bodies than terrestrial animals do.

Physical laws clearly affect body size. Just as clearly, body size has pervasive effects on how animals function. Large animals need more food than small animals do. Large animals also produce more waste, take longer to mature, reproduce more slowly, and tend to live longer. Conversely, small animals lose heat and water more rapidly than large animals do and are therefore more susceptible to damage from cold and dehydration. Juveniles

and adults of the same species face different challenges simply because their body sizes are different.

Why is body size such an important factor in how animals work? How do biologists study the consequences of size? Let's consider each question in turn.

Surface Area/Volume Relationships: Theory

From microscopic roundworms to gigantic blue whales, animals span an incredible range of body masses—a total of 12 orders of magnitude. Many of the challenges posed by increasing size are based on the fundamental relationship between surface area and volume.

The relationship between the surface area and volume of the roots and shoots of plants affects water and light absorption by the plant (see Chapter 34). Similarly, surface area is important in animals because oxygen and nutrients must diffuse into an animal's cells, and waste products such as urea and carbon dioxide must diffuse out. The rate at which these and other molecules and ions diffuse depends in part on the surface area available for diffusion. In contrast, the rate at which nutrients are used and heat and waste products are produced depends on the volume of the animal.

The contrast between processes that depend on surface area and those that depend on volume is important for a simple reason. As an animal gets larger, its volume increases much more rapidly than its surface area does.

Reviewing a little basic geometry will convince you why this is so. As **Figure 39.9a** shows:

- The surface area of a cube increases as a function of its linear dimension *squared*. Because a cube has six sides, the surface area of a cube of length ℓ is $6\ell^2$ (six times the area of any one side).

- The volume of the same structure increases as a function of its linear dimension *cubed*. Hence, the volume of a cube of length ℓ is ℓ^3.

(a) What are the surface area and volume of each cube?

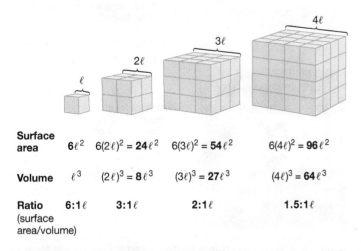

Surface area	$6\ell^2$	$6(2\ell)^2 = 24\ell^2$	$6(3\ell)^2 = 54\ell^2$	$6(4\ell)^2 = 96\ell^2$
Volume	ℓ^3	$(2\ell)^3 = 8\ell^3$	$(3\ell)^3 = 27\ell^3$	$(4\ell)^3 = 64\ell^3$
Ratio (surface area/volume)	$6:1\ell$	$3:1\ell$	$2:1\ell$	$1.5:1\ell$

(b) Surface area and volume of a cube versus length of a side

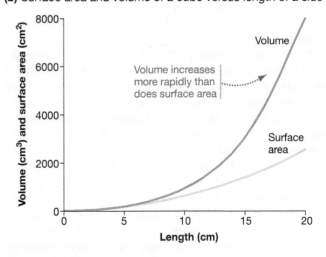

Figure 39.9 Surface Area and Volume Change as a Function of Overall Size. (a) The surface area of an object increases as the square of the length (ℓ). The volume increases as the cube of the length. **(b)** Volume increases much more rapidly than does surface area as linear dimensions increase.

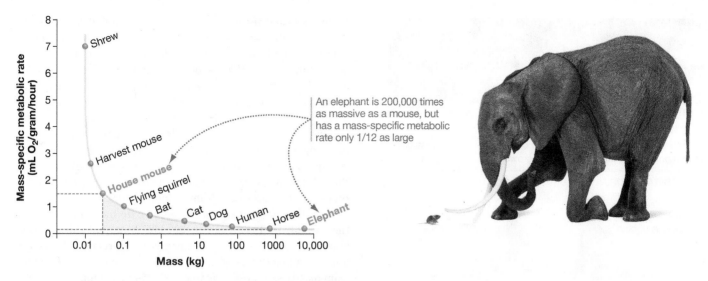

Figure 39.10 Small Animals Have Higher Relative Metabolic Rates than Large Animals Do.

✔ Which mammal must eat more to support each gram of its tissue: a Chihuahua or a Great Dane?

Area has two dimensions; volume has three. In general:

$$\text{Surface area} \propto (\text{length})^2$$

$$\text{Volume (or mass)} \propto (\text{length})^3$$

$$\text{Surface area} \propto (\text{volume})^{2/3}$$

(The symbol $\propto$ means "is proportional to.")

Figure 39.9b graphs the consequences of these relationships. The x-axis plots the length of a side in a cube; the y-axis plots the cube's volume (orange line) or surface area (yellow line). As a cube gets bigger, its surface area increases much more slowly than does its volume (or mass).

The same general relationship holds for cells, tissues, organs, organ systems, and whole organisms. Larger cells, for example, have lower surface area/volume ratios than smaller cells. Quantities that are based on volume, such as body mass, increase disproportionately fast with increases in linear dimensions. How does the relationship between surface area and volume affect animal form and function?

Surface Area/Volume Relationships: Data

As an example of how surface area/volume relationships affect an animal's physiology, consider the metabolic rate of mammals. **Metabolic rate** is the overall rate of energy consumption by an individual. Because consumption and production of energy in mammals depend largely on aerobic respiration, metabolic rate is often measured in terms of oxygen consumption, and it is typically reported in units of milliliters of O_2 consumed per hour.

Because it is so much larger, an elephant consumes a great deal more oxygen per hour than a mouse does. But what is going on at the levels of cells and tissues in these animals?

Comparing Mice and Elephants   To compare metabolic rates in different species, biologists divide metabolic rate by body mass and report a mass-specific metabolic rate in units of milliliters

of oxygen per gram per hour (mL O_2/g/hr). This mass-specific, or relative, metabolic rate gives the rate of oxygen consumption per gram of tissue.

Because an individual's metabolic rate varies dramatically with its activity, the accepted convention is to report the **basal metabolic rate (BMR)**—the rate at which an animal consumes oxygen while at rest, with an empty stomach, under normal temperature and moisture conditions.

Figure 39.10 plots per-gram or "mass-specific" BMR as a function of body mass. Notice that the x-axis on the graph has a logarithmic scale, making it easier to compare very small species with very large ones (for help with logarithms, see BioSkills 5).

What is the take-home message of this graph? On a per-gram basis, small animals have higher BMRs than do large animals. An elephant has more mass than a mouse, but a gram of elephant tissue consumes much less energy than a gram of mouse tissue does.

The leading hypothesis to explain this pattern is based on surface area/volume ratios. Many aspects of metabolism—including oxygen consumption, food digestion, delivery of nutrients to tissues, and removal of wastes and excess heat—depend on exchange across surfaces. As an organism's size increases, its mass-specific metabolic rate must decrease. Otherwise the surface area available for exchange of materials would fail to keep up with the metabolic demands generated by the organism's enzymes.

Changes during Development   A salmon weighs a few milligrams or less at hatching but grows into an adult weighing 50 kg or more in some species—a millionfold increase in body mass. To explore the consequences of this change, biologists have studied how gas exchange—uptake of oxygen and removal of carbon dioxide—occurs in newly hatched Atlantic salmon.

Like most fish species, young salmon have rudimentary gills but also exchange gases across their skin. In aquatic animals, **gills** are organs that allow the exchange of gases and dissolved substances between the animals' blood and the surrounding water.

QUESTION: Newly hatched salmon can breathe through their skin and through their gills. Which predominates?

HYPOTHESIS: The relative amount of oxygen uptake across gills and skin changes as a salmon grows.

NULL HYPOTHESIS: The relative amount of oxygen uptake across gills and skin does not change as a salmon grows.

EXPERIMENTAL SETUP:

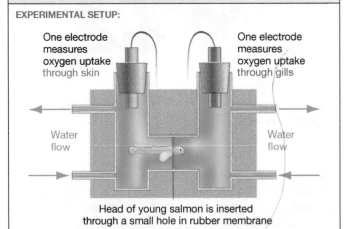

One electrode measures oxygen uptake through skin

One electrode measures oxygen uptake through gills

Water flow

Water flow

Head of young salmon is inserted through a small hole in rubber membrane

PREDICTION: Juveniles will take up a higher percentage of oxygen across gills and a lower percentage of oxygen across skin than larvae.

PREDICTION OF NULL HYPOTHESIS: Juveniles and larvae will take up the same percentage of oxygen across gills and skin.

RESULTS:

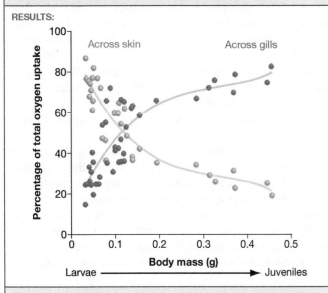

Across skin   Across gills

Percentage of total oxygen uptake

Body mass (g)

Larvae ⟶ Juveniles

CONCLUSION: Breathing changes from skin to gills as larvae grow. Interpretation: Gills provide larger surface area relative to increasing volume of body.

Figure 39.11 How Do Young Salmon Breathe?

SOURCE: Wells, P. R., and A. W. Pinder. 1996. The respiratory development of Atlantic salmon. *Journal of Experimental Biology* 199: 2737–2744.

✔ **PROCESS OF SCIENCE** Based on the experimental results, predict the relative usage of skin versus gills in breathing by adult salmon. Where would the data for adult salmon fall on the graph?

To document the amount of gas exchange that occurs in the gills versus the skin, researchers inserted the heads of individual larval and juvenile salmon through a pinhole in a soft rubber membrane and then recorded the rate of oxygen uptake on either side of the membrane. As the "Experimental Setup" section of **Figure 39.11** indicates, the gills were responsible for oxygen uptake on one side of the membrane, and the skin was responsible for oxygen uptake on the other side of the membrane. The graph in the figure's "Results" section plots the percentage of total oxygen uptake that took place across the skin (green line) and across the gills (purple line) as a function of body mass. Each data point represents the recordings from an individual fish.

Note that newly hatched larvae take up most of the oxygen they need by diffusion across the skin. As an individual grows, however, its skin surface area decreases in relation to its volume. At a body mass of about 0.1 gram, young salmon switch from mostly skin breathing to mostly gill breathing. What is the advantage of this switch?

Adaptations That Increase Surface Area

If the function of a biological structure depends on diffusion, that structure usually has a shape that increases its surface area relative to its volume. Flattening, folding, and branching are effective ways for structures to have a high surface area/volume ratio:

- *Flattening* Fish have **gill lamellae** (Figure 39.12a)—thin sheets of epithelial cells that provide the gill with an extremely high surface area relative to its volume. Because the surface area is so large, gases are able to diffuse across the gills rapidly enough to keep up with the growth in the volume of a developing fish.

- *Folding* In portions of the digestive tract where nutrients are transported into the body, the surface of the structure is folded. Extending from these folds are narrow projections called **villi** (Figure 39.12b). Together, the folds and villi make an extensive surface area available. Folded surfaces are common in diffusion-dependent organs.

- *Branching* The highly branched network shown in **Figure 39.12c** is a system of small, thin-walled blood vessels called

---

CHECK YOUR UNDERSTANDING

If you understand that . . .

- An animal's size is important in part because body mass is affected by an array of physical forces.
- The amount of heat and waste that an animal produces and the amount of food and oxygen that it requires are proportional to its mass or volume.
- The amount of surface area available relative to that mass or volume is critical because heat exchange and other important processes take place across surfaces.

✔ **You should be able to . . .**

Predict whether salamanders that lack lungs and breathe entirely through their skin are small or large compared to salamanders that have lungs. Explain your reasoning.

Answers are available in Appendix A.

(a) Flattening: fish gill lamellae

(b) Folding: intestinal folds and villi

(c) Branching: capillaries

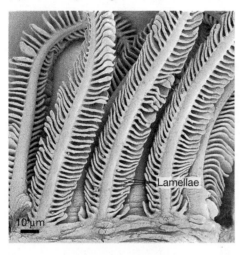

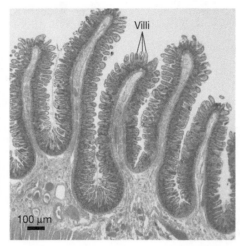

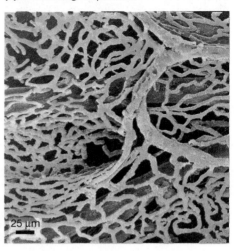

Lamellae

10 μm

Villi

100 μm

25 μm

Figure 39.12 Certain Structures Increase the Surface Area of Tissues. The micrograph in part **(c)** has been colorized to highlight capillaries (pink).

capillaries. Capillaries are the sites where gases, nutrients, and waste products diffuse into and out of blood, and branching greatly increases their surface area. In general, highly branched structures increase the surface area available for diffusion.

The amount of surface area created by flattening, folding, and branching can be impressive. The highly branched capillaries in a human have a surface area of up to 1000 m^2; extensive folding gives a surface area of about 250 m^2 in your small intestine. For comparison, a doubles tennis court has a surface area of 261 m^2.

Surface area/volume relationships have a pervasive influence on the structure and function of animals. They will be an issue in almost every chapter in this unit.

39.4 Homeostasis

Adaptation and surface area/volume ratios are important themes in the analysis of animal form and function. So is homeostasis.

Homeostasis (literally, "alike-standing") is defined as stability in the chemical and physical conditions within an organism's cells, tissues, and organs. Although conditions in an organism's environment can change, internal chemical and physical states vary slightly but are usually kept within a tolerable range.

Homeostasis: General Principles

Many of the structures and processes observed in animals can be interpreted as mechanisms for maintaining homeostasis with respect to some measure, such as pH, temperature, or calcium ion concentration. Let's review some important general ideas about homeostasis and then analyze how homeostasis can be maintained in the face of environmental fluctuations.

Homeostasis Is Achieved via Regulation Many organisms are able to **regulate** their internal conditions—to actively maintain relatively constant internal conditions even when the environment fluctuates. A dog maintains a body temperature of about 38°C whether it's cold or hot outside. If the dog's body temperature rises, it might pant to cool off and maintain homeostasis. If its body temperature falls, it might shiver to bring its temperature back up to the target value. Because dogs have to spend energy on panting and shivering, it's reasonable to conclude that maintaining a relatively constant body temperature is very important.

However, maintaining a constant body temperature might not be feasible in some environments. For example, many aquatic animals do not maintain their body temperature above the ambient temperature because they would lose heat quickly to the surrounding water. Instead, these animals **conform** to environmental conditions. The body temperature of freshwater invertebrates, fishes, and turtles, for example, changes as the water warms or cools. These animals save energy by not using metabolic heat to regulate their body temperature, but they might experience trade-offs such as swimming too slowly to escape from predators in cold water.

It is important to note that regulation and conformation lie at the two extreme ends of a spectrum, and most animals fall somewhere in between. For example, some animals conform to a range of mild ambient temperatures but expend energy to regulate their body temperature when their environment becomes dangerously cold or hot. These concepts also apply to homeostasis of other factors, such as water and ion concentration of body fluids (see Chapter 40).

The Role of Epithelia Because epithelia are the interface between the internal and external environments, they play a key role in achieving homeostasis. Epithelia are responsible for forming an internal environment that can be dramatically different from the external environment and for allowing physical and chemical conditions inside an animal to be maintained at relatively constant levels.

As subsequent chapters will show, many epithelial cells are studded with membrane proteins that regulate the transport of ions, water, nutrients, and wastes. No molecule can enter or leave the body without crossing an epithelium. Homeostasis is possible because epithelia control this exchange.

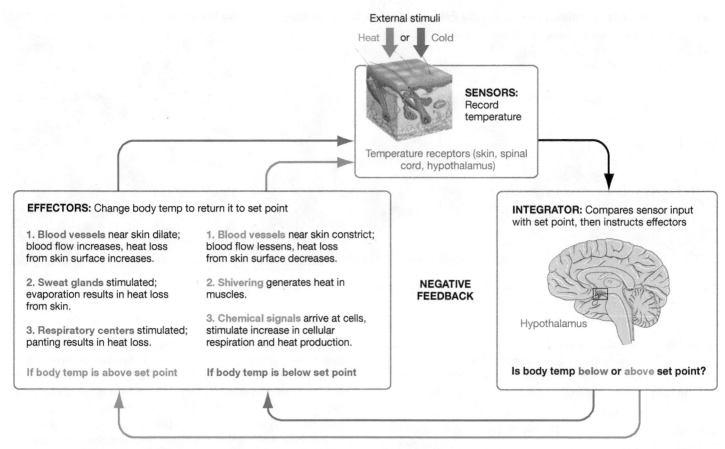

Figure 39.13 Mammals Regulate Body Temperature through Negative Feedback. In mammals, a set point for body temperature is maintained by a complex negative feedback system that includes integrators in the hypothalamus as well as sensors and effectors located throughout the body. The set point varies among species, from 30°C in monotremes to over 39°C in rabbits.

Why Is Homeostasis Important? Much of the answer to this question is based on enzyme function. Recall that enzymes are proteins that catalyze chemical reactions within cells (see Chapter 8). Temperature, pH, and other physical and chemical conditions have a dramatic effect on the structure and function of enzymes. Most enzymes function best under a narrow range of conditions.

Other processes depend on homeostasis, too. Temperature changes affect membrane permeability and how quickly solutes diffuse. The expansion of water as it freezes can rip cells apart if tissues are allowed to cool much below 0°C. Conversely, extremely high temperatures can denature proteins—meaning that they lose their tertiary structure and cease to function.

When homeostasis occurs, conditions inside the body allow molecules, cells, tissues, organs, and organ systems to function at an optimal level. However, occasional departures from homeostasis can represent important adaptations. For example, a fever is a response to an infection by a pathogen. This increase in body temperature can help fight off the pathogen.

The Role of Regulation and Feedback

Most animals achieve homeostasis by using regulatory systems that monitor internal conditions such as temperature, blood pressure, blood pH, and blood glucose concentration. If one of these variables changes, a homeostatic system acts quickly to modify it. Like the thermostat in a home heating system, each of these systems has a **set point**—a normal or target range of values for the controlled variable.

Animals have a set point for blood pH, blood oxygen and nutrient concentrations, and other parameters. In most mammals, the set point for body temperature is somewhere between 35°C and 39°C. How does an individual maintain its tissues at the set point despite changes in activity and the environment?

A homeostatic system consists of three general components: a sensor, an integrator, and an effector. Figure 39.13 shows how these components interact, to regulate temperature in mammals:

1. A **sensor** is a structure that senses some aspect of the external or internal environment.

2. An **integrator** evaluates the incoming sensory information by comparing it to the set point and determines whether a response is necessary to achieve homeostasis.

3. An **effector** is any structure that helps restore the internal condition being monitored by the system.

In mammals, the sensors are temperature receptors located throughout the body that constantly monitor information about body temperature. For example, temperature receptors in the skin sense cooling or heating, and they respond by altering the pattern of electrical signals that they send to adjacent neurons. Receptors in the brain region called the **hypothalamus** respond in a similar fashion to changes in blood temperature.

The electrical signals that originate with temperature receptors are transmitted to an integrator, also located in the hypothalamus. Current evidence indicates that separate centers in the hypothalamus sense and integrate changes in body temperature.

If a mammal is cold, cells in the hypothalamus send signals to effectors that return body temperature to the set point. Signals from the hypothalamus might induce shivering to generate warmth and fluffing of fur to improve insulation and retain heat. Signals from the same or nearby cells can also result in the release of blood-borne chemical signals that increase the rate of cellular respiration throughout the body, generating more body heat.

But if the same individual is too hot, the integrator in the hypothalamus sends signals that initiate sweating or panting—responses that cool the body. Other signals can induce behavioral changes that slow heat gain and production, such as seeking shade or a cool burrow and resting.

Homeostatic systems are based on negative feedback. When **negative feedback** occurs, effectors reduce or oppose the change in internal conditions. In response to either cooling or heating, behavioral and physiological responses move the body temperature back toward the set point via negative feedback. Figure 39.13 makes several points about the effectors that maintain homeostasis:

- Redundancy is common in feedback systems—there are usually several ways to change a parameter.

- Feedback systems usually work in "antagonistic pairs": One set of responses increases a parameter while a corresponding set of responses decreases it.

- Input from sensors and integrators happens continuously, so feedback systems are constantly making fine adjustments relative to the set point.

✔ If you understand the homeostatic system for maintaining body temperature in mammals, you should be able to explain how this system might change in a species of mammal as global temperatures rise.

Homeostatic systems are a key aspect of one of the five attributes of life (see Chapter 1): acquiring information from the environment and responding to it. Subsequent chapters in this unit explore how animals use sensor–integrator–effector systems to achieve homeostasis with respect to the solute concentrations of their cells and tissues, their oxygen supply, and nutrient availability. In the rest of this chapter, let's focus in more detail on how different animals achieve homeostasis with respect to body temperature. How do animals **thermoregulate,** or control their body temperature?

39.5 Thermoregulation: A Closer Look

All animals exchange heat with their environment. Heat flows "downhill," from regions of higher temperature to regions of lower temperature. If an individual is warmer than its surroundings, it will lose heat; if it is cooler than its environment, it will gain heat.

How does heat exchange occur?

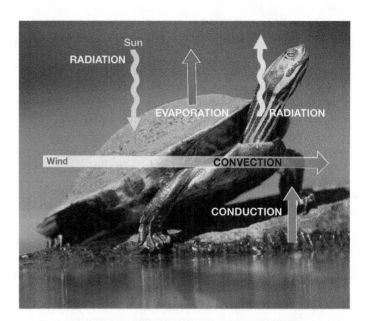

Figure 39.14 There Are Four Methods of Heat Exchange. The arrows indicate the direction of heat exchange.

Mechanisms of Heat Exchange

As **Figure 39.14** shows, animals exchange heat with the environment in four ways: conduction, convection, radiation, and evaporation.

1. **Conduction** is the direct transfer of heat between two physical bodies that are in contact with each other. For instance, when a turtle sits on a warm rock, heat is transferred from the rock to its body. The rate at which conduction occurs depends on the surface area of transfer, the steepness of the temperature difference between the two bodies, and how well each body conducts heat.

2. **Convection** is a special case of conduction. During conduction, heat is transferred between two solids; but during convection, heat is exchanged between a solid and a moving liquid or gas. For example, the heat loss that occurs when wind blows on your skin is due to convection. As the speed of the air or water flow increases, so does the rate of heat transfer.

3. **Radiation** is the transfer of heat between two bodies that are not in direct physical contact. All objects, including animals, radiate energy as a function of their temperature. The Sun radiates heat; so does your body, but to a much lesser degree.

4. **Evaporation** is the phase change that occurs when a liquid becomes a gas. Conduction, convection, and radiation can cause heat gain or loss, but evaporation leads only to heat loss. The turtle in the photograph is losing heat as water evaporates off its shell and skin. Because of the extensive hydrogen bonding in liquid water, a large amount of energy is needed to heat water and produce evaporation (see Chapter 2). If you get overheated on a summer day, splashing water on your skin and sweating will allow you to use evaporative heat loss to cool your body. Conversely, getting wet on a cold day can be deadly. The water on your skin absorbs so much heat from your body that your temperature may drop dangerously.

Heat exchange is critical in animal physiology because individuals that get too hot or too cold may die. Overheating can cause enzymes and other proteins to denature and cease functioning. It may also lead to excessive water loss and dehydration. A sharp drop in body temperature, in contrast, can slow enzyme function and energy production. In humans, both heat stroke and hypothermia ("under-heating") are life-threatening conditions.

You've already seen how mammals regulate body temperature through negative feedback. Let's now take a broader look at strategies for temperature regulation in animals.

Thermoregulatory Strategies

The ability of animals to thermoregulate varies widely. Two ways to organize this variation are by examining (1) how animals obtain heat, and (2) whether body temperature is held constant.

An **endotherm** ("inner-heat") produces adequate heat to warm its own tissues, while an **ectotherm** ("outer-heat") relies principally on heat gained from the environment. Endotherms and ectotherms represent two extremes along a continuum of heat sources. Many animals fall somewhere between these extremes.

There are also two extremes on a continuum describing whether animals hold their body temperature constant: **Homeotherms** ("alike-heat") keep their body temperature constant, while **poikilotherms** ("varied-heat") allow their body temperature to rise or fall depending on environmental conditions.

Humans, along with most birds and most other mammals, are strictly endothermic homeotherms. These species produce their own heat and maintain a constant body temperature. In contrast, most freshwater and terrestrial invertebrates, fishes, amphibians, and non-avian reptiles are ectothermic poikilotherms whose body temperatures change throughout the day and seasonally. But many animal species lie somewhere between these extremes:

- Some mammals, such as the African elephant featured in the chapter introduction, allow their body temperature to rise during the hotter part of the day—meaning they are somewhat poikilothermic.

- Small mammals that inhabit cold climates lose heat rapidly because their surface area is large relative to their volume. To survive when the ambient temperature is low, species such as dormice reduce their metabolic rate and allow their body temperature to drop, a form of poikilothermy. This condition is called **torpor.** Torpor that persists for weeks or months is called **hibernation.**

- Naked mole rats are mammals that lack insulation because they have no fur. They live in underground tunnels and allow their body temperature to rise and fall with burrow temperatures. They are poikilothermic and intermediate between ectotherms and endotherms.

- Japanese honeybees exhibit poikilothermy when defending their hives from predatory hornets. The honeybees swarm an invading hornet and contract their flight muscles repeatedly to collectively produce heat endothermically (Figure 39.15). The temperature within the swarm rises to 47°C (117°F), killing the hornet but not the honeybees, which can tolerate temperatures up to 50°C (122°F).

Even in a homeothermic endotherm such as a mammal or bird, body temperature can vary widely in different body regions. When a Canada goose is standing on ice, its feet may be at a temperature of just 9°C, even though its body core is at 35°C. Similar variations exist in tuna and mackerel. These fish are ectotherms but generate heat to warm certain sections of their bodies, such as their eyes or swimming muscles.

Comparing Endothermy and Ectothermy

Endotherms can warm themselves because their basal metabolic rates are extremely high—the heat given off by the high rate of chemical reactions is enough to warm the body. Mammals and birds retain this heat because they have elaborate insulating structures, such as fur or feathers.

Ectotherms can also generate heat as a by-product of metabolism. The amount of heat they generate is small compared with

(a) A hornet preys on a honeybee.

(b) A swarm of bees surrounds a hornet ...

(c) ... forming a hot defensive ball.

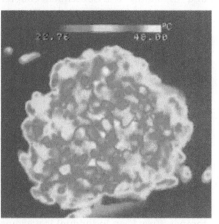

Figure 39.15 Honeybees Use Heat to Kill Predators. The infrared image in panel **(c)** shows the heat generated by the bees.

the amount generated by endotherms, however, because ectotherms have relatively low metabolic rates. The most important sources of heat gain in ectotherms are radiation and conduction: Ectotherms bask in sunlight or lie on warm rocks or soil.

You might have heard the terms "warm-blooded" and "cold-blooded" used to describe endotherms and ectotherms, respectively. But these terms are technically inaccurate, because the blood is not always warm in endotherms and cold in ectotherms. For example, an ectothermic lizard basking in the sun can attain a body temperature far above the ambient temperature, even higher than that of an endotherm.

Endothermy and ectothermy are best understood as contrasting adaptive strategies. Because endotherms maintain a high body temperature at all times, they can be active in winter and at night. Their high metabolic rates also allow them to sustain high levels of aerobic activities, such as running or flying.

These abilities come at a cost, however: To fuel their high metabolic rates, endotherms have to obtain large quantities of energy-rich food. The energy used to produce heat is then unavailable for other energy-demanding processes, such as reproduction and growth.

In contrast, ectotherms are able to thrive with much lower intakes of food. And because they are not oxidizing food to provide heat, they can use a greater proportion of their total energy intake to support reproduction.

What's the downside of ectothermy? Chemical reaction rates are temperature dependent, so muscle activity and digestion slow dramatically as the body temperature of an ectotherm drops. As a result, ectotherms are more vulnerable to predation in cold weather and in general are less successful than endotherms at inhabiting cold environments or remaining active on cool nights.

In short, each suite of adaptations has advantages and disadvantages. Like all adaptations, endothermy and ectothermy involve trade-offs.

Countercurrent Heat Exchangers

Homeothermic endotherms such as birds and mammals have sophisticated systems for thermoregulation. Among their most impressive adaptations are those that minimize heat loss from the body in cold environments. Heat loss is a particularly important problem for aquatic mammals. If you've ever gone swimming in cold water, you can appreciate the problem faced by seals, otters, and whales. Water is such an effective conductor of heat that aquatic organisms lose metabolic heat rapidly. The dense, water-repellent fur of otters conserves heat by maintaining a layer of trapped air next to the skin. Seals and whales are insulated by thick layers of fatty blubber.

Some marine mammals have body parts containing specially arranged blood vessels that minimize heat loss. For example, the tongue of a gray whale, which is exposed to cold water during feeding, contains bundles of arteries and veins. Each bundle includes an artery that carries warm, oxygenated blood from the body core. The artery is encircled by smaller veins, which transport cool blood from the tongue surface back toward the body core (**Figure 39.16a**).

This type of arrangement, in which fluids flow through adjacent pipes in opposite directions, is called a **countercurrent exchanger.** The "exchanger" part of the name is apt because, in a case like the whale's tongue, heat is exchanged between the warm blood in the artery and the cool blood in the veins.

The countercurrent exchange system is key to minimizing heat loss in the whale tongue. To see how it works, study the diagram on the left in **Figure 39.16b**. In this diagram, the fluid that enters the countercurrent heat exchanger is initially warm but steadily transfers heat to the adjacent, cooler fluid flowing in the opposite direction. There is a warmer-to-cooler gradient between the two fluids at every point along the length of the countercurrent exchanger.

(a) Tongue of gray whale

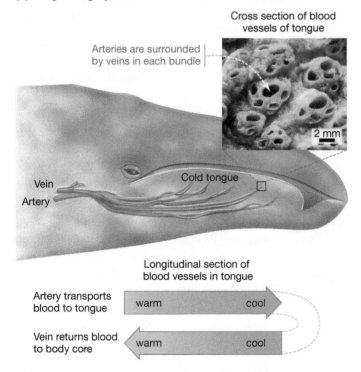

(b) Contrasting countercurrent with "concurrent" heat exchange

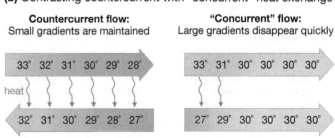

Figure 39.16 Countercurrent Exchangers Conserve Heat. (a) Bundles of arteries and veins in a whale tongue form heat exchangers that minimize heat loss from the tongue to the cold ocean water during feeding. **(b)** Countercurrent arrangements are much more efficient than "concurrent" arrangements. The data given here are hypothetical.

If the two fluids ran in the same direction, as in the diagram on the right in Figure 39.16b, the gradient between them would disappear quickly as the arterial current cooled and the venous current heated. The physical arrangement, in which an artery is tightly wrapped with several small veins, increases the rate of heat transfer beyond what would occur if there were a single large vein. Countercurrent exchangers, including heat exchangers, are effective because they maintain a gradient between the two fluids along their entire length.

Similar heat-conserving arrangements of arteries and veins are found in the flippers of whales and dolphins and in the legs of many mammals and birds that live in cold terrestrial environments.

Countercurrent exchangers are just one of many sophisticated adaptations you'll encounter in this unit—structures and systems that allow animals to thrive in a wide array of environments.

CHAPTER 39 REVIEW

For media, go to MasteringBiology

39.1 Form, Function, and Adaptation

- Animal structures and their functions represent adaptations, which are heritable traits that improve survival and reproduction in a certain environment.

- Adaptations involve trade-offs, or inescapable compromises between traits.

- Acclimatization is a reversible response to the environment that improves physiological function in that environment.

39.2 Tissues, Organs, and Systems: How Does Structure Correlate with Function?

- Animal cells with a common function are grouped together into four general types of tissue: connective tissue, nervous tissue, muscle tissue, and epithelial tissue.

- Organs are structures that are composed of two or more tissues that together perform specific tasks.

- Organ systems comprise organs that work together in an integrated fashion to perform one or more functions.

39.3 How Does Body Size Affect Animal Physiology?

- Large animals have smaller surface area/volume ratios than small animals. As animals grow, their volume increases more rapidly than their surface area.

- Large animals have low mass-specific metabolic rates, in keeping with their relatively small surface area for exchanging the oxygen and nutrients required to support metabolism and the wastes and heat produced by metabolism.

- The relatively high surface area of small animals means that they lose heat extremely rapidly.

39.4 Homeostasis

- Homeostasis refers to relatively constant physical and chemical conditions inside the body.

- Homeostasis in a fluctuating environment is usually achieved by regulation.

- Animals have set points, or target values, for various body parameters. When a parameter is not at its set point, negative feedback occurs. Responses to negative feedback return the parameter to the set point and result in homeostasis.

- Most animals have a set point for body temperature. If an individual overheats, it may pant, sweat, or seek a cool environment; if an individual is cold, it may shiver, bask in sunlight, or fluff its fur or feathers.

39.5 Thermoregulation: A Closer Look

- Animals vary from endothermic to ectothermic and from homeothermic to poikilothermic.

- Endotherms can be active in cold environments but must obtain a lot of energy to fuel their metabolism. Ectotherms do not require as much energy, but their activity depends on environmental temperature.

- Countercurrent heat exchangers have vessels in close contact that carry warm and cool fluids in opposite directions.

Answers are available in Appendix A

✓ TEST YOUR KNOWLEDGE

1. True or False: The increase in red blood cell count in tourists visiting Tibet is an example of acclimatization.

2. Which of the following examples best describes the concept that form facilitates function?
   a. Crickets must balance their resources between spermatophore production and immune defenses.
   b. A desert jackrabbit has large ears that help eliminate excess heat.
   c. An Antarctic fish maintains homeostasis by conforming to the stable, external temperature.
   d. Honeybees will swarm around a predatory wasp and contract their flight muscles to generate a lethal ball of heat.

3. As an animal gets larger, which of the following occurs?
   a. Its surface area grows more rapidly than its volume.
   b. Its volume grows more rapidly than its surface area.
   c. Its volume and surface area increase in perfect proportion to each other.
   d. Its volume increases, but its total surface area decreases.

4. Which of the following is an advantage that ectotherms have over endotherms of the same size?
   a. They require much less food.
   b. They are less vulnerable to predation during cold weather.
   c. They can remain active in cold weather or on cold nights.
   d. They have higher metabolic rates and grow more quickly.

✔ TEST YOUR UNDERSTANDING

5. For each of the following, explain how structure relates to function: absorptive sections of the digestive tract; capillaries; beaks of Galápagos finches; fish gills.

6. The metabolic rate of a frog in summer (at 35°C) is about eight times higher than in winter (at 5°C). Compare and contrast the frog's ability to move, exchange gases, and digest food at the two temperatures. During which season will the frog require more food energy, and why?

7. Explain why most endotherms are homeothermic and most ectotherms are poikilothermic.

8. QUANTITATIVE Consider three spheres with radii of 1 cm, 5 cm, and 10 cm. Calculate the surface area and the volume of each sphere, and plot the results on a graph with radius on the x-axis and surface area and volume on the y-axis. (Surface area of a sphere = $4\pi r^2$; volume of a sphere = $(4/3)\pi r^3$.) Explain how the graph shows the relationship between size and surface area/volume ratio.

✔ TEST YOUR PROBLEM-SOLVING SKILLS

9. Explain why it would be impossible for a gorilla the size of King Kong to have fur. (Your answer should explain how the surface area/volume ratio of a normal-sized gorilla would compare to Kong's; relate this to the role of surface area and volume in heat generation and heat transfer; and consider the function of fur.)

10. The dinosaur *Apatosaurus (Brontosaurus)* is one of the largest terrestrial animals that ever lived—over 20 m in length and weighing over 20 metric tons. Is it more likely that *Apatosaurus* was homeothermic or poikilothermic? Explain.

MasteringBiology®

Students Go to MasteringBiology for assignments, the eText, and the Study Area with animations, practice tests, and activities.
Professors Go to MasteringBiology for automatically graded tutorials and questions that you can assign to your students, plus Instructor Resources.

✔ PUT IT ALL TOGETHER: Case Study

How does gigantism affect the physiology of animals?

Many species of animals on islands are larger than related species on the mainland. Scientists hypothesize that this phenomenon, called island gigantism, evolved in response to the scarcity of competitors and predators on islands. Reduced competition and predation allows species to exploit more resources and frees them from the need to hide in small refuges.

11. QUANTITATIVE The graph shown here compares the average carapace (shell) length of mainland and island tortoises. Summarize the results (*** means $P < 0.001$, see BioSkills 3), then use the data to predict whether the surface area/volume ratio is higher in mainland or island tortoises.

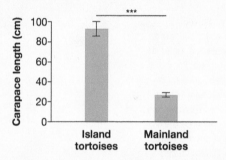

Source: Jaffe, A. L., G. J. Slater, and M. E. Alfaro. 2011. *Biology Letters* 7: 558–561.

12. Which tortoises, mainland or island, need to eat more food per gram of their body mass?

13. Which of the following might be a trade-off of gigantism experienced by giant island tortoises?
    a. They cool very rapidly during cold weather.
    b. It would be difficult to sustain their high mass-specific metabolic rates on a diet of plants alone.
    c. It could be more difficult to avoid thermally unfavorable conditions.
    d. They could hide from nonnative predators more easily.

14. CAUTION True or false: The body temperatures of island tortoises always closely match the temperatures in their environments.

15. Suppose that a small mainland tortoise and a large island tortoise are placed in the same pen at a zoo. Which tortoise will be more poikilothermic, the small or large tortoise? Why?

16. CAUTION On a trip to the Galápagos Islands, you overhear a group of tourists refer to tortoises as "cold blooded." Explain why this word is not accurate to describe a giant tortoise.

40 Water and Electrolyte Balance in Animals

Terrestrial animals lose water every time they breathe, defecate, and urinate. For many animals, drinking is an important way to replace lost water and achieve homeostasis. This chapter explores how terrestrial and aquatic animals maintain water balance.

In this chapter you will learn that

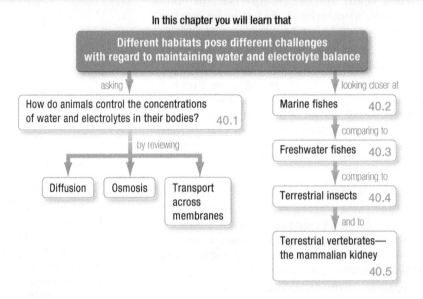

Different habitats pose different challenges with regard to maintaining water and electrolyte balance

asking

How do animals control the concentrations of water and electrolytes in their bodies? 40.1

by reviewing

Diffusion   Osmosis   Transport across membranes

looking closer at

Marine fishes   40.2

comparing to

Freshwater fishes   40.3

comparing to

Terrestrial insects   40.4

and to

Terrestrial vertebrates—the mammalian kidney   40.5

This chapter is part of the Big Picture. See how on pages 816–817.

The chemical reactions that make life possible occur in an aqueous solution. If the balance of water and dissolved substances in the solution is disturbed, those chemical reactions—and life itself—may stop. Humans can survive just three days without drinking water. Many marine animals die if a hurricane introduces enough freshwater to the ocean shore to disrupt normal salt concentrations.

An animal achieves water balance when its water intake equals its water loss. Water balance is an important component of homeostasis—the maintenance of constant and favorable conditions in cells and tissues.

Water balance is intimately associated with sustaining a balanced concentration of electrolytes throughout the body. An **electrolyte** is a compound that dissociates into ions when dissolved in water. Electrolytes got their name because they conduct electrical current.

In many animals, the most abundant ions of electrolytes are sodium (Na^+), chloride (Cl^-), potassium (K^+), and calcium (Ca^{2+}). Cells require precise concentrations of these ions to function normally. In humans, imbalances can lead to muscle spasms, confusion, irregular heart rhythms, fatigue, paralysis, or even death.

Water and electrolyte balance is also associated with excretion. Animals produce urine to excrete wastes. Urine contains water, so excretion of urine inevitably leads to water loss. The amount of water an animal loses in its urine depends both on its hydration state and on the type of wastes it produces.

This chapter is focused on a single question: How do animals maintain water and electrolyte balance in marine, freshwater, and terrestrial environments? Answering it will introduce you to some of the most complex and important homeostatic systems known. You can review the importance of maintaining water and electrolyte balance in the Big Picture on pages 816–817.

40.1 Osmoregulation and Excretion

Recall that uncharged solutes move down their concentration gradients via **diffusion** (see Chapter 6). Because solutes in aqueous solutions interact with water molecules, an increase in solute concentration effectively lowers the water concentration. The movement of water down its gradient across a semipermeable membrane is called **osmosis** (see Figure 6.13).

The concentration of solutes in a solution, measured in osmoles[1] per liter, is the solution's **osmolarity.** If the solutes are separated by a selectively permeable membrane and cannot cross that membrane, water moves from the side of lower osmolarity—that is, lower solute concentration and higher water concentration—to the side of higher osmolarity—higher solute concentration and lower water concentration.

Now let's examine how osmosis and diffusion affect water and ion balance in animals that live in different environments.

What Is Osmotic Stress?

Osmotic stress occurs when the concentration of dissolved substances in a cell or tissue is abnormal. It means that water and solute concentrations are different from their set points.

Many organisms respond to osmotic stress by osmoregulating, just as they respond to heat or cold stress by thermoregulating (see Chapter 39). **Osmoregulation** is the process by which organisms control the concentration of water and solutes in their bodies.

Not all animals encounter osmotic stress. For many marine invertebrates, such as sponges, jellyfish, and flatworms, achieving homeostasis with respect to water and solute balance is straightforward. Seawater is a fairly constant ionic and osmotic environment, and the concentrations of electrolytes and other solutes found in these animals nearly match those of the sea. Such animals are **osmoconformers.**

---

[1]The unit *osmole* is similar to the unit *mole* except that an osmole takes into account molecules that dissociate in solution. For example, because NaCl dissociates into Na^+ and Cl^- in solution, adding 1 mole of NaCl to water is equivalent to adding 2 osmoles of solute.

Seawater is **isosmotic** with the tissues of osmoconforming animals. Stated another way, the solute concentrations inside and outside these animals are equal. Because the body fluids of osmoconforming marine invertebrates are isosmotic with seawater, osmosis doesn't alter water and solute balance and induce osmotic stress.

Osmotic Stress in Seawater, in Freshwater, and on Land

In contrast to most marine invertebrates, marine and freshwater bony fishes and terrestrial animals are **osmoregulators.** These animals actively regulate osmolarity inside their bodies to achieve homeostasis. Osmoregulation in seawater, in freshwater, and on land involves very different challenges and solutions.

By osmoregulating, marine bony fishes keep the osmolarity of their tissues lower than that of seawater. The difference in osmolarity is most important in gills, which are organs involved in gas exchange. For gas exchange to occur with the environment, the epithelial cells on the surfaces of the gills must be in direct contact with seawater.

Seawater is **hyperosmotic** to the tissues of marine bony fishes—the solution outside the body has a higher solute concentration than the solution inside (Figure 40.1). Because there is a large difference in osmolarity between the inside of each cell and the seawater outside, water tends to flow by osmosis out of the gill epithelium. If the water that these fishes lose across their gills is not replaced, their cells will shrivel and die. These

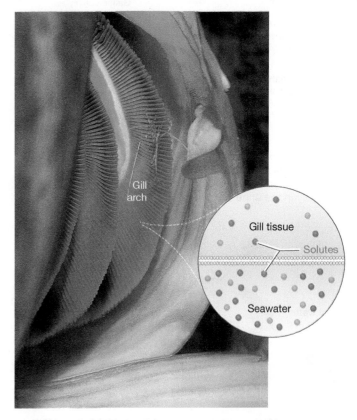

Figure 40.1 **Seawater Is Hyperosmotic Compared to Fish Gill Tissue.**

(a) Marine fishes lose water by osmosis and gain electrolytes by diffusion.

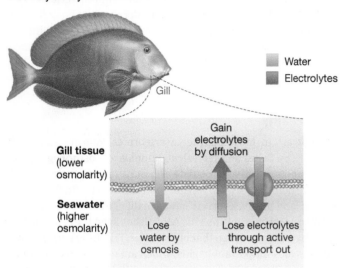

Water
Electrolytes

Gill

Gain electrolytes by diffusion

Gill tissue (lower osmolarity)

Seawater (higher osmolarity)

Lose water by osmosis

Lose electrolytes through active transport out

(b) Freshwater fishes gain water by osmosis and lose electrolytes by diffusion.

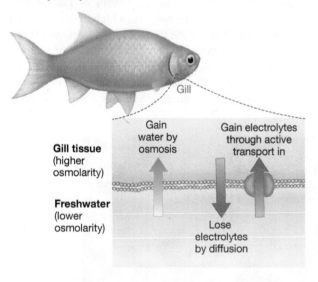

Gill

Gain water by osmosis

Gain electrolytes through active transport in

Gill tissue (higher osmolarity)

Freshwater (lower osmolarity)

Lose electrolytes by diffusion

(c) Terrestrial animals lose water by evaporation from gas-exchange and other body surfaces. Electrolytes are lost primarily in the urine and feces.

Lose water by evaporation from other body parts

Lose water from lungs during breathing

Gain metabolic water

Gain water by drinking and eating

Lose water in urine and feces

Gain electrolytes in food

Lose electrolytes in urine

Figure 40.2 Marine, Freshwater, and Terrestrial Animals Face Different Osmoregulatory Challenges.

animals face a trade-off between gas exchange and maintaining water and electrolyte balance.

Marine bony fishes replace the lost water by drinking large quantities of seawater. Drinking brings in excess electrolytes, however. Electrolyte balance is disrupted even further because ions diffuse into the gill epithelium, following a concentration gradient from seawater to tissues.

To rid themselves of these excess electrolytes, marine bony fishes actively pump ions out of their bodies and back into the seawater, using membrane proteins located in the gill epithelium (**Figure 40.2a**). They also lose electrolytes by excreting small quantities of highly concentrated urine.

Freshwater fishes osmoregulate in an environment dramatically different from the ocean. Unlike their marine relatives, which lose water by osmosis and gain solutes by diffusion, freshwater fishes gain water and lose solutes.

Why? In the gills of freshwater fishes, epithelial cells have a higher solute concentration than the freshwater outside. The freshwater is **hyposmotic** to the fishes' tissues. As a result, these fishes gain water via osmosis across the gill epithelium (**Figure 40.2b**), which puts them under osmotic stress. Just as in marine fishes, there is a trade-off between gas exchange and osmoregulation.

If a freshwater fish does not get rid of incoming water, its cells will burst and it will die. To achieve homeostasis and survive, freshwater fishes excrete large amounts of water in their urine and do not drink.

Freshwater fishes also undergo osmotic stress because electrolytes tend to diffuse out of the gill epithelium into the environment, along their concentration gradients. These animals must replace the lost electrolytes by obtaining them in food or by actively transporting them into the body from the surrounding water—usually across the gills.

What about land animals? In terms of water balance terrestrial environments are similar to the ocean. Like marine bony fishes, land animals constantly lose water to the environment (**Figure 40.2c**). On land, however, the process involved is not osmosis but evaporation (see Chapter 39).

The epithelial cells that line a turtle's lung and a fruit fly's gas-exchange structures have a moist surface, which protects the integrity of the cells' plasma membranes and promotes diffusion of gases across the epithelia. Because the atmosphere is almost always drier than this surface, terrestrial animals lose water by evaporation. Once again, there is a trade-off between gas exchange and osmoregulation.

Water balance in land animals is further complicated because water is lost in urine and, in some species, when they sweat or pant to lower body temperature. The lost water is replaced by drinking, ingesting water in food, or gaining metabolic water—water produced during cellular respiration (see Chapter 9). The relative importance of each of these methods of replacing water depends on the species. For example, many desert animals do not have access to drinking water throughout much of the year, so they rely more on water in food and metabolic water.

✔ If you understand this concept, you should be able to explain why maintaining water and electrolyte homeostasis poses similar challenges to marine and terrestrial animals.

How Do Electrolytes and Water Move across Cell Membranes?

What molecular mechanisms allow animals to cope with the diverse challenges they face in maintaining water and electrolyte balance? Recall that solutes move across cell membranes by passive or active transport (see Chapter 6). *Passive transport* occurs by diffusion along an electrochemical gradient and does not require an expenditure of energy by the cell. *Active transport*, in contrast, occurs when a source of energy like ATP powers the movement of a solute, establishing a concentration gradient or an electrochemical gradient.

In *primary* active transport, a source of energy like ATP is used to move ions against their gradients. The sodium–potassium pump, or Na^+/K^+-ATPase, is a very important pump in animals. *Secondary* active transport, or *cotransport*, relies on membrane proteins that use an electrochemical gradient established by a pump during primary active transport. A cotransporter that moves different solutes in the same direction is called a *symporter*; a cotransporter that moves different solutes in opposite directions is called an *antiporter* (see Chapter 35).

How does water cross cell membranes? To date, there are no known mechanisms for actively transporting water across membranes. Instead, cells use pumps to transport ions and set up an osmotic gradient; water then follows by osmosis—often through the specialized membrane channels called **aquaporins** (see Chapter 6). In essence, cells move water by moving solutes.

Animals excrete excess solutes, along with waste products, using a urinary system. Because solutes and wastes often must be dissolved in water to be excreted, water balance is fundamentally related to excretion.

Types of Nitrogenous Wastes: Impact on Water Balance

Animal cells contain amino acids and nucleic acids that are used to synthesize proteins, RNA, and DNA. Excess amino acids and nucleic acids can be broken down in catabolic reactions that produce **ammonia** (NH_3). Ammonia is toxic to cells because at high concentrations it raises the pH of intracellular and extracellular fluids enough to inactivate enzymes.

How do animals avoid these toxic effects? They get rid of the ammonia—by excreting it or by converting it to other nitrogen-containing compounds, which are then excreted. Ammonia and these other compounds are referred to as nitrogenous wastes.

Forms of Nitrogenous Waste Vary among Species Because nitrogenous wastes must be dissolved in water, their excretion inevitably leads to water loss. However, the amount of water an animal loses during excretion depends on the type of nitrogenous waste it excretes (see Table 40.1).

- In freshwater fishes, ammonia is diluted to a low concentration and excreted in watery urine.

- In freshwater and marine bony fishes, ammonia diffuses across the gills into the surrounding water along its concentration gradient.

- In mammals (including humans) and adult amphibians, enzyme-catalyzed reactions convert ammonia to a much less toxic compound called **urea,** which is excreted in urine.

- In terrestrial arthropods, birds, and other reptiles, reactions convert ammonia to **uric acid,** the white, paste-like substance that you have probably seen in bird feces. Compared with urea and ammonia, uric acid is much less soluble in water—which explains why it is so difficult to wash bird droppings off a car. As a result, animals that excrete uric acid can get rid of excess nitrogen while losing little water.

Why Do Nitrogenous Wastes Vary among Species? The type of nitrogenous waste produced by an animal correlates with its lineage—its evolutionary history. For example, mammals excrete urea while reptiles (including birds) excrete uric acid (Table 40.1).

Evolutionary history is not the entire story, however. Nitrogenous waste production is also related to the amount of

SUMMARY Table 40.1 Attributes of Three Forms of Nitrogenous Waste			
Attribute	**Ammonia**	**Urea**	**Uric Acid**
Solubility in water	high	medium	very low
Amount of water required for excretion	high	medium	very low
Toxicity	high	medium	low
Groups where it is the primary waste	most bony fishes, aquatic invertebrates	mammals, most adult amphibians, sharks, rays, skates	birds and other reptiles, most terrestrial arthropods (insects, spiders)
Method of synthesis	product of breakdown of amino acids and nucleic acids	synthesized in liver, starting with ammonia or amino groups from amino acids	synthesis starts with nucleic acids
Energy cost of synthesis	low	high	high
Method of excretion	in urine, and diffuses across gills	in urine (mammals); diffuses across gills (sharks)	with feces

osmotic stress that a species endures, which is influenced by the habitat it occupies.

- Terrestrial birds conserve water by excreting about 90 percent of their nitrogenous waste as uric acid and only 3–4 percent as ammonia, but aquatic birds such as ducks excrete just 50 percent of their excess nitrogen as uric acid and 30 percent as ammonia.

- Tadpoles are aquatic and excrete ammonia, but many adult frogs and toads are terrestrial and excrete urea.

- Production of urea and uric acid is particularly common in animals—such as reptiles—that live in dry habitats.

To make sense of these observations, consider the fitness trade-off between the energetic cost of synthesizing each type of waste and the benefit of conserving water. Ammonia excretion requires a large water loss but little energy expenditure because the molecule isn't processed by enzymes. Uric acid excretion, in contrast, requires almost no loss of water but a series of enzyme-catalyzed, energy-demanding reactions. Different trade-offs are favored in different environments.

Now that you have a basic understanding of the osmoregulatory and excretory challenges facing animals, let's take a closer look at how marine, freshwater, and terrestrial animals maintain water and electrolyte homeostasis.

40.2 Water and Electrolyte Balance in Marine Fishes

Marine bony fishes and cartilaginous fishes (sharks, rays, and skates) experience severe osmotic stress because they live in water with a very high osmolarity. Distinct strategies for dealing with osmotic stress have evolved in these vertebrate lineages since they diverged over 400 million years ago.

Osmoconformation versus Osmoregulation in Marine Fishes

Osmoregulation and osmoconformation are two strategies for living in the ocean, and each has its own costs and benefits. Marine bony fishes are osmoregulators. Recall that they maintain a lower blood osmolarity than that of seawater by drinking seawater to replace water lost via osmosis and by actively transporting electrolytes out of the body. This process comes with a significant energetic cost.

Sharks, rays, and skates are osmoconformers. However, the composition of their blood is quite different from that of seawater. Shark blood contains low concentrations of ions but relatively high concentrations of urea. This increases their blood osmolarity so that it is nearly isosmotic with seawater. The result? Sharks lose little water by osmosis. However, sharks must expend energy to make proteins that protect their cells from the toxic effects of high urea concentrations.

Even though they are osmoconformers, sharks still maintain a relatively low concentration of salt (NaCl) in their blood. To do so, sharks must excrete salt because sodium and chloride ions

diffuse into their gill cells from seawater, along the ions' concentration gradients. Research on the molecular mechanism of salt excretion in sharks revealed two key points:

1. The mechanism is found in a wide array of species, including *Homo sapiens*. It is functioning in your kidneys, right now.

2. The mechanism represents a critically important concept in physiology. Plant and animal cells use active transport to set up a strong electrochemical gradient for one ion—typically Na^+ in animals and H^+ in plants. The sodium or proton gradient is then used to transport a variety of other substances without further expenditure of energy.

Salt excretion is fundamental to life. Let's dig in.

How Do Sharks Excrete Salt?

Research on salt excretion in sharks focused on an organ called the **rectal gland,** which secretes a concentrated salt solution. To determine how this gland works, researchers studied it in vitro—meaning outside the shark's body, in a controlled laboratory environment. The basic approach was to dissect rectal glands, immerse them in a solution with a defined composition and osmolarity, and analyze the fluid that the glands produced.

Early experiments showed that normal salt excretion occurred only if the solution in the rectal gland contained ATP. This result supported the hypothesis that salt excretion involves active transport. A concentrated salt solution can be produced only if ions are actively transported against a concentration gradient. How do ions become concentrated?

The Role of Na^+/K^+-ATPase An energy-demanding mechanism for salt excretion implies that a protein in the plasma membrane of epithelial cells is actively pumping Na^+, Cl^-, or both. The best-characterized candidate was Na^+/K^+-ATPase.

To test the hypothesis that Na^+/K^+-ATPase is involved in salt excretion by shark rectal glands, biologists used a plant defense compound called **ouabain** (pronounced *WAA-bane*). This molecule is toxic to animals because it binds to Na^+/K^+-ATPase and prevents it from functioning.

Just as predicted, rectal glands that were treated with ouabain stopped producing a concentrated salt solution. This was strong evidence that Na^+/K^+-ATPase is essential for salt excretion.

A Molecular Model for Salt Excretion Subsequent work has shown that salt excretion in sharks is a multistep process, summarized in **Figure 40.3**.

1. Na^+/K^+-ATPase pumps Na^+ out of epithelial cells across the basolateral surface, into the **interstitial fluid**—the extracellular fluid surrounding the rectal gland. The pump creates an electrochemical gradient favoring the diffusion of Na^+ into the cell. This gradient allows the cell to transport other ions without an additional expenditure of energy.

2. Na^+, Cl^-, and K^+ all enter the cell by secondary active transport through a cotransporter, powered by the Na^+ master gradient. Note that this cotransporter allows Na^+ to diffuse into the cell *along* its electrochemical gradient, causing Cl^- and K^+ to move into the cell *against* their electrochemical

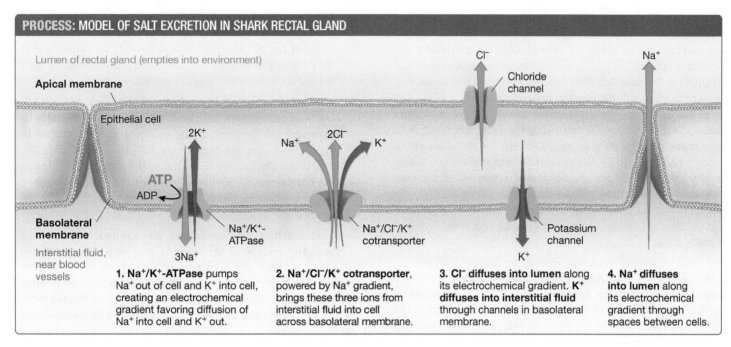

Lumen of rectal gland (empties into environment)

Apical membrane

Epithelial cell

Cl⁻ Chloride channel

Na⁺

$2K^+$

ATP
ADP

Na⁺ $2Cl^-$ K⁺

Na⁺/K⁺-ATPase

$3Na^+$

Na⁺/Cl⁻/K⁺ cotransporter

Potassium channel

K^+

Basolateral membrane

Interstitial fluid, near blood vessels

1. **Na^+/K^+-ATPase** pumps Na^+ out of cell and K^+ into cell, creating an electrochemical gradient favoring diffusion of Na^+ into cell and K^+ out.

2. **$Na^+/Cl^-/K^+$ cotransporter**, powered by Na^+ gradient, brings these three ions from interstitial fluid into cell across basolateral membrane.

3. **Cl^- diffuses into lumen** along its electrochemical gradient. **K^+ diffuses into interstitial fluid** through channels in basolateral membrane.

4. **Na^+ diffuses into lumen** along its electrochemical gradient through spaces between cells.

Figure 40.3 The Rectal Gland Rids the Shark Body of Excess Salt.

gradients. This entry of Cl^- and K^+ is possible only because these ions move through a cotransporter with Na^+.

3. As Cl^- builds up inside the cell, Cl^- diffuses down its concentration gradient into the lumen of the gland through a chloride channel located in the apical membrane.

4. Following its electrochemical gradient, Na^+ diffuses into the lumen of the gland through spaces between the cells.

In many animals, epithelial cells that transport sodium and chloride ions contain the same combination of membrane proteins found in the shark rectal gland. These species include

- marine birds and other reptiles that drink seawater and excrete NaCl via salt glands in their nostrils;

- marine fishes that excrete salt from their gills (see Figure 40.2a);

- mammals that transport salt in their kidneys.

Research on the shark rectal gland also produced an unforeseen benefit for understanding cystic fibrosis, the most common genetic disease in human populations of northern European extraction (see Chapter 6). Several years after the shark chloride channel was characterized, investigators identified a protein called cystic fibrosis transmembrane regulator (CFTR). Although the disease was known to be associated with defects in CFTR, no one knew what the protein did.

When investigators realized that the amino acid sequence of CFTR is 80 percent identical to that of the shark chloride channel, it was their first hint that CFTR is involved in Cl^- transport. Subsequent studies supported the hypothesis that cystic fibrosis results from a defect in a chloride channel. With this result, research on water and electrolyte balance in sharks shed light on an important human disease.

CHECK YOUR UNDERSTANDING

If you understand that ...

- Marine bony fishes lose water by osmosis. To replace it, they drink seawater.
- Marine sharks, rays, and skates osmoconform.
- Marine fishes must rid themselves of the salt they gain when they drink seawater or when Na^+ and Cl^- diffuse into their blood along concentration gradients.

✔ **You should be able to ...**

List the advantages and disadvantages of osmoregulating and osmoconforming in a marine environment.

Answers are available in Appendix A.

40.3 Water and Electrolyte Balance in Freshwater Fishes

Research on the shark rectal gland and the gills of marine bony fishes has uncovered the molecular mechanisms of salt balance in these animals. How do freshwater fishes achieve homeostasis with respect to electrolytes?

How Do Freshwater Fishes Osmoregulate?

Recall from Figure 40.2b that freshwater fishes have to cope with an osmotic stress that is opposite the challenge facing marine animals. Freshwater fishes lose electrolytes across their gill epithelium by diffusion. To maintain homeostasis, they must actively transport ions back into the body across the gill epithelium. How do they do this?

Salmon and Sea Bass as Model Systems To understand how freshwater fishes gain electrolytes, researchers have focused on sea bass and several species of salmon. Over the course of a lifetime, individuals of these species move between seawater and freshwater. In doing this, they move between environments that present dramatically different osmotic stressors.

In marine bony fishes, specialized cells in the gill epithelium called chloride cells move salt using the same combination of membrane proteins used by epithelial cells in the shark rectal gland (see Figure 40.3). When sea bass and salmon are in seawater, chloride cells are abundant and active. What happens to these cells when individuals move into freshwater? Do the changes that occur provide any insight into how these species acclimatize to their new environment and avoid dying of osmotic stress?

A Freshwater Chloride Cell? The results of research on sea bass and salmon support the hypothesis that there is a freshwater version of the classical chloride cell—one that moves ions in the opposite direction of the seawater version. Instead of excreting salt, these cells import it.

Three lines of evidence have accumulated to date:

1. *Osmoregulatory cells may be in different locations.* Salmon taken from freshwater and seawater have chloride cells in different locations on the gills. The same is true for other fish species that switch between freshwater and seawater habitats. This observation suggests that when the nature of the osmotic stress changes, the structure of the gill epithelium changes. Specifically, active pumping of ions takes place in different populations of cells in seawater and freshwater.

2. *Different forms of Na^+/K^+-ATPase may be activated.* The salmon genome contains genes for several different forms of Na^+/K^+-ATPase. There is now strong evidence that the form activated when salmon are in seawater differs from the one activated when they are in freshwater.

3. *The orientation of key transport proteins "flips."* In sea bass, researchers have been able to stain epithelial cells to reveal the location of the cotransporter illustrated in Figure 40.3—the one that brings Na^+, Cl^-, and K^+ into the cell. When the fish are in seawater, the protein is located in the basolateral membrane of chloride cells. But when they are in freshwater, the protein is located in the apical membrane (Figure 40.4).

Taken together, the data suggest that freshwater fishes have a freshwater version of the chloride cell, with different forms of Na^+/K^+-ATPase and transporters that result in the import rather than export of ions. Identifying the mechanisms of electrolyte uptake in freshwater fishes is an important challenge for researchers who want to know how aquatic organisms cope with osmotic stress.

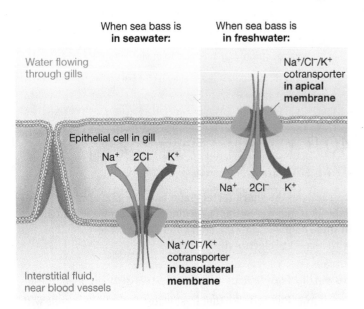

Figure 40.4 **A Key Ion Cotransporter Can Change Locations in Gill Epithelial Cells of Sea Bass.** Changing the location of the $Na^+/Cl^-/K^+$ cotransporter helps sea bass deal with the different osmotic stresses caused by seawater and freshwater environments. (Other membrane channels and pumps are present but not shown here.)

Labels in figure:
- When sea bass is in seawater:
- When sea bass is in freshwater:
- Water flowing through gills
- Epithelial cell in gill
- Na^+ $2Cl^-$ K^+
- Interstitial fluid, near blood vessels
- $Na^+/Cl^-/K^+$ cotransporter in basolateral membrane
- $Na^+/Cl^-/K^+$ cotransporter in apical membrane
- Na^+ $2Cl^-$ K^+

40.4 Water and Electrolyte Balance in Terrestrial Insects

By studying extreme situations or unusual organisms, biologists can often gain insight into how organisms cope with more moderate environments. In studies on the molecular mechanisms of water and electrolyte balance in terrestrial insects, the most valuable model organisms have been the desert locust and a common household pest called the flour beetle. (You may have seen the larvae of flour beetles, called mealworms, in bags of flour that were not shut tightly enough to keep adults from entering and breeding.)

Desert locusts and flour beetles live in environments where osmotic stress is severe. These insects rarely, if ever, drink—simply because little or no water is available in their habitats.

How do they maintain water and electrolyte balance? The answer has two parts: They minimize water loss from their body surface, and they carefully regulate the amount of water and electrolytes that they excrete in their urine and feces. Let's look at each issue in turn.

(a) Most of an insect's surface is covered with wax.

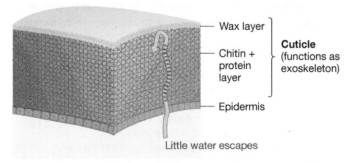

Wax layer
Chitin + protein layer
Cuticle (functions as exoskeleton)
Epidermis

Little water escapes

(b) Spiracles can be closed to minimize water loss from tracheae.

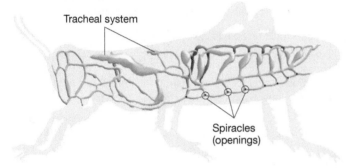

Tracheal system

Spiracles (openings)

Figure 40.5 In Terrestrial insects, Adaptations Limit Water Loss from the Body Surface and from the Respiratory System.

✔ In what season would a desert insect's cuticle likely have the most wax? Explain.

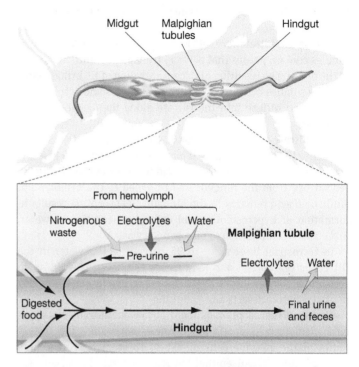

Midgut Malpighian tubules Hindgut

From hemolymph
Nitrogenous waste Electrolytes Water
Malpighian tubule
Pre-urine
Electrolytes Water
Digested food
Final urine and feces
Hindgut

Figure 40.6 In Insects, Urine Forms in the Malpighian Tubules and Is Modified in the Hindgut. The isosmotic filtrate that forms in the Malpighian tubules empties into the hindgut, where it mixes with fecal material. Valuable substances such as electrolytes and water are selectively reabsorbed from the hindgut, leaving wastes to be excreted with feces.

How Do Insects Minimize Water Loss from the Body Surface?

Terrestrial animals breathe by exposing an extremely thin respiratory epithelium to the atmosphere (see Chapter 42). Oxygen diffuses into this epithelium, and carbon dioxide diffuses out. Water also crosses the respiratory surface and is lost to the atmosphere via evaporation.

Evaporation from the rest of the body is another threat—this is a particular challenge to insects because they are small. Small organisms have a high surface area/volume ratio (see Chapter 39). Insects have a relatively large surface area from which to lose water but a small volume in which to retain it.

Figure 40.5a shows how insects minimize evaporation from the surface of their bodies. This diagram is a cross-sectional view of an insect's exoskeleton, which consists of a layer of chitin—a tough, nitrogen-containing polysaccharide—and protein covered by a layer of wax. This combination of chitin, protein, and wax is known as the **cuticle.**

Recall that waxes, a type of lipid, are highly hydrophobic and thus highly impermeable to water (see Chapter 6). Researchers who removed the wax from insect exoskeletons found that the rate of water loss from the body surface increased sharply. This observation indicates that the wax layer is an adaptation that minimizes evaporative water loss.

In terrestrial insects, gas exchange occurs across the membranes of epithelial cells that line the **tracheae,** an extensive

system of tubes. The insect tracheal system connects with the atmosphere at openings called **spiracles** (Figure 40.5b). Muscles just inside each spiracle open or close the opening, much as guard cells open or close the stomatal pores in plant leaves and stems (see Chapter 37).

When investigators manipulated assassin bugs (*Rhodnius*) so that their spiracles stayed open and then placed the animals in a dry environment, the insects died within three days. These data support the hypothesis that the ability to close spiracles is an important adaptation for minimizing water loss during respiration. If an insect is under osmotic stress, it may be able to close its spiracles, reduce its metabolic rate, and wait until conditions improve before resuming activity.

For insects, minimizing water loss is only half the battle in avoiding osmotic stress. To maintain homeostasis, insects must also carefully regulate the composition of a blood-like fluid called **hemolymph.** Hemolymph is pumped by the heart and transports electrolytes, nutrients, and waste products.

The Malpighian Tubules Allow Insects to Make Concentrated Urine To maintain water and electrolyte balance, insects rely on excretory organs called **Malpighian tubules** and on their hindgut—the posterior portion of their digestive tract. As **Figure 40.6** shows, Malpighian tubules have a large surface area, are in direct contact with the hemolymph, and empty into the hindgut. The Malpighian tubules are responsible for forming a **filtrate,** a filtered liquid, from the hemolymph. This "pre-urine" then passes into the hindgut, where it is processed and modified before excretion.

How is the filtrate formed? Epithelial cells in the Malpighian tubules contain pumps that actively transport K^+ into the lumen of the organ. The resulting high concentration of K^+ brings water into the tubules by osmosis. Other electrolytes and nitrogenous wastes then diffuse into the filtrate along their concentration gradients.

The filtrate that accumulates inside the Malpighian tubules flows into the hindgut, where it joins digested food. If an insect is osmotically stressed, electrolytes and water from the filtrate are reabsorbed from the hindgut and returned to the hemolymph, while uric acid remains in the hindgut. Reabsorption results in formation of hyperosmotic final urine, conservation of water, and efficient elimination of nitrogenous wastes.

In terrestrial insects, 80 to 95 percent of the water in the filtrate is reabsorbed and kept inside the body. The ability to recover this water allows these insects to live in extremely dry habitats such as deserts and flour bins.

How does reabsorption happen? The mechanism involves specific membrane pumps and channels, not unlike the system found in the chloride cells of fishes. To study it, researchers removed the hindgut epithelium from a desert locust and set it up as a sheet dividing two solutions. When they removed K^+ and Na^+ from the solution on the lumen side of the organ, water reabsorption stopped. This result established that the hindgut's ability to recover water from urine depends on ion movement: The epithelial cells in the hindgut transport specific ions out of the filtrate and into the hemolymph. Water follows by osmosis, forming concentrated urine.

Regulating Water and Electrolyte Balance: An Overview

Several general principles that have emerged from studies of insect excretion turn out to be relevant to vertebrate systems as well:

- Water is not pumped directly. Water moves between cells or body compartments via osmotic gradients that are set up by the active transport of ions.

- The formation of the filtrate is not particularly selective. Most of the molecules present in the hemolymph are also present in the Malpighian tubules.

- In contrast to filtrate formation, reabsorption is highly selective. The membrane pumps and channels involved in reabsorption are highly specific for certain ions and molecules. Waste products do not pass through the hindgut membrane. Instead, they remain in the hindgut and are eliminated along with the feces. Only valuable ions and molecules such as nutrients are reabsorbed.

- In contrast to filtrate formation, reabsorption is tightly regulated. The membrane pumps and channels involved in reabsorption are activated and deactivated in response to osmotic stress. If an insect is dehydrated, nearly all of the water in the filtrate is reabsorbed. But if it has plenty to drink, reabsorption does not occur and the urine is watery and hyposmotic to the hemolymph. The system is dynamic and allows precise control over water and electrolyte balance.

Considering the numbers of species and individuals and the array of habitats that insects occupy, it is clear that their systems for maintaining water and electrolyte balance are remarkably effective.

40.5 Water and Electrolyte Balance in Terrestrial Vertebrates

In dealing with water loss, terrestrial vertebrates face the same hazards as terrestrial insects do. Crocodiles, turtles, lizards, frogs, birds, and mammals lose water from their body surfaces, from the surface of their lungs every time they breathe, and in their urine. Electrolytes are also lost in urine and, in some species, in sweat. To replace the water they lose, most terrestrial vertebrates drink. They replace lost electrolytes by eating.

In land-dwelling vertebrates, osmoregulation occurs primarily through events that take place in the key organ of the urinary system, the **kidney.** The kidney is responsible for water and electrolyte balance as well as the excretion of nitrogenous wastes. Its function is analogous to the Malpighian tubules and hindgut of insects. Let's take a closer look at the kidney in mammals.

The Structure of the Mammalian Kidney

Mammalian kidneys occur in pairs and tend to be bean shaped. A large blood vessel called the renal artery brings blood that contains nitrogenous wastes into the organ; another large blood vessel, the renal vein, carries away blood that has been cleared of wastes.

The urine that forms in the kidney is transported via a long tube called the **ureter** to a storage organ, the **bladder.** From the bladder, urine is transported to the body surface through the **urethra** and then excreted. In most vertebrates, the kidneys are located near the dorsal (back) side of the body. **Figure 40.7a** summarizes the parts of the human urinary system.

Most of the kidney's mass is made up of small structures called nephrons. The **nephron** is the basic functional unit of the kidney. The work involved in maintaining water and electrolyte balance occurs in the nephron.

(a) Urinary system **(b)** Kidney

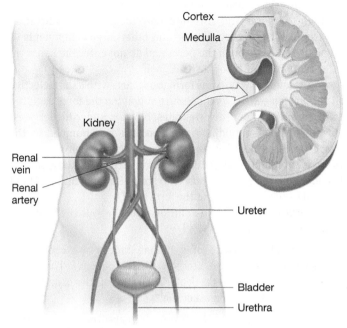

Figure 40.7 The Human Urinary System Consists of the Kidneys, Ureters, Bladder, and Urethra. (a) The kidneys are paired organs. The urine they produce is stored in the bladder. **(b)** Each kidney has an outer region called the cortex and an inner area called the medulla.

Most of the approximately 1 million nephrons in a human kidney are located almost entirely in the outer region of the organ, or **cortex** (Figure 40.7b). But some nephrons extend from the cortex into the kidney's inner region, or **medulla.**

The Function of the Mammalian Kidney: An Overview

The nephron shares important functional characteristics with the insect excretory system:

- Water cannot be transported actively—it crosses membranes only by osmosis.

- To move water, cells in the kidney set up a strong osmotic gradient in the interstitial fluid surrounding the nephrons.

- By regulating these gradients and specific channel proteins, kidney cells exert precise control over loss or retention of water and electrolytes.

Figure 40.8a provides a detailed view of the nephron. Note that it has four major regions, the last of which is connected to a structure called the collecting duct. Each nephron is basically a tube that is closed at one end and open at the other. The closed end is the beginning of the nephron; the open end empties its contents into collecting ducts.

The four major nephron regions and the collecting duct each have a distinct function:

1. The *renal corpuscle* filters blood, forming a filtrate or pre-urine consisting of ions, nutrients, wastes, and water.

(a) The structure of the nephron and collecting duct   **(b)** Blood vessels serve each nephron.

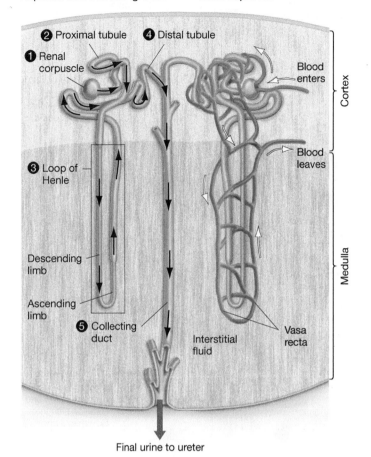

Final urine to ureter

Figure 40.8 A Nephron Has Four Major Regions, Empties into a Collecting Duct, and Is Served by Blood Vessels. Urine formation begins in the renal corpuscle and ends in the collecting duct.

2. The *proximal tubule* has epithelial cells that reabsorb nutrients, ions, and water from the filtrate into the blood.

3. The *loop of Henle* establishes a strong osmotic gradient in the interstitial fluid surrounding the loop. Osmolarity of the interstitial fluid increases as the loop descends into the medulla.

4. The *distal tubule* reabsorbs ions and water in a regulated manner—one that helps maintain water and electrolyte balance according to the body's needs.

5. The *collecting duct* may reabsorb more water to maintain homeostasis. In addition, urea moves from the urine to the interstitial fluid at the base of the collecting duct and contributes to the osmotic gradient set up by the loop of Henle.

Figure 40.8b shows that each of a nephron's four regions is intimately associated with blood vessels. The vessels play a key role in kidney function: They bring waste-containing blood into the nephron and then take away the molecules and ions that are reabsorbed from the initial filtrate.

Now let's delve into the details. The sections that follow trace the flow of material through each region of the nephron and out of the collecting duct.

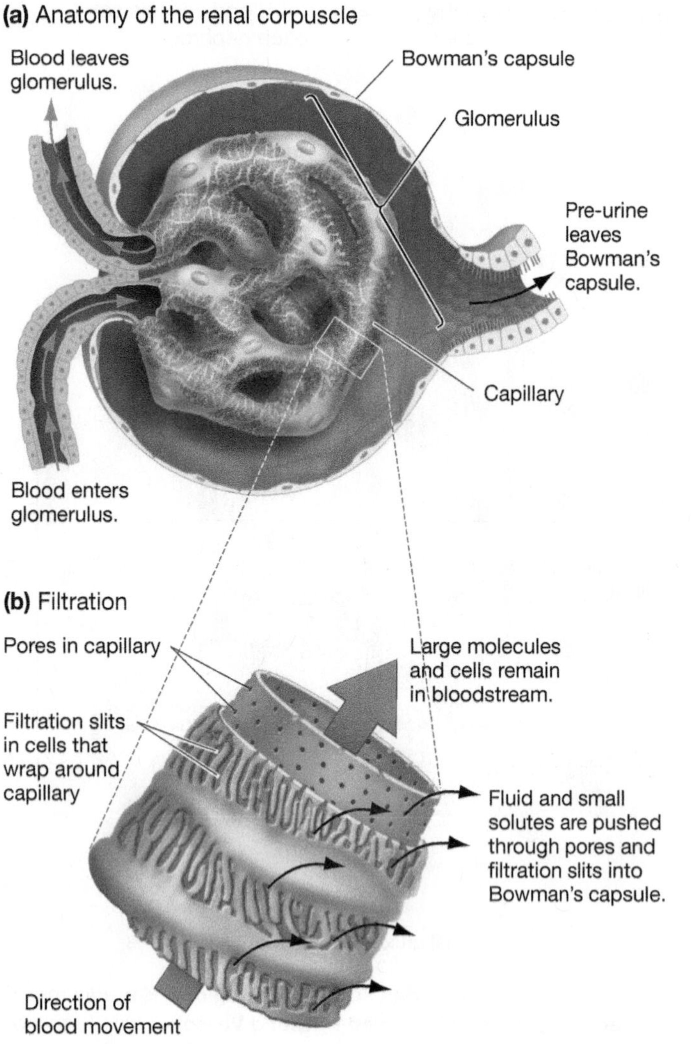

(a) Anatomy of the renal corpuscle

Blood leaves glomerulus.

Bowman's capsule

Glomerulus

Pre-urine leaves Bowman's capsule.

Capillary

Blood enters glomerulus.

(b) Filtration

Pores in capillary

Filtration slits in cells that wrap around capillary

Large molecules and cells remain in bloodstream.

Fluid and small solutes are pushed through pores and filtration slits into Bowman's capsule.

Direction of blood movement

Figure 40.9 Urine Formation Begins When Blood Is Filtered in the Renal Corpuscle. (a) The renal corpuscle consists of Bowman's capsule and the glomerulus. **(b)** The capillaries in the glomerulus have pores and are surrounded by cells that have filtration slits. Blood pressure forces water and small molecules out of the capillaries, through the slits, and into Bowman's capsule.

Filtration: The Renal Corpuscle

In terrestrial vertebrates, urine formation begins in the **renal corpuscle** (literally, "kidney little-body"). As Figure 40.9a shows, the renal corpuscle forms a capsule that encloses a cluster of tiny blood vessels, or capillaries. These vessels bring blood to the nephron from the renal artery. Collectively, the cluster of capillaries is called the **glomerulus** ("ball of yarn"). The region of the nephron that surrounds the glomerulus is named **Bowman's capsule.** Together, the glomerulus and Bowman's capsule make up the renal corpuscle.

Figure 40.9b illustrates a key feature of the glomerular capillaries: They have large pores, or openings. In addition, they are surrounded by unusual cells whose membranes fold into a series of slits and ridges.

The structure of the renal corpuscle allows it to function as a **filtration** device. Water and small solutes from the blood pass through the pores and slits into Bowman's capsule. Filtration is based on size: Proteins, cells, and other large components of blood do not fit through the pores and do not enter the nephron. They remain in the blood instead.

Stated another way, urine formation starts with a size-selective filtration step—with blood pressure supplying the force required to perform filtration. In vertebrates, blood is under higher pressure than the surrounding tissues because it is pumped by the heart through a closed system of vessels. This pressure is enough to force water and small solutes through the pores in the glomerulus, allowing the renal corpuscle to strain large volumes of fluid without expending energy in the form of ATP.

It is critical to note two additional facts about the filtration step in urine formation:

1. The renal corpuscles of a human kidney are capable of producing about 180 liters of filtrate per day. This is an impressive volume—think of 90 two-liter bottles of soft drink arranged on a supermarket shelf.

2. About 99 percent of the filtrate is reabsorbed—only a tiny fraction of the original volume is actually excreted as urine.

Filtering large volumes from the blood allows wastes to be removed effectively; pairing this process with selective reabsorption allows waste excretion to occur with a minimum of water and nutrient loss.

Reabsorption: The Proximal Tubule

Where does filtrate reabsorption begin? Filtrate leaves Bowman's capsule and enters a convoluted structure called the **proximal tubule.** The filtrate inside this tubule contains water and small solutes such as urea, glucose, amino acids, vitamins, and electrolytes. Some of these solutes are waste products; others are valuable nutrients.

Active Transport Occurs in Epithelial Cells The epithelial cells of the proximal tubule have a prominent series of small projections, called **microvilli** ("little shaggy hairs"), facing the lumen (**Figure 40.10a**). The microvilli greatly increase the surface area of this epithelium. A large surface area provides space for membrane proteins that act as pumps, channels, and cotransporters.

Epithelial cells in the proximal tubule are also packed with mitochondria, which suggests that these cells carry out extensive ATP-demanding active transport. Based on these observations, biologists hypothesized that the proximal tubule functions in the active transport of selected molecules out of the filtrate.

By injecting solutions of known composition into isolated rabbit and rat proximal tubules in the presence or absence of ATP, researchers confirmed that selected electrolytes and nutrients are actively reabsorbed from the filtrate that enters the tubules.

When solutes move from the proximal tubule into epithelial cells and then into the bloodstream, water follows along the osmotic gradient. In this way, valuable solutes and water are reabsorbed and returned to the bloodstream.

(a) Microvilli increase surface area of epithelium in proximal tubule.

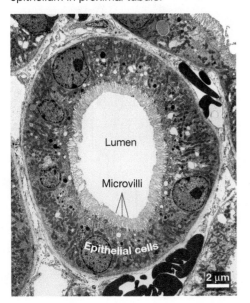

(b) Model of selective reabsorption in proximal tubule

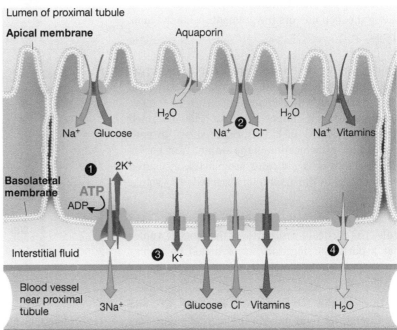

Figure 40.10 Water, Electrolytes, and Nutrients Are Reabsorbed in the Proximal Tubule.

Ion and Water Movement Is Driven by a Concentration Gradient in the Interstitial Fluid

Figure 40.10b summarizes the current model of the molecular mechanisms involved in selective reabsorption in the proximal tubule:

1. Na^+/K^+-ATPase in the basolateral membrane moves Na^+ from the interior of the cell to the interstitial fluid. The active transport of Na^+ out of the cell creates a gradient favoring the entry of Na^+ from the lumen.

2. In the apical membrane adjacent to the lumen, Na^+-dependent cotransporters use this gradient to remove ions and nutrients selectively from the filtrate. The movement of Na^+ into the cell, *along* its electrochemical gradient, provides the means for moving other solutes *against* their gradients.

3. The solutes that move into the cell diffuse across the basolateral membrane into the interstitial fluid and then into nearby blood vessels.

4. Water follows the movement of solutes from the proximal tubule into the cell and then out of the cell and into blood vessels. Recall that water moves by osmosis across the membranes of these epithelial cells through membrane proteins called aquaporins.

Almost all of the nutrients, along with about two-thirds of the NaCl and water that is originally filtered by the renal corpuscle, are reabsorbed in the proximal tubule. The osmolarity of the tubular fluid is unchanged despite this huge change in volume, however, because water reabsorption is proportional to solute reabsorption.

✔ If you understand this concept, you should be able to assign one of the following transport mechanisms to each of the four steps above: simple diffusion, facilitated diffusion, primary active transport, secondary active transport.

In effect, then, the cells that line the proximal tubule act as a recycling center. The filtration step in the renal corpuscle is based on size; the reabsorption step in the proximal tubule selectively retrieves small substances that are valuable. The pumps and cotransporters in the proximal tubule reabsorb nutrients, electrolytes, and water but leave wastes. As the filtrate flows into the loop of Henle, it has a relatively high concentration of waste molecules and a relatively low concentration of nutrients.

Creating an Osmotic Gradient: The Loop of Henle

In mammals, the fluid that emerges from the proximal tubule enters the **loop of Henle**—named for Jacob Henle, who described it in the early 1860s. In most nephrons, the loop is short and barely enters the medulla. But in about 20 percent of the nephrons present in a human kidney, the loop is long and plunges from the cortex of the kidney deep into the medulla.

In 1942 Werner Kuhn offered a hypothesis, inspired by countercurrent heat exchangers, to explain what the loop of Henle does. Recall that a countercurrent heat exchanger is a system in which two fluids of different temperatures flow through adjacent pipes in opposite directions (see Chapter 39). In the medulla, fluid flows through the descending and ascending limbs of the loop of Henle in opposite directions (see Figure 40.8a). Kuhn proposed that this opposite flow enables the loop of Henle to function as a countercurrent exchanger and multiplier. It doesn't exchange heat, however. Instead, it sets up and maintains an osmotic gradient in the interstitial fluid that surrounds it.

Specifically, Kuhn proposed that the osmolarity of the filtrate in the loop of Henle is low in the cortex and high in the medulla. Further, Kuhn maintained that the osmolarity in the interstitial fluid surrounding the loop mirrors the gradient inside the loop. This is a key point.

Testing Kuhn's Hypothesis

A series of papers published during the 1950s and early 1960s supplied important experimental support for the countercurrent exchange model. **Figure 40.11** reproduces two particularly important data sets, obtained by comparing the osmolarity of kidney tissue slices. In both graphs, the *x*-axis shows the location in the kidney, from cortex to inner medulla. The *y*-axis indicates osmolarity, measured either as the percentage of the maximum observed or as solute concentration.

- Figure 40.11a shows data on the osmolarity of fluid inside the loop of Henle. The vertical lines represent the range of values observed at a particular location. As predicted by Kuhn's model, a strong gradient in osmolarity exists from the cortex to the inner medulla.

- Figure 40.11b shows that the concentrations of Na^+, Cl^-, and urea in the interstitial fluid outside the loop of Henle also increase sharply from the cortex to the inner medulla.

These results suggested that the solutes responsible for the gradient outside the loop are Na^+, Cl^-, and urea. The change in concentration of urea turned out to be particularly important.

How Is the Osmotic Gradient Established?

The loop of Henle has three distinct regions: the descending limb, the thin ascending limb, and the thick ascending limb (**Figure 40.12a**). The thin and thick ascending limbs differ in the thickness of their walls. Do the three regions also differ in their permeability to water and solutes?

It took over 15 years of experiments performed in laboratories around the world to formulate a definitive answer to that question. Researchers punctured the loop of Henle of rodents with a micropipette, analyzed the composition of the fluid inside, and compared it with the composition of the nephron's final product—urine.

In the ascending limb of the loop of Henle, Na^+ and Cl^- constituted at least 60 percent of the solutes; urea constituted about 10 percent. But in the distal tubule, urea was the major solute. These data suggested that Na^+ and Cl^-, but not urea, were being removed somewhere in the ascending limb. How?

Na^+ and Cl^- were also present at high concentrations in the tissue surrounding the thick ascending limb, so researchers hypothesized that sodium might be actively pumped out of this portion of the nephron. The hypothesis was that the active transport of Na^+ out of the filtrate in the thick ascending limb would create an electrical gradient that would also favor the loss of Cl^-.

Follow-up experiments using ouabain and other poisons supported the hypothesis that sodium ions are actively transported out of the solution inside the thick ascending limb, and chloride ions follow along an electrochemical gradient. The epithelial cells responsible for salt excretion are configured almost exactly like the epithelium of the shark rectal gland (see Figure 40.3).

(a) Fluid inside the loop of Henle

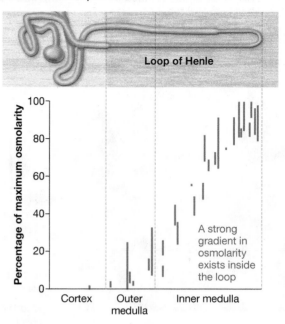

(b) Interstitial fluid outside the loop of Henle

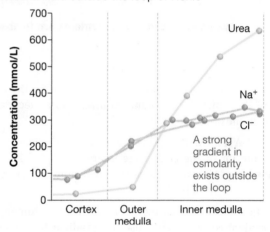

Figure 40.11 Data Confirm the Existence of a Strong Osmotic Gradient Both Inside and Outside the Loop of Henle. As the nephron plunges into the inner medulla, the concentration of dissolved solutes increases both inside **(a)** and outside **(b)** the loop of Henle.

DATA: Ullrich, K. J., K. Kramer, and J. W. Boyer. 1961. *Progress in Cardiovascular Diseases* 3: 395–431.

What is happening in the descending limb and the thin ascending limb of the loop of Henle? By injecting solutions of known concentration into the nephrons of rabbits, biologists documented that the descending limb is highly permeable to water but almost completely impermeable to solutes. The thin ascending limb of the loop, in contrast, is highly permeable to Na^+ and Cl^-, moderately permeable to urea, and almost completely impermeable to water.

A Comprehensive View of the Loop of Henle

All of the observations just summarized came together in 1972 when two papers, published independently, proposed the same comprehensive model for how the loop of Henle works. To understand this model, follow the events in **Figure 40.12b**:

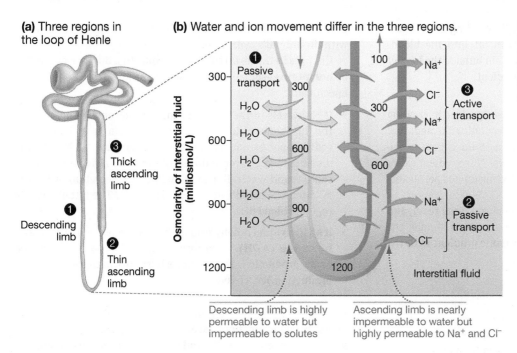

(a) Three regions in the loop of Henle

① Descending limb

③ Thick ascending limb

② Thin ascending limb

(b) Water and ion movement differ in the three regions.

Osmolarity of interstitial fluid (milliosmol/L)

① Passive transport

③ Active transport

② Passive transport

Interstitial fluid

Descending limb is highly permeable to water but impermeable to solutes

Ascending limb is nearly impermeable to water but highly permeable to Na^+ and Cl^-

Figure 40.12 The Loop of Henle Maintains an Osmotic Gradient Because Water Leaves the Descending Limb and Salt Leaves the Ascending Limb. The values inside the loop in part (b) represent the osmolarity of the filtrate.

1. As fluid flows down the descending limb, the fluid inside the loop loses water to the interstitial fluid surrounding the nephron. This movement of water is passive—it does not require an expenditure of ATP. The water follows an osmotic gradient created by the ascending limb. At the bottom of the loop—in the inner medulla—the fluids inside and outside the nephron have high osmolarity. The filtrate does not continue to lose water, though, because the membrane in the ascending limb is nearly impermeable to water.

2. The fluid inside the nephron loses Na^+ and Cl^- in the thin ascending limb. The ions move passively, along their electrochemical gradients.

3. Near the cortex, the osmolarity of the surrounding interstitial fluid is low. Additional Na^+ and Cl^- ions are actively transported out of the nephron in the thick ascending limb.

The countercurrent flow of fluid, combined with changes in permeability to water and in the types of channels and pumps that are active in the epithelium of the nephron, creates a self-reinforcing system. The presence of an osmotic gradient stimulates water and ion flows that in turn maintain an osmotic gradient.

Here's how it works: Movement of NaCl from the ascending limb into surrounding tissue increases the osmolarity of the fluid outside the descending limb, which results in an outward flow of water across the water-permeable epithelium of the descending limb, via osmosis. This loss of water in the descending limb increases the osmolarity of the fluid entering the ascending limb. The high concentration of salt in the fluid at the base of the ascending limb triggers a passive flow of ions out—reinforcing the osmotic gradient.

✔ If you understand this concept, you should be able to predict what happens to the osmotic gradient when the drug furosemide inhibits membrane proteins that pump sodium and chloride ions out of the thick ascending limb. Specifically, how does this drug affect (1) water reabsorption in the descending limb, (2) the osmolarity of the filtrate at the bottom of the loop of Henle, and (3) reabsorption of salt in the thin ascending limb?

The Vasa Recta Removes Water and Solutes That Leave the Loop of Henle What happens to the water and salt that move out of the loop from the filtrate into the interstitial fluid? They diffuse into the **vasa recta**, a network of blood vessels that runs along the loop. As a result, the water and electrolytes that are reabsorbed are returned to the bloodstream instead of being excreted in urine (**Figure 40.13**). The vasa recta joins up with small veins at the top of the medulla, which prevents the reabsorption of water and electrolytes from disrupting the concentration gradient in the medulla.

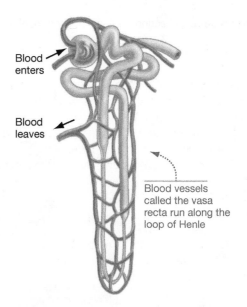

Blood enters

Blood leaves

Blood vessels called the vasa recta run along the loop of Henle

Figure 40.13 Blood Vessels Are Closely Associated with the Nephron. Water and solutes reabsorbed from the loop of Henle enter a system of blood vessels, the vasa recta.

The removal of water that leaves the descending limb is particularly important. If it were not drawn off into the bloodstream, it would dilute the concentrated fluid outside the loop of Henle and quickly destroy the osmotic gradient.

The Collecting Duct Leaks Urea   Urea is also involved in creating the steep osmotic gradient in the space surrounding the nephron. The concentration of urea in the interstitial fluid is high in the inner medulla and low in the outer medulla. This gradient exists because the innermost section of the collecting duct is permeable to urea.

Although the system created by the nephron, vasa recta, and collecting duct may seem complex, its outcome is simple: the creation and maintenance of a strong osmotic gradient with the minimum possible expenditure of energy.

Regulating Water and Electrolyte Balance: The Distal Tubule and Collecting Duct

The first three steps in urine formation—filtration, reabsorption, and establishment of an osmotic gradient—result in a fluid that is slightly hyposmotic to blood. Once the filtrate has passed through the loop of Henle, the major solutes that it contains are urea and other wastes along with a low concentration of ions.

The filtrate that enters the distal tubule is always dilute. In contrast, the urine that leaves the collecting duct is dilute when the individual is well hydrated but concentrated when the individual is dehydrated. How is this possible?

Urine Formation Is under Hormonal Control   The answer is based on two observations about the activity of the **distal tubule** and **collecting duct: (1)** It is highly regulated, and **(2)** it is altered in response to osmotic stress. The amount of Na$^+$, Cl$^-$, and water that is reabsorbed in the distal tubule and collecting duct varies with the animal's hydration.

Changes in the distal tubule and collecting duct are controlled by **hormones**—signaling molecules in the blood (see Chapter 46). Specifically:

- If Na$^+$ levels in the blood are low, the adrenal glands release the hormone **aldosterone,** which leads to activation of sodium–potassium pumps and reabsorption of Na$^+$ in the distal tubule. Water follows by osmosis. Aldosterone saves sodium and water. It also stimulates the secretion of K$^+$ and H$^+$ from the blood into the distal tubule. The latter helps to regulate blood pH.

- If an individual is dehydrated, the brain releases **antidiuretic hormone (ADH).** (The term "diuresis" refers to increased urine production, so antidiuresis means inhibition of urine production.) ADH saves water.

How Does ADH Work?   Epithelial cells of the collecting duct are joined by tight junctions (see Chapter 11), making the epithelium impermeable to water and solutes. ADH has two important effects on epithelial cells in the collecting duct:

1. ADH triggers the insertion of aquaporins into the apical membrane. As a result, cells become much more permeable to water and large amounts of water are reabsorbed.

2. ADH increases the cells' permeability to urea, which is reabsorbed into the surrounding fluid. This helps create a concentration gradient favoring water reabsorption from the filtrate.

As **Figure 40.14a** shows, water leaves the collecting duct passively—following the concentration gradient maintained by the loop of Henle. When ADH is present, water is conserved by the body, and the urine is strongly hyperosmotic to the

(a) ADH present: Collecting duct is highly permeable to water.

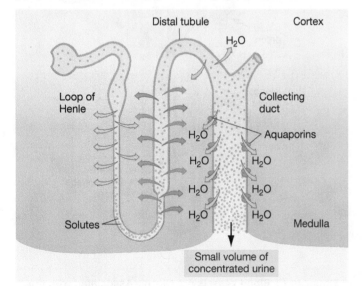

(b) No ADH present: Collecting duct is not permeable to water.

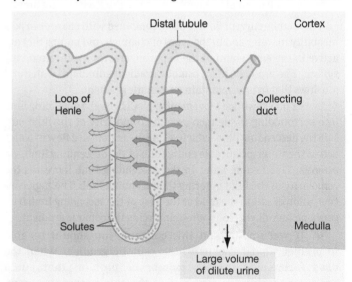

Figure 40.14 ADH Regulates Water Reabsorption by the Collecting Duct.

Structure	Function
Renal Corpuscle (Bowman's capsule and glomerulus)	Size-selective filtration: forms filtrate from blood (water and other small substances enter nephron)
Proximal Tubule	Reabsorbs electrolytes (active transport), nutrients, water
Loop of Henle	Maintains osmotic gradient in interstitial fluid from outer to inner medulla
• Descending limb	• Permeable to water (passive transport out of filtrate)
• Thin ascending limb	• Permeable to Na^+, Cl^- (passive transport out of filtrate)
• Thick ascending limb	• Active transport of Na^+, Cl^- out of filtrate
Distal Tubule	Aldosterone present: reabsorbs Na^+ No aldosterone present: does not reabsorb Na^+
Collecting Duct	Regulates water retention
• Main portion	• ADH present: water leaves filtrate; produces small volume of urine that is hyperosmotic to blood No ADH present: water stays in filtrate; produces large volume of urine that is hyposmotic to blood
• Innermost portion	• Urea leaks out by passive transport, establishing and/or maintaining high osmolarity of inner medulla

blood. The collecting duct is the final place where the composition of the filtrate can be altered. Urine exiting the collecting ducts moves from the kidneys into ureters and then is stored in the bladder until urination.

When ADH is absent, however, few aquaporins are found in the epithelium of the collecting duct, and the structure is relatively impermeable to water (**Figure 40.14b**). In this case, a larger quantity of hyposmotic urine is produced.

✔ If you understand ADH's effect on the collecting duct, you should be able to predict how urine formation is affected by ethanol, which inhibits ADH release, and by nicotine, which stimulates ADH release.

Table 40.2 reviews the functions of the four major regions of the nephron and the collecting duct.

Urine Formation in Nonmammalian Vertebrates

The loop of Henle is an important adaptation in mammals and some birds. Water loss is reduced because these animals can produce urine that is hyperosmotic to their blood. In contrast, fishes, amphibians, and non-avian reptiles lack loops of Henle, and their kidneys are therefore unable to produce concentrated urine.

Many fishes and amphibians do not need to produce concentrated urine. But conserving water is important in reptiles, especially those inhabiting deserts. Recall that reptiles produce nitrogenous wastes in the form of uric acid, which is excreted with very little water in urine that is hyperosmotic to their body tissues. However, the kidneys of non-avian reptiles produce

isosmotic urine. How, then, does it become hyperosmotic before it's excreted?

In most reptiles, the ureters empty isosmotic urine into the **cloaca,** a cavity into which the urinary, gastrointestinal, and reproductive tracts all empty (**Figure 40.15**). Reptiles are able to absorb water from urine across the wall of the cloaca into the bloodstream. Eventually, a semisolid uric acid paste is excreted along with the feces.

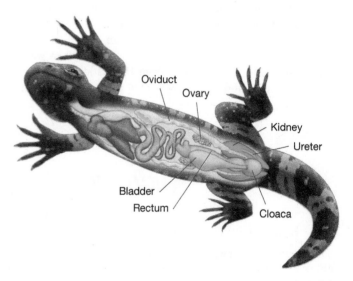

Figure 40.15 The Cloaca of Reptiles Is a Cavity into Which the Urinary, Gastrointestinal, and Reproductive Tracts Empty.

(a) Change following injection of radioactive water into bladder

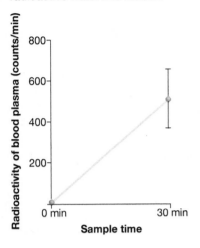

(b) Change following injection of water into bladder or stomach

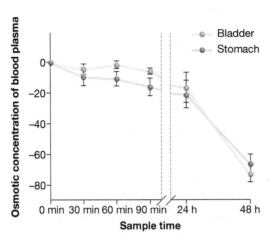

- Bladder
- Stomach

Figure 40.16 Gila Monsters Can Reabsorb Water from Their Bladders. (a) Radioactively labeled water passes from the bladder into the bloodstream. **(b)** Water reduces blood osmolarity at a similar rate in dehydrated lizards whether added to the stomach or the bladder.

DATA: Davis, J. R., and D. F. DeNardo. 2007. *Journal of Experimental Biology* 210: 1472–1480.

✔ What physiological trade-offs might be imposed by carrying a large amount of water in the bladder?

Some reptiles also have a bladder that collects the isosmotic urine from the ureters and stores it before emptying it into the cloaca. When water is available, these reptiles drink a lot, and their bladders fill up with dilute urine. Researchers hypothesized that the bladder acts as a "canteen" to store water for when it is unavailable.

To test this hypothesis, the investigators injected the bladders of dehydrated Gila monsters—large desert lizards—with radioactively labeled water and drew blood samples over time. The radioactivity of the lizards' blood plasma increased within a half hour, which meant that the radioactively labeled water from the bladder was being absorbed into the bloodstream (**Figure 40.16a**).

The researchers also examined whether water in the bladder can rehydrate lizards to the same extent as drinking water. Working with two groups of dehydrated Gila monsters, they injected water into the bladders of one group, and—to mimic drinking—they injected water into the stomachs of the second group. They found that the osmolarity of the plasma decreased at the same rate in both groups (**Figure 40.16b**).

These results indicate that the bladder can indeed allow lizards to carry a water supply that they can access when water is scarce. As water is reabsorbed from the bladder, the urine becomes more and more concentrated, but the osmolarity of the blood remains low.

Studies of the mammalian nephron and the Gila monster bladder demonstrate that the vertebrate urinary system is remarkably effective in regulating water and electrolyte balance and achieving homeostasis.

CHECK YOUR UNDERSTANDING

If you understand that ...

- The mammalian kidney is specialized for the production of hyperosmotic urine.
- The loop of Henle is a countercurrent system that maintains a strong osmotic gradient in the medulla.
- The characteristics of urine change in response to hormonal signals. The signals trigger changes in the nephron and collecting duct that either save or eliminate water and electrolytes.

✔ **You should be able to ...**

Predict how the following events would affect urine production: drinking massive amounts of water, eating large amounts of salt, and refraining from drinking water for 48 hours.

Answers are available in Appendix A.

40.1 Osmoregulation and Excretion

- Solutes move across membranes via passive transport, facilitated diffusion, or active transport. Water moves across membranes by osmosis.

- In most animals, epithelial cells that selectively transport water and electrolytes are responsible for homeostasis.

- The mechanisms involved in regulating water and electrolyte balance vary widely among animal groups because different habitats present different types of osmotic stress.

- The type of nitrogenous waste excreted by an animal is affected by its phylogeny and its habitat type. Most fishes excrete ammonia; mammals and most adult amphibians excrete urea; and insects and reptiles excrete uric acid.

40.2 Water and Electrolyte Balance in Marine Fishes

- Seawater is strongly hyperosmotic to the tissues of marine bony fishes, so they tend to lose water by osmosis and gain electrolytes by diffusion.
- Marine bony fishes are osmoregulators, whereas cartilaginous fishes including sharks are osmoconformers.
- Epithelial cells in the shark rectal gland and in the gills of marine bony fishes excrete excess salt using Na^+/K^+-ATPase and $Na^+/Cl^-/K^+$ cotransporters located in the basolateral membrane.
- Similar salt-excreting cells also exist in the salt glands of marine birds and other reptiles and in the kidneys of mammals.

40.3 Water and Electrolyte Balance in Freshwater Fishes

- Freshwater is strongly hyposmotic to the blood of freshwater fishes, so they tend to gain water by osmosis and lose electrolytes by diffusion.
- Epithelial cells in the gills of freshwater fishes import ions using Na^+/K^+-ATPase located in the basolateral membrane and $Na^+/Cl^-/K^+$ cotransporters located in the apical membrane.

40.4 Water and Electrolyte Balance in Terrestrial Insects

- A waxy coating on the insect exoskeleton limits evaporative water loss. Spiracles, the openings to the insect respiratory system, close when osmotic stress is severe.
- The Malpighian tubules of insects form a filtrate that is isosmotic with the hemolymph. If pumps in the epithelium of the hindgut are activated, then electrolytes and water are reabsorbed from the filtrate and returned to the hemolymph.
- Insects can form hyperosmotic urine that minimizes water loss during the excretion of nitrogenous wastes.

40.5 Water and Electrolyte Balance in Terrestrial Vertebrates

- Nephrons in the vertebrate kidney form a filtrate in the renal corpuscle and then reabsorb valuable nutrients, electrolytes, and water in the proximal tubule.
- A solution containing urea and electrolytes flows through the loop of Henle of mammalian kidneys, where changes in the permeability of epithelial cells to water and salt—along with active transport of salt—create a steep osmotic gradient.
- Antidiuretic hormone increases the water permeability of the collecting duct, causing water to be reabsorbed along the osmotic gradient and hyperosmotic urine to be produced.
- The nephrons of fishes, amphibians, and non-avian reptiles do not have loops of Henle and therefore cannot produce urine that is hyperosmotic to the body fluids. However, some of these vertebrates can produce hyperosmotic urine by reabsorbing water from the cloaca or bladder.

Answers are available in Appendix A

✔ TEST YOUR KNOWLEDGE

1. Which of the following statements is true of fishes that live in freshwater?
   a. Water moves across the gills via osmosis until equilibrium is established, at which time the water molecules stop moving.
   b. They lose water to their environment primarily through the gills. They replace this water by drinking.
   c. Water enters epithelial cells in their gills via osmosis. Electrolytes leave the same cells via diffusion.
   d. They have specialized epithelia that actively pump Na^+ and Cl^- from the blood into their environment.

2. Which of the following organisms would lose the most water by osmosis across its gills?
   a. marine bony fish
   b. shark
   c. freshwater fish
   d. freshwater invertebrate

3. What effect does antidiuretic hormone (ADH) have on the nephron?
   a. It increases water permeability of the descending limb of the loop of Henle.
   b. It decreases water permeability of the descending limb of the loop of Henle.
   c. It increases water permeability of the collecting duct.
   d. It decreases water permeability of the collecting duct.

4. Fill in the blank: In Gila monsters, the organ in which water from urine is reabsorbed into the bloodstream is the _____.

✔ TEST YOUR UNDERSTANDING

5. Compare and contrast the types of nitrogenous wastes excreted by animals. Identify which type can be excreted with the least water, which is most toxic, and which waste is excreted by bony fishes, by mammals, and by insects. Which type would you expect to be produced by embryos inside eggs laid on land?

6. The chloride cells of fish gills have a high density of mitochondria. How does this characteristic relate to the functional role of chloride cells? Would you expect other epithelial cells involved in ion transport to contain large numbers of mitochondria? Explain.

7. Explain why mammals would not be able to produce concentrated urine if they lacked loops of Henle.

8. Scientists have noted that marine invertebrates tend to be osmoconformers, while freshwater invertebrates tend to be osmoregulators. Suggest an explanation for this phenomenon.

✔ TEST YOUR PROBLEM-SOLVING SKILLS

9. Biologists have been able to produce mice that lack functioning genes for aquaporins. How would the urine of these mice compare to that of mice with normal aquaporins?
   a. lower volume and lower osmolarity
   b. lower volume and higher osmolarity
   c. higher volume and lower osmolarity
   d. higher volume and higher osmolarity

10. **QUANTITATIVE** To test the hypothesis that mussels are osmoconformers, researchers exposed mussels to water of varying osmolarities and then drew hemolymph samples from the mussels. Graph the data below. Put the independent variable on the *x*-axis and the dependent variable on the *y*-axis. Is the researchers' hypothesis supported by the data? Explain.

Water Osmolarity (milliosmol/L)	Hemolymph Osmolarity (milliosmol/L)
250	261
500	503
750	746
1000	992

✓ PUT IT ALL TOGETHER: Case Study

How does water pollution affect osmoregulation in fishes?

Fish and other aquatic organisms are exposed to many types of water pollutants, including metals such as aluminum. Although low levels of aluminum are found in unpolluted water, many lakes and streams have increased levels because of mining, sewage treatment, and accidental spills of toxic materials. Aluminum pollution can result in mass fish die-offs like the one pictured here. How does this occur?

11. Which of the following is an osmoregulatory challenge that freshwater fishes need to overcome?
    a. Diffusion of sodium out of the body
    b. Diffusion of water out of the body
    c. Active transport of sodium out of the body
    d. Active transport of water out of the body

12. **QUANTITATIVE** In a laboratory, scientists exposed freshwater bony fish (*Prochilodus lineatus*) to water high in aluminum and compared their blood osmolarity to that of fish exposed to water with normal aluminum levels (control). The results of the experiment are shown below (asterisks indicate $P < 0.05$ between control and treated groups at a given time, see BioSkills 3). Do the data support the hypothesis that aluminum interferes with osmoregulation in freshwater fish? Explain.

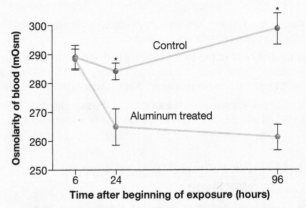

Source: Camargo, M. M. P., M. N. Fernandes, and C. B. R. Martinez. 2009. *Aquatic Toxicology* 94: 40–46.

13. **PROCESS OF SCIENCE** Why did the scientists do this experiment in a laboratory instead of simply collecting fish from a river with high aluminum levels and documenting their osmoregulatory ability?

14. The scientists also measured the activity of Na^+/K^+-ATPase in the gills of the fish exposed to aluminum and compared it to that of the control fish. What do you suppose were their results? Explain.

15. **CAUTION** True or false: Water moves by osmosis across a fish's gills to an area with a higher sodium ion concentration because water molecules are attracted to the sodium ions.

16. **MODEL** Draw a graph similar to the one above showing how the results would be different if the experiment had been performed on marine bony fish in seawater. (Assume that the osmolarity of seawater is 1100 mOsm and the set point osmolarity of marine bony fishes is 290 mOsm.)

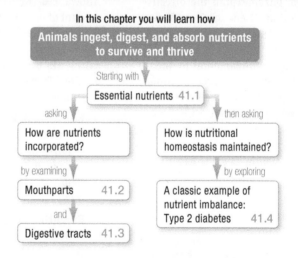

41 Animal Nutrition

A crocodile has just caught a fish. Animals obtain nutrients by ingesting food.

In this chapter you will learn how

Animals ingest, digest, and absorb nutrients to survive and thrive

Starting with ▼

Essential nutrients 41.1

asking ▼   then asking ▼

How are nutrients incorporated?

How is nutritional homeostasis maintained?

by examining ▼   by exploring ▼

Mouthparts 41.2

A classic example of nutrient imbalance: Type 2 diabetes 41.4

and ▼

Digestive tracts 41.3

BIG PICTURE

This chapter is part of the Big Picture. See how on pages 816–817.

Animals get the two basic requirements for life—**(1)** chemical energy for synthesizing ATP and **(2)** carbon-containing compounds and minerals for building complex macromolecules—by ingesting other organisms. In short, animals are heterotrophs: They eat to live.

The types of food that are available to different animals vary widely, and food is often in dangerously short supply. From these observations, you might expect that many different means for obtaining food have evolved in animals and that animals are under intense natural selection for making efficient use of the food they have. How do animals get their food, and how do they process it? Which substances in food are used as nutrients, and how do humans and other animals maintain appropriate levels of key nutrients in their bodies?

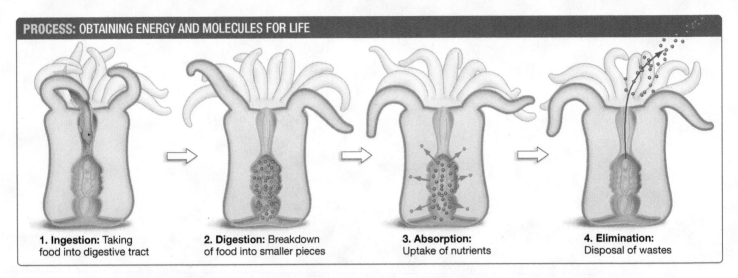

1. Ingestion: Taking food into digestive tract

2. Digestion: Breakdown of food into smaller pieces

3. Absorption: Uptake of nutrients

4. Elimination: Disposal of wastes

Figure 41.1 Animal Nutrition Is a Four-Step Process. Ingestion is followed by digestion, where food is broken down into absorbable components. Anything not absorbed is eliminated as waste.

For you or any other animal to stay alive, food must be ingested, digested, and absorbed, and then the wastes must be eliminated (**Figure 41.1**). **Ingestion** is the process of bringing food into the **digestive tract**—also known as the alimentary (literally, "nourishment") canal or gastrointestinal (GI) tract. The digestive tract is a chamber or tube where **digestion,** the breakdown of food, takes place. Various glands secrete enzymes into the digestive tract that digest food into particles small enough for efficient **absorption**—the uptake of specific ions and molecules across the epithelium that lines the digestive tract.

Research on feeding and digestion is fundamental to understanding basic aspects of animal biology, but research on animal nutrition has important practical applications as well. For example, it addresses questions about why several nutrition-related diseases, including diabetes mellitus and obesity, are on the rise in many human populations.

Let's begin with a look at what animals must eat to live.

41.1 Nutritional Requirements

Humans and other animals get the chemical energy and carbon-containing building blocks they need from carbohydrates, proteins, and fats. All these substances are carbon compounds with high potential energy. Chapters 5 and 6 analyzed the structures of carbohydrates and fats, and Chapter 9 detailed how these compounds are used to synthesize ATP and key macromolecules.

A carbohydrate, protein, or fat is an example of a **nutrient:** a substance that an organism needs to remain alive. **Food** is any material that contains nutrients.

The amount of energy provided by foods is measured in kilocalories (on food labels, kilocalories are referred to as Calories). Because fats are rich in C–H bonds, they provide more energy than other nutrients: about 9 kcal/g versus about 4 kcal/g for carbohydrates and proteins.

Understanding which nutrients an individual needs, and in what amounts, are basic issues in research on nutrition in humans and other animals. Let's consider what humans need to maintain good health.

In 1943 the Food and Nutrition Board of the U.S. National Academy of Sciences[1] published the first Recommended Dietary Allowances (RDAs). The goal of the RDAs was to specify the amount of each essential nutrient that an individual must ingest to meet the needs of most healthy people. Although all nutrients are necessary for growth and survival of animals, **essential nutrients** are those that cannot be synthesized and must be obtained from the diet.

Humans require four classes of essential nutrients:

- **Essential amino acids** are amino acids that an animal cannot synthesize from simpler building blocks. The human diet requires nine essential amino acids, which must be obtained from food. (Recall from Chapter 3 that all 20 amino acids are required to manufacture most proteins; humans can synthesize 11 of them.)

- **Essential fatty acids** are fatty acids that an animal must obtain in its diet. (Fatty acids were introduced in Chapter 6.) Humans can synthesize all fatty acids except two, which must be obtained from eating certain plants or fish.

- **Vitamins** are organic, or carbon-containing, compounds that are vital for health but are required in only minute amounts. They have a variety of roles; several function as coenzymes in critical reactions (see Chapter 8). Table 41.1 lists a few of the vitamins for which RDAs have been established, notes their functions, and indicates the problems that develop if they are missing in the diet.

---

[1] The National Academy of Sciences is a group of scientists and engineers that advises the U.S. Congress on scientific and technical matters. Its Food and Nutrition Board is made up of biologists who specialize in animal nutrition.

Table 41.1 Some Important Vitamins Required by Humans

	Source	Function	Effects if Deficient
Vitamin B$_1$ (thiamine)	legumes, whole grains, potatoes, peanuts	formation of coenzyme in citric acid cycle	beriberi (fatigue, nerve disorders, anemia)
Vitamin B$_{12}$	red meat, eggs, dairy products; also synthesized by bacteria in intestine	coenzyme in synthesis of proteins and nucleic acids and in formation of red blood cells	anemia (fatigue and weakness due to low hemoglobin content in blood)
Niacin	meat, whole grains	component of coenzymes NAD$^+$ and NADP$^+$	pellagra (digestive problems, skin lesions, nerve disorders)
Folate	green vegetables, oranges, nuts, legumes, whole grains; also synthesized by bacteria in intestine	coenzyme in nucleic acid and amino acid metabolism	anemia
Vitamin C (ascorbic acid)	citrus fruits, tomatoes, broccoli, cabbage, green peppers	used in collagen synthesis, prevents oxidation of cell components, improves absorption of iron	scurvy (degeneration of teeth and gums)
Vitamin D	fortified milk, egg yolk; also synthesized in skin exposed to sunlight	aids absorption of calcium and phosphorus in small intestine	rickets (bone deformities) in children; bone softening in adults

- **Minerals** are inorganic substances used as components of enzyme cofactors or structural materials (see Table 41.2). Some, such as calcium and phosphorus, are needed in relatively large quantities. Others, such as iron and copper, are required in small or trace amounts. Minerals include ions of electrolytes, which influence osmotic balance and are required for normal membrane function (see Chapter 40). Sodium (Na$^+$), potassium (K$^+$), and chloride (Cl$^-$) are the major ions of electrolytes in the human body.

To obtain nutrients, animals must ingest them, usually via a mouth. The structure of animal mouthparts is therefore often highly specialized for the capture of specific types of food.

Table 41.2 Major Minerals Required by Humans

	Source in Diet	Function	Effects if Deficient
Calcium (Ca)	dairy products, green vegetables, legumes	bone and tooth formation, nerve signaling, muscle response	loss of bone mass, slow growth
Chlorine (Cl)	table salt or sea salt, vegetables, seafood	fluid balance in cells, protein digestion in stomach (HCl), acid–base balance	weakness, loss of muscle function
Fluorine (F)	fluoridated water, seafood	maintenance of tooth structure	higher frequency of tooth decay
Iodine (I)	iodized salt, algae, seafood	component of the thyroid hormones thyroxine and T$_3$	goiter (enlarged thyroid gland)
Iron (Fe)	meat, eggs, whole grains, green leafy vegetables, legumes	enzyme cofactor; synthesis of hemoglobin and electron carriers	anemia, weakness
Magnesium (Mg)	whole grains, green leafy vegetables	enzyme cofactor	nerve disorders
Phosphorus (P)	dairy products, meat, grains	bone and tooth formation; synthesis of nucleotides and ATP	weakness, loss of bone mass
Potassium (K)	dairy products; meat; nuts; fruits; potatoes, legumes, and other vegetables	nerve signaling, muscle response, acid–base balance	weakness, muscle cramps, loss of muscle function
Sodium (Na)	table salt or sea salt, seafood	nerve signaling, muscle response, blood pressure regulation	weakness, muscle cramps, loss of muscle function, nausea, confusion
Sulfur (S)	any source of protein	amino acid synthesis	swollen tissues, degeneration of liver, mental retardation

(a) The large canines of saber-toothed cats stabbed and sliced prey.

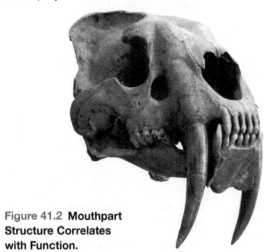

Figure 41.2 **Mouthpart Structure Correlates with Function.**

(b) Having a highly flexible cranium and jaws allows snakes to swallow large prey whole.

41.2 Capturing Food: The Structure and Function of Mouthparts

Instead of making their own food, as the vast majority of plants do, animals obtain the energy and nutrients they need by feeding on other organisms. Biologists assign animal feeding techniques to one of four strategies (see Chapter 30):

1. **Suspension feeders,** such as sponges and tubeworms, filter small organisms or bits of organic debris from water by means of cilia, mucus-lined "nets," or other structures.

2. **Deposit feeders,** including earthworms and sea cucumbers, swallow sediments and other types of deposited material rich in organic matter.

3. **Fluid feeders** suck or lap up blood, nectar, or other fluids.

4. **Mass feeders** are the majority of animals. They seize and manipulate chunks of food.

Mouthparts as Adaptations

The types of food that animals harvest range from soupy solutions in decaying carcasses to nuts inside hard shells. Solutions have to be lapped up; nuts have to be cracked. Given the diversity of food sources that animals exploit, it is not surprising that they capture and process food using a wide variety of mouthpart structures, including jaws, teeth, beaks, and toxin-injecting organs.

Natural selection has closely matched the structure of animal mouthparts to their function in obtaining food. For example,

- Most mammals chew their food and swallow distinct packets or boluses. The extinct mammal in **Figure 41.2a** illustrates one example of the many tooth shapes that evolved from the relatively simple and uniform teeth in the common ancestor of all mammals. Diversification of tooth shape has allowed mammals to exploit a wide range of foods.

- Snakes have highly mobile skull bones and complex associated musculature that allow them to ingest large prey without chewing or biting off pieces (**Figure 41.2b**).

The reason that there's such a close correlation between the structure and function of mouthparts is simple: Natural selection is particularly strong when it comes to food capture because obtaining nutrients is so fundamental to fitness—the ability to produce offspring.

Let's pursue the correlation between mouthparts and food sources further, by analyzing the structure and function of jaws and teeth in what may be the most diverse lineage within any vertebrate family: the cichlid fishes of Africa.

A Case Study: The Cichlid Throat Jaw

The cichlids that inhabit the Rift Lakes of East Africa are a spectacular example of **adaptive radiation**—the diversification of a single ancestral lineage into many species, each of which lives in a different habitat or exhibits a distinct form (see Chapter 25). Lake Victoria, for example, is home to 300 cichlids that live nowhere else.

Pharyngeal jaws

Oral jaws

Figure 41.3 **Rift Lake Cichlids Have Two Sets of Biting Jaws.** This X-ray image shows the oral jaws, which capture food, and the pharyngeal jaws, which process it.

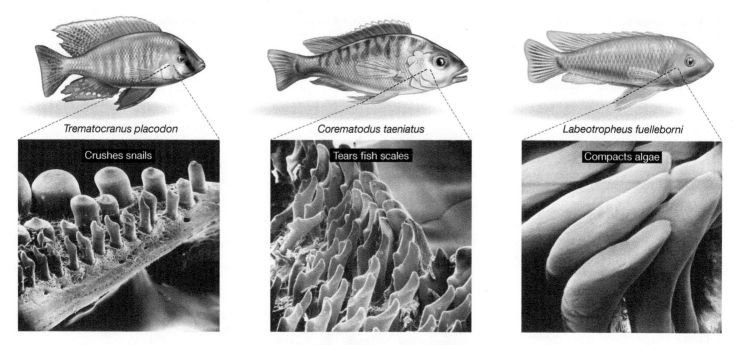

Trematocranus placodon   Crushes snails

Corematodus taeniatus   Tears fish scales

Labeotropheus fuelleborni   Compacts algae

Figure 41.4 **In Cichlids, the Structure of the Pharyngeal Jaw Correlates with the Type of Food Ingested.**

Each Lake Victoria cichlid species feeds on a different specific item, but as a group they exploit almost every food source in the lake: planktonic organisms, crust-forming algae, leaflike algae, eggs, fish scales, fish fins, whole fish, plants, insects, and snails.

How can a group of closely related species exploit so many different food sources? Many fish species have pharyngeal (throat) jaws located well behind the oral (mouth) jaws (**Figure 41.3**). Most non-cichlids use their pharyngeal jaws to move food down their throats, but cichlids and some other species can also use theirs to bite. In cichlids this is possible because the upper pharyngeal jaw attaches to the skull, and because muscles connecting their lower pharyngeal jaw to the cranium allow it to move against the upper jaw.

In addition to acting as a second set of biting jaws that make food processing more efficient, the pharyngeal jaws provide a more specialized set of toothlike structures. These protuberances vary in size and shape among cichlids, correlating with their function, such as crushing snail shells, tearing fish scales, or compacting algae (**Figure 41.4**).

These observations are part of a large body of evidence supporting a general pattern in animal evolution: In response to natural selection, mouthparts have diversified, enabling animals to exploit a diversity of food sources. The structures of jaws, teeth, and other mouthparts correlate with their functions in harvesting and processing food.

41.3 How Are Nutrients Digested and Absorbed?

Digestion is a key process in animals because, unlike plants, unicellular organisms, and fungi, most animals do not acquire nutrients as individual molecules. (Some animals that live as internal parasites are exceptions.) Instead, most animals take in packets of food that must be broken down into small pieces. Nutrients must be extracted from the small pieces, and waste materials must be eliminated. How and where does this processing occur?

An Introduction to the Digestive Tract

Digestive tracts come in two general designs:

1. **Incomplete digestive tracts** have a single opening, the mouth, through which the animal both ingests food and eliminates wastes. The mouth opens into a chamber, called a gastrovascular cavity, where digestion takes place (**Figure 41.5**).

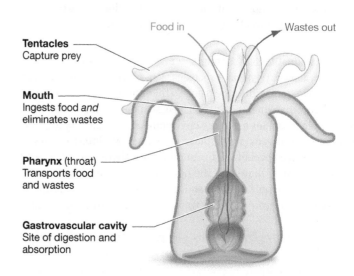

Food in   Wastes out

Tentacles
Capture prey

Mouth
Ingests food *and*
eliminates wastes

Pharynx (throat)
Transports food
and wastes

Gastrovascular cavity
Site of digestion and
absorption

Figure 41.5 **Sea Anemones Have an Incomplete Digestive Tract.** Sea anemones use stinging cells located on their tentacles to capture small fishes, crustaceans, and other prey. Prey are taken into the mouth and digested in the gastrovascular cavity; then wastes are eliminated through the mouth.

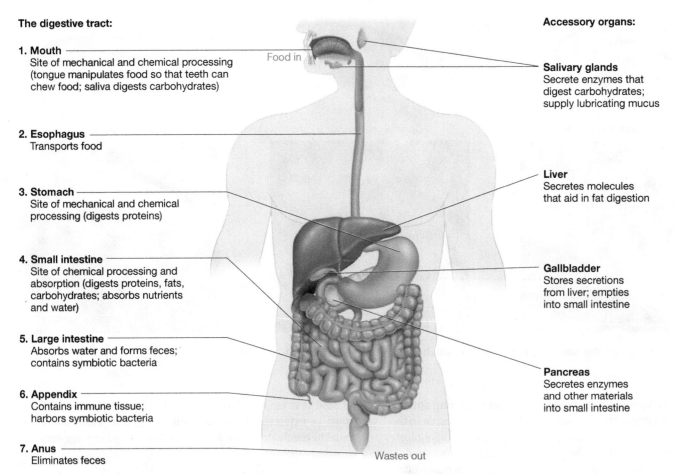

The digestive tract:

1. Mouth
Site of mechanical and chemical processing (tongue manipulates food so that teeth can chew food; saliva digests carbohydrates)

Food in

2. Esophagus
Transports food

3. Stomach
Site of mechanical and chemical processing (digests proteins)

4. Small intestine
Site of chemical processing and absorption (digests proteins, fats, carbohydrates; absorbs nutrients and water)

5. Large intestine
Absorbs water and forms feces; contains symbiotic bacteria

6. Appendix
Contains immune tissue; harbors symbiotic bacteria

7. Anus
Eliminates feces

Wastes out

Accessory organs:

Salivary glands
Secrete enzymes that digest carbohydrates; supply lubricating mucus

Liver
Secretes molecules that aid in fat digestion

Gallbladder
Stores secretions from liver; empties into small intestine

Pancreas
Secretes enzymes and other materials into small intestine

Figure 41.6 Humans Have a Complete Digestive Tract. In humans, as in all vertebrates and most other animals, the digestive tract is a tube that runs from the mouth to the anus. The salivary glands, liver, gallbladder, and pancreas are not part of the tract itself. Instead, they secrete material into the tract at specific points.

2. **Complete digestive tracts** have two openings—they start at the mouth and end at the anus. The interior of this tube communicates directly with the external environment via these openings (**Figure 41.6**).

One advantage of a complete digestive tract is that different chemical and physical processes can be confined to different compartments within the tract, so that they occur independently of each other and in a prescribed sequence. The stomach, for example, provides an acidic environment for digestion. Ingested material proceeds from there to the small intestine, where enzymes are specialized to function in a slightly alkaline environment. Also, thanks to the one-way flow of food and wastes, material can be ingested and digested without interruption, instead of alternating with waste removal as in an incomplete digestive tract.

The digestive tract is only one part of the digestive system, however. Several vital organs and glands are connected to the digestive tract. These accessory structures are not part of the digestive tract because food does not pass through them. However, they contribute digestive enzymes and other products to specific portions of the tract and therefore play a key role in digestion. In vertebrates, they include the salivary glands, liver, gallbladder, and pancreas (see Figure 41.6).

An Overview of Digestive Processes

Before analyzing the function of each component of the digestive system in detail, let's consider the general changes that happen to food as it is digested, both mechanically and chemically, on its way through the digestive tract. In this brief overview and in the detailed discussion that follows, humans will serve as a model species—simply because so much is known about human digestion.

In mammals, digestion begins with chewing—the tearing and crushing activity of teeth. Chewing reduces the size of food particles and softens them. Humans augment the mechanical breakdown of food by their use of knives and cooking. In fact, the invention of cutting tools and cooking, which make food easier to chew, is the leading hypothesis to explain why average tooth size has declined steadily over the past several million years of human evolution.

Distinct chemical changes occur as food moves through each compartment in the digestive tract (**Figure 41.7**):

- In the mouth, enzymes in the saliva begin the chemical breakdown of carbohydrates and lipids.

- Chemical digestion of protein begins in the acidic environment of the stomach.

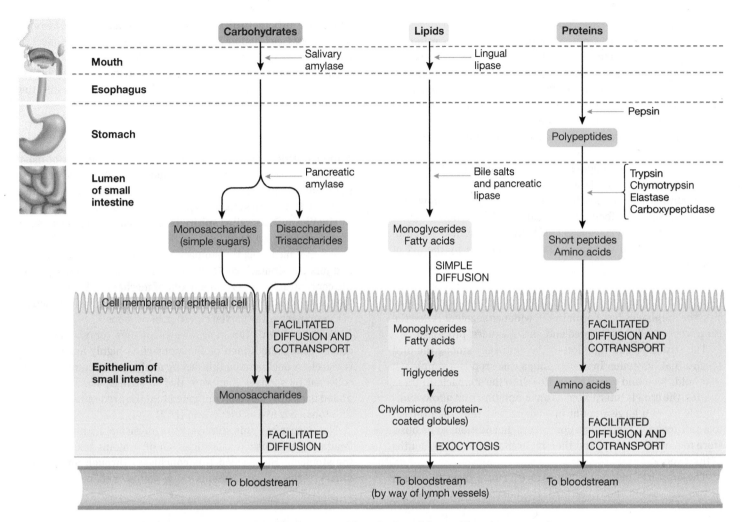

Figure 41.7 Carbohydrates, Lipids, and Proteins Are Processed in a Series of Steps. Three key types of macromolecules enter the digestive system (top of diagram). As they proceed through the digestive tract, they are broken apart by various enzymes. Simple sugars, monoglycerides, fatty acids, and amino acids then enter epithelial cells in the small intestine and are transported to the bloodstream.

- Chemical processing of the three major types of macromolecules—carbohydrates, proteins, and lipids—is completed in the small intestine (see Chapter 9 for an overview of catabolic and anabolic pathways). The small molecules that result from the digestion of these macromolecules are absorbed in the small intestine, along with water, vitamins, and ions.

- In the large intestine, more water is absorbed. The material remaining in the large intestine is **feces,** which are eventually excreted.

Because digestion is so important to understanding how animal bodies work, let's examine each step more closely. As the following sections track food from the mouth to the anus in humans, watch for notes highlighting the diversity of structures found in the digestive tracts of nonhuman animals.

The Mouth and Esophagus

If you hold a cracker in your mouth long enough, it will start to taste sweet. The sensation occurs because an enzyme in your saliva hydrolyzes some of the starch molecules in the cracker to

maltose (see Chapter 5). Maltose is a disaccharide that is split in the small intestine to form two glucose monomers.

Starch breakdown was actually the first enzyme-catalyzed reaction ever discovered (see Chapter 8 for a review of enzyme function). In the early 1800s several researchers found that a component of certain plant extracts digested starch; in 1831 the same activity was discovered in human saliva.

Digestion Starts in the Mouth **Salivary amylase,** the enzyme responsible for starch digestion in the mouth, is one of the best-studied enzymes. Amylase cleaves bonds to release maltose from starch and glycogen, initiating the digestion of those macromolecules.

Cells in the tongue synthesize and secrete another important salivary enzyme, **lingual lipase** ("lingual" refers to the tongue), which begins the digestion of lipids by breaking triglycerides into diglycerides and fatty acids.

Salivary glands in the mouth not only secrete amylase but also produce the slimy substance called **mucus.** The combination of water and mucus makes food soft and slippery enough to be swallowed.

Peristalsis Moves Material Down the Esophagus Once food is swallowed, it enters a muscular tube called the **esophagus,** which connects the mouth and stomach. A wave of muscular contractions called **peristalsis** propels food down the esophagus. About 6 seconds after being swallowed, food reaches the bottom of the esophagus. Because peristalsis actively moves material along the esophagus, you can swallow even when your mouth is lower than your stomach, such as when you bend over to drink from a drinking fountain.

In response to nerve signals, the smooth muscles in the esophagus contract and relax in a coordinated fashion (**Figure 41.8**). The resulting wave of muscle contractions propagates down the tube, propelling the food mass ahead of it. These nerve signals are not the result of conscious choice but are a reflex—an automatic reaction to a stimulus—that is stimulated by the act of swallowing.

A Modified Esophagus: The Bird Crop In an array of bird species, the esophagus has a prominent, widened segment called the **crop** where food can be stored and, in some cases, processed.

The structure and function of the crop vary among the bird species that have one. In many groups, the crop is a simple sac that holds food and regulates its flow into the stomach. In these species, the crop is interpreted as an adaptation that allows individuals to eat a large amount in a short time; they then retreat to a safe location while digestion occurs. In addition, some birds store food in their crops and then regurgitate it into the mouths of their young.

The crop has independently evolved into a digestive organ in two leaf-eating species of bird, the hoatzin and the kakapo.

Leaves are difficult to digest because they contain a large amount of cellulose (see Chapter 5). In the enlarged crop of these species, bacteria that are capable of breaking down cellulose perform digestion. The bacterial cells, along with the fatty acids that result from bacterial metabolism, leak out of the crop into the stomach and are used as food by the birds.

The Stomach

Although little if any digestion occurs in the esophagus of most animals, the situation changes dramatically when food reaches the stomach. The **stomach** is a tough, muscular pouch in the digestive tract, bracketed on both the superior and inferior ends by ringlike muscles called **sphincters,** which control the passage of material (**Figure 41.9**).

When a meal fills the stomach, muscular contractions churn and mix the stomach contents to a uniform consistency and solute concentration. A certain amount of mechanical breakdown of food also results from this churning. The other main function of the stomach is the partial digestion of proteins.

Compared with the mouth or esophagus (or virtually any other tissue), the lumen of the stomach is highly acidic. Early researchers documented this fact by analyzing vomit or material collected by sponges that were tied to strings, swallowed, and pulled back up; chemists confirmed that the predominant acid in the stomach is hydrochloric acid (HCl).

Not long after this discovery, a physician named William Beaumont established that digestion of proteins takes place in the stomach. He reached this conclusion through an extraordinary series of experiments on a young man named Alexis St. Martin.

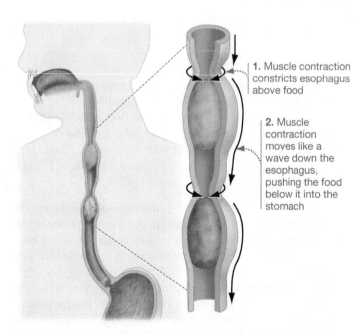

1. Muscle contraction constricts esophagus above food

2. Muscle contraction moves like a wave down the esophagus, pushing the food below it into the stomach

Figure 41.8 In the Esophagus, Peristalsis Transports Food to the Stomach. Peristalsis is a wave of contraction and relaxation of smooth muscle. Contraction constricts the esophagus behind food, and relaxation expands it in front of food. The wave begins at the oral end of the esophagus and propels the food toward the stomach.

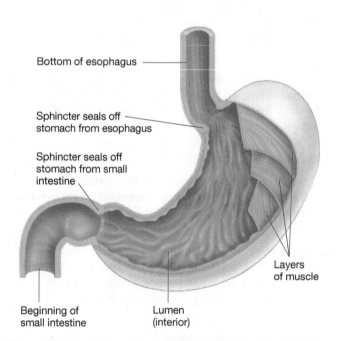

Bottom of esophagus

Sphincter seals off stomach from esophagus

Sphincter seals off stomach from small intestine

Layers of muscle

Beginning of small intestine

Lumen (interior)

Figure 41.9 The Stomach Is a Muscular Pocket of the Digestive Tract. The stomach provides an acidic environment for protein digestion. Its muscular contractions mix food and break it into smaller pieces.

The Stomach as a Site of Protein Digestion In 1822, when St. Martin was 19 years old, a shotgun accidentally discharged into his abdomen, leaving a series of wounds. Despite repeated attempts, Beaumont was unable to close a hole in St. Martin's stomach. Eventually Beaumont inserted a small tube through the opening; the tube remained in St. Martin's body for the rest of his life. (Today, biologists insert tubes into various parts of the digestive tract of cows or sheep to study how these animals digest different types of feed.)

With the tube in place, Beaumont was able to tie a string onto small pieces of meat or vegetables, insert the food directly into St. Martin's stomach, and draw it out after various intervals. Beaumont also removed liquid from inside the stomach and observed how this gastric (stomach) juice acted on food in vitro. His experiments showed that gastric juice digests food—particularly meat.

Theodor Schwann later purified the enzyme that is responsible for digesting proteins in the stomach and named it **pepsin.** Because it breaks down proteins, biologists hypothesized that pepsin must be synthesized and stored in cells while it is in an inactive form—otherwise it would kill the cells that make it.

In 1870 a microscopist established the presence of granules in specialized stomach cells called chief cells. These granules were hypothesized to be a pepsin precursor. Follow-up work confirmed this hypothesis. The precursor compound, which came to be called pepsinogen, is converted to active pepsin by contact with the acidic environment of the stomach.

Secretion of a protein-digesting enzyme in inactive form is important: It prevents digestion of proteins in the cells where the enzyme is synthesized.

Which Cells Produce Stomach Acid?

The acidic environment of the human stomach denatures (unfolds) proteins, making it easier for pepsin to digest them. But where does the acid come from?

Researchers who were studying the anatomy of the stomach wall noticed clusters of distinctive **parietal cells** located in pits in the stomach lining (Figure 41.10a). An investigator also documented that the shape and activity of these cells appeared to vary as the digestion of a meal proceeded. Based on these observations, he inferred that parietal cells are the source of the HCl in gastric juice, which may have a pH as low as 1.5.

Earlier microscopists had shown that another type of cell, called a **mucous cell,** secretes additional mucus that is found in gastric juice. Mucus lines the gastric epithelium and protects the stomach from damage by HCl. To summarize, these anatomical studies showed that the epithelium of the stomach contains several types of secretory cells, each of which is specialized for a particular function.

How Do Parietal Cells Secrete HCl?

The first clue to how parietal cells manufacture HCl emerged in the late 1930s, when a researcher found a high concentration of an enzyme called carbonic anhydrase in parietal cells.

This result was interesting because **carbonic anhydrase** catalyzes the formation of carbonic acid (H_2CO_3) from carbon dioxide and water. In solution, the carbonic acid that is formed

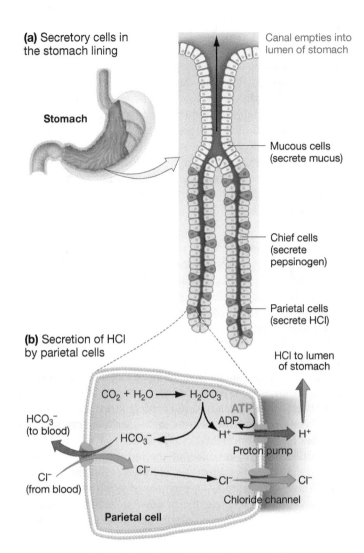

(a) Secretory cells in the stomach lining

Stomach

Canal empties into lumen of stomach

Mucous cells (secrete mucus)

Chief cells (secrete pepsinogen)

Parietal cells (secrete HCl)

(b) Secretion of HCl by parietal cells

HCl to lumen of stomach

$CO_2 + H_2O \longrightarrow H_2CO_3$

HCO_3^- (to blood)

HCO_3^-

ATP
ADP
H^+
H^+
Proton pump

Cl^- (from blood)

Cl^- → Cl^- → Cl^-
Chloride channel

Parietal cell

Figure 41.10 Cells in the Stomach Lining Secrete Mucus, Pepsinogen, and Hydrochloric Acid.

immediately dissociates to form a proton (H^+) and a bicarbonate ion (HCO_3^-):

$$CO_2 + H_2O \rightleftharpoons H_2CO_3 \rightleftharpoons H^+ + HCO_3^-$$

A second clue to the formation of HCl came in the 1950s, when transmission electron microscopes allowed researchers to analyze parietal cells at high magnification (see BioSkills 9). The micrographs showed that parietal cells are packed with mitochondria. Because mitochondria produce ATP, the structure of parietal cells suggested that they might function in active transport.

Later work confirmed this hypothesis by showing that the protons formed by the dissociation of carbonic acid are actively pumped into the lumen of the stomach. Subsequent studies showed that chloride ions from the blood enter parietal cells in exchange for bicarbonate ions, via a cotransport protein, and then move into the lumen through a chloride channel. **Figure 41.10b** diagrams the current model for HCl production.
✔ If you understand this model, you should be able to explain why many heartburn (acid reflux) drugs contain proton pump inhibitors.

Ulcers as an Infectious Disease An **ulcer** is an eroded area in an epithelium; it exposes the underlying tissues to damage. Ulcers in the lining of the stomach or the duodenum—the initial section of the small intestine—can cause intense abdominal pain.

For decades, physicians thought that gastric and duodenal ulcers resulted from the production of excess acid in the stomach. They treated ulcers by prescribing basic compounds that neutralized hydrochloric acid in the stomach. (To review acids and bases, see Chapter 2.) In the 1980s, however, scientists discovered that most ulcers are associated with infections from the bacterium *Helicobacter pylori*. Physicians now routinely prescribe antibiotics to relieve ulcers.

The Ruminant Stomach The structure and function of the stomach can vary, depending on the nature of the diet. In cattle, sheep, goats, deer, antelope, giraffe, and pronghorn—species that are collectively called **ruminants**—the stomach is specialized for digesting cellulose instead of proteins.

Animals do not produce the enzymes required to digest cellulose. Yet cellulose is the main carbohydrate in the leaves, stems, and twigs that ruminants ingest.

Like the hoatzin and kakapo described earlier in this chapter, ruminants are able to harvest energy from cellulose thanks to a combination of specialized anatomical structures and symbiotic relationships with bacteria and unicellular protists. The microbes ferment the cellulose to produce food for themselves; meanwhile, other by-products of the fermentation, as well as some of the microbes themselves, are used as food by the ruminant. This relationship is an example of **symbiosis,** in which members of different species live in close contact with each other.

As **Figure 41.11** shows, ruminants have four-chambered stomachs.

1. Food initially enters the largest chamber, the rumen, which serves as a fermentation vat. The rumen is packed with symbiotic bacteria and protists. These organisms have **cellulase,** an enzyme capable of breaking the chemical bonds in cellulose, yielding glucose. The rumen is an oxygen-free environment, and the symbiotic organisms produce ATP from this glucose via fermentation, releasing fatty acids as a by-product (see Chapter 9). These fatty acids are absorbed by the ruminant and used as an energy source.

2. The chamber adjacent to the rumen, called the reticulum, is similar in function. After plant material has been partially digested in the rumen and the reticulum, the animal regurgitates portions of that material into its mouth, forming a cud. The ruminant chews that regurgitated material further to enhance mechanical breakdown and then re-swallows it.

3. Processed cud enters the third chamber, the omasum, where water and some minerals are absorbed.

4. The final chamber, the abomasum, contains pepsin and other digestive enzymes produced by the ruminant and functions much like the stomachs of other mammals.

Most of a ruminant's food consists of **(1)** fatty acids and other compounds produced as waste products of fermentation reactions in symbiotic organisms, and **(2)** the symbiotic cells themselves.

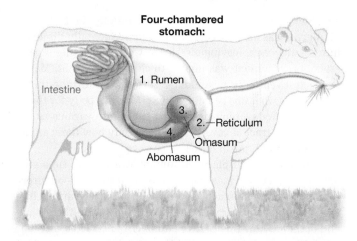

Four-chambered stomach:

Intestine
1. Rumen
3.
2.—Reticulum
4.
Omasum
Abomasum

Figure 41.11 Ruminant Stomachs Facilitate the Digestion of Cellulose by Symbiotic Organisms. Ruminants obtain many of their nutrients from symbiotic bacteria and protists that live in two chambers of the stomach, the rumen and reticulum.

The Avian Gizzard The avian gizzard is another prominent type of modified stomach. Birds do not have teeth and cannot chew food into small pieces. Instead, most species swallow sand and small stones that lodge in the gizzard. As this muscular sac contracts, food is pulverized by the grit.

The gizzard is particularly large and strong in bird species that eat coarse foods such as seeds and nuts. The gizzard of a wild turkey, for example, can crack large walnuts.

Like the crop, the gizzard is interpreted as an adaptation that allows birds to ingest food quickly—without needing to chew—and digest it later. Biologists invoke the same hypothesis to explain why ruminants chew cud. The ability to regurgitate material and finish chewing while hiding in a place safe from predators is thought to increase fitness.

The Small Intestine

In humans, the stomach is responsible for mixing the contents of a meal into a homogenous slurry, breaking the food up mechanically, and providing the acid and enzymes required to partially digest proteins. Peristalsis in the stomach wall then moves small amounts of material through the sphincter at the base of the stomach and into the small intestine.

The **small intestine** is a long tube that is folded into a compact space within the abdomen. In the small intestine, partially digested food mixes with secretions from the pancreas and the liver and begins a journey of about 6 m (20 ft). When passage through this structure is complete, digestion is finished, and most nutrients—along with large quantities of water—have been absorbed.

Folding and Projections Increase Surface Area The surface area available for nutrient and water absorption in the small intestine is nothing short of remarkable (see Chapter 39). As **Figure 41.12** shows, the organ's epithelial tissue is folded and covered with fingerlike projections called **villi** (singular: **villus**). In turn,

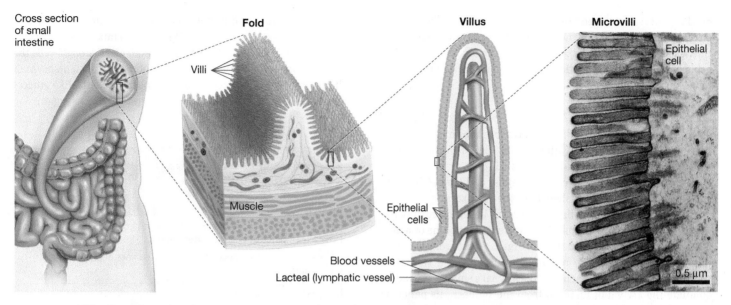

Figure 41.12 The Small Intestine Has an Extremely Large Surface Area. The villi that project from folds in the small intestine are covered with microvilli (colorized brown in the micrograph at the far right).

the cells that line the surface of villi have tiny projections on their apical surfaces called **microvilli** (singular: **microvillus**). Microvilli project into the lumen of the digestive tract.

If the small intestine lacked folds, villi, and microvilli, it would have a surface area of about 3300 cm² (3.6 ft²). Instead, the epithelium covers about 2 million cm² (over 2200 ft²)—an area about the size of a tennis court.

The enormous surface area of the small intestine increases the rate of nutrient absorption. And because each villus contains blood vessels and a lymphatic vessel called a **lacteal**, nutrients pass quickly from epithelial cells into the body's transport systems (see Chapter 42).

To understand how digestion is completed and absorption occurs, let's explore what happens to proteins, lipids, and carbohydrates as they move through this section of the digestive tract. Again, humans are the model organism.

Protein Processing by Pancreatic Enzymes The acidic environment of the stomach disrupts the secondary and tertiary structures of proteins. In addition, pepsin cleaves the peptide bonds next to certain amino acids, reducing long polypeptides to relatively small chains of amino acids. In the small intestine, protein digestion is completed, yielding individual amino acids that can enter the bloodstream and be transported to cells throughout the body.

How do these final stages of protein digestion occur? By the end of the nineteenth century, it was established that enzymes in the small intestine digest polypeptides to monomers. Later work showed that each of these protein-digesting enzymes, or **proteases**, is specific to certain types or configurations of amino acids in a polypeptide chain. Therefore, a suite of proteases is required to completely digest polypeptides to amino acid monomers.

In addition, by 1900 biologists had determined that proteases are synthesized in an inactive form in the **pancreas**, which is

connected to the small intestine by the pancreatic duct. Like the production of inactive pepsinogen by chief cells in the stomach, the production of pancreatic enzymes in an inactive conformation prevents pancreatic cells from digesting themselves.

How are pancreatic enzymes activated in the small intestine? A breakthrough in understanding came when Russian physiologist Ivan Pavlov showed that contact with juice from the upper part of the small intestine activates pancreatic enzymes. Activation ceased to occur when he heated the intestinal juice, and because he knew that heat denatures enzymes (like all proteins), he hypothesized that what activated the pancreatic enzymes was also an enzyme.

Decades later, scientists figured out how this enzyme, called enteropeptidase, works. Other researchers demonstrated that enteropeptidase removes a short section from the N-terminus of trypsinogen, an inactive pancreatic protein, resulting in the active enzyme **trypsin.** Trypsin then triggers the activation of other proteases, such as chymotrypsin, elastase, and carboxypeptidase (**Figure 41.13**). These enzymes are also synthesized

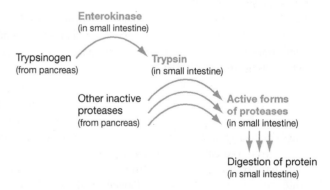

Figure 41.13 Enterokinase Triggers an Enzyme-Activation Cascade in the Small Intestine.

by the pancreas and secreted in an inactive form. Once these enzymes are activated in the upper reaches of the small intestine, each begins cleaving specific peptide bonds between amino acids. Eventually, polypeptides are broken up into amino acid monomers.

What Regulates the Release of Pancreatic Enzymes?
Digestive enzymes are needed only when food reaches the small intestine. Based on this simple observation, it was logical to predict that their release would be carefully controlled.

A classic experiment by William Bayliss and Ernest Starling, published in 1902, established how the release of pancreatic enzymes is controlled. Bayliss and Starling began by cutting the nerves that connect to the pancreas and small intestine of a dog. Electrical signaling between the two organs via neurons was now impossible. But when the researchers introduced a weak HCl solution into the upper reaches of the animal's small intestine, to simulate the arrival of material from the stomach, its pancreas secreted enzymes in response.

This observation was startling: The small intestine had successfully signaled the pancreas that food had arrived, even though the nerves connecting the two organs had been cut.

Starling hypothesized that a chemical messenger must be involved, and that the chemical messenger must originate in the small intestine and travel to the pancreas via the blood. He tested this hypothesis by cutting off a small piece of the small intestine, grinding it up, and injecting the resulting solution into a vein in the animal's neck. Minutes later, the pancreas sharply increased secretion.

Bayliss and Starling had discovered the first **hormone**—a chemical messenger that influences physiological processes at very low concentrations. The molecule they detected, which they called **secretin,** is produced by the small intestine in response to the arrival of food from the stomach.

Follow-up work showed that secretin's primary function is to induce a flow of bicarbonate ions (HCO_3^-) from the pancreas to the small intestine. Bicarbonate is important because it neutralizes the acid arriving from the stomach (see Chapter 2).

Researchers also discovered a second hormone produced in the small intestine, called **cholecystokinin** (pronounced *ko-la-sis-ta-KAY-nin*). Cholecystokinin (literally, "bile-bag-mover") stimulates the secretion of digestive enzymes from the pancreas and the secretion of molecules from the gallbladder that aid in processing lipids.

Hormones are involved in stomach function as well. For example, after being stimulated by nerves or the arrival of food, certain stomach cells produce the hormone **gastrin.** In response, parietal cells begin secreting HCl.

How Are Carbohydrates Digested and Transported?
In addition to manufacturing protein-digesting enzymes, the pancreas produces nucleases and an amylase that is similar to the salivary enzyme introduced earlier. **Nucleases** digest the RNA and DNA in food; **pancreatic amylase** continues the digestion of carbohydrates that began in the mouth. Carbohydrate digestion ends with the release of monosaccharides such as glucose.

When digestion of proteins and carbohydrates is complete in the small intestine, the resulting slurry is a mixture of nutrients, water, indigestible plant fibers from food, and bacterial cells that live symbiotically in the gut. What molecular mechanisms make it possible for epithelial cells to transport nutrients, like glucose, from the lumen of the small intestine into the bloodstream?

RESEARCH

QUESTION: How is glucose transported into epithelial cells of the small intestine?

HYPOTHESIS: Glucose enters epithelial cells along with sodium ions via a Na^+-glucose cotransporter protein.

NULL HYPOTHESIS: Glucose transport does not depend on Na^+ transport.

EXPERIMENTAL SETUP:

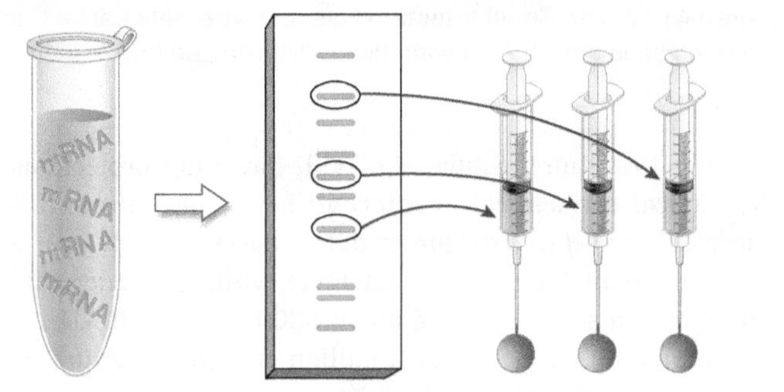

1. **Purify mRNA** from rabbit intestinal cells.
2. **Separate mRNAs** by size via gel electrophoresis.
3. **Inject individual mRNAs into frog eggs.** Test each egg—can it absorb Na^+ and glucose?

PREDICTION: An egg will be able to absorb Na^+ and glucose because it received the mRNA that codes for the Na^+-glucose cotransporter.

PREDICTION OF NULL HYPOTHESIS: None of the eggs will be able to absorb Na^+ and glucose.

RESULTS:

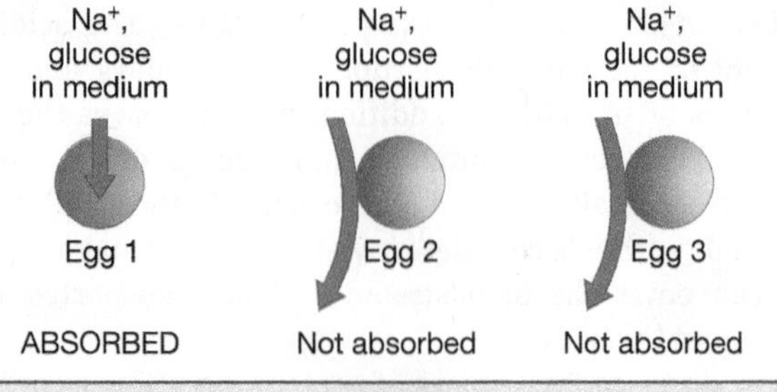

Na^+, glucose in medium — Egg 1 — ABSORBED

Na^+, glucose in medium — Egg 2 — Not absorbed

Na^+, glucose in medium — Egg 3 — Not absorbed

CONCLUSION: The egg that absorbs Na^+ and glucose received the mRNA from the Na^+-glucose cotransporter gene.

Figure 41.14 The Experimental Protocol for Locating the Na^+-Glucose Cotransporter Gene.

SOURCE: Wright, E. M. 1993. The intestinal Na^+/glucose cotransporter. *Annual Review of Physiology* 55: 575–589.

✔ **PROCESS OF SCIENCE** Why did the researchers inject the RNAs into frog eggs instead of into rabbit epithelial cells?

Two general principles apply to monosaccharide and amino acid absorption: **(1)** It is highly selective, in that proteins in the plasma membranes of microvilli are responsible for bringing specific nutrients into epithelial cells; and **(2)** it is active, meaning ATP is expended to transport nutrients into the cells against their concentration gradients.

Work over the past several decades has demonstrated both of these principles. One of the key results grew out of a series of experiments during the 1980s, which established that glucose absorption depends on the presence of an electrochemical gradient favoring an influx of sodium ions into the epithelium. Based on this finding, biologists hypothesized that the apical membranes of epithelial cells must contain a variety of cotransporters—membrane proteins that bring a nutrient molecule into the cell along with sodium ions. To confirm that a sodium–glucose cotransporter exists, investigators set out to find the gene that codes for it.

The researchers began by purifying mRNAs from rabbit intestinal cells (**Figure 41.14**), which presumably were transcribing the cotransporter genes. Then the team separated the mRNAs by size via gel electrophoresis (see **BioSkills 6**) and injected one of each type of mRNA into a series of frog eggs—cells that do not normally transport glucose. The frog eggs translated the rabbit mRNAs into proteins.

One of the injected eggs was able to import Na^+ and glucose in tandem. The researchers concluded that this egg had received the mRNA for the rabbit Na^+-glucose cotransporter. They made a DNA copy of the mRNA (using techniques introduced in Chapter 20), analyzed it to determine the sequence of the gene, and from that inferred the amino acid sequence of the membrane protein.

The discovery of the Na^+-glucose cotransporter inspired a three-step model for glucose absorption:

1. Na^+/K^+-ATPase (sodium–potassium pump) in the basolateral membrane of the epithelial cells creates an electrochemical gradient that favors the entry of Na^+.

2. Glucose from digested food enters the cell along with sodium via the Na^+-glucose cotransporter in the apical membrane.

3. Glucose diffuses into nearby blood vessels through a glucose carrier in the basolateral membrane.

If this configuration of pumps, cotransporters, and carriers sounds familiar, there is a good reason: The same combination of membrane proteins occurs in the proximal tubule of the kidney, where the proteins are responsible for the reabsorption of sodium and glucose from urine (see Chapter 40).

Follow-up work showed that in the small intestine—just as in the proximal tubule—other cotransporters are responsible for the absorption of other monosaccharides and of amino acids, and that specific channels and carriers in the basolateral membrane are responsible for the transport of each substance to the blood.

Digesting Lipids: Bile and Transport The pancreatic secretions include digestive enzymes that act on fats, in addition to enzymes that act on proteins and carbohydrates. Like the lingual lipase added to saliva in the mouth, the enzyme **pancreatic lipase** breaks certain bonds present in fats and results in the release of fatty acids and other small lipids.

Recall that fats are insoluble in water (see Chapter 6). As a result, they tend to form large globules as they are churned in the stomach. Before pancreatic lipase can act, the large fat globules that emerge from the stomach must be broken up—a process known as **emulsification.**

In the small intestine, emulsification results from the action of small molecules called bile salts. As **Figure 41.15** shows, bile salts function like the detergents that researchers use to break up the lipids in plasma membranes (see Chapter 6).

Bile salts are synthesized in the **liver,** an organ that performs an array of functions related to digestion, and secreted in a complex solution called **bile,** which is stored in the **gallbladder.** When bile enters the small intestine, it raises the pH and emulsifies fats. Once fats are broken into small globules, which increases

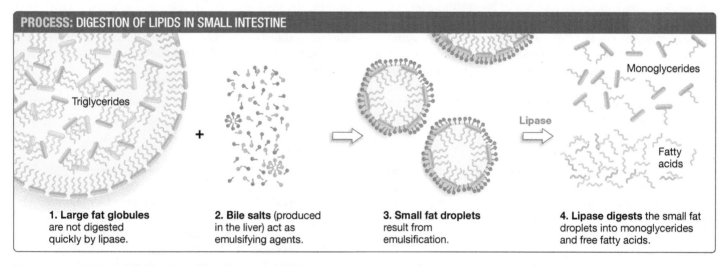

PROCESS: DIGESTION OF LIPIDS IN SMALL INTESTINE

Triglycerides

+

Lipase

Monoglycerides

Fatty acids

1. Large fat globules are not digested quickly by lipase.

2. Bile salts (produced in the liver) act as emulsifying agents.

3. Small fat droplets result from emulsification.

4. Lipase digests the small fat droplets into monoglycerides and free fatty acids.

Figure 41.15 Lipid Digestion in the Small Intestine Depends on Bile Salts and Pancreatic Lipase. Bile salts break up large fat globules, enabling pancreatic lipase to digest fats quickly.

Digestion is accomplished by the enzymes listed here, by HCl produced in the stomach in response to the hormone gastrin, and by bile salts from the liver. Bile salts are stored in the gallbladder. They are released in response to the hormone cholecystokinin and emulsify fats in the small intestine.

	Where Synthesized	Regulation	Function
Carboxypeptidase	Pancreas	Released in inactive form in response to cholecystokinin from small intestine; activated by trypsin	In small intestine, breaks peptide bonds in polypeptides—releasing amino acids
Chymotrypsin	Pancreas	Released in inactive form in response to cholecystokinin from small intestine; activated by trypsin	In small intestine, breaks peptide bonds in polypeptides—releasing amino acids
Elastase	Pancreas	Released in inactive form in response to cholecystokinin from small intestine; activated by trypsin	In small intestine, breaks peptide bonds in polypeptides—releasing amino acids
Lingual lipase	Salivary glands	Released in response to taste and smell stimuli	In mouth and stomach, breaks bonds in fats—releasing fatty acids and monoglycerides
Nucleases	Pancreas	Released in response to cholecystokinin from small intestine	In small intestine, break apart nucleic acids—releasing nucleotides
Pancreatic amylase	Pancreas	Released in response to cholecystokinin from small intestine	In small intestine, breaks apart carbohydrates—releasing sugars
Pancreatic lipase	Pancreas	Released in response to cholecystokinin from small intestine	In small intestine, breaks bonds in fats—releasing fatty acids and monoglycerides
Pepsin	Stomach	Released in inactive form (pepsinogen); activated by low pH in stomach lumen	In stomach, breaks peptide bonds between certain amino acids in proteins—releasing polypeptides
Salivary amylase	Salivary glands	Released in response to taste and smell stimuli	In mouth, breaks apart carbohydrates—releasing sugars
Trypsin	Pancreas	Released in inactive form (trypsinogen) in response to cholecystokinin from small intestine; activated by enteropeptidase from small intestine	In small intestine, breaks specific peptide bonds in polypeptides—releasing amino acids

their surface area, they can be attacked by pancreatic lipase and digested. Table 41.3 summarizes the major digestive enzymes.

The monoglycerides and fatty acids released by lipase activity enter small intestine epithelial cells by simple diffusion and are processed into protein-coated globules called chylomicrons, which move by exocytosis into lacteals—see Figure 41.12—near the epithelial cells. The lacteals merge with larger lymph vessels, which then merge with large veins. In this way, fats enter the bloodstream without clogging small blood vessels.

How Is Water Absorbed? When solutes from digested material are absorbed into the epithelium of the small intestine, water follows passively by osmosis. This is an important mechanism for **(1)** absorbing water that has been ingested, and **(2)** reclaiming liquid that was secreted into the digestive tract in saliva, mucus, and pancreatic fluid.

This mechanism of water absorption inspired an important medical strategy called oral rehydration therapy. If a patient has diarrhea, clinicians frequently prescribe dilute solutions of glucose and electrolytes to be taken orally. When the solutes in the drink are absorbed in the small intestine through sodium-glucose cotransporters, enough water follows to prevent the life-threatening effects of dehydration. This simple treatment saves thousands of lives every year. ✔ If you understand this strategy, you should be able to predict at least two digestive effects of a molecule that selectively blocks the sodium-glucose cotransporter.

The Large Intestine

By the time digested material reaches the large intestine of a human, a large amount of water (approximately 5 liters per day) and virtually all of the available nutrients have been absorbed. The primary function of the **large intestine** is to form feces by absorbing additional water and compacting the wastes that remain.

These processes occur in the **colon**—the main section of the large intestine. Feces are held in the **rectum,** which is the final part of the large intestine, until they can be eliminated. Although the kidneys are responsible for maintaining water balance, water absorption in the large intestine is important for keeping the body well hydrated.

In addition to compacting wastes and absorbing water, the human colon contains symbiotic microorganisms that digest cellulose. Fermentation of cellulose is not as important to an omnivorous human as it is to an herbivore like a ruminant. However, bacteria in the human colon also produce several important nutrients, such as vitamin K, that are absorbed into the bloodstream.

Variations in Structure and Function The size and function of the large intestine vary dramatically among animals. In insects, the posteriormost portion of the digestive tract, called the hindgut, reabsorbs water and ions and excretes uric acid and feces (see Chapter 40). Among vertebrates, various lineages of fishes have no large intestine at all.

In some herbivorous vertebrates, the **cecum,** a blind sac at the anterior end of the large intestine, is greatly enlarged and functions in cellulose digestion. These vertebrates include rabbits, many rodents, some marsupials, horses, elephants, tapirs, and leaf-eating primates. Like the crop of some birds and the modified stomach of ruminants, the cecum of these vertebrates contains symbiotic bacteria and protists that ferment cellulose.

In humans, a narrow pouch called the **appendix** emerges from the cecum. The function of the appendix has long been debated. It has often been described as vestigial—referring to a reduced or incompletely developed trait that is a vestige of evolutionary ancestry (see Chapter 22)—partly because it does not perform any obvious vital function. Indeed, if it becomes inflamed, it can be surgically removed from a patient without any ill effects. However, while not vital, the appendix may have important functions: It contains immune system cells, and it appears to act as a haven for symbiotic microorganisms that inhabit the colon. After an episode of diarrhea flushes symbiotic bacteria from the colon, the appendix may provide the additional bacteria needed for recolonizing the colon.

Rabbits and some other mammals are able to eliminate the cecum's contents as pellets, which the animal then re-ingests and

passes through the digestive tract a second time. This particular example of **coprophagy,** or feces eating, allows the animal to absorb more nutrients from food.

Another striking structural variation occurs in the rectum of amphibians, reptiles, and birds. Their urine flows from the kidneys into the **cloaca,** an enlarged portion of the large intestine into which the reproductive tract also empties (see Chapter 40).

41.4 Nutritional Homeostasis— Glucose as a Case Study

When digestion is complete, amino acids, fatty acids, ions, and sugars enter the bloodstream and are delivered to the cells that need them. The body uses or stores these nutrients in order to maintain homeostatic levels in the blood and avoid imbalances. Too much of a nutrient or too little can be problematic or even fatal.

The illness **diabetes mellitus** is a classic example of nutrient imbalance. People with diabetes mellitus have abnormally high levels of glucose in their blood because cells cannot import the glucose. Over the course of a lifetime, chronically elevated blood glucose levels can lead to an array of complications, including blindness, impaired blood circulation, and heart failure. What causes the imbalance? More important, how is glucose homeostasis normally maintained?

The Discovery of Insulin

In 1879, researchers removed the pancreas from a dog and observed that the dog's blood glucose level became very high. This experiment suggested that the pancreas secretes a compound needed for removing glucose from the blood.

When other investigators cut up pancreatic tissues and injected extracts into diabetic dogs, however, they observed no response. Eventually, they decided that digestive enzymes in the pancreas were probably destroying the active agent during the extraction process.

Then, in 1921, Frederick Banting and Charles Best conducted a breakthrough experiment:

1. They began by tying off a dog's pancreatic duct—the tube through which digestive enzymes flow to the small intestine. The logic was that blocking the secretion of digestive enzymes might kill the cells that synthesize them.

2. The investigators waited several weeks for the cells near the duct to die and then removed the pancreas.

3. They froze the pancreatic tissue, ground it up, and injected an extract into a diabetic dog.

4. To their delight, the dog's blood glucose levels stabilized, and the dog became more active and healthy looking.

After Banting and Best repeated the experiment and observed the same result, they grew increasingly confident that they had located the source of the molecule responsible for lowering blood glucose levels. The molecule came to be called insulin.

Insulin's Role in Homeostasis

Insulin is a hormone that is secreted by cells in the pancreas when blood glucose levels are too high. It travels through the bloodstream and binds to receptors on cells throughout the body. (See Chapter 46 for more detail on the structure and function of hormones and other chemical signals.) In response, cells that have insulin receptors increase their rate of glucose uptake and processing. Specifically, insulin stimulates cells in the liver and skeletal muscle to import glucose from the blood and synthesize glycogen from glucose monomers. As a result, glucose levels in the blood decline (**Figure 41.16**, top).

If blood glucose levels fall too low, as they do when food is lacking, other cells in the pancreas secrete a hormone called **glucagon.** In response to glucagon, liver cells catabolize stored glycogen and produce glucose via **gluconeogenesis,** the synthesis of glucose from non-carbohydrate compounds. As a result, glucose levels in the blood rise (**Figure 41.16**, bottom).

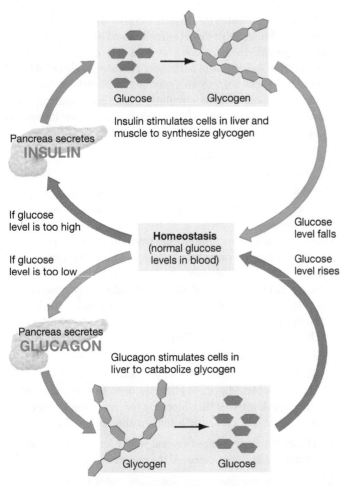

Figure 41.16 Insulin and Glucagon Provide Negative Feedback in a Homeostatic System. Both insulin and glucagon are secreted by cells in the pancreas but have opposite effects on blood glucose levels.

✔ After reading the descriptions of type 1 and type 2 diabetes mellitus, decide which arrow is disrupted in individuals with type 2 diabetes mellitus and which arrow is disrupted in individuals with type 1 diabetes mellitus.

Insulin and glucagon interact to form a negative feedback system capable of achieving homeostasis with respect to glucose concentrations in the blood.

Diabetes Mellitus Has Two Forms

Diabetes mellitus develops in people who **(1)** do not synthesize sufficient insulin or **(2)** are resistant to insulin, meaning that insulin does not effectively activate its receptor in target cells. The first condition is called type 1 diabetes mellitus; the second condition is type 2 diabetes mellitus. In both types, effector cells do not receive the signal that would result in a drop in blood glucose levels.

Glucose imbalance has a direct effect on urine formation. Normally, signals from insulin keep blood glucose levels low enough that all of the glucose can be reabsorbed from the filtrate formed in the kidney. But when blood glucose levels are very high, so much glucose enters the nephron that it cannot all be reabsorbed. High glucose levels in the filtrate increase its osmolarity and decrease the amount of water reabsorbed from it. More water leaves the body, leading to high urine volume in both types of diabetes mellitus.

The word "diabetes" means "to run through"; water "runs through" people with diabetes. The word "mellitus" means "honeyed (sweet)." Before chemical methods of analyzing urine were available, physicians would taste the patient's urine. If the urine was sweet, then the patient very likely was suffering from diabetes mellitus.

How do these diseases develop? Type 1 diabetes mellitus is an autoimmune disease, meaning that the body's immune system mistakenly targets its own cells for destruction. In the case of type 1 diabetes mellitus, the insulin-producing cells of the pancreas are destroyed. Type 2 diabetes mellitus occurs when the receptors for insulin no longer function correctly or are reduced in number. The primary risk factors for developing type 2 diabetes mellitus are obesity, a high-sugar diet, lack of exercise, and genetic predisposition to the disease.

High blood glucose levels are not the only problem with diabetes. The levels are high because glucose cannot be imported into cells, so cells that require glucose to function, such as brain neurons, can be starved unless the disease is treated.

Currently, type 1 diabetes mellitus is treated with insulin injections and careful attention to diet; type 2 diabetes mellitus is managed primarily through prescribed diets, exercise, and monitoring blood glucose levels, as well as taking drugs that increase cellular responsiveness to insulin. The challenge is to achieve homeostasis with respect to blood glucose levels in the absence of the body's normal regulatory mechanisms.

✔ If you understand the difference between type 1 and type 2 diabetes mellitus, you should be able to explain why insulin injections are more effective in controlling blood glucose levels in individuals with type 1 diabetes mellitus.

The Type 2 Diabetes Mellitus Epidemic

An epidemic of type 2 diabetes mellitus is currently under way in certain human populations. In the United States, 11 percent of persons aged 20 and over and 27 percent of persons aged 65

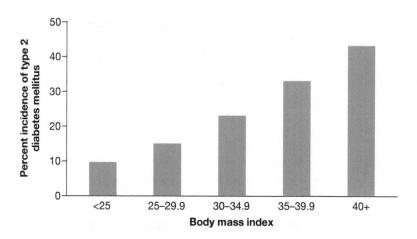

Figure 41.17 The Incidence of Type 2 Diabetes Mellitus Is Correlated with Obesity.
DATA: N. T. Nguyen, et al. 2011. *Obesity Surgery* 21: 351–355.

✔ **QUANTITATIVE** A 1.8-m (6-ft) tall man has a BMI of 40. How much weight would he need to lose to reduce his risk for type 2 diabetes mellitus to less than 10 percent?

and over were diabetic in 2013. About 90–95 percent of these individuals had type 2 diabetes mellitus. Minority groups such as African Americans and Hispanics have much higher rates of new cases of type 2 diabetes mellitus than white non-Hispanic Americans.

Because there is a strong association between the prevalence of diabetes mellitus in parents and their children, researchers have long suspected that some individuals have a genetic predisposition for developing the disease. To date, alleles at 38 different genes that predispose individuals to type 2 diabetes mellitus have been identified (using techniques introduced in Chapter 20).

However, there is also evidence that obesity has an important impact on the incidence of type 2 diabetes mellitus. From 1999 to 2006, researchers collected data on more than 20,000 middle-aged and elderly Americans, 2900 of whom developed type 2 diabetes mellitus. As **Figure 41.17** shows, the researchers found a strong relationship between the incidence of type 2 diabetes mellitus and **body mass index (BMI),** a measure of obesity. BMI is calculated as body mass (in kilograms) divided by height (in meters) squared. A person with a BMI of 30 or higher is considered obese and has a far greater risk of developing type 2 diabetes mellitus than people with lower BMIs.

Type 2 diabetes mellitus used to be called adult-onset diabetes because the disease typically appeared in adults. The current epidemic of type 2 diabetes mellitus is not restricted to adults, however, and that name was abandoned as more and more young people were diagnosed with the disease. At present, one of every three children born in the United States will develop type 2 diabetes mellitus in their lifetimes, and childhood diabetes rates are increasing by 3 percent every year worldwide. Two-thirds of American adults are overweight, and one-third are obese. It is clear that type 2 diabetes mellitus and obesity are modern-day epidemics.

CHECK YOUR UNDERSTANDING

If you understand that ...

- Insulin and glucagon interact to regulate glucose levels in the blood.
- Diabetes mellitus results from a lack of homeostasis in blood glucose levels.

✔ You should be able to ...

1. Identify the causes of each type of diabetes mellitus.
2. Explain what a person with type 1 diabetes mellitus should do when her or his blood glucose level is too high and when it is too low.

Answers are available in Appendix A

For media, go to MasteringBiology

41.1 Nutritional Requirements

- The diets of animals include fats, carbohydrates, and proteins that provide energy; vitamins that serve as coenzymes and perform other functions; minerals that are used as components of enzyme cofactors or structural materials; and ions of electrolytes required for osmotic balance and normal membrane function.

- Fats contain more energy (about 9 kcal/g) than carbohydrates or proteins (about 4 kcal/g), making fats an efficient way to store energy in the body.

41.2 Capturing Food: The Structure and Function of Mouthparts

- Most animals are mass feeders that obtain food by seizing and manipulating it.

- Animal mouthparts include teeth, jaws, beaks, and toxin-injecting organs.

- Through natural selection, mouthparts in different animal species have become adapted for obtaining particular types of food.

41.3 How Are Nutrients Digested and Absorbed?

- Most animals have a digestive tract that begins at the mouth and ends at the anus.

- In many animals, chemical digestion of food begins in the mouth. In mammals, salivary amylase hydrolyzes bonds in starch and glycogen, and lingual lipase hydrolyzes bonds in fats.

- Once food is swallowed, it is propelled down the esophagus by peristalsis.

- Digestion continues in the stomach. In the human stomach, a highly acidic environment denatures proteins, and the enzyme pepsin begins the cleavage of peptide bonds that link amino acids.

- Food passes from the stomach into the small intestine, where it is mixed with secretions from the pancreas and liver.

- In the small intestine, carbohydrate digestion is continued by pancreatic amylase; fats are emulsified by bile salts and digested by pancreatic lipase; and protein digestion is completed by a suite of pancreatic proteases.

- Cells that line the small intestine absorb the nutrients released by digestion. In many cases, uptake is driven by an electrochemical gradient established by Na^+/K^+-ATPase that favors the diffusion of Na^+ into the cells.

- As solutes leave the lumen of the small intestine and enter cells, water follows by osmosis.

- Water reabsorption is completed in the large intestine, where feces form.

- The structure of organs in the digestive tract varies widely among species, in ways that support processing of the food each species ingests.

41.4 Nutritional Homeostasis— Glucose as a Case Study

- Diabetes mellitus is a condition in which the level of glucose in the blood is abnormally high.

- Type 1 diabetes mellitus is caused by a defect in the production of insulin—a hormone secreted by the pancreas that promotes the uptake of glucose from the blood.

- Type 2 diabetes mellitus is characterized by a failure of cells to respond to insulin.

- The development of type 2 diabetes is correlated with obesity. The incidence of this disease has reached epidemic proportions in many populations.

Answers are available in Appendix A

✔ TEST YOUR KNOWLEDGE

1. **QUANTITATIVE** Calculate and compare the caloric content of skim milk and whole milk. Per serving, skim milk contains 12 g carbohydrates, 8 g protein, and no fat; whole milk contains 12 g carbohydrates, 8 g protein, and 8 g fat.

2. In mammals, how and where are carbohydrates digested?
   a. by lipases in the small intestine
   b. by pepsin and HCl in the stomach
   c. by nucleases in the small intestine
   d. by amylases in the mouth and small intestine

3. Cellulose is fermented in which of the following structures in rabbits?
   a. small intestine
   b. cecum
   c. abomasum
   d. rumen

4. A hormone that reduces blood glucose levels is _____, and a hormone that increases blood glucose levels is _____.

✔ TEST YOUR UNDERSTANDING

5. Look in the mirror at your teeth. What do their shapes suggest about their functions in terms of the types of food humans are adapted to eat?

6. Explain the role in nutrition of each of the following structures: bird crop, cow rumen, and elephant large intestine.

7. Why is oral rehydration therapy with a solution of sodium chloride and glucose an effective treatment for dehydration?
   a. The sodium and glucose decrease urine output.
   b. The sodium and glucose facilitate water absorption by the small intestine.
   c. The sodium and glucose help kill intestinal bacteria.
   d. The sodium and glucose make the person thirsty.

8. Why is it important that the small intestine has a much greater surface area than the stomach or esophagus?

✔ TEST YOUR PROBLEM-SOLVING SKILLS

9. Why is fat the most efficient form of energy stored for later use?

10. Among vertebrates, the large intestine exists only in lineages that are primarily terrestrial (amphibians, reptiles, and mammals). Propose a hypothesis to explain this observation.

✔ PUT IT ALL TOGETHER: Case Study

What is the relationship between diet and the structure of the digestive tract?

Minnows are mainly carnivorous, eating insects and other small animals. However, herbivory has evolved independently in minnows several times. What changes in digestive structure and function are associated with the evolution of herbivory?

11. Like cichlids, minnows use their pharyngeal jaws to process food. Suggest some possible structural differences between the teeth on the pharyngeal jaws of carnivorous and herbivorous minnows.

12. Which of the following is true of the digestive tracts of minnows?
    a. They are incomplete but have both a mouth and an anus.
    b. They are complete, facilitating compartmentalization of digestion in different organs.
    c. They are incomplete, with no accessory organs.
    d. They are complete and include a large gastrovascular cavity.

13. QUANTITATIVE Researchers compared the relative gut length—the length of the digestive tract divided by body length—in four species of herbivorous minnows and four species of carnivorous minnows. The results are shown in the graph that follows (*** means $P < 0.001$; see BioSkills 3). Based on these data, what conclusion can you draw about the relationship between diet and gut length?

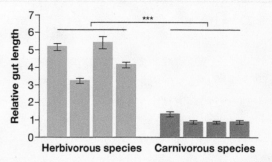

Source: D. P. German et al. 2010. *Physiological and Biochemical Zoology* 83: 1–18.

14. Suggest a function of the difference in relative gut lengths of herbivorous and carnivorous minnows.

15. Which minnows, herbivorous or carnivorous, should exhibit higher cellulase activity in the gut? Explain.

16. PROCESS OF SCIENCE Why did the researchers compare relative gut length instead of absolute gut length?

MasteringBiology®

Students Go to MasteringBiology for assignments, the eText, and the Study Area with animations, practice tests, and activities.
Professors Go to MasteringBiology for automatically graded tutorials and questions that you can assign to your students, plus Instructor Resources.

42 Gas Exchange and Circulation

During intense exercise, animal circulatory systems deliver large amounts of oxygen to tissues and remove large amounts of carbon dioxide. This chapter explores how gas exchange occurs in animals that live in aquatic or terrestrial environments.

In this chapter you will learn that

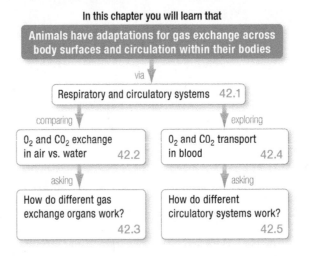

Animals have adaptations for gas exchange across body surfaces and circulation within their bodies

via

Respiratory and circulatory systems   42.1

comparing

O_2 and CO_2 exchange in air vs. water   42.2

asking

How do different gas exchange organs work?   42.3

exploring

O_2 and CO_2 transport in blood   42.4

asking

How do different circulatory systems work?   42.5

This chapter is part of the Big Picture. See how on pages 816–817.

Animal cells are like factories that run 24 hours a day. Inside the plasma membrane, the chemical reactions that sustain life require a steady input of raw materials. Those reactions also produce a steady stream of wastes. Earlier in this unit, you learned how waste materials are excreted from the body (see Chapter 40). You also examined how nutrients enter the body (see Chapter 41). Let's now turn our attention to two other major questions:

1. How are two of the most important molecules in the economy of the cell—the oxygen (O_2) required for cellular respiration and the carbon dioxide (CO_2) produced by cellular respiration—exchanged with the environment?

2. How are these gases—along with wastes, nutrients, and other types of molecules—transported throughout the body?

Understanding gas exchange and circulation is fundamental to understanding how animals work. If either process fails, the consequences are dire. Let's begin with an overview of animal respiratory and circulatory systems and then plunge into the details of how gases are exchanged and transported.

42.1 The Respiratory and Circulatory Systems

When the mitochondria inside animal cells are producing ATP via cellular respiration, they consume oxygen and produce carbon dioxide. To support continued ATP production, cells have to obtain oxygen and expel excess carbon dioxide continuously (see the Big Picture, Energy for Life, on pages 232–233).

How does this gas exchange occur between an animal's environment and its mitochondria? In most cases, gas exchange involves the five steps illustrated in **Figure 42.1**:

1. *Ventilation,* the movement of air or water through a specialized gas exchange organ, such as a lung or gill.

2. *Diffusion at the respiratory surface,* where O_2 moves from the air or water into the blood and CO_2 moves from the blood into the air or water.

3. *Circulation,* the transport of dissolved O_2 and CO_2 throughout the body—along with nutrients, wastes, and other types of molecules—via the circulatory system.

4. *Diffusion at the tissues,* where O_2 moves from the blood into the tissues and CO_2 moves from the tissues into the blood.

5. *Cellular respiration,* the cell's use of O_2 and production of CO_2. In tissues, where cellular respiration has led to low O_2 levels and high CO_2 levels, gas exchange occurs between blood and cells.

Steps 1 and 2 are accomplished by the **respiratory system,** the collection of cells, tissues, and organs responsible for gas exchange between the animal and its environment. In essence, a respiratory system consists of structures for conducting air or water to a surface where gas exchange takes place.

In some animals the gas exchange surface is the skin, but in most species it is located in a specialized organ like the gills found in mollusks, arthropods, and fishes, the tracheae of insects, or the lungs of tetrapods. Section 42.3 analyzes the structure and function of gills, tracheae, and lungs in detail.

Step 3 in Figure 42.1 is usually accomplished by a **circulatory system,** which moves O_2, CO_2, and other materials around the body. In many cases, a muscular heart propels a specialized, liquid transport tissue throughout the body via a system of vessels.

Keeping in mind this broad overview of respiratory and circulatory systems, let's dive into the details by exploring how oxygen and carbon dioxide move between an animal's body and its environment.

42.2 Air and Water as Respiratory Media

Gas exchange between the environment and cells is based on diffusion. Under normal conditions, oxygen concentrations are relatively high in the environment (for example, in air that you inhale or in ocean water) and low in tissues, while carbon dioxide levels are relatively high in tissues and low in the environment. So oxygen tends to move from the environment into tissues, and carbon dioxide tends to move from tissues into the environment.

How much oxygen and carbon dioxide are present in the atmosphere versus the ocean? What factors in air and water influence how quickly these gases move by diffusion?

How Do Oxygen and Carbon Dioxide Behave in Air?

The atmosphere is composed primarily of nitrogen (76 percent) and oxygen (21 percent) and has trace amounts of argon (0.93 percent) and CO_2 (0.04 percent). Nitrogen (N_2) and argon are not important to animals living at sea level and are usually ignored in analyses of gas exchange.

However, the data are actually a little misleading. To understand why, consider that the *percentage* of O_2 in the atmosphere does not vary with elevation. The atmosphere at the top of Mt. Everest is composed of 21 percent oxygen, just as it is at sea level. The key difference is that far fewer molecules of oxygen

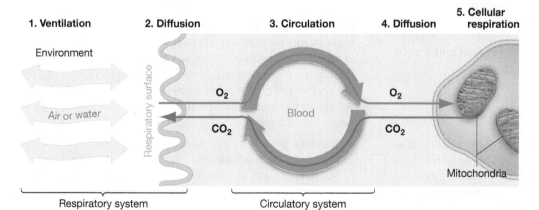

1. Ventilation   **2. Diffusion**   **3. Circulation**   **4. Diffusion**   **5. Cellular respiration**

Environment

Respiratory surface

Air or water

O_2

CO_2

Blood

O_2

CO_2

Mitochondria

Respiratory system

Circulatory system

Figure 42.1 Gas Exchange Involves Ventilation, Diffusion, Circulation, and Respiration. In animals, oxygen and carbon dioxide are exchanged by diffusion across the surface of a lung, a gill, the skin, or some other gas exchange organ. In many species these gases are transported to and from cells—where gas exchange also takes place—in a fluid connective tissue such as blood.

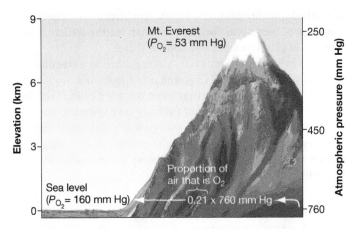

Figure 42.2 Oxygen Makes Up 21 Percent of the Atmosphere, but Its Partial Pressure Depends on Elevation. Atmospheric pressure, and thus oxygen partial pressure (P_{O_2}), fall with increasing elevation.

and other atmospheric gases are present per unit volume of air at high elevations than at sea level, because atmospheric pressure is lower at high elevations. To understand how gases move by diffusion, it is important to express their presence in terms of partial pressures instead of percentages. Pressure is force exerted per unit area. A **partial pressure** is the pressure of a particular gas in a mixture of gases.

To calculate the partial pressure of a particular gas, multiply the fractional composition (the fraction of air the gas comprises) by the total pressure exerted by the entire mixture (atmospheric pressure). The calculation is valid because the total pressure of a mixture of gases is the sum of the partial pressures of all the individual gases. This relationship is called Dalton's law.

For example, **Figure 42.2** shows that the total atmospheric pressure at sea level is 760 mm Hg (millimeters of mercury). If you multiply this value by 0.21, which is the fraction of air that is O_2, you obtain a partial pressure of oxygen, abbreviated P_{O_2}, at sea level of 160 mm Hg. Because the atmospheric pressure is only about 250 mm Hg at the top of Mt. Everest, the P_{O_2} there is only $0.21 \times 250 = 53$ mm Hg.

Oxygen and carbon dioxide diffuse between the environment and cells along their respective partial pressure gradients, just as solutes diffuse along their electrochemical gradients. In both air and water, O_2 and CO_2 move from regions of high partial pressure to regions of low partial pressure. It's hard to breathe at the top of Mt. Everest because the partial pressure of oxygen is low there—meaning that the diffusion gradient between the atmosphere and your lung tissues is small, so fewer molecules of O_2 diffuse into your tissues when you take a breath.

How Do Oxygen and Carbon Dioxide Behave in Water?

To obtain oxygen, water breathers face a much more challenging environment than air breathers do. Aquatic animals live in an environment that contains much less oxygen than the environments inhabited by terrestrial animals. At 15°C, a liter of air can contain up to 209 milliliters (mL) of O_2, while a liter of water

may contain a maximum of only 7 mL of O_2. To extract a given amount of oxygen, an aquatic animal has to process 30 times more water than the amount of air a terrestrial animal breathes.

In addition, water is about a thousand times denser than air and much more viscous. As a result, water breathers have to expend much more energy to ventilate their respiratory surfaces than do air breathers.

What Affects the Amount of Gas in a Solution? Oxygen and carbon dioxide diffuse into water from the atmosphere, but the amount of gas that dissolves in water depends on several factors:

- *Solubility of the gas in water* Oxygen has very low solubility in water. Only 0.003 mL of oxygen dissolves in 100 mL of water for each increase of 1 mm Hg in oxygen partial pressure. Animals compensate for the low solubility of oxygen in water by having a molecule in blood that binds to oxygen and delivers it to tissues. Without this carrier molecule, the rate of blood flow to tissues would have to increase dramatically to meet oxygen demand.

- *Temperature of the water* As the temperature of water increases, the amount of gas that dissolves in it decreases. Other things being equal, warm-water habitats have much less oxygen available than cold-water habitats do. For a fish, breathing in warm water is comparable to a land-dwelling animal breathing at high elevation.

- *Presence of other solutes* Because seawater has a much higher concentration of solutes than does freshwater, seawater can hold less dissolved gas. At 10°C, up to 8.02 mL of O_2 can be present per liter of freshwater versus only 6.35 mL of O_2 per liter of seawater. As a result, freshwater habitats tend to be more oxygen rich than marine environments.

- *Partial pressure of the gas in contact with the water* Gases move from regions of high partial pressure to regions of low partial pressure. So if the partial pressure of a gas dissolved in a liquid exceeds that of the gas in the adjacent atmosphere, the gas will bubble up out of the liquid. This is what happens when the cap is removed from a bottle of carbonated beverage. The partial pressure of carbon dioxide in the newly opened drink is much higher than it is in the atmosphere.

What Affects the Amount of Oxygen Available in an Aquatic Habitat? The partial pressure of oxygen varies in different types of aquatic habitats, just as it varies with altitude on land. In addition to the four factors just listed, other important considerations affect oxygen's availability in water. These include the presence of photosynthetic organisms and decomposers, the amount of mixing that occurs, and the surface area of the body of water. For example,

- Habitats with large numbers of photosynthetic organisms tend to be relatively oxygen rich. In contrast, oxygen content is extremely low in bogs and other stagnant-water habitats because oxygen is quickly depleted by decomposers that use it in cellular respiration.

- Unless currents mix water almost continuously, water near the surface has much higher oxygen content than water near the bottom of the same habitat.

- Shallow ponds and streams tend to be much better oxygenated than deep bodies of water because shallower bodies have a higher ratio of surface area to volume.

- Rapids, waterfalls, and breaking waves are the most highly oxygenated of all aquatic environments because a large surface area is exposed to the atmosphere as water splashes and because air bubbles are incorporated into the water.

Now let's consider the structure and function of ventilatory organs. How do the gills of fishes, the tracheae of insects, and the lungs of mammals cope with the differences between air and water?

CHECK YOUR UNDERSTANDING

If you understand that ...

- O_2 and CO_2 move from regions of high partial pressure to regions of low partial pressure.
- The partial pressure of oxygen in a body of water depends on the water's temperature, surface area, and amount of mixing and on the impacts of photosynthetic organisms and decomposers, among other factors.
- Water breathing is much more difficult than air breathing, in part because the partial pressure of oxygen in water is much lower than its partial pressure in air.

✔ **You should be able to ...**

Decide, for each of three aquaria (A, B, and C), whether a large or a small amount of air should be bubbled in to maintain oxygenation of the water. A contains warm water and several fish; B contains cold water, several fish, and aquatic algae; and C contains warm water and sedentary animals.

Answers are available in Appendix A.

42.3 Organs of Gas Exchange

Many small animals lack specialized gas exchange organs, such as gills or lungs. Instead, they obtain O_2 and eliminate CO_2 by diffusion across the body surface. This is possible because their size and shape give them an extraordinarily high ratio of surface area to volume (see Chapter 39). In sponges, jellyfish, flatworms, and other species, diffusion across the body surface is rapid enough to fulfill their requirements for taking in O_2 and expelling CO_2.

Most of these animals are restricted to living in wet environments, however. Gas exchange surfaces must be kept moist to facilitate diffusion of gases across them. The surfaces must also be thin, and thin tissues are prone to water loss. Living in wet or humid environments allows animals to exchange gases across their outer surface while avoiding dehydration.

In contrast, animals that are large or that live in dry habitats need some sort of specialized respiratory organ. Respiratory organs provide a greater surface area for gas exchange—enough

to meet the demands of a large body filled with cells. In terrestrial animals, respiratory organs are located inside the body, which helps minimize water loss from the moist surfaces.

Biologists have long marveled at the efficiency of gills and lungs. To appreciate why, let's examine the physical factors that control diffusion rates and then look at the structure and function of these respiratory organs.

Physical Parameters: The Law of Diffusion

In 1855 Adolf Fick derived an equation regarding diffusion, based on the results of experiments he had performed on the behavior of gases. **Fick's law of diffusion** states that the rate of diffusion of a gas depends on five parameters: the solubility of the gas in the aqueous film lining the gas exchange surface; the temperature; the surface area available for diffusion; the difference in partial pressures of the gas across the gas exchange surface; and the thickness of the barrier to diffusion (**Figure 42.3**).

Fick's law identifies traits that allow animals to maximize the rate at which oxygen and carbon dioxide diffuse across respiratory surfaces. Specifically, Fick's law states that gases diffuse at the highest rates when three conditions are met:

1. A is large, meaning a large area is available for gas exchange. Given Fick's law, it is not surprising that the respiratory surface in the human lungs would cover about 140 m^2—about a third of a basketball court—if the epithelium were spread flat.

2. D is small, meaning the respiratory surface is extremely thin. In the human lung, this barrier to diffusion is only 0.2 μm thick—about 1/200th of the thickness of this page.

3. $P_2 - P_1$ is large, meaning the partial pressure gradient of the gas across the surface is large. Large partial pressure gradients are maintained in part by having a circulatory system in close contact with the gas exchange surface. When blood flows close to the respiratory surface, oxygen is rapidly taken away from the area where inward diffusion is occurring, and carbon dioxide is rapidly brought into the area where outward diffusion is occurring. As a result, $P_2 - P_1$ stays high.

What other aspects of gill and lung structure affect the diffusion rate? To answer this question, let's delve into the anatomy of these respiratory organs.

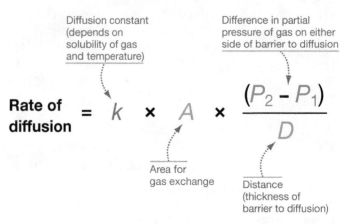

Diffusion constant (depends on solubility of gas and temperature)

Difference in partial pressure of gas on either side of barrier to diffusion

$$\text{Rate of diffusion} = k \times A \times \frac{(P_2 - P_1)}{D}$$

Area for gas exchange

Distance (thickness of barrier to diffusion)

Figure 42.3 Fick's Law Describes the Rate of Diffusion.

How Do Gills Work?

Gills are outgrowths of the body surface or throat that are used for gas exchange in aquatic animals as well as for osmoregulation (see Chapter 40). Gills are efficient solutions to the problems posed by water breathing, primarily because they present a large surface area for the diffusion of gases across a thin epithelium.

In some species of invertebrates, such as the red tubeworm (Figure 42.4a), gills project from the body surface and contact the surrounding water directly.

In other invertebrate species, such as the crayfish (Figure 42.4b), gills are located inside the exoskeleton or body wall. If gills are internal, water must be driven over them by cilia, the limbs, or other specialized structures.

In contrast to the diversity of gills found in aquatic invertebrates, the gills of bony fishes are all similar in structure. Fish gills are located on both sides of the head and in teleosts (see Chapter 32) the gills consist of four arches, as Figure 42.5 shows.

How Do Fishes Ventilate Their Gills?

To move water through their gills so gas exchange can take place, most fishes open and close their mouth and **operculum**, the stiff flap of tissue that covers the gills. The pumping action of the mouth and operculum creates a pressure gradient that moves water over the gills.

In contrast, tuna and other fishes that are particularly fast swimmers force water through their gills by swimming with their mouths open. This process is called ram ventilation.

Regardless of how fish gills are ventilated, water flows in one direction through gills, passing over long, thin structures called **gill filaments** that extend from each gill arch. Each gill filament is composed of hundreds or thousands of **gill lamellae.** Gill lamellae are sheetlike structures, shown in detail at the bottom of Figure 42.5. Note that a bed of small blood vessels called capillaries runs through each lamella.

The Fish Gill Is a Countercurrent System

The one-way flow of water through gill lamellae has a profound impact on gill function, for a simple reason: The flow of blood through the capillaries in each lamella is in the opposite direction to the flow of water. As a result, each lamella functions as a countercurrent exchanger.

Recall that countercurrent exchangers are based on two adjacent fluids flowing in opposite directions (see Chapter 39). Figure 42.6 illustrates why the countercurrent flow is so critical.

Note two key points about the left side of the figure, where water and blood flow in opposite directions:

1. A slight gradient in partial pressure of oxygen between the water and blood (here, 10 percent) exists along the entire length of the lamella.

2. A large difference in oxygen partial pressure exists between the start and end of the system. In this example, the difference is 100% − 15% = 85% in the water and 90% − 5% = 85% in the blood.

The upshot? Most of the oxygen in the incoming water has diffused into the blood.

Now look at the right side of the figure, where water and blood flow in the same direction.

1. A large gradient in partial pressure of oxygen (here, 100 percent) exists at the start of the system. The gradient in oxygen partial pressures declines rapidly and eventually disappears.

2. A relatively small difference in oxygen partial pressure exists between the start and end of the system. In this example, the difference is 100% − 50% = 50% in the water and 50% − 0% = 50% in the blood.

With this arrangement, only half of the oxygen in the incoming water has diffused into the blood.

Countercurrent flow makes fish gills extremely efficient at extracting oxygen from water because it ensures that a difference

(a) External gills are in direct contact with water.

(b) Internal gills must have water brought to them.

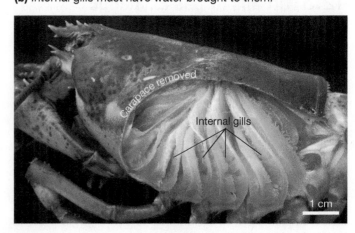

Figure 42.4 **Gills Can Be External or Internal. (a)** Red tubeworms are marine polychaetes with gills that protrude from the body. **(b)** Crayfish gills are located inside the main body wall. In this photo, a portion of the carapace (exoskeleton covering the head and thorax) has been removed to expose the gills.

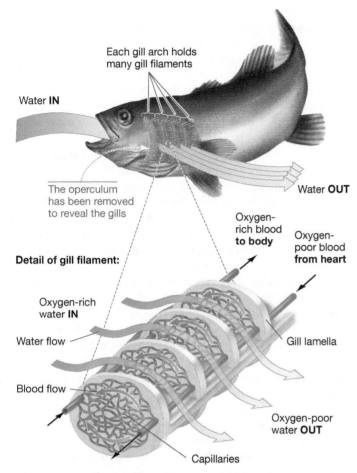

Figure 42.5 **Fish Gills Are a Countercurrent Exchange System.** In fish gills, water and blood flow in opposite directions. In the blood vessels, red represents oxygenated blood, blue represents deoxygenated blood, and purple represents mixed blood.

in the partial pressure of oxygen in water versus blood is maintained over the entire gas exchange surface.

The effect of countercurrent exchange is to maximize the $P_2 - P_1$ term in Fick's law of diffusion, averaged over the entire gill surface. Based on this observation, biologists cite countercurrent exchange as another example of how gills are optimized for efficient gas exchange.

How Do Insect Tracheae Work?

As noted earlier, air and water are dramatically different ventilatory media because they have different densities, viscosities, and abilities to hold oxygen and carbon dioxide. In addition, the consequences of exposing the gas exchange surface to air versus water differ.

In aquatic habitats, ventilation tends to disrupt water and electrolyte balance, and homeostasis must be maintained by an active osmoregulatory system. Osmosis causes marine animals to lose water across their gas exchange surface and freshwater animals to gain water (see Chapter 40). Diffusion tends to cause marine animals to gain sodium, chloride, and other ions, and freshwater animals to lose them.

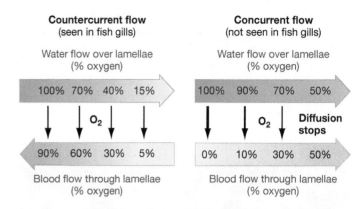

Figure 42.6 **Countercurrent Exchange Is Much More Efficient than Concurrent Exchange.** In the countercurrent system of fish gills, oxygen is transferred along the entire length of the capillaries.

✔ If you understand this concept, you should be able to predict what would happen to oxygen transfer from water to blood if flow were concurrent.

In contrast, breathing leads to a loss of water by evaporation in terrestrial environments. How do terrestrial animals minimize water loss while maximizing the efficiency of gas exchange?

To answer this question, consider the tracheal system of insects. Recall that insects have an extensive system of air-filled tubes called **tracheae** located within the body (see Chapter 40). These tubes connect to the exterior through openings in the exoskeleton called **spiracles,** which can be closed to minimize the loss of water by evaporation (**Figure 42.7**). The interior ends of tracheae are tiny and highly branched. This structure allows the tracheal system to transport air close enough to cells that gas exchange can take place directly across their plasma membranes.

Air moves from the atmosphere into the spiracles and then through the tracheae to the tissues in the insect's body. Is simple diffusion enough to ventilate the system, or is some type of breathing mechanism involved?

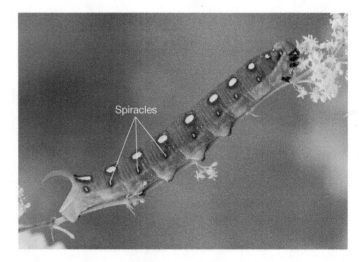

Figure 42.7 **Spiracles of the Hawkmoth Caterpillar.** Openings along the side of the caterpillar allow air to move in and out of the tracheae.

If insects ventilate their tracheal system with simple diffusion, then according to Fick's law, the distance that the air would have to diffuse down the tracheae would be very important. In other words, the rate of diffusion of air down the tracheae would be limited in part by the length of the tracheae. In reality, only very small insects have tracheae that are short enough to be ventilated by simple diffusion.

RESEARCH

QUESTION: Does physical activity affect air movement through the insect tracheal system?

HYPOTHESIS: Air moves through the tracheal system faster during physical activity.

NULL HYPOTHESIS: Physical activity does not affect the rate of air movement.

EXPERIMENTAL SETUP:

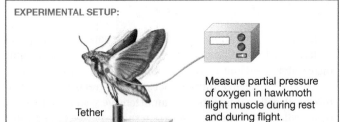

Tether

Measure partial pressure of oxygen in hawkmoth flight muscle during rest and during flight.

PREDICTION: Flying will increase ventilation of tracheal system, causing increase in P_{O_2} in flight muscle.

PREDICTION OF NULL HYPOTHESIS: Flying will not increase ventilation of tracheal system; P_{O_2} in flight muscle will decline steadily during flight.

RESULTS:

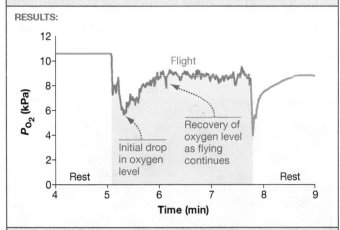

CONCLUSION: Muscular contractions may help ventilate the tracheal system in at least some insects.

Figure 42.8 Research Suggests the Insect Tracheal System Is Ventilated during Movement. On the graph's y-axis, kPa stands for kilopascal, a unit of pressure.

SOURCE: Komai, Y. 1998. Augmented respiration in a flying insect. *The Journal of Experimental Biology* 201: 2359–2366.

✔ **PROCESS OF SCIENCE** Why was it important for the researcher to repeat this experiment on several individuals?

Many insects are far too large to deliver gases to and from their tissues by simple diffusion alone. How do these large insects ventilate their tracheal system?

Consider a study on the sweet potato hawkmoth by Yutaka Komai. To investigate how the amount of O_2 delivered to the flight muscles changes during flight, Komai inserted a needle-like electrode into the muscles. The electrode was attached to an instrument that measured the partial pressure of oxygen, and the hawkmoth was tethered to a stand (Figure 42.8).

Komai recorded P_{O_2} as the insect rested and then stimulated the moth to fly by exposing it to wind. The "Results" section of Figure 42.8 shows how P_{O_2} changed during one such experiment. Note that the P_{O_2} level in the flight muscles dropped initially. This is not surprising because flight is an energetically demanding activity. As flying continued, however, the P_{O_2} level recovered until it was nearly as high as it was at rest. The same pattern was observed in several individuals.

To explain this observation, biologists propose that the tracheae are alternately compressed and dilated as the muscles around them contract and relax. The muscle contractions and relaxations produce pressure changes that alter the volume of the tracheal system (Figure 42.9). This key point is known as Boyle's law: If the volume occupied by a fixed amount of gas increases, the gas pressure decreases. If that volume declines, the gas pressure increases.

The volume of the tracheal system increases when muscles relax, causing pressure inside the system to go down and air from the atmosphere to rush in. What happens when muscles contract? The opposite—the volume of the tracheae decreases, pressure inside the system increases, and gas moves out of the tracheae into the atmosphere.

The action of the abdominal and flight muscles therefore stimulates air flow through the insect tracheal system, causing gases to move more quickly than they would by diffusion alone.

In large insects, the movement of gases is further promoted by larger tracheal diameters. These larger diameters increase another variable in Fick's law, the cross-sectional area for gas exchange. As evidence, researchers have shown that the diameter of the tracheae in large beetles is disproportionally larger than that in small beetles. Disproportionally large tracheae allow effective ventilation even in the largest beetles, which can weigh over 50 g and reach impressive lengths of over 15 cm (6 inches), the size of a submarine sandwich!

Why don't beetles get even larger than this? Researchers hypothesize that if they did, the diameter of their tracheae would have to be so large that there would not be enough space in their bodies for much else. The beetles would lack sufficient muscles and other tissues to support their huge bodies.

In the Paleozoic era about 300 million years ago (mya), however, giant insects flourished. While the largest dragonflies today have a wingspan of about 15 cm, during the Paleozoic they had wingspans as large as 70 cm (2.3 feet)! How can this be explained?

One major hypothesis posits that giant insects evolved during the Paleozoic era because the atmospheric oxygen concentration was much higher than it is today (Figure 42.10). Recall that according to Fick's law, the rate of diffusion of a gas from one

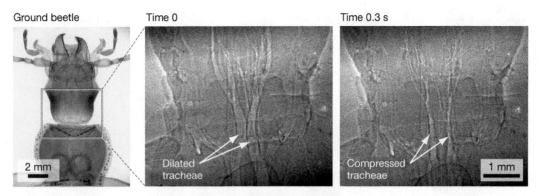

Ground beetle   Time 0   Time 0.3 s

2 mm

Dilated
tracheae

Compressed
tracheae

1 mm

Figure 42.9 Tracheae Are Dilated and Compressed during Ventilation. Muscle relaxation and contraction during flight or other activity alternately dilates and compresses tracheae, causing pressure changes that promote air flow in and out of the tracheae. Beetles and other insects can inhale and exhale one-half the volume of their trachea, similar to humans who exchange about half their lung volume during mild exercise.

point to another is affected by the difference in partial pressures of the gas at the two points. During the latter part of the Paleozoic, the value of $P_2 - P_1$ was increased in the equation shown in Figure 42.3. This may have increased the rate of diffusion of oxygen across the respiratory surfaces in insects, permitting adequate ventilation even in extremely large insects.

By the start of the Mesozoic era about 50 to 100 million years later, the atmospheric oxygen concentration had declined precipitously. Giant insects went extinct, likely in part because they could no longer supply their tissues with enough oxygen.

How Do Vertebrate Lungs Work?

In most terrestrial vertebrates, air enters the body through both the nose and mouth. A tube known as the **trachea** (not to be confused with the tracheae of insects) carries the inhaled air to narrower tubes called **bronchi** (singular: **bronchus**). The bronchi branch off into yet narrower tubes, the **bronchioles.** The organs

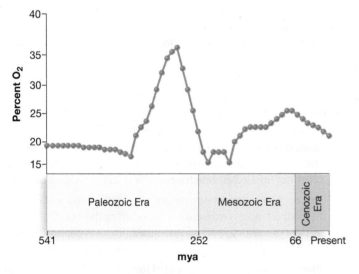

Figure 42.10 Atmospheric Oxygen Levels Peaked during the Paleozoic Era.

DATA: Berner, R. A. 1999. *Proceedings of the National Academy of Sciences* 96: 10955–10957.

of ventilation, the lungs, enclose the bronchioles and part of the bronchi (see **Figure 42.11a** on page 882).

Lungs are internal organs that are used for gas exchange. Terrestrial vertebrates—amphibians, reptiles (including birds), and mammals—have lungs, as do certain fishes and invertebrates.

Lung Structure and Ventilation Vary among Species The amount of lung surface area available for gas exchange varies a great deal among species. In frogs and other amphibians, the lung is a simple sac lined with blood vessels. The lungs of mammals, in contrast, are finely divided into tiny sacs called **alveoli** (singular: **alveolus;** **Figure 42.11b**).

Each human lung contains approximately 150 million alveoli, which give mammalian lungs about 40 times more surface area for gas exchange than an equivalent volume of frog lung tissue. As **Figure 42.11c** shows, an alveolus provides an interface between air and blood that consists of a thin aqueous film, a layer of epithelial cells, some extracellular matrix (ECM) material, and the wall of a capillary.

Apart from total surface area, the other major feature of lungs that varies among species is mode of ventilation. In the lungs of snails and spiders, air movement takes place primarily by diffusion. Vertebrates, in contrast, actively ventilate their lungs by pumping air via muscular contractions.

One mechanism for pumping air is **positive pressure ventilation,** used by frogs and some other amphibians. A frog lowers the floor of its throat, increasing the volume there and drawing in air from the atmosphere through the nasal passages and into the oral cavity. The animal then closes the nasal passages and contracts its throat muscles. These actions increase the air pressure in the oral cavity, forcing air into the lungs.

In effect, frogs push air into their lungs. In contrast, humans and other mammals pull air into their lungs. How does this **negative pressure ventilation** work?

Ventilation of the Human Lung The pressure inside the human chest cavity is about 5 mm Hg less than atmospheric pressure. This negative pressure surrounding the lung is just enough to keep the lung expanded. If a wound penetrates the chest wall and

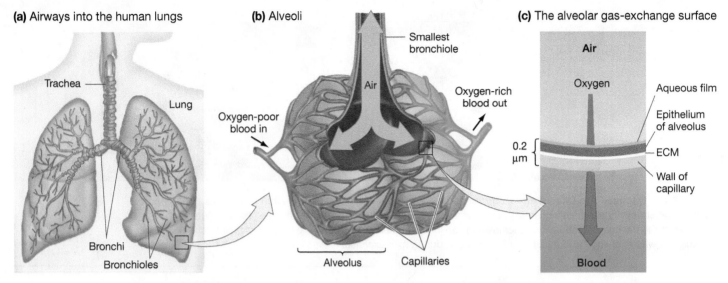

(a) Airways into the human lungs

Trachea

Lung

Bronchi

Bronchioles

(b) Alveoli

Smallest bronchiole

Air

Oxygen-poor blood in

Oxygen-rich blood out

Alveolus

Capillaries

(c) The alveolar gas-exchange surface

Air

Oxygen

Aqueous film

Epithelium of alveolus

0.2 µm

ECM

Wall of capillary

Blood

Figure 42.11 Lungs Offer a Thin Membrane with a Large Surface Area for Gas Exchange between Air and Blood. (a) The human respiratory tract branches repeatedly from the largest airway, the trachea, to the smallest, called bronchioles. The system of airways ends in clusters of tiny sacs called alveoli. **(b)** Alveoli are covered with capillary networks and are **(c)** the site of gas exchange.

the pressure differential between the chest cavity and the atmosphere disappears, the lung on the side of the injury will collapse like a deflated balloon.

Humans ventilate their lungs by changing the pressure within their chest cavity between about −5 mm Hg and −8 mm Hg relative to the atmosphere. As **Figure 42.12a** shows, inhalation is based on increasing the volume of the chest cavity and thus lowering the pressure. The change in volume is caused by a downward motion of the thin muscular sheet called the **diaphragm** and an expansion of the rib cage. As the pressure surrounding the lungs drops, air flows into the airways along a pressure gradient.

Exhalation, in contrast, is a passive process—the volume of the chest cavity decreases as the diaphragm and rib muscles relax. Because the lung is elastic, it returns automatically to its original shape if it is not stretched or compressed. During exercise, though, exhalation is an energy-demanding, active process.

The changes in pressure that occur during negative pressure ventilation are analogous to changing the pressure within a jar, as shown in **Figure 42.12b**.

About 450 mL of air moves into and out of the lungs in an average breath. Only about two-thirds of this volume actually participates in gas exchange, however, because 150 mL of the air occupies **dead space**—air passages that are not lined by a respiratory surface. The trachea and bronchi shown in Figure 42.11a, for example, represent dead space.

During exercise, the chest cavity undergoes larger changes in volume, allowing much more gas to be exchanged. When a person is breathing hard, over 2500 mL of air can move with each inhalation–exhalation cycle, but the 150 mL of dead space stays the same.

Ventilation of the Bird Lung Flight is one of the most energy-demanding activities performed by animals. Even so, some birds fly tens of thousands of kilometers during annual migrations.

Even more impressive, geese regularly fly at elevations of 5500 m (18,000 feet). How are birds able to extract enough oxygen from the atmosphere to support long flights and to fly at high elevations?

Figure 42.13 provides a diagram of ventilation in birds.

1. During inhalation, air flows through the trachea and enters two large air sacs posterior to the lungs.

2. During exhalation, air leaves the posterior air sacs and enters tiny, branching airways, called parabronchi, in the posterior portion of the lungs.

3. During the next inhalation, air moves into parabronchi in the anterior part of the lungs and on to a system of air sacs anterior to the lungs.

4. During the next exhalation, air moves out of the anterior sacs, through the trachea, and out to the atmosphere. Meanwhile, air from the second inhalation is now flowing through the lungs.

The key conclusion from these observations? Airflow through the avian lung is unidirectional, which relates to its efficiency.

Why is the avian respiratory system so efficient?

- Dead space is restricted to the short stretch of trachea between the mouth and the opening of the anterior air sacs. As a result, birds use inhaled air much more efficiently than mammals do.

- Gas exchange occurs during both inhalation and exhalation. In contrast, no gas exchange occurs during the exhalation half of the respiratory cycle in mammals. Bird ventilation resembles the continuous ventilation of fish gills in this respect.

- Blood circulates through the bird lung in capillaries that cross the parabronchi perpendicularly. This crosscurrent pattern is less efficient than the countercurrent circulation of fish gills but far more efficient than the weblike arrangement of capillaries that surround mammalian alveoli.

(a) Lungs expand and contract in response to changes in pressure inside the chest cavity.

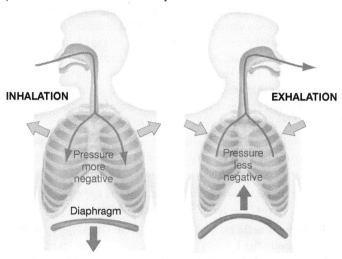

INHALATION   EXHALATION

Pressure more negative

Pressure less negative

Diaphragm

(b) Ventilatory forces can be modeled by a balloon in a jar.

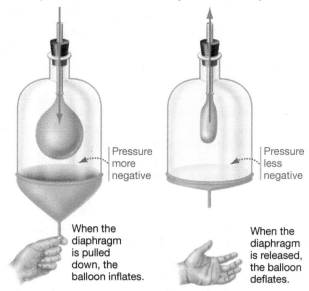

Pressure more negative

Pressure less negative

When the diaphragm is pulled down, the balloon inflates.

When the diaphragm is released, the balloon deflates.

Figure 42.12 Changes in the Volume of the Chest Cavity Drive Negative Pressure Ventilation. (a) Inhalation: When the diaphragm and rib muscles contract, the volume of the chest cavity increases, lowering pressure within the lungs. In response, air flows into the lungs. Exhalation: When the diaphragm and rib muscles relax, the volume of the chest cavity decreases, causing internal pressure to increase. In response, lung volume decreases—due to elasticity of the lungs—and air flows out. **(b)** A model of negative pressure ventilation.

Homeostatic Control of Ventilation

An animal is in trouble if its mechanisms of homeostasis fail to maintain blood oxygenation or to eliminate carbon dioxide. Adequate adenosine triphosphate (ATP) production depends on maintaining the partial pressures of oxygen and carbon dioxide within a narrow range, during both rest and vigorous exercise. How is ventilation controlled to achieve this critical homeostasis?

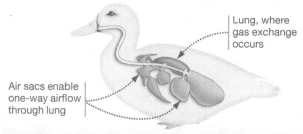

Lung, where gas exchange occurs

Air sacs enable one-way airflow through lung

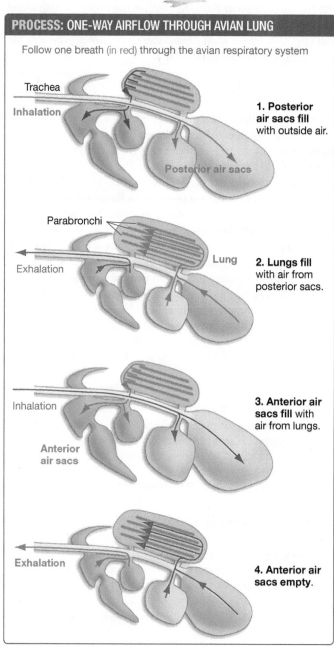

PROCESS: ONE-WAY AIRFLOW THROUGH AVIAN LUNG

Follow one breath (in red) through the avian respiratory system

Trachea

Inhalation

1. Posterior air sacs fill with outside air.

Posterior air sacs

Parabronchi

Exhalation

Lung

2. Lungs fill with air from posterior sacs.

Inhalation

3. Anterior air sacs fill with air from lungs.

Anterior air sacs

Exhalation

4. Anterior air sacs empty.

Figure 42.13 Air Flows in One Direction through the Bird Lung, Maximizing Gas Exchange.

When mammals are resting, the rate of breathing is established by the medullary respiratory center, an area at the base of the brain, just above the spinal cord. This center stimulates the rib and diaphragm muscles to contract about 12 to 14 times per minute in humans.

But during exercise, things change. Active muscle tissue takes up more oxygen from the blood. As a result, the partial pressure of oxygen (P_{O_2}) in blood drops. Those same muscles release larger quantities of carbon dioxide to the blood, raising its partial pressure (P_{CO_2}) in blood.

The rise in P_{CO_2} in blood—not the drop in blood P_{O_2}—is the major factor controlling breathing rate in mammals. When carbon dioxide reaches the brain, it rapidly diffuses from the blood into the cerebrospinal fluid that bathes the brain. In both blood and cerebrospinal fluid, CO_2 reacts with water to form carbonic acid (H_2CO_3), which then dissociates to release a hydrogen ion (H^+) and a bicarbonate ion (HCO_3^-):

$$CO_2 + H_2O \rightleftharpoons H_2CO_3 \rightleftharpoons H^+ + HCO_3^-$$

The result is a slight drop in the pH of blood and cerebrospinal fluid. The change in blood pH is sensed by specialized neurons in the brain and in the large arteries that travel from the heart into the neck and to the base of the brain.

Signals from these neurons and from pH detectors in the medullary respiratory center are responsible for sustained increases in breathing rate and depth during exercise. The rise in ventilation rate and depth increases the rate of oxygen delivery to the tissues and the rate at which carbon dioxide is eliminated from the body, restoring P_{O_2} and P_{CO_2} to their resting levels. This control system is so effective that it can maintain stable blood levels of oxygen and carbon dioxide even during intense exercise.

Now let's look more closely at how blood transports oxygen and carbon dioxide between the gas exchange surface and an animal's tissues.

CHECK YOUR UNDERSTANDING

If you understand that …

- The rate of diffusion of gases across a respiratory surface depends on the area of the surface, the thickness of the surface, and the difference in partial pressures of the gases across the surface.
- Most large-bodied animals exchange gases via gills, tracheae, or lungs.

✔ **You should be able to …**

1. Identify two features that are common to gills, tracheae, and lungs, as well as one trait that is unique to each.
2. Describe what happens to the P_{O_2}, P_{CO_2}, and pH of your blood when you hold your breath.

Answers are available in Appendix A.

42.4 How Are Oxygen and Carbon Dioxide Transported in Blood?

Blood is a connective tissue that consists of cells in a watery extracellular matrix. Besides carrying oxygen and carbon dioxide between cells and the lungs or gills, blood transports nutrients from the digestive tract to other tissues in the body, moves waste products to the kidney and liver for processing, conveys hormones from glands to target tissues, delivers immune system cells to sites of infection, and distributes heat throughout the body.

Given the wide variety of functions that blood serves, it is not surprising that it is a complex tissue. In an average human, 50–65 percent of the blood volume is composed of an extracellular matrix called **plasma.** The remainder of the volume comprises cells and cell fragments that are collectively called formed elements.

The formed elements in blood include platelets, several types of white blood cells, and red blood cells.

- **Platelets** are cell fragments that act to minimize blood loss from ruptured blood vessels. They do so by releasing material that helps form the blockages known as clots.
- **White blood cells** are part of the immune system. They fight infections (as Chapter 48 will explain in detail).
- **Red blood cells** transport oxygen from the lungs to tissues throughout the body. They also play a role in transporting carbon dioxide from tissues to the lungs. In humans, red blood cells make up 99.9 percent of the formed elements.

The human body synthesizes new red blood cells at the rate of 2.5 million per second to replace old red blood cells, which die at the same rate. New red blood cells last for about 120 days. Red blood cells, white blood cells, and platelets develop from stem cells located in the tissue inside bone (bone marrow).

Vertebrates other than mammals transport oxygen in red blood cells that retain their nuclei. But in mammals, red blood cells lose their nuclei as they mature, along with their mitochondria and most other organelles. Mammalian red blood cells are essentially bags filled with approximately 280 million copies of the oxygen-carrying molecule **hemoglobin.**

Structure and Function of Hemoglobin

Even though oxygen is not highly soluble in water, it is often found in high concentrations in blood. Blood has a high oxygen-carrying capacity because O_2 readily binds to the hemoglobin molecules in red blood cells.

The evolution of hemoglobin was a key event in the diversification of animals. By increasing the oxygen-carrying capacity of blood, hemoglobin made it possible for cellular respiration rates to increase. High rates of ATP production, in turn, support high rates of growth, movement, digestion, and other activities.

Hemoglobin is a tetramer, meaning that it consists of four polypeptide chains (**Figure 42.14**). Each of the four polypeptide chains binds to a nonprotein group called **heme** (represented by black circles in the figure). Each heme group, in turn, contains an iron ion (Fe^{2+}) that can bind to an oxygen molecule. As a result, each hemoglobin molecule can bind up to four oxygen molecules. In blood, 98.5 percent of the oxygen is bound to hemoglobin; only 1.5 percent is dissolved in plasma.

What Is Cooperative Binding?
Blood leaving the human lungs has a P_{O_2} of about 100 mm Hg, while at rest the muscles and other tissues have a P_{O_2} of about 40 mm Hg. This partial pressure difference creates a diffusion gradient that unloads O_2 from hemoglobin to the tissues.

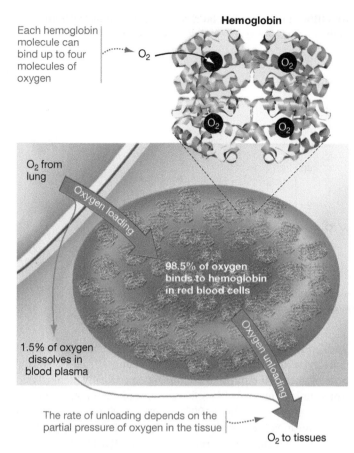

Each hemoglobin molecule can bind up to four molecules of oxygen

Hemoglobin

O_2

O_2

O_2

O_2

O_2 from lung

Oxygen loading

98.5% of oxygen binds to hemoglobin in red blood cells

1.5% of oxygen dissolves in blood plasma

Oxygen unloading

The rate of unloading depends on the partial pressure of oxygen in the tissue

O_2 to tissues

Figure 42.14 Hemoglobin Transports Oxygen to Tissues.

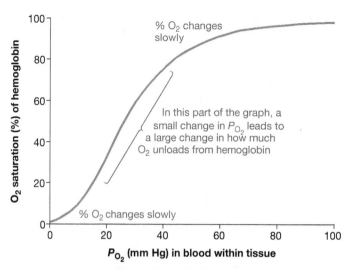

% O_2 changes slowly

In this part of the graph, a small change in P_{O_2} leads to a large change in how much O_2 unloads from hemoglobin

% O_2 changes slowly

O_2 saturation (%) of hemoglobin

P_{O_2} (mm Hg) in blood within tissue

Figure 42.15 The Oxygen–Hemoglobin Equilibrium Curve Is Sigmoidal. A sigmoidal curve has three distinct regions.

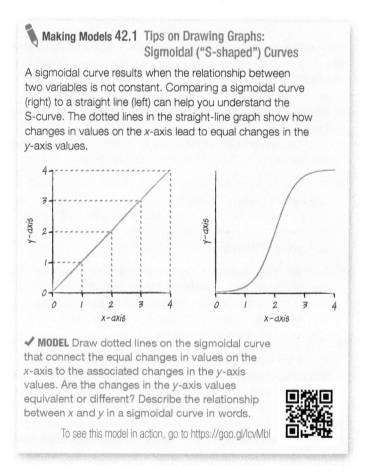

✏ **Making Models 42.1 Tips on Drawing Graphs: Sigmoidal ("S-shaped") Curves**

A sigmoidal curve results when the relationship between two variables is not constant. Comparing a sigmoidal curve (right) to a straight line (left) can help you understand the S-curve. The dotted lines in the straight-line graph show how changes in values on the x-axis lead to equal changes in the y-axis values.

✔ **MODEL** Draw dotted lines on the sigmoidal curve that connect the equal changes in values on the x-axis to the associated changes in the y-axis values. Are the changes in the y-axis values equivalent or different? Describe the relationship between x and y in a sigmoidal curve in words.

To see this model in action, go to https://goo.gl/IcvMbl

Researchers who studied the dynamics of O_2 unloading in tissues found the pattern shown in **Figure 42.15**. This graph plots the percentage of O_2 saturation of hemoglobin in red blood cells versus the P_{O_2} in the blood within tissues. If the saturation of hemoglobin approaches 100 percent, it means that every possible binding site in hemoglobin contains an oxygen molecule.

The graph in Figure 42.15 is called an **oxygen–hemoglobin equilibrium curve,** an oxygen dissociation curve, or a hemoglobin saturation curve. Note that the x-axis plots the partial pressure of oxygen in tissues. In effect, this represents "demand." Oxygen-depleted tissues, where demand for oxygen is high, are toward the left on the horizontal axis; oxygen-rich tissues are toward the right. The y-axis, in contrast, plots the percentage of hemoglobin molecules in blood that are saturated with oxygen—a measure of "supply," or how many oxygen molecules on average are bound to hemoglobin. Each 25 percent change in saturation corresponds to an average of one additional oxygen molecule bound per hemoglobin molecule or one oxygen molecule delivered to tissues.

The most remarkable feature of the oxygen–hemoglobin equilibrium curve is that it is sigmoidal, or S-shaped (see **Making Models 42.1** for tips on understanding S-shaped curves). The sigmoidal pattern occurs because the binding of each successive oxygen molecule to a subunit of the hemoglobin molecule causes a conformational change in the protein that makes the remaining subunits much more likely to bind oxygen.

This phenomenon is called **cooperative binding.** Conversely, the loss of a bound oxygen molecule changes hemoglobin's conformation in a way that makes the loss of additional oxygen molecules more likely.

(a) With cooperative binding, there is a large difference the amount of O_2 delivered to resting and exercising tissues.

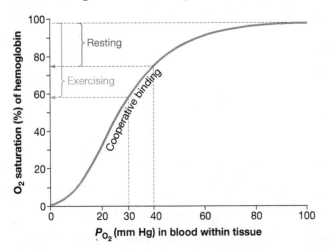

(b) Without cooperative binding, there is a smaller difference in the amount of O_2 delivered to resting and exercising tissues.

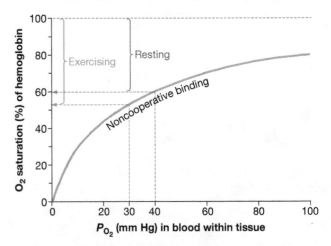

Figure 42.16 Cooperative Binding of O_2 by Hemoglobin Results in Greater O_2 Delivery than Noncooperative Binding. Hemoglobin is almost 100 percent saturated with oxygen until it arrives at tissues.

Why Is Cooperative Binding Important?

To understand why cooperative binding is important, use **Figure 42.16a** to figure out what happens to hemoglobin saturation when oxygen demand in tissues changes.

Let's begin with some basic observations. When blood arrives at tissues from the lungs, its hemoglobin saturation is close to 100 percent. At rest, tissue P_{O_2} is typically about 40 mm Hg. But during exercise, cells are using so much oxygen in cellular respiration that tissue P_{O_2} drops to about 30 mm Hg. Now,

- Put your finger on the x-axis at 40 mm Hg, trace the dashed line up until it hits the equilibrium curve, and check where this point is on the y-axis. The answer is about 75 percent. This means that when tissues are at rest, hemoglobin unloads 25 percent of its oxygen to the tissues.

- Now put your finger on the x-axis at 30 mm Hg, trace the dashed line up, and check hemoglobin saturation at this point on the curve. The answer is about 58 percent. This means that when tissues are exercising, hemoglobin unloads about 42 percent of its oxygen to tissues.

Here's the punch line: In response to a relatively small change in tissue P_{O_2}, there is a relatively large change in the percentage of saturation of hemoglobin. The large change occurs because the equilibrium curve is extremely steep in the range of P_{O_2} values commonly observed in tissues. The curve is steep because of cooperative binding. Thus, cooperative binding is important because it makes hemoglobin exquisitely sensitive to changes in the P_{O_2} of tissues.

If cooperative binding did not occur, all four subunits of hemoglobin would load or unload oxygen independently of each other. They would lose or gain oxygen in direct proportion to the partial pressure of oxygen in the blood. The curve would not be as steep in the center—meaning that there is only a small change in the percentage saturation of hemoglobin when tissue P_{O_2} changes.

Figure 42.16b shows how the oxygen–hemoglobin equilibrium curve might look if binding were noncooperative. As the dashed lines on this graph indicate, a relatively small change in oxygen delivery would occur when tissue P_{O_2} changes from its resting level of about 40 mm Hg to 30 mm Hg. Specifically, hemoglobin would unload about $100\% - 60\% = 40\%$ of its oxygen when tissues are at rest, and about $100\% - 53\% = 47\%$ of its oxygen during exercise. This difference—about 7 percent—is much less than the 17 percent change observed with cooperative binding.

How Do pH and Temperature Affect Oxygen Unloading from Hemoglobin?

Cooperative binding is only part of the story behind oxygen delivery. Hemoglobin—like other proteins—is sensitive to changes in pH and temperature.

As noted earlier, the partial pressure of CO_2 rises in active muscle tissue during exercise. The CO_2 produced by exercising muscle reacts with the water in blood to form carbonic acid, which dissociates and releases a hydrogen ion. As a result, the pH of the blood in exercising muscle drops.

Decreases in pH alter hemoglobin's conformation. These shape changes make hemoglobin more likely to unload O_2 at any given value of tissue P_{O_2}. As **Figure 42.17** shows, this phenomenon, known as the **Bohr shift,** causes the oxygen–hemoglobin equilibrium curve to shift to the right when pH declines.

The Bohr shift is important because it makes hemoglobin more likely to release oxygen during exercise or other conditions in which P_{CO_2} is high, pH is low, and tissues are under oxygen stress.

During exercise, active tissues also produce heat, causing their temperature to rise. Increasing temperature has the same result as decreasing pH: It shifts the oxygen–hemoglobin equilibrium curve to the right, representing a greater unloading of oxygen to tissues at any given P_{O_2}.

Oxygen Delivery by Hemoglobin Is Extremely Efficient

To appreciate cooperative binding and the Bohr shift in action, consider an experiment on how the oxygen transport system in rainbow trout responds to sustained exercise.

To begin, biologists had fish swim continuously against a current in a water tunnel. As the researchers increased the speed of

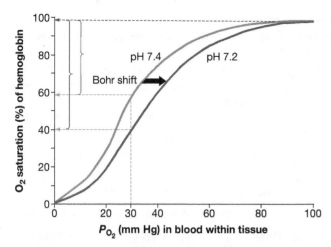

Figure 42.17 **The Bohr Shift Makes Hemoglobin More Likely to Release Oxygen to Tissues with Low pH.** As pH drops, oxygen becomes less likely to stay bound to hemoglobin at all values of tissue P_{O_2}. Exercising tissues have lower pH than resting tissues and so receive more oxygen from hemoglobin.

✔ **QUANTITATIVE** Estimate how much more oxygen is unloaded from hemoglobin at pH 7.2 than at pH 7.4 when the tissue has a P_{O_2} of 30 mm Hg.

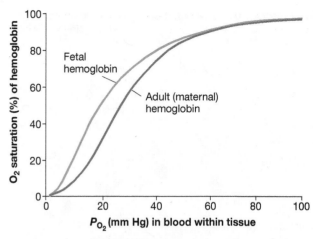

Figure 42.18 **Fetal Hemoglobin Binds Oxygen More Tightly than Maternal Hemoglobin.**

the current and thus the swimming speed of the fish, they periodically sampled the O_2 content of arterial and venous blood. Arterial blood is freshly oxygenated and moving from the gills to tissues; venous blood is returning to the heart from the tissues.

Not surprisingly, the biologists found that arterial O_2 levels remained fairly constant as swimming speed increased—meaning the gills continued to saturate hemoglobin with oxygen.

In contrast, the O_2 content of venous blood, which had undergone gas exchange with the tissues, dropped steadily as swimming speed increased. When the fish had reached their maximum sustainable speed, virtually all the oxygen that had been available in the blood had been extracted. The data show that in hard-working tissues, the combination of increased temperature, lower pH, and lower P_{O_2} caused hemoglobin to become almost completely deoxygenated.

Comparing Hemoglobins Hemoglobin molecules from different individuals or species may vary in ways that affect fitness—the ability to survive and produce viable offspring. As an example, consider the oxygen–hemoglobin equilibrium curves in **Figure 42.18**. The curve in dark red is from a pregnant woman; the curve in light red is from a fetus she is carrying.

The hemoglobin found in fetuses is encoded by different genes than adult hemoglobin and has a distinctive structure and function. The difference in structure causes the oxygen–hemoglobin equilibrium curve for fetal hemoglobin to be shifted to the left with respect to the curve for adult hemoglobin.

Recall that a rightward shift of the curve means that hemoglobin is more likely to release oxygen. The leftward shift in Figure 42.18 means that fetal hemoglobin is less likely to give up oxygen—it binds oxygen more tightly. Stated another way, fetal hemoglobin has a higher affinity for oxygen than adult hemoglobin does at every P_{O_2}.

This shift is crucial. In the placenta, hemoglobin in the mother's blood gets close to hemoglobin in the fetus's blood. Because fetal hemoglobin has a higher affinity for oxygen, there is a transfer of oxygen from the mother's blood to the fetus's blood. The difference in hemoglobin structure and function ensures an adequate supply of oxygen to the fetus as it develops.

CO_2 Transport and the Buffering of Blood pH

The carbon dioxide that is produced by cellular respiration in the tissues enters the blood, where it reacts with water to form carbonic acid, which dissociates into bicarbonate and hydrogen ions. Recall that the resulting drop in blood pH stimulates an increase in breathing rate. Rapid exhalation of CO_2 then counteracts the drop in blood pH.

Homeostasis with respect to blood pH is reinforced by a series of events that take place inside red blood cells. Biologists were able to work out what was happening when they discovered large amounts of the enzyme **carbonic anhydrase** in red blood cells.

The Role of Carbonic Anhydrase and Hemoglobin Recall that carbonic anhydrase catalyzes the formation of carbonic acid from carbon dioxide in water (see Chapter 41). Consequently, CO_2 that diffuses into red blood cells is quickly converted to bicarbonate ions and protons. The same reaction occurs in the plasma surrounding red blood cells, although much more slowly in the absence of the enzyme. Why is the carbonic anhydrase activity in red blood cells so important? The answer has two parts.

1. The protons produced by the enzyme-catalyzed reaction induce the Bohr shift, which makes hemoglobin more likely to release oxygen.

2. The partial pressure of CO_2 in blood drops when carbon dioxide is converted to soluble bicarbonate ions, maintaining a strong partial pressure gradient favoring the entry of CO_2 into red blood cells.

Thus, carbonic anhydrase activity promotes both O_2 delivery and CO_2 uptake in active tissues.

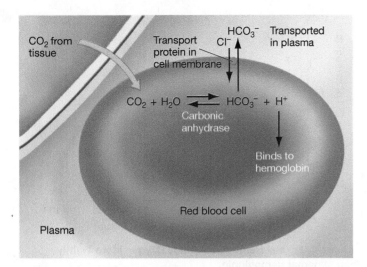

Figure 42.19 Carbonic Anhydrase Is Vital to CO$_2$ Transport in Blood. When CO$_2$ diffuses into red blood cells, carbonic anhydrase quickly converts it to carbonic acid, which dissociates into a bicarbonate ion (HCO$_3^-$) and a proton (H$^+$). This reaction maintains the partial pressure gradient favoring the entry of CO$_2$ into red blood cells. The protons produced by the reaction bind to deoxygenated hemoglobin. Most CO$_2$ in blood is transported to the lungs in the form of HCO$_3^-$.

✔ This diagram shows the sequence of events in tissues. After reading the rest of Section 42.4, explain what happens when the red blood cell in the diagram reaches the lungs.

Once bicarbonate ions form in the red blood cell, they are transported into the blood plasma. The outcome is that most CO$_2$ is transported in blood (specifically in plasma) in the form of the bicarbonate ions. In contrast, the protons produced by the reaction stay inside red blood cells (**Figure 42.19**).

What ultimately happens to these protons? When hemoglobin is carrying few oxygen molecules, it has a high affinity for protons. As a result, it takes up much of the H$^+$ that is produced by the dissociation of carbonic acid. The hemoglobin acts as a **buffer**—a compound that minimizes changes in pH.

CHECK YOUR UNDERSTANDING

If you understand that ...

• In blood, oxygen is bound to hemoglobin and transported inside red blood cells. Carbon dioxide is converted to bicarbonate ions and transported in plasma.
• Hemoglobin has several properties that make it an effective transport protein, including cooperative binding of oxygen, the Bohr shift response to low pH, and the ability to bind the protons that are generated when carbon dioxide is converted to bicarbonate ions.

✔ **You should be able to ...**

Predict how the oxygen–hemoglobin equilibrium curves of Tibetan people, whose ancestors have lived at high elevations for thousands of years, compare to curves of people whose ancestors have lived at sea level for many generations.

Answers are available in Appendix A.

What Happens When Blood Returns to the Lungs? When deoxygenated blood reaches the alveoli, its environment changes dramatically. In the lungs, a partial pressure gradient favors the diffusion of CO$_2$ from plasma and red blood cells to the atmosphere within the alveoli. As CO$_2$ diffuses from the blood into the alveoli, P_{CO_2} in the blood declines.

The drop in blood P_{CO_2} reverses the chemical reactions that occurred in tissues:

1. Hydrogen ions (protons) leave their binding sites on hemoglobin.

2. Protons react with bicarbonate to form CO$_2$.

3. CO$_2$ diffuses into the alveoli and is exhaled from the lungs.

In the meantime, hemoglobin has picked up O$_2$. Hemoglobin's affinity for oxygen is high in the alveoli because blood pH rises as P_{CO_2} declines.

When blood leaves the lungs, it has unloaded its carbon dioxide, and its hemoglobin is saturated with oxygen. The cycle begins anew.

42.5 Circulation

According to Fick's law, differences in the partial pressure of gases are only part of the story when it comes to understanding diffusion rates. Surface area—*A* in the equation featured in Figure 42.3—also plays a key role.

Animals without circulatory systems have various ways of maximizing the surface area available for diffusion of gases and other key solutes:

• Animals that are only a few millimeters in size, like rotifers and tardigrades, have a small enough volume that diffusion over their body surface is adequate to keep them alive.

• The flattened bodies of flatworms and tapeworms give these animals a high surface-area-to-volume ratio (see Chapter 39). In these species, too, molecules are exchanged with the environment directly across the outer body surface.

• Diffusion across the body wall also occurs in roundworms, where gas exchange is facilitated by muscular contractions in the body wall. Diffusion is enhanced as roundworms circulate fluids by sloshing them back and forth.

• Jellyfish and corals have a large, highly folded gastrovascular cavity that offers a large surface area for exchange of molecules with the environment.

In larger animals, however, the problem of providing a large enough surface area for diffusion is solved by a circulatory system. A circulatory system carries transport tissues called blood or hemolymph into close contact with every cell in the body. In this case, "close contact" is a distance of about 0.1 mm or less between the blood or hemolymph and cells within tissues. Diffusion is rapid at this scale.

To explore how circulatory systems work, let's start by distinguishing the two most basic types—open and closed. Open circulatory systems occur in most invertebrates, while all vertebrates have closed systems.

What Is an Open Circulatory System?

In an **open circulatory system,** a fluid connective tissue called hemolymph is actively pumped throughout the body in a limited system of vessels. The hemolymph is not confined exclusively to the vessels, however. Instead, hemolymph comes into direct contact with tissues. As a result, the molecules being exchanged between hemolymph and tissues do not have to diffuse across the wall of a vessel. Hemolymph transports wastes and nutrients and may also contain oxygen-carrying pigments, some cells, and clotting agents.

Figure 42.20 illustrates the open circulatory system in a spider. Note that a muscular organ called the **heart** pumps hemolymph into vessels that empty into open, fluid-filled spaces. When the heart relaxes and its internal pressure drops below the pressure in these spaces, hemolymph enters the heart via little holes in its surface. General body movements also help hemolymph to and from the heart.

Because it moves throughout the volume of the body, hemolymph is under relatively low pressure in open circulatory systems. As a result, hemolymph flow rates may also be low. These features make open circulatory systems most suitable for relatively sedentary organisms, which do not have high oxygen demands.

Insects, with their rapid movements and more active lifestyles, are an exception to this rule. In the open circulatory systems of insects, the limitations imposed by low hemolymph pressure are overcome by their tracheal respiratory system, which delivers oxygen directly to the tissues.

Another characteristic of open circulatory systems, because they lack discrete, continuous vessels, is that the flow of hemolymph cannot be directed toward tissues that have a high oxygen demand and CO_2 buildup. An open circulatory system moves hemolymph throughout an animal's body in much the same way that a ceiling fan moves air throughout a room in a house.

Crustaceans are an important exception to this rule, however. Even though their circulatory system is classified as open, these species have a network of small vessels that can preferentially send hemolymph to tissues with the highest oxygen demands.

What Is a Closed Circulatory System?

In a **closed circulatory system,** blood flows in a continuous circuit through a series of vessels in the body, under pressure generated by a heart. Because the blood is confined to vessels, a closed system can generate enough pressure to maintain a high flow rate.

In a closed circulatory system, blood flow can also be directed in a precise way in response to the tissues' needs. For example, blood can be shunted to leg muscles during exercise, to the intestines after a meal, or to regions of the brain engaged in particular mental tasks.

Which Lineages Have Closed Circulatory Systems? Closed circulatory systems are found in vertebrates and a few other lineages where individuals tend to be active. Earthworms and other annelids, for example, have a closed circulatory system and exchange gases with the environment across their thin, moist skin, which has a dense supply of capillaries. As a result, annelids are able to obtain and circulate enough oxygen to support intense muscular activity. Most live as active burrowers and hunters.

A similar situation occurs in squid, octopuses, and other cephalopods that hunt down prey. The closed circulatory system of these mollusks generates high rates of blood flow, which oxygenates their muscles well enough to support rapid movements and a predatory lifestyle.

Closed circulatory systems contain various types of blood vessels, each having a distinct structure and function. Let's review the major types of blood vessels and then consider how the vessels of a closed circulatory system interact with the lymphatic system.

Types of Blood Vessels An enormous amount of tubing is required to distribute blood within "diffusion distance" of every cell in the body. If all the blood vessels in a human body were laid end to end, they would stretch about 100,000 km (over 60,000 miles).

Blood vessels are classified as follows:

- **Arteries** are tough, thick-walled vessels that take blood away from the heart. Small arteries are called **arterioles.**

- **Capillaries** are vessels whose walls are just one cell thick, allowing exchange of gases and other molecules between blood and tissues. Networks of capillaries are called **capillary beds.**

- **Veins** are thin-walled vessels that return blood to the heart. Small veins are called **venules.**

The structure of arteries, capillaries, and veins correlates closely with their functions in a closed circulatory system. For

Figure 42.20 Spiders Have an Open Circulatory System. Red arrows show the direction of hemolymph flow.

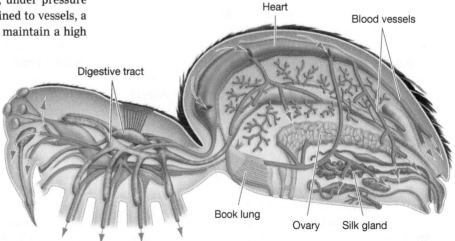

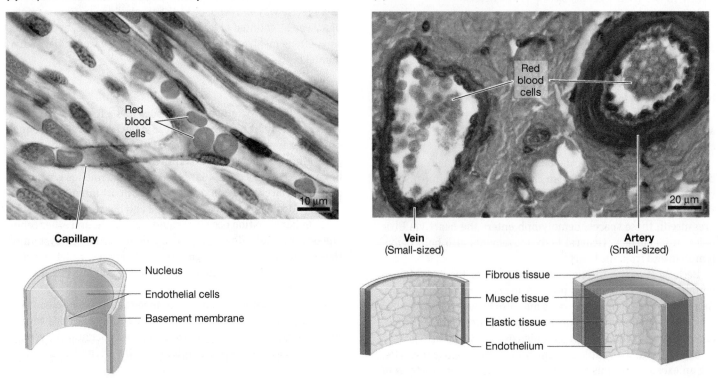

(a) Capillaries are small and extremely thin walled.

Red blood cells

10 μm

Capillary

Nucleus

Endothelial cells

Basement membrane

(b) Veins and arteries differ in structure.

Red blood cells

20 μm

Vein
(Small-sized)

Artery
(Small-sized)

Fibrous tissue

Muscle tissue

Elastic tissue

Endothelium

Figure 42.21 The Structures of Capillaries, Veins, and Arteries Reflect Their Different Functions.
Notice the differences in relative wall thickness and overall size.

example, the heart ejects blood into a large artery, usually called the **aorta.** All arteries have both muscle fibers and elastic fibers in their walls, but elastic fibers dominate the walls of the aorta. As a result, the aorta can expand when blood enters it under high pressure from the heart.

When a contraction of the heart ends, the diameter of the aorta returns to its resting state. This elastic response propels blood away from the heart and augments the force generated by the heart contraction. Similar types of secondary pumping action occur to some extent in other arteries as well. This feature helps maintain forward blood flow in the period between heart contractions.

The walls of arteries and arterioles have a thick layer composed of smooth muscle fibers. When the muscle fibers relax, the vessel diameter increases, resistance to flow is reduced, and blood flow increases in the tissues served by the vessel. But when these muscle fibers contract, the vessel diameter decreases, increasing resistance to flow and slowing the flow of blood in the vessel. In this way, blood flow to specific tissues can be carefully regulated by signals from the nervous system to muscle fibers in the vessels supplying those tissues.

Capillaries are the smallest blood vessels. Their walls are only one cell layer thick, and they are just wide enough to let red blood cells through one at a time (**Figure 42.21a**). The extreme thinness of capillaries and the dense network they form throughout the body make them suitable sites for the exchange of gases, nutrients, and wastes between blood and the other tissues.

In some organs, such as the liver, the walls of capillaries contain many small openings that further diminish the barrier to diffusion

between blood and the tissues. Despite their thinness, it is rare for capillaries to rupture because blood pressure drops dramatically as blood passes through arterioles on its way to capillary beds.

After blood from arteries and arterioles passes through capillaries, veins carry it back to the heart. Because blood is under relatively low pressure by the time it exits the tissues, veins have thinner walls and larger interior diameters than arteries do (**Figure 42.21b**).

Blood flow in veins is speeded by skeletal muscle activity in the extremities, which compresses large veins. Larger veins also contain one-way **valves,** which are thin flaps of tissue that prevent any backflow of blood.

All veins contain some muscle fibers, which contract in response to signals from the nervous system, decreasing the diameter and overall volume of the vessels. Blood pressure in a closed circulatory system is regulated, in part, by actively adjusting the volume of blood contained within the veins.

Exchange between Blood Plasma and Interstitial Fluid The relatively high operating pressure of closed circulatory systems, combined with the thinness of capillaries, produces a small but steady leakage of fluid from these blood vessels into the surrounding space. The area between cells is called interstitial space; the extracellular fluid that fills it is interstitial fluid (see Chapter 40). Blood cells are retained within capillaries, so interstitial fluid resembles plasma in its electrolyte composition.

Why does interstitial fluid build up? In 1896 Ernest Starling proposed that two forces were at work (**Figure 42.22**):

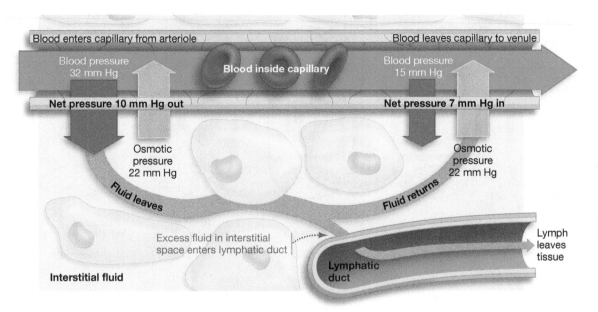

Figure 42.22 **Pressure Differences in Capillaries Create Interstitial Fluid and Lymph.** The balance of blood pressure and osmotic forces favors fluid loss from the beginning (inflow) end of capillaries and fluid recovery at the other (outflow) end. Fluid that is not recovered by the capillaries is transported out of the tissue as lymph, which eventually rejoins the blood circulation.

Labels in figure:
Blood enters capillary from arteriole
Blood pressure 32 mm Hg
Blood inside capillary
Blood leaves capillary to venule
Blood pressure 15 mm Hg
Net pressure 10 mm Hg out
Net pressure 7 mm Hg in
Osmotic pressure 22 mm Hg
Osmotic pressure 22 mm Hg
Fluid leaves
Fluid returns
Excess fluid in interstitial space enters lymphatic duct
Interstitial fluid
Lymphatic duct
Lymph leaves tissue

1. There is an outward-directed hydrostatic force in capillaries, created by the blood pressure generated by the heart. This force is analogous to the pressure that drives water through the wall of a leaky garden hose.

2. There is also an inward-directed osmotic force across the capillary walls, created by the higher concentration of solutes in the blood plasma than in the interstitial space.

Starling reasoned that at the end of the capillary nearest to an arteriole, the hydrostatic force (the blood pressure) would exceed the osmotic force. If so, then in that location fluid would move out of the capillary into the interstitial space. But because blood pressure drops as fluid passes through a long, thin tube, Starling proposed that at the venous end of the capillary, the inward-directed osmotic force would exceed the outward-directed hydrostatic force. Thus, the fluid that was lost at the arteriolar end of the capillary would be largely reclaimed at the venous end.

Note the adverb "largely," however—not all interstitial fluid is reabsorbed by capillaries. In Figure 42.22, not all of the fluid entering the interstitial space at the arteriolar end of the capillary bed has reentered the bloodstream at the venous end—there is a net buildup of interstitial fluid. What happens to this fluid?

The Role of the Lymphatic System Starling proposed that because interstitial fluid is continually added to the interstitial space, there must be a mechanism for draining the excess fluid. In fact, the fluid is collected in the **lymphatic system:** a collection of thin-walled, branching tubules called lymphatic vessels that permeate all tissues. Interstitial fluid that enters the lymphatic ducts is called **lymph.** Lymphatic vessels join with one another, like the tributaries of a river, to form larger vessels. The largest lymphatic vessels return excess interstitial fluid, in the form of lymph, to the major veins entering the heart.

The importance of the lymphatic system becomes evident when lymphatic vessels are damaged or blocked. For example, a disease called elephantiasis results when the lymphatic vessels in the extremities are blocked by parasitic worms that are transmitted from person to person via mosquito bites. The affected limbs swell dramatically because the lymph cannot be drained, and the skin thickens, cracks, and becomes very painful.

How Does the Heart Work?

In vertebrates, the heart contains at least two chambers: There is at least one thin-walled **atrium** (plural: **atria**), which receives blood, and at least one thick-walled **ventricle,** which generates the force required to propel blood out of the heart and through the circulatory system. Atria are separated from ventricles by atrioventricular (AV) valves.

The phylogenetic tree in **Figure 42.23** on page 892 shows the evolutionary relationships among some major vertebrate lineages and a simplified sketch of the heart and circulatory system for each lineage. Two points are particularly important to note:

1. The number of atria and ventricles in the heart increased as vertebrates diversified. Fish hearts have one atrium and one ventricle; amphibians, turtles, lizards, and snakes have two atria and one ventricle; crocodilians, birds, and mammals have two atria and two ventricles. It is common to refer to these as two-, three-, and four-chambered hearts, respectively.

2. In fishes, the circulatory system forms a single circuit—one loop services the gills and the body. In other lineages, there are separate circuits to the lungs and to the body.

Why Did Multichambered Hearts and Multiple Circulations Evolve? Lungs evolved in some lineages of fishes about 400 million years ago, facilitating air-breathing and supplementing the water-breathing capacity of gills. In these animals, exemplified by the extant lungfish, a **pulmonary artery** carries blood to the lungs, and **pulmonary veins** return freshly oxygenated blood to the heart. Circulation is partially split into two circuits—a **pulmonary circuit** that takes blood to the lungs and gills, and a **systemic circuit** that takes blood to the body.

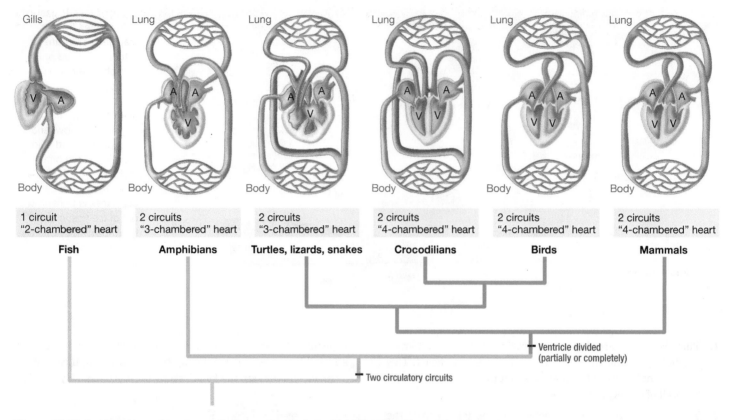

Figure 42.23 As Vertebrate Circulatory Systems Evolved, the Number of Atria and Ventricles Increased.
"A" denotes the atria—chambers that receive blood coming into the heart from the body and the gills or lungs.
"V" denotes the ventricles—chambers that pump blood out to the gills or lungs and the body.

Because fishes live in the neutrally buoyant environment of water, gravity has little effect on blood flow. Even though blood pressure drops as blood passes through the gills—due to the mechanical resistance to flow that occurs in the gills' capillary beds—blood pressure stays high enough to move blood throughout the body.

The situation changed dramatically in those lineages that evolved into terrestrial vertebrates, whose lungs became their primary gas exchange organ. Gravity has a much larger effect on circulation in land-dwelling vertebrates than in aquatic vertebrates, especially in the case of blood flow to elevated portions of the body. To overcome gravity in terrestrial environments, blood must be pumped at high pressure. However, the capillaries and alveoli of the lungs are too thin to withstand high pressures. The evolution of pulmonary and systemic circuits allowed the best of both worlds—a high-pressure systemic circuit that pumps blood throughout the body, and a low-pressure pulmonary circuit that sends blood to the lungs.

Paired atria evolved in the ancestors of modern amphibians, but the pulmonary and systemic circulations are only partially separated in amphibians, turtles, lizards, and snakes. In these lineages, blood from the right and left atria may mix in the common ventricle before being expelled from the heart to the lungs or to the body. Turtles, lizards, and snakes, however, have partially divided ventricles that can limit the amount of mixing that occurs there (see Figure 42.23).

In addition, turtles, lizards, and snakes have a bypass vessel running from the right side of the ventricle directly into the systemic circulation. This bypass vessel is also observed in the unusual four-chambered hearts of crocodilians. The bypass vessels have an important function: They shunt blood from the pulmonary to the systemic circulation when the animal is underwater and not breathing. The result is a great reduction in blood flow to the lungs at those times.

Unlike turtles, lizards, and snakes, birds and mammals have fully divided ventricles and lack a bypass vessel. This configuration completely separates the pulmonary and systemic circuits. Complete separation prevents mixing of blood in the ventricles, causing the highly oxygenated blood returning from the lungs to be ejected exclusively into the systemic circuit. As a result, tissues receive more oxygen and can produce more ATP to fuel energy-intensive processes such as aerobic exercise—flight, for example—and endothermy.

The Human Heart Your heart is located in your chest cavity, between your lungs, and is roughly the size of your fist. As **Figure 42.24** shows, the human circulatory system returns blood from the body to the right atrium of the heart. This blood is low in oxygen, and it arrives via two large veins called the inferior (lower) and superior (upper) **venae cavae** (singular: **vena cava**).

When the muscles that line the right atrium contract, they send deoxygenated blood to the right ventricle. The right ventricle, in turn, contracts and sends blood out to the lungs, via the pulmonary artery. In this way, the right ventricle powers the movement of blood through the pulmonary circulation.

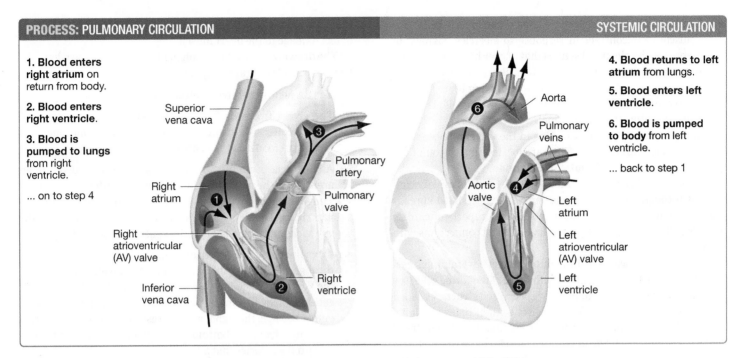

1. Blood enters right atrium on return from body.

2. Blood enters right ventricle.

3. Blood is pumped to lungs from right ventricle.

... on to step 4

Superior vena cava

Pulmonary artery

Pulmonary valve

Right atrium

Right atrioventricular (AV) valve

Inferior vena cava

Right ventricle

4. Blood returns to left atrium from lungs.

5. Blood enters left ventricle.

6. Blood is pumped to body from left ventricle.

... back to step 1

Aorta

Pulmonary veins

Aortic valve

Left atrium

Left atrioventricular (AV) valve

Left ventricle

Figure 42.24 The Human Heart Maintains Separation of Oxygenated and Deoxygenated Blood. Blood flows through the chambers in the sequence shown.

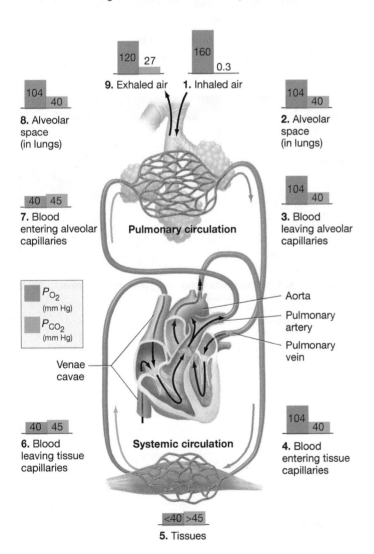

120   27   160   0.3

9. Exhaled air   **1.** Inhaled air

104   40

8. Alveolar space (in lungs)

104   40

2. Alveolar space (in lungs)

40   45

7. Blood entering alveolar capillaries

Pulmonary circulation

104   40

3. Blood leaving alveolar capillaries

P_{O_2} (mm Hg)

P_{CO_2} (mm Hg)

Aorta

Pulmonary artery

Pulmonary vein

Venae cavae

40   45

6. Blood leaving tissue capillaries

Systemic circulation

104   40

4. Blood entering tissue capillaries

<40   >45

5. Tissues

Blood flows from atrium to ventricle to artery in only one direction because one-way valves separate the heart's chambers from each other and from the adjacent arteries. As Figure 42.24 indicates, the valves are flaps, oriented to ensure a one-way flow of blood with little or no backflow. If heart valves are damaged or defective, the resulting backflow can be heard through a stethoscope. The backflow reduces the organ's efficiency and is called a **heart murmur.**

After blood circulates through the capillary beds in the lung's alveoli and becomes oxygenated, it returns to the heart through the pulmonary veins. The oxygenated blood enters the left atrium.

When the left atrium contracts, it pushes blood into the left ventricle. The walls of the left ventricle are so thick with muscle cells that their contraction sends oxygenated blood at high pressure through the aorta and into the arteries and capillaries that make up the systemic circulation.

Figure 42.25 summarizes the flow pattern through the human circulatory system and the partial pressures of O_2 and CO_2 at various points in the pulmonary and systemic circulations. Notice that blood vessels are called arteries or veins according to the direction of blood flow relative to the heart, not because of the oxygen content of the blood in them. So the pulmonary artery is called an artery because it takes blood away from the heart, even though this blood is low in oxygen.

Figure 42.25 Partial Pressures of O_2 and CO_2 Vary throughout the Human Circulatory System.

✔ Why are the partial pressures of oxygen and carbon dioxide in exhaled air intermediate in magnitude between the partial pressures in inhaled and alveolar air?

Electrical Activation of the Heart Like other muscle cells, cardiac muscle cells contract in response to electrical signals. In invertebrates, the electrical signals that trigger heart contraction come directly from the nervous system. But a vertebrate heart will continue to beat even if all nerves supplying it are severed. Why? In vertebrates, a group of cells in the heart itself is responsible for generating the initial signal.

The cells that initiate contraction in the vertebrate heart are known as **pacemaker cells.** They are located in a region of the right atrium called the **sinoatrial (SA) node.**

The electrical signal generated in the SA node is rapidly conducted throughout the right and left atria. The signal spreads quickly from cell to cell thanks to a striking property of cardiac muscle cells: They form physical and electrical connections with each other.

All cardiac muscle cells branch to contact several other cardiac muscle cells, join end to end with these neighboring cells (see Figure 39.5), and connect to them by specialized structures called **intercalated discs.** Because these discs contain many gap junctions (cell-to-cell connections described in Chapter 11), electrical signals pass directly from one cardiac muscle cell to the next.

The electrical activation of the heart is reflected in the orange line at the bottom of Figure 42.26. This line is called an **electrocardiogram,** or **EKG**—a recording of the electrical events that occur as the heart beats. An EKG recording is generated by amplifying the overall electrical signal conducted from the heart to the chest wall through the tissues of the body. By inspecting an EKG, physicians can diagnose disturbances of heart rhythm and detect damage to the heart muscle.

The drawings above the graph in Figure 42.26 show where the key electrical events are happening.

1. The SA node generates an electrical signal.

2. The signal from the SA node quickly propagates to atrial muscle cells. As a result, the atria contract simultaneously and eject blood into the ventricles.

3. As the atria begin to contract, the signal is conducted to an area of the heart called the **atrioventricular (AV) node.** The AV node delays the signal slightly before passing it to the ventricles. The delay allows the atria to completely fill the ventricles with blood before the ventricles contract.

4. After the delay, the electrical impulse is rapidly transmitted through specialized fibers in the muscular wall that separates the ventricles. The impulse spreads through both ventricles, causing them to contract as the atria relax. The ventricles empty because the signal and the resulting muscular contraction move from the bottom up to the top of each ventricle—toward the arteries that allow blood to exit.

5. The final electrical event occurs as the ventricles relax and their cells recover—restoring their electrical state before contraction.

✔ If you understand these concepts, you should be able to predict how the amount of blood ejected from the ventricles would change if there were no delay at the AV node.

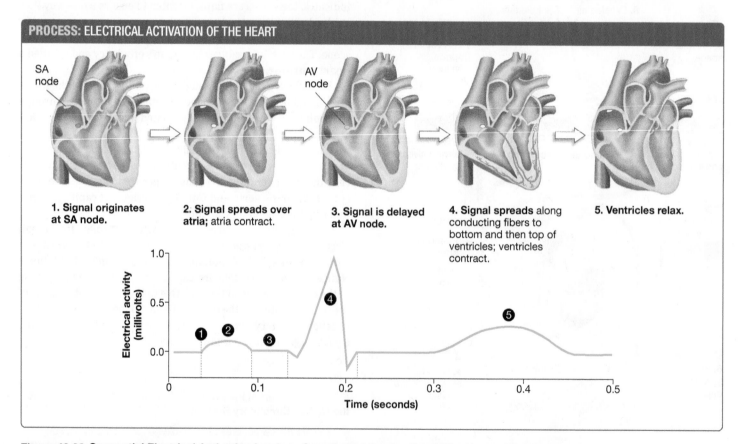

PROCESS: ELECTRICAL ACTIVATION OF THE HEART

SA node

AV node

1. Signal originates at SA node.

2. Signal spreads over atria; atria contract.

3. Signal is delayed at AV node.

4. Signal spreads along conducting fibers to bottom and then top of ventricles; ventricles contract.

5. Ventricles relax.

Figure 42.26 **Sequential Electrical Activation Leads to Coordinated Contraction of the Human Heart.** The rate and strength of contractions control the pressure in the heart chambers and arteries.

The SA node and the muscle cells of the heart receive input from the nervous system and from chemical messengers carried in the blood. These inputs are important for regulating both the heart rate and the strength of ventricular contraction. In this way, the rate of blood flow through the circulatory system varies in response to electrical signals and hormones. During the "fight-or-flight" response (discussed in Chapter 46), for example, a chemical signal called epinephrine causes both heart rate and contraction strength to increase—sending blood more quickly through the body in preparation for rapid movement.

The Cardiac Cycle The electrical signals originating from the SA node ensure that the atria contract simultaneously, and the delay at the AV node ensures that the atria are relaxed by the time the ventricles contract. The contraction phases of the atria and the ventricles, called **systole,** are therefore closely coordinated with their relaxation phases, or **diastole.** This sequence of contraction and relaxation is called the **cardiac cycle** and consists of one diastole and one systole for both atria and ventricles.

Ventricular contraction (ventricular systole) leads to a rapid increase in pressure within both ventricles, as recorded in the dark purple line in **Figure 42.27.** Blood is ejected into the pulmonary artery and the aorta when ventricular pressure exceeds the pressure within each respective artery. Blood pressure measured

in the systemic arterial circulation at the peak of ventricular ejection into the aorta is called the **systolic blood pressure.** Blood pressure measured just before ventricular ejection is called the **diastolic blood pressure.**

Clinicians report blood pressure measurements in fractional notation, where systolic pressure is the numerator and diastolic pressure is the denominator. People with blood pressures consistently higher than 140/90 mm Hg have high blood pressure, or **hypertension.**

Hypertension is a serious disease because it can lead to a variety of defects in the heart and circulatory system. Abnormally high blood pressure puts mechanical stress on arteries. If the walls of an artery fail, the individual may experience heart attack, stroke, kidney failure, or burst or damaged vessels.

Patterns in Blood Pressure and Blood Flow

As blood moves through capillaries, blood pressure drops dramatically—as the top graph in **Figure 42.28** indicates. This happens because, as arteries branch, rebranch, and eventually form networks of capillaries, the total cross-sectional area of blood vessels in the circulatory system increases, as shown on the bottom graph. As the total cross-sectional area of the vessels increases, the blood encounters less resistance, resulting in a drop in pressure.

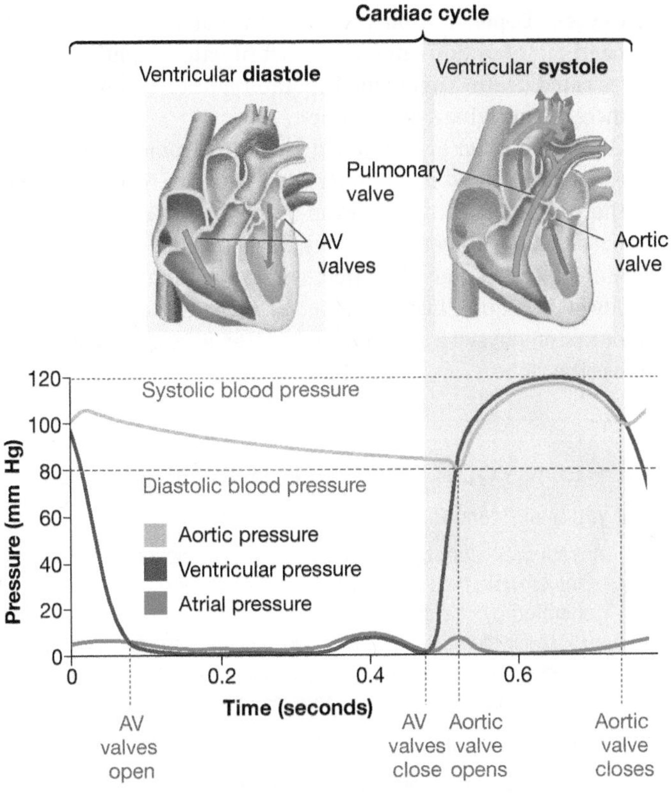

Figure 42.27 Blood Pressure Changes during the Cardiac Cycle. These data show the pressures in the left atrium, left ventricle, and aorta in the course of a cardiac cycle. In this example, the blood pressure measured in the upper arm would be 120/80 mm Hg. Right ventricle and pulmonary artery pressures would produce a similar pattern, but the blood pressure in the pulmonary artery would be much lower—closer to 25/8 mm Hg.

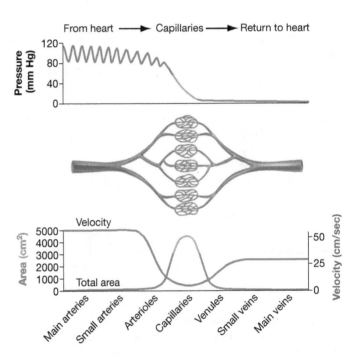

Figure 42.28 Blood Pressure Drops Dramatically in the Circulatory System. The top graph shows how blood pressure changes as blood leaves the heart and travels through arteries, capillaries, and veins, as in the branching pattern of the middle diagram. In arteries near the heart, each heartbeat causes fluctuations in blood pressure. These pressure pulses disappear in the capillaries, so blood flows there at a steady speed. The bottom graph plots the total area of blood vessels shown in the diagram, as well as the velocity of blood flow through the vessels.

As the line labeled "Velocity" in the bottom graph in Figure 42.28 indicates, the velocity of blood flow also decreases significantly in capillary beds relative to arteries and veins, because the same amount of fluid is passing through a much larger area. Recall that the slow flow of blood through capillaries is important: It provides sufficient time for gases, nutrients, and wastes to diffuse between tissues and blood.

Why Is Regulation of Blood Pressure and Blood Flow Important?

The general patterns of blood pressure and blood flow diagrammed in Figure 42.28 don't tell the entire story, however. Blood movement is carefully regulated at an array of points throughout the circulatory system.

Recall that the walls of arterioles are comprised partially of smooth muscle. Contraction or relaxation of this muscle can restrict or allow blood flow to specific tissues. For example, arterioles in the skin dilate during exercise, diverting blood flow to the skin to eliminate excess heat. This accounts for the flushed facial appearance induced by vigorous exercise.

As another example of how blood pressure and blood flow are regulated, consider what happens if you sit long enough for blood to pool in your legs, under the influence of gravity. If you stand up rapidly, your blood pressure can drop enough to reduce blood flow to your brain and cause dizziness or even a blackout. More serious drops in blood pressure, due to severe dehydration or blood loss, can be fatal. Fortunately, decreases in blood pressure elicit a powerful homeostatic response.

Homeostatic Control of Blood Pressure

Recall that all homeostatic responses involve **(1)** sensors that detect the change in condition, **(2)** an integrator that processes information about the change, and **(3)** effectors that diminish the impact of the change (see Chapter 39).

Specialized pressure-sensing receptors called **baroreceptors** detect changes in blood pressure. Baroreceptors are found in the walls of the heart and some of the major arteries. When baroreceptors transmit nerve signals to the brain (the integrator) indicating a serious fall in blood pressure, a rapid, three-component effector response ensues:

1. Cardiac output—the volume of blood leaving each ventricle per minute—increases. This is due to an increase in heart rate and an increase in stroke volume, which is the amount of blood ejected from each ventricle during each cardiac cycle. (Cardiac output = heart rate × stroke volume.)

2. Arterioles serving the capillaries of certain tissues constrict to divert blood to more critical organs. (This occurs in tissues like the skin and intestines, which can endure short-term restrictions in their blood supply without damage.)

3. Veins constrict, decreasing their overall volume. Because more than half of the blood in the circulatory system is contained within the veins, constriction of these vessels shifts blood volume toward the heart and arteries to maintain blood pressure and flow to vital organs.

This coordinated response is mediated both by a portion of the nervous system called the sympathetic nervous system (see Chapter 43) and by hormones produced by the adrenal glands (see Chapter 46). Sympathetic nerves and the hormones involved in regulating blood pressure deliver their messages directly to **(1)** the SA node to increase heart rate, **(2)** the ventricles of the heart to increase stroke volume, and **(3)** the muscular walls of the arteries and veins to modify their total volume.

Cardiovascular Disease

A healthy circulatory system is obviously critical to your overall well-being. Indeed, **cardiovascular disease,** which is a group of ailments collectively affecting the heart and blood vessels, is the number one cause of death in humans worldwide.

Many factors contribute to cardiovascular disease, including age, tobacco use, poor diet, obesity, inactivity, and genetics. As people age, their blood vessels harden and lose elasticity—a condition called **arteriosclerosis.**

High-fat diets and lack of physical activity can compound the problem by leading to the deposit of fatty plaques on the walls of blood vessels, effectively reducing their diameter. Nicotine in tobacco also constricts blood vessels. The loss of elasticity and the reduced diameter of the vessels combine to cause increased blood pressure, which can weaken the walls of arteries.

If the arteries that deliver blood to the heart muscle become completely blocked, a **myocardial infarction,** or heart attack, can occur. Contrary to popular thought, this condition is not defined as stopping of the heartbeat. In a myocardial infarction, a portion of heart tissue dies within minutes when it is deprived of oxygen. Depending on the location and extent of damage, myocardial infarction can affect heart function slightly, or it can cause rapid death. Timely medical intervention can improve the chances of surviving a heart attack.

Over 17 million people worldwide died from cardiovascular disease in 2013, and the number is projected to reach 23 million by the year 2030. It may get even higher because the incidences of obesity and diabetes mellitus have reached epidemic proportions (see Chapter 41). Effectively combating cardiovascular disease will require improved diet, reduced tobacco use, greater amounts of physical activity, and better access to health care across the globe.

CHECK YOUR UNDERSTANDING

If you understand that …

- Animal circulatory systems may be open or closed, but both types of systems circulate blood or hemolymph via pressure generated by one or more hearts.
- In closed systems, regulated changes in the diameter of blood vessels can direct blood to specific regions, and overall blood pressure is carefully regulated through changes in cardiac output.

✔ **You should be able to …**

1. Make a labeled diagram showing how blood circulates through the mammalian heart.
2. **CAUTION** In a medical drama on television, a patient's heart stops beating, and a doctor says the patient is in cardiac arrest. Is this the same thing as a myocardial infarction? Why or why not?

Answers are available in Appendix A.

42.1 The Respiratory and Circulatory Systems

- Animal gas exchange involves ventilation, exchange of gases between the environment and the blood, and exchange of gases between blood and tissues.

- Animal circulation involves transportation of gases, nutrients, wastes, and other substances throughout the body.

42.2 Air and Water as Respiratory Media

- As media for exchanging oxygen and carbon dioxide, air and water are dramatically different.

- Compared with water, air contains much more oxygen and is much less dense and viscous. As a result, terrestrial animals have to process a much smaller volume of air to extract the same amount of O_2, and the amount of work required to do so is less than in aquatic animals.

- Both terrestrial and aquatic animals pay a price for exchanging gases: Land-dwellers lose water to evaporation; freshwater animals lose ions and gain excess water; marine animals gain ions and lose water.

42.3 Organs of Gas Exchange

- The structure of gills, tracheae, lungs, and other gas exchange organs minimizes the cost of ventilation while maximizing the diffusion rates of O_2 and CO_2.

- Consistent with predictions made by Fick's law of diffusion, respiratory epithelia tend to be extremely thin and to be folded to increase surface area.

- In fish gills, countercurrent exchange ensures that the differences in O_2 and CO_2 partial pressures between water and blood are favorable for gas exchange over the entire length of the ventilatory surface.

- Insect tracheae carry air directly to and from tissues.

- In bird lungs, structural adaptations lead to a high ratio of useful ventilatory space to dead space.

- Breathing rate is regulated to keep the carbon dioxide content of the blood stable during rest and exercise.

42.4 How Are Oxygen and Carbon Dioxide Transported in Blood?

- The tendency of hemoglobin to give up oxygen varies as a function of the P_{O_2} in surrounding tissue in a sigmoidal fashion. As a result, a relatively small change in tissue P_{O_2} causes a large change in the amount of oxygen released from hemoglobin.

- Oxygen binds less tightly to hemoglobin when pH is low. Because CO_2 reacts with water to form carbonic acid, the existence of high CO_2 partial pressures in exercising muscle tissues lowers their pH and makes oxygen less likely to stay bound to hemoglobin and more likely to be unloaded into tissues.

- The CO_2 that diffuses into red blood cells from tissues is rapidly converted to carbonic acid by the enzyme carbonic anhydrase. The protons that are released as carbonic acid dissociates bind to deoxygenated hemoglobin. In this way, hemoglobin acts as a buffer that takes protons out of solution and prevents large fluctuations in blood pH.

42.5 Circulation

- In many animals, blood or hemolymph moves through the body via a circulatory system consisting of a pump (heart) and vessels.

- In open circulatory systems, overall pressure is low and tissues are bathed directly in hemolymph.

- In closed circulatory systems, blood is contained in vessels that form a continuous circuit. Containment of blood allows higher pressures and flow rates, as well as the ability to direct blood flow accurately to tissues that need it the most.

- In organisms with a closed circulatory system, a lymphatic system collects excess fluid that leaks from the capillaries and returns it to the circulation.

- In amphibians and some reptiles, blood from the pulmonary and systemic circuits may be mixed in the single ventricle.

- In mammals and birds, a four-chambered heart pumps blood into two circuits, which separately serve the lungs and the rest of the body. Crocodilians have a similar heart with a bypass vessel that can shunt blood from the pulmonary to the systemic circuit.

- In vertebrates, the cardiac cycle is controlled by electrical signals that originate in the heart itself.

- Heart rate, cardiac output, and constriction of both arterioles and veins are regulated by chemical signals and by electrical signals from the brain.

- Cardiovascular disease is the leading cause of death in humans.

Answers are available in Appendix A

✓ TEST YOUR KNOWLEDGE

1. In insects, what is the adaptive significance of spiracles?
   a. They dilate and constrict during flight or other types of movement, functioning as a "breathing" mechanism.
   b. They open into the body cavity, allowing direct contact between hemolymph and tissues.
   c. They are thin and highly branched, offering a large surface area for gas exchange.
   d. They close off tracheae to minimize water loss.

2. Which of the following is *not* an advantage of breathing air over breathing water?
   a. Air is less dense than water, so it takes less energy to move during ventilation.
   b. Air is less viscous than water, so it takes less energy to move during ventilation.
   c. The oxygen content of air is greater than that of an equal volume of water.
   d. Air breathing leads to high evaporation rates from the respiratory surface.

3. Which of the following promotes oxygen release from hemoglobin?
   a. a decrease in temperature
   b. a decrease in CO_2 levels
   c. a decrease in pH
   d. a decrease in carbonic anhydrase activity

4. Describe the disadvantages of an open circulatory system relative to a closed circulatory system.

✓ TEST YOUR UNDERSTANDING

5. Why is ventilation in birds considered much more efficient than ventilation in humans and other mammals?

6. Explain how each parameter in Fick's law of diffusion is reflected in the structure of the mammalian lung.

7. Carp are fishes that thrive in stagnant-water habitats with low oxygen partial pressures. Compared with the hemoglobin of many other fish species, carp hemoglobin has an extremely high affinity for O_2. Is this trait adaptive? Explain your answer.

8. Frog lungs have a lower surface area for gas exchange than mammalian lungs. How do frogs compensate for this difference?
   a. Frog tissue absorbs more oxygen from the blood than mammalian tissue does.
   b. Frogs breathe more quickly than mammals.
   c. Frogs also obtain oxygen via diffusion across the skin.
   d. Frog lung tissue has a greater density of capillary beds than mammalian lung tissue.

✓ TEST YOUR PROBLEM-SOLVING SKILLS

9. Predict how Antarctic icefish can transport enough oxygen in their blood to meet their needs even though they lack hemoglobin.

10. Why did separate systemic and pulmonary circulations evolve in species that have the high-pressure circulatory system required for rapid movement of blood?

✓ PUT IT ALL TOGETHER: Case Study

How do the cardiovascular systems of athletes adjust to strenuous exercise?

During exercise, the cardiovascular system must supply muscles with large amounts of oxygen and fuel and get rid of a lot of wastes. How do the cardiovascular systems of athletes respond to prolonged exercise?

11. During athletic training, the oxygen–hemoglobin dissociation curve
    a. shifts to the right, unloading more oxygen to tissues.
    b. shifts to the right, unloading less oxygen to tissues.
    c. shifts to the left, unloading more oxygen to tissues.
    d. shifts to the left, unloading less oxygen to tissues.

12. CAUTION When athletes exercise, what is the primary physiological variable responsible for their sustained increase in ventilation rate?
    a. decreased blood P_{O_2}
    b. increased blood P_{CO_2}
    c. increased blood pH
    d. increased body temperature

13. QUANTITATIVE Researchers used echocardiography, a sonogram of the heart, to estimate the mass of the left ventricle in current athletes, non-athletes, and ex-athletes. The data are graphed below (*** means $P < 0.001$, and the P value comparing non-athletes and ex-athletes is > 0.05; see BioSkills 3). What conclusion can be drawn from the graph?

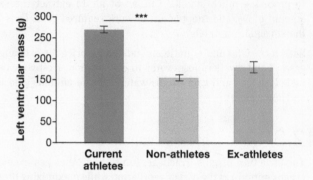

Source: Shapiro, L. M. 1984. *British Heart Journal* 52: 130–135.

14. Explain the advantage of the observed difference between current athletes and non-athletes in the graph above.

15. Researchers have also observed that athletes and non-athletes have the same mean resting cardiac output, even though athletes have a far lower resting heart rate. How is this possible?

16. SOCIETY Athletes are not the only people with enlarged hearts. Many patients with cardiovascular disease also have enlarged hearts. Suggest a cause of this enlargement.

MasteringBiology®

Students Go to MasteringBiology for assignments, the eText, and the Study Area with animations, practice tests, and activities.
Professors Go to MasteringBiology for automatically graded tutorials and questions that you can assign to your students, plus Instructor Resources.

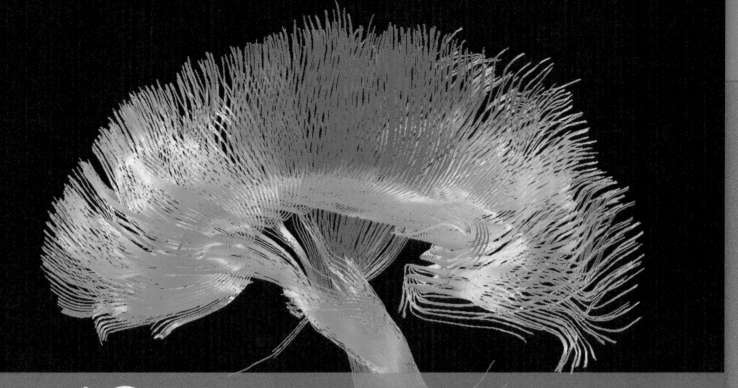

43 Animal Nervous Systems

Diffusion spectrum imaging reveals the trajectory of neural pathways in the brain. Such advances in brain imaging are allowing neurobiologists to study how neurons in the brain communicate with one another.

In this chapter you will learn how

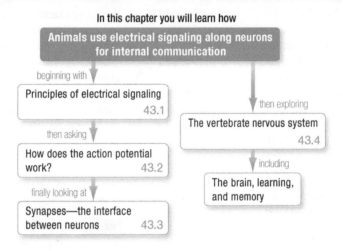

Animals use electrical signaling along neurons for internal communication

beginning with

Principles of electrical signaling
43.1

then asking

How does the action potential work? 43.2

finally looking at

Synapses—the interface between neurons 43.3

then exploring

The vertebrate nervous system
43.4

including

The brain, learning, and memory

This chapter is part of the Big Picture. See how on pages 816–817.

ost students and professional biologists are attracted to the study of neurobiology because they want to understand the human brain as well as higher-order processes like consciousness, intelligence, emotion, learning, and memory. However, the human brain is very challenging to study as a whole structure. It contains billions of cells, interconnected through a myriad of neural pathways, only a tiny fraction of which are highlighted in the photo above.

Faced with this challenge, early researchers in neurobiology started simple: They focused on the function of individual nerve cells, or **neurons,** the cells mainly responsible for the working of the brain and the rest of the nervous system. Neurons conduct information in the form of electrical signals from point to point in the body at speeds of up to 120 m/sec (270 mph). Thus, electrical signaling is a crucial aspect of information processing—one of the five attributes of life (introduced in Chapter 1).

Initial research on the electrical properties of single neurons laid a broad foundation for more recent studies of how the human brain works. This chapter proceeds in the same way. Let's begin by focusing on the neurons themselves and how they use electrical signaling to communicate with each other. In the last section of the chapter we'll consider how the brain is organized and how phenomena like memory work.

43.1 Principles of Electrical Signaling

The evolution of neurons was a key event in the diversification of animals, along with the evolution of muscles (see Chapter 30). All animals except sponges have neurons and muscle cells. Neurons transmit electrical signals; muscles can respond to signals from neurons by contracting.

Neurons are organized into two basic types of nervous systems:

1. The diffuse arrangement of cells called a **nerve net,** found in cnidarians (jellyfish, hydra, anemones) and ctenophores (comb jellies).

2. A **central nervous system (CNS)** that includes large numbers of neurons aggregated into clusters called ganglia.

Most animals with a CNS have a large cerebral ganglion, or brain, located in their anterior end. You also might recall that this phenomenon—the evolution of a bilaterally symmetric body with structures for information gathering and processing located at the head end—is known as cephalization (see Chapter 30).

Cephalization made most animals into efficient eating and moving machines: They face the environment in one direction, and sensory appendages take in information and send it to a nearby brain for processing. After integrating information from an array of sensory cells, the brain sends electrical signals to muscles and other organs that respond to the sensory stimuli.

Types of Neurons

The sensory cells that are responsible for gathering information respond to light, sound, touch, or other stimuli. Sensory cells in an animal's skin, eyes, ears, mouth, and nose transmit information about the environment. Sensory cells inside the body monitor conditions that are important in homeostasis, such as blood pH and temperature. In this way, sensory cells monitor conditions both outside and inside the body. Many sensory cells are **sensory neurons** (Figure 43.1), which carry information to the CNS. In vertebrates, the CNS consists of the brain and spinal cord.

One function of the CNS is to integrate information from sensory neurons. Cells in the CNS called **interneurons** (literally, "between-neurons"), which pass signals from one neuron to another, perform this integration.

Some interneurons make connections to **motor neurons,** which are nerve cells that send signals to effector cells in glands or muscles. Recall that effectors are structures that bring about a physiological change in an organism (see Chapter 39). Motor neurons and sensory neurons are bundled together into long strands of nervous tissue called **nerves.**

All neurons and other components of the nervous system that are outside the CNS are considered part of the **peripheral nervous system,** or **PNS.** Section 43.4 describes the structure and function of the vertebrate PNS.

Typically, sensory information is transmitted via the PNS to the CNS, where it is processed. Then a response is transmitted back through the PNS to appropriate parts of the body via motor neurons. For example, if you prick your finger on a rose thorn, pain sensors in your finger relay information to your spinal cord, which then causes you to react by withdrawing your hand to avoid further injury. This reaction is an example of a **reflex,** an involuntary response to an environmental stimulus. In the reflex illustrated in Figure 43.1, sensory neurons stimulate interneurons in the spinal cord that then stimulate motor neurons; the motor neurons make the biceps muscle contract, causing you to withdraw your hand even before your brain becomes aware of the pain.

Figure 43.1 The CNS Integrates Sensory Information and Sends Signals to Effector Cells. Sensory neurons send information to the CNS, where it is integrated with information from other sources. Once integration is complete, a response is sent to effector cells through motor neurons.

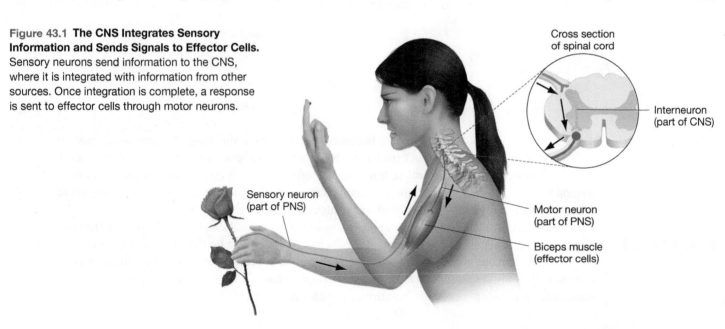

Cross section of spinal cord

Interneuron (part of CNS)

Motor neuron (part of PNS)

Biceps muscle (effector cells)

Sensory neuron (part of PNS)

The Anatomy of a Neuron

Neurons are difficult to study because they are small, transparent, and structurally complex. So when Camillo Golgi discovered that some neurons become visible when preserved nervous tissue is treated with a silver nitrate solution, his finding was a major advance. The year was 1873.

Through the early decades of the twentieth century, the work of Golgi and Santiago Ramón y Cajal revealed several important points about the anatomy of neurons. Most neurons have the same three parts, shown in **Figure 43.2a:**

1. A **cell body,** or **soma,** which contains the nucleus

2. A highly branched group of relatively short projections called **dendrites**

3. One or more relatively long projections called **axons**

Dendrites are rarely more than 2 mm long, but axons can be over a meter in length. The number of dendrites and their arrangement vary greatly from neuron to neuron.

Dendrites receive signals from the axons of other neurons; a neuron's axon sends signals to the dendrites and cell bodies of other neurons (**Figure 43.2b**). In short, dendrites and cell bodies receive signals; axons pass them on. In each neuron, incoming signals are integrated in the dendrites and cell body, and an outgoing signal is sent along the axon.

How do neurons produce the electrical signals that they transmit?

An Introduction to Membrane Potentials

Ions carry an electric charge. In virtually all cells, the cytoplasm and extracellular fluids adjacent to the plasma membrane contain unequal distributions of ions. As a result, there is a difference in charge across the membrane.

A difference in charge between any two points creates an **electrical potential,** or a **voltage.** When an electrical potential exists across a plasma membrane, the separation of charges is called a **membrane potential.** If there is a large difference in charge across the membrane, the membrane potential is large.

It is important to remember that membrane potentials refer only to a separation of charge immediately adjacent to the plasma membrane, on either side of the membrane. Even if there is a large membrane potential, there may be no charge separation slightly farther from the membrane.

Units and Signs Membrane potentials are measured in units called millivolts. The **volt** is the standard unit of electrical potential, and a **millivolt (mV)** is 1/1000 of a volt. As a comparison, an AA battery that you buy in a store has an electrical potential of 1500 mV between its positive and negative terminals. In resting neurons, the difference in electrical potential across a plasma membrane typically ranges from 65 to 80 mV.

By convention, membrane potentials are always expressed in terms of inside relative to outside, and the outside value is defined as 0 mV. Because there are usually more negatively charged ions and fewer positively charged ions on the inside surface of a membrane relative to its outside surface, membrane potentials are usually negative (for example, −65 mV).

Electrical Potential, Electric Currents, and Electrical Gradients Membrane potentials are a form of potential energy. Recall that potential energy is energy based on the position of matter.

To convince yourself that ions have potential energy when a membrane potential exists, consider what would happen if the membrane were removed. Ions would spontaneously move from the region of like charge to the region of unlike charge—causing a flow of charge. This flow of charge, which is called an

(a) Information flows from dendrites to the axon.

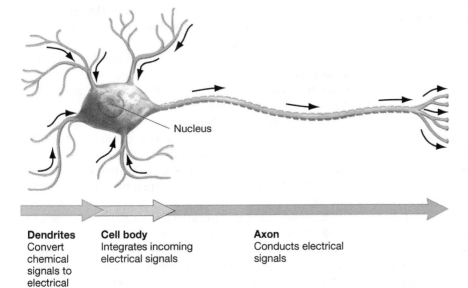

Dendrites	Cell body	Axon
Convert chemical signals to electrical signals	Integrates incoming electrical signals	Conducts electrical signals

(b) Neurons form networks for information flow.

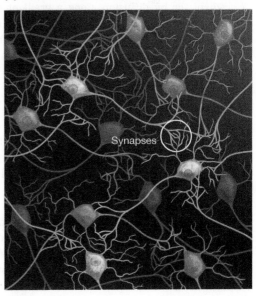

Figure 43.2 **How Does Information Flow in a Neuron? (a)** The structure of a generalized neuron.
(b) Most neurons receive inputs from and send projections to many other neurons.

electric current, would occur because like charges repel and unlike charges attract.

However, charge is not the only contributor to the potential energy of a membrane potential. Ions also have different concentrations across membranes. Therefore, a membrane potential also includes energy stored as the concentration gradients of charged ions on the two sides of the membrane. Recall that the combination of an electrical gradient and a concentration gradient is an **electrochemical gradient** (see Chapter 6).

What do all these facts have to do with neuron function? Neurons use the electrochemical gradient of ions across their membranes to power the signals that allow neurons to communicate with one another and with other cells.

How Is the Resting Potential Maintained?

When a neuron is not communicating with other cells, the difference in charge across its membrane is called the **resting potential.** To understand why the resting potential exists, consider the distribution of the various ions on the two sides of the neuron's plasma membrane, shown in **Figure 43.3:**

- The interior side of the membrane has relatively low concentrations of sodium (Na^+) and chloride (Cl^-) ions, a relatively high concentration of potassium ions (K^+), and some organic anions—proteins, amino acids, and other organic molecules that have dropped one or more protons and thus carry a negative charge.

- In the extracellular fluid, sodium and chloride ions predominate.

If each type of ion diffused across the membrane in accordance with its concentration gradient, organic anions and K^+ would leave the cell, while Na^+ and Cl^- would enter.

Ions cannot cross phospholipid bilayers readily, however. They cross plasma membranes mainly in three ways (see Chapter 6): by primary or secondary active transport against a gradient, or by diffusion along a gradient through an **ion channel**—a protein that forms a pore in the membrane through which specific ions can diffuse. Let's examine how these types of transport are involved in establishing and maintaining a neuron's resting potential.

The Role of Na^+/K^+-ATPase The sodium–potassium pump, Na^+/K^+-ATPase, actively pumps Na^+ out of the cell and K^+ into the cell. More specifically, the energy gained by the sodium–potassium pump when it receives a phosphate group from one ATP is used to move three Na^+ ions out of the cell and two K^+ ions into the cell (see Figure 6.25).

Active transport via Na^+/K^+-ATPase ensures that eventually the concentration of K^+ is much higher on the inside of the plasma membrane than the outside, while the concentration of Na^+ is lower on the inside than the outside. In addition to setting up concentration gradients of K^+ and Na^+, the pump establishes an electrical gradient: The outward movement of three positive charges and inward movement of two positive charges each time the ATPase pumps makes the interior of the membrane less positive (more negative) than the outside.

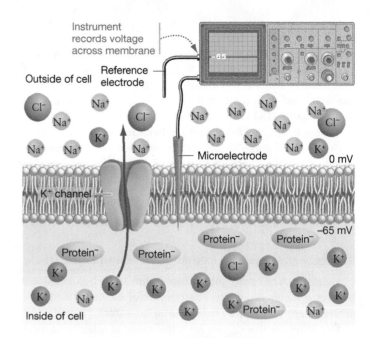

Figure 43.3 Neurons Have a Resting Potential. In resting neurons, the membrane is selectively permeable to K^+. As K^+ leaves the cell along its concentration gradient, the inside of the membrane becomes negatively charged relative to the outside. To measure a neuron's membrane potential, researchers use two electrodes: a reference electrode outside the cell and a microelectrode inserted into the cell.

✔ Will K^+ continue to leave the cell indefinitely? Explain why or why not.

The Role of the K^+ Leak Channel At rest, the plasma membrane of a neuron is relatively impermeable to most cations. However, neurons have a relatively high number of potassium channels, called K^+ **leak channels,** that allow K^+ to leak across the membrane.

The K^+ concentration gradient established by Na^+/K^+-ATPase (high K^+ inside the cell, low K^+ outside) favors the net diffusion of K^+ out of the cell through leak channels. As K^+ moves from the interior of the cell to the exterior, the inside of the membrane becomes more and more negatively charged relative to the outside. This buildup of negative charge inside the membrane begins to attract K^+ and counteract the concentration gradient that had favored the movement of K^+ out.

These counteracting influences cause the membrane to reach a voltage at which equilibrium exists between the concentration gradient that favors movement of K^+ out and the electrical gradient that favors movement of K^+ in. At this voltage, called the **equilibrium potential** for K^+, there is no longer a net movement of K^+.

Although Cl^- and Na^+ cross the plasma membrane much less readily than does K^+, some movement of these ions also occurs through a small number of leak channels that are selective for each of them. As a result, each type of ion has an equilibrium potential. The membrane as a whole has a membrane potential that combines the effects of the individual ions.

To summarize, the neuron has a negative resting membrane potential because Na^+/K^+-ATPase pumps three cations out for only two cations in, and because K^+ exits the neuron through leak channels along its electrochemical gradient. The resting potential represents energy stored as concentration and electrical gradients of specific ions. ✔ If you understand this concept, you should be able to predict what would happen to the membrane potential if Na^+ or K^+ were allowed to diffuse freely across the membrane.

Using Electrodes to Measure Membrane Potentials

During the 1940s, A. L. Hodgkin and Andrew Huxley focused on what has become a classic model system in the study of electrical signaling: the "giant" axons of squid.

Squid live in the ocean and are preyed on by fishes and whales. When a squid is threatened, electrical signals travel down the giant axons to muscle cells, causing the cells to contract. Their contraction expels water from a cavity in the squid's body. As a result, the squid lurches away from danger by jet propulsion (see Chapter 31). This extremely rapid response to threats is an adaptation that helps squid avoid predation.

Hodgkin and Huxley decided to study the squid giant axon simply because it is so large. Many of the axons found in humans are a mere 2 μm in diameter, but the squid giant axon is about 500 μm in diameter—large enough that the researchers could insert a wire down its length. By measuring the voltage difference between the wire inside the axon and another wire outside, Hodgkin and Huxley could record the membrane potential of the axon.

Later researchers developed glass microelectrodes with tips tiny enough to penetrate smaller axons and other parts of neurons. This development made it possible to record membrane potentials from a wide variety of neurons in many animal species.

Recordings made with electrodes inserted into neurons revealed that the resting potential can be disrupted by an event called the action potential when a neuron is stimulated.

What Is an Action Potential?

An **action potential** is a rapid, temporary change in a membrane potential. It may qualify as the most important type of electrical signal in cells. When stimulated, neurons produce action potentials that allow them to communicate with other neurons, muscles, or glands.

Although Hodgkin and Huxley initially studied the action potential in the squid giant axon, subsequent work has shown that action potentials have the same general characteristics in all species and in all types of neurons.

A Three-Phase Signal **Figure 43.4** shows the form of the action potential that Hodgkin and Huxley recorded from the squid giant axon—the signal that allows the squid to jet away from predators. The action potential has three distinct phases:

1. **Depolarization** of the membrane. In its resting state, a membrane is said to be polarized because the charges on the two sides are different. Depolarization means that the membrane becomes less polarized than before. During the depolarization phase, the membrane potential changes from highly negative, crosses zero, and then is briefly positive.

2. A rapid **repolarization,** which changes the membrane potential back to negative.

3. A **hyperpolarization** phase, when the membrane potential is slightly more negative than the resting potential.

Together, all three phases of an action potential occur within a few milliseconds.

For an action potential to begin in a squid giant axon, the membrane must depolarize from the resting potential (−65 mV in Figure 43.4) to about −55 mV. If the membrane depolarizes less than that, an action potential does not occur. But if this **threshold potential** is reached, certain channels in the axon membrane open, allowing ions to rush into the axon along their electrochemical gradients. The inside of the membrane becomes less negative and then positive with respect to the outside.

When the membrane potential reaches about +40 mV, an abrupt change occurs and the repolarization phase begins. The change is triggered by the closing of certain ion channels and the opening of other ion channels in the membrane.

To summarize, an action potential occurs because specific ion channels in the plasma membrane open or close in response to changes in membrane voltage. An action potential always has the same three-phase form, even though the values of the resting potential, threshold potential, and peak depolarization may vary among species or even among types of neurons in one species.

Figure 43.4 Action Potentials Have the Same General Shape. An action potential is a stereotyped change in membrane potential—meaning that it occurs the same way every time.

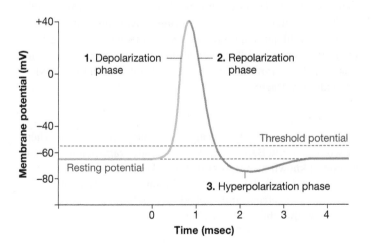

An "All-or-None" Signal That Propagates Hodgkin and Huxley made other important observations about the action potential. Besides being fast and having three distinct phases, it is an all-or-none event.

- There is no such thing as a partial action potential.

- All action potentials for a given neuron are identical in magnitude and duration.

- Action potentials are always propagated down the entire length of the axon.

For example, when an action potential was recorded at a particular point on a squid axon, an action potential that was identical in shape and magnitude would be observed farther down the same axon soon afterward. Neurons are said to have **excitable membranes** because they are capable of generating action potentials that propagate rapidly along the length of their axons.

Taken together, these observations suggested a mechanism for electrical signaling. In the nervous system, information is coded in the form of action potentials that propagate along axons. In the squid giant axon, action potentials signal muscles to contract. As a result, the animal escapes from danger.

CHECK YOUR UNDERSTANDING

If you understand that ...

- The plasma membrane of a neuron has a negative resting potential because Na^+/K^+-ATPase pumps 3 Na^+ ions out of the cell and 2 K^+ ions into the cell and because the membrane is selectively permeable to K^+ ions, which leak out.
- Action potentials are three-phase, all-or-none signals that propagate down the length of an axon.

✔ **You should be able to ...**

1. Predict what would happen to the resting potential of a squid axon if potassium leak channels were blocked.
2. Explain why the first phase of an action potential is called depolarization and why the second phase is called repolarization.

Answers are available in Appendix A.

43.2 Dissecting the Action Potential

Of Na^+, Cl^-, and K^+, which ion or ions are most important in the electric currents that form the action potential? Are different ions responsible for the depolarization and repolarization phases of the event?

Hodgkin made a crucial start in answering this question when he realized that the peak of the action potential in the squid giant axon, about +40 mV, was close to the equilibrium potential for Na^+. If sodium channels opened early in the action potential, then Na^+ should flow into the neuron until the membrane potential reached this equilibrium potential. How could this hypothesis be tested?

Distinct Ion Currents Are Responsible for Depolarization and Repolarization

To understand the currents responsible for the action potential, Hodgkin and Huxley recorded electrical activity in squid giant axons that were bathed in solutions containing different concentrations of ions.

- Removing Na^+ from the solution surrounding the axon abolished the production of action potentials.

- When axons were bathed in solutions with various concentrations of Na^+, the peak of the action potential paralleled the concentration of Na^+. If the Na^+ concentration outside the axon was high, the peak was high. If the Na^+ concentration outside the axon was low, the peak was low. (Note that this change in the peak of the action potential occurred because the scientists altered the Na^+ concentration gradient. In a living animal, action potentials in the same neuron always have the same magnitude.)

These experiments furnished strong support for the hypothesis that the action potential begins when Na^+ flows into the neuron. In other words, sodium ions are responsible for the depolarization phase.

What happens during the repolarization phase? Using radioactive K^+, Hodgkin and Huxley showed that there was a strong flow of potassium ions out of the cell during the repolarization phase.

The action potential consists of a strong inward flow of sodium ions followed by a strong outward flow of potassium ions. ✔ If you understand this concept, you should be able to add labels that read, "Sodium channels open, Na^+ enters" and "Potassium channels open, K^+ leaves" to Figure 43.4.

How Do Voltage-Gated Channels Work?

The action potential depends on **voltage-gated channels**—membrane proteins that open and close in response to changes in membrane voltage. The shape of a voltage-gated channel, and thus its ability to admit ions, changes in response to the charges present at the inside of the membrane. **Figure 43.5** shows a simple model of how voltage-gated sodium channels change shape as the membrane potential changes.

To confirm that voltage-gated channels exist, Hodgkin and Huxley used a technique called voltage clamping. **Voltage clamping** allows researchers to hold the voltage of a cell's plasma membrane at any desired value and record the electrical currents that occur at that voltage. When the researchers held the squid giant axon membrane at various voltages, different currents resulted. These experiments supported the hypothesis that the membrane contained ion channels whose behavior depends on voltage.

Patch Clamping and Studies of Single Channels Studying individual ion channels became possible in the 1980s when Erwin Neher and Bert Sakmann perfected a variation of voltage clamping known as **patch clamping.** As **Figure 43.6** shows, the researchers touched a tiny patch of axon membrane with a fine-tipped microelectrode and applied suction to capture a single ion channel within the electrode's tip.

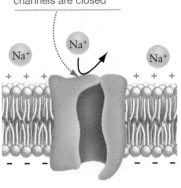

At the resting potential, voltage-gated Na⁺ channels are closed

A shape change opens the channels when the membrane is depolarized

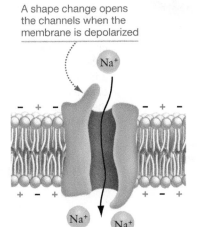

Figure 43.5 The Shape of a Voltage-Gated Channel Depends on the Membrane Potential. Changes in the shape of voltage-gated channels are responsible for changes in a neuron's permeability to ions.

Using this technique, Neher and Sakmann were able to document for the first time the currents that flowed through individual channels, and they showed that different ion channels behave differently:

- Voltage-gated channels are either open or closed. There is no gradation in channel behavior. This conclusion is based on the shape of the recorded current: Current flow starts and stops instantly, and the size of the current is always the same.

- Sodium channels open quickly when the membrane is depolarized. They stay open for about a millisecond, close, and remain inactive for 1 to 2 msec. That explains why the cell can repolarize: Once the sodium channels close, there is a lag before they can open again.

- Potassium channels open with a delay during depolarization. They continue to flip open and closed until the membrane repolarizes. Once the membrane returns to the resting potential, these channels remain closed.

Positive Feedback Occurs during Depolarization More detailed experiments on Na⁺ channels also explained why the action potential is an all-or-none event. The key observation was that Na⁺ channels become more likely to open as a membrane depolarizes. As a result, an initial depolarization leads to the opening of more Na⁺ channels, which depolarizes the membrane further, which leads to the opening of additional Na⁺ channels.

The opening of Na⁺ channels exemplifies **positive feedback**—meaning that the occurrence of an event makes the same event more likely to recur. Positive feedback is rare in organisms: It cannot be employed as a regulatory mechanism under many circumstances because it often leads to uncontrolled events. The opening of Na⁺ channels during an action potential is one of the few examples known.

Using Neurotoxins to Identify Channels and Dissect Currents In addition to using voltage clamping and patch clamping, researchers have used neurotoxins to explore the dynamics of voltage-gated channels. **Neurotoxins** are poisons that affect neuron function—often resulting in convulsions, paralysis, or unconsciousness. They come from sources as diverse as venomous snakes and foxglove plants.

For example, when biologists treated giant axons from lobsters with tetrodotoxin from puffer fish, they found that the resting potential in treated neurons was normal, but action potentials were abolished. More specifically, the flow of K⁺ out of the cell was normal but the influx of Na⁺ was wiped out. Researchers concluded that tetrodotoxin blocks the voltage-gated Na⁺ channel, probably by binding to a specific site on the channel protein.

How Is the Action Potential Propagated?

To explain how action potentials propagate down an axon, Hodgkin and Huxley suggested the model illustrated in **Figure 43.7a** on page 906.

Step 1 The influx of Na⁺ at the start of an action potential repels intracellular cations, causing them to spread away from the sodium channels.

Step 2 As positive charges are pushed farther from the initial sodium channels, they depolarize adjacent portions of the membrane.

Step 3 Nearby voltage-gated Na⁺ channels open when the adjacent membrane reaches threshold, resulting in a new action potential there.

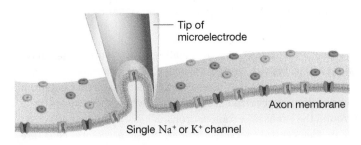

Tip of microelectrode

Axon membrane

Single Na⁺ or K⁺ channel

Figure 43.6 Patch Clamping Provides Insights into the Behavior of Ion Channels. In patch clamping, researchers use extremely fine-tipped microelectrodes to record electric currents through individual ion channels.

(a) PROCESS: PROPAGATION OF ACTION POTENTIAL

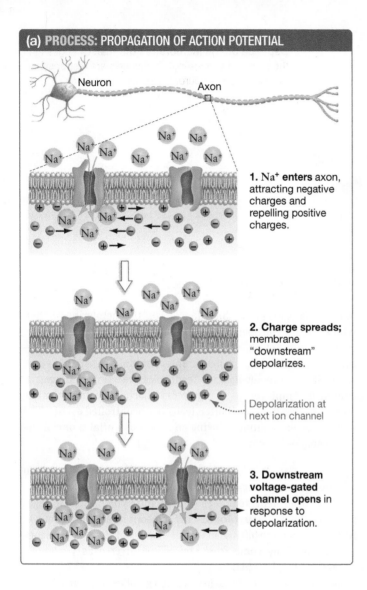

1. Na⁺ **enters** axon, attracting negative charges and repelling positive charges.

2. **Charge spreads;** membrane "downstream" depolarizes.

Depolarization at next ion channel

3. **Downstream voltage-gated channel opens** in response to depolarization.

Figure 43.7 Action Potentials Propagate because Charge Spreads Down the Membrane. (a) An action potential starts with an influx of Na⁺. The influx of positive charge attracts negative charges inside the cell and repels positive charges. As a result, cations spread away from the channel where the Na⁺ enters and depolarize nearby regions of the neuron. Voltage-gated Na⁺ channels open in response. **(b)** Action potentials propagate down the axon without getting smaller, because new action potentials are continuously generated along the axon membrane.

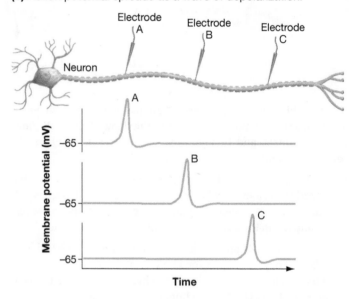

(b) Action potential spreads as a wave of depolarization.

In this way, new action potentials are continuously generated at adjacent areas of the plasma membrane (**Figure 43.7b**). Action potentials are all or none because new action potentials are always generated along the entire length of the axon.

Why don't action potentials propagate back up the axon in the direction of the cell body? To answer this question, recall that once Na⁺ sodium channels have opened and closed, they are less likely to open again for a short period. This condition is known as the **refractory** state. Action potentials propagate in one direction only because "upstream" sodium channels, in the direction of the cell body, are in the refractory state.

The hyperpolarization phase, in which the membrane is more negative than the resting potential, also keeps the positive charges that spread upstream from triggering an action potential in that direction. During the hyperpolarization phase, a much stronger stimulus would be necessary to raise the membrane potential to the threshold potential.

Axon Diameter Affects Speed Understanding how the action potential propagates helped researchers explain why the squid's axons are so large. When sodium ions enter the axon interior

at the start of an action potential, they repel intracellular cations, causing them to spread along the inside of the membrane. Cations moving down axons with larger diameters meet less resistance than those moving down narrow axons. As a result, the charge spreads along the membrane more quickly.

The upshot is that the squid giant axon and other large-diameter axons transmit action potentials much more quickly than small axons can. The squid giant axon's large size is an adaptation that makes particularly rapid signaling possible.

Myelination Affects Speed Relatively few vertebrates have giant axons. Instead, vertebrates—and some invertebrates—have another adaptation that increases the speed of action potential propagation: specialized accessory cells whose membranes wrap around the axons of certain neurons.

In the central nervous system, these accessory cells are **oligodendrocytes.** In the peripheral nervous system, described in Section 43.4, they are **Schwann cells** (**Figure 43.8a**). Oligodendrocytes and Schwann cells are two examples of **glia,** which are nervous system cells that support neurons.

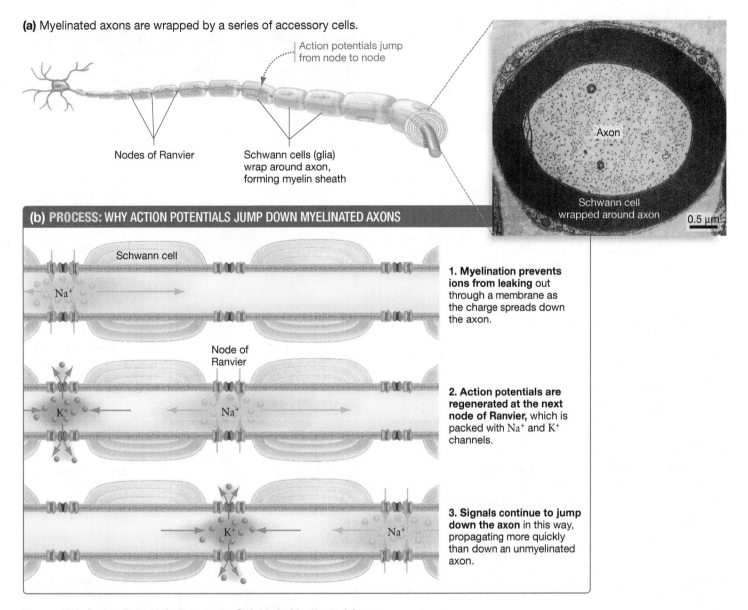

(a) Myelinated axons are wrapped by a series of accessory cells.

Action potentials jump from node to node

Nodes of Ranvier

Schwann cells (glia) wrap around axon, forming myelin sheath

Axon

Schwann cell wrapped around axon

0.5 μm

(b) PROCESS: WHY ACTION POTENTIALS JUMP DOWN MYELINATED AXONS

Schwann cell

Na⁺

1. Myelination prevents ions from leaking out through a membrane as the charge spreads down the axon.

Node of Ranvier

K⁺

Na⁺

2. Action potentials are regenerated at the next node of Ranvier, which is packed with Na⁺ and K⁺ channels.

K⁺

Na⁺

3. Signals continue to jump down the axon in this way, propagating more quickly than down an unmyelinated axon.

Figure 43.8 Action Potentials Propagate Quickly in Myelinated Axons.

When oligodendrocytes or Schwann cells wrap around an axon, they form a **myelin sheath,** which acts as a type of electrical insulation. As intracellular cations spread down an axon during the propagation of action potentials, the myelin sheath prevents ions from leaking back out across the plasma membrane of the axon.

Consequently, the cations moving down the membrane are able to spread until they reach a gap in the myelin sheath, called a **node of Ranvier** (Figure 43.8b). The nodes have a dense concentration of voltage-gated Na⁺ and K⁺ channels, so new action potentials can be generated at the nodes.

Action potentials "jump" from node to node down a myelinated axon much more rapidly than they can move down an unmyelinated axon of the same diameter. In an unmyelinated axon, voltage-gated sodium and potassium channels are found all along its length, and action potentials propagate continuously

down the axon. Myelination is an adaptation that makes rapid transmission of electrical signals possible in axons that have a small diameter. The effect is dramatic: Myelination can increase the speed of action potential propagation in neurons 15-fold.

To appreciate the importance of myelination, consider what happens when it is disrupted. If myelin degenerates, the transmission of action potentials slows considerably. The autoimmune disease **multiple sclerosis (MS)** develops when the immune system targets oligodendrocytes, destroying myelin in the CNS. As damage to myelin increases, electrical signaling becomes more impaired, affecting coordination among neurons and causing muscles to weaken. The symptoms of MS are highly variable; in severe cases, the disease can be crippling.

Once action potentials have been initiated in a neuron, they are propagated down the entire length of the axon. What happens when action potentials reach the end of the axon?

43.3 The Synapse

Ramón y Cajal maintained that the plasma membrane of each neuron is separated from those of adjacent cells. This hypothesis was confirmed in the 1950s, when images from transmission electron microscopes revealed that most neurons are separated from one another at their junctions by tiny spaces called **synapses.** Despite this separation, neurons can communicate with one another. Therefore, some indirect mechanism must exist that transmits signals from cell to cell, across their plasma membranes.

In the 1920s, Otto Loewi showed that this indirect mechanism involves **neurotransmitters.** Neurotransmitters are chemical messengers that transmit information from one neuron to another neuron, or from a neuron to a target cell in a muscle or gland.

Loewi knew that signals from the vagus nerve slow the heart rate. To test the hypothesis that the signal from nerve to heart muscle is delivered by a chemical, he performed the experiment diagrammed in Figure 43.9.

First, Loewi isolated the vagus nerve and heart of a frog. As predicted, the heart rate slowed when he stimulated the vagus nerve electrically. Next, he took the solution that bathed the first heart and applied it to another frog heart—without stimulating the vagus nerve to that heart. He found that the second heart's rate slowed as well.

This result provided strong evidence for the chemical transmission of signals by the nervous system. The vagus nerve had released a neurotransmitter.

Synapse Structure and Neurotransmitter Release

As Figure 43.10 shows, **(1)** the membranes of axons and the cells they communicate with are separated by a tiny space, the **synaptic cleft,** and **(2)** the ends of axons contain numerous sac-like structures, called **synaptic vesicles.** Synaptic vesicles were hypothesized to be storage sites for neurotransmitters.

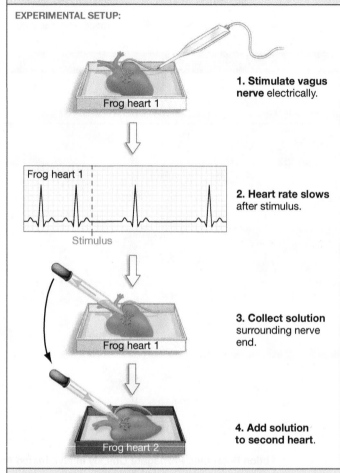

1. **Stimulate vagus nerve** electrically.

2. **Heart rate slows** after stimulus.

3. **Collect solution** surrounding nerve end.

4. **Add solution** to second heart.

PREDICTION: The rate of the second heart will slow.

PREDICTION OF NULL HYPOTHESIS: There will be no change in the second heart's rate.

RESULTS:

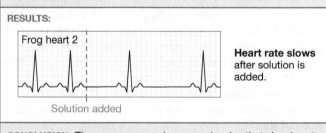

Heart rate slows after solution is added.

CONCLUSION: The vagus nerve releases molecules that slow heart rate. Neurotransmitters carry information.

Figure 43.9 Experimental Evidence for the Existence of Neurotransmitters.

SOURCE: Loewi, O. 1921. Über humorale Übertragbarkeit der Herznervenwirkung. *Pflügers Archiv European Journal of Physiology* 189: 239–242.

✔ **PROCESS OF SCIENCE** What would be an appropriate control for this experiment?

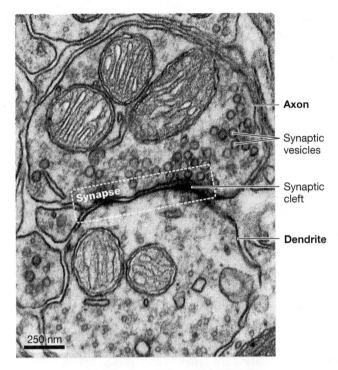

Figure 43.10 **Synaptic Vesicles Cluster Near Synapses.** A cross section of the site where an axon meets a dendrite.

At a synapse, the neuron that contains the synaptic vesicles is called the **presynaptic neuron,** and the cell on the other side of the synaptic cleft is called the **postsynaptic cell.**

Anatomical observations such as these, combined with chemical studies of the synapse, led to the model of synaptic transmission illustrated in **Figure 43.11.**

Step 1 An action potential arrives at the end of the axon.

Step 2 The depolarization created by the action potential opens voltage-gated calcium channels located near the synapse, in the plasma membrane of the presynaptic neuron. The electrochemical gradient for Ca^{2+} results in the inflow of calcium ions through the open channels.

Step 3 In response to the increased calcium concentration inside the axon, synaptic vesicles fuse with the membrane and release neurotransmitters into the gap between the cells, the synaptic cleft. The delivery of neurotransmitters into the cleft is an example of exocytosis (see Chapter 7).

Step 4 Neurotransmitters bind to receptors on the postsynaptic cell. thus, each neurotransmitter functions as a **ligand,** a molecule that binds to a specific site on a receptor molecule. Neurotransmitter-receptor binding leads to a change in the membrane potential of the postsynaptic cell. The combined effect on membrane potential of many neurotransmitters binding may trigger an action potential in the postsynaptic cell.

Step 5 The response ends when the neurotransmitters unbind from their receptors and diffuse out of the synaptic cleft, are broken down, or are taken back up by the presynaptic cell.

Is the model correct? Let's begin by analyzing the role of neurotransmitters.

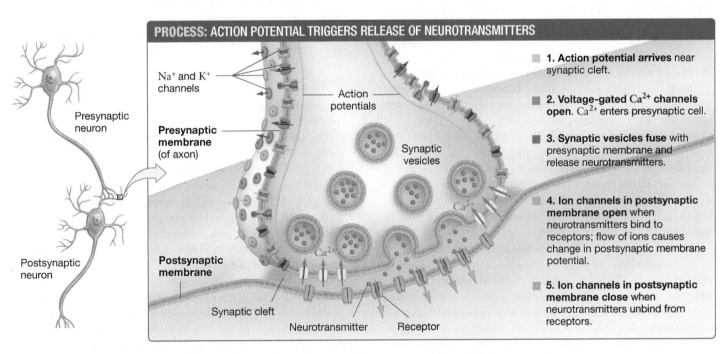

PROCESS: ACTION POTENTIAL TRIGGERS RELEASE OF NEUROTRANSMITTERS

1. **Action potential arrives** near synaptic cleft.

2. **Voltage-gated Ca^{2+} channels open.** Ca^{2+} enters presynaptic cell.

3. **Synaptic vesicles fuse** with presynaptic membrane and release neurotransmitters.

4. **Ion channels in postsynaptic membrane open** when neurotransmitters bind to receptors; flow of ions causes change in postsynaptic membrane potential.

5. **Ion channels in postsynaptic membrane close** when neurotransmitters unbind from receptors.

Figure 43.11 **Neurons Meet and Transfer Information at Synapses.** The sequence of events that occurs when an action potential arrives at a synapse.

Table 43.1 Categories of Neurotransmitters

Neurotransmitter	Site of Action	Action*	Drugs That Interfere†
Acetylcholine	Neuromuscular junction, some CNS pathways	Excitatory (inhibitory in some parasympathetic neurons)	• Botulism toxin blocks release • Black widow spider venom increases, then eliminates, release • Alpha-bungarotoxin (in some snake venoms) binds to and blocks receptor
Monoamines			
Norepinephrine	Sympathetic neurons, some CNS pathways	Excitatory or inhibitory	• Ritalin (used for attention deficit hyperactivity disorder) increases release • Some antidepressants prevent reuptake
Dopamine	Many CNS pathways	Excitatory or modulatory	• Cocaine and amphetamine prevent reuptake
Serotonin	Many CNS pathways	Inhibitory or modulatory	• MDMA (ecstasy) increases levels for several hours, then reduces levels for days to weeks
Amino Acids			
Glutamate	Many CNS pathways	Excitatory	• PCP (angel dust) blocks receptor
Gamma-aminobutyric acid (GABA)	Some CNS pathways	Inhibitory	• Ethanol mimics response to GABA
Peptides			
Endorphins, enkephalins, substance P	Sensory pathways (pain)	Excitatory, modulatory, or inhibitory	• Natural and synthetic opiates (e.g., opium, heroin, morphine, and others) bind to and stimulate receptors • Naloxone blocks receptors; used to treat opiate drug overdose

*Excitatory neurotransmitters make action potentials more likely in postsynaptic cells; inhibitory neurotransmitters make action potentials less likely; modulatory neurotransmitters modify the response at other synapses.

†Drugs that prevent reuptake of neurotransmitters increase their activity.

What Do Neurotransmitters Do?

Researchers can look for neurotransmitters by stimulating a neuron, collecting the molecules that are released, and analyzing them chemically. To find the receptor for a particular neurotransmitter, researchers can attach a radioactive atom or other type of label to the neurotransmitter and add the labeled neurotransmitter to nervous tissue. Receptors that are bound to the labeled neurotransmitter can then be isolated and analyzed.

Using techniques such as these, biologists have discovered and characterized a wide array of neurotransmitters and receptors. Some of them are listed in Table 43.1.

By patch-clamping receptors, biologists confirmed that many receptors are also ion channels. Such channels, called **ligand-gated channels,** have a binding site for a specific ligand on the part of the channel protein that faces the synaptic cleft. In contrast to voltage-gated channels, which open in response to a change in membrane voltage, ligand-gated channels open in response to binding by a specific neurotransmitter.

When a neurotransmitter binds to a ligand-gated ion channel in the postsynaptic membrane, the channel opens and allows ions to diffuse along their electrochemical gradient. In this way, the neurotransmitter's chemical signal is transduced to an electrical signal—a change in the membrane potential of the postsynaptic cell.

Not all neurotransmitters bind to ion channels, however. Some bind to receptors that activate enzymes whose action leads to the production of a second messenger in the postsynaptic cell.

Recall that **second messengers** are chemical signals produced inside a cell in response to a chemical signal that arrives at the cell surface (see Chapter 11).

The second messengers induced by neurotransmitters may trigger changes in enzyme activity, gene transcription, or membrane potential. (Chapter 46 explores the cellular role of second messengers in detail.)

Postsynaptic Potentials

What happens when a neurotransmitter binds to a ligand-gated ion channel in the postsynaptic cell?

Ligand-gated sodium channels on the membranes of dendrites are in particularly high concentration near synapses. When neurotransmitters bind, these channels open and allow cations like sodium to enter the cell, causing depolarization (Figure 43.12a). In most cases, depolarization makes an action potential in the postsynaptic cell more likely. Changes in the membrane potential of a postsynaptic cell that make the cell more likely to produce an action potential are called **excitatory postsynaptic potentials (EPSPs).**

If neurotransmitter-receptor binding leads to an outflow of potassium ions or an inflow of chloride ions or other anions in the postsynaptic cell, the postsynaptic membrane hyperpolarizes—making action potentials less likely to occur in the postsynaptic cell (Figure 43.12b). Changes in the membrane potential of a postsynaptic cell that make the cell less likely to produce an action potential are called **inhibitory postsynaptic potentials (IPSPs).**

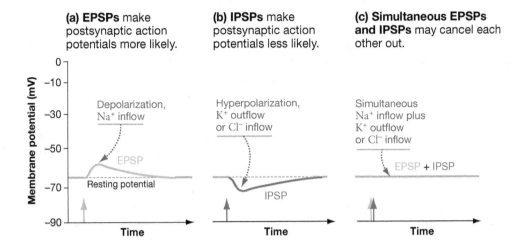

(a) EPSPs make postsynaptic action potentials more likely.

(b) IPSPs make postsynaptic action potentials less likely.

(c) Simultaneous EPSPs and IPSPs may cancel each other out.

Depolarization, Na⁺ inflow

EPSP

Resting potential

Time

Hyperpolarization, K⁺ outflow or Cl⁻ inflow

IPSP

Time

Simultaneous Na⁺ inflow plus K⁺ outflow or Cl⁻ inflow

EPSP + IPSP

Time

Figure 43.12 Events at the Synapse May Depolarize or Hyperpolarize the Postsynaptic Membrane. These recordings show what happens to the membrane potential of a postsynaptic neuron in response to the release of neurotransmitters that cause **(a)** depolarization or **(b)** hyperpolarization. In **(c)**, the simultaneous release of both neurotransmitters results in no change because the depolarization and hyperpolarization cancel each other out.

If an EPSP and an IPSP occur at the same time in the same postsynaptic cell, they may cancel each other out (**Figure 43.12c**). Synapses also can be modulatory—meaning that their activity modifies a postsynaptic cell's response to input from other synapses.

Postsynaptic Potentials Are Graded It is critical to realize that, unlike action potentials, EPSPs and IPSPs are not all-or-none events. Instead, they are graded in magnitude.

The magnitude of an EPSP or IPSP depends on the amount of neurotransmitter that is released at the synapse at a given time. A higher concentration of neurotransmitter in the synaptic cleft leads to a larger EPSP or IPSP. Both types of signal are short lived because neurotransmitters do not bind irreversibly to receptors. When they unbind, they may be quickly inactivated by enzymes or taken up by the presynaptic cell and recycled.

Anything that changes the amount or life span of neurotransmitters in the synaptic cleft may alter the normal functioning of neurons. The drugs cocaine and amphetamine, for example, exert their effects by inhibiting the uptake and recycling of the neurotransmitter dopamine (see Table 43.1).

Summation and Threshold How do EPSPs and IPSPs affect the postsynaptic cell? As **Figure 43.13a** shows, the dendrites and cell body of a neuron typically make hundreds or thousands of synapses with other neurons. Therefore, the postsynaptic neuron may receive a great many EPSPs and IPSPs at any instant.

If an IPSP and EPSP occur close together in space or time, the changes in membrane potential tend to cancel each other out. But if several EPSPs occur close together in space or time, they sum and make the neuron more likely to reach threshold and fire an action potential (**Figure 43.13b**). The additive nature of postsynaptic potentials is termed **summation.**

The sodium channels that trigger action potentials in a neuron are typically located near the place where the axon emerges from the cell body, a site called the **axon hillock** (see Figure 43.13a). As IPSPs and EPSPs are received throughout the dendrites and cell body, charge spreads to the axon hillock. If the membrane at the axon hillock depolarizes to the threshold potential, enough voltage-gated sodium channels open to trigger positive feedback and an action potential. Once an action potential starts at the axon hillock, it propagates down the axon to the next synapse.

(a) Most neurons receive information from many other neurons.

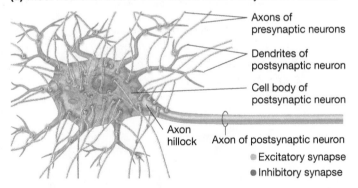

Axons of presynaptic neurons

Dendrites of postsynaptic neuron

Cell body of postsynaptic neuron

Axon hillock

Axon of postsynaptic neuron

● Excitatory synapse
● Inhibitory synapse

(b) Postsynaptic potentials sum.

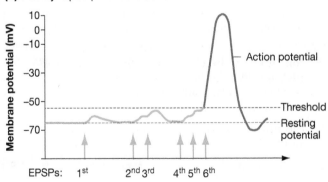

Action potential

Threshold

Resting potential

EPSPs: 1ˢᵗ   2ⁿᵈ 3ʳᵈ 4ᵗʰ 5ᵗʰ 6ᵗʰ

Figure 43.13 Neurons Integrate Information from Many Synapses. (a) The dendrites and cell body of a neuron typically receive signals from hundreds or thousands of other neurons. **(b)** When presynaptic action potentials arrive close together in time, the postsynaptic potentials sum. Here the first EPSP is insufficient to generate an action potential; two EPSPs arriving close together undergo summation but do not reach the threshold; the summation of three EPSPs arriving close together does reach the threshold. This example is simplified—in reality, hundreds or thousands of IPSPs and EPSPs sum to determine action potential frequency.

Summation is critically important. Because neurons receive input from many synapses, and because IPSPs and EPSPs sum, information in the form of electrical signals is modified at the postsynaptic neuron before being passed along. An action potential in a presynaptic neuron does not always lead to an action potential in a postsynaptic neuron—the response by the postsynaptic cell depends on the information it receives from a wide array of neurons.

43.4 The Vertebrate Nervous System

The first three sections of this chapter examined electrical signaling at the level of molecules, membranes, and individual cells. This section discusses electrical signaling at the levels of tissues, organs, and systems.

To begin, let's consider the overall anatomy of the vertebrate nervous system and how researchers explore the function of the most complex organ known: the human brain. The chapter concludes by returning to the molecular level (and to studies of invertebrates) to introduce recent work on learning and memory.

What Does the Peripheral Nervous System Do?

Recall from Section 43.1 that the vertebrate central nervous system (CNS) is made up of the brain and spinal cord and is concerned primarily with integrating information. The peripheral nervous system (PNS) is made up of neurons outside the CNS.

What functions do the cells of the PNS control? Anatomical and functional studies indicate that the PNS consists of two divisions with distinct functions:

1. The **afferent division** transmits sensory information to the CNS.

2. The **efferent division** carries commands from the CNS to the rest of the body.

Neurons in the afferent division monitor conditions inside and outside the body. Once information from afferent neurons has been processed in the CNS, neurons in the efferent division carry signals that allow the body to respond to changed conditions in an appropriate way.

As **Figure 43.14** shows, the afferent and efferent divisions are part of a hierarchy of PNS functions. The efferent division is further divided into a somatic nervous system and an autonomic nervous system.

- The **somatic nervous system** carries out voluntary responses, which are under conscious control. Skeletal muscles serve as the effectors.

- The **autonomic nervous system** carries out involuntary responses, which are not under conscious control. Autonomic neurons control internal processes such as digestion and heart rate. Smooth muscle, cardiac muscle, and glands serve as the effectors.

Many organs are served by two functionally distinct types of autonomic nerves, summarized in **Figure 43.15**: The two types often have opposite effects on the same organ.

1. Nerves in the **parasympathetic nervous system** promote "rest and digest" functions that conserve or restore energy. For example, the parasympathetic nerves that synapse on the heart slow it down, while those that serve the digestive tract stimulate its activity.

2. Nerves in the **sympathetic nervous system** typically prepare organs for stressful "fight or flight" situations. Sympathetic nerves speed up the heart rate, stimulate the release of glucose from the liver, and inhibit action by digestive organs.

In addition to the afferent and efferent divisions, some researchers have proposed a third division of the PNS, consisting of neurons embedded in the wall of the gastrointestinal tract, from esophagus to anus. This **enteric nervous system** interacts with autonomic nerves but can also function independently (for example, if the vagus nerve is cut). The enteric nervous system plays a major role in regulating digestion, but it may also be important in immune function, mental health, cognition, and memory formation in the CNS.

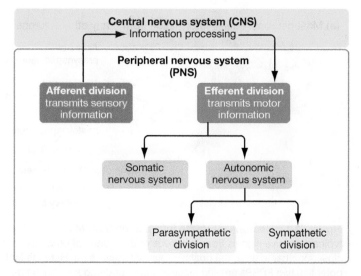

Figure 43.14 The Vertebrate Nervous System Has Several Functional Divisions.

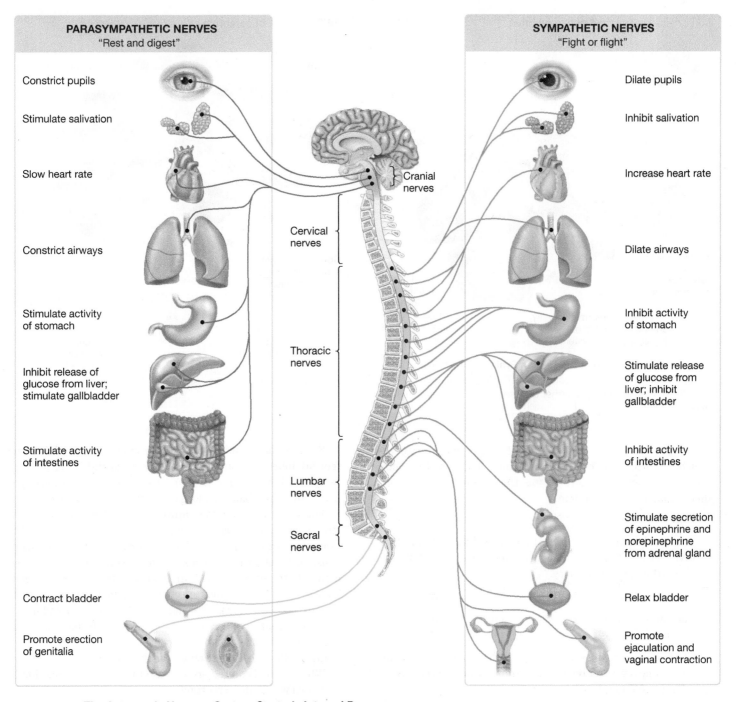

Figure 43.15 The Autonomic Nervous System Controls Internal Processes.

✔ Explain how the responses listed here for the pupils, heart rate, liver, and gallbladder are part of the "rest and digest" function or the "fight or flight" function.

Functional Anatomy of the CNS

Parasympathetic nerves originate at the base of the brain or the base of the spinal cord (see Figure 43.15). Most sympathetic nerves also originate in the spinal cord, but they emerge along the middle of its length. Similarly, most sensory neurons project axons to the spinal cord, and most somatic motor neurons project from the spinal cord.

In effect, then, the spinal cord serves as an information conduit. It collects and transmits information throughout the body.

Virtually all the sensory information that enters the spinal cord must be sent to the brain for processing. The main exceptions involve spinal reflexes, such as the one illustrated in Figure 43.1, in which sensory neurons stimulate interneurons or motor neurons within the spinal cord itself.

What happens once sensory signals arrive at the brain? How are thousands of signals integrated to allow an animal to respond to stimuli? Let's begin our exploration by delving into the anatomy of the brain.

(a) Longitudinal section of human brain

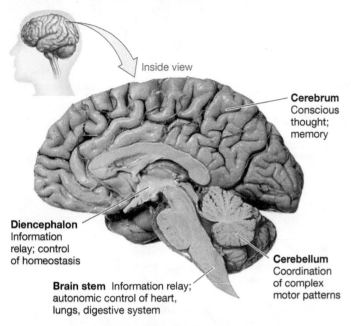

Cerebrum
Conscious
thought;
memory

Diencephalon
Information
relay; control
of homeostasis

Cerebellum
Coordination
of complex
motor patterns

Brain stem Information relay;
autonomic control of heart,
lungs, digestive system

Figure 43.16 **Structure of the Human Brain. (a)** The brain
is composed of four main structures. **(b)** The largest of these
structures, the cerebrum, is further divided into two hemispheres
and four distinct lobes.

(b) Four lobes of cerebrum

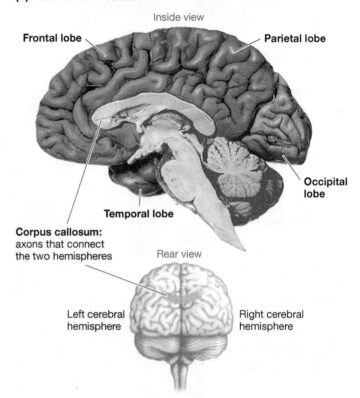

Inside view

Frontal lobe

Parietal lobe

Occipital lobe

Temporal lobe

Corpus callosum:
axons that connect
the two hemispheres

Rear view

Left cerebral
hemisphere

Right cerebral
hemisphere

General Anatomy of the Human Brain Nineteenth-century anatomists established that the human brain is made up of the four
structures labeled in **Figure 43.16a**: the cerebrum, cerebellum,
diencephalon, and brain stem.

Each has distinct functions:

- The **cerebrum** makes up the bulk of the human brain. It is
  divided into left and right hemispheres and is the seat of conscious thought and memory.

- The **cerebellum** coordinates complex motor patterns.

- The **diencephalon** relays sensory information to the cerebrum and controls homeostasis.

- The **brain stem** connects the brain to the spinal cord. It is the
  autonomic center for regulating cardiovascular, digestive, and
  other involuntary functions.

Each cerebral hemisphere has four major areas, or lobes: the
frontal lobe, the **parietal lobe,** the **occipital lobe,** and the
temporal lobe (**Figure 43.16b**). The two hemispheres are connected by a thick band of axons called the **corpus callosum.**

The relative size of the entire brain, and of its component
structures, varies greatly among vertebrates (**Figure 43.17**). For
example, compare the size of the cerebrum in fishes and mammals. In fishes, the cerebrum is quite small and is involved
mainly in the sense of smell. In mammals, the cerebrum is very
large and contains regions specialized for memory and reasoning, in addition to the processing of multiple sensory and motor
functions. Your own cerebrum is three times as large as those
of comparably sized mammals, reflecting its role in the higher
brain functions that are so advanced in humans.

What methods do researchers use to explore the function of
each area within the cerebrum?

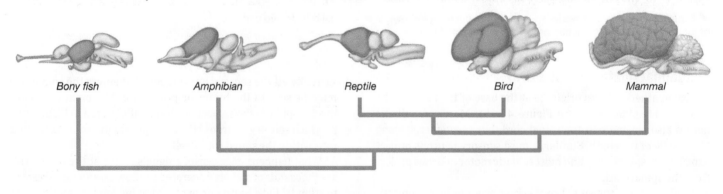

Bony fish   Amphibian   Reptile   Bird   Mammal

Figure 43.17 **The Relative Sizes of Brain Regions Differ among Vertebrate Lineages.** For example, the
cerebrum (highlighted in brown) is larger in birds and mammals than in bony fishes, amphibians, and reptiles.

Mapping the Brain I: Lesion Studies Early work on brain function focused on people with specific mental deficits caused by areas of brain damage, or lesions. In 1848, for example, Phineas Gage was working on a railroad construction site when an iron rod over 3 cm in diameter was blasted through his skull. The rod entered beneath his left eye, exited through his forehead, and landed more than 20 m away. Miraculously, Gage survived this accident. However, his personality did not fare well. After the accident, Gage's physician reported him to be "fitful," "irreverent," and "obstinate," a dramatic change from his previous personality. The iron rod had damaged Gage's frontal lobe, providing some of the first clues that this part of the brain plays a role in personality and emotion.

The French physician Paul Broca formulated the hypothesis that specific regions of the brain are specialized for coordinating particular functions. Broca's hypothesis arose from his study of an individual who could understand language but could not speak. After the person's death in 1861, Broca examined the patient's brain and discovered a lesion in the left frontal lobe. Broca proposed that this region is responsible for speech.

Broca's hypothesis that functions are localized to specific brain areas has been verified through extensive efforts to map the cerebrum. Important advances were made by studying the behavior of people who had specific portions of their brains removed during surgery.

One such case is that of a 27-year-old man named Henry Gustav Molaison (referred to as "H.M." until his death). In 1953, surgeons treated him for life-threatening seizures by removing a small portion of his temporal lobe and about two-thirds of his **hippocampus,** a structure at the inner edge of the temporal lobe. Molaison recovered and lived for another 55 years. For the rest of his life, he had normal intelligence and vividly remembered his childhood, but he had no short-term memory. Brenda Milner, who studied Molaison for over 40 years, had to introduce herself to him every time they met; he could not even recognize a recent picture of himself.

Based on case histories like Molaison's and studies of memory in laboratory animals, a consensus has emerged that several aspects of memory are governed by the hippocampus and interior sections of the temporal lobe. In particular, the hippocampus is responsible for the formation of new memories, which are then "stored" in the cerebrum to be retrieved later. How did scientists discover this role of the cerebrum?

Mapping the Brain II: Electrical Stimulation of Conscious Patients Wilder Penfield pioneered a different approach to studying brain function. Penfield studied people who were suffering from severe seizures and were scheduled to have seizure-prone areas of their brains surgically removed. While the patients were awake and under a local anesthetic, Penfield electrically stimulated portions of their cerebrums. His immediate goal was to map essential areas that should be spared from removal if possible.

When Penfield stimulated specific areas, patients reported sensations or experienced movement in particular regions of the body. From these responses, Penfield was able to map

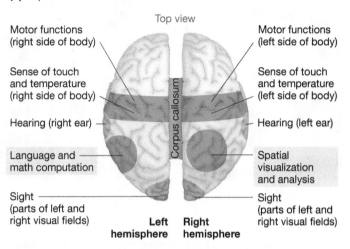

(a) Top view of cerebrum

Top view

Motor functions (right side of body)
Sense of touch and temperature (right side of body)
Hearing (right ear)
Language and math computation
Sight (parts of left and right visual fields)

Corpus callosum

Motor functions (left side of body)
Sense of touch and temperature (left side of body)
Hearing (left ear)
Spatial visualization and analysis
Sight (parts of left and right visual fields)

Left hemisphere **Right hemisphere**

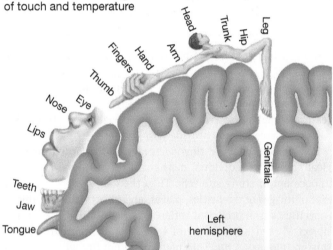

(b) Cross section through area of cerebrum responsible for sense of touch and temperature

Head, Trunk, Hip, Leg, Arm, Hand, Fingers, Thumb, Eye, Nose, Lips, Teeth, Jaw, Tongue, Genitalia

Left hemisphere

Figure 43.18 Specific Brain Areas Have Specific Functions.
(a) A map of the cerebrum, in top view (as if the person is looking at the top of the page), showing the functions of some major regions. The map was compiled from studies of people with brain lesions or in whom brain regions had been removed surgically. Note that the corpus callosum is not actually as wide as shown here.
(b) Researchers mapped the cerebral area responsible for the sense of touch and of temperature by stimulating neurons in the brains of patients who were awake. The size of the icons corresponds to the amount of cerebral area devoted to processing sensory information from those parts.

✔ Is there a correlation between the size of the cerebral area devoted to sensing a particular body part and the size of that body part? Explain.

regions of the cerebrum involved in sensory and motor processing **(Figure 43.18)**. Brain surgeons still use this technique to map critical locations near tumors and seizure-prone areas.

Perhaps the most striking of Penfield's findings was that, on occasion, patients would respond to stimulation of their temporal lobe by having what appeared to be flashbacks. After one region was stimulated, a woman said, "I hear voices. It is late at night around the carnival somewhere—some sort of traveling

| 0 action potentials/sec | 8 action potentials/sec | 0 action potentials/sec | 6 action potentials/sec | 0 action potentials/sec |

Figure 43.19 Single-Neuron Recording Reveals that Some Neurons in the Brain Recognize Specific Concepts. The recordings below each photograph show how a single neuron fires in response to images of actress Jennifer Aniston but not to other images.

DATA: Quiroga, R. Q., L. Reddy, G. Kreiman, et al. 2005. *Nature* 435: 1102–1107.

circus....I just saw lots of big wagons that they used to haul animals in."

Was this a memory, stored in a small set of neurons that Penfield happened to stimulate? The hypothesis that memories are somehow stored in specialized cells is controversial. However, a recent study provided support for it.

Researchers attached tiny electrodes that recorded the electrical activity of individual neurons in the temporal lobes and hippocampi of study subjects. They then showed each subject a set of images of celebrities, places, and objects. In one subject, a specific neuron produced action potentials ("fired") when the subject viewed any of several images of the actress Jennifer Aniston (**Figure 43.19**). That neuron did not fire when the subject viewed images of spiders, buildings, other actresses, or even Aniston with another person. The neuron fired only when the subject viewed images of the actress alone, or even an image of her name spelled out. It appeared that, through experience, at least one of this person's neurons became singularly devoted to the concept of Jennifer Aniston.

It is important to note that the researchers were testing only a tiny subset of the neurons present in the human brain, so there may be more than one "Jennifer Aniston neuron" in the brain. But the take-home message is that the formation or retrieval of memories associated with specific concepts involves specific neurons. Researchers are still examining exactly how these neurons interact with other parts of the brain during the processes of learning and remembering.

Methods such as lesioning and single-cell recording are powerful because they provide strong evidence for the functions of specific brain regions and even neurons. However, these methods merely establish a correlation between specific neurons or brain regions and a given function. In 1979, Francis Crick, known for his codiscovery of the double-helix structure of DNA but also an accomplished neurobiologist, suggested that major breakthroughs in neuroscience would come with the development of techniques that could stimulate or inhibit certain

neurons without affecting others. In the early 2000s, shortly before Crick's death, this idea became a reality with the invention of optogenetics.

Mapping the Brain III: Optogenetics The technique known as **optogenetics** uses light to control the activity of targeted types of neurons in the brain. In one of the earliest applications of optogenetics, researchers inserted an algal gene that codes for a light-activated ion channel into the DNA of specific types of neurons in the brains of mice. By surgically implanting light-emitting probes in the brains of those mice (**Figure 43.20**), the researchers were able to study the behavior of the mice while stimulating action potentials in the neurons that expressed the algal ion channel. This technique made it possible to directly observe the role of specific neurons in specific behaviors.

In the past 15 years, optogenetics has exploded in popularity as a tool for studying the functions of neurons responsible for

Figure 43.20 Optogenetics Allows Researchers to Stimulate Specific Neurons. Neurons genetically engineered to be depolarized by light are stimulated by a light-emitting brain implant.

sleeping, running, mating, and many other behaviors. In addition, researchers are developing optogenetic tools to stimulate neurons that may be compromised in neurodegenerative diseases, including Parkinson's disease and Alzheimer's disease. Optogenetics is also being used to examine detailed neural mechanisms behind learning and memory, for example by elucidating the roles of specific sub-regions of the hippocampus in memory formation.

What other approaches to studying learning and memory have been productive?

How Do Learning and Memory Work?

Learning is an enduring change in behavior that results from a specific experience in an individual's life. **Memory** is the retention of learned information. Learning and memory are thus closely related and are often studied in tandem. As an introduction to how researchers explore these phenomena, let's first examine work that focuses on neurons and then review research at the molecular level.

Recording from Single Neurons during Memory Tasks

How do the action potentials generated by a neuron change as learning and memory take place? Researchers have attempted to answer this question by recording from individual neurons in the temporal lobes of humans.

Physicians placed electrodes in specific brain regions of patients who were about to undergo surgery to remove seizure-prone areas of their brains. While the patients were still awake, the researchers projected words or names of objects on a screen and asked the patients to read them silently, read them aloud, or remember them and repeat them later. The data showed that individual neurons in the cerebrum's temporal lobe were relatively inactive while patients identified objects but extremely active when patients remembered the objects and repeated their names aloud.

What do such data mean? Neurons in the temporal lobe are most active during memory tasks. How can action potentials in particular neurons make memory possible?

Documenting Changes in Synapses

Research on the molecular basis of memory is based on the idea that learning and memory must involve some type of short-term or long-term change in the neurons responsible for these processes. This change could be structural or chemical in nature. Structural changes might include modifications in the number of synapses that a particular neuron makes, the destruction of neurons, or the formation of new neurons. Chemical changes might involve alterations in the amount of neurotransmitter released at certain synapses or changes in the number of receptors present in postsynaptic cells.

To explore the molecular basis of learning and memory, Eric Kandel's group has focused on an animal much easier to study than any vertebrate—the sea slug *Aplysia californica* (**Figure 43.21a**). Much of their work has explored the reflex diagrammed in **Figure 43.21b**: When the siphon, a structure on the animal's back, is touched—for example, by a stream of water—the sea slug responds by withdrawing its gill. Withdrawing the gill protects it from predators. The reflex is produced by sensory neurons that are activated by touch and motor neurons that project to a gill muscle.

Early work established that this simple reflex is modified by learning. For example, *Aplysia* also withdraw their gills when their tails are given an electrical shock. If a tail shock is repeatedly paired with a very light touch to the siphon—too light to normally produce a response on its own—an *Aplysia* will learn to withdraw its gill in response to a light siphon touch alone.

Follow-up studies showed that the neurons involved in learning in this reflex release the neurotransmitter **serotonin.** Repeated application of serotonin mimics what happens at the synapse during learning, when sensory neurons from the siphon

(a) Sea slug *Aplysia californica*

(b) Gill-withdrawal reflex protects the gills during an attack.

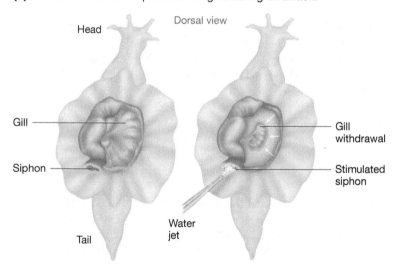

Figure 43.21 The Gill-Withdrawal Reflex in *Aplysia* Is a Model System in Learning and Memory.

(a) *Aplysia* sensory neuron and motor neurons in culture

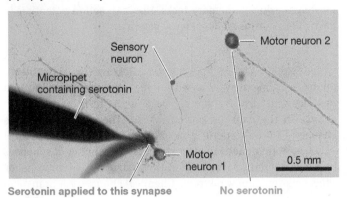

Serotonin applied to this synapse   No serotonin

(b) Effect of serotonin on EPSP

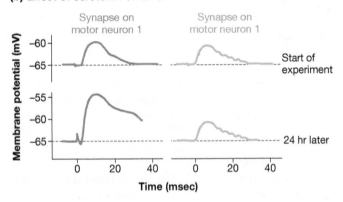

(c) Percentage change in EPSP size caused by serotonin

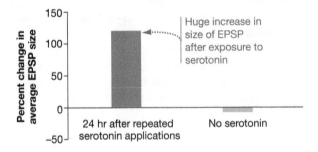

Figure 43.22 Learning and Memory Involve Changes in Synapses. **(a)** In this experiment, a single *Aplysia* sensory neuron was grown in culture with two motor neurons. A micropipet was used to apply serotonin to the synapse between the sensory neuron and one of the motor neurons. **(b)** Stimulating the sensory neuron produced EPSPs in both motor neurons. One day after repeated serotonin application, the EPSP was much larger at the serotonin-treated synapse but not at the untreated synapse. **(c)** Bar graph quantifying the results of 18 experiments.

DATA: Martin, K. C., A. Casadio, H. Zhu, et al. 1997. *Cell* 91: 927–938.

exposed to serotonin had changed, based on its experience. The motor neuron that had not been exposed to serotonin had no increase in the size of its EPSPs or the number of its synapses.

Documenting Changes in Neurons Synapses change over time, but can new neurons form in the central nervous system? When early neurobiologists dissected brains from adult cadavers, they found that none of the brain neurons showed signs of mitosis. From these observations, they concluded that **neurogenesis**—the formation of new neurons—does not occur in adults.

In 1983, Steven Goldman and Fernando Nottebohm revisited this long-standing idea by examining the brains of songbirds. Songbirds were chosen because in their brains, specific regions that control singing behavior undergo dramatic seasonal changes in size. The researchers hypothesized that these changes result from an increased rate of neurogenesis during the reproductive season.

To test this hypothesis, the researchers injected canaries (**Figure 43.23a**) with radiolabeled thymidine, which becomes incorporated into newly synthesized DNA. The researchers later collected the birds' brains, cut them into very thin slices, mounted the slices on microscope slides, and brought the slides into contact with photographic film. In this technique, called autoradiography (see BioSkills 6), any cells with radiolabeled thymidine in their DNA would expose the film, thereby indicating the presence and location of cells that were produced after the bird was injected.

The researchers found that adult songbirds are indeed able to produce large numbers of new neurons. Dozens of studies since Goldman and Nottebohm's experiment have confirmed that new neurons are incorporated into the song-control regions of the brain each spring, causing these regions to grow dramatically (**Figure 43.23b**). The new neurons promote learning and memory in the song-control system.

Other scientists around the same time and, indeed, even earlier obtained autoradiographic evidence of neurogenesis in adult mammals. However, the sheer number of new cells was much lower in mammals than in birds, so these reports did not convince all researchers. Skeptics initially suggested that the labeled cells in mammals might actually be glia rather than neurons.

A breakthrough came in the early 1990s with the development of new techniques that specifically label neurons. The markers used in these techniques bind to proteins that are found only in neurons. Since that time, neurogenesis has been definitively shown to occur in all adult vertebrates, including humans.

and the tail fire repeatedly. These results suggest that in *Aplysia*, changes in the nature of the synapse form the molecular basis of learning and memory. A change in the responsiveness or structure of a synapse is termed **synaptic plasticity.**

To take a closer look at synaptic plasticity in *Aplysia*, Kandel's team replicated these results with sensory and motor neurons growing in culture. **Figure 43.22a** shows an *Aplysia* sensory neuron that synapses with two motor neurons on a culture plate. To mimic the learning process, the investigators applied serotonin to the synapse on one motor neuron five times over a short period.

When they stimulated the sensory neuron a day later, they found a huge increase in the size of EPSPs in the motor neuron postsynaptic to that synapse (**Figure 43.22b** and **c**). That motor neuron had also established additional synapses with the sensory neuron. The structure and behavior of the motor neuron

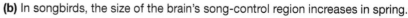

(a) Male canaries (left) sing to attract females (right).

(b) In songbirds, the size of the brain's song-control region increases in spring.

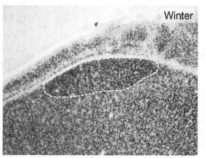
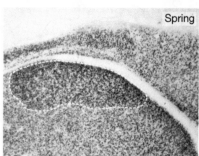

Winter

Spring

Figure 43.23 Neurogenesis Occurs in the Adult Songbird Brain.

Scientists are only beginning to understand the functional roles of these new neurons. Do they have the same roles as neurons made during development? Can neurogenesis be used to help heal brain injuries? Some studies have even suggested that chronic stress during childhood (the stress of poverty or bullying, for example) can reduce the ability to make new neurons, thereby negatively affecting learning in adults.

Results like these reinforce a growing consensus that learning, memory, and the control of complex behaviors involve not only molecular and structural changes in synapses but also changes in the number of neurons. Further, most researchers now agree that at least some aspects of long-term memory involve changes in gene expression. Chemical messengers called hormones also cause changes in gene expression in target cells (see Chapter 46). But before investigating how hormones work, let's focus on the electrical signals involved in vision, hearing, taste, and movement (the subjects of Chapters 44 and 45).

CHECK YOUR UNDERSTANDING

If you understand that ...

- The CNS and PNS work together to gather information about the external and internal environments, process that information, and signal muscles, glands, and other organs to make appropriate responses to the information.
- Brain regions have specific functions.
- Changes in synapses and neurogenesis allow animals to learn and create memories.

✔ **You should be able to ...**

1. **PROCESS OF SCIENCE** Describe the research strategies that allowed biologists to localize particular functions to specific regions in the brain.
2. **CAUTION** Critique the concept that all brain damage is always permanent. What physiological mechanism(s) might be involved in brain repair after damage?

Answers are available in Appendix A.

CHAPTER 43 REVIEW

For media, go to MasteringBiology (MB)

43.1 Principles of Electrical Signaling

- Most neurons have a cell body, multiple short dendrites that receive signals from other cells, and a single axon that transmits electrical signals to other neurons or to effector cells in glands or muscles.

- Studies of the squid giant axon established that neurons have a resting potential maintained by the sodium–potassium pump and potassium leak channels. When Na^+/K^+-ATPase hydrolyzes ATP, it transports 3 Na^+ out of the cell and 2 K^+ in.

43.2 Dissecting the Action Potential

- Studies of the squid giant axon established that the action potential is a rapid, all-or-none change in membrane potential.

- An action potential begins with an inflow of Na^+ that depolarizes the membrane. An outflow of K^+ follows and repolarizes the membrane.

- Both Na^+ and K^+ flow through voltage-gated channels.

- As Na^+ flows in, it repels cations, which spread along the inside of the cell from the site of the action potential, causing the adjacent portion of the membrane to depolarize enough to trigger an action potential there.

- Action potentials propagate most rapidly in axons that are large or myelinated.

43.3 The Synapse

- When an action potential arrives at a synapse, synaptic vesicles fuse with the axon's membrane and deliver neurotransmitters into the synaptic cleft. The neurotransmitters bind to receptors on the membrane of the postsynaptic cell.

- Some receptors are ligand-gated channels. These channels open in response to binding by a neurotransmitter, enabling ion flow that depolarizes or hyperpolarizes the postsynaptic cell's membrane.

- Postsynaptic potentials sum.

- If the membrane at the axon hillock of a postsynaptic neuron depolarizes to the threshold potential, an action potential is triggered.

43.4 The Vertebrate Nervous System

- The vertebrate CNS consists of the brain and spinal cord; the PNS consists of all nervous system components outside the CNS.

- In vertebrates, the PNS contains somatic and autonomic components. The somatic nervous system carries out voluntary responses by signaling skeletal muscles; the autonomic nervous system carries out involuntary responses by signaling effector cells that change internal conditions.

- Early efforts to map functional regions of the brain were based on analyzing deficits in individuals with brain lesions or on stimulating certain regions of the cerebrum.

- Research has established that learning and memory involve synaptic changes, including the release of more or less neurotransmitter and the formation of additional synapses.

- Neurogenesis (formation of new neurons) occurs in adult vertebrates and may be an important component of learning and memory.

Answers are available in Appendix A

✓ TEST YOUR KNOWLEDGE

1. Which ion most readily leaks across a neuron's membrane, helping to establish the resting potential?
   a. Ca^{2+} **b.** K^+ **c.** Na^+ **d.** Cl^+

2. How does myelination affect the propagation of an action potential?
   a. It speeds propagation by increasing the density of voltage-gated channels all along the axon.
   b. It slows propagation by increasing electrochemical gradients favoring Na^+ entry.
   c. It speeds propagation by preventing cations from leaking out across the membrane as they spread down the axon.
   d. It slows propagation by restricting voltage-gated Na^+ channels to gaps in the myelin (nodes of Ranvier).

3. In a neuron, what creates the electrochemical gradient favoring the outflow of K^+ when the cell is at rest?
   a. Na^+/K^+-ATPase
   b. voltage-gated K^+ channels
   c. voltage-gated Na^+ channels
   d. ligand-gated Na^+/K^+ channels

4. Which of the following brain regions is responsible for formation of new memories?
   a. brain stem
   b. cerebellum
   c. frontal lobe
   d. hippocampus

✓ TEST YOUR UNDERSTANDING

5. Explain the difference between a ligand-gated K^+ channel and a voltage-gated K^+ channel.

6. Describe the role of summation in postsynaptic cells.

7. Compare and contrast the somatic nervous system and autonomic nervous system.

8. Why is memory thought to involve changes in particular synapses?
   a. At some synapses, more neurotransmitters are released after learning takes place.
   b. At some synapses, a different type of neurotransmitter is released after learning takes place.
   c. When researchers stimulated certain neurons electrically, individuals replayed memories.
   d. When researchers changed synapses in the brains of patients during surgery, the patients' memories changed.

✓ TEST YOUR PROBLEM-SOLVING SKILLS

9. Explain why drugs that prevent neurotransmitters from being taken back up by a presynaptic neuron have dramatic effects on the activity of postsynaptic neurons.

10. Alzheimer's disease is a common form of dementia affecting millions of people, especially the elderly. Two regions of the brain are particularly affected, often shrinking dramatically and accumulating large deposits of extracellular material. Based on your knowledge of memory, what two brain regions do you think these are? Explain.

✓ PUT IT ALL TOGETHER: Case Study

Phyllobates terribilis

How can a frog kill with its skin?

Certain species of frogs in the genus *Phyllobates* have a powerful defensive adaptation—their skin can secrete a milky fluid that contains an extremely toxic compound called batrachotoxin (BTX). These frogs, which are found in Colombia, are known as poison dart frogs because some indigenous Colombian hunters coat the tips of their blowgun darts with the frogs' skin secretions. An animal hit by one of these darts dies quickly. What is the mechanism of action of BTX?

11. QUANTITATIVE The graph below shows the effect of BTX on the membrane potential of a squid giant axon.

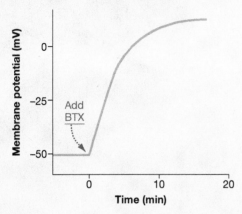

Source: Narahashi, T., E. X. Albuquerque, and D. Deguchi. 1971. *The Journal of General Physiology* 58: 54–70.

Which of the following is the most likely explanation for the effect of BTX on the squid giant axon?
a. Inactivation of Na$^+$/K$^+$-ATPase
b. Closing of sodium channels
c. Opening of sodium channels
d. Opening of potassium channels

12. PROCESS OF SCIENCE Identify a research technique that could be used to discover how BTX affects specific membrane proteins. Based on the graph in Question 11, what would you expect this technique to show?

13. As shown by the graph in Question 11, BTX depolarizes the membrane and prevents repolarization. What effect would this have on electrical signaling by the nervous system?

14. MODEL Like neurons, cells in skeletal and cardiac muscle also produce action potentials. Create a concept map (see BioSkills 12) showing how BTX could kill a mammal through its effects on nervous and muscle tissues.

15. Predict the effects of each of the following on the membrane potential of a neuron simultaneously poisoned with BTX: (a) removing extracellular sodium; (b) increasing the intracellular potassium concentration; and (c) adding tetrodotoxin from puffer fish.

16. BTX is a powerful antipredator poison. However, one snake species in Colombia eats poison dart frogs. Suggest a hypothesis that explains how the snake is resistant to the toxin.

MasteringBiology®

Students Go to MasteringBiology for assignments, the eText, and the Study Area with animations, practice tests, and activities.
Professors Go to MasteringBiology for automatically graded tutorials and questions that you can assign to your students, plus Instructor Resources.

44 Animal Sensory Systems

In many species of moth, males have much larger antennae than females do. Receptor cells on the males' feathery antennae detect airborne chemical signals that are produced by sexually mature females. As a result, males can locate females in total darkness.

In this chapter you will learn how

Animals transform sound, smell, and other stimuli into signals the brain can understand

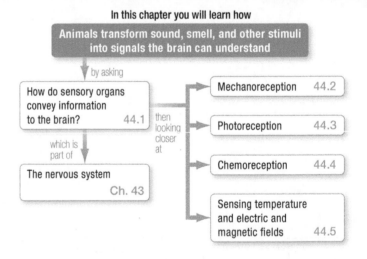

by asking

How do sensory organs convey information to the brain? 44.1

which is part of

The nervous system Ch. 43

then looking closer at

Mechanoreception 44.2

Photoreception 44.3

Chemoreception 44.4

Sensing temperature and electric and magnetic fields 44.5

BIG PICTURE

This chapter is part of the Big Picture. See how on pages 816–817.

Many adult moths are active at night, when it is difficult or impossible to see. Instead of *looking* for a mate under these challenging circumstances, sexually mature female moths release a chemical attractant into the air. Male moths can detect even a single molecule of the attractant by using receptor cells located on their large, feathery antennae. Guided by an airborne gradient of attractant molecules, a male moth flies unerringly toward a female.

As they patrol in search of these airborne molecules, however, male moths are hunted by bats. Like moths, bats are active almost exclusively at night. Instead of hunting by sight, like a falcon or a cheetah, bats hunt with the aid of sonar: They emit a train of high-pitched sounds as they fly and then listen for echoes that indicate the direction and shape of objects in their path. If the object is a moth, the bat flies toward it, catches the moth in its mouth, and eats it.

But some moth species can hear the sounds bats emit. When moths detect sounds from an onrushing bat, they tumble out of the sky in chaotic escape flights.

If you were out at night as these dramas unfolded, you might be only dimly aware that bats and moths were flying about. Humans cannot smell moth attractants or hear the sounds that most bats emit when flying. It took decades of careful experimentation for biologists to understand how moths and bats sense the world around them and respond to the information they receive.

Sensing and interpreting changes in the environment are fundamental to how animals work. Let's begin with a basic question: How are sounds, smells, and other stimuli transformed into a signal that the brain can understand?

44.1 How Do Sensory Organs Convey Information to the Brain?

As a moth flies through the night, its brain receives streams of signals from an array of sensory organs. Antennae collect information about the concentration of female attractant molecules; ears located on various parts of the body send data on the presence of high-pitched sounds; detectors for balance and gravity transmit signals about the body's orientation in space.

Each type of sensory information is detected by a sensory neuron or by a specialized receptor cell that makes a synapse with a sensory neuron. As **Figure 44.1** shows, the moth's nervous system integrates the sensory input—the information from sensory neurons—and responds with motor output, via electrical signals, to specific muscle groups (effectors).

The ability to sense a change in the environment depends on two processes:

1. *Transduction,* the conversion of an external stimulus to an internal signal in the form of action potentials along sensory neurons

2. *Transmission* of the signal to the central nervous system (CNS)

The first process, **transduction,** requires a sensory receptor cell specialized for converting light, sound, touch, or some other signal into an electrical signal. Sensory receptors are located throughout the body and are categorized by type of stimulus:

- **Mechanoreceptors** respond to distortion caused by pressure.
- **Photoreceptors** respond to particular wavelengths of light.
- **Chemoreceptors** detect specific molecules.
- **Thermoreceptors** detect changes in temperature.
- **Nociceptors** sense harmful stimuli such as tissue injury.
- **Electroreceptors** detect electric fields.
- **Magnetoreceptors** detect magnetic fields.

With such a broad range of possible sensory receptors, it is no wonder that animals can monitor and respond to a wide array of changes in their environments.

Now, how do sensory cells receive information from the environment and report it to the brain, so an appropriate response can occur?

Sensory Transduction

During the resting state in most sensory cells, the inside of the plasma membrane is negative relative to the outside (see Chapter 43). When ion flows cause the inside to become less negative than the resting potential, the membrane is depolarized. When ion flows cause the inside to become more negative than the resting potential, the membrane is hyperpolarized.

Although sensory receptors can detect a remarkable variety of stimuli, they all transduce sensory input—such as light, sounds, touch, and odors—to a change in membrane potential. In this way, different types of information are transduced to a common type of signal—one that can be interpreted by the brain.

If a sensory stimulus induces a large change in a sensory receptor's membrane potential, there is a change in the firing rate of action potentials sent to the brain. The amount of depolarization that occurs in a sound-receptor cell, for example, is proportional to the loudness of the sound. If the depolarization passes threshold, enough voltage-gated sodium channels open to trigger action potentials that are relayed to the brain.

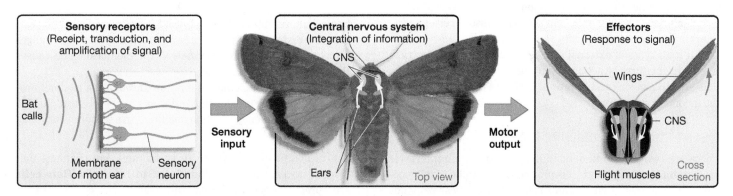

Figure 44.1 Sensory Systems, the CNS, and Effectors Are Linked. Sensory neurons relay information about conditions inside and outside an animal to the central nervous system. After integrating information from many sensory neurons, the CNS sends signals to muscles.

(a) Sound-receptor cells depolarize in response to sound.

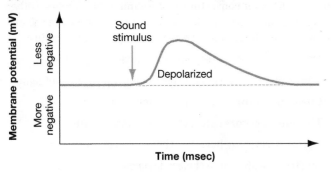

(b) Sensory neurons respond more strongly to louder sounds.

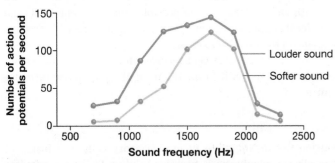

Figure 44.2 Sensory Inputs Change the Membrane Potential of Receptor Cells. (a) In response to sensory stimuli, ions flow across the membranes of receptor cells and either depolarize or hyperpolarize the membrane. **(b)** The rate at which action potentials occur in a sensory neuron provides information about the nature and intensity of the sensory stimulus. (The frequency of a sound, measured in hertz, determines its pitch.)

DATA: Rose, J. E., J. E. Hind, D. J. Anderson, et al. 1971. *Journal of Neurophysiology* 34: 685–699.

Figure 44.2a shows the membrane potential from a sound-receptor cell. When the experimenter played a sound, the sound-receptor cell depolarized for a short time in response. Other sensory cells work in a similar way.

Recall that all action potentials from a given neuron are identical in size and shape (see Chapter 43). **Figure 44.2b** graphs the action potential "firing rate" recorded from a sensory neuron when sounds at various frequencies were played at two distinct intensities. Notice that loud sounds induce a higher rate of action potentials than do soft sounds. In this way sensory cells provide information about the intensity of a stimulus.

But if all types of external stimuli are converted to electrical signals in the form of action potentials, and if all action potentials are alike in size and duration, how does the brain interpret the incoming signals properly?

Transmitting Information to the Brain

There are two keys to understanding how the brain interprets sensory information. First, receptor cells tend to be highly specific. For example, each receptor cell in a human ear responds best to certain pitches of sound. Some receptors are more sensitive to low-pitched sounds, and others respond best to high-pitched sounds. The pattern of action potentials from a cell contains information about the pitch of the sound that is being detected, its intensity, and its duration.

The second key point: Each type of sensory neuron sends its signals to a specific portion of the brain. Axons carrying sensory information from the human ear project to the temporal lobes at the sides of the brain, but axons carrying sensory information from the eye deliver action potentials to the occipital lobe at the back of the brain. Different regions of the brain are specialized for interpreting different types of stimuli.

Now that the basic principles of sensory transduction and transmission have been introduced, let's delve into the details of the major sensory systems.

44.2 Mechanoreception: Sensing Pressure Changes

Animals have a variety of mechanisms for **mechanoreception**—the sensation of pressure changes. Crabs, for example, have a fluid-filled organ that helps them sense the pressure created by gravity. The organ, known as a **statocyst,** is lined with pressure-receptor cells and contains a small calcium-rich particle that normally rests on the bottom of the organ. But if the crab is tipped or flipped over, this particle presses against receptors that are *not* on the bottom of the organ. When the brain receives action potentials from these receptors, it responds by activating muscles that restore the animal to its normal posture.

It's also common for animals to have cells that are responsible for detecting direct physical pressure on skin, as well as pressure-receptor cells that monitor how far muscles or blood vessels are stretched. Animals hear by detecting sound waves, which produce pressure changes in air, and some aquatic animals detect pressure waves in water via a lateral line system. These pressure-sensing systems are all based on the same mechanism.

Let's briefly examine the general structure of a mechanoreceptor cell and its response to pressure, and then investigate the specific structures involved in vertebrate hearing and the lateral line system.

How Do Sensory Cells Respond to Sound Waves and Other Forms of Pressure?

In mechanoreception, direct physical pressure on a plasma membrane or distortion of membrane structures by bending changes the conformation of ion channels in the membrane and causes the channels to open or close.

The consequent change in ion flow through the channel proteins results either in a depolarization or a hyperpolarization. This changes the frequency of action potentials in a sensory neuron.

The Structure of Hair Cells In vertebrates, ion channels that respond to pressure are often found in hair cells. **Hair cells** are pressure-receptor cells, illustrated in **Figure 44.3a,** named for their stiff outgrowths called **stereocilia** (singular: **stereocilium**). The "hairy-looking" stereocilia are microvilli that are reinforced by actin filaments.

(a) Hair cells have many stereocilia and one kinocilium.

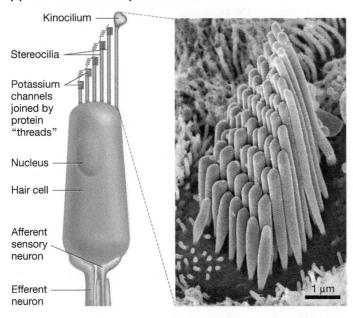

(b) PROCESS: BENDING OPENS ION CHANNELS

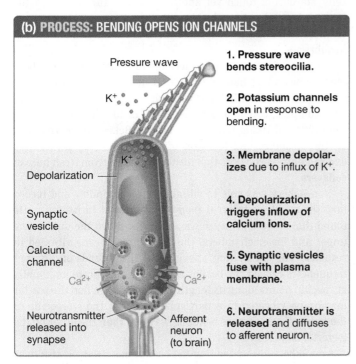

1. **Pressure wave bends stereocilia.**

2. **Potassium channels open** in response to bending.

3. **Membrane depolarizes** due to influx of K⁺.

4. **Depolarization triggers inflow of calcium ions.**

5. **Synaptic vesicles fuse with plasma membrane.**

6. **Neurotransmitter is released** and diffuses to afferent neuron.

Figure 44.3 Hair Cells Transduce Sound Waves to Electrical Signals.

Many hair cells also have a single **kinocilium,** a true cilium that contains a 9 + 2 arrangement of microtubules (introduced in Chapter 7). Hair cells are found in the ears of land-dwelling vertebrates and the lateral line system in many species of fishes and some amphibians.

As Figure 44.3a shows, the stereocilia in a hair cell are arranged in order of increasing length; if a kinocilium is present, it is the longest of all the projections. These structures extend into a fluid-filled chamber.

Signal Transduction in Hair Cells If stereocilia are bent in the direction of the kinocilium in response to pressure (**Figure 44.3b**), the distortion causes potassium ion (K⁺) channels in the stereocilia to open. This is the common theme connecting pressure-sensing cells: Bending opens or closes ion channels.

Recall that the opening of K⁺ channels usually causes an outflow of K⁺ that hyperpolarizes neurons (see Chapter 43). Hair-cell plasma membranes respond differently, however, because they are bathed by extracellular fluid with an extraordinarily high K⁺ concentration. As a result, when the channels open, K⁺ rushes in and causes the cells to depolarize.

In hair cells, depolarization causes an inflow of calcium ions, which triggers an increase in the amount of neurotransmitter released at the synapse between the hair cell and a sensory neuron. The end result is excitation of the afferent sensory neuron, meaning that it becomes more likely to fire action potentials. You might recall that afferent neurons are part of the peripheral nervous system and conduct information to the CNS (see Chapter 43).

If sound-pressure waves bend stereocilia the other way, however, the K⁺ channels close, and the cell hyperpolarizes. This decreases the amount of neurotransmitter released at the synapse and inhibits the postsynaptic sensory neuron, making it less likely to fire action potentials.

How can bending affect ion channels? Electron micrographs show that tiny threads connect the tips of stereocilia to each other. One hypothesis contends that when the stereocilia are bent, the threads somehow pull on the ion channels in the membrane of the next longest stereocilium and open them like tiny trapdoors (see Figure 44.3b, step 2). Researchers still do not fully understand how the ion channels involved in pressure reception work.

Hearing: The Mammalian Ear

Hearing is the sensation produced by the wavelike changes in air pressure called sound. A sound consists of waves of pressure in air or in water. The number of pressure waves that occur in 1 second is the **frequency** of the sound, reported in units called hertz (Hz), or cycles per second. When you hear different sound frequencies, you perceive them as different **pitches.** A high-pitched sound may have a frequency in the range of 8000 Hz, whereas a low-pitched sound frequency might be 1000 Hz.

The ear transduces sound waves into action potentials that carry information to the brain. To understand how changes in the membrane potential of hair cells result in hearing, let's focus on the human ear as a case study. The human ear has three sections: the **outer ear, middle ear,** and **inner ear,** as shown in **Figure 44.4** on page 926. A membrane separates each section from the next.

The path of sound through the ear is traced in Figure 44.4. The outer ear, which projects from the head, collects incoming pressure waves and funnels them into a tube known as the ear canal. At the inner end of the ear canal (see the lower part of Figure 44.4), the waves strike the **tympanic membrane,** or eardrum, which separates the outer ear from the middle ear.

The repeated cycles of air compression cause the tympanic membrane to vibrate back and forth with the same frequency as the sound wave. The vibrations are passed to three tiny bones

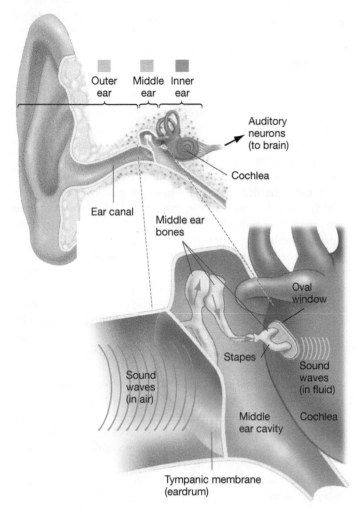

Figure 44.4 **Mammals Have an Outer Ear, Middle Ear, and Inner Ear.** The middle ear starts with the tympanic membrane and ends in the oval window of the cochlea.

in the middle ear that vibrate against one another in response. One of these bones, the **stapes** (pronounced *STAY-peez*), vibrates against a membrane called the **oval window,** which separates the middle ear from the inner ear. The oval window oscillates in response and generates waves in the fluid inside a chamber known as the **cochlea** (pronounced *KOK-lee-ah*). These pressure waves are sensed by hair cells in the cochlea.

In effect, the ear translates airborne waves into fluid-borne waves. The system seems extraordinarily complex, though, for such a simple result. Why doesn't the outer ear canal lead directly to the oval window? Why have a middle ear at all?

The Middle Ear Amplifies Sounds Biologists began to understand the function of the middle ear when they recognized two key aspects of its structure. First, the size difference between the tympanic membrane and the oval window is important. The tympanic membrane is about 15 times as large as the oval window, causing the amount of vibration induced by sound waves to increase by a factor of 15 when it reaches the oval window. This phenomenon is similar to taking the same amount of force used to bang on a very large door and applying it to a very small door.

In addition, the three middle ear bones act as levers that further amplify vibrations from the tympanic membrane. The overall effect in mammals is to amplify sound by a factor of 22—meaning that soft sounds are amplified enough to stimulate hair cells in the cochlea. Thus, biologists interpret the mammalian middle ear as an adaptation for increasing sensitivity to sound.

To summarize, the mammalian outer ear transmits sound waves from the environment to the middle ear; the middle ear amplifies these waves enough to stimulate the hair cells within the cochlea of the inner ear.

If all hair cells responded equally to all frequencies of sound, you would be able to perceive only one pitch. Everyone's voice—indeed, every noise—would sound the same. How can hair cells distinguish different frequencies?

The Cochlea Detects the Frequency of Sounds As **Figure 44.5a** shows, the cochlea is a coiled tube with a set of internal membranes that divide it into three chambers. Hair cells, forming rows in the middle chamber, are embedded in a tissue that sits atop the **basilar membrane** (**Figure 44.5b**). In addition, the hair cells' stereocilia touch yet another, smaller surface called the **tectorial membrane.** (The kinocilium is not present in a mature cochlear hair cell.) In effect, hair cells are sandwiched between membranes.

Researchers struggled for decades to understand how these membranes affect hair cell function. It is virtually impossible to study cochleas in living organisms, because the cochleas are tiny, complex, coiled, and buried deep inside the skull. During the 1920s and 1930s, however, Georg von Békésy pioneered work on the structure and function of these organs by performing experiments on cochleas that he had dissected from fresh human cadavers.

Von Békésy was able to vibrate the oval window and record how the cochlea's internal membranes moved in response. He found that when a pressure wave traveled down the fluid in the upper and lower chambers, the basilar membrane vibrated in response. His key finding, though, was that sounds of different frequencies caused the basilar membrane to vibrate maximally at specific points along its length (**Figure 44.6**). When the basilar membrane vibrated in a particular location, the stereocilia of the hair cells there were bent one way and then the other by the tectorial membrane.

Von Békésy also noted that the basilar membrane is stiff near the oval window and flexible at the other end. This is why each segment vibrates in response to a different frequency of sound. Just as a stiff drumhead produces a high-pitched sound and a loose drumhead yields a low-pitched sound, high-frequency sounds cause the stiff part of the basilar membrane to vibrate; low-frequency sounds cause the flexible part to vibrate.

To summarize, certain portions of the basilar membrane vibrate in response to specific frequencies and result in the bending of hair-cell stereocilia. In this way, hair cells in a particular place on the membrane respond to sounds of a certain frequency. When the occipital lobe of the cerebrum receives action potentials from neurons associated with specific hair cells, it interprets the action potentials as a particular pitch—meaning a specific frequency of sound. The result is the sense called hearing.

(a) The middle chamber of the fluid-filled cochlea contains hair cells.

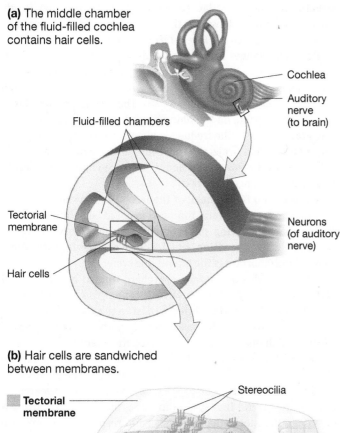

Cochlea

Auditory nerve (to brain)

Fluid-filled chambers

Tectorial membrane

Hair cells

Neurons (of auditory nerve)

(b) Hair cells are sandwiched between membranes.

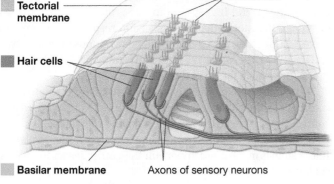

Stereocilia

Tectorial membrane

Hair cells

Basilar membrane

Axons of sensory neurons

Figure 44.5 The Human Cochlea Contains Fluid-Filled Chambers Separated by Membranes.

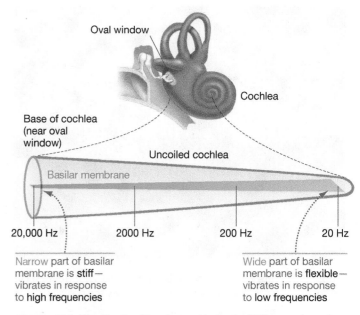

Oval window

Cochlea

Base of cochlea (near oval window)

Uncoiled cochlea

Basilar membrane

20,000 Hz   2000 Hz   200 Hz   20 Hz

Narrow part of basilar membrane is **stiff**— vibrates in response to **high** frequencies

Wide part of basilar membrane is **flexible**— vibrates in response to **low** frequencies

Figure 44.6 The Basilar Membrane Varies in Stiffness along Its Length. Different parts of the basilar membrane vibrate in response to different sound frequencies.

Complex sounds contain a wide variety of frequencies and trigger particular combinations of hair cells. Through experience, the brain learns which combinations of frequencies represent music, a fire alarm, or a best friend's voice.

Humans can hear sounds between 20 Hz and 20,000 Hz (20,000 Hz is equal to 20 kHz, or kilohertz). But some mammals can hear low-frequency infrasounds that are too low for humans to hear (*infra*— means "below or under"); others can hear high-frequency ultrasounds that are above the range of human hearing (*ultra*— means "beyond").

Elephants Detect Infrasound When Katherine Payne was observing elephants at a zoo in the mid-1980s, she noticed a subtle throbbing in the air. Payne knew that infrasound can produce such sensations.

To test the hypothesis that the elephants were producing infrasonic vocalizations, Payne returned to the zoo with a tape recorder and microphones that could pick up sounds at extremely low frequencies. Played at normal speed, the tape she made was silent. But when she raised the pitch of the sounds by speeding up the tape, she heard a chorus of cow-like noises. The elephants were calling to each other, using low-frequency sounds.

Follow-up research showed that elephants have the best infrasonic hearing of any land mammal. Because infrasound can travel exceptionally long distances, biologists hypothesize that infrasonic calls allow wild elephants to communicate when they are miles apart.

Bats Detect Ultrasound Ultrasonic hearing in bats was discovered in the late 1930s, when Donald Griffin borrowed the only ultrasonic apparatus then in existence from Robert Galambos, a fellow graduate student. Griffin used the machine to demonstrate that flying bats constantly emit ultrasounds. In subsequent experiments, he documented that a bat with cotton in its ears, or with its mouth taped shut, crashed into walls when released in a room. Blindfolded bats, in contrast, never crashed.

Griffin and Galambos concluded that bats use sound echoes (sonar) to navigate. This concept, termed **echolocation,** was an outlandish idea at the time. When Galambos described it at a meeting in 1940, another scientist shook him by the shoulders and said, "You can't really mean that!"

Bats generate high-frequency sound waves with their larynx, or voice box. These waves "bounce" off surfaces (including those of insects), producing echoes that the bat detects in its inner ear (see **Figure 44.7** on page 928). Recall that hair cells on different sections of the basilar membrane sense sound waves of different frequencies. In bats, a huge area of the basilar membrane is

Figure 44.7 Bats Emit Ultrasonic Sound Waves That Bounce Off Surfaces. Returning sound waves are sensed by the bat's inner ear.

- Bat sonar
- Returning sound waves

specialized for sensing the high-frequency sounds of the returning echoes. Similarly, the part of the brain used to process sound is unusually large in bats, highlighting the extremely important role of echolocation in their navigation and hunting.

More recent research has shown that dolphins, shrews, and certain other animals besides bats use sonar. In fact, it is likely that at least some of these species perceive shapes with their ears better than they do with their eyes.

The Lateral Line System in Fishes and Amphibians

Hair cells in the ear allow mammals to sense changes in air pressure that are perceived as sound. But in fishes and aquatic amphibians, hair cells in a different organ allow the perception of pressure changes in water. In most fishes and larval amphibians, groups of hair cells are embedded in gel-like domed structures called cupulae (pronounced *KEWP-yoo-lay*) inside canals that run the length of the body (Figure 44.8a), forming a sensory organ called the **lateral line system.**

Pressure changes in the surrounding water—whether resulting from waves, an animal swimming nearby, or some other force—cause changes in the pressure of water moving through the lateral line system (Figure 44.8b). These changes cause kinocilia and stereocilia on the hair cells to bend, and the distortion leads to a change in the frequency of action potentials along sensory neurons that project to the brain. In this way, most aquatic vertebrates get information about pressure changes at specific points along the head and body.

What use do fishes make of the lateral line system? It seems reasonable that the lateral line system could be helpful for identifying mates, locating prey, or avoiding predators. However, fishes could also use vision, smell, or other senses for these functions. How important is the lateral line system?

To answer this question, researchers studied how nocturnal catfish locate prey. At night, catfish cannot use vision to hunt, so they must detect stimuli that persist in the wake of their prey after it has moved on. The researchers hypothesized that the nocturnal catfish hunt smaller fishes using the lateral line system.

To test this hypothesis, they conducted an ablation experiment on the catfish (Figure 44.9). Ablation is the removal or blocking of a structure or process. In this case, the researchers ablated the lateral line system in one group of catfish, using a chemical that blocks the hair cells from responding to pressure waves. In another group of catfish, they ablated the ability to smell or taste the water by surgically removing the lobes of the brain responsible for these senses.

While the catfish whose smell and taste were ablated captured about the same percentage of guppies as the non-ablated control group, the catfish whose lateral line was ablated had very poor hunting success. The researchers concluded that the lateral line system is much more important than other senses in successful hunting by nocturnal catfish.

(a) The lateral line system consists of a series of canals running along the head and body.

(b) Water enters the canals through pores and bends kinocilia on hair cells, activating sensory neurons.

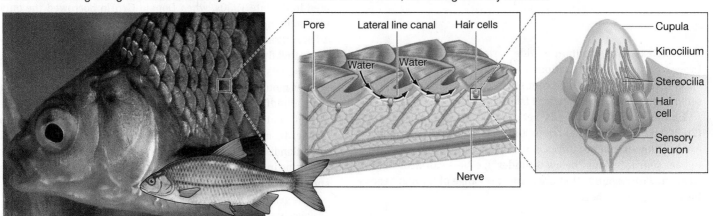

Figure 44.8 The Lateral Line System Detects Pressure Waves in Water. (a) Lateral line canals lie just under the fish's epidermis. **(b)** Hair cells within the canals have kinocilia and stereocilia embedded in a gel-like cupula.

QUESTION: What cues do predatory fish use to detect prey at night?

HYPOTHESIS: Predatory fish detect prey using the lateral line system.

ALTERNATE HYPOTHESIS: Predatory fish detect prey using smell and taste.

NULL HYPOTHESIS: Predatory fish use none of these senses to detect prey.

EXPERIMENTAL SETUP:

1. Three experimental groups of catfish ($n = 16$ for each group):

Lateral line ablated	Smell and taste ablated	Control fish

2. Acclimate catfish to dark tank at night.

3. Add guppies to tank and record capture success rate.

PREDICTION: Fish with their lateral line ablated will have lower capture success than control fish.

PREDICTION OF ALTERNATE HYPOTHESIS: Fish with smell and taste ablated will have lower capture success than control fish.

PREDICTION OF NULL HYPOTHESIS: There will be no capture success difference among groups.

RESULTS:

Percentage of Guppies Captured

Lateral line ablated	Smell and taste ablated	Control fish
17%	60%	65%

CONCLUSION: Nocturnal predatory catfish use the lateral line system to detect prey.

Figure 44.9 The Lateral Line System Is Used for Predation.
SOURCE: Pohlmann, K., J. Atema, and T. Breithaupt. 2004. The importance of the lateral line in nocturnal predation of piscivorous catfish. *The Journal of Experimental Biology* 207: 2971–2978.

✔ **PROCESS OF SCIENCE** If you wanted to conduct a study similar to this one on a diurnal species of catfish, what other sense would you need to control for, and how would you do it?

If you understand that …

- In vertebrate hair cells, mechanoreception begins when the stereocilia bend in response to changes in pressure. The bending opens ion channels and results in a change in membrane potential.
- The mammalian ear consists of specialized structures that function in transmitting and amplifying sound and in responding to specific frequencies as well as recognizing changes in intensity.
- The lateral line system in fishes and aquatic amphibians allows them to sense pressure waves in water caused by prey, predators, and potential mates.

✔ **You should be able to …**

1. Predict and explain the effect on hearing in each of the following cases: a punctured eardrum, a mutation that results in dramatically shortened stereocilia, and an age-related loss of flexibility in the basilar membrane.
2. Which of the following animals would you expect to have a more developed lateral line system, the aquatic clawed frog or the semiaquatic bullfrog? Explain.

Answers are available in Appendix A.

44.3 Photoreception: Sensing Light

Most animals have a way to sense light. The organs involved in **photoreception** range from simple light-sensitive eyespots in flatworms to the sophisticated, image-forming eyes of vertebrates, cephalopod mollusks, and arthropods.

Variation in the structure of light-sensing organs illustrates an important general principle about the sensory abilities of animals: In most cases, a species' sensory abilities correlate with the environment it lives in and its mode of life—how it finds food and mates. Eyes and other sensory structures are adaptations that allow individuals to thrive in a particular environment. Salamander species that live in meadows and forests have sophisticated eyes; those that live in lightless caves have no functional eyes at all.

Keep this principle in mind as you delve into the details of how insects and vertebrates see.

The Insect Eye

Insects have **compound eyes** composed of hundreds or thousands of light-sensing columns called **ommatidia.** As **Figure 44.10** on page 930 shows, each ommatidium has a lens that focuses light onto a small number of receptor cells—usually four. The receptor cells, in turn, send axons to the brain.

Each ommatidium acts like a single pixel on a computer monitor: It contributes information about one small piece of the visual field. Therefore, a compound eye with more ommatidia has higher resolution—meaning greater resolving power, or ability to distinguish objects.

(a) Ommatidia are the functional units of insect eyes.

(b) Each ommatidium contains receptor cells that send axons to the CNS.

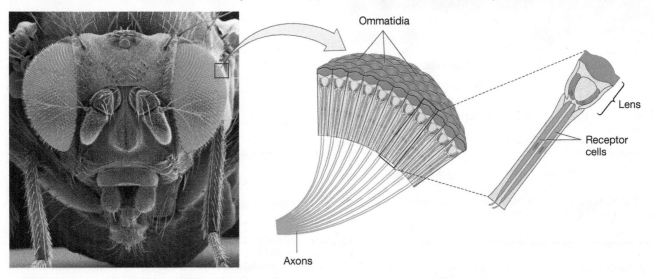

Figure 44.10 In the Compound Eyes of Insects, Each Ommatidium Sees Part of the Visual Field. The micrograph in part (a) is colorized to match the drawings in part (b).

In addition, the presence of many light-sensing columns makes species with compound eyes particularly good at detecting movement. Insects that hunt by sight, such as damselflies and dragonflies, have particularly large numbers of ommatidia.

The Vertebrate Eye

Compound eyes are found in insects, crustaceans, and certain other arthropods. Because compound eyes appear only in species that are part of the same monophyletic group (see Chapter 25), researchers conclude that this type of eye structure evolved just once—in an ancestor of today's arthropods.

In contrast, the **simple eye**—a structure with a single lens that focuses incoming light onto a layer of many receptor cells—evolved independently in several widely divergent groups, including annelids, cephalopod mollusks (squid and octopuses), and vertebrates. Let's examine the vertebrate version of the simple eye more closely.

The Structure of the Vertebrate Eye Figure 44.11a shows the major structures in a typical vertebrate eye:

- The outermost layer of the eye is a tough rind of white tissue called the sclera. This is the "white of the eye."

- The front of the sclera forms the **cornea,** a transparent sheet of connective tissue.

- The **iris** is a pigmented, round muscle just inside the cornea. The iris can contract or expand to control the amount of light entering the eye.

- The **pupil** is the hole in the center of the iris.

- Light enters the eye through the cornea and passes through the pupil and a curved, clear **lens.**

- Together, the cornea and lens focus incoming light onto the retina in the back of the eye. The **retina** contains a layer of photoreceptors and several layers of neurons.

Figure 44.11b provides a closer look at the retina, which is attached to the rest of the eye by a single layer of pigmented epithelial cells. From back to front, the retina comprises three distinct cell layers:

1. The photoreceptors, sensory cells that respond to light, are held in place by the pigmented epithelium.

2. Photoreceptors synapse with an intermediate layer of connecting neurons called **bipolar cells.**

3. Bipolar cells synapse with neurons called **ganglion cells,** which form the innermost layer of the retina. The axons of the ganglion cells project to the brain via the **optic nerve.**

Note that vertebrate eyes—including yours—have a blind spot because there are no photoreceptor cells where the optic nerve leaves the retina. If light falls in this area, there are no sensory cells available to respond. No signal is sent to the brain, so the light isn't seen.

What Do Rods and Cones Do? Early anatomists established that the photoreceptors in vertebrate eyes come in two distinct types: small rod-shaped cells and cone-shaped cells, called **rods** and **cones** (Figure 44.12a). When technical advances allowed changes in the membrane potentials of these cells to be recorded, it became clear that rods and cones differ in function as well as structure.

Rods are sensitive to dim light but not to color. Cones, in contrast, are much less sensitive to faint light but respond to different wavelengths (i.e., colors). These discoveries explained why night vision is largely black and white—at night, the rods do most of the work.

How Do Rods and Cones Detect Light? As Figure 44.12a shows, rods and cones have segments that are packed with membrane-rich disks. The membranes contain large quantities of a transmembrane protein called **opsin.** Each opsin molecule is associated with a molecule of the pigment **retinal.** In rod cells, the two-molecule complex is called **rhodopsin** (Figure 44.12b).

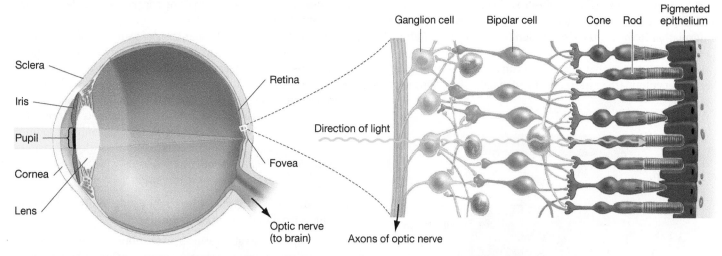

(a) The structure of the vertebrate eye

Sclera
Iris
Pupil
Cornea
Lens
Retina
Fovea
Optic nerve (to brain)

(b) In the retina, cells are arranged in layers.

Ganglion cell
Bipolar cell
Cone
Rod
Pigmented epithelium
Direction of light
Axons of optic nerve

Figure 44.11 Simple Eyes Have a Single Lens That Focuses Incoming Light on Receptor Cells. (a) Light passes through the pupil of the eye and is focused onto the retina. **(b)** The photoreceptor cells (rods and cones), which respond to light, are in the "outermost" layer of the retina, farthest from the light source.

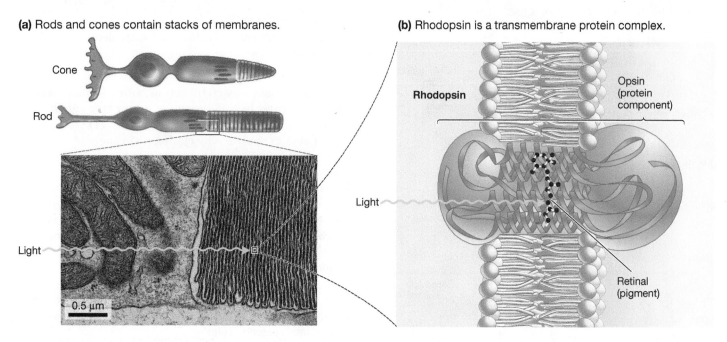

(a) Rods and cones contain stacks of membranes.

Cone
Rod
Light
0.5 µm

(b) Rhodopsin is a transmembrane protein complex.

Rhodopsin
Opsin (protein component)
Light
Retinal (pigment)

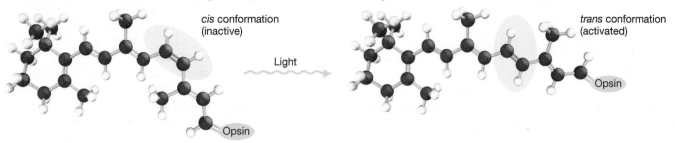

(c) The retinal molecule inside rhodopsin changes shape when retinal absorbs light.

cis conformation (inactive)
Opsin
Light
trans conformation (activated)
Opsin

Figure 44.12 Rods and Cones Are Packed with Transmembrane Proteins That Contain the Pigment Retinal. (a) Rods and cones have membranous disks containing thousands of opsin and retinal molecules (together called rhodopsin in rods). **(b)** Each opsin holds one retinal molecule. **(c)** Retinal changes conformation when it absorbs light. In response, opsin also changes shape.

Experiments with isolated retinal molecules confirmed that retinal changes shape when it absorbs light. Specifically, the number-11 carbon in the retinal molecule changes from the *cis* conformation to the *trans* conformation (Figure 44.12c). Retinal is a light switch.

The shape change that occurs in retinal triggers a series of events that culminate in a stream of action potentials being sent

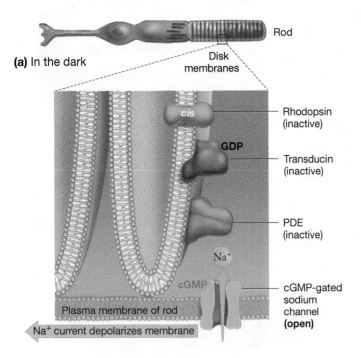

(a) In the dark

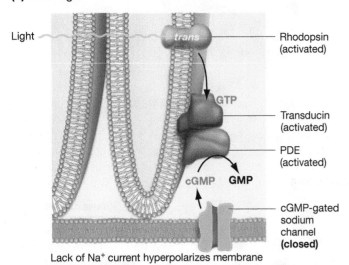

(b) In the light

Lack of Na⁺ current hyperpolarizes membrane

Figure 44.13 A Signal-Transduction Pathway Connects Light Absorption to Changes in Membrane Potential. (a) In the dark, sodium ions flow into the photoreceptor, depolarizing the membrane. **(b)** In the light, activation of rhodopsin leads to a reduction in cGMP concentration. With less cGMP available, cGMP-gated sodium channels close, and the membrane hyperpolarizes.

✔ The inflow of sodium ions into a photoreceptor cell is called "the dark current." Why?

to the brain. The sequence of events is unusual, though, because light does not open ion channels or trigger the release of a neurotransmitter to a sensory neuron.

In vertebrates, the molecular basis of vision is a shape change in retinal that *closes* ion channels and decreases the amount of neurotransmitter being released to the sensory neuron. In rod cells, electrical activity across the membrane, as well as neurotransmitter release, are maximized in the dark. When retinal has not been activated by light, sodium channels in the rod's plasma membrane are open (Figure 44.13a), and entry of sodium continually depolarizes the rod cells. Exposure to light transmits information by *inhibiting* both processes.

Figure 44.13b shows how the inhibition happens:

1. Rhodopsin is activated when light causes retinal to change shape from the *cis* to *trans* conformation.

2. Rhodopsin activation causes a membrane-bound molecule called transducin to activate the enzyme phosphodiesterase (PDE).

3. PDE breaks down a nucleotide called cyclic guanosine monophosphate (cGMP) to guanosine monophosphate (GMP).

4. As cGMP levels decline, cGMP-gated sodium channels in the plasma membrane of the rod cell close.

5. When sodium channels close, Na⁺ entry decreases and the membrane hyperpolarizes.

✔ If you understand this sequence of events, you should be able to explain why cGMP acts as both a second messenger and a ligand in this system, and how transducin compares to G proteins (introduced in Chapter 11). You should also be able to explain why closing Na⁺ channels results in hyperpolarization.

In response to the ensuing change in membrane potential, smaller quantities of the neurotransmitter glutamate are released at the synapse. The decrease in neurotransmitter release indicates to the postsynaptic bipolar cell that the rod has absorbed light. As a result, a new pattern of action potentials is sent to the brain, via neurons called ganglion cells. Axons from ganglion cells are bundled into the optic nerve.

This system is exquisitely sensitive: Biologists have recorded a measurable change in the membrane potentials of rod cells in response to a single photon of light. But how do humans and other animals perceive color?

Color Vision: The Puzzle of Dalton's Eye   To answer this question, consider the research program initiated by John Dalton[1] in the late eighteenth century. At the age of 26, Dalton realized that he and his brother saw colors differently than other people did. To them, red sealing wax and green laurel leaves appeared to be the same color, and a rainbow exhibited only two hues. Dalton and his brother could not differentiate the colors red and green. This condition is called red–green color blindness (Figure 44.14).

---

[1]Dalton was an accomplished physicist. He was the first proponent of the atomic theory of matter and formulated Dalton's law on the partial pressures of gases (introduced in Chapter 42). Red–green color blindness is sometimes called daltonism in his honor.

Figure 44.14 People with Red–Green Color Blindness Cannot Distinguish Red from Green. These images show what a person with red–green color blindness would see, compared to a person with normal color vision.

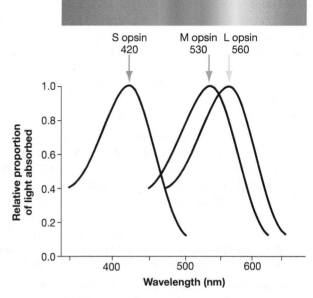

Figure 44.15 Color Vision Is Possible because Different Opsins Absorb Different Wavelengths of Light. Each human cone cell contains one of three different types of opsin. Each opsin absorbs a different range of wavelengths.

✔ The retinal molecules in S, M, and L opsins are identical. What is the likely reason that the opsins respond to different wavelengths of light?

In a lecture delivered in 1794, Dalton explained his perceptions by hypothesizing that red wavelengths failed to reach his retinas. Further, he hypothesized that because a normal eyeball is filled with clear fluid, and because blue fluids absorb red light, his defective vision resulted from the presence of bluish fluid rather than clear fluid in his eyes.

To test this hypothesis, Dalton left instructions that his eyes should be removed after his death and examined to see if the fluid inside was blue. When he died 50 years later, an assistant dutifully removed the eyes from Dalton's corpse and examined them. The fluid inside the eye was not blue at all, however, but slightly yellow—the normal color for an older person. Further, when the back was cut off one eye and colored objects were viewed through the lens, the objects looked perfectly normal. Dalton's hypothesis was incorrect.

Color Vision: Multiple Opsins What, then, caused Dalton's color blindness? The key to answering this question was the discovery that the human retina contains three types of color-sensitive photoreceptors: blue, green, and red cones, named for the colors to which they are most sensitive.

To follow up on this result, biologists analyzed opsin molecules from the three cone types and found that each had a distinct amino acid sequence. The three proteins are now called the blue, green, and red opsins (or S, M, and L, for short, medium, and long wavelengths, respectively). Although retinal is the light-absorbing molecule in all photoreceptor cells, the different opsin molecules cause each type to respond to a different range of wavelengths of light.

Based on these results, biologists hypothesized that the brain distinguishes colors by combining signals initiated by the three classes of opsins. **Figure 44.15**, for example, graphs how much light is absorbed across a range of wavelengths by the S, M, and L opsins of humans. Notice that light at a wavelength of 560 nanometers (nm) is absorbed strongly by L cones, to an intermediate degree by M cones, and not at all by S cones. In response to the corresponding signals from these cells, the brain perceives the color yellow.

Does this hypothesis explain Dalton's color blindness? According to the data in Figure 44.15, wavelengths from green to red are not absorbed by S opsin at all. It is thus unlikely that S opsin is involved in red–green color blindness. Did Dalton fail to distinguish red and green because his M or L cones were defective? Research has shown that red–green color-blind people lack either functional M or L cones, or both. Was the same true of Dalton?

This question was answered in the 1990s, when the genes for the M and L opsins were sequenced. Remarkably, Dalton's eyes had been preserved. Researchers managed to extract DNA from the 150-year-old tissue and analyze his M opsin genes and L opsin genes. They found that Dalton had a normal *L* allele but lacked a functional *M* allele. As a result, he did not have green-sensitive cones. The puzzle of Dalton's color vision was solved.

Red–green color blindness, or the inability to distinguish red and green due to an absence of either M or L cones, is estimated to affect about 5 to 10 percent of men and less than 0.5 percent of women. It is more prevalent in men than in women because it is an X-linked trait (see Chapter 14).

Do Other Animals See Color? What about other animals—do they see color the way humans do? The answer is, probably not. Animals that are active at night have relatively few cone cells and many rods, giving them high sensitivity to light but poor color vision. On the other hand, many vertebrate and invertebrate species have four or more types of opsins and probably perceive a world of colors that is much richer than ours.

In general, the types of opsins found in a species correlate with the environment it inhabits and its mode of life. For example,

- A marine fish called the coelacanth (pronounced *SEE-luh-kanth*), which lives in water 200 m deep, has two opsins that respond to the blue region of the spectrum (with absorption peaks at 478 nm and 485 nm). As a result, coelacanths perceive several distinct hues of blue that we would perceive as a single color. Presumably, these opsins offer an adaptive advantage to coelacanths because wavelengths in the yellow and red parts of the spectrum do not penetrate well into deep water—only blue light exists in the coelacanth's habitat.

- In humans and other primates that eat fruit, two of the three opsins are sensitive to wavelengths around 550 nm. The presence of these opsins allows individuals to distinguish between the greens, yellows, and reds of unripe and ripe fruits.

- Many animals (for example, some insects and birds) have opsins that are sensitive to ultraviolet (UV) light, which has shorter wavelengths than humans can see. Certain flowers have UV patterns that serve as signals for insect pollinators. Also, many birds have strong UV patterns in their plumage that are important criteria used by females for selecting mates.

44.4 Chemoreception: Sensing Chemicals

Chemoreception occurs when chemicals bind to chemoreceptors, initiating action potentials in sensory neurons. The sense of taste, called **gustation,** and the sense of smell, called **olfaction,** originate in chemoreceptors. A chemoreceptor detects the

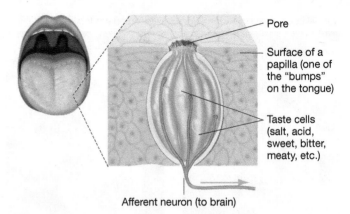

Figure 44.16 Taste Buds Contain Many Types of Chemoreceptors. A single taste bud, shown in this figure, is comprised of many taste cells.

presence of a specific molecule by undergoing a change in membrane potential when that molecule is present. In this way, information about the presence of a particular molecule is transduced to an electrical signal in the body.

Taste: Detecting Molecules in the Mouth

In humans, the chemoreceptor cells that sense taste are clustered in structures known as **taste buds.** Although taste buds are scattered around the mouth and throat, most taste buds are located on the tongue (**Figure 44.16**). A taste bud contains about 100 spindle-shaped taste cells, which make synapses with sensory neurons.

How do taste cells work on a molecular level, and how do they produce the sensation of taste? Early taste research focused on the hypothesis that four "basic tastes" existed: salty, sour, bitter, and sweet.

Salty and Sour Researchers who analyzed the membrane proteins in taste cells found strong evidence that salty and sour sensations result from the activity of ion channels.

- The sensation of saltiness is due primarily to sodium ions (Na^+) dissolved in food. These ions flow into certain taste cells through open Na^+ channels and depolarize the cells' membranes.

- Sourness is due in part to the presence of protons (H^+), which flow directly into certain taste cells through H^+ channels and depolarize the membrane.

The sour taste of grapefruit and other citrus fruits, for example, results from the release of protons by citric acid. In general, the lower the pH of a food, the more it depolarizes a taste cell's plasma membrane, and the more sour the food tastes.

Compared to saltiness and sourness, the molecular mechanisms responsible for the sensations of bitterness and sweetness have been much more difficult to identify.

Why Do Many Different Foods Taste Bitter? Bitterness has been difficult to understand because molecules with very different structures, such as those in orange peel or unsweetened cocoa, are all perceived as bitter. How is this possible?

An answer began to emerge after researchers confirmed that some humans genetically lack the ability to taste certain bitter substances. In 1931, Arthur Fox was synthesizing phenylthiocarbamide (PTC) and accidentally released some of it into the air. A nearby colleague complained of a bitter taste in his mouth, but Fox could not taste anything. Follow-up research confirmed that the ability to taste PTC is inherited and polymorphic. About 25 percent of Americans cannot sense the molecule.

To find the gene responsible for this trait, biologists compared the distribution of genetic markers observed in "tasters" and "nontasters." The mapping effort recently narrowed down this gene's location to several candidate chromosomal regions. (Chapter 20 introduced this type of gene hunt.) In one of the regions, researchers found a family of 40 to 80 genes that encode transmembrane receptor proteins.

Follow-up work has documented that each protein in the family binds to a different type of bitter molecule. A taste cell, however, can have many different receptor proteins from this family. As a result, many different molecules can depolarize the same cell and cause the sensation of bitterness.

Why are so many genes devoted to detecting bitterness? Many of the molecules that bind to these receptor proteins are found in toxic plants; most animals react to bitter foods by spitting them out and avoiding them in the future. In essence, bitterness indicates, "This food is dangerous; don't swallow it."

What Is the Molecular Basis of Sweetness and Other Tastes?

Inspired by progress on bitter receptors, research teams used a similar approach—analyzing mutant mice that could not sense sweetness—to understand how sweet receptors work.

In humans and mice, three closely related membrane receptor proteins are responsible for detecting sweetness as well as glutamate and other amino acids. Glutamate triggers the sensation called **umami,** which is the meaty taste of the molecule monosodium glutamate (MSG). Glutamate is sensed by one particular pair of the three receptor proteins. Sweetness is sensed by a different pair.

Recent work has answered a long-standing question about the sweet sensation—why so many different types of sugars trigger the same sensation. As it turns out, a single receptor protein has binding sites for multiple types of sweet compounds, meaning that a variety of molecules can stimulate each sweet receptor cell.

The tongue appears to have receptors that are responsible for sensations other than salty, sour, bitter, sweet, and umami. For example, scientists are currently studying whether our tongues can detect calcium, other metals, and carbon dioxide. There is also evidence that mechanoreception in the tongue plays an important role in taste by giving foods a certain texture or "mouth feel." Although taste is beginning to reveal its secrets, the complete story will probably not be known for many years.

Olfaction: Detecting Molecules in the Air

Taste allows animals to assess the quality of their food before swallowing it. Olfaction, in contrast, allows animals to monitor airborne molecules that convey information. Wolves and domestic dogs, for example, can distinguish millions of different airborne molecules at vanishingly small concentrations. The molecules that constitute odor contain information about the movements and activities of prey and other members of an animal's own species.

Odorants Provide Information about the Environment Airborne molecules that convey information about food or the environment are called **odorants.** When they reach the nose, they diffuse into a mucus layer in the roof of the nose (**Figure 44.17**). There, they activate olfactory neurons by binding to membrane-bound receptor proteins. Axons from these neurons project to the **olfactory bulb,** the part of the brain where olfactory signals are processed and interpreted.

Understanding the anatomy of the odor-recognition system was a relatively simple task. Understanding how receptor neurons distinguish one molecule from another was much more difficult. Initially, investigators hypothesized that receptors respond

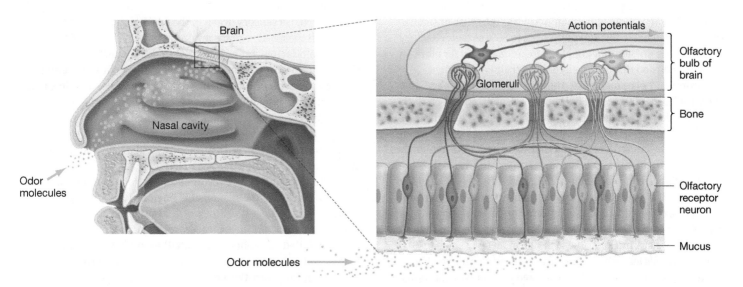

Figure 44.17 In Mammals, Chemoreceptor Cells in the Nose Respond to Specific Odorants. Each of the chemosensory neurons in the nose has one type of odor receptor protein on its dendrites. Sensory neurons with the same receptor protein project to the same glomerulus, or section within the olfactory bulb of the brain.

Figure 44.18 **Bloodhounds Have an Excellent Olfactory Sense.**

to a small set of "basic odors," such as musky, floral, minty, and so on. The idea was that each basic odor would be detected by its own type of receptor, much like the way gustation works.

In 1991, Linda Buck and Richard Axel discovered a gene family in mice that comprises hundreds of distinct coding regions and encodes receptor proteins on the surface of olfactory receptor neurons. Follow-up experiments confirmed that each receptor protein binds to a small set of molecules.

Further work established that most, if not all, vertebrates possess this family of genes. The number of olfactory receptor genes varies widely among mammals, from around 700 in some primates to over 4000 in elephants. But about half of the receptor genes in most mammal species have mutations that render them nonfunctional. For example, humans have about 800 receptor genes, but only half code for receptor proteins. This observation may explain why the sense of smell is so poor in humans compared with that of most other mammals. But the sense of smell is even worse in whales and dolphins—70% to 80% of their olfactory receptor genes are nonfunctional. These animals rely far more on hearing and vision than on smell to sense their environment.

In contrast, mammals like rodents, horses, and elephants express at least 1000 types of functional receptor proteins, reflecting their reliance on olfaction to sense the environment. Humans take advantage of the strong olfactory sense of another mammal species, the dog, to sense odorants that we cannot detect, including explosives, drugs, and missing persons or criminals on the run. Bloodhounds have the strongest sense of smell of any dog (Figure 44.18). The combination of many functional receptor protein types expressed in millions of olfactory cells spread over a vast surface area of olfactory epithelium makes the bloodhound an exquisite scent tracker. They can detect as few as one or two human skin cells left behind on a rock or branch in the woods.

Further research on olfaction centered around two questions. How many different receptor proteins occur in the membrane of each neuron involved in odor reception? How does the brain make sense of the input from so many different receptors?

Scientists determined that each olfactory neuron has only one type of receptor protein and that axons of neurons that respond to this receptor protein project to the same region in the olfactory bulb of the brain. These regions are called **glomeruli** (meaning "little balls"). For example, each smell recognized by mice is associated with the activation of a different subset of the 2000 glomeruli in the olfactory bulb. Thus the activation of several specific glomeruli might be perceived as the smell "fresh bread." In essence, then, the sensing of odorants is similar to the eye's use of three cones to sense many colors; but odor reception works on a much larger scale.

Interestingly, odorant receptor proteins have recently been identified in locations other than the nose—for example, in tissues of the heart and pancreas. The proteins have also been identified in the cell membranes of sperm cells, where they appear to play an important role in guiding the sperm toward the egg. Research on this complex and impressive sense continues at a furious pace.

Pheromones Provide Information about Members of the Same Species Recall from the introduction to this chapter that male silk moths can locate female moths from miles away. Males have much larger antennae than females, suggesting that they use these antennae in a sex-specific manner.

These factors led scientists to hypothesize that female moths release a chemical into the environment that binds to chemoreceptors on the males' antennae and acts as an attractant. In 1959, scientists identified this chemical and named it bombykol, after the scientific name of the silk moth (*Bombyx mori*). Bombykol was the first chemically characterized **pheromone,** meaning a chemical that is secreted into the environment and that affects the behavior or physiology of animals of the same species.

Thousands of pheromones have since been identified in invertebrates and vertebrates alike, performing such roles as alerting other members of a beehive to an intruder or signaling a male rodent that a female is ovulating. In insects, pheromones typically bind to receptors on the antennae. In tetrapod vertebrates, pheromone receptors are often localized in the **vomeronasal organ** (VNO), a sensory organ in the nasal cavity. The VNO is distinct from the nasal region containing sensory neurons that project to the olfactory bulb. The VNO and the olfactory bulb send signals to different parts of the brain, although some animals also sense odorants with their VNO. For example, a male snake may use its VNO to follow a pheromone trail of a female snake or a scent trail of a prey animal.

Do humans release pheromones? This is a hotly debated question. In 1971, Martha McClintock reported that the menstrual cycles of women living in close contact with one another become synchronized as a result of a secretion from the women's armpits. However, the responsible chemical was not identified. Furthermore, the methodology of this study has been criticized and its results have become controversial, as other researchers have failed to replicate them. Other studies have suggested that secretions from men's armpits can alter hormone levels in women, but both the amount of the chemical secreted and the reaction to it vary dramatically. Until scientists more fully understand the mechanisms by which these human "pheromones" achieve their effects, the jury is out.

44.5 Other Sensory Systems

The stimuli and senses discussed so far are the ones you are likely most familiar with. But animals can sense much more than pressure waves, light, and chemicals. All animals can sense temperature and painful stimuli, and some can even perceive electric or magnetic fields. Let's start with temperature and examine each of these other stimuli and senses in turn.

Thermoreception: Sensing Temperature

Recall that many animals thermoregulate to maintain body temperature within an acceptable range (see Chapter 39). Virtually every physiological process, from digestion to metabolism, is temperature-dependent, so the ability to sense temperature changes in the environment and respond accordingly is crucial.

Thermoreception Helps Animals Thermoregulate Animals detect heat energy by **thermoreception** and adjust their behaviors or physiological processes, such as shivering and sweating, in response.

Some thermoreceptors are located in the central nervous system. In mammals, the hypothalamus is the brain region that senses departures from homeostatic body temperature and sends signals to effectors to restore homeostasis (see Figure 39.13).

Thermoreceptors also are commonly found on skin and other outer surfaces of animals, so that changes in the temperature of the environment can be sensed. As an example, several types of thermoreceptors have been identified in mammals. Some receptors depolarize in response to cooling, and others depolarize in response to heating. Picking up a cold object stimulates "cold receptors" in your skin, resulting in an increase in the rate of action potentials in sensory neurons that inform your brain that the object is cold.

Interestingly, extreme temperatures are sensed by a different type of receptor, called a nociceptor, that also senses other painful stimuli such as those produced by certain chemicals, excessive pressure, and tissue damage. If you touch a hot stove burner, the pain you feel arises primarily via stimulation of nociceptors.

Pit Vipers Have Extremely Sensitive Thermoreceptors The pit vipers are a group of snakes named after the two temperature-sensitive pits just beneath their nostrils (**Figure 44.19a**). Inside each pit is a membrane lined with exquisitely sensitive thermoreceptors—a rattlesnake's thermoreceptors can sense changes in temperature as little as 0.003°C.

Pit vipers use these thermoreceptors to sense the heat energy given off by prey or predators, and to detect potential burrows in which to hide. The brains of these snakes may combine visual and thermal stimuli into a "thermal image" that might look something like an image from an infrared camera (**Figure 44.19b**). Even in complete darkness, rattlesnakes can strike prey with deadly accuracy.

✔ If you understand thermoreception, you should be able to predict whether a rattlesnake could strike effectively at its prey with (1) its eyes covered but pits exposed, (2) its eyes and pits covered with cotton cloth, and (3) its eyes and pits covered with an opaque, heat-blocking material.

(a) Pit vipers have temperature-sensitive pits.

(b) Warm animals emit infrared radiation.

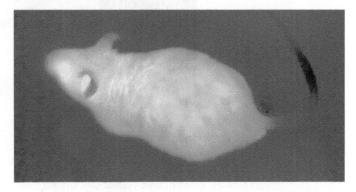

Figure 44.19 Pit Vipers Use Thermoreception to Detect Prey.
(a) Pits are lined with extremely sensitive thermoreceptors. **(b)** Pit vipers can detect infrared radiation given off by rodents and other prey.

Figure 44.20 **Ampullae of Lorenzini on a Shark's Head Detect Electric Fields to Help Locate Prey.**

Electroreception: Sensing Electric Fields

All animals give off weak electrical impulses that arise from the activity of their nerves and muscles. Since water is a good conductor of these electrical impulses, many kinds of fishes use **electroreception,** or sensation of electric fields, to locate prey, detect predators, and navigate.

Sharks Use Electroreception to Hunt

In sharks, some parts of the lateral line system are specialized to detect electric fields rather than pressure. Tiny pores scattered across a shark's head contain structures called **ampullae of Lorenzini** (Figure 44.20). These ampullae are lined with hair cells that detect electrical potentials in the water and send signals to the shark's brain via sensory neurons.

The sensitivity of these ampullae is remarkable—sharks can detect electrical potentials as small as a nanovolt (a billionth of a volt). This ability allows sharks to sense prey that are far away or even buried in the sand on the ocean floor. Combined with their exquisite sense of olfaction—sharks can detect a single drop of blood in a million drops of ocean water—electroreception makes them finely tuned predators.

Although data are scarce, scientists have some evidence to suggest that sharks also use electroreception to navigate. Ocean currents moving through the Earth's magnetic field generate weak electrical currents. Sharks have been observed orienting themselves to these fields in the ocean as well as to artificially created fields in the laboratory.

Electrogenic Fishes Generate Electric Fields

Electrogenic fishes have specialized organs near their tails that generate electric fields stronger than those of regular nerves or muscles. The currents produced by these fields move in an arc through the water (Figure 44.21). Any item located within that arc will disrupt the currents, allowing the fish's electroreceptors to detect it. In this way, electrogenic fishes use their electric organs to locate prey, sense predators, navigate through murky water, and even communicate with other members of the same species.

Some electrogenic fishes have the ability to produce extremely strong currents that stun or kill their prey. The electric organs of electric eels take up over 80 percent of their body mass and can generate a 500-volt change in electrical potential and 1 ampere of current in the water around them. This amount of current is enough to kill a person swimming in water with an electric eel.

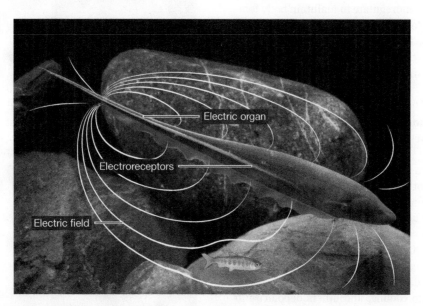

Figure 44.21 **Electrogenic Fishes Can Create a Strong Electric Field.** The field, generated by the fish's electric organ, produces an electrical current in the surrounding water. When a prey animal disrupts the current, the fish detects its presence using electroreceptors.

Magnetoreception: Sensing Magnetic Fields

The Earth produces a magnetic field as it rotates on its axis. Just as a compass responds to this magnetic field to indicate direction, animals may home in on magnetic fields while navigating. **Magnetoreception** has been described in many groups of organisms, including bacteria, fungi, invertebrates, and all vertebrate classes.

In general, studies of the mechanisms by which animals sense the Earth's magnetic field are in their infancy. However, scientists are confident that several distinct mechanisms have evolved. Recall that sharks can sense Earth's magnetic field indirectly via electric fields produced by ocean currents. Terrestrial animals, in contrast, have the ability to sense magnetic fields directly.

In 1968, German scientists noticed that European robins being kept in the laboratory with no visual cues to the outside began to sit at one end of their cages at the beginning of the migratory season. This behavior led the scientists to hypothesize that birds use magnetoreception to determine direction as they migrate.

Since then, support for this hypothesis has accumulated. For example, when European robins were placed into circular chambers with artificial magnetic fields, the birds always oriented themselves in relation to the artificial field. Furthermore, disruption of the magnetic field prevents birds from navigating properly. When scientists fitted homing pigeons with little caps that reversed the polarity of the magnetic field, the pigeons flew in the direction opposite to the one they were trained to fly in.

What enables birds to sense magnetic fields? It is likely a combination of factors. One hypothesis is that deposits of iron inside sensory neurons in the beak play a role in the response to changes in the magnetic field. In support of this hypothesis,

cutting the axons of these neurons prevents birds from responding to artificial changes in the magnetic field in the lab.

To complicate matters, however, magnetoreception in birds is apparently also dependent on vision. Covering the right eye—but not the left eye—of migrating birds interferes with their ability to navigate using magnetic cues. Scientists have recently found evidence for magnetoreceptors in the retinas of birds.

This complication highlights a key feature of sensory perception: Animals do not use individual senses in isolation, but rather combine sensations of many types when locating prey, evading predation, or communicating with other individuals. Whether it is a homing pigeon using magnetoreception and photoreception to find its way home, or a rattlesnake using a visual and thermal image to strike at a mouse, all animals depend on sensory systems that work together to provide the animal with the information it requires to survive.

CHECK YOUR UNDERSTANDING

If you understand that ...

- Thermoreceptors, nociceptors, electroreceptors, and magnetoreceptors convey information about temperature, painful stimuli, electric fields, and magnetic fields, respectively.
- Animals combine input from multiple senses to locate prey, escape from predators, and communicate.

✔ **You should be able to ...**

1. Suggest a sensory adaptation that could help vampire bats, which feed exclusively on the blood of large mammals such as cattle and humans, locate prey.
2. Propose a mechanism by which a female sea turtle migrates to lay eggs on the beach where she was born decades earlier.

Answers are available in Appendix A.

CHAPTER 44 REVIEW

For media, go to MasteringBiology

44.1 How Do Sensory Organs Convey Information to the Brain?

- Sensory stimuli as different as sound and light are transduced to changes in membrane potential in receptor cells. These changes alter the pattern of action potentials that sensory neurons send to the brain.

- The brain is able to distinguish different types of stimuli because axons from different types of sensory neurons project to different regions of the brain.

44.2 Mechanoreception: Sensing Pressure Changes

- Pressure receptors detect direct physical stimulation, including stimulation from sound.

- Hair cells, the major sensory receptors in the vertebrate ear, undergo a change in membrane potential in response to bending of their stereocilia.

- Sound waves of a certain frequency cause a certain part of the cochlea's basilar membrane to vibrate. Hair cells at this location stimulate action potentials in sensory neurons in response to the vibration.

- Hair cells in the lateral line systems of fishes and aquatic amphibians are stimulated by pressure changes in the water.

44.3 Photoreception: Sensing Light

- In the vertebrate eye, photoreceptors (rods and cones) contain light-sensitive molecules that consist of retinal paired with an opsin protein.

- The rhodopsin found in rods is stimulated by even the faintest light.

- Color vision is possible because cones contain opsins that respond to specific wavelengths of light absorbed by retinal.
- Humans distinguish colors based on the pattern of stimulation of three types of opsins found in cones. People who lack one of the functional cone opsins are color blind, meaning they cannot distinguish as many colors as people with all three opsins can.

44.4 Chemoreception: Sensing Chemicals

- Chemoreceptors detect the presence of specific chemicals.
- Taste buds contain taste cells with membrane proteins that play key roles in the response to chemicals. Sodium ions and protons enter taste cells via channels and depolarize the membrane directly, producing the sensations of saltiness and sourness, respectively. Sugars and some toxic compounds bind to membrane receptors, resulting in action potentials in sensory neurons that are interpreted by the brain as sweet and bitter flavors, respectively.
- Smell, or olfaction, is used to detect molecules from the outside environment. Airborne chemicals are detected by hundreds of different odor-receptor proteins located in the membranes of receptor cells in the nose.

44.5 Other Sensory Systems

- Thermoreceptors respond to changes in temperature.
- Nociceptors respond to painful stimuli, including extreme temperatures, certain chemicals, excessive pressure, and tissue damage.
- Electroreceptors contain modified hair cells that respond to electric fields.
- Magnetoreceptors respond to magnetic fields and are often used in navigation and orientation.

Answers are available in Appendix A

✔ TEST YOUR KNOWLEDGE

1. In the human ear, how do different hair cells respond to different frequencies of sound?
   a. Waves of pressure move through the fluid in the cochlea.
   b. Hair cells are "sandwiched" between membranes.
   c. Receptor proteins in the stereocilia of each hair cell are different; each protein responds to a certain range of frequencies.
   d. Because the basilar membrane varies in stiffness, it vibrates in certain places in response to certain frequencies.

2. Which of the following comparisons of rods and cones is *false*?
   a. Most human eyes have one type of rod and three types of cones.
   b. Rods are more sensitive to dim light than cones are.
   c. Nocturnal animals have fewer rods than diurnal animals.
   d. Both rods and cones use retinal and opsins to detect light.

3. Which of the following statements about taste is *true*?
   a. Sweetness is a measure of the concentration of hydrogen ions in food.
   b. Sodium ions from foods can directly depolarize certain taste cells.
   c. All bitter-tasting compounds have a similar chemical structure.
   d. Membrane receptors are involved in detecting acids.

4. What type of sensory system do migrating birds use to detect direction?

✔ TEST YOUR UNDERSTANDING

5. Considering that sounds and odors both trigger changes in the patterns of action potentials in sensory neurons, how does the brain perceive which sense is which when the action potentials reach the brain?
   a. The action potentials stimulated by sounds are different in size and shape from those stimulated by odors.
   b. The axons from different sensory neurons go to different areas of the brain.
   c. Mechanoreception is not consciously perceived by the brain, whereas chemoreception is.
   d. Chemoreception is not consciously perceived by the brain, whereas mechanoreception is.

6. Give three examples of how the sensory abilities of an animal correlate with its habitat or method of finding food and mates.

7. Compare and contrast the lateral line system of fishes with electroreception in sharks.

8. Scientists generally think that a "good hypothesis" is one that is reasonable and testable and inspires further research into a phenomenon. Using these criteria, explain whether Dalton's hypothesis about color vision was a good hypothesis. Was it correct?

✔ TEST YOUR PROBLEM-SOLVING SKILLS

9. **QUANTITATIVE** Scientists collected data on the date of onset of the menstrual cycles of a group of women who moved into a college dormitory together in the fall. The y-axis of the graph shows the mean difference (in days) between the onset of a woman's cycle and the average onset date of the rest of the women. Evaluate whether these data provide evidence for the existence of a human pheromone.

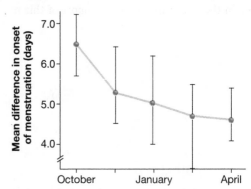

DATA: McClintock, M. K. 1971. *Nature* 229: 244–245, Figure 1.

10. **PROCESS OF SCIENCE** Design experiments to test the hypothesis that electric eels are both electrogenic and electroreceptive.

✓ PUT IT ALL TOGETHER: Case Study

How do pheromones keep a hive of honeybees buzzing?

Honeybees live in social groups consisting of a queen, up to several hundred male drones, and thousands of infertile female workers. The drones mate with the queen only, and the workers protect the hive, forage, and feed and groom the queen. The health of the hive depends on the female workers performing these duties instead of reproducing. What roles do pheromones play in maintaining a functional beehive?

11. Scientists have identified dozens of pheromones used by honeybees for communication. Which type of sensory system are pheromones used in?
    a. mechanoreception
    b. photoreception
    c. chemoreception
    d. thermoreception
    e. electroreception

12. Honeybees produce an alarm pheromone when their hive is molested. This pheromone stimulates the bees to protect the hive. If you were to count the number of alarm pheromone receptors in honeybee tissues, which type of bee would likely have the most—a queen, a drone, or a worker? Why?

13. Why might an alarm pheromone be more effective for triggering a protective response in a hive than signals that involve other senses, such as vision or hearing?

14. **QUANTITATIVE** Researchers observed that the queen produces a pheromone that is very attractive to both drones and workers. They hypothesized that this pheromone inhibits ovarian development in the workers, making the workers infertile. To test this hypothesis, they exposed workers to a synthetic version of the queen pheromone and then recorded their "ovary development score." (Higher scores indicate more fully developed ovaries.) The results are shown in the graph below. Do these results support the researchers' hypothesis? Why or why not? (*** signifies $P < 0.001$; see BioSkills 3 for more on statistical significance.)

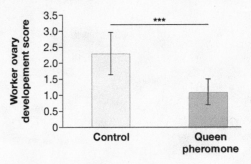

Source: Hoover, S. E. R., C. I. Keeling, M. L. Winston, et al. 2003. *Naturwissenschaften* 90: 477–480.

15. **PROCESS OF SCIENCE** In the experiment described in Question 14, the researchers dissolved the queen pheromone in diethyl ether, a chemical that helps volatilize the pheromone, making it easier for the workers to detect it in the air. The control treatment consisted of plain diethyl ether. Why did they use this as the control, instead of simply not exposing the workers to any chemical?

16. **SOCIETY** Beekeepers carefully manage their beehives by adding mated queens, drones, and workers at appropriate times. However, sometimes the bees abandon a new hive before the queen can mature, and the result is inefficient hive management and honey production. Suggest a potential use of queen pheromone in controlling this problem.

45 Animal Movement

Basilisk lizards are able to run on water—literally. This impressive escape strategy demonstrates the extent to which muscle-generated movements have diversified among animals. For most animals, complex muscle movements make the difference between life and death.

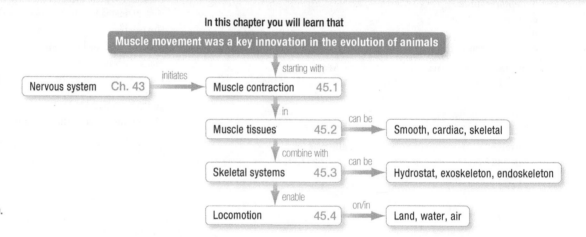

In this chapter you will learn that

Muscle movement was a key innovation in the evolution of animals

| | starting with | |
| Nervous system Ch. 43 | —initiates→ | Muscle contraction 45.1 |

in

| Muscle tissues 45.2 | —can be→ | Smooth, cardiac, skeletal |

combine with

| Skeletal systems 45.3 | —can be→ | Hydrostat, exoskeleton, endoskeleton |

enable

| Locomotion 45.4 | —on/in→ | Land, water, air |

This chapter is part of the Big Picture. See how on pages 816–817.

You may have discovered while studying biology that plants and animals are more similar to each other than they initially appear. For example, plants and animals both require water and nutrients in specific quantities, have highly specialized tissues and complex reproductive structures, and launch defenses against parasites and predators. You can see a comparison of these and other traits in the Big Picture of Plant and Animal Form and Function on pages 816–817.

However, animals possess a quality that clearly distinguishes them from plants and other organisms: movement by virtue of muscle contractions. Muscle-generated movements were a key innovation in animal evolution. Rapid movements, along with sophisticated sensory structures (Chapter 44) and complex information processing systems (Chapter 43), were vital to animal diversification (Chapter 30), and these attributes made animals efficient eating machines in diverse ecosystems.

Muscles generate movement by exerting force and causing shape changes. Movement falls into two general categories:

1. ***Movement of the entire animal relative to its environment.*** **Locomotion,** the movement of an organism or cell from place to place under its own power, enables animals to avoid predators and to seek food, water, mates, and shelter. Modes of animal locomotion include undulating, jetting, swimming, walking, running, jumping, gliding, and flying.

2. ***Movement of one part of the animal relative to other parts (not involved in locomotion).*** This type of movement also has important functions—for example, to ventilate gills for gas exchange and to grasp prey. Even sessile animals like corals and barnacles use complex, muscle-generated movements to survive and reproduce.

How do animals accomplish their spectacular movements? This chapter starts by probing into the mechanism of muscle contraction, which serves as the "engine" for most animal movements. It then considers how muscle and skeletal systems work together to produce locomotion. The latter discussion introduces a research field called **biomechanics,** in which the principles of physics and engineering are applied to questions about the mechanical structure and function of organisms. Let's jump in.

45.1 How Do Muscles Contract?

The mechanism responsible for the contraction of muscle has fascinated and perplexed scientists for many centuries. Before the advent of microscopes and modern research techniques, scientists could only speculate about what makes muscles contract and relax.

Early Muscle Experiments

In the second century C.E., Roman physician and philosopher Galen proposed that spirits flowed from nerves into muscles, inflating them and increasing their diameter. This "inflation"

hypothesis persisted into the seventeenth century, when French philosopher René Descartes suggested that nerves carry fluid from the pineal gland—a part of the brain then considered to be the seat of the soul—to the muscles, making them shorten and swell.

Later that century, Dutch anatomist Jan Swammerdam tested Descartes' inflation hypothesis with a simple yet elegant experiment. He placed a piece of frog muscle into an airtight syringe with the nerve protruding through a small hole in the side and a small drop of water in the tip of the syringe. He then stimulated the nerve, causing the muscle to contract. If the muscle's volume changed during contraction, the drop of water in the tip would move. But it did not. The volume of the muscle remained constant.

Swammerdam's experiment demonstrated an important point: The contraction mechanism is inherent to the muscle itself—muscle is not like a balloon, and the nerve is not like a water hose filling a balloon. This insight was confirmed by Italian scientist Luigi Galvani in the 1790s, when he cut the nerve to a frog's leg muscle and then connected the two sides of the cut with a metal conductor. The muscle contracted. He concluded that the nerve and muscle possess "animal electricity" that can induce contraction.

If the shape of a muscle does not change by inflation, what is the mechanism of muscle contraction?

The Sliding-Filament Model

Early microscopists established that the muscle tissue in vertebrate limbs and hearts is composed of slender fibers. A **muscle fiber** is a long, thin muscle cell. Within each muscle cell are many threadlike, contractile structures called **myofibrils.** The myofibrils inside muscle fibers often look striped or striated due to the alternating light–dark units called **sarcomeres,** which repeat along the length of a myofibril (**Figure 45.1**).

The microscopists observed that sarcomeres shorten as myofibrils contract. Sarcomeres then lengthen when the cell relaxes and an external force stretches the muscle. Based on these

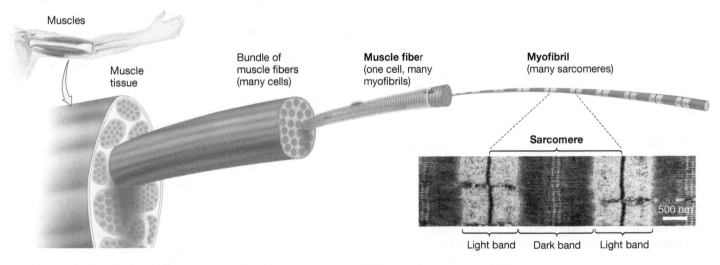

Muscles
Muscle tissue
Bundle of muscle fibers (many cells)
Muscle fiber (one cell, many myofibrils)
Myofibril (many sarcomeres)

Sarcomere

500 nm

Light band   Dark band   Light band

Figure 45.1 **Muscle Cells Contain Many Myofibrils, Which Contain Many Sarcomeres.** Skeletal muscle cells (fibers) have a striped appearance due to repeating sarcomeres, which are units of alternating light–dark bands.

Relaxed sarcomere

Thin filament (actin)   Thick filament (myosin)   Z disk

A   B   C   D

A   B   C   D

Contracted sarcomere

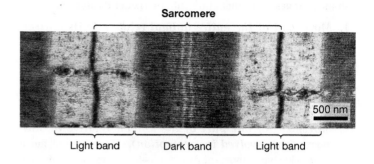

Sarcomere

500 nm

Light band   Dark band   Light band

Figure 45.2 The Sliding-Filament Model Explains Important Aspects of Sarcomere Contraction. When a sarcomere contracts, the lengths of the thin filaments (distance from A to C) and thick filaments (distance from B to D) do not change. Rather, the filaments slide past one another.

✔ According to the model shown here, why is the dark band in a sarcomere dark and the light band light?

observations, it became clear that the question of how muscles contract simplifies to the question of how sarcomeres shorten.

Biologists knew that the answer must involve the two types of protein that had been found in sarcomeres: **actin** and **myosin.** But they did not know the shapes of these molecules or how they were arranged within the sarcomere. Did both types of molecules span the entire length of the sarcomere? Or were they restricted to certain bands within the sarcomere?

In 1952, biologist Hugh Huxley produced electron micrographs of sarcomeres in cross section. He observed that there were two types of filaments, **thin filaments** and **thick filaments,** and that these filaments overlapped in the dark bands but not in the light bands. Huxley and his collaborator Jean Hanson also observed that sarcomeres stripped of their myosin had no dark bands. They concluded that the thick filaments must be composed of myosin, and the thin filaments must be composed of actin.

How did myosin and actin interact to shorten the sarcomere? In 1954, Huxley and Hanson hit on the key insight when they observed how the light and dark bands in sarcomeres changed when a muscle contracted. Overall, the width of the dark bands did not change during a contraction, but the light bands became narrower.

To explain these observations, Huxley and Hanson proposed the **sliding-filament model** illustrated in **Figure 45.2.** They hypothesized that the filaments slide past one another during a contraction. That is, the sarcomere shortens with no change in the lengths of the thin and thick filaments themselves:

- The distance from point A to point C does not change, and the distance from point B to point D does not change.

- Points A and B move closer to each other during contraction, as do points C and D.

Interestingly, another pair of researchers, Andrew F. Huxley (no relation to Hugh) and Rolf Niedergerke, published the same result at the same time and in the same issue of *Nature*. In the years that followed, research has confirmed that the Huxley–Hanson model is correct in almost every detail.

Each thin filament is composed of two coiled chains of actin, a common component of the cytoskeleton of eukaryotic cells (Chapter 7). One end of a thin filament is anchored to a structure called the **Z disc,** which forms the end wall of the sarcomere. The other end of a thin filament is free to interact with thick filaments. Thick filaments are composed of multiple strands of myosin. They span the center of the sarcomere and are free at both ends to interact with thin filaments.

To appreciate how the sliding-filament model works, consider the following analogy: Two large trucks are parked 50 m apart, facing each other. Each has a long rope attached to the front bumper. Six burly weightlifters stand in a line on a platform in front of each truck, grab onto the rope, and pull, hand over hand, so that the two trucks roll toward one another. ✔ If you understand the sliding-filament model, you should be able to explain which elements in this analogy represent the Z discs, which represent the thin filaments, and which represent the thick filaments.

How Do Actin and Myosin Interact?

How does this sliding action occur at the molecular level? Early work on the three-dimensional structure of myosin revealed that a myosin molecule contains a pair of subunits whose "tails" are coiled around one another and whose "heads" are bent to the side. Each myosin head can bind to actin, and the head region can catalyze the hydrolysis of ATP into adenosine diphosphate (ADP) and a phosphate ion.

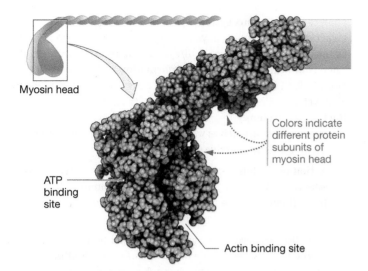

Myosin head

Colors indicate
different protein
subunits of
myosin head

ATP
binding
site

Actin binding site

Figure 45.3 Myosin's "Head" Binds ATP and Actin. A myosin molecule includes two myosin proteins, each of which has a head that contains binding sites for ATP and actin.

In addition, electron microscopy revealed that myosin and actin are locked together shortly after an animal dies, and its muscles enter the stiff state known as rigor mortis. Because ATP is unavailable in dead tissue, the data suggested that ATP is required for myosin to release from actin once the two molecules have bound to each other.

Later, Ivan Rayment and colleagues solved the detailed three-dimensional structure of the myosin head (**Figure 45.3**). Using X-ray crystallography (see BioSkills 6), Rayment's group determined the location of the actin-binding site. They also showed that myosin's conformation was significantly different when ATP was bound to the head than when ADP was bound.

Based on these data, Rayment and co-workers proposed a four-step model for actin–myosin interaction (**Figure 45.4**):

Step 1 ATP binds to the myosin head, causing a conformational change that releases the head from the actin in the thin filament.

Step 2 When ATP is hydrolyzed to ADP and inorganic phosphate, the neck of the myosin straightens and the head pivots. The myosin head then binds to a new actin subunit farther down the thin filament. In this position, the myosin head is "cocked" in its high-energy state, ready for the power stroke.

Step 3 When inorganic phosphate is released, the neck bends back to its original conformation. This bending, called the power stroke, moves the entire thin filament relative to the thick filament.

Step 4 After ADP is released, the myosin head is ready to bind to another molecule of ATP.

As ATP binding and hydrolysis continue, myosin continues to bind actin, move the thin filament, release actin, and bind again, much like when you swing along on monkey bars. This movement of the thin filament along the thick filament causes the

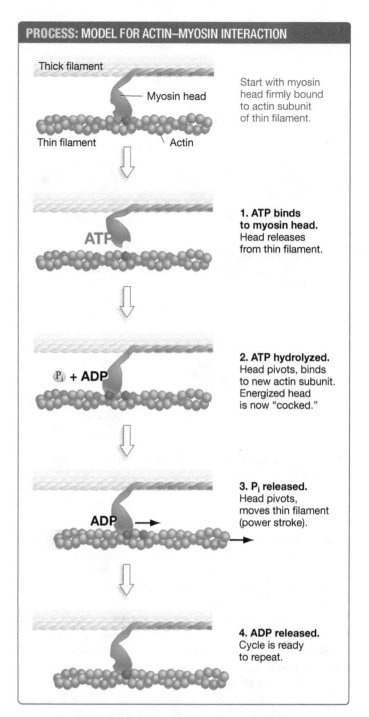

PROCESS: MODEL FOR ACTIN–MYOSIN INTERACTION

Thick filament

Myosin head

Thin filament   Actin

Start with myosin head firmly bound to actin subunit of thin filament.

ATP

1. ATP binds to myosin head. Head releases from thin filament.

P_i + ADP

2. ATP hydrolyzed. Head pivots, binds to new actin subunit. Energized head is now "cocked."

ADP

3. P_i released. Head pivots, moves thin filament (power stroke).

4. ADP released. Cycle is ready to repeat.

Figure 45.4 Myosin and Actin Interact during Muscle Contraction. Summary of the current model of how myosin and actin interact as a sarcomere contracts. The four steps repeat rapidly. (Only one head of the myosin molecule is shown, for simplicity.)

two ends of the sarcomere to be pulled closer together, as long as ATP is available and the muscle is being stimulated. (Note that the transition from step 4 to step 1 cannot occur when ATP supplies run out, which explains why rigor mortis sets in after death.)

The same basic ratcheting mechanism between actin and myosin is responsible for the amoeboid movement observed in

(a) Muscle relaxed: Tropomyosin and troponin work together to block the myosin binding sites on actin.

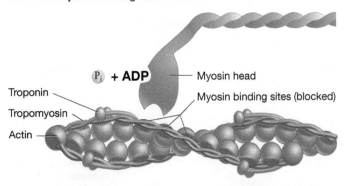

(b) Contraction begins: When a calcium ion binds to troponin, the troponin–tropomyosin complex moves, exposing myosin binding sites.

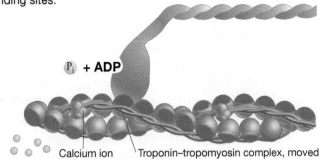

Figure 45.5 Troponin and Tropomyosin Regulate Muscle Activity. Note that the myosin head is in its energized state when a muscle is relaxed.

amoebae and slime molds (Chapter 27) and the streaming of cytoplasm observed in algae and land plants. Actin and myosin have played a critical role in the diversification of eukaryotes because they make movement possible in the absence of cilia and flagella.

Considering that ATP is almost always available in living muscles, how do muscles ever stop contracting and relax? Besides actin, thin filaments contain two key proteins called **tropomyosin** and **troponin,** which work together to block the myosin binding sites on actin. When these sites are blocked, the myosin–actin interaction cannot occur, and thick and thin filaments cannot slide past each other. As a result, the muscle relaxes (**Figure 45.5a**).

But when calcium ions bind to troponin, the resulting troponin–tropomyosin complex moves in a way that exposes the myosin binding sites on actin. As **Figure 45.5b** shows, myosin then binds, and contraction can begin.

How are calcium ions released so that contraction can begin? The process begins when the muscle cell is stimulated by a neuron.

How Do Neurons Initiate Contraction?

You are probably sitting as you read. If so, contract your calf muscles to point your toes. Your nervous system just played a critical role in controlling the timing of your muscle contractions. First,

your central nervous system—your brain—received input from an array of sensory cells in your peripheral nervous system, such as the ones in the retina of your eyes as you read this paragraph. Then your brain integrated this information and triggered action potentials in the motor neurons that cause your calf muscles to contract. (See Chapter 43 to review the structure and function of the nervous system.)

Figure 45.6 summarizes what happens when action potentials from a motor neuron arrive at a muscle cell:

1. Action potentials trigger the release of the neurotransmitter **acetylcholine** (ACh) from the motor neuron into the synaptic cleft between the motor neuron and the muscle cell. (See Figure 43.11 for a review of the synaptic cleft.)

2. ACh diffuses across the synaptic cleft and binds to receptors on the plasma membrane of the muscle cell. Binding of ACh opens a ligand-gated ion channel in the receptor protein, resulting in depolarization of the muscle cell. If enough ACh is released by the motor neuron, the depolarization triggers action potentials in the muscle cell.

3. The action potentials propagate along the length of the muscle cell and spread into the interior of the cell via invaginations of the plasma membrane called **T tubules.** (The T stands for *transverse*, meaning "extending across.")

4. T tubules intersect with extensive sheets of smooth endoplasmic reticulum called the **sarcoplasmic reticulum.** When an action potential passes down a T tubule and reaches one of these intersections, a protein in the T-tubule membrane changes conformation and opens calcium channels in the sarcoplasmic reticulum. Calcium diffuses through these channels into the cytoplasm, where the sarcomeres are located.

5. Calcium causes the myosin binding sites on the actin filaments to be exposed, enabling the contraction to begin.

By this series of events, the interaction of the nervous system and muscle tissue at the neuromuscular junction precisely regulates muscle contractions—and thus complex movement.

CHECK YOUR UNDERSTANDING

If you understand that …

- Muscles shorten when thick filaments of myosin slide past thin filaments of actin in a series of binding events mediated by the hydrolysis of ATP.
- Muscle cells shorten in response to action potentials, which trigger the release of calcium ions that enable actin and myosin to interact.

✔ **You should be able to …**

1. Describe the sliding-filament model.
2. Predict the effect on muscle function of drugs that have the following actions: increase acetylcholine release at the neuromuscular junction, prevent conformational changes in troponin, and block uptake of calcium ions into the sarcoplasmic reticulum.

Answers are available in Appendix A.

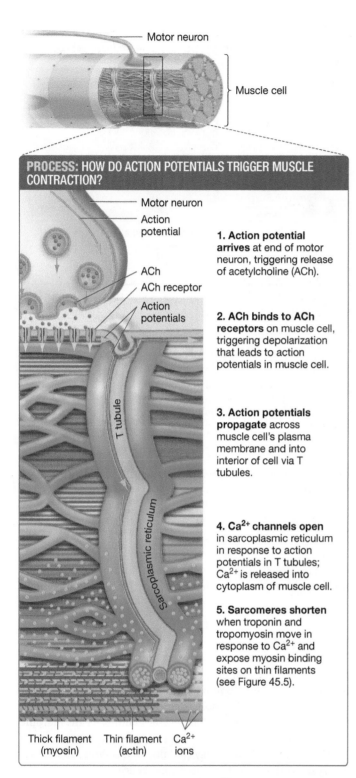

PROCESS: HOW DO ACTION POTENTIALS TRIGGER MUSCLE CONTRACTION?

Motor neuron
Action potential
ACh
ACh receptor
Action potentials
T tubule
Sarcoplasmic reticulum

1. Action potential arrives at end of motor neuron, triggering release of acetylcholine (ACh).

2. ACh binds to ACh receptors on muscle cell, triggering depolarization that leads to action potentials in muscle cell.

3. Action potentials propagate across muscle cell's plasma membrane and into interior of cell via T tubules.

4. Ca²⁺ channels open in sarcoplasmic reticulum in response to action potentials in T tubules; Ca^{2+} is released into cytoplasm of muscle cell.

5. Sarcomeres shorten when troponin and tropomyosin move in response to Ca^{2+} and expose myosin binding sites on thin filaments (see Figure 45.5).

Thick filament (myosin)   Thin filament (actin)   Ca²⁺ ions

Motor neuron
Muscle cell

Figure 45.6 Action Potentials Trigger Ca²⁺ Release. Action potentials at the neuromuscular junction trigger the release of Ca^{2+} inside the muscle cell. Ca^{2+} binds to troponin, moving the troponin–tropomyosin complex and allowing myosin to form a cross-bridge with actin.

45.2 Muscle Tissues

How do muscle cells and muscle tissues vary? After years of careful anatomical study, biologists concluded that animals have three classes of muscle tissue: **(1)** smooth muscle, **(2)** cardiac muscle, and **(3)** skeletal muscle. You, and all other vertebrates, have all three.

Smooth, cardiac, and skeletal muscle share several properties. They all contract as described by the sliding-filament model, and they all contract in response to electrical stimulation. However, the three classes of muscle also differ in important ways, summarized in Table 45.1 on page 948:

- **Voluntary versus involuntary** **Voluntary muscles** can contract in response to conscious thought (and also by unconscious reflexes) and are stimulated by neurons in the somatic division of the peripheral nervous system. **Involuntary muscles** contract only in response to unconscious electrical activity and are stimulated and inhibited by neurons in the autonomic division of the peripheral nervous system. (See Chapter 43 for a review of the somatic and autonomic divisions of the nervous system.)

- **Multinucleate versus uninucleate** Muscle cells may have one or many nuclei depending on the size of the cells.

- **Striated versus unstriated** As shown in Figure 45.1, the actin and myosin filaments in some muscle cells are aligned in rows forming sarcomeres, giving the cells and tissues a banded appearance; for this reason, such muscle tissue is often called **striated muscle.** Other muscle cells are unstriated.

Let's apply these characteristics to each class of muscle tissue in more detail.

Smooth Muscle

Smooth muscle cells are unbranched, tapered at each end, and often organized into thin sheets. They lack the sarcomeres that are found in skeletal and cardiac muscle; hence, they are unstriated and appear smooth. Smooth muscle cells are relatively small and have a single nucleus.

Smooth muscle is essential to the function of the lungs, blood vessels, digestive system, urinary bladder, and reproductive system. Bronchioles in the lungs have a layer of smooth muscle that controls the size of airways; similarly, smooth muscles in blood vessels can contract or relax to alter blood-flow patterns and blood pressure. Layers of smooth muscle in the gastrointestinal tract help mix and move food, and uterine smooth muscle is responsible for expelling the fetus during birth.

Smooth muscle is innervated by autonomic motor neurons and is thus involuntary. In the digestive system, ACh released by parasympathetic ("rest-and-digest") neurons stimulates contraction of smooth muscle in the stomach and intestine, aiding digestion (Chapter 43). In contrast, sympathetic ("fight-or-flight") neurons release the neurotransmitter norepinephrine, and the adrenal glands adjacent to the kidneys release the hormone epinephrine (also called adrenaline).

Smooth Muscle	Cardiac Muscle	Skeletal Muscle
25 μm	25 μm	25 μm
Location Intestines, arteries, other	Heart	Attached to the skeleton
Function Move food, help regulate blood pressure, etc.	Pump blood	Move skeleton
Cell characteristics	Intercalated discs	Nuclei
Single nucleus	1 or 2 nuclei	Multinucleate
Unstriated	Striated	Striated
Unbranched	Branched; intercalated discs form direct cytoplasmic connections between cells	Unbranched
No sarcomeres	Contains sarcomeres	Contains sarcomeres
Activity is "involuntary," meaning that signal from motor neuron is not required	Activity is "involuntary," meaning that signal from motor neuron is not required	Activity is "voluntary," meaning that signal from somatic motor neuron is required

Norepinephrine and epinephrine have the opposite effect to that of acetylcholine: They inhibit contraction of smooth muscle in the gut.

Cardiac Muscle

Cardiac muscle makes up the walls of the heart and is responsible for pumping blood throughout the body. Unlike smooth muscle cells, cardiac muscle cells contain sarcomeres and are striated. Further, cardiac muscle cells have a unique branched structure, and they are directly connected end to end via specialized regions called intercalated discs. These discs are critical to the flow of electrical signals from cell to cell and thus to the coordination of the heartbeat.

Like smooth muscle, cardiac muscle is involuntary—it contracts following spontaneous depolarizations. During rest, parasympathetic neurons release acetylcholine onto the heart. This neurotransmitter slows the rate of depolarization of cardiac cells. The result is a lower heart rate. During exercise, or when an animal is frightened, stressed, or otherwise stimulated, sympathetic neurons release norepinephrine onto the heart, and the adrenal glands release epinephrine. Norepinephrine and epinephrine increase heart rate and strengthen the force of cardiac

muscle contraction. The result is that more blood is pumped from the heart—an essential component of the fight-or-flight response.

Skeletal Muscle

Skeletal muscle consists of exceptionally long, unbranched muscle fibers. For example, a skeletal muscle fiber of a cat may be 0.4 mm wide and 40 mm long—enormous compared to most cells. These large cells result from the fusion of many smaller embryonic cells during development, accounting for the multiple nuclei spread out along the cell. Each muscle fiber is packed with myofibrils, each of which may contain thousands of sarcomeres, giving skeletal muscle its striated appearance.

Skeletal muscle is so named because it usually attaches to the skeleton. When skeletal muscle contracts, it exerts a pulling force on the skeleton, causing it to move—powering the sprint of cheetahs, the flight of hummingbirds, and the pinch of crab claws. In addition, skeletal muscle encircles the openings of the digestive and urinary tracts and controls swallowing, defecation, and urination.

A significant fraction of the body of many animals is composed of skeletal muscle. For example, 63 percent of the body

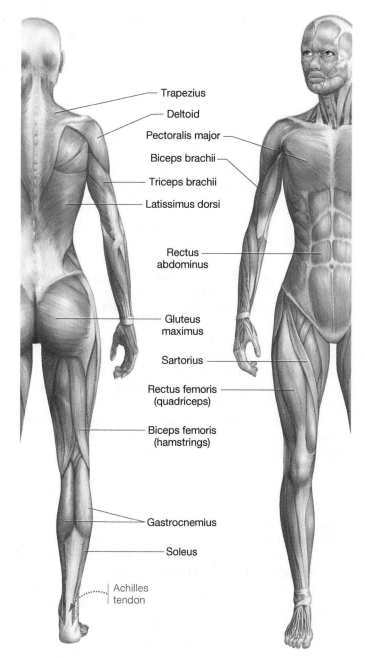

Figure 45.7 Major Skeletal Muscles Make Up a Large Portion of the Human Body.

Labels (top to bottom, both views):
Trapezius
Deltoid
Pectoralis major
Biceps brachii
Triceps brachii
Latissimus dorsi
Rectus abdominus
Gluteus maximus
Sartorius
Rectus femoris (quadriceps)
Biceps femoris (hamstrings)
Gastrocnemius
Soleus
Achilles tendon

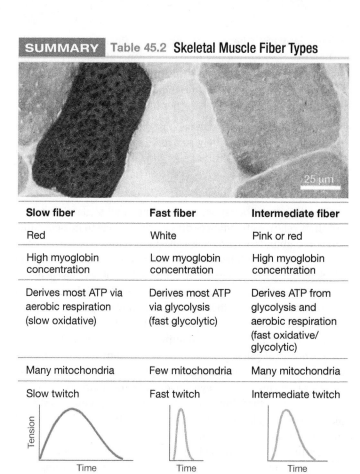

25 µm

Slow fiber	Fast fiber	Intermediate fiber
Red	White	Pink or red
High myoglobin concentration	Low myoglobin concentration	High myoglobin concentration
Derives most ATP via aerobic respiration (slow oxidative)	Derives most ATP via glycolysis (fast glycolytic)	Derives ATP from glycolysis and aerobic respiration (fast oxidative/glycolytic)
Many mitochondria	Few mitochondria	Many mitochondria
Slow twitch	Fast twitch	Intermediate twitch
(Tension vs. Time graph)	*(Tension vs. Time graph)*	*(Tension vs. Time graph)*
Fatigues slowly	Fatigues quickly	Intermediate fatigue

weight of trout is skeletal muscle, and mammals—including humans—of all sizes are 40 to 45 percent muscle. When animals engage in load-bearing exercise, like weight-lifting by humans, existing muscle fibers synthesize additional contractile proteins and become larger; no new cells are formed. The increased size of the muscle fibers allows a muscle to do more work—for example, to pull on bones with greater force to lift heavier weights.

Clearly, skeletal muscle plays an important role in animal biology. Some of the major skeletal muscles in the human body are shown in Figure 45.7.

Skeletal muscle is distinguished from cardiac and smooth muscle in being voluntary. Skeletal muscle must be stimulated by somatic motor neurons to contract. If these motor neurons are damaged, as can occur with a spinal cord injury, skeletal muscle cannot contract and becomes paralyzed.

Although all muscles contract as described by the sliding-filament model, not all skeletal muscle fibers have the same contractile properties. The force output of skeletal muscles depends on **(1)** the relative proportion of different fiber types, **(2)** the organization of fibers within the muscle, and **(3)** how the muscle is used. Let's take a closer look at these sources of variation in muscle performance.

Skeletal Muscle Fiber Types Skeletal muscle fibers can be divided into general types based on their structural and functional characteristics, summarized in Table 45.2:

- **Slow muscle fibers** (slow oxidative fibers) appear red because they contain a high concentration of myoglobin, an iron-bearing pigment that carries oxygen (similar to but distinct from hemoglobin in the blood). Slow fibers contract slowly because the myosin hydrolyzes ATP at a slow rate. They also fatigue slowly because they have many mitochondria and can generate steady quantities of ATP using oxidative phosphorylation—that is, aerobic respiration (Chapter 9)—thanks to the plentiful supply of oxygen delivered by myoglobin.

- **Fast muscle fibers** (fast glycolytic fibers) appear white because they have a low myoglobin concentration. They contract rapidly because the myosin hydrolyzes ATP at a rapid rate, but they also fatigue rapidly because their primary source of ATP is glycolysis rather than aerobic respiration.
- **Intermediate muscle fibers** (fast oxidative/glycolytic fibers) appear pink or red. Their contractile properties vary but are intermediate between those of slow and fast fibers because intermediate fibers derive ATP from both glycolysis and aerobic respiration.

The different fiber types are present in all skeletal muscles, but their relative abundances differ from muscle to muscle. Slow fibers are abundant in muscles specialized for endurance—such as the leg muscles of birds that excel at swimming or walking (the "dark meat" of chicken legs). In humans, the soleus muscle in the back of the calf is an example of a muscle with a high proportion of slow fibers—it helps to keep you upright when you stand.

Fast fibers contract and relax up to three times as fast as slow fibers, making fast fibers well suited for bursts of activity. The "white meat" of chicken breasts, specialized only for quick bursts of flight to escape predators, is made primarily of fast fibers. The muscles that control your eye movements are another example.

✔ If you understand muscle fiber types, you should be able to predict the most abundant fiber type in the postural muscles of the human neck.

Can humans change their muscle fiber types through training? Experiments have shown that endurance training can increase the density of mitochondria and myoglobin in muscle fibers as well as the number of blood vessels in muscles, enabling athletes to improve their muscle performance. However, training does not change slow fibers to fast fibers, nor the reverse.

Skeletal Muscle Fiber Organization The length change of a muscle is determined by the length of its muscle fibers—how many sarcomeres are lined up in a row in each fiber. By contrast, the force exerted by a muscle is proportional to the cross-sectional area of the muscle—the number of sarcomeres lined up side by side exerting a pull in synchrony. Thus, the arrangement of fibers within a muscle influences the contractile properties of the muscle.

For a given muscle volume, some muscles are organized to maximize length change, because the fibers are parallel to each other in long bands (**Figure 45.8**, left)—a longer chain of sarcomeres in a myofibril produces a greater length change. The sartorius muscle in the human thigh has parallel fibers.

Other muscles are organized to maximize force, because the fibers are in a diagonal, or pennate, pattern ("penna" means feather; Figure 45.8, right)—more sarcomeres pulling in parallel produce a greater force. The gastrocnemius muscle in the human calf is a pennate muscle.

Context of Muscle Contraction The relative abundances of fiber types and organization of muscle fibers are not sufficient to account for the diverse contraction properties of skeletal muscles. Muscle force also varies according to how extended the muscle is when it contracts and how rapidly it is allowed to

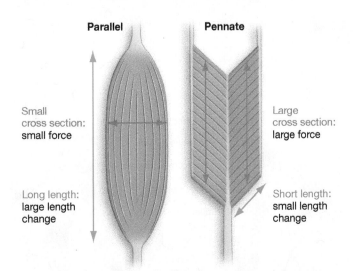

Figure 45.8 Muscle Fiber Patterns Affect Contractile Properties. Most muscles have fibers arranged in either a parallel or pennate pattern. The orientation of muscle fibers affects the contractile properties of the muscle.

shorten—if at all. Muscles like the quadriceps in your thigh can even exert a force while they are lengthening, such as when you ease your weight down a step.

These circumstances depend on the interaction between the muscle and the skeleton. Let's take a closer look at how the muscle and skeletal systems interact to produce movement.

45.3 Skeletal Systems

All a muscle can do is pull. How can complex movements be accomplished using an engine that can only pull? Also, muscles are limited in how much they can shorten. How, then, can they cause dramatic shape changes in animal bodies?

Muscle forces and shape changes are transmitted to other parts of the body and to the environment via the skeleton. Skeletal systems perform four main functions:

1. *Protection* from physical and biological assaults.
2. *Maintenance of body posture* despite the downward pull of gravity and the vagaries of wind and waves.
3. *Re-extension of shortened muscles* If no mechanism of re-extension existed, muscles would shorten only once.
4. *Transfer of muscle forces* to other parts of the body and to the environment, enabling a much greater range of force production and shape change than can be accomplished by muscle alone.

The relative importance of these roles varies among animals according to their lifestyles and environments. For example, natural selection has favored turtles with robust shells in some environments—a skeletal adaptation for protection. In other environments, natural selection has favored highly reduced shells—an adaptation for rapid locomotion. There are trade-offs between protection and mobility.

(a) Earthworms are one example of **hydrostatic skeletons**.

(b) Vertebrates (e.g., frogs) have internal **endoskeletons**.

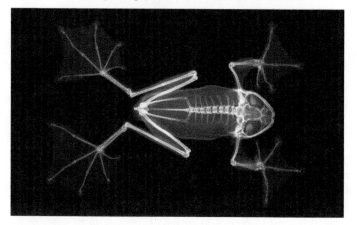

Figure 45.9 **Three Types of Skeletal Systems Allow Animals to Move.**

(c) Arthropods (e.g., crabs) have external **exoskeletons**.

the tongues and penises of humans and the tube feet of echinoderms (Chapter 32).

The structures of hydrostatic skeletons are diverse as well. The body wall of hydrostats may include different numbers and orientations of muscle layers and fiber-reinforced cuticles or connective tissues. The interior may include seawater, coelomic fluid, blood, or soft organs such as intestines. Hydrostatic skeletons composed mostly of muscle, such as tongues and tentacles, are called muscular hydrostats.

Function How do animals with hydrostatic skeletons move? Consider an earthworm. Its body wall consists of a cuticle reinforced with collagen fibers as well as two layers of muscle—longitudinal muscles, oriented along the length of the animal, and circumferential muscles, oriented in bands around each segment. When the circumferential muscles contract, they make the segments narrower and squeeze the coelomic fluid and internal tissues, thus increasing internal pressure. The pressure pushes outward in all directions, extending the relaxed longitudinal muscles and lengthening the segment (**Figure 45.10**).

Despite the stunning diversity in animal bodies, virtually all animals can be considered to have one (or more) of three types of skeletal systems (**Figure 45.9**):

1. Hydrostatic skeletons use the hydrostatic pressure of enclosed body fluids or soft tissues to support the body (Figure 45.9a).

2. Endoskeletons have rigid structures inside the body (Figure 45.9b).

3. Exoskeletons have rigid structures on the outside of the body (Figure 45.9c).

Let's consider how each skeletal system transmits muscle forces and shape changes.

Hydrostatic Skeletons

Despite their squishy appearance, soft-bodied animals do have skeletons—hydrostatic skeletons. First let's look at how they are built, and then consider how they function.

Structure **Hydrostatic skeletons** ("still-water skeletons"), or hydrostats, are constructed of an extensible body wall in tension surrounding a fluid or deformable tissue under compression. When fluid is under compression, its pressure increases. The pressurized internal fluid, rather than a rigid structure, enables soft-bodied animals to maintain posture, re-extend muscles, and transfer muscle forces to the environment.

Hydrostatic skeletons occur in diverse animals, from sea anemones and jellyfish to mollusks and many types of worms (Chapter 31). Hydrostats also support *parts* of animals, such as

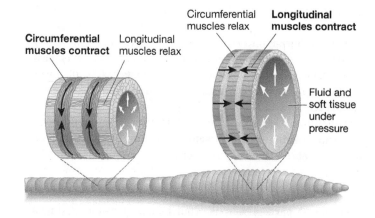

Figure 45.10 **Antagonistic Muscle Groups Cause Shape Changes in Hydrostatic Skeletons.** The pressure of the internal fluid or tissue transmits forces between muscle groups and between muscles and the environment.

(a) Bones of the human endoskeleton

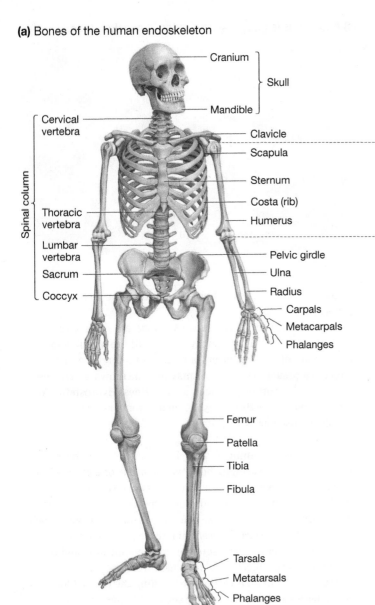

(b) Joints enable movement.

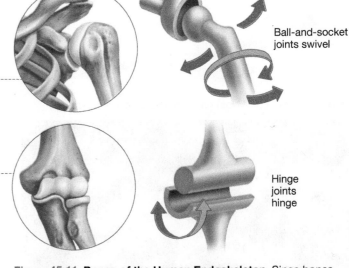

Ball-and-socket joints swivel

Hinge joints hinge

Figure 45.11 Bones of the Human Endoskeleton. Since bones are rigid and cannot change shape themselves, they articulate at joints that make specific types of movement possible, such as swiveling and hinging.

When the longitudinal muscles contract and the circumferential muscles relax, the reverse occurs—the segments become wider and shorter, pushing sideways against the soil. Alternating contractions of longitudinal and circumferential muscles pass down the earthworm in waves, called **peristalsis.** In this way, earthworms move forward (or backward) within their underground burrows.

Longitudinal and circumferential muscles in earthworms make up an **antagonistic muscle group,** a group of two or more muscles that re-extend one another via the skeleton.

Endoskeletons

Even though parts of you, like your tongue, are supported by a hydrostatic skeleton, your endoskeleton is what keeps you standing up and on the move.

Structure **Endoskeletons** ("inside skeletons") are rigid structures that occur within the body. Even the most ancient of animal

lineages, the sponges, secrete spicules—stiff spikes of silica or calcium carbonate—that provide structural support for the body. In echinoderms, the endoskeleton consists of calcium carbonate plates just beneath the skin—fused into a rigid case in sea urchins, but suspended in a flexible matrix that enables bending of the arms in sea stars.

The vertebrate endoskeleton differs from those of most sponges and echinoderms—and from hydrostatic skeletons—in that it is composed of rigid levers (the bones) separated by joints. Vertebrates change the shapes of their bodies largely by changing the *joint angles* between bones in the limbs and between the limbs and the rest of the body, rather than changing the shapes of body segments themselves.

Vertebrate skeletons are composed of three main elements:

1. **Bones** are made up of cells in a hard extracellular matrix of calcium phosphate with small amounts of calcium carbonate and protein fibers. The adult human body contains 206 bones (**Figure 45.11a**). The meeting places where adjacent bones interact are called **articulations,** or **joints.** Bones articulate in ways that limit the range of motion, for example enabling a swivel in the shoulder joint but a hinge in the elbow joint (**Figure 45.11b**).

2. **Cartilage** is made up of cells scattered in a gelatinous matrix of polysaccharides and protein fibers. Cartilage can be quite rigid, as in the clam-crushing jaws of some stingrays, or more rubbery, as in the pads that cushion the joints in your knees and back.

3. **Ligaments** are bands of fibrous connective tissue, primarily collagen, that bind bones to other bones. Ligaments stabilize the joints.

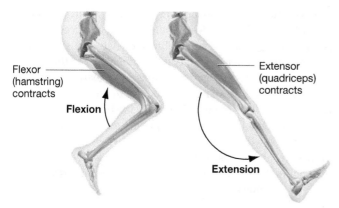

Figure 45.12 **Endoskeletons Move by Contraction and Relaxation of Flexor and Extensor Muscles.** The muscles are attached to the outside of the skeleton.

✔ Use this figure along with Figure 45.7 to assign the roles of flexor or extensor to the biceps brachii and triceps brachii muscles.

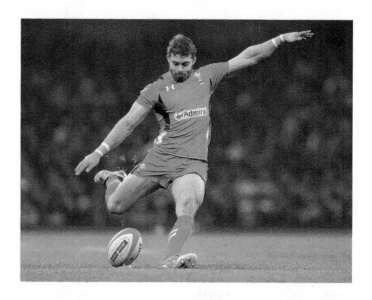

Bones attach to skeletal muscle via bands of fibrous connective tissue called **tendons.** The ropelike structure of tendons transmits muscle forces to precise locations on the bones, sometimes quite a distance away from the muscle itself.

Function: Movement Bones and cartilage do a good job of resisting compression (pushing) and bending, whereas tendons and ligaments do a good job of resisting tension (pulling). These structures interact with muscle in ways that enable the efficient transmission of muscle forces and shape changes.

Vertebrate skeletons move by means of changes in joint angles controlled by antagonistic muscle groups. For example, consider how your thigh muscles flex and extend your knee joint. The hamstring muscles in the back of your thigh are **flexors,** muscles that pull bones closer together, decreasing the joint angle between them. They swing your lower leg back toward your thigh, reducing the angle of your knee joint. The quadriceps muscles in the front of your thigh are **extensors,** muscles that increase the angle of a joint. They straighten your leg at the knee joint (**Figure 45.12**).

The hamstrings and quadriceps muscles accomplish the large swing of the lower leg by inserting into different locations on the tibia (shin bone). The articulation of the tibia with the femur (thigh bone) serves as the pivot point for this lever. Along with enabling a shape change, the bone transmits the forces exerted by the thigh muscles to the foot—such as when the extension of your leg enables you to kick a ball.

Function: Calcium Homeostasis In addition to their mechanical functions, bones serve several physiological functions. Chief among these is storage of calcium and other minerals. Calcium is necessary for the proper functioning of many physiological processes, including cell division, release of neurotransmitters, and muscle contraction (Section 45.1). The calcium in bone is the main stored source of calcium for these functions. When blood calcium levels fall, the bones release calcium, maintaining blood–calcium homeostasis so that essential physiological functions can occur.

Several cell types work together to keep blood calcium levels relatively constant. **Osteoblasts** are bone-building cells—they secrete the protein- and calcium-rich extracellular matrix that hardens to form bone. **Osteoclasts,** on the other hand, are bone-resorbing cells. When blood calcium levels are low, osteoclasts secrete acid onto bone tissue, causing small amounts of minerals to be resorbed into the blood.

The relative rates of bone building and bone resorption are affected by many factors, including hormones, aging, diet, and exercise. In healthy adults, bone building and breakdown are balanced, so bone mass remains constant even though the turnover rate is high. Weight-bearing exercise helps to increase bone mass, while aging and malnutrition can reduce it. **Osteoporosis** ("bone pores"), a disease in which reduced bone mass can make bones brittle and susceptible to fracture, is a common affliction of elderly people.

Bones perform other physiological functions as well. The interior of long bones, called bone marrow, is the source of red blood cells needed to carry oxygen in the blood (Chapter 42) and white blood cells needed for the immune system (Chapter 48).

Exoskeletons

The mechanical function of rigid cuticle in exoskeletons is similar in many ways to the function of endoskeletons. Exoskeletons occur primarily in arthropods, including insects, crustaceans, and arachnids (spiders, ticks, scorpions).

Structure An **exoskeleton** ("outside skeleton") is an exterior skeleton that encloses and protects an animal's body. The origin of the exoskeleton was a key innovation that preceded the spectacular diversification of arthropods, the most diverse and abundant animals on Earth (Chapter 31).

The material composition of exoskeletons varies. Insect exoskeletons consist of a cuticle formed from a composite of proteins and the polysaccharide chitin (see Table 5.1). Chitinous ingrowths of the skeleton form **apodemes,** where muscles attach. Crustaceans such as crabs and lobsters have a cuticle that is mineralized with calcium carbonate, making their exoskeletons relatively thick and hard—and heavy. Most crustaceans are aquatic, and their buoyancy in water helps support their weight.

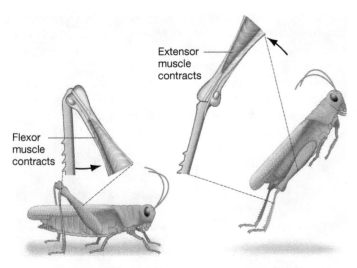

Figure 45.13 Exoskeletons Move by Contraction and Relaxation of Flexor and Extensor Muscles. The muscles are contained within the skeleton.

Function Like vertebrates, arthropods have paired flexor–extensor muscles that operate their jointed skeletons, causing movements that are based on changes in joint angles rather than changes in the dimensions of the segments themselves (Figure 45.13). Unlike vertebrate muscles, however, the muscles of arthropods must be packed *within* the skeleton.

In many arthropods, the problem of the interior placement of muscles is solved by having the pennate, or feather-like arrangement of muscle fibers illustrated in Figure 45.8. This arrangement boosts force output by effectively increasing the muscle cross-sectional area but not the muscle width during a contraction.

The disadvantage of pennate muscles is that their length change is small, so they have a limited range of motion. Arthropods compensate for this constraint in part by the placement of their apodemes, which can convert a small shortening of muscle to a large change in joint angle.

The rigid levers of vertebrate skeletons can grow continuously as the rest of the body grows. But since the rigid exoskeletons of

arthropods encase the growing soft tissue like a suit of armor, they must be shed—molted—periodically and replaced with a bigger one. Arthropods are vulnerable to predation during molts because their skeleton is soft and dysfunctional at that time.

Hydrostatic skeletons, endoskeletons, and exoskeletons all transmit muscle forces and shape changes to other parts of the body and to the environment. While hydrostatic skeletons are the most widespread in terms of the number of animal phyla that contain species with skeletons of this type (virtually all—even arthropods, echinoderms, and vertebrates), the lever-based, segmented, jointed skeletons of arthropods and vertebrates win the prize for overall functional diversity.

45.4 Locomotion

The most spectacular capability conferred on animals by the combination of muscle contractions and skeletal systems is efficient locomotion. Some animals migrate thousands of miles every year, and others perform astonishing feats of acrobatics. Locomotion has been shaped by natural selection and has been central to complex ecological relationships since the radiation of animals during the Cambrian Explosion more than 500 million years ago (Chapter 30).

Many of the diverse modes of locomotion are already familiar to you. Here are some examples.

- **On land** Crawling, walking, running, climbing, hopping, jumping, burrowing
- **In water** Undulating, jetting, swimming, rowing
- **In air** Flying, gliding

What variables do biologists analyze to unlock the secrets of animal locomotion?

How Do Biologists Study Locomotion?

The number of experimental studies on locomotion has increased exponentially in recent years, partly due to the conceptual breakthrough offered by the field of biomechanics—applying the principles of engineering to quantify the mechanics of organisms. Biomechanics studies the physical act of locomotion at different levels, including material properties, structures, motions, forces, and energetics. Let's examine each of these levels, starting with materials.

How Are the Material Properties of Tissues Important to Locomotion? A great deal of research has been devoted to analyzing the active contractile properties of muscle because they are central to understanding how forces are generated in locomotion. However, the passive material properties of the skeletal elements are essential to understanding the transmission of forces.

Consider how you walk and run. A pioneer of biomechanics, R. McNeill Alexander, observed that, in terms of the movement and energy exchange of the center of mass, walking is mechanically similar to the swinging of an upside-down pendulum, whereas running is mechanically similar to a bouncing ball. Based on this insight, Alexander hypothesized that the large tendons of the lower legs of terrestrial animals—for example, the

---

CHECK YOUR UNDERSTANDING

If you understand that ...

- Hydrostatic skeletons, endoskeletons, and exoskeletons transmit muscle forces and shape changes to other parts of the animal and to the environment.
- Antagonistic muscles re-extend one another via the skeleton.
- Shape changes in hydrostatic skeletons involve changes in body segments, whereas shape changes in endoskeletons and exoskeletons involve changes in angles between segments.

✔ You should be able to ...

1. Compare and contrast the structure and function of hydrostatic skeletons, endoskeletons, and exoskeletons.
2. Predict what would happen if neurons simultaneously stimulated the biceps brachii and triceps brachii muscles to contract.

Answers are available in Appendix A.

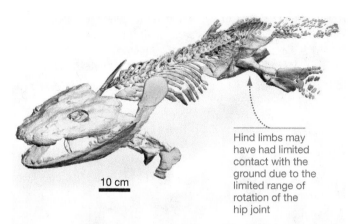

10 cm

Hind limbs may have had limited contact with the ground due to the limited range of rotation of the hip joint

Figure 45.14 The Relationship between Structure and Function Can Be Studied Using Computer Models. This computer image of an early tetrapod, *Ichthyostega*, was built using high-resolution scans of fossil bones. The 3-D model measures the range of rotation of the major limb joints based on skeleton geometry, determining the overall range of motion of the limbs. The model found that the range of rotation of the shoulder and hip joints was more limited than previously thought, rejecting the hypothesis that these animals could walk on all four limbs.

Achilles tendon at the back of your ankle (Figure 45.7)—work as springs when animals run.

To test this hypothesis, Alexander measured the elastic properties of tendon by clamping a piece of tendon in a device that measures the pulling force of the tissue as it is stretched to different lengths and released. The tendon returned 93 percent of the energy invested, losing only 7 percent to heat. This high rate of elastic-energy storage explains how tendons add a spring to the steps of runners, reducing the amount of muscle-generated power that must be generated from step to step.

The importance of the material properties of muscles and skeletal tissues is most obvious when they fail, whether in subtle or catastrophic ways. You may have firsthand experience with the debilitating consequences of broken bones or strained tendons.

How Is Musculoskeletal Structure Adapted for Locomotion?
Many biologists begin their study of locomotion by examining the size and shape of the skeletal elements. Careful measurements of skeleton geometries can reveal a great deal about the posture of the animal, range of motion of joints, and skeletal function in general. For example, a team of biologists recently used structural analysis to test the hypothesis that an early tetrapod, called *Ichthyostega*, could walk on all four limbs like today's salamanders (**Figure 45.14**).

Similar mechanical principles can be applied to relate the shapes of wings to flying ability and the shapes of aquatic animals to swimming ability. Sometimes, however, you just have to watch the action itself to understand how an animal uses its body to locomote.

What Does Locomotion Look Like in Living Animals?
All the motions of different parts of the skeleton, such as the angular rotation of limbs and the pattern of footfall on the ground, together produce locomotion.

Photographer Eadweard Muybridge is famous for his pioneering photo sequences of locomotion. His work with animals reportedly began when he was commissioned by a racehorse owner to settle a wager on whether horses are ever completely airborne during a gallop. His results are shown in the top sequence of **Figure 45.15**. High-speed video and digital images of many other animals have since been recorded, providing insights into many forms of locomotion, such as

- The gait of human sprinters (Figure 45.15, bottom)
- The complex wing-beat patterns of hovering bees and hummingbirds
- The upright, bipedal (two-footed) gait of basilisk lizards running across the surface of water (see chapter opening image)
- The footfall pattern that prevents centipedes from tripping on their own legs
- The aerial undulating of snakes that glide down from treetops
- The limb-like use of fins in lungfish "walking"
- Peristalsis in the muscular feet of crawling snails

Figure 45.15 The Motions of Locomotion Can Be Captured on Film. Eadweard Muybridge shot many photo series of animals during locomotion to enable precise analysis of limb and body motions over time.

For most animals, the pattern of movement during locomotion varies with speed. For example, horses walk at slow speeds, trot at intermediate speeds, and gallop at fast speeds—each gait has a distinct pattern of leg motions.

Computers facilitate the analysis of the many images captured in motion studies. The results are themselves insightful, but they also serve as an important stepping-stone to understanding the forces involved in locomotion.

What Forces Are Involved in Locomotion?

If an animal wants to move forward, it must push something backward, as predicted by Newton's third law of motion. Otherwise, the animal could move but not get anywhere, like a person with smooth shoes on slick ice. The types of forces that are important in locomotion vary according to whether the animal is locomoting on land, in water, in air, or some combination of the three.

On land, gravitational forces and inertial forces dominate. The gravitational force experienced by an animal is its weight, which is the product of its mass and the acceleration due to gravity (9.8 m/sec^2 on Earth). Weight is important on land because most terrestrial animals must hold themselves up to move forward. Inertial forces are proportional to mass and velocity, and they represent resistance of bodies and limbs to acceleration and deceleration. Note in the horse and human photo sequences in Figure 45.15 that the arms and legs must swing back and forth dramatically—an energy-intensive process of acceleration and deceleration.

In water, gravitational forces are less important than on land, due to the counteracting buoyant forces supporting the animal's weight in water. However, aquatic animals must overcome drag, the force that resists forward motion through fluids. Convergent evolution of torpedo-shaped bodies has occurred in diverse aquatic animals, from tuna to dolphins and ichthyosaurs, due to the strong selection for bodies that minimize drag during rapid locomotion (Chapter 25). Aquatic animals that move more slowly face less drag and thus are morphologically more diverse.

Water and air are both fluids, but air is a thousand times less dense than water. Buoyant forces are therefore negligible in air, making gravitational forces very important to fliers—most animals that locomote by flying or gliding have adaptations that make them lightweight. They must produce a force called lift to counteract gravity, and they must also minimize drag. As a result, fast fliers tend to have very streamlined shapes.

How are forces measured? Scientists can measure ground force—the force with which a terrestrial animal strikes the substratum during a step—by coaxing an animal to walk, run, or hop upon an instrument called a force plate. Quantifying forces in fluids is more nuanced. It often requires indirect measurement by visualizing the flow of air or water around the animal (Figure 45.16).

What Is the Cost of Locomotion?

Animals must spend energy to find food and mates and escape from predators. However, the more energy an animal spends on locomotion, the less it can spend on producing offspring. There is strong selection pressure to minimize the cost of locomotion. How do biologists measure this cost?

Figure 45.16 Visualization of Airflow Is Used to Analyze the Forces Involved in the Hovering of a Bat. The lift and drag forces acting on flying and swimming animals can be measured by observing fluid flow around the animal. The arrows represent the velocity of tiny water droplets illuminated by a laser in front of a high-speed camera.

To get a sense of variables that determine the cost of locomotion, consider the classic studies by Alexander on the gait transition from walking to running in humans. Alexander discovered that walking is an efficient mode of transport because you exchange potential energy at the top of your stride with kinetic energy midstride. However, the resulting pendulum-like motion of your center of mass is not efficient at higher speeds, when it becomes more cost effective to run using your spring-like tendons and other skeletal tissues to store energy between strides.

Alexander hypothesized that animals locomote using the most energy-efficient gait at each speed. To test this hypothesis in horses, physiologists Dan Hoyt and Richard Taylor trained horses to walk, trot, and gallop at a range of unnatural speeds—for example, trotting at a speed where the horse would normally have preferred to gallop. Hoyt and Taylor fitted each horse with an oxygen mask and ran it on a treadmill, so that they could measure oxygen consumption and speed simultaneously. The rate of oxygen consumption is a measure of energy use because oxygen consumption is proportional to ATP production during aerobic respiration. The researchers then plotted energy use versus speed for each gait.

Hoyt and Taylor also filmed the horses moving freely around their paddock and measured the speeds at which the horses used different gaits when given free choice. The researchers then compared the lab data to the gait preference in the paddock.

The graph in **Figure 45.17** shows Hoyt and Taylor's results. The three curves at the top represent the energy used per distance traveled at the three gaits—the dips in the curves indicate the speeds at which the gaits were most efficient. The bars at the bottom of the graph show the speeds and gaits chosen by the horses when they were able to locomote freely in the paddock. The data support the hypothesis that the horses use the most energy-efficient gaits at different speeds and avoid intermediate speeds where the cost of locomotion is higher.

QUESTION: Do horses minimize the cost of locomotion?

HYPOTHESIS: Horses choose gaits that minimize energy use at different speeds.

NULL HYPOTHESIS: Horses do not choose gaits based on the cost of locomotion.

EXPERIMENTAL SETUP:

1. Measure oxygen consumption of horses trained to walk, trot, and gallop at a range of speeds on a treadmill. Calculate energy used per distance traveled at different speeds.

5.6 m/s

Oxygen mask

Treadmill

2. Videotape the same horses locomoting freely in the paddock, and measure the gaits and speeds they choose to use naturally.

PREDICTION: For each gait, there is a range of speeds where energy use is minimized. Horses will favor these gaits and speeds.

PREDICTION OF NULL HYPOTHESIS: There will be no correlation between chosen gaits and energy consumption.

RESULTS:

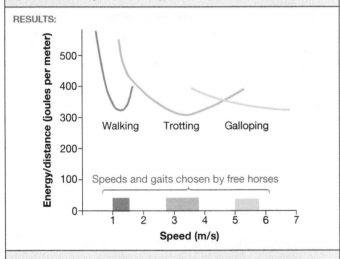

CONCLUSION: Horses choose gaits that minimize energy use at different speeds and avoid speeds with high energy consumption.

Figure 45.17 Horses Minimize the Cost of Locomotion by Choosing Appropriate Gaits.

SOURCE: Hoyt, D. F., and C. R. Taylor. 1981. Gait and the energetics of locomotion in horses. *Nature* 292: 239–240.

✔ **QUANTITATIVE** Use the graph to estimate the relative cost of galloping rather than trotting at 3.5 meters/second (m/s).

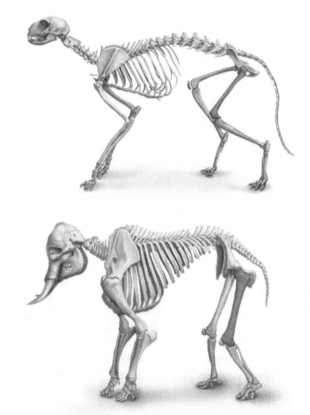

Figure 45.18 Size Influences Skeleton Geometry. When scaled to the same size, an elephant has thicker bones and a more upright stance than a cat does, due to the disproportionate burden of gravity on larger animals. The femurs are highlighted for comparison.

Similar studies have been conducted for diverse animals running, swimming, and flying, with similar results. Natural selection favors animals that locomote efficiently because they have more energy available for other vital activities.

Size Matters

Animals that use muscles to power locomotion span a vast range of sizes—an astonishing 10 orders of magnitude (10,000,000,000)—from tiny ants to giant whales. Many of these animals also grow over a large size range during their development. As is true for many other aspects of animal structure and function, size matters.

Two organisms may be geometrically similar—that is, they may have exactly the same proportions—but if they are different sizes, they are more different than they seem. To start, the ratio of surface area to volume decreases as the organism gets larger, because surface area is proportional to length squared, while volume is proportional to length cubed (Chapter 39). This concept has far-reaching implications for physiology. It also has important mechanical implications.

The weight of an animal is proportional to its volume, and the ability of leg bones to support the weight is proportional to their cross-sectional area. Thus, large terrestrial animals must have disproportionately hefty skeletal elements to avoid breaking their legs—something that Galileo observed 400 years ago when he compared skeletons of small and large animals (**Figure 45.18**).

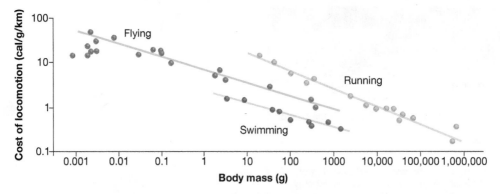

Figure 45.19 Cost of Locomotion for Running, Flying, and Swimming Animals Decreases with Body Mass.
DATA: Schmidt-Nielsen, K. 1972. Locomotion: Energy cost of swimming, flying, and running. *Science* 177: 222–228.

✔ **QUANTITATIVE** About how much more costly is it to run than to swim for animals with a body mass of 100 g?

So, in the late 1980s, it was surprising when Andrew Biewener discovered that animals of different sizes maintain similar stresses in their skeletal tissues. How do they do that?

Biewener observed that posture and behavior are important variables. Small animals locomote in a more crouched posture and make great leaps, while large animals like elephants are more straight-legged, so that their skeletons, rather than their muscles, can support their body weight. Larger animals also locomote more gently. If a house cat were enlarged to the size of an elephant, it would break its own bones when trying to pounce.

Size is also of paramount importance in determining how animals locomote through fluids. Fluids have an inherent viscosity, or stickiness, that is of minor concern to animals that are very large and/or fast (and thus have high inertia), like dolphins, which can glide through water with little effort. But viscosity is of enormous concern to animals that are very small and/or slow (and thus have low inertia), like plankton. If you were the size of a grain of rice and went for a swim in a lake, the water would feel like corn syrup.

Size also affects the cost of locomotion. In the 1970s, physiologist Knut Schmidt-Nielsen compared the energy costs of different modes of locomotion. To account for widely different body sizes and distances traveled, he normalized all the data to the energy cost in calories per gram of body tissue per kilometer traveled and then plotted the data on a log–log plot (see BioSkills 5).

Schmidt-Nielson's data showed that larger animals use less energy per gram of body tissue per distance traveled than smaller animals—all the lines slope down to the right (Figure 45.19). The data also showed that for a given body size, running is a more expensive mode of transport than flying, and swimming is the least expensive.

Many other aspects of locomotion can also be plotted as a function of body size. The results reveal general principles that can be used to make predictions for diverse animals, even those that are extinct.

The take-home message? The laws of physics establish definite constraints on the possible sizes, shapes, and modes of locomotion in animals. Understanding these principles helps illuminate themes and variations among the diversity of animals.

CHAPTER 45   **REVIEW**

For media, go to MasteringBiology

45.1 How Do Muscles Contract?

- The muscles of vertebrate limbs are composed of cells, called muscle fibers, that contain contractile elements called myofibrils, each divided into contractile units called sarcomeres.

- Sarcomeres appear striated, or banded, due to the aligned arrangement of thick filaments (myosin) and thin filaments (actin).

- Sarcomeres shorten when thick filaments of myosin slide past thin filaments of actin in a series of binding events mediated by the hydrolysis of ATP.

- Calcium ions play an essential role in muscle contraction by making the actin in thin filaments available for binding by myosin.

- Acetylcholine released from somatic motor neurons is the neurotransmitter that stimulates contraction of skeletal muscle.

45.2 Muscle Tissues

- Smooth muscle lines bronchioles, blood vessels, the gastrointestinal tract, and certain reproductive organs. Smooth muscle cells are small and unstriated and have a single nucleus. Contractions are involuntary.

- Cardiac muscle occurs in the heart and forces blood through the circulatory system. Cardiac muscle cells are striated, branched, and connected to one another by intercalated discs. Contractions are involuntary.

- Most skeletal muscles are attached to the skeleton and are responsible for voluntary movement of the body. Skeletal muscle cells are long, striated, and multinucleate.

- Skeletal muscle fibers are specialized to contract slowly or quickly and to have a high or low endurance. These properties depend on the concentration of myoglobin present and the use of aerobic respiration and/or glycolysis for the production of ATP.

- Skeletal muscle fibers are organized in a parallel arrangement, which maximizes shortening, or a pennate pattern, which maximizes force production.

45.3 Skeletal Systems

- Hydrostatic skeletons are composed of a body wall in tension surrounding fluid or soft tissue under compression.

- Endoskeletons are internal skeletons, surrounded by soft tissue. In vertebrates, the jointed endoskeleton is composed of bones, cartilage, and ligaments.

- Bones are involved in movement, protection of organs, storage of calcium, and production of blood cells.

- Exoskeletons are external skeletons, enclosing soft tissue. In arthropods, the muscles occur within the rigid, jointed cuticle composed of chitin, proteins, and sometimes minerals. Exoskeletons must be shed to enable growth.

- Movement is based on antagonistic muscle groups that act on a skeleton. Examples include flexors and extensors, which change the joint angle between rigid skeletal segments—especially in limbs.

45.4 Locomotion

- Locomotion is movement relative to the environment and requires the transmission of muscle forces to the land, water, or air surrounding the animal.

- Locomotion can be studied at different levels: material properties, structures, motions, forces, and energetics.

- Locomotion on land is usually dominated by gravitational and inertial forces. Swimmers must overcome drag. Fliers must overcome drag and must generate enough lift to counteract gravity.

- Body size is important to the mechanics of locomotion.

Answers are available in Appendix A

✔ TEST YOUR KNOWLEDGE

1. Which of the following classes of muscle is/are voluntary?
   a. skeletal muscle
   b. cardiac muscle
   c. smooth muscle
   d. all of the above

2. In muscle cells, myosin molecules continue moving along actin molecules as long as
   a. ATP is present and troponin is not bound to Ca^{2+}.
   b. ADP is present and tropomyosin is released from intracellular stores.
   c. ADP is present and intracellular acetylcholine is high.
   d. ATP is present and intracellular Ca^{2+} is high.

3. Which of the following is critical to the function of most exoskeletons, endoskeletons, and hydrostatic skeletons?
   a. Muscles interact with the skeleton in antagonistic groups.
   b. Muscles attach to each of these types of skeleton via tendons.
   c. Muscles extend joints by pushing skeletal elements.
   d. Segments of the body or limbs are extended when paired muscles relax in unison.

4. True or false: A large animal will experience twice the gravitational force of a small animal half its length if their geometries are the same.

✔ TEST YOUR UNDERSTANDING

5. How did data on sarcomere structure inspire the sliding-filament model of muscle contraction? Explain why the observation that muscle cells contain many mitochondria and extensive smooth endoplasmic reticulum turned out to be logical once the molecular mechanism of muscular contraction was understood.

6. Rigor mortis is the stiffening of a body after death that occurs when myosin binds to actin but cannot unbind. What prevents myosin from unbinding?

7. R. McNeill Alexander discovered that the arch of the human foot operates like a spring during running. Predict how a runner's oxygen consumption would change if a runner wore shoes that prevented the arches from changing shape. Explain your reasoning.

8. Explain why the energetic cost of swimming decreases as a fish grows.

✔ TEST YOUR PROBLEM-SOLVING SKILLS

9. Atropine is a compound found in many poisonous nightshade plants. It blocks acetylcholine receptors in the heart. Predict the effect of ingestion of atropine on heart rate. Explain your logic.

10. QUANTITATIVE The speed at which you switch from a walk to a run can be predicted using what is called the Froude number, based on the relative importance of gravitational and inertial forces of your pendulum-like walking gait.

$$\text{Froude number} = \frac{(\text{speed of locomotion})^2}{\text{gravitational acceleration} \times \text{leg length}}$$

Most mammals change from a walk to a run at a Froude number of 0.5. If gravitational acceleration is 9.8 m/s², and your leg length is 0.9 m, at what speed are you likely to switch from a walk to a run?
   a. 2.0 m
   b. 1.9 m/s
   c. 2.1 m/s
   d. 2.0 m/s²

✔ PUT IT ALL TOGETHER: Case Study

Is athletic performance related to muscle fiber type?

Distance runner Paula Radcliffe has won dozens of long-distance races and has held the world record in the marathon for over a decade. Scientists, trainers, and athletes alike have wondered about the extent to which muscle structure and function contribute to success in athletes like Radcliffe. What makes elite distance runners so good? Are their muscles somehow different from those of less successful athletes and non-athletes?

11. Compare and contrast the structure and function of the three types of skeletal muscle fibers.

12. Predict who would likely have a greater proportion of fast glycolytic fibers in their gastrocnemius (calf) muscle—an elite distance runner or an elite sprinter. Explain.

13. **CAUTION** Predict the effect of training for a marathon on the number of muscle cells in the gastrocnemius. Explain.

14. **QUANTITATIVE** To discover the relationship between muscle-fiber types and performance, researchers obtained tiny biopsies of the gastrocnemius of 14 elite distance runners, 18 trained but non-elite distance runners, and 19 untrained subjects. They

categorized the fiber types as slow or fast. (At the time of the study, intermediate fibers had not been identified as a third type.) Some of their data are shown below (* means $P < 0.05$; see BioSkills 3). What conclusions can you draw from these data?

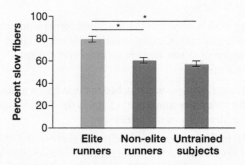

Source: Fink, W. J., D. L. Costill, and M. L. Pollock. 1977. *Annals of the New York Academy of Sciences* 301: 323–327.

15. The researchers looked more closely at the data within the group of elite runners. Although the mean proportion of slow fibers was 79 percent in this group, individual values ranged from 27 percent in one runner to 98 percent in another. How does this finding affect your interpretation of the relationship between athletic performance and muscle-fiber types?

16. Imagine that Paula Radcliffe is racing against a bird and a fish, each with the same mass as Paula. Which organism would have the highest cost of locomotion during the race?

MasteringBiology®

Students Go to MasteringBiology for assignments, the eText, and the Study Area with animations, practice tests, and activities.
Professors Go to MasteringBiology for automatically graded tutorials and questions that you can assign to your students, plus Instructor Resources.

46 Chemical Signals in Animals

The spectacular transformation that occurs during insect metamorphosis is triggered by chemical signals called hormones.

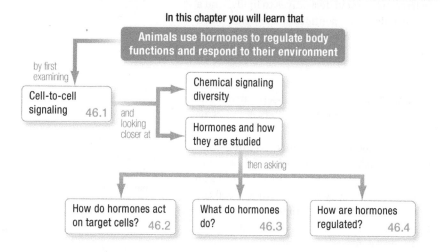

In this chapter you will learn that

Animals use hormones to regulate body functions and respond to their environment

by first examining

Cell-to-cell signaling 46.1

and looking closer at

Chemical signaling diversity

Hormones and how they are studied

then asking

How do hormones act on target cells? 46.2

What do hormones do? 46.3

How are hormones regulated? 46.4

This chapter is part of the Big Picture. See how on pages 816–817.

n response to sights, sounds, and other sensory stimuli, an animal's nervous system sends rapid messages, in the form of action potentials, to precise locations in the body. In many cases, these messages result in immediate, temporary responses such as muscle contractions and movement.

In response to changes in external or internal conditions, cells in the nervous system or the endocrine system also release molecules that produce longer-term responses in a broad range of tissues and organs. The **endocrine system** is a collection of organs and cells that secrete chemical signals into the bloodstream. A chemical signal that circulates through body fluids and affects distant target cells is called a **hormone.**

The goal of this chapter is to explore how hormones and other types of internal chemical signals work in animals. Together, animal nervous systems and endocrine systems process information about the internal and external environment—a function that is one of the five key attributes of life (see Chapter 1).

Let's begin with an overview of chemical signaling systems and then plunge into analyzing how hormones regulate the activity of target cells.

46.1 Cell-to-Cell Signaling: An Overview

Animal chemical signals are present in extremely low concentrations but can have enormous effects on their target cells. Unlike action potentials, which are electrical impulses that have a short-term effect on a single cell or on a small population of adjacent cells, the messages that chemical signals carry can have a relatively long-lasting effect.

In combination, electrical and chemical signals allow animals to coordinate the activities of cells throughout the body. They are the mechanism responsible for maintaining trillions of cells as an integrated unit called an individual.

Major Categories of Chemical Signals

The chemical signals found in animals have diverse structures and functions. Table 46.1 summarizes how biologists organize the diversity of chemical signals, based on where the molecules originate and where they act. Notice that the names for most of the categories use the Greek word root *crin*, meaning "separated." Its use captures something essential about how chemical signals act: They are released from cells and thus are separated from them.

It's important to note that these five classes of chemical messenger do not coincide with five structurally distinct classes of molecules. For example, the endocrine signals found in a particular organism routinely belong to several families of chemical compounds, ranging from amino acid derivatives to lipids. And a particular family of molecules—say, peptides or the lipids called steroids—may function as endocrine, autocrine, and paracrine signals in the same individual.

Autocrine Signals Act on the Same Cell That Secretes Them
Translated literally, "autocrine" means "same-separated." The name is appropriate because **autocrine** signals affect the same cell that releases them.

Perhaps the best-studied autocrine signals are **cytokines** ("cell-movers"). Most cytokines amplify the response of a cell to a stimulus. An example is interleukin 2, which in the course of fighting an infection is synthesized and released by a type of white blood cell called a T cell. Interleukin 2 activates T cells to help eliminate the infection. It also causes the cells to divide repeatedly, producing more activated T cells for host defense (see Chapter 48).

Paracrine Signals Act on Neighboring Cells
Translated literally, **paracrine** means "beside-separated." Paracrine signals diffuse locally and act on target cells near the source cell. Cytokines, for example, may act as paracrine signals as well as autocrine signals, because they can trigger responses by other nearby cells of the immune system.

It is common, in fact, to observe that a single chemical messenger can be assigned to more than one category of signal, based on its mode of action. Like some cytokines, the cell–cell signals named **insulin** and **glucagon** cross categories. These molecules are produced by two distinct populations of cells within the regions of the **pancreas** called the islets of Langerhans. The molecules act on nearby pancreatic cells as paracrine signals

and ensure a smooth, steady response to changing blood-glucose levels. But they also act as hormones, in that they are released into the blood or other body fluids and affect distant cells—in this case, controlling the concentration of glucose in the blood.

Endocrine Signals Are Hormones
Endocrine ("inside-separated") signals are carried to distant cells by blood or other body fluids. The cells that produce endocrine signals may be organized into discrete organs called **glands** or may be interspersed among the cells of other organs—as are the islets of Langerhans in the pancreas.

Because hormones are well studied and particularly important to understanding how animals work, they serve as the focus of this chapter. Many or most of the principles discussed are relevant to the other categories of animal cell–cell signals as well, however.

Neural Signals Are Neurotransmitters
You might recall that when an action potential arrives at a synapse, it triggers the release of neurotransmitters, which bind to receptors on the postsynaptic cell and induce a change in membrane potential—altering the tendency for the postsynaptic cell to fire action potentials (see Chapter 43).

Five Categories of Chemical Signals in Animals

Type of Chemical Signal	Source and Target
Autocrine signals act on the same cell that secretes them.	
Paracrine signals diffuse locally and act on nearby cells.	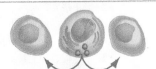
Endocrine signals are hormones carried between cells by blood or other body fluids.	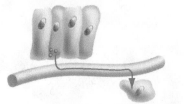
Neural signals (neurotransmitters) diffuse a short distance between neurons.	
Neuroendocrine signals (neurohormones) are hormones released from neurons.	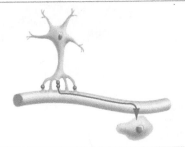

(a) Endocrine pathway

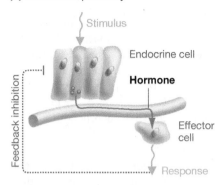

(b) Neuroendocrine pathway

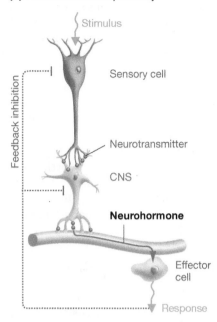

(c) Neuroendocrine-to-endocrine pathway

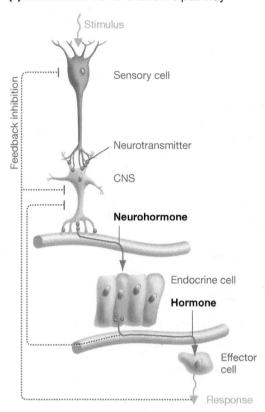

Figure 46.1 Hormones Act via Three Pathways and Are Regulated by Negative Feedback. For help in diagramming feedback loops similar to those used here, see **Making Models 46.1.**

Neural signaling can be very fast, because action potentials propagate rapidly and neurotransmitters have to diffuse only a short distance—across the tiny gap between two neurons, called the synaptic cleft. Neural signals also tend to be short lived, because the signaling molecules are quickly broken down or taken back up by the presynaptic cell.

Neuroendocrine Signals Act at a Distance Contrary to popular belief, the endocrine and nervous systems do not function independently of each other. Even though they are released from neurons, **neuroendocrine** ("nerve-inside-separated") signals share a key attribute with endocrine signals: They act on distant cells. For this reason, they are called **neurohormones**.

Antidiuretic hormone (ADH; also called vasopressin) is a particularly well-studied neuroendocrine signal. ADH is produced by neurons that have their cell bodies in a brain region called the **hypothalamus.** But instead of acting as a neural signal, ADH acts on cells in the collecting duct of the kidney to help regulate water excretion (see Chapter 40).

Hormone Signaling Pathways

In plants, sensory cells perceive changes in the environment and broadcast a hormonal signal that triggers an appropriate response from effector cells (see Chapter 37). In animals, some endocrine cells also respond directly to an environmental stimulus by secreting hormones (**Figure 46.1a**). But frequently, hormonal signaling in animals involves additional steps.

In many cases, information about external or internal conditions is gathered by sensory receptors and then integrated by neurons in the central nervous system (CNS) before the production of a hormonal signal. Neurons in the CNS respond by releasing neurohormones, which act on effector cells directly (**Figure 46.1b**) or stimulate cells in the endocrine system, which respond by producing hormones (**Figure 46.1c**).

All three types of signaling pathway—endocrine, neuroendocrine, and neuroendocrine-to-endocrine—are regulated by **negative feedback,** or **feedback inhibition.** In feedback inhibition, the product of a process inhibits its production. **Positive feedback,** in contrast, occurs when the product of a process *stimulates* its production, resulting in greater and greater production of that product.

> **✎ Making Models 46.1 Tips on Drawing Feedback Loops**
>
> Using arrows to show stimulation and bar-headed lines to show inhibition is a useful way to conceptualize feedback loops. The model below shows a negative feedback system, in which endocrine gland A releases hormone A, which stimulates endocrine gland B to release hormone B. Hormone B inhibits the release of hormone A.
>
>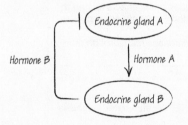
>
> **MODEL** Draw a model showing a positive feedback loop. What will happen to the secretion of hormone B over time?
>
> To see this model in action, go to https://goo.gl/WM9OBt
>
>

Negative feedback is key to homeostasis (see Chapter 39). In the endocrine pathway, the hormone produced by the effector cells feeds back on the endocrine cells that secrete it, lowering production of the hormone and down-regulating the response (Figure 46.1a). The response of effector cells also feeds back to cells that initiate the neuroendocrine and neuroendocrine-to-endocrine pathways. A change in input from these initiating cells then lowers production of the neurohormone and reduces the response (see Figures 46.1b and 46.1c). Neuroendocrine-to-endocrine signaling pathways have an additional layer of regulation, because the hormonal signal usually inhibits production of the neurohormone (Figure 46.1c).

The take-home message? The nervous system and endocrine system are tightly integrated into a neuroendocrine system. Endocrine signals are released in response to electrical signals; in turn, endocrine signals modulate the electrical signals transmitted by the nervous system.

Feedback inhibition in the endocrine system is analogous to temperature control by a heat-sensitive thermostat. If the temperature is too high, the thermostat sends a signal that turns the furnace off; if the temperature is too low, the thermostat sends a signal that turns the furnace on. The result is a relatively constant air temperature. In animal cell–cell signaling, feedback inhibition reduces the production or secretion of a hormone, or both.

What Makes Up the Endocrine System?

The endocrine system is the collection of cells, tissues, and organs responsible for hormone production and secretion. Organs that secrete a hormone into the bloodstream are called **endocrine glands.**

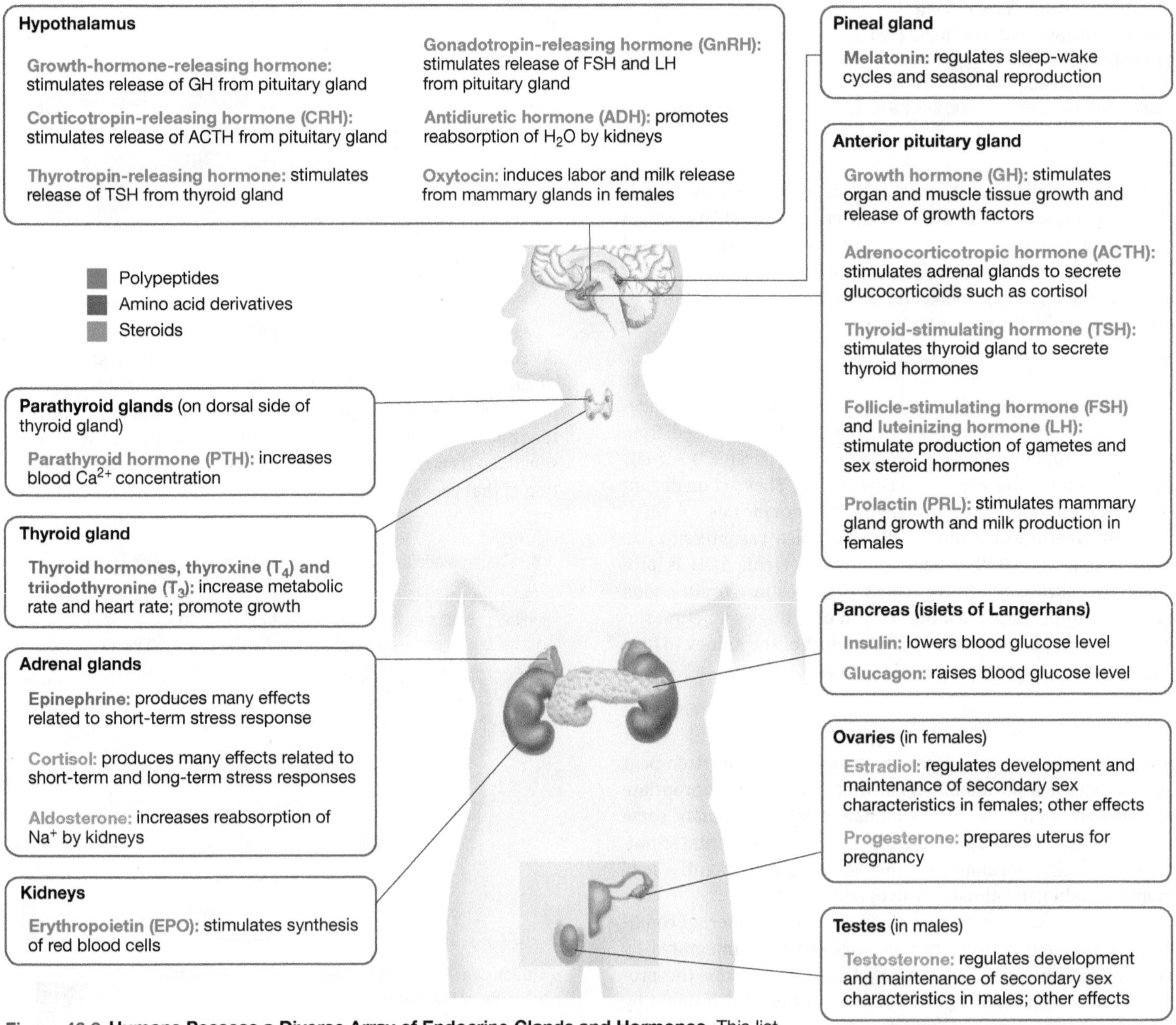

Hypothalamus

Growth-hormone-releasing hormone: stimulates release of GH from pituitary gland

Corticotropin-releasing hormone (CRH): stimulates release of ACTH from pituitary gland

Thyrotropin-releasing hormone: stimulates release of TSH from thyroid gland

Gonadotropin-releasing hormone (GnRH): stimulates release of FSH and LH from pituitary gland

Antidiuretic hormone (ADH): promotes reabsorption of H_2O by kidneys

Oxytocin: induces labor and milk release from mammary glands in females

Pineal gland

Melatonin: regulates sleep-wake cycles and seasonal reproduction

Anterior pituitary gland

Growth hormone (GH): stimulates organ and muscle tissue growth and release of growth factors

Adrenocorticotropic hormone (ACTH): stimulates adrenal glands to secrete glucocorticoids such as cortisol

Thyroid-stimulating hormone (TSH): stimulates thyroid gland to secrete thyroid hormones

Follicle-stimulating hormone (FSH) and luteinizing hormone (LH): stimulate production of gametes and sex steroid hormones

Prolactin (PRL): stimulates mammary gland growth and milk production in females

■ Polypeptides
■ Amino acid derivatives
■ Steroids

Parathyroid glands (on dorsal side of thyroid gland)

Parathyroid hormone (PTH): increases blood Ca^{2+} concentration

Thyroid gland

Thyroid hormones, thyroxine (T_4) and triiodothyronine (T_3): increase metabolic rate and heart rate; promote growth

Adrenal glands

Epinephrine: produces many effects related to short-term stress response

Cortisol: produces many effects related to short-term and long-term stress responses

Aldosterone: increases reabsorption of Na^+ by kidneys

Kidneys

Erythropoietin (EPO): stimulates synthesis of red blood cells

Pancreas (islets of Langerhans)

Insulin: lowers blood glucose level

Glucagon: raises blood glucose level

Ovaries (in females)

Estradiol: regulates development and maintenance of secondary sex characteristics in females; other effects

Progesterone: prepares uterus for pregnancy

Testes (in males)

Testosterone: regulates development and maintenance of secondary sex characteristics in males; other effects

Figure 46.2 Humans Possess a Diverse Array of Endocrine Glands and Hormones. This list is only partial. The heart, gastrointestinal tract, adipose (fat) tissue, and many other organs and cells also produce hormones.

The tissues and organs that make up the endocrine system vary widely among animals. For example, neurons that manufacture and secrete hormones are particularly important in insects, where they regulate molting, metamorphosis, and other processes. Salmon have an unusual gland that secretes a hormone responsible for regulating calcium ion concentration.

Even within one species, the diversity of endocrine system components can be impressive. For example, **Figure 46.2** shows major human glands with endocrine functions. As mentioned earlier, hormone-secreting cells are not always organized into discrete glands. In many cases, they are located in other kinds of organs. The islets of Langerhans in the pancreas are one example.

It's important to note that not all glands in the body are part of the endocrine system. **Exocrine glands,** in contrast to endocrine glands, deliver their secretions through outlets called ducts into a space other than the circulatory system. Most of the digestive glands are either exocrine glands—an example is the salivary glands—or mixed endocrine and exocrine glands, such as the pancreas (see Chapter 41). The exocrine cells of the pancreas secrete digestive enzymes through ducts into the intestine. The endocrine portion of the pancreas consists of cells that secrete insulin and glucagon directly into the bloodstream.

Researchers have identified hundreds of hormones involved in every physiological system, and new hormones are still being discovered. However, scientists initially thought that all internal communication was accomplished via the nervous system, because nerves are visible during dissection and hormones are not. How did scientists discover hormones?

How Do Researchers Identify a Hormone?

Research on animal hormones began in the mid-1800s, when the Swiss-German biologist Arnold Berthold performed an experiment on roosters. Berthold hypothesized that the testes release a chemical signal that causes male roosters to act aggressively toward one another. His hypothesis stemmed from the observation that when young male roosters are castrated (have their testes removed so that more tender meat develops), they do not act aggressively toward one another and do not grow the large combs and wattles typical of roosters (**Figure 46.3**).

To test his hypothesis, Berthold castrated a group of young male chickens. In some, he re-implanted one of the testes he had just removed into the birds' own abdominal cavities or those of other castrated chickens. As these birds matured, Berthold found that they acted aggressively and grew large wattles and combs, like normal roosters, whereas the control castrated birds did not.

The genius of Berthold's experiment was that it separated hormonal from neural influences. The testes that he implanted in the birds' abdominal cavities did not form new neural connections with the body, but they did establish new blood vessels. When the castrated birds with re-implanted testes developed typical male anatomy and behavior, Berthold concluded that these characteristics were stimulated not by nerves, but by a blood-borne chemical signal. Although this chemical was not isolated and named until years after his death, Berthold had discovered **testosterone,** the hormone that controls development of male reproductive anatomy and stimulates reproductive behavior.

RESEARCH

QUESTION: What causes typical male anatomy and behavior in roosters?

HYPOTHESIS: A chemical signal released from the testes is responsible for aggression and comb and wattle growth in roosters.

NULL HYPOTHESIS: A chemical signal released from the testes is not responsible for aggression and comb and wattle growth in roosters.

EXPERIMENTAL SETUP:

Group 1: Male chicks castrated (testes removed)

Group 2: Male chicks castrated, testis re-implanted in abdominal cavity

Group 3: Male chicks castrated, testes transplanted between chicks

PREDICTION: Castrated males will fight less and have smaller wattles and combs than castrated males with testes implanted in the body.

PREDICTION OF NULL HYPOTHESIS: There will be no difference in fighting behavior and comb and wattle size between groups.

RESULTS:

Group 1: Birds have small wattles and combs; don't fight.

Groups 2 and 3: Birds develop large, red wattles and combs; fight aggressively.

Necropsy shows that implanted testes reestablished blood vessels but not nerves.

CONCLUSION: A chemical signal released from the testes into the bloodstream causes males to fight and stimulates comb and wattle growth.

Figure 46.3 The Testes Produce a Hormone Required for Male Anatomy and Behavior in Roosters. This hormone was later named testosterone.

SOURCE: Berthold, A. A. 1849. Transplantation der Hoden. *Arch. Anat. Physiol. Wiss. Med.* 16: 42–49.

✔ **PROCESS OF SCIENCE** Now that testosterone is commercially available for use in research, how could Berthold's experiment be modified to yield more specific results?

A Breakthrough in Measuring Hormone Levels

Documenting an association between a particular gland or hormone and an effect in the body is just a first step. To understand hormone action, researchers have to figure out how these signals help animals stay alive and produce offspring.

The key to this goal is the ability to quantify the levels of hormones circulating in the bloodstream. This ability eluded researchers for decades, however, because hormones are present in the blood at extremely low concentrations.

The breakthrough came in the 1950s when Rosalind Yalow developed the **radioimmunoassay,** a feat for which she later received the Nobel Prize in Medicine. In a radioimmunoassay, the quantity of hormone in a blood sample can be estimated by adding a radioactively labeled version of that hormone to the sample. The labeled and unlabeled hormones will compete with each other for binding to an antibody (see BioSkills 6).

The technique of radioimmunoassay has revolutionized the study of hormones and the treatment of endocrine diseases, allowing the concentrations of hormones to be measured precisely in blood samples drawn from animals or patients. Currently, radioimmunoassays are used every day in endocrine research and medical laboratories. Much of what researchers know about hormone function was learned in studies employing these assays.

CHECK YOUR UNDERSTANDING

If you understand that ...

• Cell-to-cell signaling occurs through a variety of pathways, and distant signaling is accomplished via the nervous system or endocrine system.
• Hormone levels are quantified using radioimmunoassay.

✔ You should be able to ...

Discuss why it is often difficult to differentiate between the functions of the nervous and endocrine systems.

Answers are available in Appendix A.

46.2 How Do Hormones Act on Target Cells?

Hormones have an astonishing array of functions, but they all share certain characteristics. Chief among these are that they can have strong effects even at very low concentrations, and they exert these effects by binding to proteins called **hormone receptors** in target tissues. Let's take a look at how these characteristics are related to the functions of various chemical classes of hormones.

Hormone Concentrations Are Low, but Their Effects Are Large

Hormones have profound effects on individuals, even though they are present at vanishingly small concentrations. As an example, consider research that led to the discovery of **growth hormone (GH).**

Several researchers noted that rats and other laboratory animals stopped growing when their pituitary glands were removed. Based on this observation, it was hypothesized that the **pituitary gland,** located at the base of the brain, produces a chemical signal that promotes cell division and other aspects of growth.

To test this hypothesis, a research group purified a polypeptide from cow pituitary glands, injected the polypeptide into lab rats, and documented rapidly accelerated growth. When the researchers injected 0.01 mg of the polypeptide each day for nine days into rats that lacked pituitary glands, the growth plates in the rats' leg bones widened by 50 percent. Those rats also gained an average of 10 g more than rats that lacked pituitary glands and did not receive the polypeptide injections. Stated another

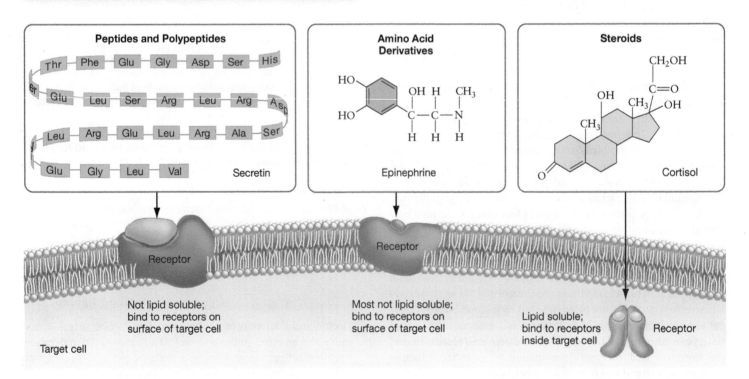

Figure 46.4 **Most Animal Hormones Belong to One of Three Chemical Classes.**

way, an additional 0.09 mg of polypeptide—now known to be GH—led to a weight gain of 10,000 mg.

Further, 1 kg of cow pituitary tissue contains a mere 0.04 g of GH. By mass, GH makes up just 4 one-thousandths of 1 percent of the cow pituitary gland, but it has a dramatic effect on animal growth.

Three Chemical Classes of Hormones

Figure 46.4 illustrates the three major classes of chemicals that can act as hormones in animals:

1. Peptides and polypeptides, which are chains of amino acids linked by peptide bonds (see Chapter 3)

2. Amino acid derivatives

3. Steroids, which are a family of lipids distinguished by a four-ring structure (see Chapter 6)

Secretin, a hormone produced in the small intestine that stimulates the exocrine portion of the pancreas, is a polypeptide; the hormone **epinephrine**, also known as **adrenaline**, is synthesized in the medulla of the **adrenal glands** from the amino acid tyrosine; and the hormone **cortisol** is synthesized in the cortex of the adrenal glands from the steroid cholesterol. (The Greek word roots *epi* and *nephron* mean "top-kidney"; the Latin word roots *ad* and *renal* also mean "top-kidney.")

Given that small amounts of polypeptide, amino-acid-derived, and steroid hormones have large effects on the activity of cells, organs, and systems, how do the three classes of hormones differ? The major difference is that steroids are lipid soluble, but polypeptides and most amino acid derivatives are not (see Figure 46.4).

Important exceptions to this rule are the **thyroid hormones, triiodothyronine** (also known as T_3) and **thyroxine** (also known as T_4), which are produced by the **thyroid gland.** The thyroid hormones are derived from the amino acid tyrosine but are lipid soluble.

Differences in solubility are important because steroids and thyroid hormones cross plasma membranes much more readily than do other types of hormones. To affect a target cell, all polypeptides and most amino acid derivatives bind to a receptor on the cell surface. Lipid-soluble hormones, in contrast, can diffuse through the plasma membrane and bind to receptors inside the cell.

To compare these two distinct paths of hormone action, let's consider how estradiol and epinephrine affect target cells. As a steroid and a nonsteroid, respectively, they serve as model systems for target cell responses to hormonal signals.

Steroid Hormones Bind to Intracellular Receptors

Estrogens are steroid hormones that direct the development of female secondary sex characteristics in many animal species. In humans and other mammals, the most important estrogen is the molecule **estradiol** (formally, 17 β-estradiol).

Because of estradiol's importance in reproduction by humans and domesticated animals, its mode of action has been the topic of intense investigation for over 50 years. How do target cells receive the signal carried by estradiol?

Identifying the Estradiol Receptor In 1966, biologists succeeded in isolating the estradiol receptor in laboratory rats. **Figure 46.5** indicates the experimental approach. In essence, the research team injected labeled estradiol into female rats and then used density-gradient centrifugation to separate molecules in the rats' uterine cells by size (see BioSkills 7).

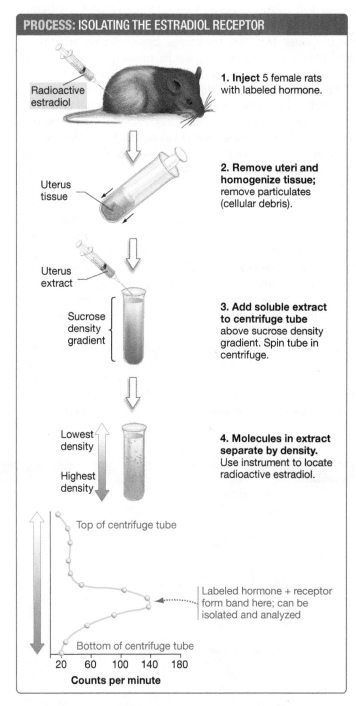

PROCESS: ISOLATING THE ESTRADIOL RECEPTOR

Radioactive estradiol

1. **Inject** 5 female rats with labeled hormone.

Uterus tissue

2. **Remove uteri and homogenize tissue;** remove particulates (cellular debris).

Uterus extract

Sucrose density gradient

3. **Add soluble extract to centrifuge tube** above sucrose density gradient. Spin tube in centrifuge.

Lowest density

Highest density

4. **Molecules in extract separate by density.** Use instrument to locate radioactive estradiol.

Top of centrifuge tube

Labeled hormone + receptor form band here; can be isolated and analyzed

Bottom of centrifuge tube

Counts per minute
20   60   100   140   180

Figure 46.5 Labeled Hormones Can Be Used to Find Hormone Receptors. If radioactive estradiol binds to its receptor in the uterus, the hormone–receptor complex should form a distinct band of radioactivity when molecules from uterine cells are separated by centrifugation.

DATA: Toft, D., and J. Gorski. 1966. *Proceedings of the National Academy of Sciences, USA* 55: 1574–1581.

When centrifugation was complete, the biologists found that the labeled estradiol was concentrated in a narrow band comprised of the hormone bound to its receptor. After purifying the receptor molecule, they discovered that proteinase enzymes could destroy it. Based on this result, they inferred that the estradiol receptor was a protein.

Follow-up experiments established that the estradiol receptor is primarily located in the nucleus but is not associated with the nuclear envelope. Further, the receptor is found only in estradiol target tissues, including the uterus, hypothalamus, and mammary glands. The latter finding was particularly exciting because it clarified how hormones act in a tissue-specific way.

This is a crucial point: Hormones are broadcast throughout the body via the bloodstream, but they act only on cells that express the appropriate receptor. Target cells respond to a particular hormone because they contain a receptor for that hormone.

What happens once the hormone–receptor complex is present inside the nucleus of a target cell?

Documenting Changes in Gene Expression During the 1970s and 1980s, work in several laboratories suggested that estradiol and other steroid hormones affect gene transcription after they bind to their receptors. For example, researchers injected laboratory animals with estradiol or other steroid hormones and documented changes in the mRNAs and proteins produced in target cells. These data showed that steroid hormones can cause dramatic changes in the amount or timing of mRNA production by a large number of genes.

How do steroid hormones accomplish this? The estradiol receptor, like other members of the steroid-hormone receptor family, has two copies of a distinctive DNA-binding domain called a zinc finger. DNA-binding domains are sections of a protein that make physical contact with DNA. The presence of zinc fingers in the estradiol receptor suggested that once estradiol binds to it, the hormone–receptor complex might affect gene expression by binding directly to DNA.

Follow-up work confirmed that steroid hormone–receptor complexes bind to specific sites in DNA called **hormone-response elements.** Hormone-response elements are located just "upstream" (in the 5′ direction) from the start of target genes. Gene expression changes when a regulatory molecule such as a steroid hormone–receptor complex binds to the hormone-response element for that gene.

Figure 46.6 summarizes the current model of how steroid hormones affect target cells. Because each hormone–receptor complex leads to the production of many copies of the gene product, the signal from the hormone is amplified. In this way, a small number of hormone molecules produce a large change in the activity of target cells and tissues.

✓If you understand how steroid hormones affect target cells, you should be able to predict what would happen to the estradiol response if an individual had mutations that changed the DNA sequence of its hormone-response element.

In contrast to steroid hormones, polypeptide hormones and most amino-acid-derived hormones are not lipid soluble and therefore cannot enter cells. How do they stimulate their target cells?

Polypeptide Hormones Bind to Receptors on the Plasma Membrane

For water-soluble messengers like polypeptide and most amino-acid-derived hormones to affect a cell, they must bind to receptors on the cell surface. Because the messenger never enters the target cell, its message must be transduced—changed into a form that is active inside the cell. This phenomenon is known as **signal transduction** (see Chapter 11).

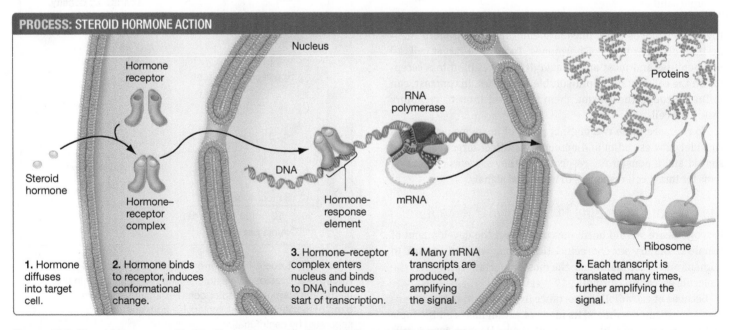

PROCESS: STEROID HORMONE ACTION

Nucleus

Hormone receptor

Proteins

RNA polymerase

Steroid hormone

DNA

Hormone–receptor complex

Hormone-response element

mRNA

Ribosome

1. Hormone diffuses into target cell.

2. Hormone binds to receptor, induces conformational change.

3. Hormone–receptor complex enters nucleus and binds to DNA, induces start of transcription.

4. Many mRNA transcripts are produced, amplifying the signal.

5. Each transcript is translated many times, further amplifying the signal.

Figure 46.6 Steroid Hormones Bind to Receptors Inside Target Cells and Affect Gene Expression.

(a) The enzyme phosphorylase has a phosphorylation site and a glycogen-binding site.

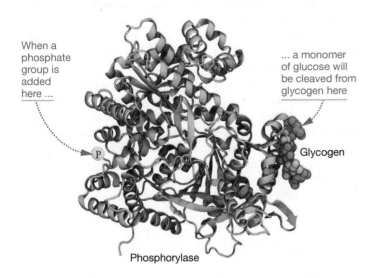

When a phosphate group is added here ...

... a monomer of glucose will be cleaved from glycogen here

Glycogen

Phosphorylase

(b) Activated phosphorylase catalyzes the cleavage of glucose from glycogen.

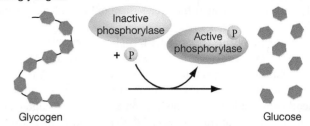

Glycogen

Glucose

(c) Phosphorylase is activated in response to epinephrine.

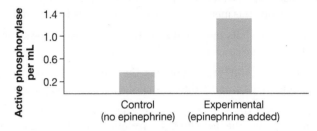

Figure 46.7 Phosphorylase Is the Enzyme That Catalyzes the Release of Glucose Monomers from Glycogen. **(a)** Activation of phosphorylase requires phosphorylation. **(b)** Glucose is released into the blood. **(c)** When epinephrine is added to extracts from liver cells, the amount of activated phosphorylase increases dramatically.

DATA: Rall, T. W., E. W. Sutherland, and J. Berthet. 1957. *Journal of Biological Chemistry* 224: 463–475.

To explore how signal transduction occurs, let's first examine hormone receptors that reside in the plasma membrane and then explore the molecules that process the message inside the cell. In both cases, epinephrine will be used as a model system.

Identifying the Epinephrine Receptor   In 1948 a biologist named Raymond Ahlquist published an exhaustive set of studies on how epinephrine affects dogs, cats, rats, and rabbits. The responses fell into two distinct categories, depending on the tissue being considered. To explain this observation, Ahlquist hypothesized that epinephrine binds two types of receptor. He called these hypothetical receptors the alpha receptor and the beta receptor.

Follow-up work with molecules that block epinephrine receptors documented that there are actually four types of epinephrine receptors: two types of alpha receptors and two types of beta receptors. Each is found in a distinct tissue type, and each induces a different response from target cells.

The discovery of four epinephrine receptors reinforces the concept of tissue specificity observed in experiments on the estradiol receptor. Hormones are transmitted throughout the body, not unlike cell phone signals that are broadcast through the atmosphere. But a hormone's message is received only by cells with the appropriate receptor—just as a cell phone signal is received only by a phone with the correct number. Since there are four epinephrine receptors, the same hormone can trigger different effects in different cells. What happens once epinephrine binds to one of these receptors?

What Acts as the Second Messenger?   Signal transduction occurs when a chemical messenger binds to a cell-surface receptor and triggers a response inside the cell.

One effect of epinephrine is an increase in the glucose level in the blood. How does a signal from epinephrine trigger this effect? To answer that question, biologists focused on the enzyme **phosphorylase** (**Figure 46.7a**), which catalyzes a reaction that cleaves glucose molecules off glycogen (**Figure 46.7b**). Phosphorylase exists in active and inactive states; the enzyme switches between these states when it is phosphorylated or dephosphorylated by another enzyme.

Phosphorylase is present in liver cells—the primary source of blood glucose during the short-term stress response. As predicted, when researchers added epinephrine to extracts from homogenized (ground up) liver cells, much larger amounts of phosphorylase were activated than in cell extracts that did not receive epinephrine (**Figure 46.7c**).

This observation suggested that something in the homogenized cells activated the phosphorylase when epinephrine was present. By purifying components of the liver cell extracts and testing them one by one, researchers eventually found the key ingredient in the activation of phosphorylase: a molecule called cyclic adenosine monophosphate, or **cyclic AMP (cAMP).**

The role of cAMP in epinephrine signaling was confirmed when researchers studied epinephrine's effects on the rat heart. During the short-term stress response, the heart beats faster and with more force, sending more blood to the tissues. When researchers injected rats with epinephrine, they found that cAMP levels increased inside heart cells *before* phosphorylase levels increased. This supported the hypothesis that cAMP is a second messenger in this system. Recall that a **second messenger** is a nonprotein signaling molecule that increases in concentration inside a cell in response to a signaling molecule that binds at the surface (see Chapter 11).

A Phosphorylation Cascade How does cAMP transfer the hormonal signal on the cell surface to phosphorylase inside the cell? Follow-up work revealed the mechanism of epinephrine action on liver cells (Figure 46.8).

When epinephrine binds to its receptor, it activates a G protein, which then activates the enzyme adenylyl cyclase. Adenylyl cyclase catalyzes a reaction that converts ATP to cAMP. Next, cAMP initiates a chain of events called a **signal transduction cascade** (also called a phosphorylation cascade; see Chapter 11), by binding to an enzyme called cAMP-dependent protein kinase A. This enzyme responds by phosphorylating the enzyme phosphorylase kinase, which then phosphorylates phosphorylase.

In studying this model, it is crucial to recognize two points:

1. cAMP transmits the signal from the cell surface to the signal transduction cascade.

2. Together, cAMP production and the subsequent phosphorylation events amplify the original signal from epinephrine.

To appreciate the second point, consider that, in response to stimulation by the activated G protein, adenylyl cyclase is thought to catalyze the formation of at least 100 molecules of cAMP. In turn, each of these cAMP molecules activates many molecules of cAMP-dependent protein kinase A. Subsequently,

each protein kinase A molecule activates many molecules of phosphorylase kinase, and so on.

In this way, the binding of just a single molecule of epinephrine may trigger the release of millions or even billions of glucose molecules. Amplification through a signal transduction cascade explains why tiny amounts of hormones can have such huge effects on an individual.

The model in Figure 46.8 was inspired by experiments on the type of epinephrine receptor called the beta-1 receptor. But other researchers showed that a completely different signal transduction event occurs when epinephrine binds to a different type of receptor, the alpha-1 receptor. In this and many other receptor systems, calcium ions (Ca^{2+}) serve as the second messenger in conjunction with a molecule called IP_3. Diacylglycerol (DAG) and 3', 5'-cyclic GMP (cGMP) are also common second messengers in hormone response systems.

Why Do Different Target Cells Respond in Different Ways?

Researchers are increasingly impressed with the diversity and complexity of signal transduction cascades. For example, target cells that have the same receptor protein may have different second messengers or different enzyme systems that are available for activation. As a result, the same hormone and receptor can give rise to different responses in different target cells.

This finding helps explain one of the most fundamental observations about hormones: The same chemical messenger can trigger different responses in cells from different organs or in cells at different developmental stages. The reason is that the cells contain different receptors, second messengers, amplification steps, protein kinases, enzymes, or transcriptionally active genes.

To summarize this section, steroid and thyroid hormones tend to exert their effects through changes in gene expression; they activate transcription factors that lead to the production of new proteins. In contrast, polypeptide and most amino-acid-derived hormones trigger signal transduction cascades that activate existing proteins, usually by phosphorylation.

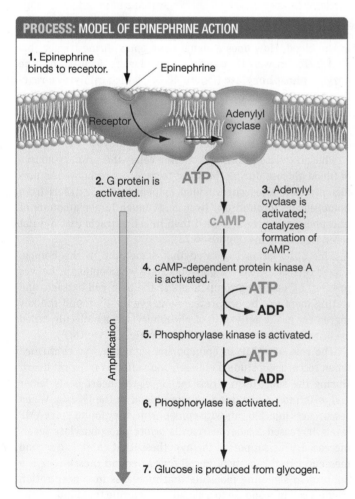

PROCESS: MODEL OF EPINEPHRINE ACTION

1. Epinephrine binds to receptor.

Epinephrine

Receptor

Adenylyl cyclase

2. G protein is activated.

ATP

3. Adenylyl cyclase is activated; catalyzes formation of cAMP.

cAMP

4. cAMP-dependent protein kinase A is activated.

ATP → ADP

Amplification

5. Phosphorylase kinase is activated.

ATP → ADP

6. Phosphorylase is activated.

7. Glucose is produced from glycogen.

Figure 46.8 Epinephrine Triggers a Signal Transduction Cascade. Epinephrine's signal is amplified at each of steps 3–6.

46.3 What Do Hormones Do?

At the beginning of this chapter, you read that hormones are chemical messengers. If that's so, what do hormones "say"?

A first step in answering this question is to recognize that a single hormone can exert various effects in an animal. In humans, for example, the thyroid hormones T_3 and T_4 stimulate metabolism and thus oxygen consumption throughout the body. But they also promote growth, increase heart rate, and stimulate the synthesis of many important macromolecules.

A second step in grasping what hormones do is to recognize that several different hormones may affect the same aspect of physiology. Insulin, glucagon, epinephrine, and cortisol all influence glucose levels in the blood.

Some hormones have extremely diverse effects; other hormones have functions that appear to overlap. These observations begin to make sense when hormone action is viewed in the context of the whole organism. Hormones coordinate the activities of cells in three arenas: (1) development, growth, and reproduction; (2) response to environmental challenges; and (3) maintenance of homeostasis. Let's analyze each of these actions in turn.

How Do Hormones Direct Developmental Processes?

In animals, as in plants, hormones play a key role in regulating growth and development. Growth hormones and sex hormones play crucial roles in promoting cell division, increasing overall body size, and promoting sexual differentiation as an individual matures; certain hormones direct the development of particular cells and tissues at critical junctures in an individual's life.

Let's explore two of the most dramatic examples of hormonal control—metamorphosis in amphibians and in insects—and then survey other developmental processes that are affected by hormone action.

The Role of T_3 in Amphibian Metamorphosis Frogs, toads, and salamanders are called amphibians ("double-lives") because in most species, juveniles (larvae) live in water while adults live on land. The process of changing from an immature, aquatic larva to a sexually mature, terrestrial frog, toad, or salamander is an example of **metamorphosis** ("change-form"; Figure 46.9).

Two sets of complementary experiments, published in 1912 and 1916, established that frog metamorphosis depends on thyroid hormones. Researchers induced frog tadpoles to undergo metamorphosis by feeding them ground-up thyroid glands from horses; they prevented metamorphosis by surgically removing the tadpoles' thyroid glands.

Follow-up work showed that T_3 is the hormone that triggers many of the changes observed in metamorphosis. In response to a signal from the brain, the pituitary gland secretes **thyroid-stimulating hormone (TSH).** TSH stimulates the thyroid gland to produce T_4, and T_4 is then converted to T_3 at target tissues.

In juvenile amphibians, an increase in the level of T_3 stimulates the growth of new structures, such as legs. Other structures—such as a tadpole's tail—disintegrate or are absorbed. Some tissues change structure and function. For example, changes in existing cells are responsible for the switch from a tadpole's long intestine, specialized for digesting plant material, to an adult's short intestine, specialized for digesting insects and other prey. In the liver, cells respond to T_3 by manufacturing the enzymes required to excrete urea—the nitrogenous waste product released by adults—instead of the ammonia produced by tadpoles.

✔ If you understand the basic principles of hormone action, you should be able to suggest a hypothesis explaining why different frog cells can respond to T_3 in such different ways.

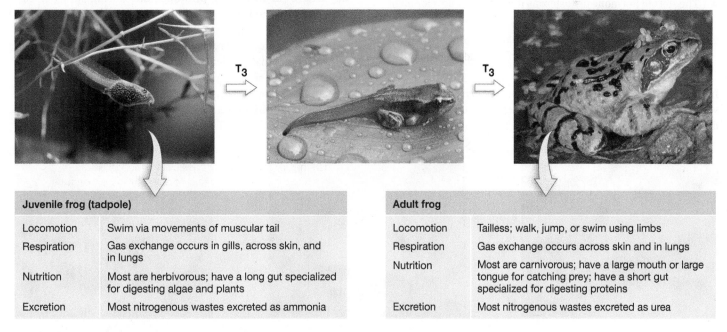

Juvenile frog (tadpole)	
Locomotion	Swim via movements of muscular tail
Respiration	Gas exchange occurs in gills, across skin, and in lungs
Nutrition	Most are herbivorous; have a long gut specialized for digesting algae and plants
Excretion	Most nitrogenous wastes excreted as ammonia

Adult frog	
Locomotion	Tailless; walk, jump, or swim using limbs
Respiration	Gas exchange occurs across skin and in lungs
Nutrition	Most are carnivorous; have a large mouth or large tongue for catching prey; have a short gut specialized for digesting proteins
Excretion	Most nitrogenous wastes excreted as urea

Figure 46.9 Amphibian Metamorphosis Is a Continuous Process. When metamorphosis begins in a frog, toad, or salamander, the individual stays active and continues to feed. The continuous and gradual transition from juvenile to adult is mediated by T_3.

Hormone Interactions Regulate Insect Metamorphosis Some insects show a remarkable type of juvenile-to-adult transition, called holometabolous ("complete") metamorphosis (see Chapter 31). In species that undergo this process, juveniles are called larvae. As in amphibians, insect larvae look completely different from adults, live in different habitats, and eat different food.

As insect larvae grow, they undergo a series of molts in which they shed their old exoskeleton, expand their bodies, and produce a new exoskeleton. After a specific number of these juvenile molts, however, they secrete a tough covering called a pupal case. Inside the pupal case, specific populations of larval cells give rise to a completely new adult body. The rest of the larval body disintegrates (**Figure 46.10**).

In insects, metamorphosis depends on interactions between two hormones. If **juvenile hormone (JH)** is present at a high concentration in the larva, surges of the hormone **ecdysone** induce the growth of the larva via molting. But if JH levels are low, ecdysone triggers a complete remodeling of the body—metamorphosis—and the transition to adulthood and sexual maturity.

Sexual Development and Activity in Vertebrates
In mammals and other vertebrates, long-distance cell-to-cell signals play key roles as embryos develop. Hormones also direct anatomical and physiological changes that occur later in life. Some of the most important of these changes involve the reproductive organs.

Events early in development dictate whether the sex organs, or **gonads,** of a vertebrate embryo become male (**testes**) or female (**ovaries**). This process is called primary sex determination. In mammals, primary sex determination depends on genes located on sex chromosomes. Expression of these genes dictates whether testes or ovaries develop, and these early gonads then begin producing different hormones. In human males, the early testes produce two hormones:

1. The steroid hormone testosterone induces early development of the male reproductive tract.

2. A polypeptide hormone called **Müllerian inhibitory substance** inhibits development of the female reproductive tract.

In females, the ovaries produce the steroid hormone estradiol, which is required for further development of the female reproductive tract.

Sex hormones also play a key role in the juvenile-to-adult transition in mammals. When humans reach early adolescence, for example, surges of sex hormones lead to the physical and emotional changes associated with **puberty.** These developmental changes create the adult phenotype and the ability to produce offspring.

In boys, surges of testosterone are responsible for changes that include enlargement of the penis and testes and growth of facial and body hair. In girls, an increased concentration of estradiol leads to the enlargement of breasts, the onset of menstruation, and other changes. In both sexes, a growth surge begins at puberty. This growth is stimulated by GH produced in the pituitary gland (see Figure 46.2). GH regulates growth factors, which are signaling molecules that control the cell cycle (see Chapter 12). Growth originates in the epiphyseal plates, which are small pieces of cartilage separating the shaft from the end at both extremities of long bones.

Puberty is associated with a growth spurt because the effect of GH on the human skeleton is enhanced by the action of sex hormones, which surge during adolescence. Although growth and sex hormones continue to be produced long after puberty, growth in humans stops when the epiphyseal plates are replaced with bone, making further growth impossible.

The sex hormones continue to play a key role in adults. In humans, sex hormones are instrumental in regulating sperm production, the menstrual cycle, and reproductive behavior (see Chapter 47). The result of the regular release of sex hormones is that humans can mate year-round. In many animals, reproductive behavior is instead confined to specific times of the year. In these species, environmental cues such as increasing day length, warmth, or onset of seasonal rains trigger the release of sex hormones (see Chapter 50).

How Photoperiod Affects Sex Hormone Release
The increase in day length—or increasing **photoperiod**—during spring is particularly important in stimulating the release of sex hormones in seasonally reproducing mammals, lizards, and birds. The lengthening photoperiod is sensed by photoreceptors, which are sensory receptors that respond to light (see Chapter 44).

The location of these photoreceptors depends on the animal. In mammals, photoreceptors in the retinas of the eyes send signals to the **pineal gland** via a pathway leading through the brain and spinal cord. The pineal gland secretes the hormone

Figure 46.10 Insect Metamorphosis Occurs during a Resting Stage. When metamorphosis begins in a holometabolous insect, the individual enters a resting stage called the pupa.

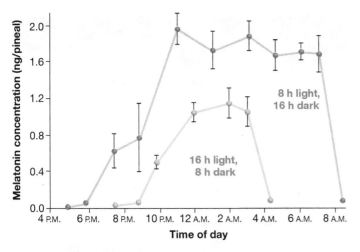

Figure 46.11 **Melatonin Levels Are Affected by Time of Day and Photoperiod in Seasonal Breeders.** Melatonin levels are highest at night, and they are higher overall when photoperiod is short (8 h light, 16 h dark) than when it is long (16 h light, 8 h dark).

DATA: Illnerova H., K. Hoffmann, and J. Vanecek. 1984. *Neuroendocrinology* 38: 226–231.

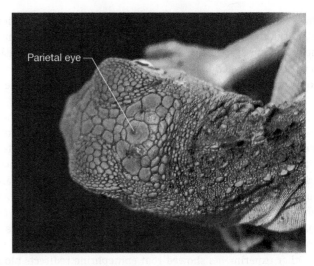

Figure 46.12 **Some Diurnal Reptiles Have a Parietal Eye.** A tiny hole in the skull allows sunlight to directly stimulate photoreceptors in the parietal eye, a brain region associated with the pineal gland.

melatonin, which relays photoperiodic information to the hypothalamus, a brain region that initiates a series of signals directing production of sex hormones. The pineal gland also regulates sleep–wake cycles.

Maximal melatonin secretion occurs in the dark, so stimulation of the pineal gland by photoreceptors *reduces* melatonin secretion. Animals therefore experience a daily rhythm in melatonin levels, which are highest at night. As photoperiod increases in spring, there are fewer hours of darkness, resulting in lower *overall* levels of melatonin (**Figure 46.11**). This decline in melatonin levels "informs" the hypothalamus to stimulate the testes and ovaries to make sex hormones, readying the body for reproduction.

Many diurnal (day-active) lizard species do not rely solely on retinal photoreceptors. These lizards also have a small hole in the top of their skull, covered only by a thin layer of skin (**Figure 46.12**). Light passes through this hole and stimulates photoreceptors in the parietal eye, a part of the brain associated with the pineal gland. Interestingly, in birds, neither retinal nor pineal photoreceptors are responsible for sending photoperiodic information to the hypothalamus. It appears that this information originates in photoreceptors located diffusely throughout the brain.

The common thread among mammals, lizards, birds, and other vertebrates is that information about photoperiod is transduced from a signal detected by photoreceptors into a hormonal signal originating at the hypothalamus. The role of the hypothalamus is discussed in more detail in Section 46.4.

Some Chemicals Can Disrupt Hormone Signaling In 1962, Rachel Carson stunned the world with her book *Silent Spring*, in which she described how commercially produced synthetic chemicals—even at low concentrations—can adversely affect humans and wildlife. Since then, evidence has continued to accumulate that many pesticides, industrial chemicals, and other pollutants interfere with normal endocrine function in many animal species.

In the early 1990s, scientists coined the term **endocrine disruptor** to describe chemicals that interfere with normal hormonal signaling. This interference can happen in a number of ways, including binding of the chemical to hormone receptors and altering the metabolism of hormones, thereby affecting physiological processes and behavior.

Many endocrine disruptors are **xenoestrogens**—foreign chemicals that bind to estrogen receptors and induce estrogen-like effects. For example, exposure to the widely used herbicide atrazine causes feminization and even sex change in male frogs, induces reproductive-tissue abnormalities and reduced spawning in fishes, and is associated with low sperm counts and increased risk of birth defects in humans.

Another well-known xenoestrogen is bisphenol A (BPA), an industrial chemical used in many plastic and metal products, including containers for food and water. Laboratory animals exposed to BPA show abnormal development of reproductive and brain tissues, along with increased risk of some types of cancers.

As research continues into the possible health effects of xenoestrogens and other endocrine disruptors, many states and countries are limiting or banning their use. For example, atrazine is currently banned in the European Union, and BPA is banned in some countries for use in products such as baby bottles.

How Do Hormones Coordinate Responses to Stressors?

When an animal is thrust into a dangerous or unpredictable situation, hormones play a part in both the short-term and long-term responses. Let's explore each of these response categories in turn.

Short-Term Responses to Stress The short-term reaction, called the **fight-or-flight response,** is triggered by the sympathetic nervous system (see Chapter 43). If you were being chased by a grizzly bear, action potentials from your sympathetic nerves would stimulate your adrenal medulla and lead to the release of epinephrine.

To determine how epinephrine affects the body, researchers injected human volunteers with a saline solution—as a control—or epinephrine and then measured five physiological parameters in the volunteers. As shown in Figure 46.13, epinephrine caused dramatic increases in the concentrations of free fatty acids and glucose in the blood, pulse rate, blood pressure, and oxygen consumption by the brain. In addition, the volunteers who were injected with epinephrine reported strong subjective feelings of anxiety and excitement.

Other experiments showed that epinephrine redirects blood away from the skin and digestive system and toward the heart, brain, and muscles. Epinephrine does this by relaxing smooth muscle surrounding blood vessels in the heart, brain, and muscles—increasing blood delivery.

Taken together, the responses to epinephrine lead to a state of heightened alertness and increased energy use that prepares the body for rapid, intense action such as fighting or fleeing. Epinephrine coordinates the activities of cells in many organs and systems throughout the body to prepare an individual to cope with a life-threatening situation.

Long-Term Responses to Stress If you have ever experienced the fight-or-flight response, you may recall that the state is short lived. Once an epinephrine "rush" wears off, most people feel exhausted and want to rest and eat.

What happens if the stress continues and turns into a long-term condition? In the course of a lifetime, it is not unusual for a person to experience periods of starvation or fasting, prolonged emotional distress, or chronic illness. How do hormones help humans and other animals cope with extended stress?

Early studies of long-term stress in human subjects suggested a role for cortisol, which is produced in the adrenal cortex. Increased levels of cortisol were found in airplane pilots and crew members during long flights, athletes who were training for intense contests, parents of children undergoing treatment for cancer, and college students who were preparing for final exams. Why?

What Does Cortisol Do? In humans, cortisol's primary role is to ensure the continuing availability of glucose for use by the brain during long-term stress. Cortisol manages three main processes that maintain glucose production:

1. Cortisol induces the synthesis of liver enzymes that make glucose from amino acids and other chemical precursors.

2. Cortisol makes adipose tissue—fat tissue—and resting muscles resistant to insulin. Insulin normally stimulates **adipocytes** and resting muscle cells to remove glucose from the bloodstream. But when cortisol makes these cells resistant to insulin, glucose is reserved for use by the brain and exercising muscles.

RESEARCH

QUESTION: How does epinephrine affect the body?

HYPOTHESIS: Epinephrine causes changes involved in the fight-or-flight response.

NULL HYPOTHESIS: Epinephrine is not involved in the fight-or-flight response.

EXPERIMENTAL SETUP:

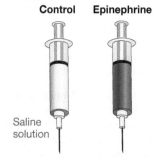

Control   Epinephrine

Saline solution

1. **Inject** human volunteers with saline solution or epinephrine.

2. **Document changes** in fatty-acid and glucose concentrations in blood, pulse rate, blood pressure, and oxygen consumption in brain.

PREDICTION: The epinephrine-treated group will have higher fatty-acid and glucose concentrations in blood, pulse rate, blood pressure, and brain oxygen consumption than the control group.

PREDICTION OF NULL HYPOTHESIS: There will be no differences in the physiological state of individuals based on the substance injected.

RESULTS:

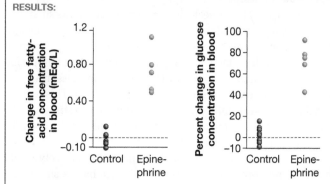

	Control	Epinephrine
Pulse rate (beats/min)	78.3	89.6
Blood pressure (mm Hg)	90.9	108.7
O₂ consumption in brain (cc O₂/100 g/min)	3.41	4.16

CONCLUSION: Epinephrine causes an array of changes associated with the fight-or-flight response.

Figure 46.13 Epinephrine Prepares the Body for Action. Each point in the graphs represents data from one volunteer; the data in the table are average values of the study participants.

SOURCES: King, B. D., L. Sokoloff, and R. L. Wechsler. 1952. The effects of *l*-epinephrine and *l*-nor-epinephrine upon cerebral circulation and metabolism in man. *Journal of Clinical Investigation* 31: 273–279. Mueller, P. S., and D. Horwitz. 1962. Plasma free fatty acid and blood glucose responses to analogues of norepinephrine in man. *Journal of Lipid Research* 3: 251–255.

✔ **PROCESS OF SCIENCE** Why did researchers bother to inject volunteers in the control group with saline? Why did they inject them with anything?

3. Cortisol promotes the release of fatty acids—the body's major fuel molecules—from adipose tissue, for use by the heart and muscles.

Because of its importance in regulating blood glucose concentration, cortisol is referred to as a **glucocorticoid.** Corticosterone, produced by some other vertebrates, is a glucocorticoid similar to cortisol.

The long-term stress response comes at a high price, however, as any victim of a serious injury or illness knows. Glucocorticoids make amino acids available for glucose synthesis by promoting the degradation of contractile proteins in muscle. The resulting loss of muscle mass may cause severe weakness. Also, glucocorticoids impair wound healing and suppress immune and inflammatory responses. These processes are costly in terms of energy use, but suppressing them makes the body more susceptible to infection.

The overall concept here is that the long-term stress response is a compromise—a fitness trade-off (see Chapter 39). The fuel requirements of the brain are met at the expense of other tissues and organs.

How Are Hormones Involved in Homeostasis?

Recall that homeostasis is the maintenance of relatively constant physical and chemical conditions inside the body. Homeostatic systems depend on three components (see Figure 39.13):

1. A sensory receptor that monitors a condition
2. An integrator that processes information from the sensor and compares it to a normal value, or set point
3. Effector cells that return the condition to the set point

In homeostatic systems, messages often travel from integrators to effectors in the form of hormones.

Insulin, Glucagon, and Blood Glucose Homeostasis The regulation of blood glucose concentrations is a good example of homeostasis regulated by hormones. It is essential to maintain blood glucose levels within a narrow range of values. If the level gets too low, the brain does not have enough fuel to function. High blood glucose levels, on the other hand, are toxic to neurons and blood vessels and can result in organ failure and amputation of extremities (see Chapter 41).

When an animal eats, rising blood glucose levels stimulate the release of insulin from the pancreas (see Figure 41.15). Insulin stimulates effector cells throughout the body to import glucose from the blood for storage or use in metabolism, causing blood glucose levels to drop to normal values.

Hours after a meal, blood glucose levels decline as glucose is used for cellular respiration, which causes glucagon to be released from the pancreas. Glucagon has basically the opposite effect of insulin: It causes glucose-storing cells in the liver to export glucose into the blood, thereby increasing blood glucose levels.

ADH, Aldosterone, and Water and Electrolyte Balance Recall that when an individual is dehydrated, antidiuretic hormone (ADH) is released from the pituitary gland (see Chapter 40).

ADH increases the permeability of the kidney's collecting ducts to water, causing water to be reabsorbed from urine and saved.

ADH is instrumental in achieving homeostasis with respect to water balance. For example, the ethanol in alcoholic beverages inhibits the release of ADH from the pituitary. Consequently, people who imbibe large quantities of these beverages produce large quantities of dilute urine. The resulting water loss can lead to dehydration and nausea—symptoms associated with an alcoholic hangover.

When the sodium concentration in body fluids is low, **aldosterone** is released from the adrenal cortex (see Chapter 40). Because aldosterone increases reabsorption of sodium ions in the distal tubules of the kidney, it plays a key role in homeostasis with respect to electrolyte concentrations and overall volume of body fluids. Adrenal hormones with this effect are called **mineralocorticoids.**

ADH saves water; aldosterone saves sodium. Together, they are key players in maintaining water and electrolyte balance.

EPO and Oxygen Availability **Erythropoietin (EPO)** is a crucial component in the homeostatic system for blood oxygen levels. When blood oxygen levels fall, the kidneys and other tissues release EPO, which stimulates the production of red blood cells. The more red blood cells there are, the higher the oxygen-carrying capacity of blood is. If you moved to a high elevation and experienced chronic oxygen deficit, your body would respond by releasing EPO and increasing your red blood cell count. This explains why many endurance athletes train at high altitudes.

Some athletes have turned to EPO injections as a way to increase the oxygen-carrying capacity of their blood and give themselves a competitive edge. This practice is dangerous as well as illegal. The increased viscosity of blood in EPO abusers is accentuated during exercise, when blood plasma volume drops due to dehydration. The combination of high blood viscosity and low blood volume can impair blood flow through capillaries, increasing the risk of tissue damage and blood clotting. If clots form in blood vessels that lead to the heart or brain, a heart attack or stroke may occur. EPO abuse is thought to be responsible for the collapse and death of several cyclists during races in the mid-1990s.

CHECK YOUR UNDERSTANDING

If you understand that ...

- Hormones usually function in directing development and sexual maturation, preparing an individual for environmental challenges, or achieving homeostasis.
- Endocrine disruptors and stressors can affect hormone signaling and homeostasis.

✔ **You should be able to ...**

1. Compare and contrast the roles of the hormones involved in metamorphosis of amphibians and insects.
2. Explain how the various changes induced by elevated cortisol levels result in a response to long-term stress.

Answers are available in Appendix A.

46.4 How Is the Production of Hormones Regulated?

Most hormones are released in response to an environmental cue or a message from an integrator in a homeostatic system. Often, the nervous system is closely involved. For example, environmental cues that signal the onset of the breeding season or the presence of a predator are received by sensory receptors and interpreted by the brain. Similarly, integration in most homeostatic systems is done by neurons in the central nervous system (CNS)—the brain and spinal cord (see Chapter 43).

Based on these observations, the short answer to the question posed in the title of this section is simple: In many cases, hormone production is directly or indirectly controlled by the nervous system.

The Hypothalamus and Pituitary Gland

The pituitary gland is directly connected to the hypothalamus. This physical link is the basis of the connection between the CNS and the endocrine system. As you read in Section 46.2, removing the entire pituitary gland in laboratory animals caused them to stop growing. The animals also lost the ability to maintain a normal body temperature and suffered atrophy (shrinkage) of their genitals, thyroid glands, and adrenal cortexes. Not surprisingly, their life span shortened dramatically.

These experiments suggested that, in addition to secreting GH, the pituitary secretes hormones that regulate the production of a wide variety of other hormones. As a case study, let's look at the pituitary hormone that acts on the adrenal glands.

Controlling the Release of Glucocorticoids Early work on rats suggested that a molecule from the pituitary gland affects the adrenal gland. This molecule soon came to be called **adrenocorticotropic hormone,** or **ACTH** (*adreno* refers to the adrenal glands; *cortico* refers to the outer portion, or cortex, of each gland; and *tropic* means "affecting the activity of"). ACTH is also known as corticotropin.

ACTH was purified and characterized in 1943. When human volunteers were injected with ACTH, cortisol levels in their blood rose. This result provided evidence that ACTH is a regulatory hormone. The adrenal cortex secretes glucocorticoids in response to ACTH released from the pituitary.

What regulates ACTH release? Biologists from two laboratories independently showed that ACTH is released in response to a molecule produced by the hypothalamus. After years of effort, a different team of researchers succeeded in purifying a peptide—just 41 amino acids long—called **corticotropin-releasing hormone (CRH).** When the hypothalamus releases CRH, it stimulates cells in the pituitary to secrete ACTH into the bloodstream.

Feedback Inhibition by Glucocorticoids What *stops* glucocorticoid secretion? The key is to recognize that glucocorticoids themselves suppress ACTH production by the pituitary gland. Glucocorticoids accomplish feedback inhibition—they suppress their own production.

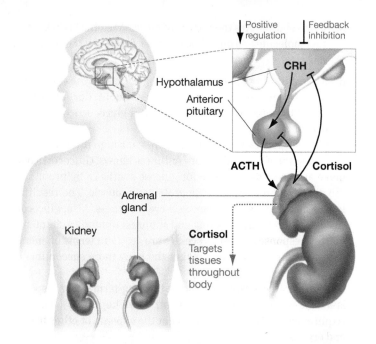

Figure 46.14 The Interaction between Cortisol, ACTH, and CRH Is an Example of Feedback Inhibition.

✔ **PROCESS OF SCIENCE** Use the figure to devise a test for adrenal failure in humans.

When human volunteers were injected with cortisol, ACTH levels in their bloodstream dropped dramatically. Cortisol also inhibits release of CRH from the hypothalamus. Thus, if glucocorticoid levels become too high, ACTH levels fall. But if glucocorticoid levels become too low, ACTH levels rise and drive a compensatory increase in glucocorticoid production. **Figure 46.14** summarizes the relationships among CRH, ACTH, and the glucocorticoid cortisol.

What happens when feedback inhibition fails? Certain pituitary tumors diminish the ability of cortisol to suppress ACTH production, leading to persistently high blood levels of ACTH and cortisol. The result is **Cushing's disease,** an unrelenting stress response that depletes the body's protein reserves. It is fatal if not treated.

Patterns in Glucocorticoid Release Under ordinary circumstances, the production of CRH by the hypothalamus displays a daily rhythm and reaches its highest level in the early morning hours. This pattern drives a corresponding daily rhythm in ACTH production and blood cortisol level.

The morning peak in blood cortisol level typically coincides with arousal and initiation of the day's activities—and the effect is saving glucose for use by the brain. The unpleasant symptoms of jet lag are due in part to the daily cortisol rhythm being out of synchrony with local time for several days after you arrive in a new time zone.

When the brain processes stimuli that produce pain or anxiety, it initiates a long-term stress response and a sustained increase in CRH production. Increased CRH production causes blood ACTH and cortisol levels to remain much higher throughout the day than they are in the unstressed state.

The Hypothalamic–Pituitary Axis: An Overview The CRH-ACTH-glucocorticoid relationship is just one of many hormone systems based on interactions among the hypothalamus, pituitary, and target glands or cells. The **hypothalamic–pituitary axis** actually forms two anatomically distinct systems because the pituitary gland has two segments: the **anterior pituitary** and the **posterior pituitary** (**Figure 46.15**). The anterior pituitary develops from cells in an embryo's mouth and throat lining; the posterior pituitary is an extension of the brain.

The hypothalamic neurons responsible for hormone secretion by the posterior pituitary are distinct from those that control hormone secretion by the anterior pituitary. Both types of hypothalamic neurons synthesize and release neurohormones and are therefore called **neurosecretory cells.** Their hormone release is under the control of brain regions responsible for integrating information about the external or internal environment. For example, information about an upcoming exam or athletic contest might trigger action potentials that lead to the release of CRH.

The Posterior Pituitary The anterior pituitary and posterior pituitary function in different ways. As Figure 46.15a indicates, the posterior portion of the pituitary is an extension of the hypothalamus itself.

Neurosecretory cells that project from the hypothalamus produce the hormones ADH and oxytocin, which are then stored in the posterior pituitary. From there, ADH and oxytocin are released into the bloodstream. This is an example of the neuro-endocrine pathway of hormone action. Recall that ADH aids in the reabsorption of water by the kidneys. **Oxytocin** helps induce labor and milk release in female mammals.

The Anterior Pituitary Unlike the situation in the posterior pituitary, the hypothalamus and anterior pituitary are connected indirectly. Neurosecretory cells in the hypothalamus secrete stimulatory or inhibitory hormones into tiny blood vessels, which carry the hormones to the anterior pituitary. In response, the anterior pituitary alters its secretion of hormones that enter the general bloodstream and act on target tissues or glands. This is an example of the neuroendocrine-to-endocrine pathway of hormone action.

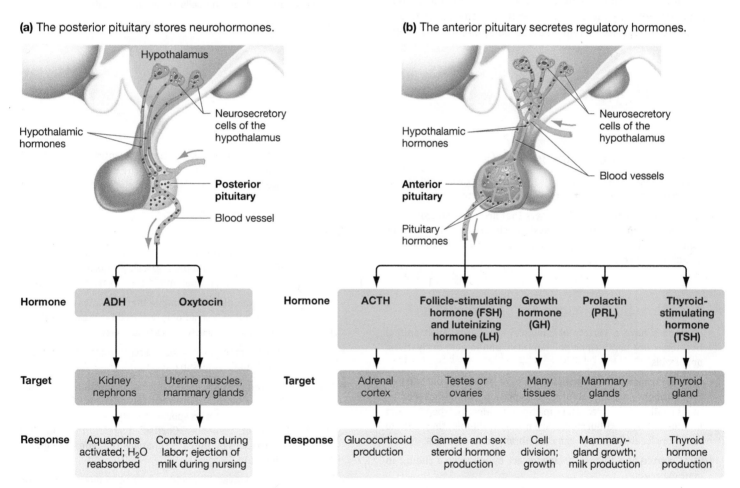

(a) The posterior pituitary stores neurohormones.

(b) The anterior pituitary secretes regulatory hormones.

Hormone	ADH	Oxytocin
Target	Kidney nephrons	Uterine muscles, mammary glands
Response	Aquaporins activated; H₂O reabsorbed	Contractions during labor; ejection of milk during nursing

Hormone	ACTH	Follicle-stimulating hormone (FSH) and luteinizing hormone (LH)	Growth hormone (GH)	Prolactin (PRL)	Thyroid-stimulating hormone (TSH)
Target	Adrenal cortex	Testes or ovaries	Many tissues	Mammary glands	Thyroid gland
Response	Glucocorticoid production	Gamete and sex steroid hormone production	Cell division; growth	Mammary-gland growth; milk production	Thyroid hormone production

Figure 46.15 The Hypothalamus and Pituitary Interact Closely. (a) Developmentally and anatomically, the posterior pituitary is an extension of the hypothalamus. Neurosecretory cells in the hypothalamus extend directly into the posterior pituitary and secrete ADH (vasopressin) and oxytocin. **(b)** The hypothalamus and the anterior pituitary communicate indirectly, via blood vessels. Hormones produced by other populations of neurosecretory cells in the hypothalamus travel in the blood to the anterior pituitary, where they control the release of pituitary hormones.

Many of the hormones produced by the anterior pituitary stimulate the production of other hormones. The anterior pituitary hormones include ACTH; **follicle-stimulating hormone (FSH)** and **luteinizing hormone (LH),** which are involved in stimulating the gonads to produce sex hormones and gametes; GH; **prolactin,** which stimulates mammary gland growth and milk production in mammals; and TSH.

Control of Epinephrine by Sympathetic Nerves

When biologists analyze how the nervous system and endocrine system interact to control the release of epinephrine, the distinction between the two systems begins to blur. Section 46.2 introduced how epinephrine acts as an endocrine signal. During the fight-or-flight response, sympathetic nerves trigger the release of epinephrine from the adrenal medulla into the bloodstream. But in addition, some sympathetic nerves release the related molecule **norepinephrine** directly onto target cells. Epinephrine and norepinephrine, which differ from one another only by the presence of an additional methyl group on epinephrine, are members of the family of molecules called **catecholamines.**

During the fight-or-flight response, the endocrine system broadcasts epinephrine by secreting it into the bloodstream, whereas the nervous system delivers norepinephrine directly to particular cells. Although the mechanisms for distributing these two chemical messengers are different, their physiological effects during the fight-or-flight response are similar.

Catecholamines function as neurotransmitters as well as hormones. This exemplifies how the nervous and endocrine systems are not separate systems, but rather are coordinated components of organisms' physiological strategies for maintaining homeostasis.

▌ CHECK YOUR UNDERSTANDING

If you understand that …

- Hormone concentrations are tightly regulated—in some cases by negative feedback, in other cases by stimulatory or inhibitory signals from the hypothalamus.

✔ **You should be able to …**

1. Explain how feedback inhibition affects the release of ACTH.
2. Discuss the relationship between processing centers in the brain, neurosecretory cells in the hypothalamus, and hormone-secreting cells in the anterior pituitary.

Answers are available in Appendix A.

CHAPTER 46   REVIEW

For media, go to MasteringBiology

46.1 Cell-to-Cell Signaling: An Overview

- Chemical signals in animals fall into five categories: autocrine, paracrine, endocrine, neural, and neuroendocrine.

- Hormones are chemical messengers that are released from neurons or cells of the endocrine system, circulate in the blood or other body fluids, and trigger a response in target cells containing an appropriate receptor.

46.2 How Do Hormones Act on Target Cells?

- Hormones have a variety of chemical structures. Most animal hormones are peptides or polypeptides, amino acid derivatives, or steroids.

- Animal hormones have two basic modes of action. Steroid and thyroid hormones are lipid soluble, cross plasma membranes readily, and usually bind to receptors inside cells. Most polypeptide and amino-acid-derived hormones are not lipid soluble; they bind to receptors located in the plasma membranes of target cells.

- Most steroid and thyroid hormones act by inducing a change in gene expression.

- Polypeptide and most amino-acid-derived hormones trigger signal transduction cascades that activate one or more target proteins by phosphorylation.

- Although they are produced in tiny concentrations, hormones have large effects because they trigger gene expression or because their message is amplified through a signal transduction cascade.

46.3 What Do Hormones Do?

- Together with the nervous system, hormones coordinate the activities of diverse cells and tissues. A single hormone may affect a wide array of cells and tissues and induce a variety of responses.

- Estradiol is an example of a hormone that regulates development and sexual maturation. Estradiol is required for the maturation of female secondary sex characteristics in adolescence.

- Melatonin is a hormone that regulates reproductive physiology in response to seasonal changes in day length.

- Epinephrine and cortisol are examples of hormones that help individuals cope with environmental changes. Epinephrine activates the short-term response to stressors by triggering the fight-or-flight response. Cortisol triggers the long-term response to stressors by inducing changes that conserve glucose for use by the brain.

- Hormones are involved in a wide array of homeostatic interactions. For example, hormones are involved in directing cells that modify the concentrations of glucose, water, sodium ions, and other substances in the blood and interstitial fluid.

46.4 How Is the Production of Hormones Regulated?

- In many cases, the release of a hormone is regulated by hormones from the anterior pituitary.

- Hormone-secreting cells in the anterior pituitary are regulated by hormones released by the hypothalamus.

- The long-term stress response is a well-studied example of hormone regulation. The brain responds to long-term stress by triggering the release of the hypothalamic hormone CRH. CRH activates the anterior pituitary to release ACTH, which stimulates the production of cortisol by cells in the adrenal cortex. Because cortisol inhibits the production of ACTH and CRH, the chain of events is regulated by feedback inhibition.

Answers are available in Appendix A

✔ TEST YOUR KNOWLEDGE

1. How do steroid hormones differ from polypeptide hormones and most amino-acid-derived hormones?
   a. Steroid hormones are lipid soluble and cross plasma membranes readily.
   b. Polypeptide and amino-acid-derived hormones are longer lived in the bloodstream and thus exert greater signal amplification.
   c. Polypeptide hormones are the most structurally complex and induce permanent changes in target cells.
   d. Only steroid hormones bind to receptors in the plasma membrane.

2. What is a hormone-response element?
   a. a receptor for a steroid hormone
   b. a receptor for a polypeptide hormone
   c. a segment of DNA where a hormone–receptor complex binds
   d. an enzyme that is activated in response to hormone binding and produces a second messenger

3. Which of the following developmental processes is *not* controlled by hormones?
   a. the initial development of male and female gonads in mammals, soon after fertilization
   b. overall growth in vertebrates
   c. molting in insects and other invertebrates
   d. metamorphosis in insects and other invertebrates

4. True or False: In hormone systems, feedback inhibition occurs when the presence of a hormone inhibits release of the hormone.

✔ TEST YOUR UNDERSTANDING

5. Compare and contrast the modes of action of lipid-soluble and water-soluble hormones.

6. Why is the observation that one hormone may bind to more than one type of receptor important?

7. Compare and contrast the structure and function of the anterior and posterior pituitary glands.

8. **PROCESS OF SCIENCE** Design a study to test the hypothesis that the symptoms of jet lag are caused by disruption of normal daily cortisol rhythms.

✔ TEST YOUR PROBLEM-SOLVING SKILLS

9. **PROCESS OF SCIENCE** Suppose that during a detailed anatomical study of a marine invertebrate, you found a small, previously undescribed structure. How would you test the hypothesis that the structure is a gland that releases one or more hormones?

10. **QUANTITATIVE** Scientists set out to test the hypothesis that the herbicide atrazine is an endocrine disruptor that feminizes male amphibians. They treated male amphibians with atrazine and then compared their circulating testosterone concentrations with those of males and females that were not treated with atrazine (controls). The results are shown below (* signifies $P < 0.05$; see BioSkills 3 for more on statistical significance). Was the hypothesis supported? Why or why not?

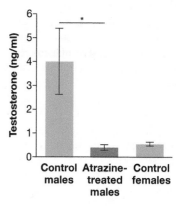

DATA: Hayes, T. B., A. Collins, M. Lee, et al. 2002. *Proceedings of the National Academy of Sciences, USA* 99: 5476–5480.

✔ PUT IT ALL TOGETHER: Case Study

Is ecotourism stressful to animals?

Ecotourism helps conserve wildlife by increasing the value of wildlife conservation for local people. In Argentina, the world's largest breeding colony of Magellanic penguins is visited by thousands of tourists every year, causing the penguins to become habituated to the presence of people. Has ecotourism affected the penguins' ability to respond to stressors? Has it affected the penguins' secretion of corticosterone?

11. Corticosterone is a(n):
    a. neurohormone
    b. steroid hormone
    c. amino-acid-derived hormone
    d. polypeptide hormone

12. In what part(s) of a target cell would you expect to find corticosterone receptors?

13. If penguins in a colony are habituated to the presence of tourists, how would their corticosterone response to being visited by tourists compare to that of penguins in a colony not previously exposed to tourists?

14. **QUANTITATIVE** Scientists tested the hypothesis that penguins habituated to tourists have a blunted stress response overall. They examined the corticosterone response of habituated and non-habituated penguins to another stressor—that of being captured and restrained for 30 minutes. They found that both habituated and non-habituated penguins secreted corticosterone in response to being captured and restrained, but that the levels

of corticosterone after 30 minutes differed between the groups. The results are shown below (* means $P < 0.05$; see BioSkills 3). Was the hypothesis supported? Explain.

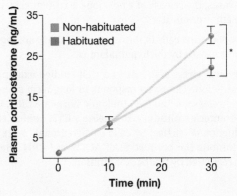

Source: Walker, B. G., P. D. Boersma, J. C. Wingfield. 2006. *Conservation Biology* 20: 146–154.

15. In response to a visit by tourists, which penguins—habituated or non-habituated—would show a greater change in expression of genes for liver enzymes involved in converting amino acids to glucose? Explain.

16. Suggest at least two distinct physiological mechanisms that could be responsible for the difference in corticosterone response to a stressor in habituated and non-habituated penguins. (Hint: Refer to Figure 46.14.)

47 Animal Reproduction and Development

The swollen, red rump of this female Hamadryas baboon indicates that she is about to produce an egg. She will probably mate with several males before the egg is fertilized.

In this chapter you will learn that

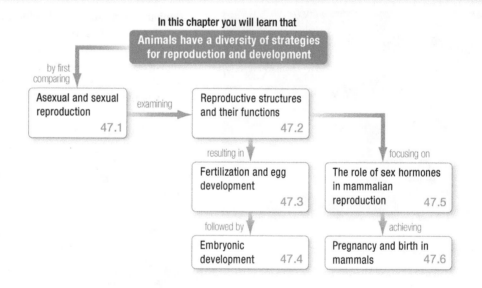

Animals have a diversity of strategies for reproduction and development

by first comparing

Asexual and sexual reproduction 47.1

examining →

Reproductive structures and their functions 47.2

resulting in ↓

Fertilization and egg development 47.3

focusing on ↓

The role of sex hormones in mammalian reproduction 47.5

followed by ↓

Embryonic development 47.4

achieving ↓

Pregnancy and birth in mammals 47.6

BIG PICTURE

This chapter is part of the Big Picture. See how on pages 816–817.

All the cells, tissues, organs, and systems introduced in Unit 7 exist for one reason: They allow animals to survive long enough and gather enough resources to reproduce. Stated another way, producing offspring is the reason that adaptations exist. Reproduction is the underlying purpose of virtually everything that an animal does. Replication is a fundamental attribute of life (see Chapter 1).

Although evolution by natural selection explains *why* animals reproduce, the goal of this chapter is to explore *how* reproduction occurs and how an animal develops from fertilization to birth. Understanding and manipulating reproductive systems is an important issue for physicians, veterinarians, farmers, zoo-keepers, conservation biologists, and many others. This chapter introduces you to some of the diversity of reproductive modes that occur in animals, but it focuses on mammalian reproduction, using humans as the primary model organism.

47.1 Asexual and Sexual Reproduction

Several earlier chapters explored how asexual and sexual reproduction differ. **Asexual reproduction** occurs without fusion of gametes and is usually based on mitosis; it typically results in offspring that are genetically identical to their parent. **Sexual reproduction,** in contrast, typically involves the fusion of haploid gametes and is based on meiosis; it results in offspring that are genetically different from each other and from their parents.

(a) Budding in hydra

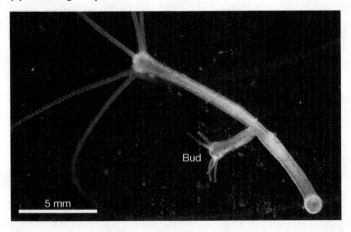

Bud

5 mm

(b) Fission in anemones

Site of fission

10 cm

(c) Parthenogenesis in some lizards

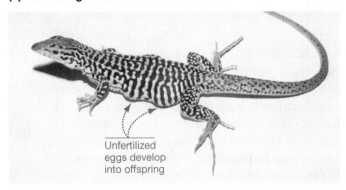

Unfertilized
eggs develop
into offspring

Figure 47.1 **Mechanisms of Asexual Reproduction in Animals Are Diverse.**

Let's first consider how animals engage in asexual reproduction to make genetically identical copies of themselves and then review the mechanisms responsible for sexual reproduction.

How Does Asexual Reproduction Occur?

In thousands of animal species, individuals can **clone** themselves—that is, produce large numbers of identical copies of themselves asexually.

There are three main mechanisms of asexual reproduction:

1. **Budding** An offspring begins to form within or on a parent (**Figure 47.1a**). The process is complete when the offspring—a miniature version of the parent—breaks free and begins to grow on its own.

2. **Fission** An individual simply splits into two or more descendants (**Figure 47.1b**).

3. **Parthenogenesis** (literally, "virgin-origin") Females produce offspring without any genetic contribution from a male. Parthenogenetic offspring may be produced by mitosis, by meiosis after a doubling of chromosome number, or by the fusion of two of the products of meiosis. Parthenogenesis occurs in a wide diversity of lineages, including certain invertebrates, fishes, lizards, snakes, and birds (**Figure 47.1c**).

Many animal species regularly switch between reproducing asexually and reproducing sexually. Why?

Switching Reproductive Modes: A Case History

Daphnia are crustaceans that live in freshwater habitats throughout the world. In a typical year, *Daphnia* produce only diploid, female offspring throughout the spring and summer, via parthenogenesis. The offspring produced by parthenogenesis develop in a structure called a brood pouch (**Figure 47.2**), and the young *Daphnia* are released when the female molts her exoskeleton.

In late summer or early fall, however, many of the parthenogenetically produced offspring develop into males. Once the males have matured, sexual reproduction ensues: Haploid **sperm,** the male gametes produced by meiosis in the *Daphnia* males, fertilize haploid **eggs,** the female gametes that the *Daphnia* females produce via meiosis.

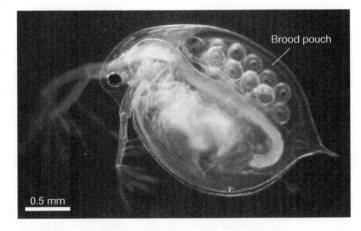

Brood pouch

0.5 mm

Figure 47.2 **Female *Daphnia* Can Produce Offspring by Parthenogenesis.**

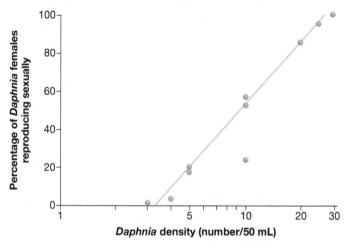

(a) Sexual reproduction is more common in crowded populations of *Daphnia pulex* than in sparse populations.

(b) In *Daphnia magna*, a combination of environmental cues triggers the switch to sexual reproduction.

Water quality	Food concentration	Day length	Sexual broods (%)
Clean	Low	Short	0
Crowded	Low	Short	44
Clean	Low	Long	0
Crowded	Low	Long	0
Clean	High	Short	0
Crowded	High	Short	0
Clean	High	Long	0
Crowded	High	Long	0

Figure 47.3 In *Daphnia*, Environmental Cues Signal the Switch from Asexual to Sexual Reproduction.
(a) There is a strong positive correlation between the percentage of females that reproduce sexually and the density of the population (plotted on a log scale here; see BioSkills 5). **(b)** Environmental conditions were varied experimentally for *Daphnia*. "Crowded" water was taken from tanks containing dense populations.
DATA: (a) Stross, R. G., and J. C. Hill. 1965. *Science* 150: 1462–1464. (b) Kleiven, O. T., P. Larsson, and A. Hoboek. 1992. *Oikos* 65: 197–206.

✔ **PROCESS OF SCIENCE** How would you determine which molecule or molecules in "crowded" water serve as a signal that triggers sexual reproduction?

Fertilization is the fusion of sperm and egg. In *Daphnia*, fertilized eggs are enclosed in a durable case that falls to the bottom of the pond or lake for the winter. In spring, only the female offspring hatch, and they begin reproducing asexually.

Biologists try to explain observations like this at two levels (see Chapter 50):

1. **Proximate causation** addresses *how* a trait is produced. When researchers identify the genetic, developmental, hormonal, or neural mechanisms responsible for a phenotype, they are working at the proximate level.

2. **Ultimate causation** addresses *why* a trait occurs, in terms of its effect on fitness. Researchers who work at the ultimate level try to understand the evolutionary history of traits.

Let's consider work on proximate aspects of the asexual–sexual switch in *Daphnia* and then consider ultimate causation.

What Environmental Cues Trigger the Switch? For decades, most researchers have contended that day length triggered the asexual–sexual switch. The idea was that the shortening days of late summer or fall affected sensors in the brain (see Chapter 46), and these receptors produced electrical or hormonal signals that induced the production of males and haploid eggs.

In 1965, however, biologists showed that high population densities are also a factor. Researchers who brought *Daphnia pulex* populations into the lab and kept day length constant found that the highest proportion of sexually reproducing females occurred at the highest population density (**Figure 47.3a**).

Another group of investigators built on this result by pinpointing the specific aspects of crowding that affected the animals. These biologists brought a closely related species—

D. magna—into the laboratory and altered day length, the amount of food available to individuals, and the quality of the water the *Daphnia* occupied. To vary water quality, the investigators used either clean water or "crowded" water taken from tanks where *D. magna* were being maintained at high density.

As **Figure 47.3b** shows, individuals in the study population switched to sexual reproduction only if they were exposed to water from crowded populations, low food availability, *and* short day lengths. In short, *D. magna* needs three different cues from the environment to switch to sexual reproduction. Two of these cues are associated with high population density; the third is associated with the onset of winter.

Why Do *Daphnia* Switch between Asexual and Sexual Reproduction? *Daphnia* appear to start sexual reproduction when conditions worsen. Why?

The leading hypothesis in answer to this question points out that sexually produced offspring are genetically diverse. Recall that genetic diversity increases fitness in environments with rapidly evolving parasites, deteriorating physical conditions, or other types of rapid environmental change (see Chapter 13). When the environment changes, genetically diverse offspring are likely to include individuals that will survive better and reproduce more than offspring that are identical to their parents.
✔ If you understand this concept, you should be able to predict the conditions under which asexual reproduction would be found as the favored method of producing offspring.

To date, however, the changing-environment hypothesis has not been tested rigorously in *Daphnia*. Research on the adaptive significance of sex in this species and other organisms continues.

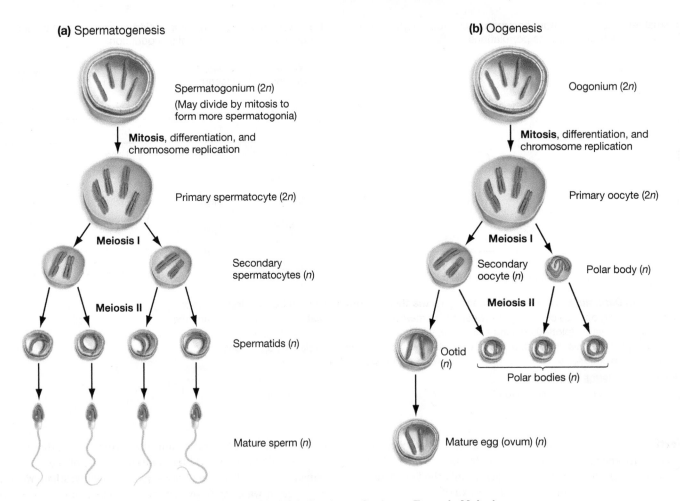

(a) Spermatogenesis

Spermatogonium (2*n*)
(May divide by mitosis to
form more spermatogonia)

Mitosis, differentiation, and
chromosome replication

Primary spermatocyte (2*n*)

Meiosis I

Secondary
spermatocytes (*n*)

Meiosis II

Spermatids (*n*)

Mature sperm (*n*)

(b) Oogenesis

Oogonium (2*n*)

Mitosis, differentiation, and
chromosome replication

Primary oocyte (2*n*)

Meiosis I

Secondary
oocyte (*n*)   Polar body (*n*)

Meiosis II

Ootid
(*n*)   Polar bodies (*n*)

Mature egg (ovum) (*n*)

Figure 47.4 Gametogenesis in Sexually Reproducing Animals Produces Sperm or Eggs via Meiosis.

Mechanisms of Sexual Reproduction: Gametogenesis

The mitotic cell divisions, meiotic cell divisions, and developmental events that produce male and female gametes are collectively called **gametogenesis. Spermatogenesis** is the formation of sperm; **oogenesis** is the formation of **ova** (singular: **ovum**) (**Figure 47.4**). An ovum is also known less formally as a mature egg.

In the vast majority of animals, gametogenesis occurs in a sex organ, or **gonad.** Male gonads are called **testes;** female gonads are called **ovaries.** Early in development, reproductive cells known as germ cells enter the testes and ovaries and give rise to diploid cells that will undergo gametogenesis.

Spermatogenesis in Mammals Figure 47.4a summarizes the events that take place during spermatogenesis. Note that in the male gonad, diploid cells called **spermatogonia** (singular: **spermatogonium**) divide by mitosis. Some of the resulting cells continue to function as spermatogonia; others differentiate to form specialized cells that are committed to developing into sperm.

The specialized cells produced by spermatogonia are called **primary spermatocytes.** They undergo meiosis I and produce two **secondary spermatocytes,** which then undergo meiosis II. The result is four haploid cells called spermatids.

Each haploid spermatid matures into a sperm—a cell that is specialized for carrying a haploid genome from the male through the female reproductive tract and fertilizing an egg. The production of spermatogonia, primary spermatocytes, and sperm occurs continuously throughout a male's adult life.

Structure and Function of Sperm As a mammalian sperm matures, it acquires the four main compartments shown in Figure 47.5: the head, neck, midpiece, and tail.

- The head contains the nucleus and an enzyme-filled structure called the **acrosome.** The enzymes stored in the acrosome allow the sperm to penetrate the barriers surrounding the egg.

- The neck encloses a centriole that will combine with a centriole contributed by the egg to form a centrosome. The centrosome is required for formation of the spindle apparatus during mitosis (see Chapter 12).

- The midpiece is packed with mitochondria, which produce the ATP required to power movement.

- The tail region consists of a **flagellum**—a long structure, composed of microtubules and surrounded by plasma membrane, that whips back and forth to make swimming possible (see Chapter 7).

Sperm are stripped down, streamlined cells that are specialized for racing other sperm to the egg. Eggs, in comparison, are bulky, far less mobile storage containers that are packed with valuable materials.

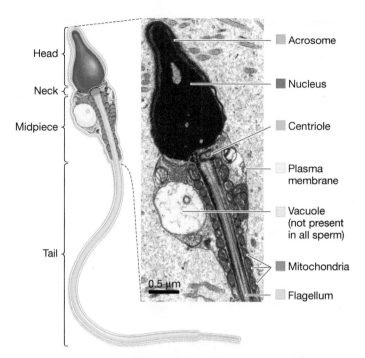

Figure 47.5 Mammalian Sperm Are Specialized for Motility and Fusing with an Egg. The morphology of human sperm is typical of many mammal species.

Oogenesis in Mammals

Figure 47.4b highlights an important similarity between spermatogenesis and oogenesis: In the female gonad, diploid cells called **oogonia** (singular: **oogonium**) divide by mitosis. Some of the resulting cells continue to function as oogonia; others differentiate to form specialized cells that are committed to producing an egg.

However, subsequent steps in gametogenesis are markedly different in females. When the specialized cells produced by an oogonium, the **primary oocytes,** undergo meiosis, only one of the haploid products will eventually mature into an egg. This **secondary oocyte** is arrested in the final stages of meiosis II until it is fertilized by a sperm. Only then does it complete meiosis to become an ootid, which matures into an ovum, or a mature egg.

The other cells produced by meiosis in females have a tiny amount of cytoplasm and do not mature into eggs. Because the distribution of cytoplasm is so unequal during each meiotic division in females, the smaller cells are called **polar bodies.** Polar bodies degenerate shortly after their formation.

Another difference between gametogenesis in males and females is that the production of primary oocytes stops early in development in many mammals; in humans, it stops before a female fetus is born. The primary oocytes enter prophase of meiosis I during fetal development but then stop developing for months, years, or decades, depending on the species.

Structure and Function of Eggs

Eggs are larger than sperm mainly because eggs contain the nutrients required for the embryo's early development. In the vast majority of species, the mature egg cell is a membrane-bound structure consisting of a haploid nucleus, a full complement of other organelles, and a large supply of nutrients provided by **yolk**—a fat- and protein-rich cytoplasm.

(a) Sea urchin eggs are surrounded by a jelly coat.

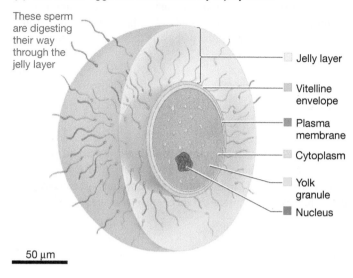

(b) Human oocytes are surrounded by a protective layer of cells called the corona radiata.

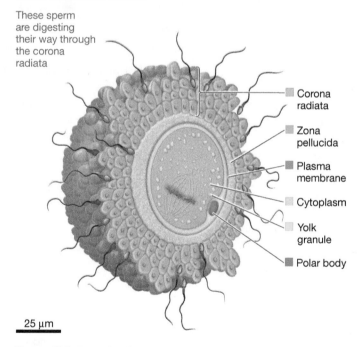

Figure 47.6 Eggs Are Surrounded by Protective Structures.

Just outside the plasma membrane of an egg, a fibrous, mat-like sheet of glycoproteins called the **vitelline envelope** forms and surrounds the egg. In many aquatic animals, such as the sea urchin, a large, gelatinous matrix known as a jelly layer surrounds the vitelline envelope, further enclosing and protecting the egg (**Figure 47.6a**). The plasma membrane and surrounding layers play a key role in binding sperm from the same species and initiating fertilization. Other animals produce amniotic eggs, which contain four membrane-bound sacs (see Chapter 32). Amniotic eggs evolved as an innovation that allowed tetrapods to lay large eggs that do not desiccate on land.

In the eggs of humans and other mammals, the vitelline envelope is unusually thick and is called the **zona pellucida.** This structure is surrounded by a layer of cells known as the corona radiata, which a sperm must penetrate before it can fertilize the oocyte (Figure 47.6b).

47.2 Reproductive Structures and Their Functions

The first section of this chapter considered the broad contrast between asexual and sexual reproduction, along with an exploration of how animals produce sperm and eggs during sexual reproduction. Now let's explore the mechanics of sexual reproduction in more detail, starting with the anatomy of the male and female reproductive systems.

The Male Reproductive System

In humans, the external anatomy, or **genitalia,** of the male reproductive system consists of the scrotum and the penis. The saclike **scrotum** holds the testes; the **penis** functions as the organ of copulation necessary for internal fertilization.

Internal Anatomy of Human Male Reproductive Organs Although it consists of many structures, the reproductive system in human males has just three basic functional components. **Figure 47.7** shows the relevant structures in side view and front view.

(a) Side view

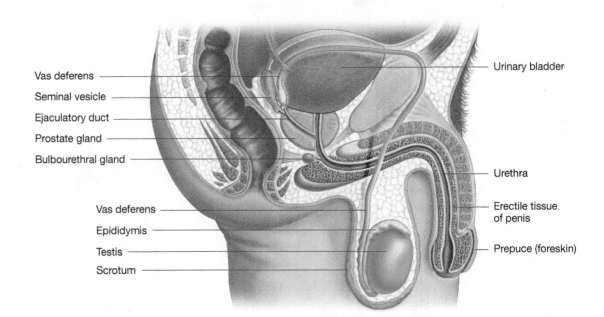

Vas deferens
Seminal vesicle
Ejaculatory duct
Prostate gland
Bulbourethral gland

Vas deferens
Epididymis
Testis
Scrotum

Urinary bladder

Urethra

Erectile tissue of penis

Prepuce (foreskin)

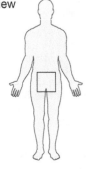

(b) Front view

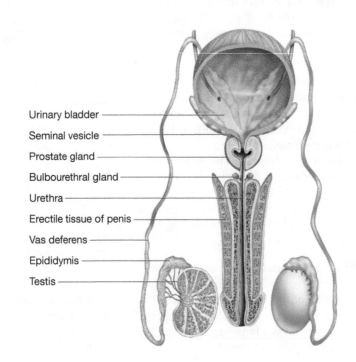

Urinary bladder
Seminal vesicle
Prostate gland
Bulbourethral gland
Urethra
Erectile tissue of penis
Vas deferens
Epididymis
Testis

Figure 47.7 The Reproductive System in a Human Male Produces, Stores, and Transports Sperm.

Source	Content	Function
Seminal vesicles	Fructose (a sugar)	Source of chemical energy for sperm movement
	Prostaglandins	Stimulate smooth muscle contractions in uterus
Prostate gland	Antibiotic compound	Prevents urinary tract infections in males
	Citric acid	Nutrient used by sperm
Bulbourethral gland	Alkaline mucus	Lubricates tip of penis; neutralizes acids in urethra

1. *Spermatogenesis and sperm storage* Sperm are produced in the testes and stored nearby in the **epididymis.**

2. *Production of accessory fluids* Complex solutions form in the **seminal vesicles, prostate gland,** and **bulbourethral gland.** These solutions, called accessory fluids, are added to sperm to form **semen.** Table 47.1 lists some components of the accessory fluids.

3. *Transport and delivery* A **vas deferens** is a muscular tube that transports sperm from the epididymis to the short **ejaculatory duct,** where the sperm are mixed with accessory fluids. The resulting semen then enters the **urethra,** a longer tube that passes through the penis and services both the reproductive and urinary systems. The semen is expelled from the body during **ejaculation.**

The composition of the accessory fluids varies widely among animals. In many insects, spiders, and vertebrates, molecules in the accessory fluids cause the semen to congeal after it arrives in the female reproductive tract, forming a plug. Experiments have shown that these copulatory plugs can serve as an effective deterrent to future matings. In some species, though, females or second males actively remove the plugs.

Another diverse aspect of male reproductive anatomy has to do with a bone inside the penis called the **baculum,** which helps stiffen the penis during copulation. Some mammal species, including humans, lack a baculum. But in rodents, the variable shape of the baculum can be used to distinguish among species. And in seals, baculum size correlates with mating system—the mating practices observed in a species. For example, in seal species in which females routinely mate with several males before becoming pregnant, males have not only large testes for their size but also a large baculum. The testes and baculum are much smaller in species in which females mate with a single male.

The Female Reproductive System

In animals, the most important part of the female reproductive system is the ovary—where meiosis occurs and mature eggs are produced. Let's consider two highly specialized examples, the reproductive systems of female birds and mammals. Birds are **oviparous** ("egg-bearing") animals that lay an amniotic egg

protected by a hard shell; most mammals are **viviparous** ("live-bearing"), and embryonic development takes place entirely within the mother's body.

The Reproductive Tract of Female Birds Figure 47.8 describes the events that take place as an egg moves through the reproductive tract of a female bird. The result is a hard-shelled egg, like the chicken eggs you buy in a store. The egg is "laid" from the **cloaca**—a chamber that the reproductive, digestive, and excretory systems flow into and that opens to the environment.

From the time the egg is released from the ovary until the zygote undergoes mitosis and the embryo begins to develop, a bird egg is a single cell. The ostrich egg, which can be over 15 cm (6 inches) in diameter, contains one of the largest single cells known in animals. A bird egg stores enough nutrients and water to sustain development until hatching.

Note that although male birds have two testes, females of most bird species have just one functional ovary. The presence of a single working ovary is thought to be an adaptation that reduces weight and makes flight more efficient.

Figure 47.8 **All Birds Are Oviparous.**

PROCESS: MATURATION OF A BIRD EGG

Left ovary

1. Meiosis and maturation of follicles. Follicles are ova (eggs) attached to yolk (yellow spheres).

2. Entry of follicle into oviduct. Fertilization takes place if the hen has mated with a cock. (Hens can store sperm for up to 30 days.)

Left oviduct

3. Addition of egg white.

4. Addition of outer membranes.

Uterus

5. Formation of eggshell.

Intestine

Vagina

Cloaca

6. Egg is laid. Egg passes through the vagina and is "laid" out of the cloaca.

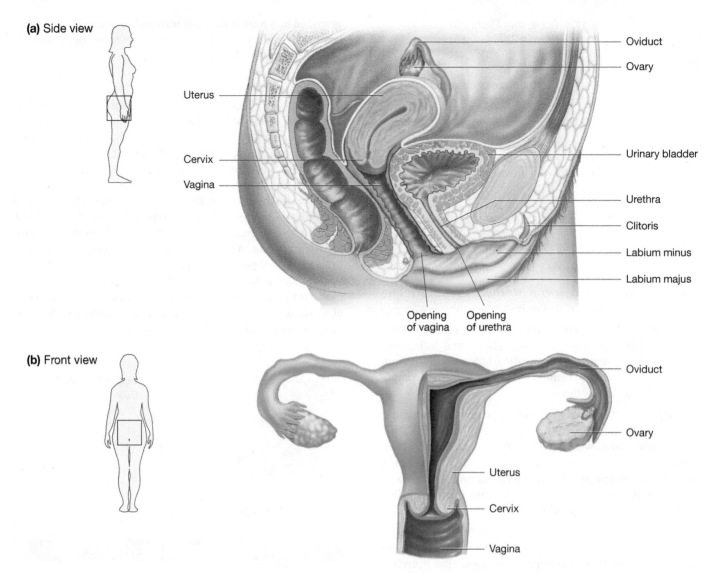

(a) Side view

Uterus

Cervix

Vagina

Oviduct

Ovary

Urinary bladder

Urethra

Clitoris

Labium minus

Labium majus

Opening of vagina   Opening of urethra

(b) Front view

Oviduct

Ovary

Uterus

Cervix

Vagina

Figure 47.9 The Reproductive System in a Human Female Produces Eggs and Nurtures the Embryo and Fetus.

✔ **PROCESS OF SCIENCE** Generate a hypothesis to explain why male and female gonads are paired in mammals. How would you test your hypothesis?

Anatomy of the Reproductive System in Human Females **Figure 47.9** shows side and front views of the human female reproductive system. Female genitalia include the **labia minora** (singular: **labium minus**) and the **labia majora** (singular: **labium majus**), the clitoris, the opening of the urethra, and the opening of the vagina.

- The labia are folds of skin that cover the urethral and vaginal openings.
- The **clitoris** is an organ that develops from the same population of embryonic cells that gives rise to the penis in males. It becomes erect during sexual stimulation and is covered with a protective sheath called the *prepuce*, which is homologous to the prepuce (foreskin) that covers the end of the penis.
- The urethral opening, where urine is expelled, is separate from the reproductive structures.
- The **vagina** is the chamber where semen is deposited during sexual intercourse. The vagina is also referred to as the birth

canal because the baby moves out of the uterus and through the vagina during childbirth.

The internal structures of the female reproductive system in humans and other mammals serve two basic functions:

1. *Production and transport of eggs* Eggs are produced in the paired ovaries. During **ovulation,** a secondary oocyte is expelled from the ovary and enters the **oviduct,** also known as the **fallopian tube,** where fertilization may take place. Fertilized eggs are then transported through the oviduct to the muscular sac called the **uterus.**

2. *Development of offspring* The uterus is where embryonic development takes place. During childbirth, the baby passes through an opening in the **cervix**—the bottom part of the uterus—and into the vagina.

How do sperm reach the egg, and how is the egg fertilized? These questions are addressed in the next section.

47.3 Fertilization and Egg Development

Fertilization is the joining of a sperm and an egg to form a diploid **zygote.** Fertilization marks the beginning of the remarkable events of animal development, the set of processes that allow the zygote to produce a multicellular organism. Development is part of a cycle that connects one generation to another: Gametes formed by adults of one generation unite in fertilization, creating a new individual that develops into an adult of the next generation. In this way, development and reproduction are inextricably linked.

Let's begin by examining different strategies for fertilization, the cellular mechanisms of fertilization, and different approaches to supplying the developing embryo with nutrients. Many species use external fertilization, the release of gametes into the environment followed by fertilization outside the mother. In other species, sperm are deposited into the reproductive tract of the female, and internal fertilization occurs.

External Fertilization

Most animals that rely on external fertilization live in aquatic environments. This is logical, because gametes and embryos must be protected from drying. If external fertilization occurred in a terrestrial environment, either the gametes or the resulting zygote would likely die of desiccation.

Animals that use external fertilization also tend to produce huge numbers of gametes. For example, female sea stars release millions of eggs into the surrounding seawater during spawning (**Figure 47.10**), and males release many times that number of sperm. The leading hypothesis to explain this pattern is that the probability of a sperm and an egg meeting in an ocean or lake is small unless large numbers of gametes are present. In addition, production of a large number of embryos is beneficial because so many of them fall prey to predators.

Sperm and eggs from different individuals must be released into the environment synchronously by males and females for external fertilization to work. How is gamete release coordinated? The answer has two parts.

1. Gametogenesis usually occurs in response to environmental cues, such as lengthening days and warming water, that indicate a favorable season for breeding.

2. Gametes are released in response to specific cues from individuals of the same species.

In fishes and other aquatic animals with well-developed eyes, external fertilization by spawning is often the culmination of an elaborate courtship ritual between a male and a female. In contrast, courtship behavior appears to be much less important—or even absent—in species such as clams, sea urchins, and sea cucumbers. How do animals that cannot see their mates time the release of their gametes? Recent research indicates that the chemical messengers called pheromones (see Chapter 44) might be involved in synchronizing gamete release.

Internal Fertilization

The vast majority of terrestrial animals as well as a significant number of aquatic animals use internal fertilization. It occurs in one of two ways:

1. After copulation, in which males deposit sperm directly into the female reproductive tract with the aid of a copulatory organ, usually called a penis.

2. After males package their sperm into a structure called a **spermatophore,** which is then picked up and placed into the female's reproductive tract by the male or the female. In some salamander species, for example, the male places the spermatophore on the ground within its territory. Later the female picks it up with her cloaca. In this case, the result is internal fertilization without sexual intercourse.

Sperm Competition and Second Male Advantage An important insight about internal fertilization came from experiments on dung flies conducted by Geoff Parker. In 1970 Parker confirmed the existence of **sperm competition**—competition between sperm from different males to fertilize the eggs of the same female.

Parker's experiments consisted of a series of matings of one female with two males. In each experiment, Parker selected the two males in such a way that he could distinguish between their offspring. He found that the proportion of offspring fathered by each male was not 50:50. Instead, whichever male was last to copulate fathered an average of 85 percent of the offspring produced.

In addition to suggesting that sperm were competing to fertilize eggs, these data indicated that, in this experiment, the second male won. Follow-up research has confirmed that

Eggs

Figure 47.10 External Fertilization Occurs in Aquatic Environments. Female seastars in the genus *Asterias* can release as many as 100 million eggs at once.

QUESTION: Does the "second-male advantage" occur in sperm competition?

HYPOTHESIS: In sperm-storage areas, sperm from the second male displace sperm from the first male.

NULL HYPOTHESIS: The mechanism does not involve sperm displacement from sperm-storage areas.

EXPERIMENTAL SETUP:

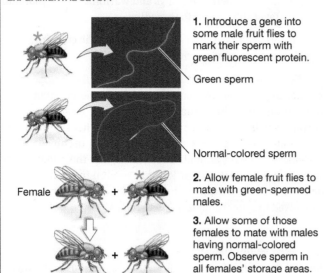

1. Introduce a gene into some male fruit flies to mark their sperm with green fluorescent protein.

Green sperm

Normal-colored sperm

Female

2. Allow female fruit flies to mate with green-spermed males.

3. Allow some of those females to mate with males having normal-colored sperm. Observe sperm in all females' storage areas.

PREDICTION: When females mate twice, little sperm from the first male remains in storage.

PREDICTION OF NULL HYPOTHESIS: When females mate twice, most or all of the sperm deposited by the first male is still present.

RESULTS:

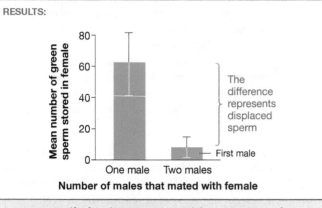

The difference represents displaced sperm

First male

Number of males that mated with female

CONCLUSION: If a female mates a second time, most sperm from the first male she mated with disappears.

Figure 47.11 Experimental Evidence Supports Second-Male Advantage in *Drosophila*. The graph shows the average number of green sperm stored in females when males with green sperm were the only male to mate or the first of two males to mate.

SOURCE: Price, C. S. C., K. A. Dyer, and J. A. Coyne. 1999. Sperm competition between *Drosophila* males involves both displacement and incapacitation. *Nature* 400: 449–452.

✔ Do these data show that sperm from the second male physically displace sperm from the first male?

second-male advantage is widespread, although not universal, in insects and some other animal groups. How does it occur?

To explore why second-male advantage occurs, biologists turned to the fruit fly *Drosophila melanogaster*. One research group introduced a gene into male fruit flies that produced sperm with green fluorescent tails (**Figure 47.11**). When a mating by a green-spermed male was followed with a second mating—by a male having normal-colored sperm—many fewer green sperm were found in the female's sperm-storage area than when no second mating took place.

To interpret this finding, the biologists suggested that the sperm of the second male physically dislodged the first male's sperm from the female's sperm-storage area. The researchers also demonstrated that the fluid that accompanies sperm during fertilization can displace stored sperm from competing males. More recent research has shown that in addition to these factors, females can eject sperm from their reproductive tracts. Together, these mechanisms result in the second male's sperm fertilizing most of the eggs laid.

Why Is Testis Size Variable among Species? Research on sperm competition has recently contributed another major finding. In species where females routinely mate with multiple males before laying eggs or giving birth, males have extraordinarily large testes for their size and produce proportionately larger numbers of sperm.

The leading hypothesis to explain this observation is that fertilization is similar to a lottery in which each sperm represents a ticket. The more tickets a male enters in the competition, the higher is his chance of "winning" fertilizations and passing his alleles on to the next generation. Males with exceptionally large testes produce exceptionally large numbers of sperm, and they are more likely to win the lottery.

The lottery model has been challenged, however, by evidence that females often store sperm and exert control over which sperm are successful in fertilization. In other words, females do not always accept the results of sperm competition passively.

Females of some species actively choose which male performs the last copulation before fertilization takes place. In other species, females physically eject sperm from undesirable males. This phenomenon has been dubbed cryptic female choice. The name is appropriate because the selection of sperm by females is hidden from males.

How Does External Anatomy Affect Sperm Competition? The structure of male genitalia varies greatly among animal species. In many groups of insects and spiders, for example, closely related species are morphologically identical except for their distinctive genitalia. Why are these organs so diverse?

The leading hypothesis is that certain shapes of genitalia give males an advantage in sperm competition. To test this hypothesis, biologists measured the size of the spines found on the tips of male genitalia in a species of seed beetle (**Figure 47.12a**) and then documented which males were most successful at fertilizing eggs when females mated with two males.

The *x*-axis in **Figure 47.12b** plots the length of genital spines; the *y*-axis plots the proportion of eggs fertilized by the second

(a) Long genital spines in males of the seed beetle *Callosobruchus maculatus*

100 μm

Male

Female

(b) During sperm competition, males with longer genital spines father more offspring.

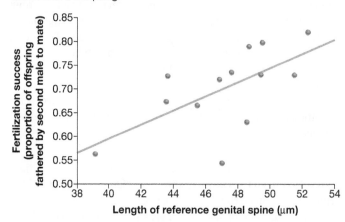

Figure 47.12 In Some Insects and Spiders, Individual Variation of Male Genitalia May Affect Reproductive Success. (a) An elaborate male reproductive structure in a seed beetle, used to transfer sperm to the female. The spikes at the top of the inset photo are called genital spines. **(b)** Data on the size of reference genital spines from experiments on reproductive success during sperm competition.

DATA: Hotzy, C., and G. Arnqvist. 2009. *Current Biology* 19: 404–407.

male to copulate with a female, during experimental matings. The line through the data points shows that second-to-mate males with longer genital spines tend to father a higher percentage of offspring. The long spines stick in the female's reproductive tract and prolong copulation time, even if the female is ready for copulation to end.

The upshot? Size matters, in seed beetles. Natural selection that occurs during sperm competition may explain why genitalia are so diverse among insect and spider species.

Now that we have explored how the size and shape of male external genitalia are related to sperm competition and reproductive success, let's examine what happens when sperm are released into the female reproductive tract and begin their hunt for the egg.

The Cell Biology of Fertilization

The first challenge of fertilization is for a sperm to find the egg. In many species, sperm accomplish this by following chemical signals secreted by the egg. In species that use external fertilization, there's an additional challenge: ensuring that only sperm and egg of the same species come together. Once in contact, the sperm and egg have to fuse, something that few other cells in the body ever do.

What's more, in most species, thousands of sperm can compete to fertilize an egg, but fusion must be limited to a single sperm so the egg does not receive extra chromosomes. Finally, the fusion of the two gametes has to trigger the onset of development. Very little is simple about fertilization.

Research on fertilization began in earnest early in the twentieth century, when biologists started to study the sperm–egg interaction that occurs during external fertilization in sea urchins. **Figure 47.13** outlines major events of this process.

Sea urchin sperm are drawn to the egg by following a gradient of a chemical secreted by the egg's jelly layer (step 1). The head of the sperm initially binds to the jelly layer (step 2). Binding triggers the acrosome reaction, a release of the contents of the sperm's acrosome (step 3). The enzymes that were contained in the acrosome digest nearby portions of the jelly layer and the vitelline envelope. Initial contact with the jelly layer also ramps up the beating of the sperm's flagellum, powering the sperm toward the egg's plasma membrane (steps 4 and 5).

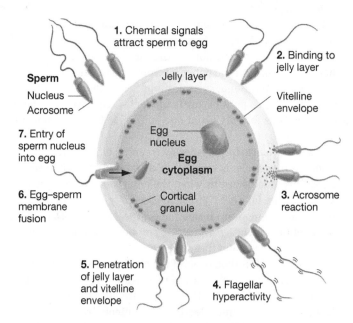

Figure 47.13 Fertilization Is a Complex Process. Steps in the fertilization of a sea urchin egg are shown in this example.

Once the sperm head contacts the egg's plasma membrane, specific proteins in the plasma membranes of the egg and sperm induce membrane fusion (step 6). The sperm nucleus then enters the egg (step 7). Contact between the sperm and egg plasma membranes also initiates many responses in the egg. The sperm and egg nuclei fuse, and the egg is now an activated machine ready for development. Fertilization is complete.

In marine habitats, sperm and eggs from different species are mixed together in the seawater. What prevents cross-species fertilization and the consequent production of dysfunctional hybrid offspring?

How Do Gametes from the Same Species Recognize Each Other?

In the 1970s, Victor Vacquier and co-workers succeeded in identifying a protein on the head of sea urchin sperm that binds to the plasma membrane of sea urchin eggs in a species-specific manner. They called this protein bindin.

Follow-up work showed that bindin proteins from even very closely related species of sea urchin are distinct, and that egg plasma membranes contain receptors that bind only to bindin from sperm of the same species. Similar types of specific protein–protein interactions occur between the sperm and eggs of mammals.

✔ If you understand the importance of protein–protein interactions in fertilization, you should be able to explain why adding a molecule that binds to a bindin-like protein on the human sperm head would be an effective contraceptive.

What Prevents More than One Sperm from Entering the Egg?

Researchers found that even when hundreds of sperm are clustered around an egg (see Figure 47.13), only one sperm participates in fertilization. This observation makes sense: Multiple fertilization, or polyspermy, would result in a zygote that had more than two copies of each chromosome, and embryos with more than two copies of each chromosome die. How do animals avoid polyspermy?

In sea urchins, there are two mechanisms that block polyspermy. The first begins immediately after sperm–egg contact and involves depolarization of the egg's plasma membrane—changing the membrane potential from negative to positive (see Chapter 43). Additional sperm cannot fuse with the egg while it is depolarized, so polyspermy is prevented. However, the depolarization lasts for only about one minute, so this mechanism is short lived.

A second block to polyspermy, seen in almost all animals, including mammals, is erection of a physical barrier to sperm entry. This process begins when the entry of the sperm nucleus causes calcium ions (Ca^{2+}) to be released from storage areas (the endoplasmic reticulum) inside the egg. As Figure 47.14a shows, a wave of Ca^{2+} release starts at the point of sperm nucleus entry and spreads throughout the egg.

The egg contains thousands of vesicles called cortical granules that lie just beneath the plasma membrane (see Figure 47.13). The release of Ca^{2+} causes the cortical granules to fuse with the plasma membrane and release their contents by exocytosis to the exterior. Recall that the same mechanism of Ca^{2+}-mediated

exocytosis is used when nerve cells communicate with other cells at synapses (Chapter 43).

Included in the contents released by the cortical granules are proteases that digest the exterior-facing portion of the receptor for sperm. This prevents any new sperm from binding to the egg surface. In addition, ions and other compounds released by the cortical granules accumulate between the egg's plasma membrane and the vitelline envelope. These concentrated solutes cause water to diffuse into the space between the plasma membrane and the vitelline envelope. The influx of water lifts the vitelline envelope away from the cell. Compounds from the cortical granules cross-link molecules in the vitelline envelope to form a tough **fertilization envelope** (Figure 47.14b). This impenetrable barrier keeps additional sperm from reaching the sea urchin egg.

Although mammalian eggs do not produce a fertilization envelope, they do experience a wave of Ca^{2+} ions that triggers the release of enzymes from cortical granules. Similar to events in the sea urchin egg, these enzymes destroy the egg's receptor for sperm and modify proteins on the egg surface and on a structure similar to the vitelline envelope. These events block polyspermy by preventing the binding of any additional sperm once the egg is fertilized.

Now that you've read about how fertilization takes place, let's look at where development occurs. Does it happen outside the mother's body or within the mother?

Why Do Some Females Lay Eggs While Others Give Birth?

In many oviparous species that release or deposit their eggs into the environment, such as sea stars, sea urchins, and most insects, the parents provide no further care. Birds, however, incubate their eggs and feed the young after hatching; fish may guard their eggs from predators and fan the eggs to oxygenate them.

In viviparous species, the embryo attaches to the reproductive tract of the mother and receives nutrition directly from her—via diffusion from her circulatory system. In **ovoviviparous** species, offspring also develop inside the mother's body but are nourished by nutrient-rich yolk stored in the egg.

Why does oviparity exist in some groups and viviparity or ovoviviparity in others? Biologists tackled this question by studying the lizard genus *Sceloporus*. Some *Sceloporus* populations are oviparous; others are ovoviviparous. The biologists analyzed a phylogenetic tree—based on molecular and morphological data—of many *Sceloporus* species (Figure 47.15). Two conclusions should make sense to you (see BioSkills 13 for help with interpreting phylogenetic trees):

1. Because the basal branches of the tree represent oviparous species, egg laying probably represents the original or ancestral condition.

2. As the red branches on the tree show, ovoviviparity evolved independently in two groups.

Using a similar research strategy, biologists have found that ovoviviparous populations of sea stars have evolved from oviparous populations on several occasions.

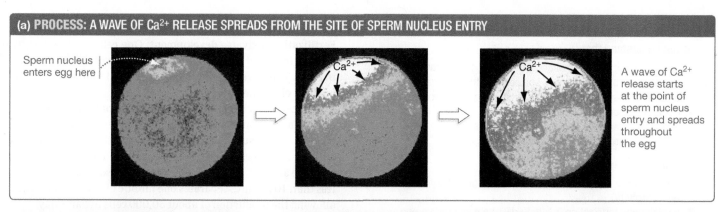

(a) PROCESS: A WAVE OF Ca²⁺ RELEASE SPREADS FROM THE SITE OF SPERM NUCLEUS ENTRY

Sperm nucleus enters egg here

Ca²⁺

Ca²⁺

A wave of Ca²⁺ release starts at the point of sperm nucleus entry and spreads throughout the egg

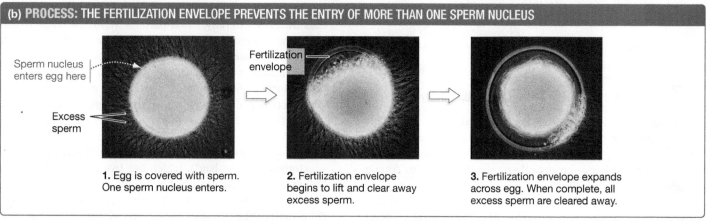

(b) PROCESS: THE FERTILIZATION ENVELOPE PREVENTS THE ENTRY OF MORE THAN ONE SPERM NUCLEUS

Sperm nucleus enters egg here

Excess sperm

Fertilization envelope

1. Egg is covered with sperm. One sperm nucleus enters.

2. Fertilization envelope begins to lift and clear away excess sperm.

3. Fertilization envelope expands across egg. When complete, all excess sperm are cleared away.

Figure 47.14 A Physical Barrier Erected after Fertilization Prevents Polyspermy. The events of sea urchin fertilization are shown here. **(a)** During fertilization, a wave of Ca²⁺ release begins at the point of sperm nucleus entry and spreads under the plasma membrane across the egg in about 30 seconds. Colors represent Ca²⁺ concentration, where white is highest and blue lowest. The Ca²⁺ concentration was measured with an injected reagent that fluoresces in the presence of Ca²⁺. **(b)** In response to the increased Ca²⁺ concentration, a fertilization envelope arises in about 40 seconds and clears away excess sperm.

Why did natural selection favor these changes between egg laying and live birth? Researchers have hypothesized that natural selection should favor live birth in cold habitats. Low temperatures slow the development of embryos. Therefore, in cold habitats, it might be advantageous for females to retain eggs inside their bodies so that they can thermoregulate to maintain the offspring at a more favorable temperature for development. This hypothesis is supported by the fact that ovoviviparous *Sceloporus* species live in the highlands of the southwestern United States and central Mexico, where temperatures can be low.

Sceloporus lizards have been a productive group in which to study this question because the trait has evolved more than once in extremely closely related species—making it easier to find correlations between live birth and other characteristics, such as living in cold habitats. The issue is much more difficult to study in mammals, where viviparity evolved just once. Monotremes (the duck-billed platypus and echidnas) are oviparous, while marsupials and eutherian mammals are viviparous (see Chapter 32). It is still not clear why, and how, viviparity evolved in mammals before the marsupial–eutherian split. Is the cold-habitats hypothesis relevant? To date, nobody knows.

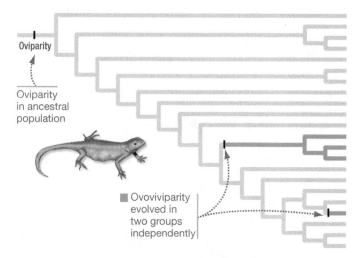

Oviparity

Oviparity in ancestral population

Ovoviviparity evolved in two groups independently

Figure 47.15 Ovoviviparity Has Evolved More than Once in *Sceloporus* Lizards. Each branch on this phylogenetic tree represents a *Sceloporus* species or population from central Mexico.

47.4 Embryonic Development

"Making Babies: 25,000 Genes, Some Assembly Required." This wry chapter title written by evolutionary-developmental biologist Sean Carroll highlights one of the most remarkable events of life. How *is* a baby—or any other animal—assembled from a single cell?

You have already learned about the basic genetic and cellular processes of development (Chapter 21). The central message was that cell–cell signaling causes different sets of transcription factors to be produced in various cells throughout the embryo, resulting in differential gene expression and differentiation.

The goal of this section is to look in more detail at how these general principles apply to embryonic development—in essence, what's involved in "some assembly required." Let's follow development through the major stages shown for humans in **Figure 47.16.**

Cleavage

Fertilization activates development. One cell becomes two, two become four, and the beginnings of a multicellular organism are in place. The stage of rapid cell divisions that follows fertilization is called **cleavage.**

In most animals, cleavage divides the cytoplasm present in the egg into a larger and larger number of smaller and smaller daughter cells. As a result, the number of cells in the embryo increases without any overall growth of the embryo. The cell divisions of cleavage are the fastest that ever occur. For example, in fruit flies, less than 10 minutes separates one mitotic division from another, allowing the production of about 50,000 cells in half a day.

The cells that are created during cleavage are called **blastomeres** (literally, "bud-parts"). When cleavage is complete, the embryo in many animals consists of a mass of blastomeres called a **blastula** ("little-sprout" or "bud").

In humans and almost all other mammals, fertilization takes place in the fallopian tube near the ovary, and cleavage occurs as the embryo moves down the fallopian tube toward the uterus (**Figure 47.17**). The embryo completes its development in the uterus.

Cleavage in mammals results in a type of blastula called a **blastocyst** ("sprout-bag"), which has two populations of cells. The exterior of the blastocyst is a thin sheet of cells called the **trophoblast** ("feeding-sprout"). Inside the trophoblast is a fluid-filled cavity (**blastocoel**) and a cluster of cells called the **inner cell mass (ICM).** There is a fundamental distinction between the trophoblast and the ICM—the embryo develops from the ICM, and the trophoblast forms part of an organ called the **placenta.** The placenta exchanges nutrients and wastes between the mother and the embryo. Cells from the mother's uterus also form part of the placenta. The placenta was a key innovation in the evolution of mammals, but it doesn't contribute any cells to the newborn.

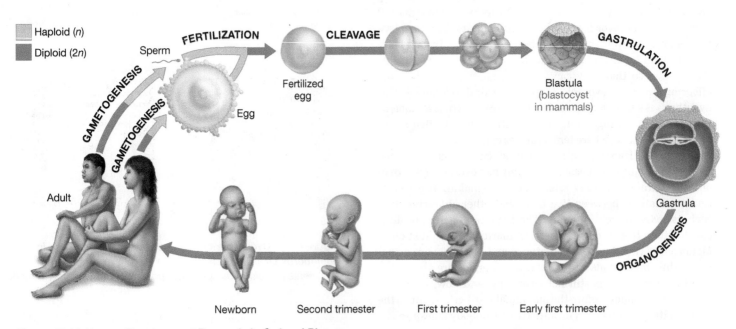

Figure 47.16 Human Development Proceeds in Ordered Phases.

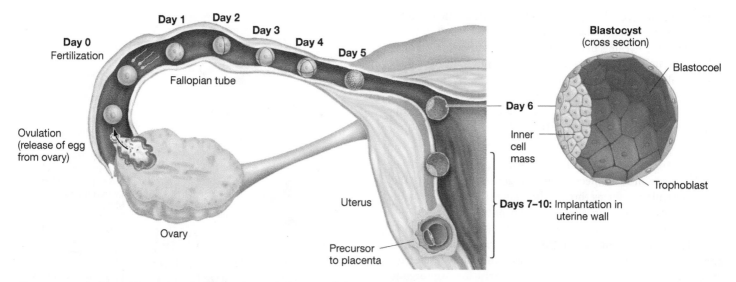

Figure 47.17 In Most Mammals, Cleavage Occurs before the Embryo Reaches the Uterus. Human cleavage and a human blastocyst are shown here.

Gastrulation

As cleavage nears completion, cell division slows, and cell movement then takes over from cell proliferation as the most important developmental process. In this stage of development, called **gastrulation,** extensive and highly organized cell movements and changes in cell shape rearrange the embryonic cells into a structure called the **gastrula. Figure 47.18** shows the dramatic reshaping of a frog embryo during gastrulation.

Intensive research on this phase of development started in the 1920s with efforts to follow the movement of individual cells during gastrulation in newts and frogs. In these early experiments, tiny blocks of agar (a gelatinous compound) were soaked

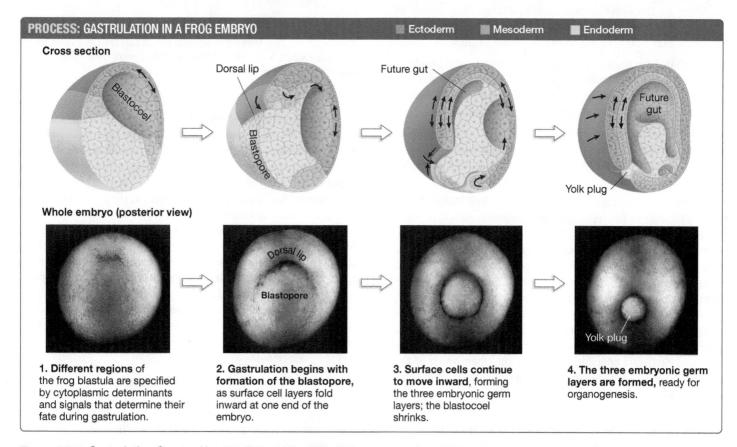

PROCESS: GASTRULATION IN A FROG EMBRYO   ▇ Ectoderm   ▇ Mesoderm   ▇ Endoderm

1. Different regions of the frog blastula are specified by cytoplasmic determinants and signals that determine their fate during gastrulation.

2. Gastrulation begins with formation of the blastopore, as surface cell layers fold inward at one end of the embryo.

3. Surface cells continue to move inward, forming the three embryonic germ layers; the blastocoel shrinks.

4. The three embryonic germ layers are formed, ready for organogenesis.

Figure 47.18 Gastrulation Creates Head-to-Tail and Back-to-Belly Axes and Three Germ Layers in the Embryo. Gastrulation in a frog is shown here. Important elements vary between species, but in every animal embryo, gastrulation requires the coordination of a remarkable set of cell movements and cell shape changes.

with a nontoxic dye. The dyed blocks were then pressed against the surface of blastula-stage embryos so that a small number of blastomeres became marked with dye. By allowing marked embryos to develop and then examining them at intervals during gastrulation, researchers were able to follow the movement of cells. Today, more sophisticated ways are used to mark individual cells and track them throughout the embryo, but the principle of marking and following cells remains the same.

Formation of Germ Layers The pattern of gastrulation varies widely among animal species, but the general outcome is the same: Gastrulation forms three embryonic tissue layers. A tissue is a group of cells that function as a unit (Chapter 39).

Most animal embryos have three primary (first) tissue layers: **(1) ectoderm** ("outside-skin"), **(2) mesoderm** ("middle-skin"), and **(3) endoderm** ("inner-skin"). These embryonic tissue layers are called **germ layers** because they give rise to all the organs and tissues of the adult. Figure 47.18 shows two views of how cell movements during gastrulation form the three germ layers in a frog embryo. Cells that will become ectoderm are shown in blue; cells destined to form mesoderm are shown in pink, and cells that will form endoderm are shown in yellow.

Step 1 The frog blastula contains a fluid-filled interior space called the blastocoel, which is present in most animal embryos.

Step 2 As gastrulation begins, an invagination (indentation) forms on the outer surface as cells change their shape. In frogs, this invagination starts out as a slit that eventually forms a circular opening known as the **blastopore.**

Step 3 Cells from the surface fold into the interior of the embryo through the blastopore, forming a tube that extends across the embryo. The tube will become the gut or digestive tract. The blastocoel is displaced and eventually disappears.

Step 4 The movement of cells into and across the embryo ultimately results in the formation of the three germ layers: endoderm on the inside, mesoderm in the middle, and ectoderm on the outside.

✔ If you understand gastrulation in a frog embryo, you should be able to describe how the ectoderm comes to completely cover the embryo.

Each germ layer forms certain tissues and organs. **Figure 47.19** shows some of the organs that the germ layers produce in a human. Remarkably, the correspondence between germ layer and organ type is the same in most animals, even those as distantly related as people and flies. Ectoderm forms the outer covering of the body and the nervous system; mesoderm produces muscle, most internal organs, and connective tissues such as bone and cartilage; endoderm produces the inner lining of the digestive tract and of the many organs that develop from the gut, such as the liver and lungs.

Creating Body Axes In addition to establishing the germ layers, gastrulation has another critical role: creating the body axes. In frogs, for example, the blastopore becomes the anus (posterior), and the opposite end of the gut tube becomes the mouth

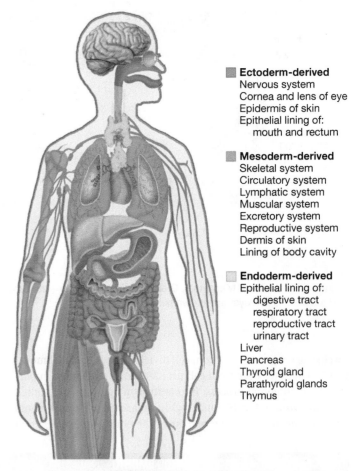

Ectoderm-derived
Nervous system
Cornea and lens of eye
Epidermis of skin
Epithelial lining of:
    mouth and rectum

Mesoderm-derived
Skeletal system
Circulatory system
Lymphatic system
Muscular system
Excretory system
Reproductive system
Dermis of skin
Lining of body cavity

Endoderm-derived
Epithelial lining of:
    digestive tract
    respiratory tract
    reproductive tract
    urinary tract
Liver
Pancreas
Thyroid gland
Parathyroid glands
Thymus

Figure 47.19 The Three Embryonic Germ Layers Give Rise to Different Adult Tissues and Organs. Each germ layer forms the same types of organs in all animals.

(anterior); the region where cells first move into the blastopore (see Figure 47.18) defines the dorsal, or back, side of the embryo, and the opposite region becomes the ventral side. In this way, the anterior–posterior and dorsal–ventral axes of the body become apparent as gastrulation proceeds.

However, well before they are revealed, the major body axes in frogs and many other animals are already at least partially determined. Determination occurs either through the action of regulatory molecules called cytoplasmic determinants or through interactions between cells, a process known as induction. Determination ultimately results in differential gene expression (see Chapter 21).

Current research on gastrulation is focused on understanding how cells coordinate their behaviors—especially the mechanisms responsible for cell movement, navigation, and changes in cell shape. Much remains to be learned.

Organogenesis

At the conclusion of gastrulation, the outside, inside, and middle layers are in place, and the positions of the head, tail, back, and belly are apparent—but this is only a start. For one thing, there are no organs within the embryo. The heart, brain, liver, and lungs all need to be formed from the germ layers, properly

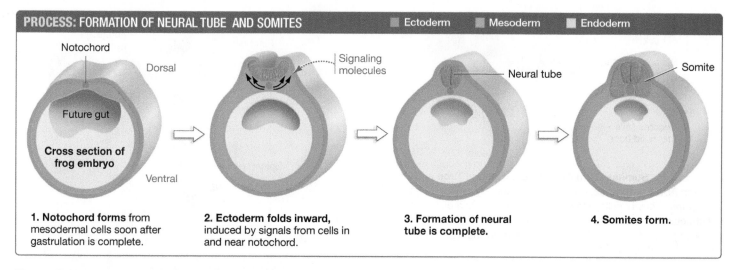

1. Notochord forms from mesodermal cells soon after gastrulation is complete.

2. Ectoderm folds inward, induced by signals from cells in and near notochord.

3. Formation of neural tube is complete.

4. Somites form.

Figure 47.20 The Notochord, Neural Tube, and Somites Form Early in Organogenesis. The figure shows a cross section of an early frog embryo at different stages of development.

positioned, and connected with other organs. **Organogenesis** ("organ-origin") gets these jobs done. During organogenesis, cells divide, move, differentiate, and assemble into tissues and organs using instructions encoded in the genome, with guidance from signals sent by other cells (see Chapter 21).

Formation of Notochord, Neural Tube, and Somites To understand the genesis of any organ, it is necessary to trace back through many earlier structures, some of which exist only in the embryo. Let's begin with the assembly of key embryonic structures: the notochord, the neural tube, and somites.

Figure 47.20 shows the developmental path to these structures. Although this figure illustrates what happens in a frog embryo, similar events occur in the embryos of chickens, humans, and all other vertebrates. First, a rod-like element called the **notochord** forms from mesodermal cells soon after gastrulation is complete (step 1). Molecular signals produced in the notochord induce the dorsal ectoderm to fold (step 2). This folding forms the **neural tube,** a tube of ectoderm that runs along the dorsal midline (middle back) of the embryo and gives rise to the brain and spinal cord (step 3).

As organogenesis continues, mesodermal cells near the notochord become organized into **somites** (step 4). Somites are paired blocks of mesodermal tissue that extend along either side of the dorsal midline of the embryo (**Figure 47.21**). Somite formation is a response to changes in the cell adhesion molecules that keep mesodermal cells attached to each other (see Chapter 11).

Note that the notochord shown in Figures 47.20 and 47.21 is unique to the group of animals called the chordates, which includes humans and all other vertebrates. In some species of chordates, the notochord is a long-lasting structure that functions as a simple internal skeleton—it stiffens the body and makes efficient swimming movements possible. But in vertebrates, such as chickens, frogs, and humans, the notochord is transient. It appears only in embryos. As organogenesis proceeds in vertebrates, many of the cells in the notochord undergo programmed cell death by apoptosis (see Chapter 21).

(a) Surface view

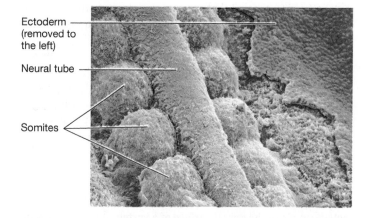

(b) Cross section

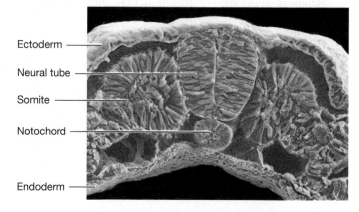

Figure 47.21 Somites Develop from Mesodermal Cells. (a) Surface view of chick embryo. **(b)** Cross section of chick embryo.

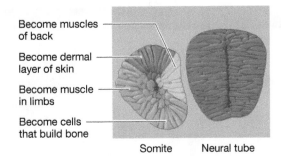

Become muscles of back

Become dermal layer of skin

Become muscle in limbs

Become cells that build bone

Somite   Neural tube

Figure 47.22 Somites Form Alongside the Neural Tube and Give Rise to Adult Structures. Each somite eventually breaks up into four populations of cells, each of which gives rise to a distinct set of structures in the adult. Signaling molecules sent from the neural tube, notochord, and nearby mesoderm specify the type of cell in each region of the somite.

Somites Are Precursors to Skin, Bone, and Muscle   Somites are transient structures, just like the notochord is. But unlike the notochord, somites produce many important structures of the adult. By marking somite cells and following them over time, researchers discovered that somites give rise not only to muscle but also to the lower (dermal) layer of the skin and much of the skeleton (**Figure 47.22**).

As organogenesis proceeds, somite cells break away in distinct groups that migrate to their final location in the developing embryo. Cell movements like these are critical to organogenesis. For example, once in their new locations, skeletal muscle precursor cells divide, begin expressing muscle-specific proteins, and eventually differentiate. The muscle cells later fuse to form long fibers within each muscle.

Formation of the Neural Tube and Central Nervous System Organogenesis of the central nervous system begins when the ectoderm along the dorsal surface of a vertebrate embryo begins folding to form the neural tube (Figure 47.20). As with somite development, molecular signaling from the notochord is crucial in determining which region of ectoderm will become part of the neural tube.

Once the neural tube is in place, organogenesis proceeds along two axes: the anterior–posterior axis and a radial axis that runs from the center of the neural tube to the periphery. The anterior portion of the neural tube contributes to the brain, and the posterior portion contributes to the spinal cord (**Figure 47.23**).

In the anterior portion, the neural tube swells out in specific regions and then is folded back on itself to form different brain structures. As this is occurring, stem cells (see Chapter 21) in the innermost layer of the neural tube divide. In every cell division, one daughter cell remains as a stem cell in the inner layer, and the other daughter cell migrates to the outermost layer of the neural tube, where it differentiates. The type of cell it becomes depends on when during development the stem cell divided. The resulting layers of different cell types are arranged along the radial axis of the neural tube like the layers of an onion. These layers of cell types are critical for both brain and spinal cord function, with each layer made up of a different type of cell.

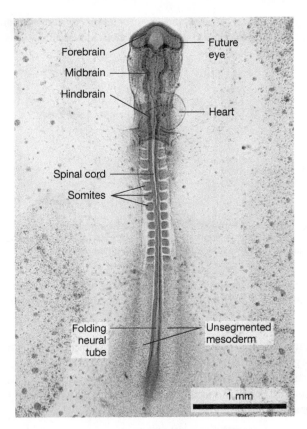

Forebrain

Midbrain

Hindbrain

Future eye

Heart

Spinal cord

Somites

Folding neural tube

Unsegmented mesoderm

1 mm

Figure 47.23 Development of Central Nervous System and Somites. This micrograph of a chick embryo was taken 33 hours into development. Development advances more rapidly in the anterior than the posterior. Brain regions have formed in the anterior even before the neural tube is fully formed in the posterior. Similarly, somites form from unsegmented mesoderm in an anterior-to-posterior wave.

Organogenesis is an elaborate, multistep process. Cells need to divide, specialize, change their shapes, migrate, and sometimes die for an organ to form. All these behaviors are ultimately the outcome of reading a shared set of genetic instructions in cell-specific ways by distinct sets of regulatory transcription factors. The whole process is controlled by signaling molecules and genetic regulatory cascades (see Chapter 21).

CHECK YOUR UNDERSTANDING

If you understand that ...

- Gastrulation consists of coordinated cell movements that reorganize the embryo and result in the formation of body axes and the embryonic germ layers.
- The notochord induces the formation of somites from surrounding mesoderm and the neural tube from overlying ectoderm.

✓ **You should be able to ...**

1. State when you would first be able to point out the future posterior and dorsal regions of a frog embryo, and explain what clues you would use to identify these regions.
2. **PROCESS OF SCIENCE** Design an experiment using chick or frog embryos to test the hypothesis that the notochord is needed for formation of the neural tube.

Answers are available in Appendix A.

Once the rudiments of organs are in place, development proceeds largely by their growth and refinement. But development doesn't occur in a vacuum. Particularly in mammals, the environment provided by the mother is critical. One class of signaling-molecule hormones plays a major role in creating an environment that supports development and reproduction. Let's take a look at how hormones control the maturation and function of the tissues that produce sperm and eggs.

47.5 The Role of Sex Hormones in Mammalian Reproduction

Recall that the sex hormones testosterone and estradiol are steroids; the latter belongs to a class of hormones known as estrogens (see Chapter 46). Testosterone and estradiol bind to receptors within the cytoplasm or nucleus of target cells. The resulting hormone–receptor complexes bind to DNA and trigger changes in gene expression.

Testosterone and estradiol are classified as gonadal hormones because they are produced in the gonads. Most testosterone is synthesized in specialized cells inside the testes; most estradiol and other estrogens are synthesized by cells that surround each developing egg in the ovaries. These surrounding cells form a structure called a **follicle.**

The sex hormones play a key role in three events:

1. Development of the reproductive tract and brain in embryos

2. Maturation of the reproductive tract during the transition from childhood to adulthood

3. Regulation of spermatogenesis and oogenesis in adults

To begin exploring the action of sex hormones, let's take a closer look at the transition from childhood to adulthood in humans.

Which Hormones Control Puberty?

In amphibians, the juvenile-to-adult transition is triggered by the hormone T₃ (triiodothyronine); in insects, it occurs in response to ecdysone (see Chapter 46). But in humans, this transition—called **puberty**—is directed by increased levels of testosterone in boys and estradiol in girls.

Gonadal hormone production is well regulated by the hypothalamic–pituitary axis (see Chapter 46). Recall that chemical signals from the hypothalamus control the release of regulatory hormones from the anterior pituitary gland, which then cause the release of hormones from other glands.

Puberty begins when the hypothalamus releases a hormone called **gonadotropin-releasing hormone (GnRH).** This hormone stimulates the anterior pituitary gland to release two hormones, luteinizing hormone (LH) and follicle-stimulating hormone (FSH), which enter the bloodstream and stimulate the testes and ovaries to secrete testosterone and estradiol, respectively (**Figure 47.24**). LH and FSH also stimulate gametogenesis.

The model in Figure 47.24 raises a question: What triggers increased GnRH secretion at the appropriate age? Although this question remains unanswered, there is some evidence that nutritional state is involved. For example:

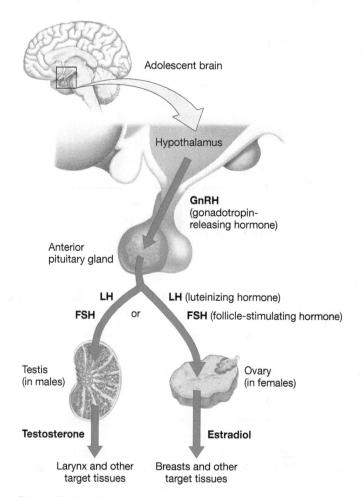

Figure 47.24 In Humans, Puberty Is Triggered by Hormones from the Hypothalamus and Anterior Pituitary.

✔ How does control of testosterone and estradiol secretion compare with control of cortisol release by the adrenal gland? (See Figure 46.14)

- The current average age for the onset of puberty in females in the United States is slightly over 12 years. During the eighteenth and nineteenth centuries, when the general nutritional state of the population was poorer, the average age was 17 years.

- Girls who have large fat stores tend to enter puberty earlier than do girls who are thin.

- Girls who exercise intensively and have little body fat, such as elite gymnasts and ballerinas, often have delayed onset of puberty.

If you recall how secretion of the adrenal hormone cortisol is controlled, however, you might suspect that the model of sex-hormone regulation in Figure 47.24 is simplified (see Chapter 46). Many hormones participate in negative feedback—also called feedback inhibition—meaning that the presence of the hormone inhibits the factor that triggers its release.

Do sex hormones participate in negative feedback? The short answer to this question is yes. To appreciate the details, let's investigate hormonal control of the human menstrual cycle.

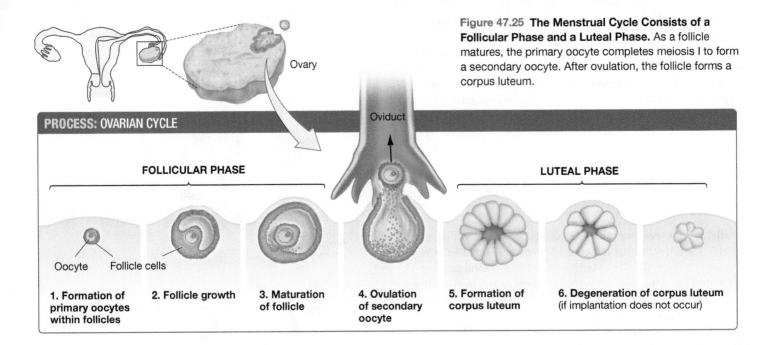

Figure 47.25 **The Menstrual Cycle Consists of a Follicular Phase and a Luteal Phase.** As a follicle matures, the primary oocyte completes meiosis I to form a secondary oocyte. After ovulation, the follicle forms a corpus luteum.

PROCESS: OVARIAN CYCLE

Ovary

Oviduct

FOLLICULAR PHASE

LUTEAL PHASE

Oocyte   Follicle cells

1. Formation of primary oocytes within follicles

2. Follicle growth

3. Maturation of follicle

4. Ovulation of secondary oocyte

5. Formation of corpus luteum

6. Degeneration of corpus luteum (if implantation does not occur)

Which Hormones Control the Menstrual Cycle in Humans?

Figure 47.25 illustrates the sequence of events in the human ovary during the **menstrual cycle,** a monthly reproductive cycle. Although the cycle's length varies among women, it averages about 28 days. In conjunction with changes in the ovary, as illustrated in the figure, the lining of the uterus undergoes a dramatic thickening followed by regression. Ultimately, if fertilization does not occur, part of the uterine lining sloughs off and is expelled through the vagina.

Day 1 in the menstrual cycle is marked by the beginning of **menstruation**—the expulsion of the uterine lining. The remainder of the cycle has two distinct phases:

1. *Follicular phase* A follicle matures during the **follicular phase,** which lasts an average of 14 days. Primary oocytes complete meiosis I during this phase. Ovulation occurs when the follicle is mature and releases its secondary oocyte into the oviduct.

2. *Luteal phase* The **luteal phase** begins with ovulation and also averages 14 days in length. Its name refers to the **corpus luteum** ("yellowish body"), a structure that forms from the ruptured follicle and degenerates if fertilization does not occur.

The regular occurrence of ovulation throughout the year makes humans extremely unusual among mammals. Although some mammals ovulate multiple times during the year, most ovulate only during a single prescribed breeding season—often in response to environmental cues such as changing photoperiod, and less often in response to cues from males.

In addition, only humans and other great apes menstruate. In the vast majority of mammals, the lining of the uterus is reabsorbed if pregnancy does not occur. The females of these mammals have an **estrous cycle** and are sexually receptive only during estrus—when they are said to be "in heat."

Whether an estrous cycle or a menstrual cycle occurs, the basic sequence of events, involving a follicular phase preceding ovulation and a luteal phase following ovulation, is shared among mammals. Hormonal control of estrous and menstrual cycles is also similar.

How Do Pituitary and Ovarian Hormones Interact during a Menstrual Cycle? By monitoring hormone concentrations in the blood or urine of a large number of women over the course of the menstrual cycle, researchers were able to document dramatic changes in the secretion of estradiol and several other hormones:

- LH and FSH are secreted by the anterior pituitary gland in response to GnRH.

- The steroid hormone **progesterone** is secreted along with estrogens, including estradiol, by the ovaries.

- In general, estradiol secretion surges during the follicular phase, and progesterone secretion surges during the luteal phase.

How are these changes regulated? Experiments helped establish that variations in the concentration of estradiol and progesterone affect the release of the pituitary hormones LH and FSH. Researchers worked with three volunteers whose ovaries had been removed because of cancerous growths or other problems. The women were receiving low doses of estradiol, which appeared to exert negative feedback on LH and FSH release.

But when the investigators injected the women with larger doses of estradiol or with progesterone, dramatic changes took place. For example, a large dose of estradiol stimulated a dramatic spike in LH levels. This result suggested that positive feedback was occurring and that estradiol's effect on anterior pituitary hormone secretion depends on the dose: High levels of estradiol increase the release of LH, whereas low doses of estradiol suppress it. In contrast, progesterone injections

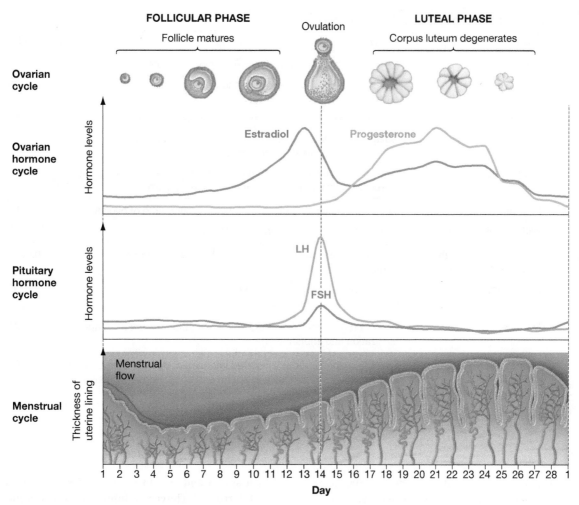

FOLLICULAR PHASE
Follicle matures

Ovulation

LUTEAL PHASE
Corpus luteum degenerates

Ovarian cycle

Ovarian hormone cycle

Estradiol

Progesterone

Hormone levels

Pituitary hormone cycle

LH

FSH

Hormone levels

Menstrual cycle

Menstrual flow

Thickness of uterine lining

1 2 3 4 5 6 7 8 9 10 11 12 13 14 15 16 17 18 19 20 21 22 23 24 25 26 27 28 1

Day

Figure 47.26 Hormones Regulate Events in the Human Menstrual Cycle.

appeared to inhibit both FSH and LH secretion, indicating that progesterone exerts only negative feedback on the pituitary hormones.

To summarize the interplay between LH, FSH, estradiol, and progesterone, let's start at day 1 in **Figure 47.26** and follow key events as the cycle progresses.

Days 1–7

- As the uterus sheds much of its lining, a follicle begins to develop in one ovary under the influence of FSH.
- The follicle secretes estradiol and a small amount of progesterone.
- While its levels are still relatively low, estradiol suppresses LH secretion through negative feedback.

Days 8–14

- As the follicle grows, its secretion of estradiol gradually increases. The increase in estradiol concentration stimulates mitosis and an increase in cell number in the uterine lining.
- The enlarged follicle produces large quantities of estradiol, which begin to exert positive feedback on LH secretion.
- Positive feedback results in a spike in the LH level, just after the estradiol concentration peaks.

- The LH spike triggers ovulation and ends the follicular phase.

Days 15–21

- As the corpus luteum develops from the remains of the ruptured follicle, it secretes large amounts of progesterone and small quantities of estradiol, in response to LH.
- The rise in progesterone concentration inhibits secretion of LH and FSH and activates the thickened uterine lining, creating a spongy tissue with a well-developed blood supply. In this way, progesterone fosters an environment that supports embryonic development if fertilization occurs.

Days 22–28

- If fertilization does not occur, the corpus luteum degenerates.
- The progesterone level falls as the corpus luteum shrinks.
- The decline in progesterone level causes the thickened lining of the uterus to degenerate. This in turn causes the menstrual bleeding that marks the first day of the next cycle.
- GnRH, LH, and FSH are released from the inhibitory control that progesterone exerts.
- The FSH level rises, and a new menstrual cycle begins.

The interplay between ovarian and pituitary hormones is similar in other mammal species that have been studied to date.

Type	Name	Mode of Action	Percent Effectiveness*
Barrier methods	Condom	Covers penis and prevents sperm from entering uterus.	85
	Female condom	Covers labia, vagina, and cervix and prevents sperm from entering uterus.	79
	Diaphragm	Covers cervix and prevents sperm from entering uterus.	84
	Sponge	Covers cervix and prevents sperm from entering uterus; also contains a molecule that immobilizes sperm.	84
	Spermicide	Foam or jelly covers cervix and prevents sperm from entering uterus; contains a molecule that immobilizes sperm.	71
Behavioral methods	Rhythm method	Couple refrains from vaginal intercourse around time of ovulation.	80
	Withdrawal	Man withdraws penis before ejaculation.	73
Hormone-based methods	The pill, the patch, the ring, the shot, the implant	Provides continuous or cyclical delivery of progesterone or progesterone plus estradiol.	92 to 99.9[†]
	Emergency contraception	Delivers progesterone or progesterone plus estradiol after unprotected vaginal intercourse.	92
Pregnancy termination	Mifepristone	Blocks progesterone receptors so menstruation occurs even after fertilization and implantation.	92
Other	Intrauterine device (IUD)	Small, T-shaped structure inserted into uterus; induces uterus to produce substances hostile to sperm and eggs. Some IUDs also secrete hormones.	99

*"Percent Effectiveness" indicates the average percentage of women who do not become pregnant during one year of typical use.

[†]Depends on delivery system used.

Manipulating Hormone Levels to Prevent Pregnancy Data on hormonal control of the menstrual cycle opened new avenues in birth control research. Specifically, researchers found that manipulating levels of progesterone and estradiol can prevent ovulation and serve as a relatively safe and effective method of **contraception,** or preventing unwanted pregnancies.

Hormone-based contraceptive methods deliver synthetic versions of progesterone or of progesterone and estradiol. These hormones suppress the release of GnRH, FSH, and LH through negative feedback.

In the United States, birth control pills are the most widely used contraceptive method. Hormone-containing pills are taken for three weeks and then stopped for one week to allow menstruation to occur. Other popular hormonal contraceptives include injections and hormone-secreting patches and implants. All hormonal contraceptives *prevent* pregnancy by preventing ovulation, but they do not terminate pregnancies that have already begun; contrary to popular belief, this statement is also true for emergency contraception (the "morning-after pill").

As **Table 47.2** indicates, hormone-based methods are just one of several approaches to preventing pregnancy. Most other methods work mainly by preventing sperm from contacting the oocyte.

The "Percent Effectiveness" column on the far right of the table indicates the average percentage of women who do not become pregnant during one year of typical use of that method. Effectiveness usually increases dramatically if couples use a method exactly as specified for optimal efficacy during every episode of sexual intercourse.

When sperm and egg do unite successfully, the menstrual cycle is interrupted. The corpus luteum does not degenerate, progesterone and estradiol levels stay high, and menstruation does not occur. Instead, the woman is now pregnant.

CHECK YOUR UNDERSTANDING

If you understand that ...

- During the follicular phase of the menstrual cycle, FSH and LH stimulate the follicle to develop and secrete estradiol, which prepares the uterine lining to support an embryo.
- During the luteal phase, progesterone protects the uterine lining. If fertilization does not occur, the progesterone level drops, and the lining is shed.

✔ You should be able to ...

1. Describe the function of FSH, and explain why the FSH level increases at the end of the menstrual cycle.
2. Predict the consequences of a drug that inhibits the release of FSH.

Answers are available in Appendix A.

47.6 Pregnancy and Birth in Mammals

Viviparity allows the mother to provide a warm, protected environment for offspring during early development. Oviparous species that guard or incubate their eggs also provide warm, safe

(a) Brushtail possum shortly after birth

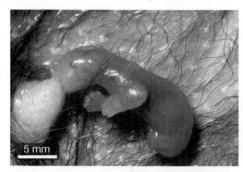

(b) 1.5 months after birth

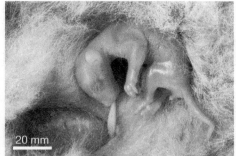

(c) 3.5 months after birth

Figure 47.27 Marsupials Trade a Long Gestation Period for a Long Lactation Period. Compared to eutherians, marsupials—like this brushtail possum—spend a short time developing in the uterus and a relatively long time being fed milk after birth.

surroundings for their young. Any investment that parents make in an offspring comes at a cost, however: The more a mother invests in each offspring, the fewer offspring she can produce.

Pregnancy and **lactation**—providing milk that nourishes offspring after birth—represent some of the most extreme forms of parental care known in animals. And in some mammal species, parental care continues long after lactation ends. Humans, for example, are largely or completely dependent on their parents for protection and nutrition until puberty or young adulthood.

Let's examine how mammals make this investment, starting with marsupials and then turning to eutherian mammals.

Gestation and Development in Marsupials

Marsupials are one of the three major monophyletic groups of mammals (see Chapter 32). In marsupials, the corpus luteum is not maintained, and the young are ejected from the mother's body at the end of the estrous cycle. As a result, they are far less developed at birth than are the young of eutherian mammals, which undergo a lengthier **gestation**—the developmental period that takes place inside the mother's uterus.

However, the jaws, gut, lungs, and forelimbs of a newly born marsupial are relatively well developed at birth. That allows the offspring to climb from its mother's vagina to a nipple, which is usually enclosed in a pouch created by a flap of skin (**Figure 47.27**). The offspring clamps onto the nipple and continues to develop, fed by the mother's milk.

Even after growing large enough to leave the pouch and begin moving and feeding on its own, the offspring will return to the pouch for protection. Marsupial mothers invest a great deal in their offspring, even though a relatively short period of development takes place in the uterus.

Major Events during Human Pregnancy

Marsupials and eutherians differ sharply in terms of how long the offspring is retained inside the mother's uterus. Let's consider humans as a model organism in eutherian reproduction.

When a secondary oocyte is released from the human ovary, the cell is viable for less than 24 hours. Human sperm, in contrast, remain capable of fertilizing an egg for up to five days.

Therefore, sexual intercourse in humans must occur less than five days before ovulation or immediately after ovulation for pregnancy to result.

Although an ejaculation may deposit hundreds of millions of sperm in the female reproductive tract, most die as they travel through the uterus. Only 100 to 300 sperm actually succeed in reaching the oviduct, where fertilization takes place.

Implantation Smooth muscle contractions in the oviduct gradually move the developing zygote toward the uterus. When the blastocyst arrives at the uterus, it undergoes **implantation**—meaning that it becomes embedded in the thickened, vascularized wall of the uterus. It will stay in the uterus for approximately 270 days (9 months).

Once the embryo is implanted in the uterine lining, its cells begin synthesizing and secreting the hormone **human chorionic gonadotropin (hCG),** which prevents the corpus luteum from degenerating; this hormone is later produced in larger quantities by the placenta. As long as hCG is present, the ovary continues secreting progesterone, and the menstrual cycle is arrested. Some hCG is excreted in the mother's urine and is used as an indicator of pregnancy in pregnancy tests.

The First Trimester Human gestation is divided into 3-month stages called trimesters (see **Figure 47.28** on page 1004). Not long after implantation is complete, mass movements of cells result in the formation of the three germ layers. By 8 weeks into gestation, these tissue layers have differentiated into the various organs and systems of the body. Also by this time, the heart has begun pumping blood through the circulatory system. The embryo at this stage is called a **fetus**.

Early in the first trimester, the trophoblast cells (see Figure 47.17) contribute to several important membranes. One of these membranes, the **amnion,** completely surrounds the embryo. The amnion eventually fills with amniotic fluid, which provides the embryo with a protective cushion.

Another key event in the first trimester is the formation of the placenta, which starts to develop on the uterine wall at the time of implantation. The placenta contains a dense supply of blood vessels from the mother, which provide nutrition for the growing

(a) 1st trimester   **(b)** 2nd trimester   **(c)** 3rd trimester

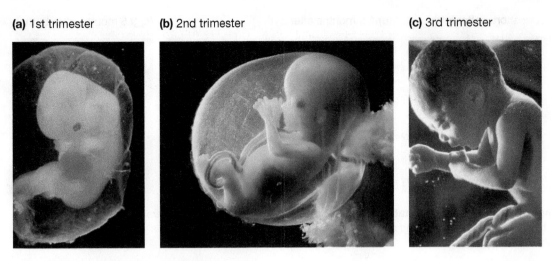

Figure 47.28 **Human Gestation Is Divided into Three Trimesters.**

fetus. Arteries transport blood from the circulatory system of the fetus, through the **umbilical cord,** to an extensive capillary bed in the placenta. This capillary bed provides a large surface area for the exchange of gases, nutrients, and wastes between maternal and fetal blood, even though the maternal and fetal blood do not commingle.

The placenta secretes a variety of hormones, including large amounts of **progesterone** and estrogens, into the maternal bloodstream. Because these hormones suppress the release of GnRH, LH, and FSH through negative feedback, they prevent the maturation and ovulation of additional follicles. By the end of the first trimester, the placenta is producing more than enough progesterone to replace the amount that had been produced by the corpus luteum, which has begun degenerating by this time. In essence, the placenta takes over from the corpus luteum in secreting the hormones required to maintain the pregnancy.

✔ If you understand how hormones influence pregnancy, you should be able to explain why women who produce low levels of progesterone from the corpus luteum are prone to miscarriage.

The Second and Third Trimesters After the fetal organs and placenta form during the first trimester, the rest of development consists mainly of growth (Figures 47.28b and 47.28c). During the last weeks of pregnancy, the brain and lungs undergo particularly dramatic growth and development. If a baby is born prematurely, intervention may be required to keep the baby alive until the lungs can complete their development.

The machinery and level of hospital care required by premature infants emphasize just how superbly adapted mothers are for nourishing a growing fetus in the uterus. It costs hundreds of thousands of dollars for health care providers to do what mothers do naturally in the last trimester. Let's take a closer look at this critical aspect of pregnancy.

How Does the Mother Nourish the Fetus?

In oviparous and ovoviviparous species, mothers produce relatively large eggs that contain all of the nutrients and fluids that the embryo needs for development until hatching. But in some viviparous species, eggs are relatively small and contain almost no nutrients.

In species such as humans, the developing embryo depends on the mother's body for oxygen, chemical energy in the form of sugars, amino acids, and other raw materials for growth, and waste removal. What physiological changes occur in human mothers to meet these demands?

Oxygen Exchange between Mother and Fetus During pregnancy, a mother's respiratory and circulatory systems change in ways that increase the efficiency of gas exchange and nutrient transfer with the fetus. For example:

- A woman's total blood volume expands by as much as 50 percent during pregnancy.

- To accommodate the increase in blood volume, maternal blood vessels dilate (widen), and blood pressure drops.

- The mother's heart enlarges and beats faster, increasing her cardiac output by almost 50 percent.

- The mother's breathing rate and breathing volume increase to meet the fetus's demand for oxygen and removal of carbon dioxide.

In addition, important adaptations in the placenta increase the efficiency of gas exchange between the mother and the fetus. In many species, such as sheep, maternal and fetal blood flow through the placenta in a countercurrent fashion. Countercurrent flows maintain gradients that increase the efficiency of diffusion or other types of exchange (see Chapter 39).

Countercurrent flow does not occur in the human placenta. Instead, another mechanism increases the efficiency of exchange between mother and fetus. Maternal arteries in humans empty into a space at the junction of the maternal and fetal portions of the placenta. This space is packed with small projections called villi, which contain the fetal blood vessels. Thus, a large surface area of fetal tissue is bathed with highly oxygenated maternal blood. The fetal villi are analogous to the villi of the small intestine (see Chapters 39 and 41), which provide a large surface area for nutrient absorption.

Toxic Chemicals Can Be Transferred from Mother to Fetus

Mothers and embryos exchange more than nutrients and wastes—they can also exchange dangerous substances. For example, children of mothers who drink alcohol during pregnancy have a higher risk for hyperactivity, severe learning disabilities, and depression. Collectively, these disorders are termed **fetal alcohol syndrome (FAS).** Brain scans of babies born with FAS reveal numerous structural abnormalities as well as reduced brain volume. These irregularities are thought to be responsible for dramatic reductions in IQ and other measures of intelligence and learning ability. On the basis of results like these, public health officials strongly advise pregnant women not to drink *any* alcohol.

Birth

Although the mechanisms responsible for initially triggering the birthing process are not completely understood, the posterior pituitary hormone oxytocin is important in stimulating smooth-muscle cells in the uterine wall to begin contractions (see Chapter 46). The contractions that expel the fetus from the uterus constitute **labor.**

Figure 47.29 shows the three stages of the birthing process in humans.

1. The uterus initially contracts at relatively low frequency. The opening in the cervix begins to dilate. Once it is fully dilated, uterine contractions become more forceful, longer lasting, and more frequent.

2. The baby is expelled through the cervix and the vagina.

3. After the baby is delivered, the placenta remains attached to the uterine wall. At this point, caregivers clamp and cut the umbilical cord, which connects the child and the placenta. When the mother delivers the placenta and accompanying membranes, birth is complete.

Although this description sounds straightforward, in reality a large number of complications are possible. For example, one study on Swedish mothers showed that in the 1700s, approximately 1.4 mothers died for every 100 infants successfully delivered. In most cases, the cause of death was blood loss or infection following delivery. In the late 1800s, the introduction of hand-washing practices by midwives caused this number to drop dramatically. The advent of antibiotics and blood transfusions in the twentieth century further reduced maternal mortality, which is now less than 0.007 percent. Improved nutrition, sanitation, and medical care have also reduced infant mortality rates in many countries.

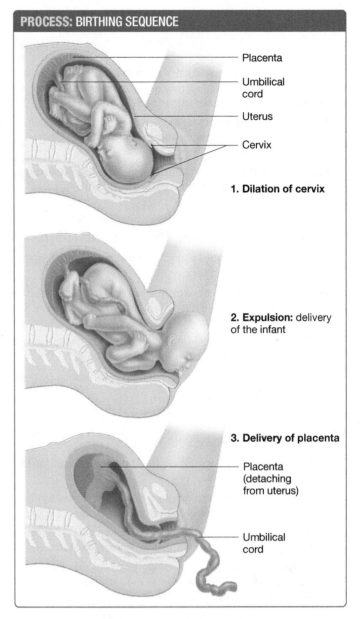

PROCESS: BIRTHING SEQUENCE

— Placenta
— Umbilical cord
— Uterus
— Cervix

1. Dilation of cervix

2. Expulsion: delivery of the infant

3. Delivery of placenta

— Placenta (detaching from uterus)

— Umbilical cord

Figure 47.29 Human Birth Occurs in Three Stages.

The huge decline in the rate of death associated with childbirth qualifies as one of the great triumphs of modern medicine. However, the mortality rates for mothers and infants remain high in many developing nations that lack sterile facilities and antibiotics.

CHAPTER 47   REVIEW

For media, go to MasteringBiology (MB)

47.1 Asexual and Sexual Reproduction

- Asexual reproduction produces offspring that have genetic material from only one parent. Sexual reproduction involves the fusion of haploid gametes from different parents during fertilization.

- Asexual reproduction may be favored in constant environments, whereas sexual reproduction may be favored in changing environments, or when food availability is low and availability of mates is high.

- In human males, spermatogenesis is continuous throughout adult life, but in human females, all primary oocytes are formed early in development. Meiosis of oocytes is arrested for long periods of time, and cell division during meiosis is so unequal in females that just one egg—not four—is produced from each primary oocyte.

47.2 Reproductive Structures and Their Functions

- In humans, the male reproductive system includes structures specialized for producing and storing sperm, synthesizing other components of semen, or transporting and delivering semen.

- The female reproductive system includes structures specialized for producing eggs, receiving sperm, and nourishing offspring during early development.

- Depending on their species, females may lay eggs (oviparity) or retain them and give birth to live offspring (viviparity).

47.3 Fertilization and Egg Development

- Fertilization is external in many aquatic animals but internal in almost all terrestrial species.

- When sperm competition occurs, males have large testes relative to their body size, and the last male to mate usually fathers a disproportionately large number of offspring.

- Fertilization is a multistep process that allows haploid sperm and eggs to fuse, forming a diploid zygote.

- Multiple mechanisms prevent polyspermy, fertilization by more than one sperm.

47.4 Embryonic Development

- The major stages of embryonic development are cleavage, gastrulation, and organogenesis.

- Cleavage is the stage of rapid cell divisions that follows fertilization and changes the fertilized egg (zygote) into a mass of cells.

- During gastrulation, coordinated cell movements and shape changes transform the cleavage-stage embryo into a gastrula.

- Gastrulation establishes the three germ layers (ectoderm, mesoderm, and endoderm) as well as the anterior–posterior and dorsal–ventral body axes.

- The germ layers give rise to distinct organs in the adult, and each germ layer produces organs of similar types in all animals.

- Organogenesis is the formation of tissues and organs from the germ layers.

- Early in vertebrate organogenesis, cells in the notochord release signals that induce the formation of two structures: (1) the neural tube—precursor to the brain and spinal cord—from overlying ectoderm, and (2) somites—precursors to muscle, bone, and the lower layer of skin—from nearby mesoderm.

47.5 The Role of Sex Hormones in Mammalian Reproduction

- In mammals, GnRH from the hypothalamus triggers the release of FSH and LH from the anterior pituitary gland. FSH and LH regulate the production of the gonadal hormones testosterone and estradiol in the testes and ovaries, respectively.

- During the human menstrual cycle, progesterone exerts negative feedback and estradiol exerts both positive and negative feedback on the production of FSH and LH. Interactions between the pituitary and ovarian hormones are responsible for regulating cyclical changes in the ovaries and uterus.

47.6 Pregnancy and Birth in Mammals

- If fertilization occurs, the developing embryo and placenta secrete the hormone hCG, which arrests the menstrual cycle and allows pregnancy to continue.

- During the first trimester, the embryo becomes implanted in the thickened uterine wall, the placenta forms, and organs develop.

- During pregnancy, the mother's blood volume, heart rate, and breathing rate increase. Nutrients and gases are exchanged efficiently in the placenta.

Answers are available in Appendix A

✓ TEST YOUR KNOWLEDGE

1. What term describes the mode of asexual reproduction in which offspring develop from unfertilized eggs?
   a. parthenogenesis   c. regeneration
   b. budding   d. fission

2. In sperm competition, what is "second-male advantage"?
   a. the observation that when females mate with two males, each male fertilizes the same number of eggs
   b. the observation that when females mate with two males, the second male fertilizes most of the eggs
   c. the observation that females routinely mate with at least two males before laying eggs or becoming pregnant
   d. the observation that accessory fluids prevent matings by second males—for example, by forming copulatory plugs

3. What happens during cleavage?
   a. The neural tube forms.
   b. The inner cell mass of the blastocyst begins dividing rapidly.
   c. The zygote divides rapidly without growth, forming a mass of cells.
   d. Massive movements of cells form the three germ layers.

4. True or false: The corpus luteum is retained upon implantation due to the presence of the hormone human chorionic gonadotropin (hCG).

✓ TEST YOUR UNDERSTANDING

5. Summarize the experimental evidence that *Daphnia* require three cues to trigger sexual reproduction. Discuss what these cues indicate about the environment.

6. Many frogs and mice are similar in size, yet a frog egg is vastly larger than a mouse egg. Propose a plausible explanation for this difference in the egg size.

7. How do spermatogenesis and oogenesis in humans differ with respect to numbers of cells produced, gamete size, and timing of the second meiotic division?

8. Give examples of negative feedback and positive feedback in hormonal control of the human menstrual cycle. Why can high estradiol levels be considered a "readiness" signal from a follicle?

✔ TEST YOUR PROBLEM-SOLVING SKILLS

9. **PROCESS OF SCIENCE** Propose an experiment to test the hypothesis that cells from only one region of a frog blastula form the ectoderm. What results from this experiment would support this hypothesis?

10. **QUANTITATIVE** The table below shows the BMI z-score of pre-pubertal and post-pubertal girls at three ages. The BMI z-score is a relative measure of body mass index (BMI; see Chapter 41) that takes into account age. Higher values represent heavier individuals for a given height.

BMI z-score

Age	Pre-pubertal	Post-pubertal
11	−0.22	0.75
12	−0.28	0.52
13	−0.56	0.34

DATA: Anderson, S. E., G. E. Dallal, and A. Must. 2003. *Pediatrics* 111: 844–850.

Which of the following conclusions can you draw from the data?
a. At a given age, there are more girls with low BMI z-scores than with high BMI z-scores.
b. At a given age, girls with high BMI z-scores are more likely to have begun puberty than girls with low BMI z-scores.
c. Girls 11, 12, and 13 years of age are equally likely to have begun puberty.
d. There is no relationship between BMI z-score and age of beginning puberty.

✔ PUT IT ALL TOGETHER: Case Study

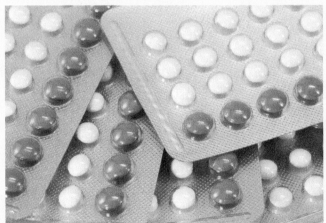

How does the birth control pill prevent pregnancy?

In the 1960s, the U.S. Food and Drug Administration approved a contraceptive that allowed women to plan desired pregnancies and prevent unwanted pregnancies. Oral hormonal contraception ("the pill") uses synthetic hormones similar in structure to progesterone and/or estradiol. What is the pill's mechanism of action?

11. Which of the following is the most effective form of contraception?
a. condom
b. diaphragm
c. withdrawal
d. the pill

12. Use your knowledge of the hormonal regulation of reproduction to predict the effect of a daily synthetic progesterone pill on (a) pituitary secretion of LH and FSH, and (b) ovarian secretion of estradiol and progesterone.

13. **QUANTITATIVE** Scientists confirmed the pill's mechanism of action by measuring plasma hormone levels in women before and after they started using the pill (* means $P < 0.05$, ** means $P < 0.01$, and *** means $P < 0.001$; see BioSkills 3). Do the data shown below support the hypothesis that the pill affects hormonal signaling?

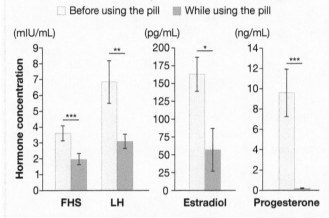

Source: Gaspard, U. J., M. A. Romus, D. Gillain, et al. 1983. Contraception 27: 577–590.

14. Use the information above to explain how the pill affects each of the following: (a) maturation of a follicle, (b) thickening of the uterine lining during the follicular phase, (c) probability of ovulation, and (d) volume of menstrual fluid.

15. **CAUTION** Use Table 47.2 to compare and contrast the mechanisms of action of emergency contraception and mifepristone to that of the pill. Which methods act as contraception and which act to terminate a pregnancy? Explain.

16. **SOCIETY** Imagine that four different contraceptives are under development. One blocks ovulation, one blocks fertilization, one blocks cleavage, and one blocks implantation. In the United States, which contraceptive is likely to be the least controversial to bring to market? Why?

MasteringBiology®

Students Go to MasteringBiology for assignments, the eText, and the Study Area with animations, practice tests, and activities.
Professors Go to MasteringBiology for automatically graded tutorials and questions that you can assign to your students, plus Instructor Resources.

Answers

Chapter 1

IN-TEXT QUESTIONS AND EXERCISES

p. 3 Fig. 1.2 *analyze* If Pasteur had done either of the things listed, he would have had more than one variable in his experiment. This would allow critics to claim that he got different results because of the differences in broth types or flask types—not the difference in exposure to preexisting cells. The results would not be definitive.

p. 5 CYU *understand* Over time, traits such as a beak shaped to retrieve a certain food type that is especially abundant in a particular habitat will become increasingly frequent in the population.

p. 7 Making Models 1.1 *apply* See Figure A1.1. Molds and other fungi are more closely related to green algae because they differ from land plants at two positions (5 and 8, counting from left to right) but differ from green algae at only one position (8).

p. 8 Fig. 1.7 *apply* The eukaryotic cell is roughly 10 times the size of the prokaryotic cell.

p. 9 CYU *analyze* From the sequence data provided, species A and B differ only in one letter of the DNA sequence (position 10 from left). Species C differs from species A and B in four letters (positions 1, 2, 9, and 10). Species A and B would be closest on a phylogenetic tree since they appear to be more closely related, while species C is more distantly related.

p. 10 Fig. 1.8 *apply* Male giraffes spend most of their time feeding on vegetation about 3.25 meters high; females spend most of their time feeding at about 2.5 meters.

p. 12 Fig. 1.10 *apply* If you used just one ant, the interpretation of the experiment would not likely change, but your confidence in the conclusions drawn would be reduced.

p. 13 CYU *create* The key here is to test predation rates during the hottest part of the day (when desert ants actually feed) versus other parts of the day. The experiment would best be done in the field, where natural predators are present. One approach would be to capture a large number of ants, divide the group in two, and measure predation rates (number of ants killed per hour) when they are placed in normal habitat during the hottest part of the day versus an hour before (or after). You would need to include a control group—ants outside during the hottest part of the day. If you didn't include a control, a critic could argue that predation

did or did not occur because of your experimental setup or manipulation, not because of differences in temperature. You also would need to make sure that there is no difference in ant body size or walking speed, how ants were captured and maintained, or other traits that might make the ants in the two groups more or less susceptible to predators. They should also be put out in the same habitat, so the presence of predators is the same in the two treatments.

✔ TEST YOUR KNOWLEDGE

1. *understand* d **2.** *remember* d **3.** *remember* b **4.** *analyze* Yes. Long necks could be advantageous for more than one reason.

✔ TEST YOUR UNDERSTANDING

5. *apply* They would need to show that the entity they discovered replicates, processes information, acquires and uses energy, and is cellular, and that its populations evolve. **6.** *understand* a **7.** *understand* Individuals with certain advantageous traits are selected, in the sense that they produce the most offspring. **8.** *understand* A null hypothesis specifies what a researcher should observe when the hypothesis being tested isn't correct.

✔ TEST YOUR PROBLEM-SOLVING SKILLS

9. *evaluate* In everyday English, the word "theory" is often used to mean a hunch or speculation about how something works. But in science, the meaning is different. A scientific theory is not just an educated guess, hunch, or speculation—it is an idea whose validity can be tested through data collection. The theory of evolution has been validated by large bodies of observational and experimental data. This theory is a scientific explanation that is so well established that no new evidence is likely to alter it. **10.** *analyze* Yes, they are likely to evolve differently. In areas of the world where HIV infection rates are high, the genes (heritable traits) that confer resistance to HIV should increase in the population over time.

✔ PUT IT ALL TOGETHER: Case Study

11. *analyze* The flow of information is from DNA to RNA to protein. Physical traits like leaf shape and size are a product of the proteins produced. **12.** *analyze* The Latin root *tri* means "three" and *foli* means "leaf." The name is appropriate because, as the photo shows, the vine consists of clusters of three-part leaves along its length.

13. *analyze* There is statistically significantly less leaf damage in the vines on leafy host trees compared to that in vines creeping on the ground or vines on bare tree trunks. This result suggests that growing among other leaves protects the vine from predation by plant eaters. But the data do not directly show that leaf mimicry reduces herbivory. To test whether mimicry reduces herbivory, researchers would need to move vines to another host and measure herbivory on vines with similar or dissimilar host leaf shapes. **14.** *analyze* If different vines were exposed to different light levels, this would add another variable to the study. Under these varying conditions, changes in the herbivory index might be due to light availability. **15.** *apply* Bare tree trunks were included in the study as a control to show that the vine was not protected merely by climbing up a support to avoid predators on the ground. **16.** *understand* "Fitness" refers to an individual's ability to survive and reproduce.

BIG PICTURE Doing Biology

p. 16 CYU (1) *understand* Biologists design and carry out a study, either observational or experimental, to test their ideas. As part of this process, they state their ideas as a hypothesis and null hypothesis and make predictions. They analyze and interpret the data they have gathered, and determine whether the data support their ideas. If not, they revisit their ideas and come up with an alternative hypothesis and design another study to test these new predictions. **(2)** *understand* There are many possible examples. Consider, for example, the experiment on navigation in foraging desert ants (Chapter 1). In addition to testing how the ants use information on stride length and number to calculate how far they are from the nest (multicellular organism and population levels), researchers also could test how the "pedometer" works at the level of cells and molecules. **(3)** *analyze* A hypothesis is a testable statement to explain a specific phenomenon or a set of observations. The word "theory" refers to proposed explanations for very broad patterns in nature that are supported by a wide body of evidence. A theory serves as a framework for the development of new hypotheses. **(4)** *analyze* The next step is to relate your findings to existing theories and the current scientific literature, and then to communicate your findings to colleagues through informal conversations, presentations at scientific meetings, and eventually publication in peer-reviewed journals.

Bioskills

BIOSKILL 1; p. 21 CYU (1) *apply* $5.0 \text{ km} \times 0.62 \text{ mile/km} = 3.1 \text{ miles}$ **(2)** *apply* $\frac{5}{9}(98.6 \, °F - 32) = 37 \, °C$ **(3)** *apply* Multiply your weight in pounds by 1 kg/2.2 pounds (0.45). **(4)** *apply* 1 gallon $\times$ 4 quarts/gallon $\times$ 1 L/1.06 quarts = 4L **(5)** *apply* The answer (4.6) has 2 significant figures. When you multiply, the answer can have no more significant figures than the least accurate measurement—in this case, 1.6.

BIOSKILL 2; p. 24 CYU (1) *apply* about 18 percent **(2)** *apply* a dramatic drop (almost 10 percent) **(3)** *analyze* No, they

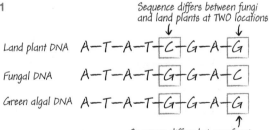

Figure A1.1

Sequence differs between fungi
and land plants at TWO locations

Land plant DNA   A—T—A—T—C—G—A—G

Fungal DNA   A—T—A—T—G—G—A—C

Green algal DNA   A—T—A—T—G—G—A—G

Sequence differs between fungi
and green algae at ONE location

would not be different. Because the data values in a bar chart are discrete or categorical rather than continuous, their order of presentation does not matter (though it's convenient to arrange the bars in a way that reinforces the overall message). **(4)** *apply* The most common height is 68 inches. 68 inches × 2.54 cm/inch = 170 cm. **(5)** *apply* The dependent variable is the percentage of children. The independent variable is the type of response. See Figure AB.1.

BIOSKILL 3; p. 26 CYU (1) *analyze* Test 2, the estimate based on the larger sample, is likely to have a smaller standard error. The more replicates or observations you have, the more precise your estimate of the average should be. **(2)** *analyze* The hummingbirds displayed a statistically significant preference for sucrose over both water and aspartame (*** means $P < 0.001$), but they consumed solutions of sucrose and erythritol with equal preference (no asterisk means no significant difference).

BIOSKILL 4; p. 27 CYU (1) *apply* ½ × ½ × ½ × ½ = ¹⁄₁₆ **(2)** *apply* ⅛ + ⅛ + ⅛ = ½

BIOSKILL 5; p. 27 CYU (1) *understand* exponential **(2)** *apply* $\ln N_t = \ln N_0 + rt$ **(3)** *apply* $pH = -\log_{10}(2.75 \times 10^{-4}) = 3.56$ **(4)** *apply* $[H^+] = 10^{-5.43} = 0.00000372 = 3.72 \times 10^{-6}$

BIOSKILL 6; p. 28 Fig. B6.1 *understand* DNA and RNA are acids that tend to lose a proton in solution, giving them a negative charge.

p. 30 Fig. B6.4 *apply* The probe must be single-stranded so that it will bind by complementary base pairing to the target DNA, and it must be labeled so that it can be detected. The probe will base-pair only with fragments that include a sequence complementary to the probe's sequence. A probe with the sequence 5· AATCG 3· will bind to the region of the target DNA that has the sequence 5· CGATT 3· as shown here:

5· AATCG 3·
3· TCCGGTTAGCATTACCATTTT 5·

p. 31 CYU (1) *analyze* The lane with no band comes from a sample where no PCR product was amplified. The faint band has very few copies of PCR product, while the bright band has many. **(2)** *evaluate* Understanding a molecule's structure is often critical to understanding how the molecule functions in cells.

BIOSKILL 7; p. 32 CYU (1) *understand* size, shape, and/or density. **(2)** *apply* Mitochondria, because they are larger than ribosomes.

BIOSKILL 8; p. 33 CYU *understand* A decrease in transmittance usually results in an increase in absorbance.

BIOSKILL 9; p. 36 CYU *analyze* It doesn't necessarily mean that the cell lacks mitochondria. It's possible that no

mitochondria happened to be present in this extremely thin section sliced through the cell.

BIOSKILL 10; p. 36 Fig. B10.1 *apply* No—each type of cDNA would be represented many times, because many copies of each type of mRNA were present in the cells, and many bacterial cells were used to prepare the library.

p. 37 Fig. B10.3 *analyze* The polymerase will begin at the 3· end of each primer. On the top strand in part (b), it will move to the left; on the bottom strand, it will move to the right. As always, synthesis is in the 5· → 3· direction.

p. 41 CYU (1) *apply* ddNTPs lack the —OH (hydroxyl) group on the 3· carbon of deoxyribose that is required to extend the DNA chain during synthesis. **(2)** *analyze* (a) Primer 1b binds to the top right strand and would allow DNA polymerase to synthesize the top strand across the target gene. Primer 1a, however, binds to the top left strand and would allow DNA polymerase to synthesize the top strand *away* from the target gene. Primer 2a binds to the bottom left strand and would allow DNA polymerase to synthesize the bottom strand across the target gene. Primer 2b, however, binds to the bottom right strand and would allow DNA polymerase to synthesize the bottom strand away from the target gene. (b) Tell her to use primer 1b with primer 2a. **(3)** *apply* Start with a microarray containing exons from a large number of human genes. Isolate mRNAs from brain tissue and liver tissue, and make labeled cDNAs from each. Probe the microarray with both cDNAs, and record where binding occurs. Binding events identify genes that are transcribed in each type of tissue. Compare the results to identify genes that are expressed in brain but not liver, or in liver but not brain.

BIOSKILL 11; p. 45 CYU (1) *analyze* Because the artificial conditions of cell culture differ from natural conditions, it may not be clear how the results apply to noncancerous cells that are not growing in cell culture. **(2)** *analyze* (a) *Caenorhabditis elegans* would be a good possibility, because the cell fates are known for each cell in a 33-cell embryo. You could find mutant individuals that lacked normal development, and compare the resulting embryos with normal embryos to identify the cells that

change and examine how they change. (b) Any of the multicellular organisms described in BioSkill 11 would be a candidate, but *Dictyostelium discoideum* might be particularly interesting because cells stick to each other only during certain points in the life cycle.

BIOSKILL 12; p. 47 CYU (1) *analyze* This model focuses on the alleles for one gene on one pair of homologous chromosomes. Other genes and other chromosomes are not shown, nor are any of the other contents of the cell. **(2)** *understand* The red balls represent oxygen atoms. These atoms have no color in real life. **(3)** *understand* DNA molecules **(4)** *apply* The arrow represents the movement of the sodium ion through a protein channel to the other side of the membrane. **(5)** *analyze* The lizard is probably about the size of a human hand (and would be too small to see clearly if drawn to the same scale as the human and the dog). **(6)** *understand* The stomata cells are too small to be seen on the leaf. **(7)** *analyze* One way is to add an arrow that points from "genes" to "alleles" and is labeled "have different versions called."

BIOSKILL 13; p. 48 CYU (1) *apply* See Figure AB.2. **(2)** *understand* Mammals, lizards/snakes, turtles, alligators/crocodiles, and birds have amniotic eggs. **(3)** *analyze* See Figure AB.2. **(4)** *analyze* See Figure AB.3. **(5)** *apply* Mammals are equally related to lizards and turtles, because the most recent common ancestor of mammals and lizards is the same as the most recent common ancestor of mammals and turtles.

BIOSKILL 14; p. 49 Fig. B14.1 *analyze* See Figure AB.4.

BIOSKILL 15; p. 50 CYU (1) *apply* "different yoked-together" **(2)** *apply* "sugary loosened" **(3)** *apply* "study of form" **(4)** *apply* "three bodies"

BIOSKILL 16; p. 52 CYU (1) *create* Many examples are possible. See Figure 1.9 as an example of the format to use for your Research box.

BIOSKILL 17; p. 52 CYU (1) *evaluate* The type of misconception is goal-oriented thinking. Evolution is not goal directed. Legs did not evolve in fish because fish wanted or needed them. (See Chapter 22 for more information on evolution by natural selection.) **(2)** *evaluate* In science, a theory is an explanation for a broad class of phenomena that is supported by a wide body of evidence. In

Figure AB.1

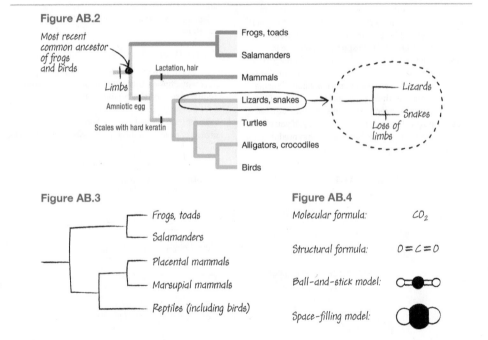

Figure AB.2

Figure AB.3

Figure AB.4

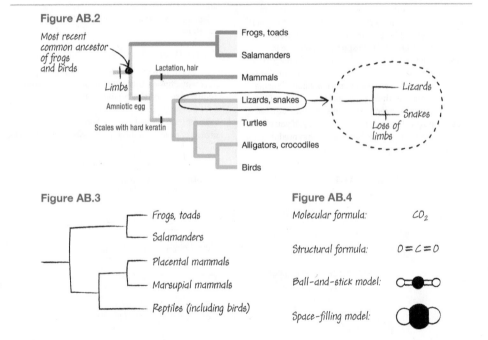

everyday use, a theory is a hunch or speculation about how something works. This difference in meaning could cause confusion because someone might dismiss a scientific theory (such as the theory of evolution or the theory of gravity) as speculation rather than treat it as a scientific explanation that is so well established that no new evidence is likely to alter it.

Chapter 2

IN-TEXT QUESTIONS AND ANSWERS

p. 57 Fig. 2.3 *apply* In phosphorus, there are 15 electrons, 3 electron shells, and 4 orbitals in the outer shell. Since isotopes of an element only vary in neutrons, the number of protons and electrons will not differ between them, so all of these values will be the same.

p. 59 Fig. 2.7 *understand* Oxygen and nitrogen have high electronegativities. They hold shared electrons more tightly than C, H, and many other atoms, resulting in polar bonds.

p. 60 *apply* *Water*: arrows pointing from hydrogens to oxygen atom; *ammonia*: arrows pointing from hydrogens to nitrogen atom; *methane*: double arrows between carbons and hydrogens; *carbon dioxide*: arrows pointing from carbon to oxygens; *molecular nitrogen*: double arrows between nitrogens.

p. 61 CYU *apply* See Figure A2.1.

p. 62 (1) *analyze* The difference in electronegativity between the C and O atoms in CO_2 is similar to the difference between H and O atoms in H_2O. Both consist of three atoms bonded together with polar covalent bonds, but CO_2 is a linear molecule with double bonds and no lone electron pairs, whereas H_2O is a bent molecule with single bonds and two lone electron pairs. **(2)** If water had a molecular shape similar to CO_2, the partial negative charge on oxygen would have partial positive charges on either side. Compared to the actual, bent molecule, the partial negative charge would be much less exposed and less able to participate in hydrogen bonding.

p. 63 Fig. 2.13 *apply* Oils, like the octane in this figure, are nonpolar. They have long chains of carbon atoms bonded to hydrogen atoms, which share electrons evenly because their electronegativities are similar. When an oil and water are mixed, the polar water molecules interact with each other via hydrogen bonding rather than with the nonpolar oil molecules, which are grouped together via hydrophobic interactions.

p. 65 Table 2.2 *understand* "Cause" (Row 1): electrostatic attractions between partial charges on water and opposite charges on ions; hydrogen bonds; water and other polar molecules. "Biological Consequences" (Row 2): ice to float; freezing solid. "Cause" (Row 4): Water molecules must absorb lots of heat energy to break hydrogen bonds and change liquid water to a gas.

p. 65 Making Models 2.1 *apply* See Figure A2.2.

p. 67 Fig. 2.16 *apply* The concentration of protons would decrease because milk is more basic (pH 6.5) than black coffee (pH 5).

p. 67 *apply* The bicarbonate concentration would increase. The protons (H^+) released from carbonic acid would react with the hydroxide ions (OH^-) dissociated from NaOH to form H_2O, leaving fewer protons free to react with bicarbonate to produce carbonic acid.

p. 69 Fig. 2.18 *remember* See Figure A2.3.

p. 69 CYU (1) *understand* The electrons are shifted farther from the nuclei of the carbon and hydrogen atoms and closer to the nuclei of the more electronegative oxygen atoms. **(2)** *analyze* The reactants have higher chemical

energy than the products. The entropy, however, is not increased or decreased based only on the number of molecules involved. The heat given off from this reaction would lead to increased entropy in the environment. Overall, the reaction would be spontaneous based on the change in potential energy.

p. 70 Fig. 2.20 *remember* The water-filled flask is the ocean; the gas-filled flask is the atmosphere; the condensed water droplets are rain; the electrical sparks are lightning.

p. 74 Table 2.3 *apply* All the functional groups in Table 2.3, except for the sulfhydryl group (−SH), are considered polar. The sulfhydryl group is only very slightly polar, since sulfur's electronegativity is only slightly higher than that of hydrogen. When present on the amino acid cysteine, the sulfhydryl group is classified as nonpolar.

✔ TEST YOUR KNOWLEDGE

1. *remember* b **2.** *remember* a **3.** *remember* c **4.** *understand* potential energy and entropy

✔ TEST YOUR UNDERSTANDING

5. *apply* c. Acetic acid has more highly electronegative oxygen atoms than the other molecules. When oxygen is bonded to carbon or hydrogen, a polar covalent bond forms. **6.** *apply* Relative electronegativities would be $F > O > H > Na$. One bond would form with sodium, and it would be ionic. **7.** *apply* The proton concentration of a pH 8.5 solution is $1.0 \times 10^{-8.5}$ M, or 3.2×10^{-9} M. This is about 32 times less concentrated than a solution with pH 7.0 (1.0×10^{-7}) **8.** *apply* If additional CO_2 were added, then the sequence of reactions would be driven to the right and make the ocean more acidic. The dissociation reaction of carbonic acid lowers the pH of the solution by releasing extra H^+ into the solution.

✔ TEST YOUR PROBLEM-SOLVING SKILLS

9. *analyze* b **10.** *analyze* In hot weather, water absorbs large amounts of heat due to its high specific heat and high heat of vaporization. In cold weather, water releases the large amount of heat that it has absorbed.

✔ PUT IT ALL TOGETHER: Case Study

11. *apply* Water is denser in its liquid form than its solid form. This results in ice floating on the surface and serving as a blanket to insulate the liquid water from the colder temperature in the air. **12.** *analyze* The water

will taste fresh. The liquid water in the ocean forms the crystalline structure of ice when water molecules interact with each other, excluding the salt ions. **13.** *apply* F, T, T, F. The freezing process is exothermic, like the condensation of water vapor into liquid. Even though the molecules have less entropy in ice, the second law of thermodynamics is preserved because the heat energy that is released will increase disorder in the environment (review Section 2.3). **14.** *create* One hypothesis might be that AFP binds to ice crystals and forms a nonpolar shell that prevents hydrogen bonding between water molecules to form a larger crystal. By limiting crystal growth, the cell would not freeze solid. **15.** *evaluate* To address the effectiveness of AFP, you might ask, "How long did the investigators keep the plants at each temperature?" **16.** *evaluate* A pro may be the prevention of lost crops due to abnormally cold weather that may occur due to climate change. A con may be the unexpected consequences in growth, taste, or nutritional value of foods that contain AFP.

Chapter 3

IN-TEXT QUESTIONS AND EXERCISES

p. 80 Fig. 3.2 *understand* The R-groups shaded in green contain mostly C and H, which have roughly equal electronegativities. Electrons are evenly shared in C−H bonds and C−S bonds, so the groups are nonpolar. All of the R-groups shaded in pink have a highly electronegative oxygen atom with a partial negative charge, making them polar.

p. 81 *apply* From most hydrophilic to most hydrophobic: (1) aspartate, (2) asparagine, (3) tyrosine, (4) valine. The most hydrophilic amino acids will have side chains with full charges (ionized), like aspartate, followed by those with the largest number of highly electronegative atoms, like oxygen or nitrogen. Highly electronegative atoms produce polar covalent bonds with carbon or hydrogen. The most hydrophobic will not have oxygen or nitrogen in their side chains, but instead will have the largest number of C−H bonds, which are nonpolar covalent.

p. 83 CYU *apply* See Figure A3.1.

p. 52 87 (1) *understand* Protein structure is hierarchical: Secondary, tertiary, and quaternary structure all depend on bonds and other interactions between amino acids that are linked in a chain in a specific order (primary structure). **(2)** *apply* Nonpolar amino acid residues

Figure A2.1

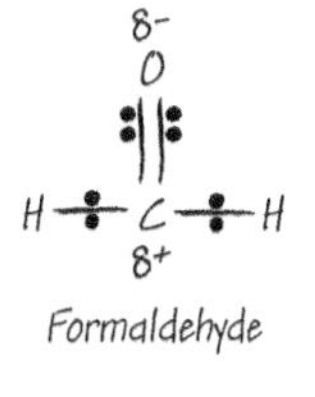

Formaldehyde

Figure A2.2

$$CH_4 + 2\, O_2 \longrightarrow CO_2 + 2\, H_2O$$

Figure A2.3

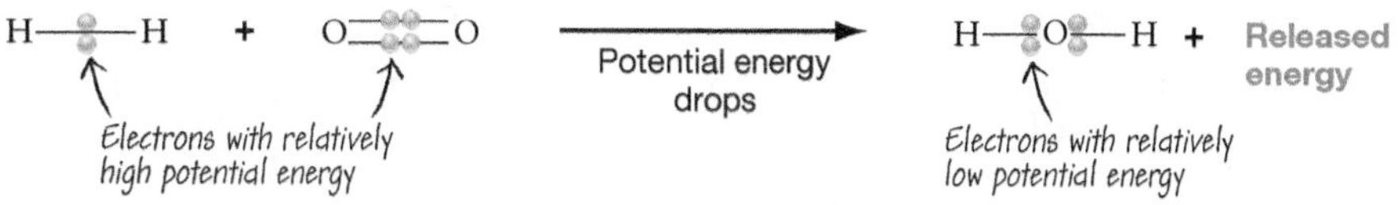

Figure A3.1

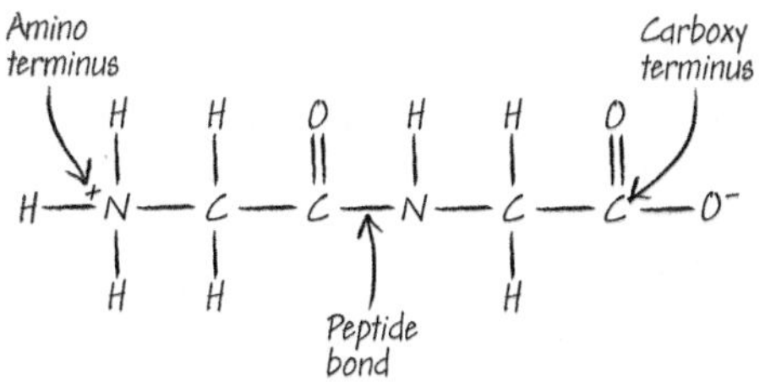

would be found in the interior of a globular protein like trypsin, grouped with other nonpolar residues due to hydrophobic interactions.

p. 91 CYU *apply* Enzymes bind to specific substrates based on the structure of the active site. An active site is formed when the polypeptide of an enzyme is folded into its tertiary structure. The information required for directing this folded state is in the primary structure of the polypeptide. The primary structure is also responsible for the specific amino acid residues in the active site that interact with the substrate.

✔ TEST YOUR KNOWLEDGE

1. *remember* d **2.** *remember* b **3.** *understand* The information present in the order and type of amino acids that make up the polypeptide (i.e., the primary structure). **4.** *remember* a

✔ TEST YOUR UNDERSTANDING

5. *apply* The protein diversity would significantly decrease. Using 20 different amino acids, a total of 20^5 (3.2×10^6) different peptides can be generated. If only 10 different amino acids were available, then the number of peptides would drop to 10^5 (1×10^5). This would be a 32-fold decrease in diversity. **6.** *understand* Molecular chaperones facilitate folding by preventing unfolded proteins from clumping together so that they can fold into the shapes that are determined by the information in their primary structures. **7.** *remember* c **8.** *understand*

A protein's activity is regulated by controlling when or where it is folded into its active form. Many proteins are in a flexible, inactive form until bound to molecules or ions. If proteins had only a single, inflexible folded conformation, this type of control could not occur.

✔ TEST YOUR PROBLEM-SOLVING SKILLS

9. *analyze* The side chain of proline is covalently bonded to the nitrogen in the core amino group as well as to the central carbon. This would restrict the movement of the side chain relative to the core nitrogen and would further restrict the backbone when the nitrogen participated in a peptide bond with a neighboring amino acid. **10.** *create* See Figure A3.2.

✔ PUT IT ALL TOGETHER: Case Study

11. *apply* There are many possible answers. Some common foods prepared with wheat flour, for example, are pizza, bagels, pasta, batter-fried chicken, and burritos. Many other condiments, such as soy sauce in Asian foods, also contain wheat flour. **12.** *understand* a **13.** *apply* You would expect proline to appear once or twice in the chain (at a frequency of 1/20 at each of the 33 positions, or 1.65 times). **14.** *analyze* Amino acid differences would be expected in the active site or in regions that affect the folded structure of this site. Either of these changes could result in a different active site that is better at either binding to the peptides or catalyzing the reaction to cleave the peptide bonds. **15.** *analyze* The AN-PEP system has fewer proline-rich peptides

in comparison to the negative control. The increase in peptide concentration in the negative control may result from the digestion of gluten by the normal gut enzymes, which would release more of the proline-rich peptide being evaluated. **16.** *create* Administering AN-PEP in pill form with a gluten-containing meal might digest the peptides before they cause an immune response, so the patient with celiac disease could at least occasionally not adhere to such a strict diet.

Chapter 4

IN-TEXT QUESTIONS AND EXERCISES

p. 95 Making Models 4.1 *understand* See Figure A4.1.

p. 96 Fig. 4.3 *apply* 5·-UAGC-·3

p. 96 CYU (1) *apply* See Figure A4.2. **(2)** *understand* Cells activate nucleotides by linking additional phosphates to an existing 5· phosphate. Activation increases the chemical energy in the nucleotides enough to offset the decrease in entropy that will result from the polymerization reaction so that the polymerization proceeds spontaneously.

p. 99 Making Models 4.2 *apply* See Figure A4.3.

p. 100 Fig. 4.7 *apply* It is not spontaneous—energy must be added (as heat) for the reaction to occur.

p. 101 CYU *apply* In the G-T pair, only one hydrogen bond could form—between the bottom N–H in guanine and one of the carbonyl groups (C=O) of thymine. The

---

Figure A3.2

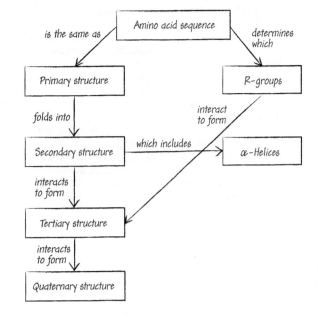

Figure A4.2

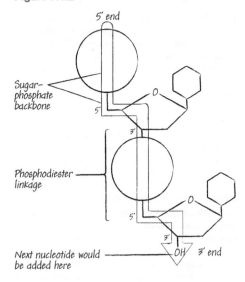

Figure A4.1

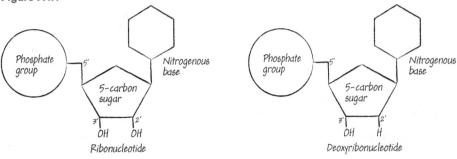

Figure A4.3

other two potential H-bonding sites in guanine would repel the similar partial charges in the aligned groups extending from the thymine base. No hydrogen bonding would be possible in an A-C pair.

p. 104 *understand* Examples would include (1) the production of nucleotides, and (2) polymerization of RNA. It is thought that nucleotides were scarce during chemical evolution, so their catalyzed synthesis by a ribozyme would have been advantageous. Catalysis by an RNA replicase would have dramatically increased the reproductive rate of RNA molecules.

✔ TEST YOUR KNOWLEDGE

1. *remember* c **2.** *remember* c **3.** *understand* d **4.** *remember* One end has a free phosphate group on the 5· carbon; the other end has a free hydroxyl group bonded to the 3· carbon.

✔ TEST YOUR UNDERSTANDING

5. *understand* DNA is a more stable molecule than RNA because it lacks a hydroxyl group on the 2· carbon and is therefore more resistant to cleavage. **6.** *apply* a; if 30 percent is adenine, then 30 percent would be thymine, since they are base-paired together. This means that 40 percent consists of G-C base pairs, which would be equally divided between the two bases. **7.** *apply* The DNA sequence of the new strand would be 5·-ATCGATATC-3·. The RNA sequence would be the same, except each T would be replaced by a U. **8.** *evaluate* No. Catalytic activity in ribozymes depends on the tertiary structure generated from folding single-stranded molecules. Fully double-stranded forms of the RNA would not form the same tertiary structure.

✔ TEST YOUR PROBLEM-SOLVING SKILLS

9. *create* See Figure A4.4 for a sample concept map.
10. *apply* See Figure A4.5.

✔ PUT IT ALL TOGETHER: Case Study

11. *analyze* The capacity for storing information would be severely limited. It would be like trying to express ideas with a language that consisted of only one 4-letter word that is repeated over and over. According to this hypothesis, DNA would not serve as an effective information storage molecule. **12.** *analyze* Watson and Crick's model had the sugar–phosphate backbones oriented toward the exterior. Pauling's structure would not likely exist in cells because the sugar–phosphate backbones of nucleic acids are negatively charged and would repel one another. **13.** *analyze* The amount of water would affect the influence of hydrophobic interactions, which push the mostly nonpolar nitrogenous bases away from water and cause the DNA to twist into a double helix. **14.** *analyze* Within each DNA sample tested, the molar ratios of A:T and that of G:C were close to one, meaning that for every adenine there is a thymine, and for every guanine there is a cytosine. A key observation was that the ratios between A:G and T:C were not close to one, meaning that all four nucleotides were not present in equal ratios. These data are contrary to what Levene's tetranucleotide model would have predicted, which is that each nucleotide would be present in the same molar amounts. In addition, since the molar ratios of A:G and T:C were quite different in the organisms tested, the primary structure of DNA appears to vary among them. **15.** *analyze* Chargaff's data show that an approximately 1:1 molar ratio exists between adenine and thymine bases, and between guanine and cytosine bases. Watson and Crick used these data to come up with complementary base pairing, which requires that every adenine pairs with a thymine and every guanine pairs with a cytosine. In RNA, Chargaff's rules do not apply since RNA is single-stranded and the pairing is not consistent throughout the molecule. **16.** *evaluate* Science is seldom advanced

in isolation. Watson and Crick could not have arrived at their model of the double helix without Levene's discovery of the structure of nucleotides and how they are linked together, Franklin's X-ray crystallography data, or Chargaff's biochemical analysis of the molar proportions of nucleotides in double-stranded DNA.

Chapter 5

IN-TEXT QUESTIONS AND EXERCISES

p. 108 Fig. 5.2 *apply* See the structure of mannose in Figure A5.1.

p. 110 CYU *apply* See Figure A5.2.

p. 113 CYU *apply* They could differ in (1) location of linkages (e.g., 1,4 or 1,6); (2) types of linkages (e.g., α or β); (3) the sequence of the monomers (e.g., two galactose and then two glucose, versus alternating galactose and glucose); and/or (4) whether the four monomers are linked in a line or whether they branch.

p. 115 Fig. 5.7 *apply* The percentage of inhibition would not change for the intact glycoprotein bar. The purified carbohydrate bar would be at zero inhibition, and the purified protein bar would be similar to the intact glycoprotein bar.

p. 116 Fig. 5.8 *understand* All of the C–C and C–H bonds should be circled.

p. 116 CYU (1) *understand* *Aspect 1:* The β-1,4-glycosidic linkages in these molecules result in insoluble fibers that most organisms cannot break down with enzymes. *Aspect 2:* When individual molecules of these carbohydrates align, bonds form between them and produce fibers or sheets that resist pulling and pushing forces. **(2)** *apply* The energy-storage molecules, like starch, are being hydrolyzed to release glucose. Disaccharides like the lactose in milk would be hydrolyzed to release

---

Figure A4.4

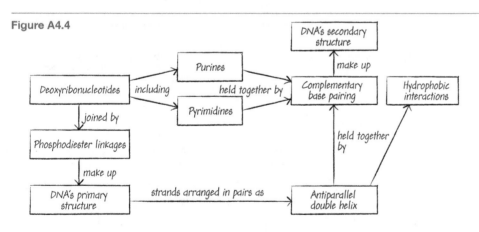

Figure A5.1

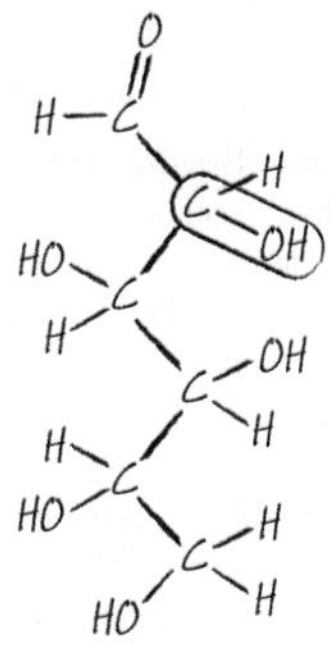

(structure of mannose)

Figure A4.5

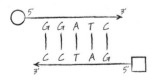

Figure A5.2

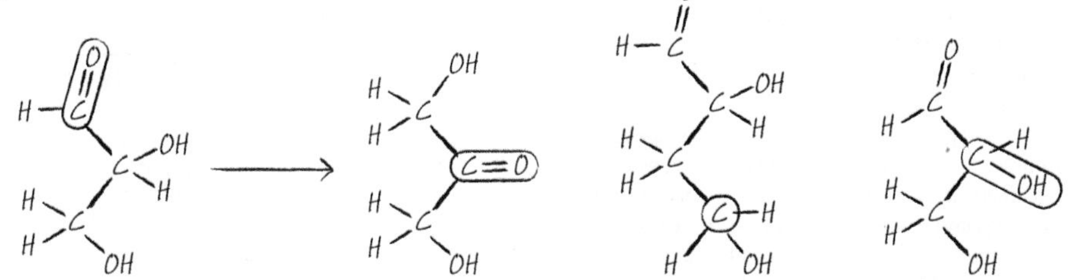

Start with a monosaccharide. This one is a 3-carbon aldose (carbonyl group at end)

Variation 1: 3-carbon ketose (carbonyl group in middle)

Variation 2: 4-carbon aldose

Variation 3: 3-carbon aldose with different arrangement of hydroxyl group glucose and galactose. These sugars may be further broken down to produce ATP and raw materials for building other molecules, such as glycolipids and glycoproteins. The insoluble cellulose that makes up dietary fiber does not get broken down, but it will help retain water and support the digestion and passage of fecal material.

✔ TEST YOUR KNOWLEDGE

1. *understand* Monosaccharides can differ from one another in three ways: (1) the location of their carbonyl group; (2) the number of carbon atoms they contain; and (3) the orientations of their hydroxyl groups. **2.** *remember* a **3.** *remember* c **4.** *remember* a

✔ TEST YOUR UNDERSTANDING

5. *understand* c. **6.** *understand* When you compare the glucose monomers in an α-1,4-glycosidic linkage versus those in a β-1,4-glycosidic linkage, the linkages are located on opposite sides of the plane of the glucose rings, and the glucose monomers are linked in the same orientation versus having every other glucose flipped in orientation. β-1,4-glycosidic linkages are much more likely to form linear fibers and sheets, so they resist degradation. **7.** *analyze* Monomers of carbohydrates vary extensively in their numbers of carbons, the position of the carbonyl group, the orientations of hydroxyl groups, and the presence of modifications (e.g., modified sugar residues in chitin and peptidoglycan). In contrast, there are only four different monomers of nucleic acids. Glycosidic linkages vary more in location and geometry than do linkages between nucleic acid residues. **8.** *apply* When bacteria contact lysozyme, the peptidoglycan in their cell walls begins to degrade, leading to the death of the bacteria. Lysozyme therefore helps protect humans against bacterial infections.

✔ TEST YOUR PROBLEM-SOLVING SKILLS

9. *apply* d; lactose is a disaccharide of glucose and galactose, which can be cleaved by enzymes expressed in the human gut to release galactose. **10.** *analyze* Amylase breaks down the starch in the cracker into glucose monomers that taste sweet.

✔ PUT IT ALL TOGETHER: Case Study

11. *apply* The monosaccharides are linked by an α-1,2-glycosidic bond because the hydroxyl is in the α position in glucose. Since the bond is formed with β-fructose, the linkage is often referred to as being an α-β-1,2-glycosidic bond. **12.** *apply* Fructose is a hexose based on having six carbons, and it is a ketose because the carbonyl is within the carbon chain (C-2). **13.** *analyze* The position of the carbonyl is the most striking structural difference between these sugars (glucose is an aldose while fructose is a ketose) and so it is most likely responsible for the disparity in taste perception. **14.** *apply* To convert the starch polymer into monosaccharides, it must be hydrolyzed by an enzyme such as amylase. Since fructose is not in starch, the second event must be to convert some of the glucose sugars into fructose. **15.** *analyze* The escape times of fructose-fed mice were almost three times slower than the control. This result suggests that the mice were impaired in their ability to recall what they had learned about finding the escape chamber. The mice that were fed omega-3 fatty acids demonstrated an enhanced memory, and it took them half the time to escape compared to those with similar diets that lacked this supplement. **16.** *evaluate* These results suggest that the best diet for performance in your classes will be rich in omega-3 fatty acids and low in fructose. Maybe it's time to replace your soda with fish oil!

Chapter 6

IN-TEXT QUESTIONS AND EXERCISES

p. 122 Fig. 6.4 *remember* A circle should be drawn around the phosphate and polar or charged group extending from the top of the molecule.

p. 123 *understand* Free fatty acids are amphipathic because their hydrocarbon tails are hydrophobic but their carboxyl functional groups are hydrophilic

p. 123 CYU (1) *understand* In general, unsaturated lipids are more fluid than saturated lipids at a given temperature. At higher temperatures, the fluidity of fats and oils will increase, and at lower temperatures they will become more solid. **(2)** *analyze* Steroids have a distinctive four-ring structure with variable side groups attached; fats consist of three fatty acids linked to glycerol; many phospholipids also have a glycerol linked to fatty acids, but instead of three fatty acids, they have two plus a hydrophilic, phosphate-containing "head" region.

p. 125 *analyze* Amino acids have amino and carboxyl groups that are ionized in water, and nucleotides have negatively charged phosphates. Due to their charge and larger size, both of these compounds would be placed below the small ions at the bottom of the permeability scale ($<10^{-12}$ cm/sec).

p. 126 Fig. 6.10 *apply* Increasing the number of phospholipids with polyunsaturated tails would increase permeability of the liposomes. Starting from the left, the first line (no cholesterol) would represent liposomes with 50 percent polyunsaturated phospholipids, the second line would be 20 percent polyunsaturated phospholipids, and the third line would contain only saturated phospholipids.

p. 127 CYU *apply* See Table A6.1.

p. 128a *apply* Since temperature is a measure of thermal motion, increasing temperature would increase the rate of diffusion and thus the rate of passive transport to achieve equilibrium across a membrane.

p. 128b *apply* No, the right side of the membrane will have a higher concentration of solute at equilibrium. If you said yes, recall that pressure from the downward pull of gravity will push water molecules back to the left, against continued transport of water toward the higher solute concentration. This opposing force would prevent the solutions separated by the membrane from achieving the same concentration.

p. 130 CYU *create* See Figure A6.1.

p. 131 Fig. 6.18 *create* Repeat the procedure using a lipid bilayer that is free of membrane proteins, such as synthetic liposomes constructed from only phospholipids. If proteins were responsible for the pits and mounds, then this control would not show these structures.

Table A6.1

Factor	Effect on permeability	Reason
Temperature	Decreases as temperature decreases.	Lower temperature shows movement of hydrocarbon tails, allowing more interactions (membrane is more dense).
Cholesterol	Decreases as cholesterol content increases.	Cholesterol molecules interact with the hydrocarbon tails, making them more tightly packed.
Length of hydrocarbon tails	Decreases as length of hydrocarbon tails increases.	Longer hydrocarbon tails have more interactions (membrane is more dense).
Saturation of hydrocarbon tails	Decreases as degree of saturation increases.	Saturated fatty acids have straight hydrocarbon tails that pack together tightly, leaving few gaps.

Figure A6.1

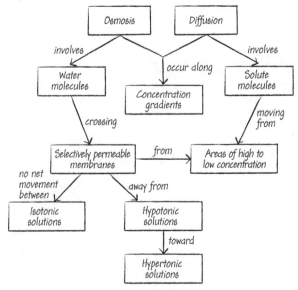

p. 132 *apply* Your arrow should point from below to above the membrane. There is no concentration gradient for chloride, but the upper side has a net positive charge, which favors the import of negative ions like chloride.

p. 133 Fig. 6.21 *evaluate* No—the 10 replicates where no current was recorded probably represent instances where the CFTR protein was damaged and not functioning properly. (In general, no experimental method works "perfectly.")

p. 135 Making Models 6.1 *apply* See Figure A6.2. In this drawing, the lipid bilayer is represented by two lines because it does not require the structural details of how the lipids are organized.

p. 136 CYU (1) *understand* Passive transport does not require an input of energy—it happens because of energy already present in an existing gradient. Active transport is active in the sense of requiring an input of energy from, for example, ATP. In cotransport, an ion or molecule is transported against its gradient along with (i.e., "co") a substance that is transported along its gradient. **(2)** *create* See Figure A6.3.

p. 137 Fig. 6.26 *understand* *Diffusion:* description as given; no proteins involved. *Facilitated diffusion:* Passive movement of ions or molecules that cannot readily cross a membrane; facilitated by channel or carrier (transmembrane) proteins. *Active transport:* Active movement of ions or molecules in a single direction, often against their gradient; made possible by pump proteins powered by an energy source such as ATP.

✔ **TEST YOUR KNOWLEDGE**

1. *understand* c **2.** *understand* b **3.** *understand* For osmosis to occur, a concentration gradient and a membrane that allows water to pass, but not the solute, must be present. **4.** *understand* d

✔ **TEST YOUR UNDERSTANDING**

5. *apply* No, because they have no polar end to interact with water. Instead, these lipids would float on the surface of water, or collect in droplets suspended in water, reducing their interaction with water to a minimum. **6.** *apply* See Figure A6.4. **7.** *analyze* Channel proteins form pores in the membrane, some of which have different closed and open conformations, and carrier proteins undergo conformational changes to shuttle molecules or ions across the membrane. **8.** *apply* b

✔ **TEST YOUR PROBLEM-SOLVING SKILLS**

9. *analyze* F, F, T, T. The first two responses are false because the interior solution in both sets of liposomes is the same. The third is true because aquaporins allow for an increased rate of water transport. The fourth is true because if the Na or Cl ions can cross the membrane in frog eggs, then osmosis may be reduced or even be prevented from occurring. **10.** *apply* At the start, NaCl will dissociated into 1 M of Na^+ and 1 M of Cl^- on the left and 1.5 M of K^+ on the right. Water would move from the right to the left, but the CFTR allows Cl^- ions to move along an electrochemical gradient from left to right. Because there is more K^+ on the right side than Na^+ on the left, at equilibrium, there will be a higher concentration of ions on the right side of the membrane. This gradient will result in the transport of water from the left side to the right via osmosis.

✔ **PUT IT ALL TOGETHER: Case Study**

11. *apply* The saturated fat in meat undergoes a change in its physical state as it is heated—from a semisolid consistency to a liquid. When meat is grilled, the liquefied fat drips off, resulting in less saturated fat in the final product. When the meat is raw, all the saturated fat remains. **12.** *understand* Saturated fats have fatty acid tails with only C–C single bonds while unsaturated fats have one or more C=C double bonds in the tails. C=C bonds normally result in kinks that increase the spacing between fats and thus make unsaturated fats more fluid than saturated fats. **13.** *apply* Hydrogenation is used because the process is likely to involve converting C=C bonds into C–C bonds by adding hydrogens. Fats with only C–H bonds (i.e., saturated) tend to be semisolid at room temperature. **14.** *analyze* Trans fats are unsaturated because they have one or more double bonds, but they have physical characteristics similar to saturated fats due to the *trans* double bond that straightens the hydrocarbon chain. **15.** *evaluate* No. The data show that there is a correlation between blood levels of trans fats and atherosclerosis (i.e., these two events appear to occur together), but these data do not show the cause. "Causation" means that one event is responsible for the occurrence of the other (e.g., studying and doing well on an exam). **16.** *create* Other factors that may affect heart disease include gender, age, weight, heart disease in the family, other dietary habits, and so on.

BIG PICTURE The Chemistry of Life

p. 140 CYU (1) *understand* Oxygen is much more electronegative than hydrogen, so within water, the electrons are unequally shared in the O–H covalent bonds. The resulting partial negative charge around the oxygen and partial positive charges around the hydrogen atoms allow for hydrogen bonds to form among water molecules. **(2)** *analyze* Unlike other macromolecules, nucleic acids can serve as templates for their own replication. RNA is generally single-stranded and can adopt many different three-dimensional structures. The flexibility in structure, combined with the presence of reactive hydroxyl groups, contribute to the formation of active sites that catalyze chemical reactions. One or more of these catalytic RNA molecules may have evolved the ability to self-replicate. DNA is not likely to have catalyzed its own replication, as it is most often double-stranded, with no clear tertiary structure, and it lacks the reactive hydroxyl groups. **(3)** *remember* In the amino acid, the nitrogen in the amino (NH_3^+) group and the carbon in the carboxyl (COO^-) group should be circled. In the nucleotide, the oxygen in the hydroxyl (OH) group and the phosphorus in the phosphate (PO_4^{2-}) group on the nucleotide should be circled. **(4)** *understand* A line representing a protein should be drawn such that it completely crosses the lipid bilayer at least once. The protein could be involved in a variety of different roles, including transport of substances across the membrane in the form of a channel, carrier, or pump.

Chapter 7

IN-TEXT QUESTIONS AND EXERCISES

p. 145 CYU *understand* (1) The ribosomes are macromolecular machines that synthesize all of the proteins in the cell. (2) Photosynthetic membranes increase food production by providing a large surface area to hold the pigments and enzymes required for photosynthesis. (3) Flagella propel cells through liquid using a motor that rotates a long, rigid filament. (4) The layer of thick, strong material stiffens the cell wall and provides protection from mechanical damage.

p. 150 Fig. 7.12 *create* Toxins are stored in vacuoles because being surrounded by a membrane prevents them from contacting and damaging the cytosolic components or other organelles in the cell.

p. 152 CYU (1) *understand* Both organelles contain specific sets of enzymes. Lysosomal enzymes digest macromolecules in the acidic lumen of this organelle, releasing monomers that can be recycled into new macromolecules. Peroxisomes contain catalase and other enzymes that process fatty acids and toxins via oxidation reactions. **(2)** *understand* From top to bottom: administrative/information hub, protein factory, large molecule manufacturing and shipping (protein synthesis and folding center, lipid factory, protein finishing and shipping line, waste processing and recycling center),

Figure A6.2

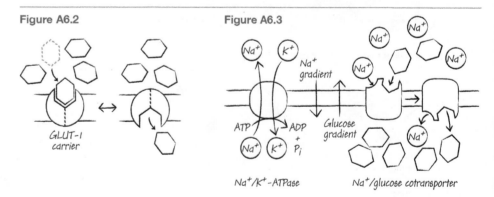

GLUT-1 carrier

Figure A6.3

Na$^+$ gradient

ATP → ADP + P$_i$

Na$^+$/K$^+$-ATPase

Glucose gradient

Na$^+$/glucose cotransporter

Figure A6.4

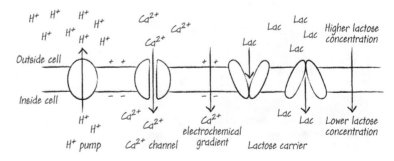

Outside cell

Inside cell

H$^+$ pump

Ca^{2+} channel

electrochemical gradient

Lactose carrier

Higher lactose concentration

Lower lactose concentration

warehouse, fatty-acid processing and detox center, power station, food-manufacturing facility, support beams, perimeter fencing with secured gates (used for plasma membrane and cell wall).

p. 154 Fig. 7.16 <remember> See Figure A7.1.

p. 156 Fig. 7.18 <apply> "Prediction": The labeled tail region fragments or the labeled core region fragments of the nucleoplasmin protein will be found in the cell nucleus. "Prediction of null hypothesis": Either both the fragments (no required signal) or neither of them (whole protein signal) will be found in the nucleus of the cell. "Conclusion": The send-to-nucleus signal is in the tail region of the nucleoplasmin protein.

p. 157 <analyze> (1) Nucleotides are small enough that they would diffuse through the nuclear pore complex along their gradients—a passive process that would not require energy. (2) Large proteins must be escorted through the nuclear pore complex in a directional manner—an active process that requires energy and results in the protein being concentrated inside the nucleus.

p. 159 <apply> During the chase period, proteins appear to have first entered the Golgi apparatus after 7 minutes and then started to move into secretory granules after 37 minutes. This means that in this experiment, it took approximately 30 minutes for the fastest-moving proteins to pass through the Golgi apparatus.

p. 161 Making Models 7.1 <apply> See Figure A7.2. Step 1: Ribosomes at the rough ER finish the polypeptide as it is moved into the ER lumen. Step 2: Polypeptide folds and is packaged into a vesicle. Step 3: Vesicle is transported to the *cis* Golgi. Step 4: Protein is processed as it moves through the Golgi apparatus and cargo receptors package it into a transport vesicle. Step 5: Secretory vesicle is transported to the plasma membrane. Step 6: Vesicle fuses with the plasma membrane and releases protein to the outside of the cell.

p. 162 CYU (1) <analyze> Proteins that enter the nucleus are fully synthesized and have an NLS that interacts with another protein to get it into the organelle. The NLS is not removed. Proteins that enter the ER have a signal sequence that interacts with the SRP during translation. The ribosome is moved to the ER and synthesis continues, moving the protein into the ER. The signal is removed once it enters the organelle. **(2)** <analyze> The protein would be in the lysosome. The ER signal would direct the protein into the ER before it is completely synthesized. The mannose-6-phosphate tag will direct the protein from the Golgi to the late endosome to the lysosome. Thus the complete protein is never free in the cytosol, where the NLS could direct it into the nucleus.

p. 167 Fig. 7.29 <apply> You should have drawn a pair of doublets that have moved past one another so that they are lined up end to end. The doublets would not bend without the links holding them together.

p. 168 CYU <analyze> Actin filaments are made up of two strands of actin monomers, intermediate filaments are made up of a number of different protein subunits, and microtubules are made up of tubulin protein dimers that form a tube. Actin filaments and microtubules exhibit polarity (or directionality), and new subunits are constantly being added or subtracted at either end (but added faster to the plus end). All three elements provide structural support, but only actin filaments and microtubules serve as tracks for motors involved in movement and cell division.

✔ TEST YOUR KNOWLEDGE

1. <understand> They have their own small, circular (or linear in some species) chromosomes; they produce their own ribosomes; and they divide in a manner that is independent of cellular division. **2.** <understand> b **3.** <remember> a **4.** <understand> The phosphate links to the motor protein and causes it to change shape, which results in the protein moving along the filament.

Figure A7.1

(a) Animal pancreatic cell: Exports digestive enzymes.

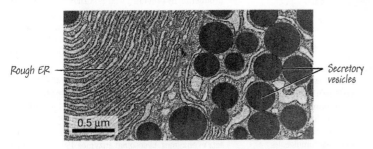

Rough ER — Secretory vesicles — 0.5 μm

(b) Animal testis cell: Exports lipid-soluble signals.

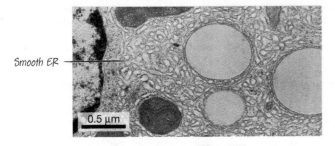

Smooth ER — 0.5 μm

(c) Plant leaf cell: Manufactures ATP and sugar.

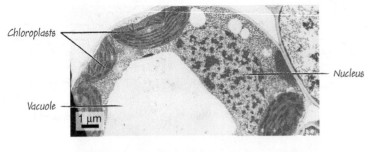

Chloroplasts — Nucleus — Vacuole — 1 μm

(d) Cardiac muscle: Uses ATP to generate the heartbeat.

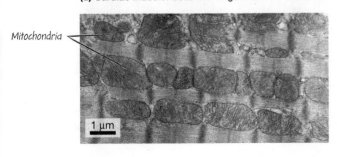

Mitochondria — 1 μm

Figure A7.2

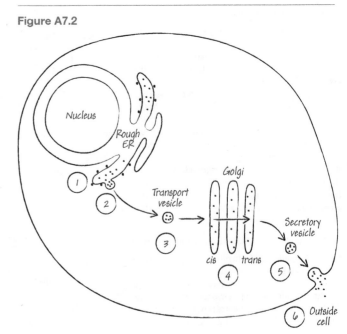

Nucleus — Rough ER — Transport vesicle — Golgi — Secretory vesicle — cis — trans — Outside cell

5. *apply* b; fimbriae are involved in bacterial attachment to surfaces and other cells, which would be important in the ability to grow on teeth. **6.** *apply* a; the endoplasmic reticulum is responsible for synthesizing the membrane proteins required for the transport of solutes across the plasma membrane. **7.** *apply* The NLS will be used to actively import the protein into the nucleus, leaving very little of the protein in the cytoplasm. Diffusion alone would not drive all the protein into the nucleus. **8.** *analyze* All cells are bound by a plasma membrane, are filled with cytoplasm, carry their genetic information (DNA) in chromosomes, and contain ribosomes (the sites of protein synthesis). Some prokaryotes have organelles not found in plants or animals, such as a magnetite-containing structure. Plant cells have chloroplasts, vacuoles, and a cell wall. Animal cells contain lysosomes and lack a cell wall.

✔ TEST YOUR PROBLEM-SOLVING SKILLS

9. *analyze* The patient may have a defect in (1) a hydrolytic enzyme that breaks down polysaccharides, (2) the process of adding a mannose-6-phosphate signal to lysosomal hydrolases, or (3) the mannose-6-phosphate receptor in the Golgi apparatus. Any of these three defects would result in lysosomes that are missing enzymes necessary to break down the polysaccharides. **10.** *analyze* The radiolabeled proteins would likely be found in the cytosol and mitochondria. Cytosolic proteins would include proteins like the actin and myosin involved in muscle contraction. Since there is a high energy demand, you would predict that many proteins are required to produce ATP in mitochondria.

✔ PUT IT ALL TOGETHER: Case Study

11. *apply* Lysosomes originate from the endomembrane system when late endosomes receive enzymes imported from the Golgi apparatus. If melanosomes have a similar origin, then they would arise from an endosome-like vesicle that receives cargo from the Golgi apparatus. **12.** *apply* See Figure A7.3. The melanosomes move along microtubule tracks using motor proteins. Microtubules originate near the nucleus of animal cells, and the positive ends project outward. Kinesin would be responsible for moving melanosomes outward to generate dark-colored cells. Dynein would be used for moving melanosomes back to the nucleus in light-colored cells. **13.** *analyze* The melansomes are taken up from the extracellular space, so the process would either be receptor-mediated endocytosis or phagocytosis. Both of these processes send the cargo to the lysosome for destruction, so if the organelles are to remain in the keratinocyte, this final step must be inhibited. **14.** *create* Hypothesis: Upon exposure to UV radiation, melanocytes will produce more melanosomes, which

are then taken up by neighboring keratinocytes to darken the skin. *Experiment*: Expose part of the skin of an individual to UV light and keep another part of the skin protected. Take samples of the skin and use microscopy to count the number of melanosomes produced in melanocytes in the two conditions. **15.** *analyze* Autophagy is the process of recycling damaged organelles and other cytoplasmic components by wrapping portions of the cytoplasm in a membrane and fusing it with lysosomes. If melanosomes were removed by autophagy, then you would expect light-skinned individuals to have a higher rate of autophagy in keratinocytes as compared to dark-skinned individuals. **16.** *analyze* When autophagy was induced, the skin appeared lighter and there was a significant decrease in melanin compared to the control. When autophagy was inhibited, the skin appeared darker and there was a significant increase in melanin compared to the control and the trial with autophagy induced. The conclusion is that autophagy can affect the appearance of skin and the amount of melanin in skin cells.

Chapter 8

IN-TEXT QUESTIONS AND ANSWERS

p. 173 *apply* (1) If ΔS is positive (products have more disorder than reactants), then according to the free-energy equation, ΔG is more likely to be negative as temperature (T) increases even if ΔH is positive. The increased temperature represents added thermal energy that may be used to drive an endothermic reaction to completion, making the reaction spontaneous. (2) Exothermic reactions may be nonspontaneous if they result in a decrease in entropy—meaning that the products are more ordered than the reactants (ΔS is negative).

p. 174 Fig. 8.4 *understand* Each point represents the data from a single test, not an average (mean) of many experiments, so it's not possible to calculate the standard error of the mean (represented by error bars).

p. 175 CYU (1) *understand* Standard free-energy equation: $\Delta G = \Delta H - T \Delta S$. ΔG symbolizes the change in the Gibbs free energy. ΔH represents the difference in enthalpy (potential energy, pressure, and volume) between the products and the reactants. T represents the temperature (in degrees Kelvin) at which the reaction is taking place. ΔS symbolizes the change in entropy (amount of disorder). **(2)** *understand* When ΔH is negative—meaning that the products have lower enthalpy than the reactants—and when ΔS is positive, meaning that the products have higher entropy (are more disordered) than the reactants.

p. 177 *apply* In part (a), the electron donor is AH_2 and the electron acceptor is FAD. In part (b), the electron donor is BH_2 and the electron acceptor is NAD^+.

p. 178 Fig. 8.9 *apply* The ΔG in the uncoupled reaction would be positive (> 0), and each of the steps in the coupled reaction would have a negative (< 0) ΔG.

p. 178 *analyze* Redox reactions transfer energy between molecules or atoms via electrons. When oxidized molecules are reduced, their potential energy increases. ATP hydrolysis is often coupled with the phosphorylation of another molecule. This phosphorylation increases the potential energy of the molecule.

p. 179 CYU (1) *understand* Electrons in C—H bonds are not held as tightly as electrons in C—O bonds, so they have higher potential energy. **(2)** *understand* The three phosphate groups in ATP have four negative charges in close proximity. The repulsive forces from the clustered negative charges result in weak, unstable bonds that have high potential energy.

p. 180 Making Models 8.1 *apply* The amino acid residues in the enzyme's active site will specifically interact with the substrate using hydrogen bonds or other weak interactions. See Figure A8.1.

p. 180 Fig. 8.12 *understand* No—a catalyst affects only the activation energy, not the overall change in Gibbs free energy (ΔG).

p. 181 *remember* (1) binding substrates, (2) transition state, (3) R-groups, (4) structure

p. 181 Fig. 8.14 *apply* Each enzyme molecule is saturated with substrate at the maximum rate of product formation, so to increase the rate, you would need to add more enzyme.

p. 184 CYU (1) *understand* The reaction rate is based primarily on the activity of the enzyme. Once the temperature reaches a level that causes unfolding and inactivation of the enzyme, the rate decreases to the uncatalyzed rate. **(2)** *analyze* Both are mechanisms that regulate the interaction between enzymes and their substrates. In competitive inhibition, the regulatory molecule binds directly to the active site and interferes with substrate binding. In allosteric regulation, the regulatory molecule binds to a different region and affects the structure of the enzyme to either open or close the active site.

p. 185 *apply* If enzyme 2 is absent, then there would be a buildup of product B because it is not being used to make C. At equilibrium, the concentration of A and B would be higher than expected in the fully functional pathway. If C is not being produced, it cannot serve as a reactant for the enzyme 3 catalyzed reaction. As a result, both C and D would be lower than expected from the functional pathway.

✔ TEST YOUR KNOWLEDGE

1. *understand* a **2.** *remember* c **3.** *remember* d **4.** *understand* The final product of a pathway inhibits the activity of an enzyme

---

Figure A7.3

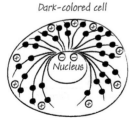

Dark-colored cell

Nucleus

Kinesin motor active

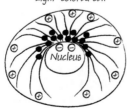

Light-colored cell

Nucleus

Dynein motor active

Figure A8.1

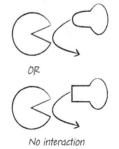

Enzyme + other molecules

OR

No interaction

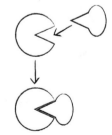

Enzyme + substrate

Interaction

early in the same pathway, thus reducing the activity of all subsequent steps in the pathway.

✔ TEST YOUR UNDERSTANDING

5. *understand* Reactions proceed when the reactant molecules (the key) fits snugly into the active site of an enzyme (the lock). Fischer's original model assumed that enzymes were rigid; in fact, enzymes are flexible and often change their shape after binding to substrates. **6.** *apply* d. Energy, such as the thermal energy in fire, must be provided to overcome the activation energy barrier before the reaction can proceed. **7.** *apply* For the coupled reaction, step 1 has a ΔG of about -3 kcal/mol and step 2 has a ΔG of about -3 kcal/mol. The uncoupled reaction has a ΔG of about $+1.3$ kcal/mol. **8.** *apply* Catabolic reactions will often have a negative ΔG based on a decrease in enthalpy and increase in entropy. Anabolic reactions are the opposite—a positive ΔG that is based on an increase in enthalpy and decrease in entropy.

✔ TEST YOUR PROBLEM-SOLVING SKILLS

9. *apply* See Figure A8.2. **10.** *apply* b. The sugar likely binds to the enzyme and changes its structure to form a functional active site.

✔ PUT IT ALL TOGETHER: Case Study

11. *analyze* If this amino acid cannot be synthesized by your cells, then it must be obtained by breaking down proteins into amino acids, which would include phenylalanine. The amount and type of protein that you consume in your diet would then affect the amount of phenylalanine available in your body. **12.** *create* See Figure A8.3. **13.** *analyze* PAH has a different structure in the presence of phenylalanine compared to when it is absent. This is shown by the different products generated after exposure to trypsin between the two conditions. These results support the hypothesis that phenylalanine is an allosteric regulatory molecule. **14.** *analyze* A defect in the production of the coenzyme, which would not allow PAH to catalyze the reaction. Another defect could be in the reactions with NADH that are responsible for regenerating the reduced form of the coenzyme. **15.** *analyze* The functional form PAH consists of four identical protein subunits, each providing one active site. **16.** *create* Two possible areas of research are (1) the development of drugs that would help PAH to form the catalytically active conformation and (2) the administration of the coenzyme to overcome defects in its production.

Chapter 9

IN-TEXT QUESTIONS AND EXERCISES

p. 191 Fig. 9.2 *understand* *Glycolysis:* "What goes in" = glucose, NAD^+, ADP, inorganic phosphate; "What comes out" = pyruvate, NADH, ATP. *Pyruvate processing:* "What goes in" = pyruvate, NAD^+; "What comes out" = acetyl CoA, NADH, CO_2. *Citric acid cycle:* "What goes in" = acetyl CoA, NAD^+, FAD, ADP or GDP, inorganic phosphate; "What comes out" = CO_2, NADH, $FADH_2$, ATP or GTP. *Electron transport and oxidative phosphorylation:* "What goes in" = NADH, $FADH_2$, O_2, ADP, inorganic phosphate; "What comes out" = NAD^+, FAD, H_2O, ATP.

p. 191 Making Models 10.1 *understand* When glucose is completely oxidized, all the carbons end up in CO_2. The processes shown by the arrows are shown in Figure A9.1.

p. 193 *apply* The radioactive carbons in glucose can be fully oxidized by the central pathways to generate radiolabeled CO_2. Other molecules, like lipids and amino acids, would end up radiolabeled since they are made using intermediates from the central pathways in other anabolic pathways.

p. 195 *apply* See Figure A9.2. If the regulatory site had a higher affinity for ATP than the active site, then when ATP is present, it would first bind to the regulatory site and inhibit the enzyme. As a result, the rate of ATP production in glycolysis would be low at all concentrations of ATP.

p. 197 *remember* Positive regulation: AMP, NAD^+, CoA (reaction substrates). *Negative regulation by feedback inhibition:* acetyl CoA, NADH, ATP (reaction products).

p. 200 Fig. 9.13 *apply* NADH would be expected to have the highest amount of chemical energy since its production is correlated with the largest drop in free energy in the graph.

p. 200 CYU (1) *understand* See Figure A9.3. **(2)** *apply* Glycolysis, pyruvate processing, and the citric acid

---

Figure A8.2

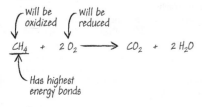

Figure A9.1

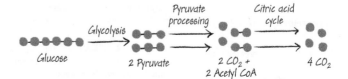

Figure A8.3

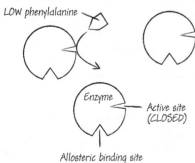

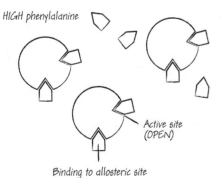

Figure A9.2

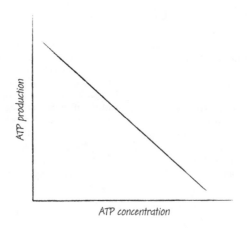

Figure A9.3

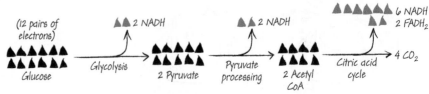

cycle all experience negative regulation. Up to the regulatory point in glycolysis, none of the molecules would have been produced. Up to the regulatory point in pyruvate processing, two NADH and two ATP would have been produced. Up to the first regulatory point in the citric acid cycle, four NADH and two ATP would have been produced.

p. 201 *apply* The O_2 at the bottom of the graph would have the highest redox potential and the FMN in complex I would have the lowest redox potential.

p. 202 Fig. 9.15 *remember* The proton gradient arrow should start above in the inner membrane space and point down across the membrane into the mitochondrial matrix. *Complex I:* "What goes in" = NADH; "What comes out" = NAD^+, e^-, transported H^+. *Complex II:* "What goes in" = $FADH_2$; "What comes out" = FAD, e^-, H^+. *Complex III:* "What goes in" = e^-, H^+; "What comes out" = e^-, transported H^+. *Complex IV:* "What goes in" = e^-, H^+, O_2; "What comes out" = H_2O, transported H^+.

p. 204 Fig. 9.17 *create* They could have placed the vesicles in an acidic solution that has a pH below that of the solution inside the vesicle. This would set up a proton gradient across the membrane to test for ATP synthesis.

p. 204 *analyze* When glucose is oxidized in glycolysis, pyruvate processing, and the citric acid cycle, reduced electron carriers (NADH or $FADH_2$) are produced. The electron carriers pass electrons to the ETC in mitochondria, which then produces a proton gradient across the inner membrane. This proton gradient powers the synthesis of ATP via the ATP synthase

p. 206 CYU *understand* See Figure A9.4.

p. 207 CYU *analyze* Both fermentation and the ETC regenerate NAD^+ from NADH. In fermentation, the only ATP produced comes from glycolysis while the proton gradient formed by the ETC is used to make many more ATP per glucose. Your cells would not survive using fermentation alone due to the low yield of ATP from this process.

✔ TEST YOUR KNOWLEDGE

1. *remember* d **2.** *understand* c **3.** *remember* Most of the energy is stored in the form of NADH. **4.** *understand* a

✔ TEST YOUR UNDERSTANDING

5. *analyze* Both processes produce ATP from ADP and P_i, but substrate-level phosphorylation occurs when enzymes remove a "high-energy" phosphate from a substrate and directly transfer it to ADP, while oxidative phosphorylation occurs when electrons move through an ETC and produce a proton-motive force that drives ATP synthase. **6.** *apply* b **7.** *analyze* Both phosphofructokinase and isocitrate dehydrogenase are regulated by feedback inhibition, where the product of the reaction or series of reactions inhibits the enzyme activity. They differ in that phosphofructokinase is regulated by allosteric inhibition while isocitrate dehydrogenase is controlled by competitive inhibition. **8.** *understand* Oxidative phosphorylation is possible via a proton gradient that is established by redox reactions in the ETC. ATP synthase consists of a membrane-associated F_0 unit and a F_1 unit joined by a rotor shaft. When protons flow through the F_0 unit, it spins the rotor shaft within the fixed F_1 unit. This spinning shaft causes structural changes in the F_1 that drives the synthesis of ATP from ADP and P_i.

✔ TEST YOUR PROBLEM-SOLVING SKILLS

9. *create* When complex IV is blocked, electrons can no longer be transferred to oxygen, the final acceptor, and cellular respiration stops. Fermentation could keep glycolysis going, but it is unable to fuel a cell's energy needs over the long term. The low production of ATP would result in death, with those cells that lack the capacity for fermentation dying first. **10.** *apply* For each glucose molecule, two ATP are produced in glycolysis and two ATP are produced in the citric acid cycle via substrate-level phosphorylation. A total of 10 NADH and 2 $FADH_2$ molecules are produced from glycolysis, pyruvate oxidation, and the citric acid cycle. If each NADH were to yield 3 ATP, and each $FADH_2$ were to yield 2 ATP, then a total of 34 ATP would be produced via oxidative phosphorylation. Adding these totals would result in 38 ATP. A cell will not produce this much ATP, because the proton-motive force is used in other transport steps and because of other issues that may reduce the overall efficiency.

✔ PUT IT ALL TOGETHER: Case Study

11. *create* The active transport of protons against the proton gradient requires energy released from redox reactions in the ETC. If the strength of the proton motive force increases above the energy released by the redox reactions, then transport of protons will be halted. When this occurs, electron transport will slow down or stop. **12.** *analyze* The greatest difference in survival occurs around week 120. This is determined by drawing a vertical line at different time points and measuring the difference in survival between the two conditions. **13.** *analyze* An additional 5.5 years would be added to the life span of the U.S. population. One way to calculate this is to first divide the life span in DNP-treated mice (770 days) by the life span of the control (719 days), then multiply this factor (1.07) by the average life span of the U.S. population (79 years). The difference between this value (84.5 years) and the current average resulted in an increase of 5.5 years. **14.** *create* Isolated mitochondria from either DNP-treated mice or control mice could be treated with the same amount of pyruvate. As in Figure 9.17, the amount of ATP produced could be determined. If DNP is reducing the proton gradient, you would expect less ATP to be produced from these mitochondria compared to those obtained from the control mice. **15.** *analyze* To meet the ATP demands of the cell, more high-energy molecules, like glucose, would be broken down in DNP-treated mice instead of using them in anabolic reactions that contribute to increased body mass. **16.** *analyze* The increased respiration likely arises from an elevated demand for O_2 to drive electron transport to address the reduced efficiency of ATP synthesis. Death is likely due to insufficient ATP being produced to keep cells alive.

Chapter 10

IN-TEXT QUESTIONS AND EXERCISES

p. 211 *apply* See Figure A10.1. This reaction requires an input of energy because there are more high-energy chemical bonds in the products compared with the reactants, and there is a decrease in entropy.

Figure A9.4

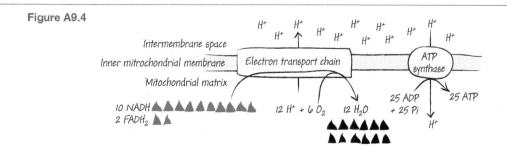

Figure A10.1

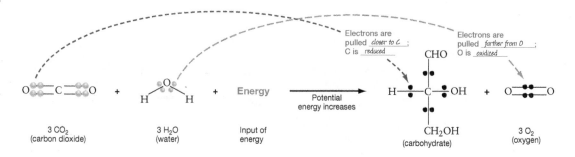

p. 211 Fig. 10.1 `apply` See Figure A10.1.

p. 212 Making Models 10.1 `understand` Figure A10.2 shows one example of a completed model.

p. 213 `apply` All of the macromolecules (proteins, nucleic acids, and carbohydrates) and lipids would be radiolabeled in a plant that is grown in $^{14}CO_2$. Because these molecules are organic, they would be made using raw materials produced by the fixation and reduction of $^{14}CO_2$ in photosynthesis.

p. 214 Fig. 10.6 `analyze` See Figure A10.3.

p. 216 Fig. 10.9 `apply` The energy state corresponding to a photon of blue light would be the same as shown, but the energy state corresponding to green light would be located between the energy states corresponding to red and blue photons.

p. 217 CYU `apply` The outer pigments would be more likely to absorb blue photons (short wavelength, high energy), and interior pigments would absorb red photons (long wavelength, low energy). This establishes a pathway to direct photon energy toward the reaction center since resonance energy is transferred from higher to lower energy levels.

p. 218 Fig. 10.11 `analyze` Yes—otherwise, changes in the production of oxygen could be due to differences in the number of chloroplasts, not differences in the rate of photosynthesis.

p. 220 `remember` Light → Antenna complex → Reaction center (electrons from water splitting are accepted here) → Pheophytin → ETC → Proton gradient → ATP synthase.

p. 223 `remember` See Figure A10.4.

p. 223 CYU `analyze` In mitochondria, electrons at a high-energy state are donated by NADH or $FADH_2$ (primary donors) and passed through an ETC to generate a proton-motive force. The electrons at a lower energy state at the end of the chain are accepted by O_2 (terminal acceptor) to form water. In chloroplasts, electrons at a lower energy state are donated by H_2O (primary donor), excited by photons or resonance energy, and passed through an ETC to generate a proton-motive

force. These electrons are then excited a second time by photons or resonance energy, and the electrons at a higher energy state are accepted by $NADP^+$ (terminal acceptor) to form NADPH.

p. 224 Fig. 10.18 `analyze` The researchers didn't have any basis for predicting these intermediates. They needed to perform the experiment to identify them.

p. 225 `apply` Each complete cycle requires 3 ATP and 2 NADPH molecules. To complete six runs through the cycle, a total of 18 ATP and 12 NADPH molecules are needed. By following the number of carbons, it is apparent that only three RuBP molecules are required, since they are fully regenerated every three cycles: 3 RuBP (15 carbons) fix and reduce 3 CO_2 to generate 6 G3P (18 carbons), yielding 1 G3P (3 carbons); the other five G3P are used to regenerate 3 RuBP (15 carbons).

p. 229 Fig. 10.25 `apply` The highest concentration of organic acids in the vacuoles of CAM plants would be found in the morning, since these acids are made during the night and used up during the day.

p. 229 CYU (1) `understand` (a) In C_3 plants, CO_2 is delivered to rubisco by diffusion through stomata. (b) In C_4 plants, the CO_2 that diffuses through stomata is first fixed by PEP carboxylase into four-carbon organic acids in mesophyll cells. These organic acids are then transported into bundle-sheath cells, where they release CO_2 to rubisco. (c) In CAM plants, CO_2 is delivered to rubisco in a two-step process similar to C_4 plants, but in the same cell. CAM plants take up CO_2 at night and the four-carbon organic acids are stored in the central vacuoles. During the day, the organic acids are processed to release CO_2 to rubisco. (2) `apply` The concentration of starch would be highest at the end of the day and lowest at the start of the day. Starch is made and stored in the chloroplasts of leaves during periods of high photosynthetic activity during the day. At night, it is broken down to make sucrose, which is transported throughout the plant to drive cellular respiration. (Cellular respiration also occurs during the day, but the impact is minimized due to the photosynthetic production of sugar.)

✔ **TEST YOUR KNOWLEDGE**

1. `remember` d **2.** `remember` d **3.** `remember` a **4.** `understand` The conversion of light energy to chemical energy first occurs when electrons are transferred from excited pigments to an electron carrier in a photosystem.

✔ **TEST YOUR UNDERSTANDING**

5. `understand` Most of the energy captured by chlorophyll in chloroplasts is converted into chemical energy by reducing electron acceptors in ETCs. When pigments are extracted, the antenna complexes, reaction centers, and ETCs have been disassembled, so the energy is given off as fluorescence and/or heat. **6.** `understand` The fixation phase is when CO_2 is fixed to RuBP by rubisco to form 3-phosphoglycerate (3PGA). The reduction phase uses ATP to phosphorylate the carbons and NADPH to reduce them with high-energy electrons to form G3P. The regeneration phase uses more ATP to convert some of the G3P to RuBP to continue the cycle. **7.** `apply` It would require 36 photons. To produce G3P from 3 CO_2 molecules and regenerate RuBP, a total of 6 NADPH and 9 ATP are required. Each NADPH is made by exciting two electrons from water in photosystem II and then again in photosystem I. This means that 24 photons are required for 6 NADPH, which would also produce 6 ATP. To make 9 ATP, three more pairs of electrons are required for a total 18 electrons that must be excited by 36 photons. **8.** `understand` Cellular respiration generates the most ATP used to drive cellular activities. If you said photosynthesis, then you might be thinking that the ATP produced in the light reactions is used in the cytosol. But the ATP produced by photosynthesis is used only in the stroma of chloroplasts for activities such as the production of G3P in the Calvin cycle.

✔ **TEST YOUR PROBLEM-SOLVING SKILLS**

9. `apply` (1) O_2, ATP, and NADPH would be formed by noncyclic electron flow. (2) No O_2 or NADPH would be formed, but ATP may be made by cyclic electron flow. (3) Initially, O_2 and NADPH would be formed by noncyclic electron flow, but no ATP would be made.

Figure A10.2

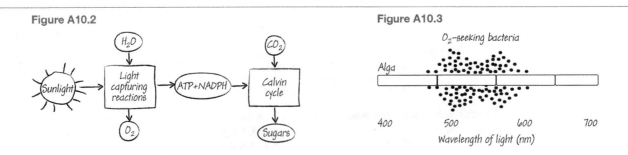

Figure A10.3

O_2-seeking bacteria

Alga

400   500   600   700

Wavelength of light (nm)

Figure A10.4

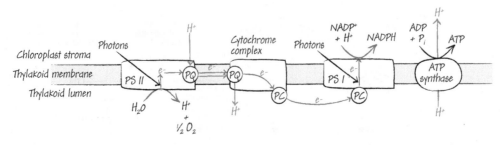

Without ATP, the Calvin cycle would halt and, once all the NADP$^+$ is reduced to NADPH, noncyclic electron flow would switch to cyclic electron flow. **10.** *analyze* b; the wavelength of light would fully excite PS I but is less likely to excite PS II, resulting in cyclic electron flow since few electrons could be harvested from water by PS II.

✓ **PUT IT ALL TOGETHER: Case Study**

11. *analyze* It is possible that some aquatic plants and algae require the C$_4$ pathway. If you said that it was not possible, you may be thinking that the role of the C$_4$ pathway is to avoid desiccation, which is not the case. This additional fixation step is used to increase the concentration of CO$_2$ to effectively drive carbon fixation by the Calvin cycle. Low CO$_2$ concentrations may (and do) exist in certain aquatic environments. **12.** *apply* The vast majority of the energy stored in the organic molecules present in fossil fuels, whether it is in plant or animal matter, originated from sunlight. **13.** *analyze* Biofuels are produced using CO$_2$ present in the atmosphere, so there would be no net release of CO$_2$ from the combustion of these molecules. **14.** *apply* The energy is likely being released from excited pigments in the form of fluorescence and/or heat. **15.** *analyze* The rate of photosynthesis increases over time in the strain with small antenna complexes when compared to the control. The engineered strain also reaches its maximum growth rate after around 24 hours, compared to 50 hours in the control. **16.** *analyze* The reduced antenna complexes would capture less light, allowing more light to pass through the water to reach microalgae at the bottom of the pool.

BIG PICTURE Energy for Life

p. 232 CYU (1) *understand* Photosynthesis uses H$_2$O as an electron donor and releases O$_2$ as a by-product; cellular respiration uses O$_2$ as an electron acceptor and releases H$_2$O as a by-product. **(2)** *understand* Photosynthesis uses CO$_2$ as a substrate to fix and reduce it to produce sugar; cellular respiration oxidizes sugar and releases CO$_2$ as a by-product. **(3)** *analyze* CO$_2$ fixation would essentially stop, but CO$_2$ would continue to be released by cellular respiration. CO$_2$ levels in the atmosphere would increase rapidly, and production of new plant tissue would cease—meaning that most animals would quickly starve to death. **(4)** *analyze* ATP "is used by" the Calvin cycle; photosystem I "yields" NADPH; FADH$_2$ "donates high-energy electrons" to the ETC.

Chapter 11

IN-TEXT QUESTIONS AND EXERCISES

p. 237 *apply* If the fibrous component of the primary cell wall were removed by digesting the microfibrils, then turgor pressure would cause the plant cell to swell until its plasma membrane burst, and the cell would die.

p. 238 CYU *analyze* Plant cell walls and animal ECMs are both fiber composites. In plant cell walls, the fibrous component consists of cross-linked cellulose fibers, and the ground substance consists of polysaccharides such as pectins. In animal ECMs, the fibrous component consists mainly of collagen fibrils, and the ground substance consists of proteoglycans.

p. 241 Fig. 11.10 *apply* *Prediction*: Cells treated with an antibody that blocks membrane proteins involved in adhesion will not adhere. *Prediction of null hypothesis*: Cells in all samples will adhere.

p. 241 *apply* All of the cells in the embryo would be capable of attaching to one another, regardless of the cell type. This would severely affect the development of different tissues and organs. The embryo would likely die.

p. 243 CYU (1) *analyze* The three structures differ in composition, but their function is similar. The middle lamella in plants is composed of pectins that glue adjacent cells together. Tight junctions are made up of membrane proteins that line up and "stitch" adjacent cells together. Desmosomes are rivet-like structures composed of proteins that link the cytoskeletons of adjacent cells. **(2)** *understand* At plasmodesmata, the plasma membranes of adjacent plant cells are continuous, and the cells share portions of the smooth endoplasmic reticulum. Gap junctions connect adjacent animal cells by forming protein-lined pores. Both structures are openings between cells that allow cytosol, including ions and small molecules, to be shared.

p. 244 Fig. 11.13 *apply* The conformational change would likely expose a nuclear localization signal on the receptor, which is required for the protein to be transported into the nucleus.

p. 247 *analyze* The spy is the signaling molecule that arrives at the cell surface (the castle gate). The guard is the G-protein-coupled receptor in the plasma membrane, and the queen is the G protein. The commander of the guard is the enzyme that is activated by the G protein to produce second messengers (the soldiers).

p. 248 *apply* After adrenaline binds to the receptor in heart and liver cells, the signal is processed via distinct signal transduction pathways that activate different proteins and thus result in different cell responses.

p. 249 Fig. 11.17 *analyze* (1) cell responses A, C, and possibly B at a low level; (2) cell responses A, B, and C; (3) cell responses B and C.

p. 249 CYU (1) *understand* Each signaling molecule binds to a specific receptor protein. A cell can respond to a signaling molecule only if it has the appropriate receptor. Only certain cell types will have the appropriate receptor for a given signaling molecule. **(2)** *understand* Signals are amplified if one or more steps in a signal transduction pathway, involving either second messengers or a phosphorylation cascade, result in the activation of multiple downstream molecules.

p. 250 *analyze* The signal transduction pathways—consisting of signaling molecules, receptors, and second messengers—are similarly organized in both unicellular and multicellular organisms. There is more variety in the means of transmitting the signal between cells in multicellular organisms than in unicellular organisms. For example, there are no gap junctions or plasmodesmata for direct intercellular signal transmission between unicellular organisms.

✓ **TEST YOUR KNOWLEDGE**

1. *understand* A fiber composite consists of cross-linked filaments that withstand tension and a ground substance that withstands compression. The cellulose microfibrils in plants and collagen fibrils in animals functionally resemble the steel rods in reinforced concrete. The pectins and other gelatinous polysaccharides in plants and proteoglycans in animals functionally resemble the concrete ground substance. **2.** *remember* a. Recall that all proteins in the ECM are made in the rough ER and then secreted into the extracellular space. **3.** *understand* d **4.** *understand* c

✓ **TEST YOUR UNDERSTANDING**

5. *analyze* b **6.** *understand* Dissociated sponge cells gradually began to aggregate, adhering to other cells of the same tissue type. Selective adhesion results from the presence of specific types of cell adhesion proteins in the plasma membrane, including cadherins. Each type of protein can bind only to proteins of the same type. **7.** *apply* For each Ras-GTP, you would need 10 pennies for kinase 1 ($0.10), 100 nickels for kinase 2 ($5.00), and 1000 dimes for kinase 3 ($100.00). Constructing the model would therefore require $105.10. **8.** *evaluate* Information from different signals may conflict or be reinforcing. Crosstalk between signaling pathways allows cells to integrate information from many signals at the same time instead of responding to each signal in isolation.

✓ **TEST YOUR PROBLEM-SOLVING SKILLS**

9. *analyze* (a) No amplification can occur because the number of signaling molecules dictates the size of the response. (b) Only one step is available for regulation, which includes either blocking the receptor or making it more responsive to the signaling molecule. (c) As with a signal transduction pathway, gene expression may be altered. Other types of responses, such as muscle contraction or the rapid mobilization of glucose, are not possible. **10.** *analyze* Antibody binding to the receptor may be causing the two parts of the receptor to dimerize. Since the signaling molecule normally activates the receptor by causing dimerization, the antibody could be activating the receptor by mimicking this interaction. The result would be activation of the phosphorylation cascade even in the absence of the signaling molecule.

✓ **PUT IT ALL TOGETHER: Case Study**

11. *understand* The pheromone–receptor complex activates the G protein by replacing the bound GDP with GTP. Activation breaks the G protein into two subunits, which then go on to affect the activity of other proteins. **12.** *apply* The protein related to Ras phosphorylates and activates a mitogen-activated protein kinase (MAPK). This active kinase phosphorylates and activates a second MAPK, which then phosphorylates and activates a third MAPK. The third kinase in this series then phosphorylates other proteins, triggering the cell response. **13.** *analyze* The scaffold protein, Ste5, increases the speed of the response by grouping the proteins that are involved. Since the number of proteins bound to Ste5 is limited, the amplification at each step in the signal transduction pathway is decreased compared to that in a pathway without a scaffold protein. **14.** *analyze* In *ptc1Δ* cells, the Ptc1 protein is not present, and the amount of binding between Fus3 and Ste5 remains high at concentrations of α factor that cause Fus3 to be released from Ste5 in wild-type cells. This suggests that Ste5 must be dephosphorylated by Ptc1 to release Fus3. **15.** *create* One possible hypothesis is that the proteins involved in signaling the assembly of microfilaments are grouped together with the receptor and have a limited ability to move beyond the area of signal reception. **16.** *create* The destruction of the cell wall may lead to osmotic lysis. To test the hypothesis that this is responsible for pheromone-induced cell death, you could add pheromone to cells in either a hypotonic solution or an isotonic solution and then measure the amount of cell death in each condition. You would expect to see more cell death in the hypotonic solution.

Chapter 12

IN-TEXT QUESTIONS AND EXERCISES

p. 255 Making Models 12.1 *apply* See Figure A12.1. Recall that after the chromosomes have replicated, each chromosome contains two attached chromatids.

p. 256 *apply* The graph would contain a straight horizontal line, indicating that the percentage of radiolabeled cells in the culture does not vary over time. The value of the line would be about 30 percent, reflecting the proportion of cells in the asynchronous culture that would have been radiolabeled during the pulse. (S phase is about a third of the cell cycle.)

p. 257 *understand* (1) DNA is the genetic material in chromosomes. (2) Chromosomes are made of chromatin, which is a complex of DNA and histone proteins. (3) Sister chromatids are identical copies of the same chromosome that are joined together.

p. 258 Fig. 12.5 *apply* (1) The prophase cell has replicated its DNA, so it will have twice as much DNA (120 picograms). Each chromosome will have two chromatids, but the number of chromosomes will remain at 22. (2) The anaphase cell still has 120 pg of DNA, but when the chromatids separate, each is defined as a daughter chromosome, so the cell has 44 chromosomes. (3) After cytokinesis, each daughter cell will have as much DNA (60 pg) and as many chromosomes (22) as the parent cell in G_1 phase. If you stated that the daughter cells have more or less DNA or chromosomes than the parent cell, recall that mitotic cell division does not change the number of chromosomes or the amount of DNA.

p. 260 *apply* See Table A12.1.

p. 261 Fig. 12.6 *apply* Daughter chromosomes will move toward the pole at the same rate as the darkened sections.

p. 263 CYU (1) *apply* See Figure A12.2. **(2)** *understand* Type 1: The shrinkage of kinetochore microtubules transports daughter chromosomes to the opposite poles of the spindle. Type 2: The push against polar microtubules

by motor proteins and the pull on astral microtubules by other motors on the plasma membrane move the spindle poles to opposite sides of the cell. **(3)** *analyze* Both cell types use cytokinesis to divide the cytoplasm into two daughter cells. Plant cells produce a cell plate that grows in the middle of the spindle and fuses with the plasma membrane. Animal cells use a cleavage furrow in the middle of the spindle to draw in the plasma membrane, which eventually fuses with itself.

p. 264 Fig. 12.10 *create* Remove a sample of cytoplasm from cells in M phase and use centrifugation to separate the cytosol from the organelles. Microinject immature oocytes with either the supernatant, which contains the cytosol, or the pellet, which contains the organelles, and evaluate the effect on inducing M phase.

p. 264 Fig. 12.11 *analyze* If the cyclin concentration did not decline, MPF would remain active and the cell would be stuck in M phase.

p. 265 *understand* MPF consists of a cyclin and a Cdk, and it is turned on by phosphorylation at the Cdk's activating site and dephosphorylation at the Cdk's inhibitory site. Enzymes that degrade cyclin reduce MPF levels.

p. 266 CYU *understand* (1) The four checkpoints are (1) the G_1 checkpoint between G_1 and S; (2) the G_2 checkpoint between G_2 and M; (3) the first M checkpoint between metaphase and anaphase; and (4) the second M checkpoint between anaphase and telophase. Without these four checkpoints, cells could be overproduced in multicellular organisms, and cell division could result in daughter cells that are inviable or have defects in their genetic material.

✔ **TEST YOUR KNOWLEDGE**

1. *remember* b **2.** *remember* d **3.** *remember* c **4.** *remember* The sister chromatids on replicated chromosomes separate, and the spindle poles are pushed farther apart.

✔ **TEST YOUR UNDERSTANDING**

5. *apply* All of the chromosomes must be replicated during S phase, the spindle apparatus must connect with the kinetochores of each sister chromatid in prometaphase, the sister chromatids of each replicated chromosome must be partitioned in anaphase, and the daughter chromosomes must be divided between two daughter cells by cytokinesis. **6.** *understand* Daughter chromosomes were observed to move toward the poles faster than the marked regions of fluorescently labeled kinetochore microtubules. **7.** *analyze* False, True, True, False. If the Rb protein is nonfunctional or G_1 cyclin is overexpressed, E2F expression would immediately cause cells to enter S phase. **8.** *analyze* The absence of growth factors in normal cells would cause the cells to arrest in G_1 phase, and eventually all the cells in the culture would be in G_1. The cancerous cells would be unlikely to depend on these growth factors, so those cells would not arrest and would continue through the cell cycle.

✔ **TEST YOUR PROBLEM-SOLVING SKILLS**

9. *analyze* a. Adding the length of time spent in each phas allows you to determine that the cell cycle is 8.5 hours long. After 9 hours, all radiolabeled cells would have passed through a full cycle and be in either S phase or G_2—none would be mitotic (in M phase). **10.** *apply* The embryo passes through multiple rounds of the cell cycle, but cytokinesis does not occur during the M phases.

✔ **PUT IT ALL TOGETHER: Case Study**

11. *apply* Microtubules are actively polymerized during the start of M phase, when the mitotic spindle is produced. During anaphase, the kinetochore microtubules are depolymerized as daughter chromosomes move to opposite poles of the cell. At the end of M phase, the spindle microtubules are depolymerized to remove the spindle before entering G_1. **12.** *apply* The second M phase checkpoint. If microtubule depolymerization were inhibited, the chromosomes would not completely separate in anaphase, and the cells would arrest in M phase. **13.** *analyze* See Figure A12.3. The asynchronous

---

Figure A12.1

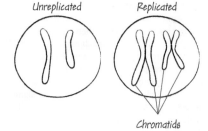

Unreplicated   Replicated

Chromatids

Figure A12.2

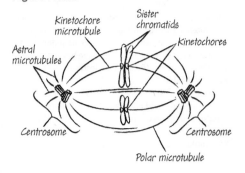

Kinetochore microtubule

Sister chromatids

Kinetochores

Astral microtubules

Centrosome   Centrosome

Polar microtubule

Table A12.1

	Prophase	Prometaphase	Metaphase	Anaphase	Telophase
Spindle apparatus	Starts to form	Contacts and moves chromosomes	Anchors poles to membrane and produces tension at kinetochores	Pulls chromatids apart	Defines site of cytokinesis
Nuclear envelope	Present	Disintegrates	Nonexistent	Nonexistent	Re-forms
Chromosomes	Condense	Attach to microtubules	Held at metaphase plate	Sister chromatids separate into daughter chromosomes	Collect at opposite poles

Figure A12.3

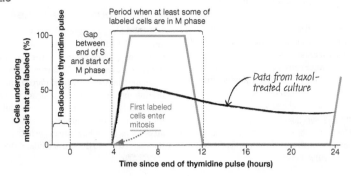

Period when at least some of labeled cells are in M phase

Gap between end of S and start of M phase

Data from taxol-treated culture

First labeled cells enter mitosis

Cells undergoing mitosis that are labeled (%)

Radioactive thymidine pulse

Time since end of thymidine pulse (hours)

culture would arrest in M phase, so after the labeled cells pass through G_2, they would remain in M phase along with other cells that were in G_2 during the pulse (resulting in only 50 percent of the M phase cells being labeled). The percentage of labeled mitotic cells would decrease over time as additional unlabeled cells accumulate in M phase. **14.** *create* The stathmin protein decreases the stability of microtubules. When stathmin is absent, the microtubule-stabilizing effect of Taxol is enhanced, and the cells are more likely to arrest. As a result, the tumors do not grow. **15.** *apply* The cyclin-dependent kinase subunit of MPF is the enzyme responsible. **16.** *create* Inactivating genes for G_1 cyclins or E2F could serve as an alternative therapy to arrest cancerous cells in G_1.

Chapter 13

IN-TEXT QUESTIONS AND ANSWERS

p. 273 *apply* Haploid number is $n = 4$; the organism is diploid, and $2n = 8$.

p. 273 Making Models 13.1 *apply* See Figure A13.1.

p. 275 *apply* See Figure A13.2. Because sister chromatids come from replication of the single double-helical molecule of DNA in the unreplicated chromosome, there is no difference in the genetic information present in the unreplicated and replicated chromosomes, so it makes sense to call both these structures one chromosome even though they look quite different from one another.

p. 279 *apply* There will be four double-helical molecules of DNA in each fruit fly gamete because the 8 replicated chromosomes in a diploid cell are reduced to 4 replicated chromosomes per cell at the end of meiosis I. Each of these replicated chromosomes contains two double-helical molecules of DNA. In meiosis II, the sister chromatids of each replicated chromosome are separated. Each cell now contains 4 unreplicated chromosomes, each with a single double-helical molecule of DNA. Note how one chromosome may contain one or two molecules of DNA depending on whether it is unreplicated or replicated.

p. 276 *apply* Because mitosis separates sister chromatids of single chromosomes and there is no need for homologous chromosomes to pair, mitosis in a triploid cell, or a cell of any level of ploidy, can occur easily. In contrast, chromosome pairing is essential for proper separation of homologous chromosomes in meiosis. Since it's impossible to pair three of anything, the three copies of each chromosome in a triploid cannot be separated into daughter cells in a reproducible way.

p. 280 CYU (1) *analyze* During anaphase I, homologs (not sister chromatids, as in mitosis) are separated, making the cells produced by meiosis I haploid. **(2)** *analyze* The separation of homologous chromosomes at meiosis I reduces both chromosome number and DNA amount in each of the daughter cells. However, each chromosome remains in a replicated state with two double-helical molecules of DNA. In meiosis II, the sister chromatids of the replicated chromosomes separate. This keeps the number of chromosomes in each daughter cell the same, but it reduces the amount of DNA in each daughter cell. The key to understanding this event is that one chromosome can contain either one double-helical DNA molecule or two, depending on whether the chromosome is unreplicated or replicated. In either case, it's still one chromosome.

p. 282 Making Models 13.2 *apply* See Figure A13.3.

p. 282 *apply* Each gamete would inherit either all maternal or all paternal chromosomes. This would limit genetic variation in the offspring by preventing many possible combinations of maternal and paternal chromosomes in gametes.

p. 282 CYU (1) *apply* Crossing over increases the genetic diversity of daughter cells by creating many different combinations of maternal and paternal alleles along each of the daughter chromosomes. **(2)** *apply* In outcrossing of $2n = 4$ individuals, each parent produces four types of gametes. Using the logic developed in the description of how many different combinations are possible in human fertilization, there would be $4 \times 4 = 16$ genetically different offspring produced by outcrossing in this situation.

p. 285 Fig. 13.14 *apply* There would be 240 more. (Notice that the number of child-producing individuals in the

sexual population doubles at each generation, but in the asexual population, there is a quadrupling of these individuals at each generation. Therefore, after 4 generations of reproduction [this is what's needed to create generation 5], there will be $2^4 = 16$ child-producing offspring in the sexual population and $4^4 = 256$ in the asexual population. The base in each equation is the fold increase at each generation, and the exponent is the number of generations; look back at Figure 13.14 to see why these numbers make sense.) This diagram shows that slight differences in population growth rate can quickly lead to big differences in the number of individuals over many generations.

p. 286 Fig. 13.15 *apply* The rate of outcrossing is predicted to rise initially, as the pathogen selects for resistant worms, and then to fall as the worms in the population gain resistance and take advantage of the increased numbers of offspring possible with self-fertilization of hermaphrodites.

✓ TEST YOUR KNOWLEDGE

1. *remember* a (If you answered c, be careful not to mistake sister chromatids for a homologous chromosome pair.) **2.** *understand* b **3.** *remember* 1/2 (This is because half of a person's chromosomes come from the father and half from the mother, regardless of the sex of the individual.) **4.** *remember* c

✓ TEST YOUR UNDERSTANDING

5. *understand* Homologous chromosomes are similar in size and shape, they have the same genes (but often different alleles), and they originate from different parents. Sister chromatids are found in replicated chromosomes. They contain exact copies of the single double-helical molecule of DNA that was present in the unreplicated chromosome and replicated during S phase. **6.** *analyze* At the end of meiosis I. (This is because in a kidney cell before DNA replication, there are pairs of each chromosome, with one double-helical molecule of DNA per chromosome; at the end of meiosis I, each cell has only one of each type of chromosome, but each chromosome has two double-helical molecules

---

Figure A13.1

Unreplicated chromosome (one double-helical molecule of DNA)

Replicated chromosome (two double-helical molecules of DNA)

Sister chromatids

Figure A13.2

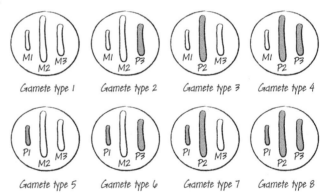

Gamete type 1   Gamete type 2   Gamete type 3   Gamete type 4

Gamete type 5   Gamete type 6   Gamete type 7   Gamete type 8

Figure A13.3

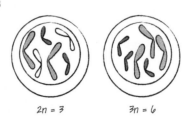

$2n = 3$ $3n = 6$

of DNA.) **7.** *apply* b (In meiosis I, chromosome number is reduced by half [78 → 39], and each chromosome retains two double-helical molecules of DNA [39 chromosomes and 78 double-helical molecules of DNA].) **8.** *analyze* Tetraploids produce diploid gametes, which combine with a haploid gamete from a diploid individual to form triploid offspring.

✔ **TEST YOUR PROBLEM-SOLVING SKILLS**

9. *apply* c (Since $2n = 3$, independent assortment creates $2^n = 2^3 = 8$ different combinations of chromosomes. One of these combinations is made up of paternal chromosomes only. Therefore, a haploid cell has a 1/8 chance of receiving only paternal chromosomes.) **10.** *create* (a) Such a study might be done in the laboratory, controlling conditions in identical populations of rotifers infected with fungus. One population would be kept moist; the other population of rotifers would be allowed to dry out. After various periods of time, water would be added to each population and then the rotifers would be observed to see if fungal infections reappeared. (b) Wind disperses the rotifer to new and often pathogen-free environments. In this case, the ticket to a sex-free existence is not genetic diversity but the evolution of an alternative means of evading pathogens. This occurs when fungus-infected rotifers rid themselves of the pathogen by drying.

✔ **PUT IT ALL TOGETHER: Case Study**

11. *evaluate* The results are consistent with the hypothesis because they show that as females age, the amount of cohesin falls, the separation between kinetochores increases, and the percentage of aneuploid eggs goes up. **12.** *understand* This relationship is logical because of cohesin's role in holding sister chromatids together. As cohesin levels fall, there is less "glue" to hold the sister chromatids together and therefore greater separation between the kinetochores on each duplicated chromosome. **13.** *analyze* This attachment is necessary to pull each homologous pair of chromosomes apart, moving one homolog to one pole and the other homolog to the other pole. This event accomplishes segregation of the homologs to different daughter cells. **14.** *analyze* One possible explanation is that the greater separation between kinetochores seen in older females allows spindle fibers from each pole to attach to a chromosome. The smaller separation between kinetochores in younger females may help to prevent this error. **15.** *analyze* There is a sharp increase in the percentage of aneuploid eggs in mice between 12 and 15 months of age. Women in their forties see a sharp increase in aneuploid children. Therefore, a 15-month-old mouse would correspond roughly to a woman in her mid-forties. **16.** *analyze* After examining the information presented in Figure 13.13, you can tell the woman that while she's right about having a greater chance of having a child with Down syndrome than if she had conceived at a younger age, her chances are still very good—roughly 59 out of 60—of having a child without Down syndrome. You can say this because a 42-year-old woman has a 1-in-60 chance of having a child with Down syndrome.

Chapter 34

IN-TEXT QUESTIONS AND ANSWERS

p. 705 Fig. 34.1 *apply* New branches and leaves should develop to the right (the plant will also lean that way); new lateral roots will develop to the left.

p. 706 Fig. 34.2 *analyze* Surface area/volume = 420,000 μm²/8,000,000 μm³ = 0.0525/μm.

p. 706 Making Models 34.1 *analyze* The long, tubelike structure will have the same volume as the large cube (8 mm³). However, the surface of the tube is 34 mm². Therefore, tube has more surface area than the cube.

p. 707 Fig. 34.3 *understand* Grasses that are shallow rooted would absorb water when it first enters soil. Plants with long taproots can reach water deep underground, which would be beneficial during periods of drought.

p. Table 34.1 *understand* Root cells need oxygen to carry out aerobic cellular respiration, which generates ATP needed to keep cells alive.

p. 709 Fig. 34.4 *understand* The individuals are genetically identical—thus, any differences in size or shape in the different habitats are due to phenotypic plasticity and not genetic differences.

p. 711 Fig. 34.5 *apply* Although parts (b) and (c) may look like multiple leaves, they each show just one leaf composed of multiple leaflets. Each compound leaf represents just one leaf defined by a single axillary bud.

p. 712 *apply* Phenotypic plasticity is more important (1) in environments where conditions vary because it gives individuals the ability to change the growth pattern of their roots, shoots, and stems to access sunlight, water, and other nutrients as the environment changes; and (2) in long-lived species because it gives individuals a mechanism to change their growth pattern as the environment changes throughout their lifetime.

p. 713 CYU (1) *remember* See Figure A34.1. **(2)** *analyze* The generalized body of a flowering plant has a taproot with many lateral roots and broad leaves. Examples of deviations from this generalized body structure follow. Modified roots: Unlike taproots, *fibrous roots* do not have one central root, and *adventitious roots* arise from stems. Modified stems: *Stolons* grow along the soil and grow roots and leaves at each node, and *rhizomes* grow horizontally underground. Both of these modified stems function in asexual reproduction. Modified leaves: The *needlelike leaves* of cacti don't lose water to transpiration compared with typical broad leaves, and they protect the plant from herbivory. *Tendrils* on climbing plants are modified leaves specialized for wrapping around trees or other substrates to facilitate climbing.

p. 715 Fig. 34.11 *understand* Many possible answers; for example, in leaf cells, genes encoding proteins involved in photosynthesis and formation of stomata, the cuticle, and trichomes would be expressed. These genes wouldn't be expressed in the root cells.

p. 717 *apply* Unlike many other plant cells, tracheids (and vessel elements) perform their function after they die. The remaining secondary cell walls serve as conduits through which water flows, by a process that does not require ATP. Therefore, the poison will have no effect on water transport through the injected tracheids.

p. 717 CYU (1) *analyze* Plant cells contain a cell wall found exterior to the cell membrane, while animal cells lack a cell wall. Plant cells are connected via plasmodesmata and may contain chloroplasts, while animals lack these structures. **(2)** *remember* Epidermal cells are flattened and lack chloroplasts; they secrete the cuticle (in shoots) or extend water and nutrient-absorbing root hairs (in roots) and protect the plant. Parenchyma cells are "metabolic workhorse cells" found throughout the plant body; they perform photosynthesis and synthesize, store, and/or transport materials. Collenchyma cells function largely in supporting the shoot. Tracheids are long, slim cells with pits in their secondary cell walls; they are found in xylem and are dead when mature, and they conduct water and solutes up the plant. Vessel elements are similar to tracheids, but are wider and have perforations in their end walls (regions with no primary or secondary cell wall). Sieve-tube elements are long, thin cells found in phloem; they are alive when mature and conduct sugars and other solutes up and down the plant.

p. 719 Fig. 34.17 *understand* The youngest tissues are found at the tip while the oldest tissues are found at the base.

p. 720 *understand* The zones of cellular division and cellular elongation are actively pushed through soil. The zone of maturation remains in place (this is why root hairs can emerge here without being torn off as the root grows through soil).

p. 721 CYU *understand* The apical meristem gives rise to the three primary meristems. The apical meristem is a single mass of cells localized at the tip of a root or shoot; the primary meristems are localized in distinctive sites behind the apical meristem.

p. 723 Fig. 34.21 *understand* Stems, branches, and roots grow from their tips. Although a tree can get taller with each passing year, the position of any existing region of the trunk will stay at that same height because new

Figure A34.1

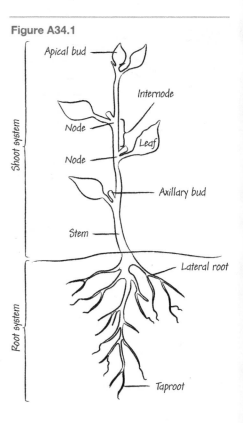

growth is initiated in the apical meristem. Thus, the birdfeeder will remain at 6 feet.

p. 724 Fig. 34.23 *understand* You should label a light band as early wood, and a dark band as late wood; both bands together comprise one growth ring.

p. 725 CYU *understand* See Figure A34.2.

✔ TEST YOUR KNOWLEDGE

1. *remember* a 2. *understand* b 3. *understand* c 4. *understand* a

✔ TEST YOUR UNDERSTANDING

5. *create* The general function of both systems is to acquire resources: The shoot system captures light and carbon dioxide; the root system absorbs water and nutrients. Vascular tissue is continuous throughout both the shoot and root systems. Diversity in roots and shoots enables plants of different species to live together in the same environment without directly competing for resources. 6. *understand* Continuous growth enhances phenotypic plasticity because it allows plants to grow and respond to changes or challenges in their environment (such as changes in light and water availability). 7. *apply* Cuticle reduces water loss; stomata facilitate gas exchange. Plants from wet habitats should have a relatively large number of stomata and thin cuticle. Plants living in dry habitats should have relatively few stomata and thick cuticle. 8. *apply* Tree trunks grow wider because of cell divisions that occur only in the vascular and cork cambia (both located just underneath the bark). Secondary xylem (wood) remains in place once it is formed. Therefore, the eggs will remain in their current position (1 inch out from the center).

✔ TEST YOUR PROBLEM-SOLVING SKILLS

9. *apply* Asparagus—stem; Brussels sprouts—lateral buds; celery—petiole; spinach—leaf (petiole and blade); carrots—taproot; potato—modified stem. 10. *apply* Girdling disrupts transport of solutes in secondary phloem. The tree's root system starves.

✔ PUT IT ALL TOGETHER: Case Study

11. *create* Acid rain may damage apical meristems and likely have a negative effect on primary growth. Trees exposed to acid rain will probably be shorter than trees exposed to neutral rain. 12. *analyze* Chinaberry trees treated with acid rain had about a 40 percent reduction in height. Trees treated with acid rain were approximately 15 cm tall while those treated with distilled water were approximately 25 cm tall—a difference of about 10 cm. Thus, 10 cm/25 cm = 40%. 13. *analyze* The apical meristem was negatively affected. 14. *evaluate* Strongly acidic rain had little effect on height (apical meristem activity) in *C. camphora*, but it had a major impact in *M. azedarach*. The *C. camphora* may have been protected from the effects of acid rain by having thick, resistant leaves with a thick cuticle; tough, resistant bark; or roots that could still function in acidic soil. 15. *create* Acid rain may cause damage to the vascular cambium and will likely have a negative impact on secondary growth in chinaberry trees (but probably not in camphor trees based on the primary growth results presented). Chinaberry trees exposed to acid rain will probably produce less wood than trees exposed to rain with a neutral pH. 16. *apply* Possibilities include negative effects on leaf production, number and quality of flowers and seeds, root formation, and any other component of plant growth.

Figure A34.2

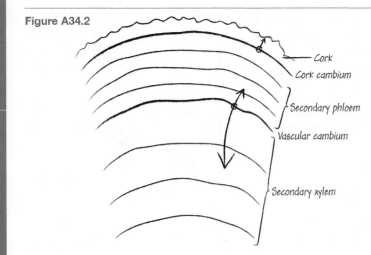

Cork
Cork cambium
Secondary phloem
Vascular cambium
Secondary xylem

Chapter 38

IN-TEXT QUESTIONS AND EXERCISES

p. 795 *evaluate* (1) The microsporocyte divides by meiosis to generate male spores; the megasporocyte divides by meiosis to generate female spores. (2) In angiosperms, the female gametophyte stays within the ovary at the base of the flower even after it matures and produces an egg cell. Fertilization and seed development take place in the same location.

p. 799 Fig. 38.7 *evaluate* A gametophyte is the multicellular individual that produces gametes by mitosis. The pollen grain is a gametophyte because it is multicellular and produces sperm by mitosis.

p. 799 CYU (1) *analyze* Both are diploid cells that divide by meiosis to produce spores. The megasporocyte produces a megaspore (female spore); a microsporocyte produces a microspore (male spore). **(2)** *analyze* Both are multicellular individuals that produce gametes by mitosis. The female gametophyte is larger than the male gametophyte and produces an egg; the male gametophyte produces sperm.

p. 802 *apply* The endosperm nucleus in the central cell is triploid; the zygote is diploid; the synergid and other cells remaining from the female gametophyte are haploid.

p. 802 CYU (1) *evaluate* Insects feed on nectar and/or pollen in flowers. Flowers provide food rewards that encourage insects to visit them. The individuals that attract the most pollinators produce the most offspring. **(2)** *understand* One product of double fertilization is the diploid zygote, which will eventually grow by mitosis into a mature sporophyte. The other product is the triploid endosperm nucleus, which will grow by mitosis to form a source of nutrients for the embryo.

p. 804 Fig. 38.13 *create* Hypothesis: Fruit changes color when it ripens as a signal to fruit eaters. The color change is advantageous because seeds are not mature in unripe fruit and are unlikely to survive. Fruit eaters disperse mature seeds in ripe fruit, and these are more likely to survive and eventually germinate.

p. 805 Fig. 38.14 *understand* Hackberries served as a control to demonstrate that animals that avoided chilies were hungry.

p. 806 Fig. 38.15 *analyze* Beans—their cotyledons are aboveground and green.

p. 807 Fig. 38.16 *apply* See Figure A38.1.

p. 808 *apply* A cotyledon and a radicle develop into organs with distinct functions, but both are composed of the same tissues: Epidermis is derived from protoderm, ground tissue is derived from ground meristem, and vascular tissue is derived from the procambium.

p. 810 CYU (1) *understand* As long as a meristem exists, it has the potential to divide and produce new cells, tissues, and organs. **(2)** *create* If the plant could be genetically engineered with a mutant form of the CLAUSA gene, then that would likely result in a shift in leaf type from simple to compound.

p. 812 *understand* Mutual inhibition between the A and C genes helps create separate regions of gene expression. If C gene expression is lost, then the inhibition of A gene expression is also lost, and A genes are expressed in their normal location and where they are normally inhibited by C gene expression.

p. 813 CYU (1) *analyze* Plants generate many reproductive structures—flowers—many times and in many places during the plant's life. Plant reproductive cells are created from vegetative cells, not cells that are set aside early in development as reproductive cells. In contrast, animals form reproductive structures (ovaries and testes) in set locations, produce reproductive structures only once during development, and set aside specialized reproductive cells (the germ line) early in their development. **(2)** *analyze* In both plants and animals, mutations in homeotic genes result in structures growing in the wrong location in place of the appropriate structure (e.g., by forming petals where stamens should be or developing legs in place of antennae).

✔ TEST YOUR KNOWLEDGE

1. *remember* c **2.** *remember* Sperm and eggs are formed by mitosis, whereas megasporocytes (female) and microsporocytes (male) undergo meiosis to generate megaspores and microspores, respectively. These divide mitotically to give rise to female and male gametophytes—the embryo sac and pollen grain, respectively. **3.** *remember* d **4.** *remember* c

✔ TEST YOUR UNDERSTANDING

5. *understand* c **6.** *analyze* Outcrossing increases genetic diversity among offspring, making them more likely to survive if environmental conditions change from the parental generation. However, outcrossing requires cross-pollination to be successful. Self-fertilization results in relatively low genetic diversity among offspring but ensures that pollination succeeds. **7.** *understand* Just like the three tissue layers in plant embryos, the tissues produced in the SAMs and RAMs of a 300-year-old oak tree can differentiate into all of the specialized cell types found in a mature plant. **8.** *understand* Human embryonic stem cells and meristem cells are both capable of extensive cell divisions that ultimately give rise to all of the cells within the adult person or plant, respectively.

✔ TEST YOUR PROBLEM-SOLVING SKILLS

9. *evaluate* Acorns have a large, edible mass and are usually animal dispersed (e.g., by squirrels that store them and forget some). Cherries have an edible fruit and are animal dispersed. Burrs stick to animals and are dispersed as the animals move around. Dandelion seeds float in wind. To estimate the distance that each type of seed is dispersed from the parent, (1) set up "seed traps" to capture seeds at various distances from the parent plant; (2) sample locations at various distances from the parent and analyze young individuals—using genetic techniques introduced in Chapter 20 to determine if they are offspring from the parent being studied; (3) mark seeds, if possible, and find them again after dispersal. **10.** *create* See Figure A38.2 for one possible solution. Notice that by using just two genes, each with two possible states (either on or off), four different outcomes, or floral structures, are possible.

✔ PUT IT ALL TOGETHER: Case Study

11. *analyze* Bees likely use visual cues such as color and patterns (possibly including ultraviolet patterns), and they also use scent when locating gooseberry flowers. Bees are likely looking for nutrient rewards such as pollen or nectar. **12.** *analyze* Flowers that were pollinated by bees did form fruits with significantly higher mass. However, there was no significant difference between number of seeds per fruit of self-pollinated and bee-pollinated flowers. **13.** *evaluate* Cross-pollination increases genetic diversity in the offspring (seeds). Self-pollination requires only one plant and therefore is advantageous because it doesn't depend on insects or other pollinators. **14.** *analyze* Fruits produce by bee-pollinated flowers are approximately 35 percent larger. **15.** *analyze* At least 240 ovules per carpel (since fruits from bee-pollinated flowers contain roughly that many seeds). **16.** *evaluate* The recent decline in bee populations is indeed a major concern for food production on a global scale. Fewer bees means lower crop production. This problem will make it more difficult to feed and sustain the increasing number of people worldwide.

Figure A38.1

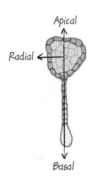

Apical

Radial

Basal

Figure A38.2

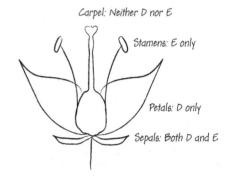

Carpel: Neither D nor E

Stamens: E only

Petals: D only

Sepals: Both D and E

BIG PICTURE — Plant and Animal Form and Function

p. 816 CYU (1) (analyze) Plants and animals may accumulate compounds in the epidermis and skin (such as waxes and other lipids) that reduce water loss. Both plants and animals evolved closable openings in this barrier to allow regulated gas exchange. Plants and animals may also change the amount of the body exposed to the sun (in plants by moving leaves, in animals by changing posture or taking shelter) to reduce evaporative water loss. **(2)** (analyze) Plants have alternation of generations including a multicellular haploid stage, whereas the haploid stage in animals is single celled. **(3)** (analyze) Very large animals and plants have strong supporting structures such as thick bones or trunks that withstand the force of gravity. They also need elaborate internal transport systems to bring nutrients to each cell and carry wastes away. **(4)** (analyze) Cellular respiration fits into one of the key functions for survival—Nutrition. Both plants and animals depend on sugar (produced by plants via photosynthesis) as their energy source to make ATP via cellular respiration.

Chapter 39

IN-TEXT QUESTIONS AND ANSWERS

p. 820 Fig. 39.2 (create) In each graph, the bars for treated and control males would have the same height.

p. 823 Fig. 39.4 (apply) Most neurons have an axon, which transmits signals to specific cells and tissues rather than widely throughout the body.

p. 824 (apply) The inside surface of the mouth contains stratified epithelium; it is subjected to wear and tear from food. The gas exchange surface of the lungs contains simple epithelium; its thinness (a single cell layer) facilitates the diffusion of gases across it.

p. 826 CYU (understand) (Many examples are possible.) *Connective tissues* consist of cells embedded in a matrix. The density of the matrix determines the rigidity of the connective tissue and its function in padding/protection, structural support, or transport. *Nervous tissue* is composed of neurons and supporting cells. Neurons have long projections that function as "biological wires" for transmitting electrical signals. *Muscle tissue* has cells that can contract in a coordinated fashion. The branching of cardiac muscle cells allows electrical signals to spread through them, resulting in their coordinated contraction and relaxation, which allows the heart to pump blood. *Epithelial tissue* consists of one or more layers of closely packed cells with distinct apical and basolateral sides. Structures that hold the cells tightly together, such as tight junctions and desmosomes, enable epithelial tissues to protect underlying tissues and to regulate the passage of materials.

p. 827 Fig. 39.10 (apply) The Chihuahua must eat relatively more because it has a higher mass-specific metabolic rate than the Great Dane.

p. 828 Fig. 39.11 (apply) Adult salmon should show virtually 100% of oxygen uptake via gills. Data for adult salmon would be in the top-right corner of the graph. (The horizontal scale would have to be extended far to the right to account for the much larger body mass of adults.)

p. 828 CYU (apply) Lungless salamanders that breathe through their skin are all small compared to salamanders with lungs. Their surface area/volume ratios are high enough that gas exchange across the skin can support the salamanders' metabolism.

p. 831 (apply) Individuals could acclimatize by normal homeostatic mechanisms (increased sweating, seeking shade, etc.). Individuals with alleles that allowed them to function better at higher temperatures would be likely to produce more offspring than individuals without those alleles. Over time, this would lead to adaptation via natural selection.

p. 834 CYU (analyze) Endotherms can remain active during the winter and at night and sustain high levels of aerobic activities such as running or flying, but they require large amounts of food energy. Ectotherms need much less food and can devote a larger proportion of their food intake to reproduction, but they have a harder time maintaining high activity levels at night or in cold weather.

✔ TEST YOUR KNOWLEDGE

1. (understand) True **2.** (understand) b **3.** (understand) b **4.** (understand) a

✔ TEST YOUR UNDERSTANDING

5. (understand) *Absorptive sections* have many folds and projections that increase their surface area for absorption. *Capillaries* have a high surface area because they are thin and highly branched, making exchange of substances more rapid. *Beaks of Galápagos finches* have sizes and shapes that correlate with the type of food each species eats. Large beaks are used to crack large seeds; long, thin beaks are used to pick insects off surfaces; etc. *Fish gills* contain thin, flattened structures with a large surface area, which facilitates the exchange of gases and wastes. **6.** (analyze) A frog can move, breathe, and digest much faster at 35°C than at 5°C because enzymes work faster (rates of chemical reactions increase) at higher temperatures. The frog will need much more food energy during the summer to support its higher metabolic rate. **7.** (understand) Because endotherms generate much of their body heat metabolically, they can adjust the amount of heat produced to maintain their body temperature near the set point. Ectotherms cannot produce as much heat metabolically, so their body temperatures will decline when ambient temperatures go down and will rise when ambient temperatures go up or when they can bask in the sun. **8.** (understand) See Figure A39.1. The graph shows that as size (radius) increases, the volume increases more rapidly than the surface area.

✔ TEST YOUR PROBLEM-SOLVING SKILLS

9. (apply) King Kong is endothermic, and his huge mass would generate a great deal of heat. His relatively small surface area compared to that of a normal-sized gorilla would not be able to dissipate the heat—especially if the surface were covered with insulating fur. **10.** (apply) *Apatosaurus (Brontosaurus)* was likely homeothermic, given its huge size. Due to its low surface area/volume ratio, its body temperature would not change much between day and night because it takes a long time to lose or gain heat across such a relatively small surface area.

✔ PUT IT ALL TOGETHER: Case Study

11. (apply) The surface area to volume ratio is higher for mainland tortoises because their body size is smaller. **12.** (understand) The mainland tortoises need to eat more food per gram of body mass because their mass-specific metabolic rate is higher. **13.** (understand) c **14.** (understand) False. The body temperature of ectotherms does not necessarily match the ambient temperature. If a tortoise is basking in a sunny field, the solar radiation might raise its body temperature well above ambient, and the tortoise's low surface area/volume ratio would cause it to retain that heat for a long time. **15.** (apply) The small tortoise from the mainland would be more poikilothermic (the temperature would rise higher during the day and drop lower at night) because heat would be transferred more readily between the environment and body of the small tortoise due to its high surface area/volume ratio. **16.** (understand) Tortoises are ectotherms, but it is inaccurate to describe them as cold blooded because their blood could actually be quite warm. This is especially true of giant tortoises, whose low surface area/volume ratios would cause them to lose heat so slowly that their body temperature could be elevated well above ambient temperature.

Chapter 40

IN-TEXT QUESTIONS AND EXERCISES

p. 838 (understand) Marine animals face dehydration because the high osmolarity of seawater causes them to lose water by osmosis. Terrestrial animals face dehydration because they constantly lose water to the air via evaporation from their body surfaces.

p. 841 CYU (understand) Marine cartilaginous fishes osmoconform, so they do not lose water to their environment. As a result, they do not need to drink seawater, so they do not absorb as much NaCl from drinking. However, they must expend energy to make proteins that protect their cells from the toxic effects of maintaining high urea concentrations in their tissues. Marine bony fishes osmoregulate, so they do not need to make those proteins. However, they must drink seawater, which increases the amount of NaCl they absorb, so they must expend energy to excrete the NaCl.

Figure A39.1

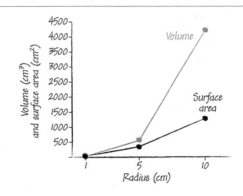

p. 842 CYU *understand* See Figure A40.1.

p. 843 Fig. 40.5 *analyze* The cuticle would likely have the most wax in the summer, when hot, dry weather would accelerate evaporation from the body surface.

p. 844 CYU (1) *understand* Uric acid has very low solubility in water and can be excreted without much water loss. **(2)** *understand* When electrolytes are reabsorbed in the hindgut epithelium, water follows along an osmotic gradient.

p. 847 *understand* In step 1, the Na$^+$/K$^+$-ATPase performs primary active transport. In step 2, the Na$^+$-dependent cotransporters perform secondary active transport. In steps 3 and 4, solutes and water move via facilitated diffusion. Simple diffusion does not occur here.

p. 849 *apply* (1) Less water will be reabsorbed because the osmotic gradient in the interstitial fluid will not be as steep. (2) Filtrate osmolarity will be lower because less water will have been reabsorbed. (3) Salt reabsorption will be reduced because the concentration of NaCl in the filtrate will be lower.

p. 851 *apply* Ethanol inhibits water reabsorption, leading to a larger volume of less concentrated urine. Nicotine increases water reabsorption, leading to a smaller volume of more concentrated urine.

p. 852 Fig. 40.16 *create* Carrying a large amount of water in the bladder may be energetically costly to the animal. The animal also might not be able to run as quickly and therefore might have an increased predation risk.

p. 852 CYU *apply* Water intake leads to lowered electrolyte concentration in the blood and filtrate and the production of large volumes of dilute urine. Eating large amounts of salt results in concentrated,

hyperosmotic urine. Water deprivation triggers ADH release and the production of concentrated, hyperosmotic urine.

✔ TEST YOUR KNOWLEDGE

1. *understand* c **2.** *understand* a **3.** *remember* c **4.** *remember* bladder

✔ TEST YOUR UNDERSTANDING

5. *analyze* Ammonia is the most toxic and must be diluted with large amounts of water to be excreted safely. Urea and uric acid are less toxic and do not have to be excreted with large amounts of water but require more energy expenditure to produce. Uric acid can be excreted with the least water. Bony fishes excrete ammonia; mammals excrete urea; and insects excrete uric acid. You would expect the embryos inside terrestrial eggs to produce uric acid, since it is the least toxic and has very low solubility in water. **6.** *analyze* Mitochondria produce ATP in cellular respiration. A key component of salt transport by chloride cells is Na$^+$/K$^+$-ATPase, which requires ATP to function. Because ATP fuels establishment of the ion gradients necessary for the cotransport mechanisms used by chloride cells as well as other epithelial cells involved in ion transport, an abundance of mitochondria would be expected in these cells.
7. *understand* Without loops of Henle, there would be no concentration gradient in the interstitial fluid of the kidney's medulla, so water could not be absorbed from the pre-urine in the collecting duct; as a result, concentrated urine could not be formed. **8.** *understand* Freshwater has such a low osmolarity that if invertebrates osmoconformed to it, the ion concentrations in their interstitial fluid would be too low to conduct electrical currents in their excitable tissues.

✔ TEST YOUR PROBLEM-SOLVING SKILLS

9. *analyze* c. Without aquaporins in the collecting duct, water cannot be reabsorbed, which would result in increased urine volume and decreased urine osmolarity. **10.** *analyze* The hypothesis that the mussels are osmoconformers is supported because the osmolarity of their hemolymph is very close to the wide range of osmolarities of the water to which they were exposed. See Figure A40.2.

✔ PUT IT ALL TOGETHER: Case Study

11. *remember* a **12.** *evaluate* Yes, the data support the hypothesis because the blood osmolarity of the aluminum-treated fish dropped between 6 hours and 24 hours after aluminum exposure began, whereas the blood osmolarity of the control fish did not change during that period. **13.** *understand* The researchers did a laboratory study to establish cause and effect by comparing two groups (the aluminum-treated fish and the control fish) that differed in only one variable (the aluminum content of the water). If they had simply sampled fish from water polluted with aluminum, they could not have attributed any observed effects on osmoregulation to aluminum with certainty because there would have been uncontrolled variables. **14.** *create* The activity of Na$^+$/K$^+$-ATPase was lower in the aluminum-treated fish than in the control fish. As a result, less sodium was imported from the water by active transport, leading to the observed reduction in blood osmolarity. **15.** *understand* False. Water moves by osmosis because there is a net diffusion of water molecules from solutions of low osmolarity to solutions of high osmolarity, not because water molecules are attracted to ions like sodium. **16.** *create* See Figure A40.3.

Figure A40.1

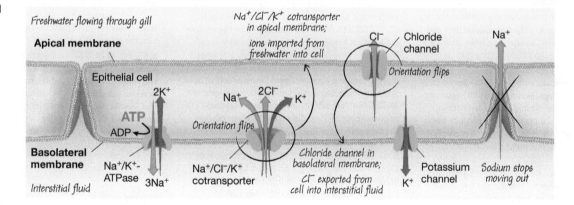

Figure A40.2

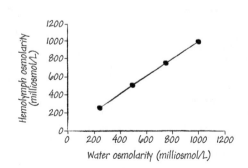

Figure A40.3

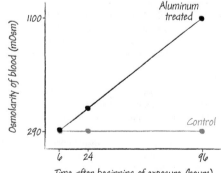

Chapter 41

IN-TEXT QUESTIONS AND EXERCISES

p. 863 `apply` Proton pump inhibitors reduce the amount of HCl that enters the lumen of the stomach, which eases the symptoms of acid reflux.

p. 866 Fig. 41.14 `understand` Frog eggs don't normally make the sodium-glucose cotransporter protein, so the researchers could be confident that if the protein appeared in the eggs, it was from the injected RNA. They would not be confident of this if they had injected RNAs into rabbit epithelial cells, where the protein was probably already present.

p. 868 `apply` (1) Decreased energy yield from foods due to reduced glucose absorption, (2) increased glucose content in feces due to the passing of unabsorbed glucose into the colon, (3) watery feces due to decreased water reabsorption in the large intestine (lower osmotic gradient). (An additional effect would be increased flatulence due to the metabolism of unabsorbed glucose by bacteria that produce gases as waste products.)

p. 869 CYU (1) `understand` *Mouth:* Food is taken in; teeth physically break down food into smaller particles; salivary amylase begins to break down carbohydrates; lingual lipase initiates the digestion of fats. *Esophagus:* Food is moved to the stomach via peristaltic contractions. *Stomach:* HCl denatures proteins; pepsin begins to digest them. *Small intestine:* Pancreatic enzymes complete the digestion of carbohydrates, proteins, lipids, and nucleic acids. Most of the water and all of the nutrients are absorbed here. *Large intestine:* More water is absorbed, and feces are formed. *Anus:* Feces accumulate in the rectum and are expelled out the anus. **(2)** `apply` If the release of bile salts is inhibited, fats would not be digested and absorbed quickly, and they would pass into the large intestine. The person would likely produce fatty feces and lose weight over time.

p. 870 Fig. 41.16 `apply` In type 2 diabetes mellitus, the top black arrow from glucose to glycogen (inside liver and muscle cells) is disrupted. In type 1 diabetes mellitus, the green arrow on the top left, indicating insulin produced by the pancreas, is disrupted.

p. 870 `understand` Individuals with type 1 diabetes mellitus do not produce sufficient insulin, so insulin injections can compensate for the missing insulin. In contrast, individuals with type 2 diabetes produce insulin but have insulin receptors that do not function correctly or are reduced in number, so insulin injections are not as effective.

p. 871 Fig. 41.17 `create` A 1.8-m tall man with a BMI of 40 weighs 130 kg. To reduce his risk for type 2 diabetes mellitus to less than 10 percent, he would need to lower his BMI below 25, so he would have to reduce his weight to less than 84 kg. Therefore, he would need to lose at least 46 kg.

p. 871 CYU (1) `understand` Type 1 diabetes mellitus is an autoimmune disease, meaning that the body's immune system mistakenly kills the insulin-producing cells of the pancreas. Type 2 diabetes mellitus is caused by a combination of factors, including genetic predisposition and obesity. **(2)** `apply` When the blood glucose level of a person with type 1 diabetes mellitus is too high, he or she should get an injection of insulin, which will trigger the absorption and storage of glucose by their cells. When their blood glucose level is too low, which might happen if they inject too much insulin, they should eat something with a high concentration of sugar (such as orange juice or a candy bar) to increase their blood glucose level quickly. (If their blood glucose level is dangerously low, a glucagon shot may be administered.)

✔ TEST YOUR KNOWLEDGE

1. `understand` One serving of skim milk has approximately $(12 \times 4) + (8 \times 4) = 80$ kcal, while one serving of whole milk has about $(12 \times 4) + (8 \times 4) + (8 \times 9) = 152$ kcal. **2.** `remember` d **3.** `remember` b **4.** `remember` insulin, glucagon

✔ TEST YOUR UNDERSTANDING

5. `apply` Humans have sharp canines and incisors, which may help to bite and tear meat. Humans also have flat molars, which help in grinding grains and other plant material. **6.** `understand` The bird crop is an enlarged sac that can hold quickly ingested food; in certain leaf-eating species, it is filled with symbiotic bacteria and functions as a fermentation vessel. The cow rumen is an enlarged portion of the stomach, and the elephant cecum is a blind sac at the anterior end of the large intestine. Both structures are filled with symbiotic organisms and function as fermentation vessels. **7.** `understand` b **8.** `understand` Nutrient absorption occurs in the small intestine but not in the stomach or esophagus, and the rate of absorption increases with surface area.

✔ TEST YOUR PROBLEM-SOLVING SKILLS

9. `understand` Fat contains more than twice the energy per gram as protein or carbohydrate, so fat storage minimizes the energetic cost of carrying stored food energy. **10.** `create` Terrestrial vertebrates are exposed to increased risk of water loss, and water reabsorption is the primary function of the large intestine. Most aquatic vertebrates do not need to reabsorb large amounts of water from their feces.

✔ PUT IT ALL TOGETHER: Case Study

11. `understand` The pharyngeal jaws of carnivorous minnows have sharp teeth specialized for puncturing animal prey, such as insects. The pharyngeal jaws of herbivorous minnows have flattened teeth specialized for grinding and compacting vegetation and algae. **12.** `understand` b **13.** `evaluate` The data show that the relative gut length of herbivorous minnows is greater than that of carnivorous minnows. **14.** `understand` The longer gastrointestinal tracts of herbivores allow more time to digest plants and algae, and provide more area to house symbiotic microbes that aid in digestion of vegetation. **15.** `apply` Cellulase activity is higher in herbivorous minnows because their diets contain more cellulose than the carnivores' diets. Cellulase is produced by gut microbes. **16.** `analyze` The minnows likely varied in overall body size, so larger fish would have had longer guts regardless of diet. Dividing gut length by body length allowed the researchers to rule out differences in gut length due solely to differences in body size.

Chapter 42

IN-TEXT QUESTIONS AND EXERCISES

p. 877 CYU `create` A: Large amount of air, because the oxygen-carrying capacity of warm water is low. B: Small amount of air, because the oxygen-carrying capacity of cold water is higher and because algae contribute oxygen to the water through photosynthesis. C: Small amount of air, because sedentary animals require relatively little oxygen.

p. 879 Fig. 42.6 `apply` If concurrent flow occurred, less oxygen would be transferred from water to blood because the partial pressure gradient driving diffusion would fall to zero partway along the length of the capillary.

p. 880 Fig. 42.7 `understand` Using several individuals increases the likelihood that the results apply to most or all members of the population instead of only one individual.

p. 884 CYU (1) `understand` Common features include large surface area, short diffusion distance (a thin gas exchange membrane), and a mechanism that keeps fresh air or water moving over the gas exchange surface. Only fish gills use a countercurrent exchange mechanism; only tracheae deliver oxygen directly to cells without using a circulatory system; only mammalian lungs contain alveoli—small air sacs surrounded by capillaries where gas exchange occurs. **(2)** `apply` The P_{O_2} decreases as oxygen is used up, the P_{CO_2} increases as CO_2 diffuses into the blood from tissues but cannot be exhaled, and the pH drops as the CO_2 dissolves in blood to form bicarbonate and H^+ ions.

p. 885 Making Models 42.1 `create` See Figure A42.1. The equal changes in x are not associated with equal changes in y in a sigmoidal curve. At low values of x (zero to x_1), y increases slowly (zero to y_1). At intermediate levels of x (x_1 to x_2), y increases much more rapidly (y_1 to y_2). At high levels of x (x_3 to x_4), y increases slowly again (y_3 to y_4).

p. 887 Fig. 42.17 `analyze` According to the data in the figure, when the tissue is 30 mm Hg, the oxygen saturation of hemoglobin is about 40 percent for blood at pH 7.2 and about 58 percent at pH 7.4. Therefore, about 60 percent of the oxygen is released from hemoglobin at pH 7.2, but only about 42 percent of the oxygen is released at pH 7.4.

p. 888 Fig. 42.19 `analyze` In the lungs, a strong partial pressure gradient favors diffusion of dissolved CO_2 from blood into the alveoli. As the partial pressure of CO_2 in the blood declines, hydrogen ions leave hemoglobin and react with bicarbonate ions to form more CO_2, which then diffuses into the alveoli and is exhaled from the lungs.

p. 888 CYU `apply` The curves of Tibetans should be shifted to the left relative to the curves of people adapted to sea level—meaning that Tibetans' hemoglobin should have a higher affinity for oxygen at all partial pressures.

p. 893 Fig. 42.25 `analyze` Air from the alveoli mixes with air in the dead space in the bronchi and trachea on its way out of the body. This dead-space air is from the previous inhalation ($P_{O_2} = 160$ mm Hg; $P_{CO_2} = 0.3$ mm Hg), so when the alveolar air mixes with it, the partial pressures in the exhaled air reach levels intermediate between those of inhaled and alveolar air.

Figure A42.1

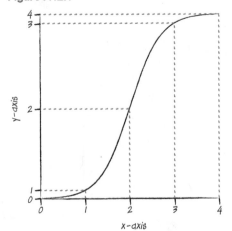

p. 894 *understand* Without the delay at the AV node, the ventricles would not have the chance to fully fill with blood from the atria. Consequently, the volume of blood ejected from the ventricles would decline.

p. 896 CYU (1) *understand* See Figure A42.2. **(2)** *remember* A myocardial infarction occurs when some of the heart tissue dies due to a lack of oxygen. It is not the same as when the heart stops beating. Only a massive infarction could interfere with proper pumping of the heart and stop it from beating.

✔ TEST YOUR KNOWLEDGE

1. *understand* d **2.** *understand* d **3.** *remember* c **4.** *understand* An open circulatory system cannot direct the hemolymph toward specific organs. Also, because the pressure is lower in an open circulatory system, there is a slower flow of hemolymph.

✔ TEST YOUR UNDERSTANDING

5. *understand* Because airflow through bird lungs is unidirectional, the gas exchange surfaces are continuously ventilated with fresh, oxygenated air. The trachea and bronchi of mammals do not have a gas exchange surface, and bidirectional airflow in these structures means that "stale" air has to be expelled before "fresh" air can be inhaled. As a result, the alveoli are not ventilated continuously. **6.** *analyze* Lungs increase the temperature of the air and are moist, allowing greater solubility of gases in the respiratory surface (increasing k); alveoli present a large surface area (large A); the epithelium of alveoli is thin (small D); and constant delivery of deoxygenated blood to alveoli maintains a steep partial pressure gradient, favoring diffusion of oxygen into the body ($P_2 - P_1$ is high). **7.** *understand* Yes—the trait compensates for the small P_{O_2} gradient between stagnant water and the blood of the carp. **8.** *understand* c

✔ TEST YOUR PROBLEM-SOLVING SKILLS

9. *apply* Cold water carries more oxygen than warm water does, so icefish blood can carry enough oxygen to supply the tissues with oxygen even in the absence of hemoglobin. The oxygen is simply dissolved in the blood. **10.** *analyze* If the pulmonary circulation were under pressure as high as that found in the systemic circulation, large amounts of fluid would be forced out of capillaries in the lungs. There is a trade-off between the thin surface required for rapid gas exchange and the thickness needed in blood vessels to withstand high pressure.

✔ PUT IT ALL TOGETHER: Case Study

11. *understand* a **12.** *understand* b (Contrary to popular belief, high P_{CO_2} plays a much more important role than low P_{O_2} in the increased ventilation rate during exercise.) **13.** *analyze* Current athletes have a higher left ventricular mass than non-athletes; this difference is statistically significant because $P < 0.001$. However, this increase in mass is not permanent, because the left ventricular masses of ex-athletes and non-athletes are not significantly different ($P > 0.05$). **14.** *understand* The increased left ventricular mass in athletes allows their hearts to pump more blood per minute to exercising muscles to meet the muscles' demand for oxygen delivery and carbon dioxide removal. **15.** *analyze* If athletes and non-athletes have the same resting cardiac output (volume of blood pumped per ventricle per minute) but athletes have a lower resting heart rate (number of beats per minute), then athletes must have a higher stroke volume (volume of blood pumped per ventricle per beat). The increased ventricular muscle mass facilitates an increased force of contraction, resulting in more blood being ejected per beat. **16.** *create* In people with cardiovascular disease, the heart muscle often enlarges as it works harder to pump blood through hardened arteries.

Chapter 43

IN-TEXT QUESTIONS AND EXERCISES

p. 902 Fig. 43.3 *apply* No—as K^+ leaves the cell along its concentration gradient, the interior of the cell becomes more negative. As a result, an electrical gradient favoring movement of K^+ into the cell begins to counteract the concentration gradient favoring movement of K^+ out of the cell. Eventually, the two opposing forces balance out, and there is no net movement of K^+.

p. 903 *apply* If Na^+ were allowed to diffuse freely (and other ions could not diffuse), the membrane potential would equal the equilibrium potential for Na^+. If K^+ were allowed to diffuse freely (and other ions could not diffuse), the membrane potential would equal the equilibrium potential for K^+.

p. 904 CYU (1) *apply* The resting potential would be much less negative because K^+ could no longer leak out of the cell. **(2)** *understand* The first phase of an action potential is called depolarization because the difference in charge across the membrane is reduced (the membrane becomes "less polarized"). The second phase is called repolarization because the difference in charge increases again.

p. 904 *understand* See Figure A43.1.

p. 908 CYU (1) *understand* If the threshold potential is attained, the probability that the voltage-gated sodium channels will open approaches 100 percent, and an action potential is produced. If the depolarization does not reach the threshold potential, the massive opening of Na^+ channels does not occur, and neither does an action potential. This is why the action potential is all or none. **(2)** *understand* Action potential propagation in the unmyelinated squid giant axon is fast because the axon's diameter is so large that cations experience less resistance as they flow down the axon. In small, myelinated axons of vertebrates, the small diameter increases resistance, but the myelination speeds propagation.

p. 908 Fig. 43.9 *apply* Collect a solution from the end of the vagus nerve at the heart *without* the nerve being stimulated. Expose a second heart to this solution. There should be no change in heart rate.

p. 912 CYU *apply* The EPSP would likely be smaller and briefer because there would be less neurotransmitter in the synaptic cleft.

p. 913 Fig. 43.15 *analyze* In the rest-and-digest mode, the pupils constrict, allowing less light to stimulate the eyes; the heart rate decreases, which conserves energy; the liver stores glucose, which enters the blood when food is digested; and the gallbladder releases products that promote digestion. In the fight-or-flight mode, the pupils open to admit more light; the heart rate increases to support muscle activity; the liver releases glucose into the blood, fueling increased muscle activity; and the gallbladder retains its contents, which are not used when food is not being digested.

p. 915 Fig. 43.18 *analyze* No—for example, part (b) indicates that the size of the cerebral area devoted to the trunk is no bigger than that devoted to the thumb.

p. 919 CYU (1) *understand* One strategy is to study individuals with known brain lesions and correlate the location of the lesion with a deficit in mental or physical function. Another is to directly stimulate brain areas or specific neurons in conscious animals and record the responses. **(2)** *evaluate* The discovery that synapses can change over time and that new neurons can be produced in adult vertebrates suggests that brain damage may not always be permanent. Following brain injury, repair might occur through synaptic plasticity or neurogenesis. The extent of repair would likely depend on many factors, including the region that was injured, the extent of the injury, and rehabilitative processes.

✔ TEST YOUR KNOWLEDGE

1. *remember* b **2.** *understand* c **3.** *remember* a **4.** *remember* d

---

Figure A42.2

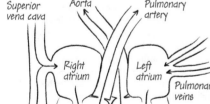
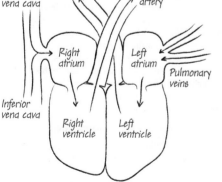

Figure A43.1

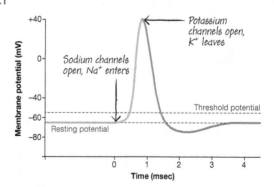

5. *analyze* The ligand-gated channel opens in response to binding by a neurotransmitter; the voltage-gated channel opens in response to membrane depolarization. **6.** *understand* Postsynaptic potentials are additive. If a postsynaptic cell receives multiple EPSPs in a short period, it may be depolarized to the threshold potential and fire an action potential. IPSPs counteract the effect of EPSPs, making the postsynaptic cell less likely to fire an action potential. **7.** *analyze* The somatic nervous system controls voluntary skeletal muscle activity, such as movement of arms and legs. The autonomic nervous system controls internal involuntary activities, such as digestion, heart contraction, and gland secretion. **8.** *understand* a

✔ TEST YOUR PROBLEM-SOLVING SKILLS

9. *apply* The neurotransmitters will stay in the synaptic cleft longer, prolonging their binding to ligand-gated channels in the postsynaptic membrane. Ion flows across that membrane will be augmented, affecting the postsynaptic cell's membrane potential and likelihood of firing action potentials. **10.** *create* Alzheimer's disease is characterized by shrinkage of the hippocampus and the outer part of the cerebrum (called the cerebral cortex). The hippocampus is responsible for the formation of new memories; the outer part of the cerebrum is involved in the storage of memories, as indicated by electrical stimulation of outer cerebral areas during brain surgery and by recordings of activity in cerebral neurons of subjects viewing photographs.

✔ PUT IT ALL TOGETHER: Case Study

11. *analyze* c. BTX opens sodium channels, causing the membrane to depolarize. In contrast to what happens during an action potential, however, the sodium channels remain open, and the membrane does not repolarize. **12.** *apply* Patch clamping could be used to study the effect of BTX on individual ion channels. If the channel inside the tip of the microelectrode was a sodium channel, you would expect BTX to cause current to flow through the channel and to continue flowing as long as BTX was present, accounting for the prolonged depolarization shown in the graph. **13.** *apply* An action potential consists of a depolarization followed by a repolarization. By preventing repolarization, BTX stops action potentials from being produced and thus abolishes electrical signaling by the nervous system. **14.** *create* See Figure A43.2. **15.** *apply* (a) Depolarization would not occur because there would be no gradient

for inward flow of sodium ions. (b) The peak depolarization would be less positive because both Na$^+$ channels and K$^+$ leak channels are open in the presence of BTX, and increasing the intracellular K$^+$ concentration shifts the equilibrium potential for K$^+$ to a more negative value. (c) Depolarization would not occur because tetrodotoxin blocks voltage-gated sodium channels. **16.** *create* One hypothesis is that in this snake species, a voltage-gated sodium channel evolved that is not affected by BTX. For example, a mutation in the gene for the sodium channel could reduce the effect of the toxin on the snake's nervous system, giving individuals with this mutation higher reproductive success and thereby causing the allele for this sodium channel to become fixed in the population by natural selection.

Chapter 44

IN-TEXT QUESTIONS AND EXERCISES

p. 929 Fig. 44.9 *create* Vision could potentially be used to detect prey in diurnal catfish. To control for this, catfish could be blinded or "blindfolded" with an opaque material over their eyes.

p. 929 CYU (1) *apply* A punctured eardrum wouldn't vibrate correctly and would result in hearing loss at all frequencies in the affected ear. If the stereocilia were too short to come into contact with the tectorial membrane, vibration of the basilar membrane would not cause them to bend, and sound would not be detected. A loss in basilar membrane flexibility would result in the inability to hear lower-pitched sounds, such as those in human speech. **(2)** *apply* The clawed frog would have a more developed lateral line system than the bullfrog because the clawed frog is entirely aquatic whereas the bullfrog spends much of its time on land. The lateral line system functions only in water.

p. 932 Fig. 44.13 *understand* This ion flow occurs when the photoreceptor cell is not receiving light—when the cell is in the dark.

p. 932 *analyze* cGMP is a second messenger in the sense that it signals the sodium channels that transducin is inactive, and it is also a ligand that binds to and opens sodium channels. Transducin is a type of G protein; like other G proteins, it binds guanosine triphosphate (GTP) in response to an activated receptor protein, switching from "off" to "on" and activating a key protein as a result. Closing Na$^+$ channels stops the entry of positive charges into the cell, making the inside of the cell more negative relative to the outside.

p. 933 Fig. 44.15 *apply* The S, M, and L opsin proteins are each different in structure. These structural differences affect the ability of retinal to absorb specific frequencies of light and change shape.

p. 934 CYU (1) *understand* Retinal acts like an on–off switch that indicates whether light has fallen on a rod cell. When retinal absorbs light, it changes shape. The shape change triggers events that result in a change in action potentials, signaling that light has been absorbed. **(2)** *apply* Retina detachment would separate the retina from the optic nerve, resulting in blindness. The mutation would produce blue–purple color blindness because the S opsin absorbs wavelengths in that region of the spectrum. A clouded lens would reduce the amount of light that reaches the retina, reducing visual sensitivity.

p. 937 CYU (1) *apply* Extremely hot food damages taste receptor proteins, which would no longer be able to respond to their chemical triggers. **(2)** *create* One hypothesis is that other complex methods of communication, including gestures, facial expressions, and language, have evolved in primates, making sensation with the vomeronasal organ less important.

p. 937 *apply* (1) A rattlesnake with its eyes covered could strike effectively because its pits could sense the prey. (2) A rattlesnake with its eyes and pits covered with cotton cloth could strike effectively. The cloth would block vision, but heat energy from the prey would penetrate the cloth and stimulate thermoreceptors in the pits. (3) A rattlesnake with its eyes and pits covered with an opaque, heat-blocking material would not be able to strike effectively because the material would block vision and heat energy.

p. 939 CYU (1) *create* Vampire bats have thermoreceptors in their noses that allow them to detect heat from their endothermic prey. **(2)** *create* Female sea turtles likely use magnetic cues to locate the beaches where they were born.

✔ TEST YOUR KNOWLEDGE

1. *remember* d **2.** *understand* c **3.** *understand* b **4.** *remember* magnetoreception

✔ TEST YOUR UNDERSTANDING

5. *understand* b **6.** *understand* The many possible examples include infrasound hearing allowing elephants to hear over long distances, ultrasonic hearing allowing bats to hunt by echolocation and moths to avoid bat predators, several blue opsins allowing coelacanths to distinguish the hues of blue light present in their deep-sea habitat, and red and yellow opsins allowing fruit-eating primates to distinguish ripe from unripe fruit. **7.** *analyze* Both the lateral line system and electroreception use hair cells to sense changes in the water. Hair cells in the lateral line system are mechanoreceptors that depolarize in response to changes in water pressure. In contrast, electroreceptive hair cells depolarize or hyperpolarize in response to changes in the electric field. **8.** *evaluate* Dalton's hypothesis was good. It was reasonable because blue fluid absorbs red light and would prevent red light from reaching the retina, and this prediction could be tested by on his eyes after his death. Although the hypothesis was not correct, it inspired a rigorous test and required researchers to think of alternative explanations.

✔ TEST YOUR PROBLEM-SOLVING SKILLS

9. *evaluate* The data show that the mean time between of a woman's menstrual cycle and that of the rest of the women declined over time after they moved into the dormitory. It declined most rapidly after they first

Figure A43.2

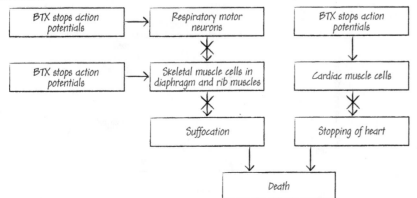

moved in together. The leveling of the graph over time shows that the onset dates became more synchronized. The data are consistent with the hypothesis that a pheromone acted to synchronize the women's menstrual cycles, but they don't provide any direct evidence for the existence of such a pheromone. **10.** (create) To determine whether electric eels are electrogenic, place an eel in a tank of water and measure the electrical currents in the water. To determine whether they are electroreceptive, place an eel in a tank in the dark and add an object the size and shape of a prey animal that emits no scent or taste. Block mechanoreceptors in the lateral line system with a chemical, as described for Figure 44.9. If the eel locates the object, it would support the hypothesis that electric eels are electroreceptive.

✔ PUT IT ALL TOGETHER: Case Study

11. (remember) c **12.** (analyze) A worker should have the most alarm pheromone receptors because workers protect the hive. **13.** (analyze) Visual signals could not be detected easily at night or inside a dark hive. Audible signals could be hard to interpret if they were produced by thousands of workers, especially if the bees made similar sounds under other conditions. In contrast, an alarm pheromone would quickly spread throughout a hive even in darkness if each worker responded to the pheromone by secreting more of it, and the specificity of receptor proteins would enable bees to associate that pheromone with a particular type of stimulus. **14.** (evaluate) The results support the hypothesis because ovaries were less fully developed in workers exposed to the queen pheromone than in workers in the control group. **15.** (analyze) The researchers used diethyl ether as the control treatment because it was present as a solvent in the queen pheromone treatment. It's possible that diethyl ether itself could affect the bees' ovarian development. By including diethyl ether in both treatment groups, the researchers could attribute any difference in ovarian development to the presence of the pheromone. **16.** (create) Beekeepers starting a new hive can add a strip of material treated with queen pheromone to that hive to prevent bees from abandoning it before the queen is mature.

Chapter 45

IN-TEXT QUESTIONS AND EXERCISES

p. 944 Fig. 45.2 (understand) The dark band includes thin filaments as well as thick filaments, which have bulbous extensions; the light band consists of thin filaments only.

p. 944 (analyze) The trucks represent the Z discs, the ropes represent the thin filaments, and the burly weightlifters represent the thick filaments.

p. 946 CYU (1) (understand) In a sarcomere, thick myosin filaments are sandwiched between thin actin filaments. When the heads on myosin contact actin and change conformation, they pull the actin filaments toward the center of the sarcomere, shortening the whole sarcomere. **(2)** (apply) Increased acetylcholine release would result in an increased rate of action potentials in muscle cells and more forceful muscle contraction. Preventing conformational changes in troponin would prevent muscle contraction. Blocking uptake of calcium ions into the sarcoplasmic reticulum would lead to sustained muscle contraction.

p. 950 (apply) The postural muscles of the human neck are composed mainly of slow oxidative fibers, which are specialized for endurance.

p. 953 Fig. 45.12 (apply) The biceps brachii is a flexor because it reduces the angle of the arm joint when it

contracts. The triceps brachii is an extensor because it increases the angle of the arm joint.

p. 954 CYU (1) (analyze) Hydrostatic skeletons are made of soft tissues that vary from animal to animal; endoskeletons are made of calcium phosphate, calcium carbonate, and proteins; and exoskeletons are made of chitin, proteins, calcium carbonate, and other substances. Hydrostatic skeletons and endoskeletons are on the inside of animals, whereas exoskeletons are on the outside. Shape changes in hydrostatic skeletons occur from changes in body segments, whereas shape changes in endo- and exoskeletons occur from changes in the angles of joints between rigid levers. All types of skeletons attach to skeletal muscle and serve to transmit muscle forces. **(2)** (apply) No movement of the arm would occur because, for these antagonistic muscles to produce movement, one of them must be contracted while the other is relaxed.

p. 957 Fig. 45.17 (apply) Galloping at 3.5 m/s would use about 33 percent more energy (about 400 J/m versus 300 J/m).

p. 958 Fig. 45.19 (apply) Running is about 10 times as costly as swimming (about 8 cal/g/km versus 0.8 cal/g/km).

✔ TEST YOUR KNOWLEDGE

1. (remember) a **2.** (understand) d **3.** (understand) a **4.** (understand) False.

✔ TEST YOUR UNDERSTANDING

5. (understand) The key observation was that the banding pattern of sarcomeres changed during contraction. As the entire sarcomere became shorter, the width of the dark bands did not change, but the light bands became narrower. This observation suggested that some portions of the structure slid past other portions. The many mitochondria in muscle cells supply the large amounts of ATP needed to power the movement of myosin heads along actin filaments; the extensive smooth ER stores the calcium that initiates contraction by binding to troponin. **6.** (understand) ATP is required for myosin and actin to unbind. Because no ATP is made after death, rigor mortis occurs when myosin and actin remain bound. **7.** (apply) The oxygen consumption of the runner would increase because the arches of his or her feet would no longer store as much elastic energy, which normally reduces the energetic cost of running. **8.** (understand) The viscosity of water has a greater effect on small fish than large fish, making it easier for large fish to move through the water.

✔ TEST YOUR PROBLEM-SOLVING SKILLS

9. (apply) In cardiac muscle, the binding of acetylcholine to its receptors causes the heart rate to slow. Ingestion of atropine would increase heart rate because it blocks acetylcholine receptors. **10.** (apply) c:

$$0.5 = v^2/(9.8 \text{ m/s}^2 \times 0.9\text{m})$$
$$0.5 = v^2/8.8 \text{ m}^2/\text{s}^2$$
$$v^2 = 0.5 \times 8.8 \text{ m}^2/\text{s}^2$$
$$v = \text{square root of } 4.4 \text{ m}^2/\text{s}^2$$
$$v = 2.1 \text{ m/s}$$

✔ PUT IT ALL TOGETHER: Case Study

11. (analyze) Slow oxidative fibers are red because they have a lot of myoglobin, which holds the oxygen necessary for the cells' high rates of aerobic respiration. These fibers contract slowly and do not fatigue readily. Fast glycolytic fibers are white due to their low myoglobin concentration; they contract and fatigue rapidly. Fast oxidative/glycolytic (intermediate) fibers

are intermediate in color (pink) and physiological properties. **12.** (apply) The sprinter would likely have a greater proportion of fast glycolytic fibers because these cells are specialized for bursts of activity. **13.** (apply) There would likely be no difference in the number of muscle cells, even though training could cause the entire muscle to enlarge. Muscle cells can become larger with training; new cells are not added. **14.** (evaluate) The elite runners on average had a significantly higher proportion of slow fibers than the non-elite runners and untrained subjects. **15.** (evaluate) Although the elite runners had a higher proportion of slow fibers on average, that proportion does not necessarily predict the athletic performance of any given athlete, as evidenced by the low percentage in some individuals who performed at the elite level. **16.** (analyze) Radcliffe would have the highest cost of locomotion because running is more energetically costly than flying or swimming.

Chapter 46

IN-TEXT QUESTIONS AND EXERCISES

p. 963 Making Models 46.1 (create) See Figure A46.1. Hormone B will increase over time.

p. 965 Fig. 46.3 (create) Rather than re-implanting testes, researchers could now castrate animals and inject them with testosterone. Doing this would show that any subsequent changes were due specifically to testosterone rather than another chemical released into the blood by the testes.

p. 966 CYU (understand) It is difficult to differentiate between the nervous and endocrine systems because some neurons secrete hormones and some endocrine glands respond to neural signals.

p. 968 (apply) The steroid-hormone–receptor complex would probably fail to bind to the hormone-response element. Then gene expression would not change in response to the hormone—the arrival of the hormone would have little or no effect on the target cell.

p. 970 CYU (analyze) Steroid hormones stimulate production of new proteins, which takes time to occur and results in long-lasting effects. In contrast, polypeptides rapidly stimulate activation of already existing proteins, which is transitory because the proteins can become inactivated just as quickly.

p. 971 (create) The cells could differ in receptors that, when bound to T_3, would induce changes in the expression of different genes.

p. 974 Fig. 46.13 (understand) The saline injection controlled for any stress induced by the injection procedure and for introducing additional fluid into the body.

p. 975 CYU (1) (analyze) In amphibians, an increase in the concentration of thyroid hormones stimulates metamorphosis from a larva to an adult without a

---

Figure A46.1

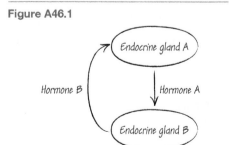

resting stage. In holometabolous insects, a decrease in the concentration of juvenile hormone and an increase in the concentration of ecdysone stimulate metamorphosis during a resting (pupal) stage. **(2)** `understand` By suppressing immune system function, promoting the release of fatty acids from storage cells and the release of amino acids from muscle cells for energy production, and preventing the uptake of glucose by adipocytes and resting muscle cells in response to signals from insulin, cortisol conserves glucose supplies for use by the brain.

p. 976 Fig. 46.14 `create` To test for adrenal failure, researchers could inject ACTH and monitor cortisol levels. If cortisol levels don't increase, adrenal failure is likely.

p. 978 CYU (1) `understand` ACTH triggers the release of cortisol, but cortisol inhibits ACTH release by blocking the release of CRH from the hypothalamus and by suppressing ACTH production by the anterior pituitary. **(2)** `understand` Processing centers in the brain are responsible for integrating a wide array of sensory input. To start a response to this sensory input, they stimulate neurosecretory cells in the hypothalamus. Neurohormones from these cells travel to the anterior pituitary, where they trigger the production and release of other hormones.

✔ **TEST YOUR KNOWLEDGE**

1. `understand` a **2.** `remember` c **3.** `remember` a **4.** `remember` True

✔ **TEST YOUR UNDERSTANDING**

5. `analyze` Lipid-soluble hormones like steroids usually bind to receptors inside the cell, forming a complex that binds to DNA and alters transcription. Water-soluble hormones like polypeptides bind to receptors on the cell surface and trigger production of a second messenger and, in some cases, a phosphorylation cascade, ending in activation of proteins already present in the cell. **6.** `analyze` This is one way that the same hormone can trigger different effects in different tissues. For example, epinephrine binds to four different types of receptors in different tissues and elicits a different response from each. **7.** `analyze` The posterior pituitary is an extension of the hypothalamus and a storage area for hypothalamic hormones. The anterior pituitary develops from nonneural tissue; it synthesizes and releases an array of hormones in response to releasing hormones from the hypothalamus. **8.** `create` Subject volunteers to travel and jet lag, measure their ACTH and cortisol levels, and correlate these results with the subjects' perceived level of jet lag symptoms.

✔ **TEST YOUR PROBLEM-SOLVING SKILLS**

9. `create` There are two basic strategies: (1) Remove the structure from some individuals and compare their behavior and condition to sham-operated individuals in the same environment, or (2) make a liquid extract from the structure, inject it into some individuals, and compare their behavior and condition to individuals in the same environment that were injected with a saline solution. **10.** `evaluate` Yes—the finding that testosterone concentrations in atrazine-treated male frogs were significantly lower than those of control males and similar to those of control females supports the hypothesis that atrazine is an endocrine disruptor that feminizes male amphibians.

✔ **PUT IT ALL TOGETHER: Case Study**

11. `remember` b **12.** `remember` Corticosterone receptors would be found in the cytoplasm or nucleus (intracellular). **13.** `apply` In response to a visit by tourists, corticosterone levels should show a smaller increase in penguins

habituated to tourists than in penguins not previously exposed to tourists. **14.** `evaluate` The hypothesis was supported because the corticosterone response to capture and restraint for 30 minutes was significantly higher in non-habituated penguins than in habituated penguins. **15.** `apply` Corticosterone is a glucocorticoid similar to cortisol, which induces the synthesis of liver enzymes that make glucose from amino acids. If corticosterone has the same effect as cortisol, and if non-habituated penguins have higher corticosterone levels than habituated penguins, then non-habituated penguins should show a greater increase in expression of genes for those enzymes. **16.** `create` There are several possibilities. In habituated penguins, the brain could become less sensitive to the stimulus of a tourist's presence, resulting in release of less CRH by the hypothalamus. Alternatively, the anterior pituitary gland could become less sensitive to CRH, secreting less ACTH. Finally, the adrenal gland could become less sensitive to ACTH, secreting less corticosterone.

Chapter 47

IN-TEXT QUESTIONS AND EXERCISES

p. 983 Fig. 47.3 `create` Isolate and identify the molecules found in "crowded" water. Test each molecule by adding it, at the same concentration found in crowded water, to clean water occupied by a single *Daphnia* and recording whether the female produces a male-containing brood. Repeat with many test females and for each molecule identified. As a control, record the number of male-containing broods produced in clean water.

p. 983 `apply` Asexual reproduction would be expected in environments where conditions change little over time.

p. 988 Fig. 47.9 `create` (Note: There is more than one possible answer—this is an example.) Having two gonads is an "insurance policy" against loss or damage. To test this hypothesis, surgically remove one gonad from a large number of male and female rats. As a control, do a similar operation on a large number of similar male and female rats, but do not remove either gonad. Once the animals have recovered, place them in a barn or other "natural" setting and let them breed. Compare reproductive success of control rats with that of rats with unpaired gonads.

p. 990 Fig. 47.11 `evaluate` No—the data are consistent with the displacement hypothesis but do not provide direct evidence for it. There are other plausible explanations for the data, such as females ejecting sperm.

p. 992 `analyze` If the added molecule blocked the bindin-like protein on the human sperm head, that protein would not be able to bind to its receptor on the egg. Fertilization would not take place.

p. 994 CYU (1) `analyze` Oviparity usually requires less energy input from the mother after egg laying, and mothers do not have to carry eggs around as long—meaning that they can lay more eggs and be more mobile. However, before egg laying, mothers have to provision the egg with all the nutrition the embryo will require, and eggs may not be well protected after they are laid. Viviparity usually increases the likelihood that the developing offspring will survive until birth, but the space available in the mother's reproductive tract limits the number of young that can be produced. If viviparous young can be nourished longer than oviparous young, they may be larger and more capable of fending for themselves. `apply` **(2)** The increase in Ca^{2+} concentration within the egg triggers formation of the fertilization envelope, which in turn blocks fertilization.

p. 996 `apply` Future ectodermal cells are initially at one pole of the spherical embryo. During gastrulation, they spread out as an expanding sheet that eventually covers the entire embryo as the future endodermal and mesodermal cells move into the interior of the embryo.

p. 998 CYU (1) `understand` The future posterior and dorsal regions could be identified as the blastopore forms and cells begin folding into the embryo. The blastopore marks the future posterior region of the embryo, and cells that are the first to be folded into the embryo mark the future dorsal side. **(2)** `create` In either type of embryo, remove a portion of the notochord. The prediction is that the neural tube would not form in the region without a notochord. Alternatively, part of a notochord could be transplanted from one embryo to a region under the ectoderm in another embryo where the neural tube does not form. In this case, the prediction is that a second neural tube would form above the transplanted notochord.

p. 999 Fig. 47.24 `analyze` In both cases, the hypothalamus produces a releasing hormone (GnRH or CRH) that stimulates the release of regulatory hormones by the anterior pituitary (LH and FSH or ACTH). The pituitary hormones travel via the bloodstream and act on the gonads or adrenal glands, inducing the release of hormones from these glands.

p. 1002 CYU (1) `understand` FSH triggers maturation of an ovarian follicle. Its level rises at the end of the menstrual cycle because its secretion is no longer inhibited by progesterone, which stops being produced at a high level when the corpus luteum degenerates. **(2)** `apply` The drug would keep the FSH level low, meaning that follicles would not mature and would not begin producing estradiol and progesterone. The uterine lining would not thicken.

p. 1004 `analyze` If the level of progesterone isn't high enough, the uterine lining will not be maintained adequately, and a miscarriage will be likely.

✔ **TEST YOUR KNOWLEDGE**

1. `remember` a **2.** `understand` b **3.** `understand` c **4.** `remember` True

✔ **TEST YOUR UNDERSTANDING**

5. `create` *Daphnia* females switched to sexual reproduction only when they were exposed to short day lengths, water from crowded populations, *and* low food concentration. These conditions are likely to occur in the fall. **6.** `apply` Frogs are oviparous, and the egg must contain everything the embryo needs to develop. This makes the egg large. Mice are viviparous, and the embryo obtains almost everything it needs from the mother. Therefore, there is no need for large eggs provisioned with everything required for development. **7.** `analyze` Spermatogenesis generates four haploid sperm from each primary spermatocyte; oogenesis produces only one haploid egg from each primary oocyte. Eggs are much larger than sperm because eggs contain more cytoplasm. In spermatogenesis, the second meiotic division occurs right after the first meiotic division; in oogenesis, the second meiotic division is delayed until fertilization. **8.** `understand` *Negative feedback*: LH triggers secretion of estradiol, but at low levels estradiol inhibits further release of LH; LH and FSH trigger secretion of progesterone, but progesterone inhibits further release of LH and FSH. *Positive feedback*: High levels of estradiol trigger release of more LH. The follicle can produce high levels of estradiol only if it has grown and matured; in that sense, high levels of estradiol can be considered a signal that the oocyte is ready for ovulation to occur.

9. *analyze* Cells from a variety of locations in many frog blastulas could be labeled with a dye. The position of these cells could be assessed relative to the blastocoel, which is displaced to one "side" of the embryo. The descendants of these labeled cells could then be followed through later stages of development. If cells from only one location came to cover the outside of the embryo and contributed to structures normally formed by the ectoderm, then the hypothesis would be supported. **10.** *analyze* b

✔ **PUT IT ALL TOGETHER: Case Study**

11. *remember* d **12.** *apply* (a) Pituitary secretion of FSH and LH would decline due to negative feedback by progesterone. (b) Because of the decline in FSH and LH secretion, follicles would not develop, and therefore the ovaries would secrete little estradiol and progesterone. **13.** *evaluate* The data from the study do support the hypothesis that the pill interferes with normal hormonal signaling because the women showed statistically significant declines in all four major reproductive hormones (FSH, LH, estradiol, and progesterone) after they started using the pill. **14.** *analyze* (a) The follicle would not develop because the FSH level is low. (b) The uterine lining would not thicken much because the estradiol level during the follicular phase would be low. (c) Ovulation would be unlikely to occur because the estradiol level would never be high enough stimulate the LH surge needed for ovulation. (d) The volume of menstrual fluid would be lower than that of women not on the pill because the uterine lining would not thicken as much. **15.** *analyze* Both the pill and emergency contraception contain progesterone or progesterone plus estradiol, and both work by preventing ovulation; they would not terminate a pregnancy. In contrast, mifepristone is a progesterone receptor blocker that does terminate a pregnancy. **16.** *analyze* A contraceptive that blocked either ovulation or fertilization is likely to be the least controversial because some people contend that a new life begins at the moment of fertilization. Contraceptives that block cleavage or implantation are likely to stir more controversy because these events occur after fertilization.

Periodic Table of Elements

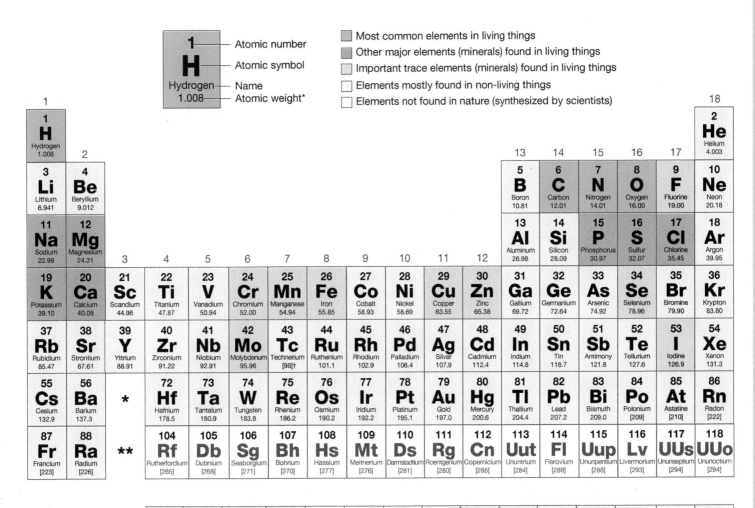

Legend:
- Atomic number
- **H** — Atomic symbol
- Hydrogen — Name
- 1.008 — Atomic weight*

- Most common elements in living things
- Other major elements (minerals) found in living things
- Important trace elements (minerals) found in living things
- Elements mostly found in non-living things
- Elements not found in nature (synthesized by scientists)

1																	18
1 H Hydrogen 1.008	2											13	14	15	16	17	**2 He** Helium 4.003
3 Li Lithium 6.941	**4 Be** Beryllium 9.012											**5 B** Boron 10.81	**6 C** Carbon 12.01	**7 N** Nitrogen 14.01	**8 O** Oxygen 16.00	**9 F** Fluorine 19.00	**10 Ne** Neon 20.18
11 Na Sodium 22.99	**12 Mg** Magnesium 24.31	3	4	5	6	7	8	9	10	11	12	**13 Al** Aluminum 26.98	**14 Si** Silicon 28.09	**15 P** Phosphorus 30.97	**16 S** Sulfur 32.07	**17 Cl** Chlorine 35.45	**18 Ar** Argon 39.95
19 K Potassium 39.10	**20 Ca** Calcium 40.08	**21 Sc** Scandium 44.96	**22 Ti** Titanium 47.87	**23 V** Vanadium 50.94	**24 Cr** Chromium 52.00	**25 Mn** Manganese 54.94	**26 Fe** Iron 55.85	**27 Co** Cobalt 58.93	**28 Ni** Nickel 58.69	**29 Cu** Copper 63.55	**30 Zn** Zinc 65.38	**31 Ga** Gallium 69.72	**32 Ge** Germanium 72.64	**33 As** Arsenic 74.92	**34 Se** Selenium 78.96	**35 Br** Bromine 79.90	**36 Kr** Krypton 83.80
37 Rb Rubidium 85.47	**38 Sr** Strontium 87.61	**39 Y** Yttrium 88.91	**40 Zr** Zirconium 91.22	**41 Nb** Niobium 92.91	**42 Mo** Molybdenum 95.96	**43 Tc** Technetium [98]†	**44 Ru** Ruthenium 101.1	**45 Rh** Rhodium 102.9	**46 Pd** Palladium 106.4	**47 Ag** Silver 107.9	**48 Cd** Cadmium 112.4	**49 In** Indium 114.8	**50 Sn** Tin 118.7	**51 Sb** Antimony 121.8	**52 Te** Tellurium 127.6	**53 I** Iodine 126.9	**54 Xe** Xenon 131.3
55 Cs Cesium 132.9	**56 Ba** Barium 137.3	*	**72 Hf** Hafnium 178.5	**73 Ta** Tantalum 180.9	**74 W** Tungsten 183.8	**75 Re** Rhenium 186.2	**76 Os** Osmium 190.2	**77 Ir** Iridium 192.2	**78 Pt** Platinum 195.1	**79 Au** Gold 197.0	**80 Hg** Mercury 200.6	**81 Tl** Thallium 204.4	**82 Pb** Lead 207.2	**83 Bi** Bismuth 209.0	**84 Po** Polonium [209]	**85 At** Astatine [210]	**86 Rn** Radon [222]
87 Fr Francium [223]	**88 Ra** Radium [226]	**	**104 Rf** Rutherfordium [265]	**105 Db** Dubnium [268]	**106 Sg** Seaborgium [271]	**107 Bh** Bohrium [270]	**108 Hs** Hassium [277]	**109 Mt** Meitnerium [276]	**110 Ds** Damstadtium [281]	**111 Rg** Roentgenium [280]	**112 Cn** Copernicium [285]	**113 Uut** Ununtrium [284]	**114 Fl** Flerovium [289]	**115 Uup** Ununpentium [288]	**116 Lv** Livermorium [293]	**117 UUs** Ununseptium [294]	**118 UUo** Ununoctium [294]

*Lanthanides

57 La Lanthanum 138.9	**58 Ce** Cerium 140.1	**59 Pr** Praseodymium 140.9	**60 Nd** Neodymium 144.2	**61 Pm** Promethium [145]	**62 Sm** Samarium 150.4	**63 Eu** Europium 152.0	**64 Gd** Gadolinium 157.3	**65 Tb** Terbium 158.9	**66 Dy** Dysprosium 162.5	**67 Ho** Holmium 164.9	**68 Er** Erbium 167.3	**69 Tm** Thulium 168.9	**70 Yb** Ytterbium 173.1	**71 Lu** Lutetium 175.0

**Actinides

89 Ac Actinium [227]	**90 Th** Thorium 232.0	**91 Pa** Protactinium 231.0	**92 U** Uranium 238.0	**93 Np** Neptunium [237]	**94 Pu** Plutonium [244]	**95 Am** Americium [243]	**96 Cm** Curium [247]	**97 Bk** Berkelium [247]	**98 Cf** Californium [251]	**99 Es** Einsteinium [252]	**100 Fm** Fermium [257]	**101 Md** Mendelevium [258]	**102 No** Nobelium [259]	**103 Lr** Lawrencium [262]

DATA: Wieser, M. E., and M. Berglund. 2009. *Pure and Applied Chemistry* 81: 2131–2156.

*Atomic weights are reported to four significant figures.

†For elements with a variable number of protons and/or neutrons, the mass number of the longest-lived isotope of the element is reported in brackets.

Glossary

5′ cap A modified guanine (G) nucleotide added to the 5′ end of eukaryotic mRNAs. Helps protect the mRNA from being degraded and promotes initiation of translation.

abdomen A region of the body; in arthropods, one of the three prominent body regions (tagmata), located posterior to the thorax.

abiotic Not alive (e.g., air, water, and some components of soil). Compare with **biotic**.

aboveground biomass The total mass of living plants in an area, excluding roots.

abscisic acid (ABA) A plant hormone that inhibits growth; it stimulates stomatal closure and triggers dormancy.

abscission In plants, the normal (often seasonal) shedding of leaves, fruits, or flowers.

abscission zone The region at the base of a petiole where cell wall degradation occurs; results in the dropping of leaves.

absorption In animals, the uptake of ions and small molecules, derived from food, across the lining of the digestive tract.

absorption spectrum The amount of light of different wavelengths absorbed by a pigment. Usually depicted as a graph of light absorbed versus wavelength. Compare with **action spectrum**.

accessory fruit A fruit-like structure (e.g., strawberry) that develops not from an ovary, but from some tissue exterior to the carpel.

acclimation A change in a study organism's phenotype that occurs in response to laboratory conditions.

acclimatization A change in an individual's phenotype that occurs in response to a change in natural environmental conditions.

acetylation Addition of an acetyl group (−COCH₃) to a molecule. Acetylation of histone proteins is important in controlling chromatin condensation.

acetylcholine (ACh) A neurotransmitter that triggers contraction of vertebrate skeletal muscle cells but slows the rate of contraction of cardiac muscle cells.

acid Any compound that gives up protons or accepts electrons during a chemical reaction or that releases hydrogen ions when dissolved in water.

acid-growth hypothesis The hypothesis that auxin triggers elongation of plant cells by increasing the activity of proton pumps, making the cell wall more acidic and leading to expansion of the cell wall and an influx of water.

acoelomate A bilaterian animal that lacks an internal body cavity (coelom). Compare with **coelomate** and **pseudocoelomate**.

acquired immune deficiency syndrome (AIDS) A human disease characterized by death of immune system cells (in particular helper T cells) and subsequent vulnerability to other infections. Caused by the human immunodeficiency virus (HIV).

acrosome A caplike structure, located on the head of a sperm, that contains enzymes capable of digesting the outer coverings of an egg.

ACTH See **adrenocorticotropic hormone.**

actin A globular protein that can be polymerized to form filaments. Actin filaments are part of the cytoskeleton and constitute the thin filaments in muscle cells.

actin filament A long fiber, about 7 nm in diameter, composed of two intertwined strands of polymerized actin protein; one of the three types of cytoskeletal fibers. Involved in cell movement. Also called a *microfilament*. Compare with **intermediate filament** and **microtubule**.

action potential A rapid, temporary change in electrical potential across a membrane, from negative to positive and back to negative. Occurs in cells, such as neurons and muscle cells, that have an excitable membrane.

action spectrum The relative effectiveness of different wavelengths of light in driving a light-dependent process such as photosynthesis. Usually depicted as a graph of some measure of the process, such as O_2 production, versus wavelength. Compare with **absorption spectrum**.

activation energy The amount of kinetic energy required to initiate a chemical reaction; specifically, the energy required to reach the transition state.

activator A protein that binds to a DNA regulatory sequence to increase the frequency of transcription initiation by RNA polymerase. See also **transcriptional activator**.

active site The location in an enzyme molecule where substrates (reactant molecules) bind and react.

active transport The movement of ions or molecules across a membrane in a single direction, often against a gradient. Requires energy (e.g., from hydrolysis of ATP) and assistance of a transport protein (e.g., pump).

adaptation Any heritable trait that increases the fitness of an individual with that trait, compared with individuals without that trait, in a particular environment.

adaptive immunity Immunity to a particular pathogen or antigen conferred by activated B and T cells in vertebrates. Characterized by specificity, diversity, memory, and self−nonself recognition. Also called *adaptive immune response.* Compare with **innate immunity**.

adaptive radiation Rapid evolutionary diversification within one lineage, producing many descendant species with a wide range of adaptive forms.

adenosine triphosphate (ATP) A molecule consisting of an adenine base, a sugar, and three phosphate groups that are linked together with covalent bonds that have high potential energy. Universally used by cells as a monomer for RNA synthesis and to store and transfer chemical energy.

adhesion The tendency of certain dissimilar molecules to cling together due to attractive forces. Compare with **cohesion**.

adipocyte A fat cell.

adrenal gland Either of two small endocrine glands, one above each kidney. The outer portion (cortex) secretes several steroid hormones; the inner portion (medulla) secretes epinephrine and norepinephrine.

adrenaline See **epinephrine**.

adrenocorticotropic hormone (ACTH) A peptide hormone, produced and secreted by the anterior pituitary, that stimulates release of steroid hormones (e.g., cortisol and aldosterone) from the adrenal cortex.

adult A sexually mature individual.

adventitious root A root that develops from a plant's shoot system instead of from the plant's root system.

aerobic Referring to any metabolic process, cell, or organism that uses oxygen as an electron acceptor. Compare with **anaerobic**.

afferent division The part of the nervous system that transmits information about the internal and external environment to the central nervous system. Consists mainly of sensory neurons. Compare with **efferent division**.

age class All the individuals of a specific age in a population.

age-specific fecundity The average number of female offspring produced by a female in a certain age class.

age structure The proportion of individuals in a population that are of each possible age.

agglutination The clumping of cells, viruses, or other particles by cross-linking molecules (e.g., antibodies).

aggregate fruit A fruit (e.g., raspberry) that develops from a single flower that has many separate carpels. Compare with **multiple** and **simple fruit**.

AIDS See **acquired immune deficiency syndrome.**

alcohol fermentation Catabolic pathway in which pyruvate produced by glycolysis is converted to ethanol in order to oxidize NADH to NAD⁺.

aldosterone A hormone that stimulates the kidney to conserve salt and water and promotes retention of sodium; produced in the adrenal cortex.

allele A particular version of a gene.

allergen Any molecule (antigen) that triggers an allergic response (an allergy).

allergy An IgE-mediated abnormal response to an antigen (allergen), usually characterized by dilation of blood vessels, contraction of smooth muscle cells in the airways, and increased activity of mucus-secreting cells.

allopatric speciation Speciation that occurs when populations of the same species become geographically isolated, often due to dispersal or vicariance. Compare with **sympatric speciation**.

allopatry Condition in which two or more populations live in different geographic areas. Compare with **sympatry**.

allopolyploidy (adjective: allopolyploid) The state of having more than two full sets of chromosomes (polyploidy) due to hybridization between different species. Compare with **autopolyploidy**.

allosteric regulation Regulation of an enzyme's (or other protein's) activity by binding of a regulatory molecule at a site that is distinct from the active site. This regulation often results in a change in the protein's shape that affects the function of the active site.

α-amylase See **amylase**.

α-helix (alpha-helix) A secondary structure in proteins formed when the polypeptide backbone coils into a spiral shape stabilized by hydrogen bonding.

alternation of generations A life cycle involving alternation of a multicellular haploid stage (gametophyte) with a multicellular diploid stage (sporophyte). Occurs in most plants and some protists.

alternative splicing In eukaryotes, the splicing of primary RNA transcripts from a single gene in different ways to produce different mature mRNAs and thus different polypeptides.

altruism Any behavior that has a fitness cost to the individual (lowered survival and/or reproduction) and a fitness benefit to the recipient. See **reciprocal altruism**.

alveolus (plural: alveoli) Any of the tiny, air-filled sacs of a mammalian lung.

ambisense Describing a single strand of RNA that contains a region with the same sequence as an mRNA required to produce viral proteins and another region that is complementary to the sequence of a different mRNA. Compare with **positive-sense** and **negative-sense**.

amino acid A small organic molecule with a central carbon atom bonded to an amino group ($-NH_3$), a carboxyl group ($-COOH$), a hydrogen atom, and a side chain. When amino acids are linked together to form proteins, they are referred to as residues.

aminoacyl tRNA A transfer RNA molecule that is covalently bound to an amino acid.

aminoacyl-tRNA synthetase An enzyme that catalyzes the addition of a particular amino acid to its corresponding tRNA molecule.

ammonia (NH_3) A small molecule, produced by the breakdown of proteins and nucleic acids, that is very toxic to cells. It is a strong base that gains a proton to form the ammonium ion (NH_4^+). The major nitrogenous waste of bony fishes and aquatic invertebrates.

amnion The innermost of the membranes surrounding the embryo in an amniotic egg.

amniotes A major lineage of vertebrates (Amniota) that reproduce with amniotic eggs. Includes all reptiles (including birds) and mammals—all tetrapods except amphibians.

amniotic egg An egg that has a watertight shell or case enclosing a membrane-bound water supply (the amnion and chorion), food supply (yolk sac), and waste sac (allantois).

amoeboid motion A sliding movement observed in some protists accomplished by the formation of cytoplasmic extensions of the cell called pseudopodia. One form of *cell crawling*.

amphibians A lineage of vertebrates, many of which breathe through their skin and feed on land but lay their eggs in water; includes frogs, salamanders, and caecilians.

amphipathic Containing hydrophilic and hydrophobic regions.

ampullae of Lorenzini Structures on the heads of sharks that contain electroreceptors.

amylase Any enzyme that can break down starch by catalyzing hydrolysis of the α-glycosidic linkages between the glucose residues.

amyloplasts Starch-storing organelles (plastids) in plants. In root cap cells, they settle to the bottom of the cell and may be used as gravity detectors.

anabolic pathway Any set of chemical reactions that synthesizes large molecules from smaller ones. Generally requires an input of energy. Compare with **catabolic pathway**.

anaerobic Referring to any metabolic process, cell, or organism that uses an electron acceptor other than oxygen, including fermentation or anaerobic respiration. Compare with **aerobic**.

anaphase The stage in mitosis or meiosis during which chromosomes are moved to opposite poles of the spindle apparatus.

anatomy The physical structure of organisms.

ancestral trait A trait found in the ancestors of a particular group.

aneuploidy (adjective: aneuploid) The state of having an abnormal number of copies of a certain chromosome.

angiosperm A flowering vascular plant that produces seeds within mature ovaries (fruits). The angiosperms form a single lineage. Compare with **gymnosperm**.

animal A member of a major lineage of eukaryotes (Animalia) whose members typically have a complex, multicellular body; eat other organisms; and move under their own power at some point in their lives.

animal model A non-human animal used by medical researchers that develops a disease with parallels to a similar disease of humans. Studied in hopes that findings may apply to human disease.

anion A negatively charged ion.

annelids Members of the phylum Annelida (segmented worms). Distinguished by a segmented body and a coelom that functions as a hydrostatic skeleton. Annelids belong to the lophotrochozoan branch of the protostomes.

annual Referring to a plant whose life cycle normally lasts only one growing season—less than one year. Compare with **perennial**.

anoxygenic Referring to any process or reaction that does not produce oxygen. Photosynthesis in purple sulfur bacteria is anoxygenic because it does not use water as an electron donor so no O_2 is produced. Compare with **oxygenic**.

antagonistic muscle group A set of two or more muscles that re-extend one another by transmitting their forces via the skeleton.

antenna (plural: antennae) A long appendage of the head that is used to touch or smell.

antenna complex Part of a photosystem; contains an array of proteins that organize chlorophyll molecules and accessory pigments to capture light and direct energy to a central reaction center during photosynthesis.

anterior Toward an animal's head and away from its tail. The opposite of posterior.

anterior pituitary The part of the pituitary gland containing endocrine cells that produce and release a variety of peptide hormones in response to other hormones from the hypothalamus. Compare with **posterior pituitary**.

anther The pollen-producing structure at the end of a stamen in flowering plants (angiosperms).

antheridium (plural: antheridia) The sperm-producing structure in most land plants except angiosperms.

anthropoids One of the two major lineages of primates, including humans and the other great apes, gibbons, and all monkeys. Compare with **prosimians**.

antibiotic Any substance, such as penicillin, that can kill or inhibit the growth of bacteria.

antibody A protein produced by B cells that can bind to a specific part of an antigen, tagging it for removal by the immune system. All monomeric forms of antibodies consist of two light chains and two heavy chains, which vary between different antibodies. Also called *immunoglobulin*.

anticodon The sequence of three bases (a triplet) in a transfer RNA molecule that can bind to an mRNA codon with a complementary sequence.

antidiuretic hormone (ADH) A peptide hormone, secreted from the posterior pituitary gland, that stimulates water retention by the kidney. Also called *vasopressin*.

antigen Any foreign molecule, often a protein, that can stimulate an innate or adaptive response by the immune system.

antigen presentation A process by which small peptides, derived from ingested or intracellular antigens, are complexed with MHC proteins and transported to the cell surface, where they are displayed and can be recognized by T-cell receptors.

antiparallel Describes the opposite orientation of nucleic acid strands that are hydrogen-bonded to one another, with one strand running in the $5' \rightarrow 3'$ direction and the other in the $3' \rightarrow 5'$ direction.

antiporter A carrier protein that allows an ion to diffuse down an electrochemical gradient, using the energy of that process to transport a different substance in the opposite direction *against* its concentration gradient. Compare with **symporter**.

antiviral Any drug or other agent that can interfere with the transmission or replication of viruses.

aorta In terrestrial vertebrates, the major artery carrying oxygenated blood away from the heart.

aphotic zone Deep water receiving no sunlight. Compare with **photic zone**.

apical Toward the top. In plants, at the tip of a branch. In animals, on the side of an epithelial layer that faces the environment and not other body tissues. Compare with **basal** and **basolateral**.

apical–basal axis The shoot-to-root axis of a plant.

apical bud A bud at the tip of a stem or branch, where growth occurs to lengthen the stem or branch.

apical dominance Inhibition of lateral bud growth by the apical meristem at the tip of a plant branch.

apical meristem A group of undifferentiated plant cells, at the tip of a shoot or root, that is responsible for primary growth. Compare with **cambium.**

apodeme Any of the chitinous ingrowths of an exoskeleton to which muscles attach.

apomixis The formation of mature seeds without fertilization occurring; a type of asexual reproduction.

apoplast In plants, the region outside plasma membranes consisting of the porous cell walls and the intervening extracellular air space. Compare with **symplast**.

apoptosis A series of tightly controlled changes in cellular activity that lead to the self-destruction of a cell. Occurs frequently during embryological development and as part of the immune response to remove infected or cancerous cells. Also called *programmed cell death.*

appendix A blind sac (having only one opening) that extends from the cecum in some mammals.

aquaporin A type of channel protein that facilitates the movement of water (osmosis) across a plasma membrane.

aqueous In a watery or in a water-based environment. Often used in describing a solution where water serves as the solvent.

aquifer An underground layer of porous rock, sand, or gravel that is saturated with water.

ara operon A set of three genes in *E. coli* that are transcribed into a single mRNA and required for metabolism of the sugar arabinose. Transcription of the *ara* operon is controlled by the AraC regulatory protein.

araC The regulatory gene (written as *araC*) or regulatory protein (when written as AraC) of the *E. coli ara* operon.

arbuscular mycorrhizal fungi (AMF) Fungi from the Glomeromycota lineage whose hyphae enter the root cells of their host plants. Also called *endomycorrhizal fungi.*

Archaea One of the three taxonomic domains of life, consisting of unicellular prokaryotes distinguished by cell walls made of certain polysaccharides not found in bacterial or eukaryotic cell walls, plasma membranes composed of unique isoprene-containing phospholipids, and ribosomes and RNA polymerase similar to those of eukaryotes. Compare with **Bacteria** and **Eukarya.**

archegonium (plural: archegonia) The egg-producing structure in most land plants except angiosperms.

arteriole A small vessel that carries blood to a capillary bed.

arteriosclerosis Hardening and loss of elasticity of arteries.

artery Any thick-walled vessel that carries blood (oxygenated or not) under relatively high pressure away from the heart to organs throughout the body. Compare with **vein**.

arthropods Members of the phylum Arthropoda. Distinguished by a segmented body; a hard, jointed exoskeleton; paired, jointed appendages; and an extensive body cavity called a hemocoel. Arthropods belong to the ecdysozoan branch of the protostomes.

articulation A point of contact between two rigid components of a skeleton, such as between bones of a vertebrate endoskeleton or between segments of cuticle in an arthropod exoskeleton. See **joint.**

artificial selection Deliberate manipulation by humans, as in animal and plant breeding, of the genetic composition of a population by allowing only individuals with desirable traits to reproduce.

ascus (plural: asci) Specialized spore-producing cell found at the ends of hyphae in "sac fungi" (Ascomycota).

asexual reproduction Any form of reproduction where offspring inherit DNA from only one parent. Includes binary fission, budding, and parthenogenesis. Compare with **sexual reproduction**.

astral microtubule A microtubule that arises from the one of the spindle poles in mitosis or meiosis and interacts with proteins on the plasma membrane.

asymmetric competition Ecological competition between two species in which one species suffers a much greater fitness decline than the other. Compare with **symmetric competition.**

atomic number The number of protons in the nucleus of an atom, giving the atom its identity as a particular chemical element.

atomic weight The average mass of an element that is based on the relative proportions of all its naturally occurring isotopes.

ATP See **adenosine triphosphate**.

ATP synthase A large membrane-bound protein complex that uses the potential energy stored in a proton gradient to couple proton transport and ATP synthesis.

atrioventricular (AV) node A region of the heart between the right atrium and right ventricle where electrical signals from the atrium are delayed briefly before spreading to the ventricle. This delay allows the ventricle to fill with blood before contracting. Compare with **sinoatrial (SA) node**.

atrium (plural: atria) A thin-walled chamber of the heart that receives blood from veins and pumps it to a neighboring chamber (the ventricle).

autocrine Relating to a chemical signal that affects the same cell that produced and released it.

autoimmunity A pathological condition in which the immune system recognizes self molecules and attacks the cells or tissues of an individual's own body.

autonomic nervous system The part of the vertebrate peripheral nervous system that controls internal organs and involuntary processes, such as stomach contraction, hormone release, and heart rate. Includes parasympathetic and sympathetic nerves. Compare with **somatic nervous system**.

autophagy The process by which damaged organelles are surrounded by a membrane and delivered to a lysosome to be recycled.

autopolyploidy (adjective: autopolyploid) The state of having more than two full sets of chromosomes (polyploidy) due to a mutation that doubled the chromosome number. All the chromosomes come from the same species. Compare with **allopolyploidy**.

autosomal inheritance The inheritance patterns that occur when genes are located on autosomes rather than on sex chromosomes.

autosome Any chromosome other than a sex chromosome (i.e., any chromosome other than the X or Y in mammals).

autotroph Any organism that can synthesize reduced organic compounds from simple inorganic sources such as CO_2 or CH_4. Most plants and some bacteria and archaea are autotrophs. Also called *primary producer.* Compare with **heterotroph**.

auxin Indoleacetic acid (IAA), a plant hormone that stimulates phototropism and cell elongation.

axillary bud A bud that forms at a node and may develop into a lateral (side) branch. Also called *lateral bud.*

axon A long projection of a neuron that can propagate an action potential.

axon hillock The site in a neuron where an axon joins the cell body and where action potentials typically are first triggered.

axoneme A structure found in eukaryotic cilia and flagella and responsible for their motion; composed of two central microtubules surrounded by nine doublet microtubules (9 + 2 arrangement).

B cell A type of lymphocyte that originates and matures in the bone marrow and, with T cells, is responsible for adaptive immunity. Produces antibodies and also functions in antigen presentation. Also called *B lymphocyte.*

B-cell receptor (BCR) A transmembrane protein in the plasma membrane of a mature B cell that can bind to a specific antigen. Its antigen-binding sites are identical to those in the antibodies produced by the same cell.

background extinction The average rate of low-level extinction that has occurred continuously throughout much of evolutionary history. Compare with **mass extinction**.

Bacteria One of the three taxonomic domains of life, consisting of unicellular prokaryotes distinguished by cell walls composed largely of peptidoglycan, plasma membranes similar to those of eukaryotic cells, and ribosomes and RNA polymerase that differ from those in archaea or eukaryotes. Compare with **Archaea** and **Eukarya**.

bacteriophage Any virus that infects bacteria.

baculum A bone inside the penis; usually present in mammals that have a penis lacking erectile tissue.

balancing selection A mode of natural selection in which no single allele is favored over time and across locations, on average. An overall balance among alleles, in terms of fitness and frequency, is maintained.

ball-and-stick model A representation of a molecule where atoms are shown as balls—colored and scaled to indicate the atom's identity—and covalent bonds are shown as rods or sticks connecting the balls in the correct geometry.

barcoding See **DNA barcoding**.

bark The protective outer layer of woody plants, composed of cork cells, cork cambium, and secondary phloem.

baroreceptor One of the specialized nerve cells in the walls of the heart and certain major arteries that detect changes in blood pressure and trigger appropriate responses by the brain.

basal Toward the base. In plants, toward the root or at the base of a branch where it joins the stem. In animals, on the side of an epithelial layer that abuts underlying body tissues. Compare with **apical**.

basal body The microtubule organizing center for cilia and flagella in eukaryotic cells. Consists of nine triplets of microtubules arranged in a circle and establishes the structure of axonemes. Structurally identical with a centriole.

basal lamina A thick, collagen-rich extracellular matrix that underlies most epithelial tissues in animals and connects it to connective tissue.

basal metabolic rate (BMR) The total energy consumption by an organism at rest in a comfortable environment. For aerobes, often measured as the amount of oxygen consumed per hour.

basal transcription factor Any of a class of proteins, present in all eukaryotic cells, that assemble on promoters and help initiate transcription. Compare with **regulatory transcription factor**.

base Any compound that acquires protons or gives up electrons during a chemical reaction or accepts hydrogen ions when dissolved in water.

basidium (plural: basidia) Specialized spore-producing cell at the ends of hyphae in "club fungi" (Basidiomycota).

basilar membrane One of the membranes in the vertebrate cochlea between which the hair cells are located. Vibrates when sound waves travel through the fluid in the cochlea.

basolateral Toward the bottom and sides. In animals, the side of an epithelial layer that faces other body tissues and not the environment.

Batesian mimicry A type of mimicry in which a harmless or palatable species resembles a dangerous or poisonous species. Compare with **Müllerian mimicry**.

behavioral ecology A discipline that focuses on behavioral adaptations that have evolved in response to ecological selection pressures; a subset of organismal ecology, which also includes morphological and physiological adapatations.

beneficial In genetics, referring to any mutation, allele, or trait that increases an individual's fitness. Compare with **deleterious** and **neutral**.

benign tumor A mass of abnormal tissue that develops due to unregulated growth but does not spread to other organs. Benign tumors are not cancers. Compare with **malignant tumor**.

benthic Living at the bottom of an aquatic environment.

benthic zone The area along the bottom of an aquatic environment.

β-pleated sheet (beta-pleated sheet) A secondary structure in proteins formed when the polypeptide backbone folds into a sheetlike shape stabilized by hydrogen bonding.

bilateral symmetry An animal body pattern in which one plane of symmetry divides the body into a left side and a right side. Typically, the body is long and narrow, with a distinct head end and tail end. Compare with **radial symmetry**.

bilaterian A member of a major lineage of animals (Bilateria) that are bilaterally symmetrical at some point in their life cycle, have three embryonic germ layers, and have a coelom (or evolved from ancestors that had a coelom). All protostomes and deuterostomes are bilaterians.

bile A complex solution produced by the liver, stored in the gallbladder, and secreted into the small intestine. Contains steroid derivatives called bile salts that are responsible for emulsification of fats during digestion.

binary fission The process of cell division used for asexual reproduction of many prokaryotic cells. The genetic material is replicated and partitioned to opposite sides of a growing cell, which then divides in half, creating two genetically identical cells.

biodiversity The diversity of life considered at three levels: genetic diversity (variety of alleles and/or genes in a population, species, or group of species); species diversity (variety and relative abundance of species present in a certain area); and ecosystem diversity (variety of communities and abiotic components in a region).

biodiversity hotspot A region that is extraordinarily rich in species.

biofilm A complex community of bacteria enmeshed in a polysaccharide-rich, extracellular matrix that allows the bacteria to attach to a surface.

biogeochemical cycle The pattern of circulation of an element or molecule among living organisms and the environment.

biogeography The study of how species and populations are distributed geographically.

bioinformatics The branch of computer science that is concerned with managing, analyzing, and interpreting biological information, particularly DNA and amino acid sequences.

biological species concept The definition of a species as a population or group of populations that are reproductively isolated from other groups. Members of a species have the potential to interbreed in nature to produce viable, fertile offspring but cannot interbreed successfully with members of other species. Compare with **morphospecies** and **phylogenetic species concepts**.

bioluminescence The emission of light by a living organism via an enzyme-catalyzed reaction.

biomagnification In animal tissues, an increase in the concentration of particular molecules that may occur as those molecules are passed up a food chain.

biomass The total mass of all organisms in a given population or geographical area; usually expressed as total dry weight.

biome A large terrestrial or aquatic region characterized by distinct abiotic characteristics and dominant types of vegetation.

biomechanics A field of biology that applies the principles of physics and engineering to analyze the mechanical structure and function of organisms.

bioprospecting The effort to find commercially useful compounds by studying organisms—especially species that are poorly studied to date.

bioremediation The use of living organisms, usually bacteria or archaea, to degrade environmental pollutants.

biosphere The thin zone surrounding Earth where all life exists; the sum of all terrestrial and aquatic ecosystems.

biotechnology The application of biological techniques and discoveries, particularly related to recombinant DNA and gene expression, to medicine, industry, and agriculture.

biotic Living, or produced by a living organism. Compare with **abiotic**.

bipedal Walking primarily on two legs; characteristic of hominins.

bipolar cell A type of cell in the vertebrate retina that receives information from one or more photoreceptors and passes it to ganglion cells.

bivalent The structure formed by synapsed homologous chromosomes during prophase of meiosis I.

bivalves A lineage of mollusks, including clams and mussels, that have shells made of two parts, or valves.

bladder An organ that holds urine until it can be excreted.

blade The wide, flat part of a plant leaf.

blastocoel A fluid-filled cavity in the blastula of many animal species.

blastocyst The mammalian blastula. A roughly spherical structure composed of trophoblast cells on the exterior, a fluid-filled cavity (the blastocoel), and a cluster of cells (the inner cell mass) that fills part of the interior space.

blastomere A cell created by cleavage in early animal embryos.

blastopore An opening (pore) in the surface of some early embryos that cells move through during gastrulation.

blastula In animals, a ball of cells (blastomeres) formed by cleavage of a zygote and typically containing a fluid-filled cavity (the blastocoel). See **blastocyst**.

blood A type of connective tissue consisting of red blood cells and leukocytes suspended in a liquid extracellular matrix called plasma. Transports materials throughout the vertebrate body.

body mass index (BMI) A mathematical relationship used to assess obesity in humans. Calculated as body mass (in kg) divided by the square of height (in m^2).

body plan The basic architecture of an animal's body, including the number and arrangement of limbs, body segments, and major tissue layers.

Bohr shift The rightward shift of the oxygen–hemoglobin equilibrium curve that occurs with decreasing pH. It results in hemoglobin being more likely to release oxygen to tissues with low pH, such as exercising muscle.

bone A type of vertebrate connective tissue consisting of living cells and blood vessels within a hard extracellular matrix composed of calcium phosphate ($CaPO_4$) and small amounts of calcium carbonate ($CaCO_3$) and protein fibers.

bone marrow The soft tissue filling the inside of large bones; contains stem cells that develop into red blood cells and leukocytes throughout life.

Bowman's capsule The hollow, double-walled, cup-shaped portion of a nephron that surrounds a glomerulus in the vertebrate kidney.

brain A large mass of neurons, located in the head region of an animal, that is involved in information processing; may also be called the cerebral ganglion.

brain stem The most posterior portion of the vertebrate brain, connecting to the spinal cord and responsible for autonomic body functions such as regulating heart rate, respiration, and digestion.

braincase See **cranium**.

branch (1) A part of a phylogenetic tree that represents populations through time. (2) A lateral extension of a plant's shoot system.

brassinosteroids A family of steroid hormones found in plants; they stimulate growth.

bronchiole Any of the small tubes in mammalian lungs that carry air from the bronchi to the alveoli.

bronchus (plural: bronchi) In mammals, one of a pair of large tubes that lead from the trachea to each lung.

budding A form of asexual reproduction in which an outgrowth from the parent breaks free as an independent individual; occurs in yeasts and some invertebrates and plants.

buffer A substance that, in solution, acts to minimize changes in the pH of that solution when acid or base is added.

bulbourethral gland In male mammals, one of a pair of small glands at the base of the urethra that secrete alkaline mucus (part of semen), which lubricates the tip of the penis and neutralizes acids in the urethra during copulation. In humans, also called *Cowper's gland*.

bulk flow The directional mass movement of a fluid due to pressure differences, such as movement of water through plant xylem and phloem, and movement of blood in animals.

bundle-sheath cell A type of cell found around the vascular tissue (veins) of plant leaves.

C_3 pathway The most common form of photosynthesis in which atmospheric CO_2 is fixed by rubisco to form 3-phosphoglycerate, a three-carbon molecule. Used in first phase of the Calvin cycle.

C_4 pathway A variant type of photosynthesis in which atmospheric CO_2 is first fixed by PEP carboxylase into four-carbon molecules, rather than the three-carbon molecules of the classic C_3 pathway. Used to concentrate CO_2 to reduce photorespiration in the Calvin cycle while stomata are closed to prevent water loss.

C_4 photosynthesis A variant type of photosynthesis in which atmospheric CO_2 is first fixed into four-carbon sugars, rather than the three-carbon sugars of classic C_3 photosynthesis. Enhances photosynthetic efficiency in hot, dry environments by reducing loss of oxygen due to photorespiration.

cadherin Any of a class of cell-surface proteins involved in selective cell–cell adhesion. Important for coordinating movements of cells and the establishment of tissues during embryological development.

callus In plants, a mass of undifferentiated cells that can generate roots and other tissues necessary to create a mature plant.

Calvin cycle In photosynthesis, the set of reactions that uses NADPH and ATP formed in the light-capturing reactions to drive the fixation of CO_2, reduction of the fixed carbon to produce sugar, and the regeneration of the substrate used to fix CO_2.

calyx All of the sepals of a flower.

CAM See **crassulacean acid metabolism**.

cambium (plural: cambia) In woody plants, tissue that consists of two types of cylindrical meristems that increase the width of roots and shoots through the process of secondary growth. See **vascular cambium** and **cork cambium**.

Cambrian explosion The rapid diversification of animal body types and lineages that occured during a 50-million-year period about 541 mya at the start of the Proterozoic eon.

cancer General term for a disease caused by cells that grow in an uncontrolled fashion, invade nearby tissues, and spread to other sites in the body.

capillary In a closed circulatory system, any of the many small, thin-walled blood vessels that permeate all tissues and organs and allow exchange of gases and other molecules between blood and body cells.

capillary action The tendency of water to move up a narrow tube due to adhesion, cohesion, and surface tension.

capillary bed A network of capillaries.

capsid A shell of protein enclosing the genome of a virus particle.

carapace In crustaceans, a large platelike section of the exoskeleton that covers and protects the cephalothorax (e.g., a crab's "shell").

carbohydrate Any of a class of molecules that contain a carbonyl group, several hydroxyl groups, and multiple carbon-hydrogen bonds. Synonymous with sugar. See **monosaccharide, disaccharide, oligosaccharide,** and **polysaccharide**.

carbon cycle, global The movement of carbon among terrestrial ecosystems, aquatic ecosystems, and the atmosphere.

carbon fixation The process of converting gaseous carbon dioxide into an organic molecule; often associated with photosynthesis. See also **PEP carboxylase** and **rubisco**.

carbon sink A resorvoir that stores carbon-containing compounds for an indefinite period of time.

carbonic anhydrase An enzyme that catalyzes the formation of carbonic acid (H_2CO_3) from carbon dioxide and water.

carboxylic acids Organic acids with one or more carboxl groups (R-COOH).

cardiac cycle One complete heartbeat cycle, including systole and diastole.

cardiac muscle The muscle tissue of the vertebrate heart; responsible for pumping blood. Consists of long, branched fibers that are electrically connected and that initiate their own contractions; not under voluntary control. Compare with **skeletal muscle** and **smooth muscle**.

cardiovascular disease A group of diseases of the heart and blood vessels that may be caused by poor diet, obesity, inactivity, genetics, tobacco use, age, and other factors.

carnivore (adjective: carnivorous) An animal whose diet consists predominantly of meat, or other animals. Most members of the mammalian taxon Carnivora are carnivores. Some plants are carnivorous, trapping and killing small animals and then absorbing nutrients from the prey's body. Compare with **herbivore** and **omnivore**.

carotenoid Any of a class of accessory pigments, found in chloroplasts, that absorb wavelengths of light not absorbed by chlorophyll; typically appear yellow, orange, or red. Includes carotenes and xanthophylls.

carpel The female reproductive organ in a flower. Consists of the stigma, to which pollen grains adhere; the style, through which the pollen tube grows; and the ovary, which houses the ovule. Compare with **stamen**.

carrier A heterozygous individual carrying a normal allele and a recessive allele for an inherited trait. The individual does not display the phenotype of the recessive trait but can pass the recessive allele to offspring.

carrier protein A transmembrane protein that facilitates diffusion of a small molecule (e.g., glucose) across a membrane by a process involving a reversible change in the shape of the protein. Also called *carrier* or *transporter*. Compare with **channel protein**.

carrying capacity (*K*) The maximum population size of a certain species that a given habitat can support.

cartilage A type of vertebrate connective tissue that consists of relatively few cells scattered in a stiff matrix of polysaccharides and protein fibers. Provides structural support.

Casparian strip In plant roots, a waxy layer containing suberin, a water-repellent substance that prevents movement of water through the walls of endodermal cells, thus blocking the apoplastic pathway of water and ion movement into the vascular tissue.

catabolic pathway Any set of chemical reactions that breaks down large, complex molecules into smaller ones, releasing energy in the process. Compare with **anabolic pathway**.

catalysis (verb: catalyze) Acceleration of the rate of a chemical reaction due to a decrease in the free energy of the transition state, called the activation energy.

catalyst Any substance that increases the rate of a chemical reaction without itself undergoing any permanent chemical change.

catecholamine Any of a class of small compounds, derived from the amino acid tyrosine, that are used as hormones or neurotransmitters. Catecholamines include epinephrine, norepinephrine, and dopamine.

cation A positively charged ion.

cation exchange The release (displacement) of cations, such as magnesium and calcium from soil particles, by protons in acidic soil water. The released cations are available for uptake by plants.

CD4 A protein on the plasma membrane of some human T cells. CD4$^+$ T cells can give rise to helper T cells.

CD8 A protein on the plasma membrane of some leukocytes in humans. CD8$^+$ T cells can give rise to cytotoxic T cells.

cDNA See **complementary DNA**.

cecum A blind sac between the small intestine and the colon. Is enlarged in some species (e.g., rabbits) that use it as a fermentation chamber for digestion of cellulose.

cell A highly organized compartment bounded by a thin, flexible structure (plasma membrane) and containing concentrated chemicals in an aqueous (watery) solution. The basic structural and functional unit of all organisms.

cell body The part of a neuron that contains the nucleus; where incoming signals are integrated. Also called the *soma*.

cell crawling A form of cellular movement involving actin filaments in which the cell produces bulges in the membrane that stick to the substrate and are used to pull the cell forward.

cell cycle An ordered sequence of events in which a eukaryotic cell increases in size, replicates its chromosomes, evenly partitions the chromosomes to two daughter nuclei, and then undergoes division of the cytoplasm.

cell-cycle checkpoint Any of several points in the cell cycle at which progression of a cell through the cycle can be regulated.

cell division Formation of new cells by division of preexisting cells.

cell-mediated (immune) response The type of immune response that involves generation of cytotoxic T cells from CD8$^+$ T cells. Defends against pathogen-infected cells, cancer cells, and transplanted cells. Compare with **humoral (immune) response**.

cell membrane See **plasma membrane**.

cell plate A flattened, sac-like structure formed in the middle of a dividing plant cell from Golgi-derived vesicles containing cell-wall material; ultimately divides the cytoplasm into two separate cells.

cell sap An aqueous solution found in the vacuoles of plant cells.

cell theory The theory that all organisms are made of cells and that all cells come from preexisting cells.

cell wall A fibrous layer found outside the plasma membrane of most bacteria and archaea and many eukaryotes.

cellular respiration A common pathway for production of ATP, involving transfer of electrons from compounds with high potential energy through an electron transport chain and ultimately to a final electron acceptor (often oxygen).

cellulase An enzyme that digests cellulose by catalyzing hydrolysis of the glycosidic linkages between glucose residues.

cellulose A structural polysaccharide composed of glucose monomers joined by β-1,4-glycosidic linkages. Found in the cell walls of algae, plants, and some bacteria and fungi.

Cenozoic era The most recent interval of geologic time, beginning 66 million years ago, during which mammals became the dominant vertebrates and angiosperms became the dominant plants.

central dogma The scheme for information flow in the cell: DNA → RNA → protein.

central nervous system (CNS) An aggregation of large numbers of neurons into clusters called ganglia in bilaterian animals. In vertebrates, the CNS consists of the brain and spinal cord. Compare with **nerve net** and **peripheral nervous system (PNS)**.

centriole One of two small cylindrical structures contained within the centrosome near the nucleus of a eukaryotic cell (found in animals but not in most plants). Consists of microtubule triplets and is structurally identical to a basal body.

centromere The region of a replicated chromosome where the two sister chromatids are joined most tightly and the kinetochore is formed during M phase.

centrosome A structure that serves as a microtubule-organizing center for the cell's cytoskeleton and for the spindle apparatus during cell division. Includes centrioles in animal cells and certain plants and fungi.

cephalization The formation in animals of a distinct anterior region (the head) where sense organs and a mouth are clustered.

cephalochordates One of the three major chordate lineages (Cephalochordata), comprising small, mobile organisms that live in marine sands and suspension feed; also called *lancelets* or *amphioxus*. Compare with **urochordates** and **vertebrates**.

cephalopods A lineage of mollusks including squid, octopuses, and nautiluses. Distinguished by large brains, excellent vision, tentacles, and (in living species) a reduced or absent shell.

cephalothorax In some arthropods, the tagma that is formed by the fusion of the head and thorax; anterior to the abdomen.

cerebellum A posterior portion of the vertebrate brain; involved in coordination of complex muscle movements, such as those required for locomotion and maintaining balance.

cerebrum The most anterior portion of the vertebrate brain; divided into left and right hemispheres and four lobes. See **frontal lobe, occipital lobe, parietal lobe**, and **temporal lobe**.

cervix The bottom portion of the uterus, containing an opening that leads to the vagina.

chaetae (singular: chaeta) Bristle-like extensions found in some annelids.

channel protein A transmembrane protein that forms a pore in a cell membrane, which may open or close in response to a signal. The structure of most channels allows them to admit just one or a few types of ions or molecules. Compare with **carrier protein**.

character Any genetic, morphological, physiological, developmental, or behavioral characteristic of an organism to be studied. Also called a *trait*.

character displacement The evolutionary tendency for the traits of similar species that occupy overlapping ranges to change in a way that reduces interspecific competition.

chelicerae A pair of clawlike appendages found near the mouth of certain arthropods called chelicerates (spiders, mites, and relatives).

chelicerate A lineage of mostly terrestrial arthropods that include spiders, scorpions, ticks, mites, daddy longlegs, and horseshoe crabs; named for their clawlike appendages called chelicerae.

chemical bond An attractive force binding two atoms together. Covalent bonds, ionic bonds, and hydrogen bonds are types of chemical bonds.

chemical energy The potential energy stored in chemical bonds between atoms.

chemical equilibrium A dynamic but stable state of a reversible chemical reaction in which the forward reaction and reverse reactions proceed at the same rate, so that the concentrations of reactants and products remain constant.

chemical evolution The theory that simple chemical compounds in the early atmosphere and ocean combined via chemical reactions to form larger, more complex substances, eventually leading to the origin of life and the start of biological evolution.

chemical reaction Any process in which substances combine or are broken down into other substances; involves the making and/or breaking of chemical bonds.

chemiosmosis An energetic coupling mechanism whereby energy stored in an electrochemical proton gradient is used to drive an energy-requiring process such as production of ATP.

chemokine Any of a subset of cytokines that acts as a chemical signal attracting leukocytes to a site of tissue injury or infection.

chemolithotroph An organism (bacteria or archaea) that produces ATP by oxidizing inorganic molecules with high potential energy, such as ammonia (NH_3) or methane (CH_4). Also called *lithotroph*. Compare with **chemoorganotroph**.

chemoorganotroph An organism that produces ATP by oxidizing organic molecules with high potential energy such as sugars. Also called *organotroph*. Compare with **chemolithotroph**.

chemoreception The detection of specific chemicals in an animal's internal or external environment.

chemoreceptor A sensory cell specialized for detecting specific chemicals or classes of chemicals.

chiasma (plural: chiasmata) The X-shaped structure formed during meiosis by crossing over between non-sister chromatids in a pair of homologous chromosomes.

chitin A structural polysaccharide composed of *N*-acetyl-glucosamine (NAG) monomers joined end to end by β-1,4-glycosidic linkages. Found in the cell walls of fungi and many algae, and in external skeletons of insects and crustaceans.

chitons A lineage of marine mollusks that have a protective shell formed of eight calcium carbonate plates.

chlorophyll Any of several closely related green pigments, found in chloroplasts, that absorb light during photosynthesis.

chloroplast A chlorophyll-containing organelle, bounded by a double membrane, in which photosynthesis occurs; found in plants and algae. Also the location of starch, amino acid, fatty acid, purine, and pyrimidine synthesis.

choanocyte A specialized, flagellated feeding cell found in sponges (the most ancient animal phylum).

cholecystokinin A peptide hormone secreted by cells in the lining of the small intestine. Stimulates the secretion of digestive enzymes from the pancreas and the release of bile by the gallbladder.

chordate Any member of the phylum Chordata. Chordates are deuterostomes distinguished by four morphological features present at some stage in their life cycles: a dorsal hollow nerve cord, pharyngeal gill slits, a notochord, and a post-anal tail. Includes vertebrates, cephalochordata, and urochordata.

chromatid One of the two identical double-stranded DNAs that are connected at the centromere and compose a replicated chromosome.

chromatin The complex of DNA and proteins, mainly histones, that compose eukaryotic chromosomes. Can be highly compact (heterochromatin) or loosely coiled (euchromatin).

chromatin remodeling The process by which the structure of chromatin is changed to allow or inhibit transcription or replication. May involve chemical modification of histone proteins or reshaping of the chromatin by large multiprotein complexes in an ATP-requiring process.

chromatin remodeling complex A group of proteins that use energy from ATP hydrolysis to shift nucleosomes on DNA so as to expose regulatory sequences to, or hide them from, transcription factors.

chromosome Gene-carrying structure consisting of a single long molecule of double-stranded DNA and associated proteins (e.g., histones). Most prokaryotic cells contain a single, circular chromosome; eukaryotic cells contain multiple noncircular (linear) chromosomes located in the nucleus.

chromosome-level mutation Any change in chromosome number, such as the loss of a chromosome (aneuploidy) or the gain of a chromosome (polyploidy), or the change in the composition of individual chromosomes as a result of inversions, translocations, deletions, or duplications during cell division. Compare with **point mutation** and **lateral gene transfer**.

chromosome theory of inheritance The principle that genes are located on chromosomes and that patterns of inheritance are determined by the behavior of chromosomes during meiosis.

cilium (plural: cilia) One of many short, filamentous projections of some eukaryotic cells, containing a core of microtubules. Used to move the cell as well as to circulate fluid or particles around the surface of a stationary cell. See **axoneme**.

circadian clock An internal mechanism found in most organisms that regulates many body processes (sleep–wake cycles, hormonal patterns, etc.) in a roughly 24-hour cycle.

circulatory system The system responsible for moving oxygen, carbon dioxide, hormones, nutrients, wastes, and other materials within the animal body.

cisternae (singular: cisterna) Flattened, membrane-bound compartments that make up the Golgi apparatus.

citric acid cycle A series of eight chemical reactions that start with citrate (deprotonated citric acid) and ends with oxaloacetate. The cycle is formed when oxaloacetate reacts with acetyl CoA to form citrate as part of the pathway that oxidizes glucose to CO_2. Also known as the *Krebs cycle* or *tricarboxylic acid* *(TCA) cycle*.

clade See **monophyletic group**.

cladistic approach A method for constructing a phylogenetic tree that is based on identifying the unique traits (shared, derived characters, called synapomorphies).

class I MHC protein A major histocompatibility protein that is present on the plasma membrane of virtually all nucleated cells of vertebrates. Functions in presenting epitopes of antigens to CD8$^+$ T cells.

class II MHC protein A major histocompatibility protein that is present on the plasma membrane of only certain cells involved in the immune response of vertebrates, including dendritic cells, macrophages, and B cells. Functions in presenting epitopes of antigens to CD4$^+$ T cells.

cleavage In animals, the series of rapid mitotic divisions, with little cell growth, that produces successively smaller cells (blastomeres) and transforms a zygote into a multicellular blastula.

cleavage furrow An indentation in the cell surface that occurs as the plasma membrane is pulled inward during cytokinesis in animal cells. The furrow deepens until the membrane fuses, dividing the cytoplasm into two daughter cells.

climate The prevailing, long-term weather conditions in a particular region.

climax community The stable, final community that develops from ecological succession.

clitoris A rod of erectile tissue in the external genitalia of female mammals. Is formed from the same embryonic tissue as the male penis and has a similar function in sexual arousal.

cloaca In a few mammals and many nonmammalian vertebrates, a body cavity into which the urinary, gastrointestinal, and reproductive tracts all empty.

clonal selection theory The dominant explanation for the generation of an adaptive immune response in vertebrates. According to the theory, the immune system retains a vast pool of inactive lymphocytes, each with a unique receptor for a unique epitope. Lymphocytes that encounter their complementary epitopes are stimulated to divide (selected and cloned), producing daughter cells that combat infection and confer immunity.

clone (1) An individual that is genetically identical to another individual. (2) A lineage of genetically identical individuals or cells. (3) As a verb, to make one or more genetic replicas of a cell or individual.

cloning vector A plasmid or other agent such as a virus used to transfer recombinant genes into cultured host cells. Also called a *vector*.

closed circulatory system A circulatory system in which the circulating fluid (blood) is confined to blood vessels and flows in a continuous circuit. Compare with **open circulatory system**.

cnidocyte A specialized stinging cell found in cnidarians (e.g., jellyfish, corals, and anemones) and used in capturing prey.

cochlea The organ of hearing in the inner ear of mammals, birds, and crocodilians. A coiled, fluid-filled tube containing specialized pressure-sensing cells (hair cells) that detect sounds of different pitches.

coding strand See **non-template strand**.

codominance An inheritance pattern in which heterozygotes exhibit both of the traits seen in each type of homozygous individual.

codon A sequence of three nucleotides in DNA or RNA that codes for an amino acid or a start or stop signal for protein synthesis.

coefficient of relatedness (r) A measure of how closely two individuals are related. Calculated as the probability that an allele in two individuals is inherited from the same ancestor.

coelom An internal, usually fluid-filled body cavity that is completely or partially lined with mesoderm.

coelomate An animal that has a true coelom, completely lined with mesoderm. Compare with **acoelomate** and **pseudocoelomate**.

coenocytic Containing many nuclei and a continuous cytoplasm through a filamentous body, without the body being divided into distinct cells. Some fungi are coenocytic.

coenzyme A small organic molecule that is required for an enzyme-catalyzed reaction. Often donates or receives electrons or functional groups during the reaction.

coenzyme A (CoA) A molecule that is required for many cellular reactions and that is often transiently linked to acetyl groups.

coenzyme Q A nonprotein molecule that shuttles electrons between membrane-bound complexes in the mitochondrial electron transport chain. Also called **ubiquinone** or *Q*.

coevolution A pattern of evolution in which two interacting species reciprocally influence each other's adaptations over time.

coevolutionary arms race A series of adaptations and counter-adaptations observed in species that interact closely over time and affect each other's fitness.

cofactor An inorganic ion, such as a metal ion, that is required for an enzyme to function normally. May be bound tightly to an enzyme or associate with it transiently during catalysis.

cohesion The tendency of certain like molecules (e.g., water molecules) to cling together due to attractive forces. Compare with **adhesion**.

cohesion-tension theory The theory that water movement upward through plant vascular tissues is due to loss of water from leaves (transpiration), which pulls a cohesive column of water upward.

cohort A group of individuals that are the same age and can be followed through time.

coleoptile A modified leaf that covers and protects the stems and leaves of grass seedlings.

collagen A fibrous, pliable, cable-like glycoprotein that is a major component of the extracellular matrix of animal cells. Various subtypes differ in their tissue distribution, some of which are assembled into large fibrils in the extracellular space.

collecting duct In the vertebrate kidney, a large, straight tube that receives filtrate from the distal tubules of several nephrons. Involved in the regulated reabsorption of water.

collenchyma Can refer to tissue or cell type. In plants, an elongated cell with cell walls thickened at the corners that provides support to growing plant parts; usually found in strands along leaf veins and stalks. Compare with **parenchyma** and **sclerenchyma**.

colon The portion of the large intestine where feces are formed by compaction of wastes and reabsorption of water.

colony An assemblage of individuals. May refer to an assemblage of semi-independent cells or to a breeding population of multicellular organisms.

commensalism (adjective: commensal) A species relationship in which one organism (the commensal) benefits and the other (the host) is unaffected. Compare with **mutualism, parasitism, consumption**, and **competition**.

commitment The gradual process by which the developmental fate of an embryonic cell is specified, directing it to become a particular type of specialized cell. Is reversible in early stages.

communication In ecology, any process in which a signal from one individual modifies the behavior of another individual.

community All the populations of different species that interact with each other in a certain area.

companion cell In plants, a cell in the phloem that is connected via many plasmodesmata to adjacent sieve-tube elements. Companion cells provide materials to maintain sieve-tube elements and function in the loading and unloading of sugars into sieve-tube elements.

compass orientation A type of navigation in which movement occurs in a specific direction.

competition In ecology, the interaction of two species or two individuals trying to use the same limited resource (e.g., water, food, living space). May occur between individuals of the same species (intraspecific competition) or different species (interspecific competition). Compare with **mutualism, consumption**, and **commensalism**.

competitive exclusion principle The principle that two species cannot coexist in the same ecological niche in the same area because one species will outcompete the other.

competitive inhibition Inhibition of an enzyme's ability to catalyze a chemical reaction via a nonreactant molecule that competes with the substrate(s) for access to the active site.

complement system A set of proteins that circulate in the bloodstream and can destroy foreign cells by forming holes in their plasma membrane.

complementary base pairing The association between specific nitrogenous bases of nucleic acids stabilized by hydrogen bonding. Adenine pairs with thymine (in DNA) or uracil (in RNA), and guanine pairs with cytosine.

complementary DNA (cDNA) DNA produced either in the lab or by retroviruses, using an RNA transcript as a template and reverse transcriptase; corresponds to the transcribed region of a gene but lacks introns.

complementary strand A strand of RNA or DNA with a base sequence that forms via complementary base-pairing with the template strand.

complete digestive tract A digestive tract with two openings: a mouth and an anus.

complete metamorphosis See **holometabolous metamorphosis**.

complex tissue A tissue consisting of two or more cell types.

compound Any substance that consists of more than one element chemically bonded together.

compound eye An eye formed of many independent lenses, each associated with a light-sensing columnar structure (ommatidium); occurs in arthropods. Compare with **simple eye**.

compound leaf A leaf consisting of two or more blades but defined by the presence of a single axillary bud where the petiole joins the branch or stem.

concentration gradient Difference across space (e.g., across a membrane) in the concentration of a dissolved substance.

condensation reaction A chemical reaction in which two molecules are joined covalently with the removal of an —OH from one and an —H from another to form water. In biology, most condensation reactions involve the joining of monomers into polymers. Also called a *dehydration reaction*. Compare with **hydrolysis**.

conduction (1) Direct transfer of heat between two objects that are in physical contact. Compare with **convection**. (2) Transmission of an electrical impulse along the axon of a nerve cell.

cone A vertebrate photoreceptor with a cone-shaped outer portion that is particularly sensitive to bright light of a certain color. Compare with **rod**.

conform To allow internal physiological conditions to vary with environmental conditions. Compare with **regulate**.

conjugation The transfer of genetic material between bacterial cells by direct cell-to-cell contact by formation of a bridge-like connection structure.

conidia Asexual spores produced by many fungi. Formed as a result of mitotic divisions; therefore, genetically identical to the parent fungus.

connective tissue An animal tissue consisting of loosely arranged cells in a liquid, jellylike, or solid extracellular matrix. Includes bone, cartilage, tendons, ligaments, and blood.

conservation biology The effort to study, preserve, and restore genetic diversity, species diversity, and diversity of ecosystem function in populations, communities, and ecosystems.

constant (*C*) region The invariant amino acid sequence in the polypeptides that comprise antibodies, B-cell receptors, and T-cell receptors. Compare with **variable (*V*) region**.

constitutive Always occurring or always present. Commonly used to describe proteins that are synthesized continuously or mutants in which one or more genetic loci are constantly expressed due to defects in gene control.

constitutive defense A defensive trait that is always manifested even in the absence of a predator or pathogen. Also called *standing defense*. Compare with **inducible defense**.

constitutive mutant An abnormal (mutated) strain that produces a product at all times, instead of under certain conditions.

consumer See **heterotroph**.

consumption In ecology, the interaction between species where one organism eats or absorbs nutrients from another. Includes predation, herbivory, and parasitism. Compare with **mutualism, commensalism**, and **competition**.

continental shelf The portion of a geologic plate that extends under seawater from a continent.

continuous strand See **leading strand**.

contraception Any of several methods to prevent pregnancy.

control In a scientific experiment, a group of organisms or samples that do not receive the experimental treatment but are otherwise identical to the group that does.

convection Transfer of heat by movement of large volumes of a gas or liquid. Compare with **conduction**.

convergent evolution The independent evolution of similar traits in different species due to adaptation to similar environmental conditions and a similar way of life.

cooperative binding The tendency of the protein subunits of hemoglobin to affect each other's oxygen binding such that each bound oxygen molecule increases the likelihood of further oxygen binding.

coprophagy The eating of feces.

coral reef A large assemblage of colonial marine corals that usually serves as shallow-water, sunlit habitat for many other species as well.

co-receptor Any membrane protein that acts with some other membrane protein in a cell interaction or cell response.

core enzyme A general term for any enzyme responsible for catalysis in a multipart holoenzyme.

core promoter A short nucleotide sequence in eukaryotic DNA that binds general transcription factors to enable RNA polymerase to begin transcription. This sequence is sometimes simply called a promoter, although "core promoter" distinguishes it from other DNA sequences important for transcription initiation.

cork cell A cell in the protective outermost layer of a woody stem and root that produces and accumulates waxes that make the cell less permeable to water and gases.

Coriolis effect The tendency for moving air or water to be deflected from a straight path, swerving in a clockwise pattern in the Northern Hemisphere and in a counterclockwise direction in the Southern Hemisphere. Caused by the spinning of the Earth on its axis.

corm A rounded, thick underground stem that can produce new plants via asexual reproduction.

cornea The transparent sheet of connective tissue at the very front of the eye in vertebrates and some other animals. Protects the eye and helps focus light.

corolla All of the petals of a flower.

corpus callosum A thick band of axons that connects the two hemispheres of the cerebrum in the mammalian brain.

corpus luteum A yellowish structure that secretes progesterone in an ovary. Formed from a follicle that has recently ovulated.

cortex (1) In animals, the outermost region of an organ, such as the kidney or adrenal gland. (2) In plants, a layer of ground tissue found outside the vascular bundles of roots and outside the pith of a stem.

corticotropin-releasing hormone (CRH) A peptide hormone, produced and secreted by the hypothalamus, that stimulates the anterior pituitary to release ACTH.

cortisol A steroid hormone, produced and secreted by the adrenal cortex, that increases blood glucose concentration and mediates the body's long-term stress response; the major glucocorticoid hormone in some mammals. Also called *hydrocortisone*.

cost–benefit analysis Decisions or analyses that weigh the fitness costs and benefits of a particular action.

cotransporter A transmembrane protein that facilitates diffusion of an ion down its previously established electrochemical gradient and uses the energy of that process to transport some other substance, in the same or opposite direction, *against* its concentration gradient. Also called *secondary active transporter*. See **antiporter** and **symporter**.

cotyledon The first leaf, or seed leaf, of a plant embryo. Used for storing and digesting nutrients and/or for early photosynthesis.

countercurrent exchanger In animals, any anatomical arrangement that allows the maximum transfer of heat or a soluble substance from one fluid to another. The two fluids must be flowing in opposite directions and have a heat or concentration gradient between them.

covalent bond A type of chemical bond in which two atoms share one or more pairs of electrons. Compare with **hydrogen bond** and **ionic bond**.

cranium A bony, cartilaginous, or fibrous case that encloses and protects the brain of vertebrates. Forms part of the skull. Also called *braincase*.

crassulacean acid metabolism (CAM) A variant type of photosynthesis that is related to the C_4 pathway in which CO_2 is fixed and stored in four-carbon organic acids. To reduce water loss and CO_2 loss by photorespiration, CO_2 is fixed at night when stomata are open and then released to feed the Calvin cycle during the day when stomata are closed.

cristae (singular: crista) Sac-like invaginations of the inner membrane of a mitochondrion. Location of the electron transport chain and ATP synthase.

Cro-Magnons A prehistoric European population of modern humans (*Homo sapiens*) known from fossils, paintings, sculptures, and other artifacts.

crop In animal anatomy, a storage organ in the digestive tract of certain vertebrates.

cross A mating between two individuals that is used for genetic analysis.

cross-pollination Pollination of a flower by pollen from another individual, rather than by self-fertilization. Also called *crossing*.

crosstalk Interactions among signaling pathways, triggered by different signals, that modify a cellular response.

crossing over The exchange of corresponding segments of non-sister chromatids between a pair of homologous chromosomes during meiosis I.

crustaceans A lineage of arthropods that includes shrimp, lobsters, and crabs. Many have a carapace (a platelike portion of the exoskeleton covering the cephalothorax) and mandibles for biting or chewing.

cryptic species A species that cannot be distinguished from similar species by easily identifiable morphological traits.

culture In cell biology, a collection of cells or a tissue growing under controlled conditions, usually in suspension or on the surface of a dish of solid growth medium.

Cushing's disease A human endocrine disorder caused by loss of feedback inhibition by cortisol on ACTH secretion. Characterized by high ACTH and cortisol levels and wasting of body protein reserves.

cuticle A protective coating secreted by the outermost layer of cells of an animal or a plant; often functions to reduce evaporative water loss.

cyanobacteria A lineage of photosynthetic bacteria formerly known as blue-green algae. Likely the first life-forms to carry out oxygenic photosynthesis.

cyclic AMP (cAMP) Cyclic adenosine monophosphate; a small molecule, derived from ATP, that is widely used by cells in signal transduction and transcriptional control.

cyclic electron flow Path of electrons in which excited electrons of photosystem I are transferred back to plastoquinone (PQ), the start of the electron transport chain normally associated with photosystem II. Instead of reducing $NADP^+$ to make NADPH, the electron energy is used to make ATP via photophosphorylation. Compare with **noncyclic electron flow**.

cyclin One of several regulatory proteins whose concentrations fluctuate cyclically throughout the cell cycle. Involved in control of the cell cycle via cyclin-dependent kinases.

cyclin-dependent kinase (Cdk) Any of several related protein kinases that are functional only when bound to a cyclin and are activated by other modifications. Involved in control of the cell cycle.

cytochrome *c* (cyt *c*) A soluble protein in the intermembrane space of mitochondria that shuttles electrons between membrane-bound complexes in the electron transport chain.

cytokine Any of a diverse group of signaling proteins, secreted largely by cells of the immune system, whose effects include increased leukocyte production, recruitment of cells to the site of an infection, tissue repair, and fever. Generally function to regulate the type, intensity, and duration of an immune response.

cytokinesis Division of the cytoplasm to form two daughter cells. In eukaryotic cells, typically occurs immediately after division of the nucleus by mitosis or meiosis.

cytokinins A class of plant hormones that stimulate cell division and retard aging.

cytoplasm All the contents of a cell bounded by the plasma membrane, excluding the nucleus (if present).

cytoplasmic determinant A regulatory molecule affecting development; it is distributed unevenly in a cell (typically an egg) and therefore is transmitted to one daughter cell but not another, specifying the fate of the cell that obtains the determinant.

cytoplasmic streaming The directed flow of cytosol and organelles that facilitates distribution of materials within some large plant and fungal cells. Occurs along actin filaments and is powered by myosin.

cytoskeleton In eukaryotic cells, a network of protein fibers in the cytoplasm that are involved in cell shape, support, locomotion, and transport of materials within the cell. Prokaryotic cells have a similar but much less extensive network of fibers.

cytosol The fluid portion of the cytoplasm, excluding the contents of membrane-enclosed organelles.

cytotoxic T cell A type of $CD8^+$ effector T cell that induces apoptosis in infected and cancerous cells. Recognizes target cells via interactions with complementary class I MHC–peptide complexes. Also called *cytotoxic T lymphocyte (CTL)* and *killer T cell*. Compare with **helper T cell**.

dalton (Da) A unit of mass approximately equal to the mass of one proton or one neutron.

daughter strand The strand of DNA that is newly replicated from a template strand of DNA.

day-neutral plant A plant whose flowering time is not affected by the relative length of day and night (the photoperiod). Compare with **long-day** and **short-day plant**.

dead space Air passages that are not involved in gas exchange with the blood; examples are the trachea and bronchi.

decomposer See **detritivore**.

decomposer food chain An ecological network of detritus, decomposers that eat detritus, and predators and parasites of the decomposers.

deep sequencing A method to learn the types of mRNAs or DNA sequences present in cells and their relative amounts. Involves preparing and extensively sequencing cDNAs prepared from the cell or tissue under investigation.

dehydration reaction See **condensation reaction**.

deleterious In genetics, referring to any mutation, allele, or trait that reduces an individual's fitness. Compare with **beneficial** and **neutral**.

deletion In genetics, refers to a loss in a DNA sequence or chromosome.

demography The study of factors that determine the size and structure of populations through time.

denaturation (verb: denature) For a macromolecule, loss of its three-dimensional structure due to breakage of chemical bonds and interactions, usually caused by exposure to heat, certain chemicals, or extreme pH conditions.

dendrite A short extension from a neuron's cell body that receives signals from other neurons.

dendritic cell A type of leukocyte that ingests and digests foreign antigens, moves to a lymph node, and presents the antigens' epitopes to $CD4^+$ and $CD8^+$ T cells in the form of MHC–peptide complexes on its plasma membrane.

dendrochronology The dating and study of annual growth rings in trees.

dense connective tissue A type of connective tissue distinguished by having an extracellular matrix dominated by collagen fibers. Found in tendons and ligaments.

density dependent In population ecology, referring to any characteristic that varies depending on population density.

density independent In population ecology, referring to any characteristic that does not vary with population density.

deoxyribonucleic acid (DNA) A nucleic acid composed of deoxyribonucleotides that carries the genetic information. Generally occurs as a double helix with two intertwined strands held together by noncovalent bonds. See also **double helix**.

deoxyribonucleoside triphosphate (dNTP) A monomer used by DNA polymerase to polymerize DNA. Consists of the sugar deoxyribose, a base (A, T, G, or C), and three phosphate groups.

deoxyribonucleotide A nucleotide consisting of a deoxyribose sugar, one or more phosphates, and one of four nitrogen-containing bases: adenine, guanine, cytosine, or thymine.

depolarization A change in membrane potential from its resting negative state to a less negative or a positive state; a normal phase in an action potential. Compare with **hyperpolarization**.

deposit feeder An animal that eats its way through a food-containing substrate.

derived trait A trait that is a modified form of an ancestral trait, found in a descendant.

dermal tissue system The tissue forming the outer layer of a plant; also called *epidermis*.

descent with modification The phrase used by Darwin to describe how species that lived in the past are the ancestors of species existing today, and that species change through time.

desmosome A type of cell—cell attachment structure in animals, consisting of cadherins and other proteins anchored to intermediate filaments. Serves to link the cytoskeletons of adjacent cells and form strong intercellular attachments throughout a tissue. Compare with **gap junction** and **tight junction**.

detergent A type of small amphipathic molecule that is water soluble and may be used to solubilize hydrophobic molecules in aqueous solution.

determination The final stage of commitment when an animal embryonic cell is locked into forming a particular type of specialized cell. Determination is typically irreversible and it occurs before differentiation. Not observed in plant cells. Compare with **commitment**.

detritivore An organism whose diet consists mainly of dead organic matter (detritus). Various bacteria, fungi, protists, and animals are detritivores. Also called *decomposer*.

detritus A layer of dead organic matter that accumulates at ground level or on seafloors and lake bottoms.

deuterostomes A major lineage of bilaterian animals that includes echinoderms and chordates; named for the embryonic development of the anus before the mouth (literally, "second mouth"). Compare with **protostomes**.

development The processes of forming a multicellular organism with specialized cells, tissues, and organs.

developmental biology The area of biology that considers the mechanisms and patterns of how organisms develop from a single cell into a multicellular adult.

developmental homology A similarity in embryonic form or developmental processes that is due to inheritance from a common ancestor.

diabetes mellitus A disease caused by a defect in insulin production (type 1) or in the response of cells to insulin (type 2). Characterized by abnormally high blood glucose levels and large volumes of glucose-containing urine.

diaphragm An elastic, sheetlike structure. In mammals, the muscular sheet that separates the chest and abdominal cavities. It contracts and moves downward during inhalation, expanding the chest cavity.

diastole The portion of the cardiac cycle during which the atria or ventricles of the heart are relaxed. Compare with **systole**.

diastolic blood pressure The force exerted by blood against artery walls during relaxation of the heart's left ventricle. Compare with **systolic blood pressure**.

dicot Any flowering plant (angiosperm) that has two cotyledons (embryonic leaves) upon germination. The dicots do not form a monophyletic group. Also called *dicotyledonous plant*. Compare with **eudicot** and **monocot**.

dideoxy sequencing A technique for determining the nucleotide sequence of DNA. Relies on the use of dideoxynucleoside triphosphates (ddNTPs), which terminate DNA replication.

diencephalon The part of the mammalian brain that relays sensory information to the cerebrum and functions in maintaining homeostasis.

differential centrifugation Procedure for separating cellular components according to their size and density by spinning a cell homogenate in a series of centrifuge runs. After each run, the supernatant is removed from the deposited material (pellet) and spun again at progressively higher speeds.

differential gene expression Expression of different sets of genes in cells with the same genome. Responsible for creating different cell types.

differentiation The process by which an unspecialized cell becomes a distinct specialized cell type (e.g., liver cell, brain cell), usually by changes in gene expression. Also called *cell differentiation*.

diffusion Spontaneous movement of a substance from one region to another, often with a net movement from a region of high concentration to one of low concentration (i.e., down a concentration gradient).

digestion The physical and chemical breakdown of food into molecules that can be absorbed into the body of an animal.

digestive tract A chamber or tube where digestion takes place. Also called *alimentary canal* or *gastrointestinal (GI) tract*.

dihybrid cross A mating between two parents that differ in alleles of two different genes.

dikaryotic Describing a fungal mycelium or hypha made up of cells containing two genetically distinct haploid nuclei.

dimer An association of two molecules that may be identical (homodimer) or different (heterodimer).

dioecious Describing an angiosperm species that has male and female reproductive structures on separate plants. Compare with **monoecious**.

diploblast (adjective: diploblastic) An animal whose body develops from two basic embryonic cell layers or tissues—ectoderm and endoderm. Compare with **triploblast**.

diploid (1) Having two sets of chromosomes $(2n)$. (2) A cell or an organism with two sets of chromosomes, one set inherited from the mother and one set from the father. Compare with **haploid**.

direct sequencing A technique for identifying and studying microorganisms that cannot be grown in culture. Involves detecting and amplifying copies of specific genes in the microorganisms' DNA, sequencing these genes, and then comparing the sequences with the known sequences from other organisms.

directed-pollination hypothesis The hypothesis that flowers are adaptations that attract specific pollinators, increasing the likelihood that pollination will occur.

directional selection A mode of natural selection that favors one extreme phenotype with the result that the average phenotype of a population changes in one direction. Generally reduces overall genetic variation in a population. Compare with **disruptive selection** and **stabilizing selection**.

disaccharide A carbohydrate consisting of two monosaccharide sugar residues linked together.

discontinuous strand See **lagging strand**.

discrete trait An inherited trait that exhibits distinct phenotypes rather than the continuous variation of a quantitative trait such as body height.

disruptive selection A mode of natural selection that favors extreme phenotypes at both ends of the range of phenotypic variation. Increases overall genetic variation in a population. Compare with **stabilizing selection** and **directional selection**.

distal tubule In the vertebrate kidney, the convoluted portion of a nephron into which filtrate moves from the loop of Henle. Involved in the regulated reabsorption of sodium and water. Compare with **proximal tubule**.

disturbance In ecology, any strong, short-lived disruption to a community that changes the distribution of living and/or nonliving resources.

disturbance regime The characteristic disturbances that affect a given ecological community.

disulfide bond A covalent bond between two sulfur atoms, typically in the side chains of certain amino acids (e.g., cysteine). Often contributes to tertiary and quaternary levels of protein structure.

DNA See **deoxyribonucleic acid**.

DNA barcoding The use of well-characterized gene sequences to identify species.

DNA cloning Any of several techniques for producing many identical copies of a particular gene or other DNA sequence.

DNA fingerprinting Any of several methods for identifying individuals by unique features of their genomes. Commonly involves using PCR to produce many copies of short tandem repeats (microsatellites) and then analyzing their lengths. Also called *DNA profiling, DNA typing*.

DNA helicase An enzyme that breaks hydrogen bonds between nucleotides of DNA, "unzipping" a double-stranded DNA molecule.

DNA ligase An enzyme that joins pieces of DNA by catalyzing the formation of a phosphodiester bond between the pieces.

DNA methylation The addition of a methyl group $(-CH_3)$ to a DNA molecule.

DNA methyltransferase A class of eukaryotic enzymes that add a methyl group to bases in DNA. In many eukaryotes, methylation of cytosine is especially important. Methylation of DNA leads to chromatin condensation and is an important means of regulating gene expression in eukaryotes.

DNA microarray A set of single-stranded DNA fragments, representing thousands of different genes that are permanently fixed to a surface such as a glass slide. Can be used to determine which genes are expressed in different cell types, under different conditions, or at different developmental stages.

DNA polymerase Any enzyme that catalyzes synthesis of DNA from deoxyribonucleoside triphosphates (dNTPs).

DNA profiling See DNA fingerprinting.

DNA typing See DNA fingerprinting.

domain (1) A taxonomic category, based on similarities in basic cellular biochemistry, above the kingdom level. The three recognized domains are Bacteria, Archaea, and Eukarya. (2) A section of a protein that has a distinctive tertiary structure and function.

dominant Referring to an allele that determines the same phenotype when it is present in homozygous or heterozygous form. Compare with **recessive**.

dormancy A temporary state of greatly reduced metabolic activity and growth in plants or plant parts (e.g., seeds, spores, bulbs, and buds).

dorsal Toward an animal's back and away from its belly. The opposite of ventral.

dorsal hollow nerve cord A bundle of nerves running the length of the body. A defining feature of chordates.

double fertilization A form of reproduction seen in flowering plants, in which one sperm cell fuses with an egg to form a zygote and the other sperm cell fuses with two polar nuclei to form the triploid endosperm.

double helix The secondary structure of DNA, consisting of two antiparallel DNA strands wound around each other. Some RNAs may also form a double helix in hairpin secondary structures.

Down syndrome A human developmental disorder caused by trisomy (3 copies) of chromosome 21.

downstream In genetics, the direction in which RNA polymerase moves along a DNA strand. Compare with **upstream**.

duplication In genetics, refers to an additional copy of a DNA sequence or part of a chromosome.

duplication and divergence An evolutionary process in which new genes are created by duplication of an original gene followed by divergence of the copied gene sequences to allow one or both copies to acquire a new function.

dynein A class of motor proteins that uses the chemical energy of ATP to "walk" toward the minus end of a microtubule. Dyneins are responsible for bending of cilia and flagella, play a role in chromosome movement during mitosis, and can transport vesicles and organelles.

early endosome A small transient organelle that is formed by the accumulation of vesicles from receptor-mediated endocytosis and is an early stage in the formation of a lysosome.

ecdysone An insect hormone that triggers either molting (to a larger larval form) or metamorphosis (to the adult form), depending on the level of juvenile hormone.

ecdysozoans A major lineage of protostomes (Ecdysozoa) that grow by shedding their external skeletons (molting) and expanding their bodies. Includes arthropods, nematodes, and other groups. Compare with **lophotrochozoans**.

echinoderms A major lineage of deuterostomes (Echinodermata) distinguished by adult bodies with five-sided radial symmetry, a water vascular system, and tube feet. Includes sea urchins, sand dollars, and sea stars.

echolocation The use of echoes from vocalizations to obtain information about the locations of objects in the environment.

ecological selection Also known as environmental selection. A type of natural selection that favors individuals with heritable traits that enhance their ability to survive and reproduce in a certain physical and/or biological environment, excluding their ability to obtain a mate. Compare with **sexual selection**.

ecology The study of how organisms interact with each other and with their surrounding environment.

ecosystem All the organisms that live in a geographic area, together with the nonliving (abiotic) components that affect or exchange materials with the organisms; a community and its physical environment.

ecosystem diversity The variety of biotic components in a region along with abiotic components, such as soil, water, and nutrients.

ecosystem function The sum of biological and chemical processes that are characteristic of a given ecosystem—such as primary production, nitrogen cycling, and carbon storage.

ecosystem services All of the benefits that humans derive, directly or indirectly, from ecosystem functions.

ecotourism Tourism that is based on observing wildlife or experiencing other aspects of natural areas.

ectoderm The outermost of the three basic cell layers (germ layers) in most animal embryos; gives rise to the outer covering and nervous system. Compare with **endoderm** and **mesoderm**.

ectomycorrhizal fungi (EMF) Fungi whose hyphae form a dense network that covers their host plant's roots but do not enter the root cells.

ectoparasite A parasite that lives on the outer surface of the host's body.

ectotherm An animal that gains most of its body heat from external sources as opposed to metabolic processes. Compare with **endotherm**.

effector Any cell, organ, or structure with which an animal can respond to external or internal stimuli. Usually functions, along with a sensor and an integrator, as part of a homeostatic system.

efferent division The part of the nervous system that carries commands from the central nervous system to the rest of the body. Consists primarily of motor neurons. Compare with **afferent division**.

egg A mature female gamete and any associated external layers (such as a shell). In animals, also called *ovum*.

ejaculation The release of semen from the copulatory organ of a male animal.

ejaculatory duct A short duct through which sperm move during ejaculation; connects the vas deferens to the urethra.

electric current A flow of electric charge. Also called *current*.

electrical potential Potential energy created by a separation of electrical charges between two points. Also called *voltage*.

electrocardiogram (EKG) A recording of the electrical activity of the heart, obtained through electrodes on the skin.

electrochemical gradient The combined effect of an ion's concentration gradient and electrical (charge) gradient across a membrane that affects the diffusion of ions.

electrogenic fishes Any of various kinds of fishes that have specialized organs that generate electric fields in the water; these fields are used to detect objects.

electrolyte Any compound that dissociates into ions when dissolved in water. In nutrition, any of the major ions necessary for normal cell function.

electromagnetic spectrum The entire range of wavelengths of radiation extending from short wavelengths (high energy) to long wavelengths (low energy). Includes gamma rays, X-rays, ultraviolet, visible light, infrared, microwaves, and radio waves (from short to long wavelengths).

electron acceptor A reactant that gains an electron and is reduced in a reduction–oxidation reaction.

electron carrier Any molecule that readily accepts electrons from and donates electrons to other molecules. Protons may be transferred with the electrons in the form of hydrogen atoms.

electron donor A reactant that loses an electron and is oxidized in a reduction–oxidation reaction.

electron shell A group of electron orbitals with similar energies. Electron shells are arranged in roughly concentric layers around the nucleus of an atom, and electrons in outer shells have more energy than those in inner shells. Electrons in the outermost shell, the valence shell, often are involved in chemical bonding.

electron transport chain (ETC) Any set of membrane-bound protein complexes and mobile electron carriers involved in a coordinated series of redox reactions. The release of energy from the redox reactions is used to actively transport protons from one side of a membrane to the other.

electronegativity A measure of the how strongly an atom pulls shared electrons toward itself in a bond.

electroreception The detection of electric fields.

electroreceptor A sensory cell specialized for detecting electric fields.

element A substance consisting of atoms with a specific number of protons. Elements preserve their identity in chemical reactions.

elongation (1) The process by which RNA lengthens during transcription. (2) The process by which a polypeptide chain lengthens during translation.

elongation factor Any of a class of proteins involved in the elongation phase of translation, assisting ribosomes in the synthesis of the growing peptide chain.

embryo An organism at an early stage of development; the stage after fertilization and zygote formation.

embryo sac The female gametophyte in flowering plants.

embryogenesis The production of an embryo from a zygote. Embryogenesis is an early event in development of animals and plants.

Embryophyta An increasingly popular name for the lineage called land plants; reflects their retention of a fertilized egg.

embryophyte A plant that nourishes its embryos inside its own body. All land plants are embryophytes.

emergent property A property that stems from the interaction of simpler elements, is not exhibited by the simple elements, and is impossible to predict from the study of individual elements. For example, homeostasis is an emergent property of the collection of molecules present in each cell.

emerging disease Any infectious disease, often a viral disease, that suddenly afflicts significant numbers of individuals for the first time; often due to changes in the host specificity of a pathogen or to radical changes in the genetic material of the pathogen.

emigration The migration of individuals away from one population to other populations. Compare with **immigration**.

emulsification (verb: emulsify) The dispersion of fat into an aqueous solution. Usually requires the aid of an amphipathic substance such as a detergent or bile salts, which can break large fat globules into microscopic fat droplets.

endangered species A species whose numbers have decreased so much that it is in danger of extinction throughout all or part of its range.

endemic species A species that lives in one geographic area and nowhere else.

endergonic Referring to a chemical reaction that has a change in Gibbs free energy greater than zero ($\Delta G > 0$) and is nonspontaneous (i.e., requires an input of energy to occur). Compare with **exergonic**.

endocrine Relating to a chemical signal (hormone) that is released into the bloodstream by a cell and acts on a distant target cell.

endocrine disruptor An exogenous chemical that interferes with normal hormonal signaling.

endocrine gland A gland that secretes hormones directly into the bloodstream or interstitial fluid. Compare with **exocrine gland**.

endocrine system All of the glands and tissues that produce and secrete hormones into the bloodstream.

endocytosis General term for any pinching off of the plasma membrane that results in the uptake of material from outside the cell. Includes phagocytosis, pinocytosis, and receptor-mediated endocytosis. Compare with **exocytosis**.

endoderm The innermost of the three basic cell layers (germ layers) in most animal embryos; gives rise to the digestive tract and organs that connect to it (liver, lungs, etc.). Compare with **ectoderm** and **mesoderm**.

endodermis In plant roots, a cylindrical layer of cells that separates the cortex from the vascular tissue and location of the Casparian strip.

endomembrane system A system of organelles in eukaryotic cells that synthesizes, processes, transports, and recycles proteins and lipids. Includes the endoplasmic reticulum (ER), Golgi apparatus, and lysosomes.

endomycorrhizal fungi See **arbuscular mycorrhizal fungi (AMF)**.

endoparasite A parasite that lives inside the host's body.

endophyte (adjective: endophytic) A fungus that lives inside the tissues of a plant in a symbiotic relationship. Compare with **epiphyte.**

endoplasmic reticulum (ER) A network of interconnected membranous sacs and tubules found inside eukaryotic cells that functions in the synthesis of lipids and proteins that reside in the endomembrane system, the plasma membrane, or are secreted from the cell. See **rough** and **smooth endoplasmic reticulum**.

endoskeleton Bony and/or cartilaginous structures within the body that provide support. Examples are the spicules of sponges, the plates in echinoderms, and the bony skeleton of vertebrates. Compare with **exoskeleton**.

endosperm A triploid ($3n$) tissue in the seed of a flowering plant (angiosperm) that serves as food for the plant embryo. Functionally analogous to the yolk in some animal eggs.

endospore A tough, resistant reproductive structure formed in certain bacteria in response to poor environmental conditions.

endosymbiont An organism that lives in a symbiotic relationship inside the body of its host.

endosymbiosis An association between organisms of two different species in which one lives inside the cell or cells of the other.

endosymbiosis theory The theory that mitochondria and chloroplasts evolved from prokaryotes that were engulfed by host cells and took up a symbiotic existence within those cells, a process termed primary endosymbiosis. In some eukaryotes, chloroplasts may have originated by secondary endosymbiosis; that is, when a cell engulfed a chloroplast-containing protist and retained its chloroplasts.

endotherm An animal that gains most of its body heat from internal metabolic processes. Compare with **ectotherm**.

endothermic Referring to a chemical reaction that absorbs heat. Compare with **exothermic**.

energetic coupling In cellular metabolism, the mechanism by which energy released from an exergonic reaction (commonly, hydrolysis of ATP) is used to make an endergonic reaction spontaneous.

energy The capacity to do work or to supply heat. May be stored (potential energy) or available in the form of motion (kinetic energy).

enhancer A regulatory sequence in eukaryotic DNA that may be located far from the gene it controls or within introns of the gene. Binding of specific regulatory transcription factor proteins to an enhancer enhances the transcription of certain genes. Typically contains binding sites for more than one transcription factor.

enrichment culture A method of detecting and obtaining cells with specific characteristics by placing a sample, containing many types of cells, under a specific set of conditions (e.g., temperature, salt concentration, available nutrients) and isolating those cells that grow rapidly in response.

enteric nervous system A network of neurons embedded in the wall of the gastrointestinal tract of vertebrates. Important in the regulation of digestion and possibly many other functions.

enthalpy (H) A quantitative measure of the amount of potential energy, or heat content, of a system plus the pressure and volume it exerts on its surroundings.

entropy (S) A quantitative measure of the amount of disorder of any system, such as a group of molecules.

envelope (viral) A membrane that encloses the capsid of some viruses. Often includes specialized proteins that attach to host-cell surfaces.

environmental sequencing See **metagenomics**.

enzyme A protein catalyst used by living organisms to increase the rate of biological reactions.

epicotyl In some embryonic plants, a portion of the embryonic stem that extends above the cotyledons.

epidemic The spread of an infectious disease throughout a population in a short time. Compare with **pandemic**.

epidermis The outermost layer of cells of any multicellular organism.

epididymis A coiled tube on the outside of each testis in reptiles, birds, and mammals. The site of the final stages of sperm maturation.

epigenetic inheritance Any pattern of inheritance involving differences in phenotype that are not due to differences in the nucleotide sequence of genes.

epinephrine A catecholamine hormone, produced and secreted by the adrenal medulla, that triggers rapid responses related to the fight-or-flight response. Also called *adrenaline*.

epiphyte (adjective: epiphytic; noun: epiphytism) A nonparasitic plant that grows on the trunks or branches of other plants and is not rooted in soil.

epithelial tissue See **epithelium**.

epithelium (plural: epithelia) An animal tissue consisting of sheetlike layers of tightly packed cells that line an organ, a gland, a duct, or a body surface. Also called *epithelial tissue*.

epitope A small region of a particular antigen that can bind to an antibody, B-cell receptor, or T-cell receptor.

equilibrium potential The membrane potential at which there is no net movement of a particular ion into or out of a cell.

ER signal sequence A short amino acid sequence that marks a polypeptide for transport to the endoplasmic reticulum, where synthesis of the polypeptide chain is completed and the signal sequence removed. See **signal recognition particle**.

erythropoietin (EPO) A peptide hormone, released by the kidney and other tissues in response to low blood-oxygen levels, that stimulates the bone marrow to produce more red blood cells.

esophagus The muscular tube that connects the mouth to the stomach.

essential amino acid Any amino acid that an animal cannot synthesize and must obtain from the diet. There are eight essential amino acids in adult humans: isoleucine, leucine, lysine, methionine, phenylalanine, threonine, tryptophan, and valine.

essential fatty acid Any fatty acid that an animal cannot synthesize and must obtain from the diet. There are two essential fatty acids in humans: linolenic acid and linoleic acid.

essential nutrient Any chemical element, ion, or compound that is required for normal growth, reproduction, and maintenance of a living organism and that cannot be synthesized by the organism.

ester linkage The covalent bond formed by a condensation reaction between a carboxyl group and a hydroxyl group. Ester linkages join fatty acids to glycerol to form a fat or phospholipid.

estradiol The major estrogen produced by the ovaries of female mammals and many other vertebrates. Stimulates development of the female reproductive tract, growth of ovarian follicles, and growth of breast tissue in mammals.

estrogen Any of a class of steroid hormones, including estradiol, estrone, and estriol, that generally promote female-like traits. Secreted by the gonads, fat tissue, and some other organs.

estrous cycle A female reproductive cycle in which the uterine lining is reabsorbed rather than shed in the absence of pregnancy and in which the female is sexually receptive only briefly during mid-cycle (estrus). Seen in all mammals except Old World monkeys and apes (including humans). Compare with **menstrual cycle**.

estuary An aquatic biome formed where streams and ocean meet, such that freshwater and salt water mix; highly productive because of abundant light and nutrients.

ethylene A gaseous plant hormone associated with senescence that induces fruits to ripen and flowers to fade.

etiolation The phenomenon in which plants grow long, thin, and spindly and tend to be pale yellow as a result of growing in shaded or dark conditions.

eudicot A member of a monophyletic group (lineage) of angiosperms that includes complex flowering plants and trees (e.g., roses, daisies, maples). All eudicots have two cotyledons, but not all dicots are members of this lineage. Compare with **dicot** and **monocot**.

Eukarya One of the three taxonomic domains of life, consisting of unicellular organisms (most protists, yeasts) and multicellular organisms (fungi, plants, animals) distinguished by a membrane-bound cell nucleus, numerous organelles, and an extensive cytoskeleton. Compare with **Archaea** and **Bacteria**.

eukaryote (adjective: eukaryotic) A member of the domain Eukarya; an organism whose cells contain a nucleus, numerous membrane-bound organelles, and an extensive cytoskeleton. May be unicellular or multicellular. Compare with **prokaryote**.

eusociality A complex social structure in which workers sacrifice most or all of their direct reproduction to help rear the queen's offspring. Common in insects such as ants, bees, wasps, and termites.

eutherians A lineage of mammals (Eutheria) whose young develop in the uterus and are not housed in an abdominal pouch. Also called *placental mammals*.

evaporation The energy-absorbing phase change from a liquid state to a gaseous state. Many organisms evaporate water as a means of heat loss.

evo-devo Popular term for evolutionary developmental biology, a research field focused on how changes in developmentally important genes have led to the evolution of new phenotypes.

evolution (1) The theory that all organisms on Earth are related by common ancestry and that they have changed over time, and continue to change, via natural selection and other processes. (2) Any change in the genetic characteristics of a population over time, especially a change in allele frequencies.

ex situ conservation Preserving species outside of natural areas (e.g., in zoos, aquaria, or botanical gardens).

excitable membrane A plasma membrane that is capable of generating an action potential. Neurons, muscle cells, and some other cells have excitable membranes.

excitatory postsynaptic potential (EPSP) A depolarization of a cell that makes the cell more likely to generate an action potential.

exergonic Referring to a chemical reaction that has a change in Gibbs free energy less than zero ($\Delta G < 0$) and can occur spontaneously, releasing heat and/or increasing entropy. Compare with **endergonic**.

exocrine gland A gland that secretes some substance through a duct into a space other than the circulatory system, such as the lumen of the digestive tract or the exterior of the body. Compare with **endocrine gland**.

exocytosis Secretion of intracellular molecules (e.g., hormones, collagen), contained within membrane-bound vesicles, to the outside of the cell by fusion of vesicles to the plasma membrane. Compare with **endocytosis**.

exon A transcribed region of a gene or region of a primary transcript that is retained in the mature RNA. Except for 5′ and 3′ UTRs, mRNA exons code for amino acids. Compare with **intron**.

exoskeleton A hard covering secreted on the outside of the body, used for body support, protection, and muscle attachment. Examples are the shell of mollusks and the outer covering (cuticle) of arthropods. Compare with **endoskeleton** and **hydrostatic skeleton**.

exothermic Referring to a chemical reaction that releases heat. Compare with **endothermic**.

exotic species A nonnative species that is introduced into a new area. Exotic species often are competitors, pathogens, or predators of native species.

expansin Any of a class of proteins that break hydrogen bonds between components in the primary cell wall of plants, allowing it to expand for cell growth.

experiment A powerful scientific tool in which researchers test the effect of a single, well-defined factor on a particular phenomenon.

exponential population growth The accelerating increase in the size of a population that occurs when the per capita growth rate is constant and density independent. Compare with **logistic population growth**.

expressed sequence tag (EST) A cDNA from a portion of a transcribed gene that is used to find the physical location of that gene in the genome and to confirm that a region of DNA is transcribed.

extant species A species that is living today.

extensor A muscle that pulls two bones farther apart, increasing the angle of the joint between them, as in the extension of a limb or the spine. Compare with **flexor**.

extinct species A species that no longer exists.

extracellular digestion Digestion that takes place outside of an organism, as occurs in many fungi that make and secrete digestive enzymes.

extracellular matrix (ECM) A complex fiber composite in which animal cells are embedded, consisting of proteins (e.g., collagen, proteoglycan, and laminin) and polysaccharides produced by the cells.

extremophile An organism that thrives in an "extreme" environment (e.g., high-salt, high-temperature, low-temperature, or high-pressure).

F_1 generation First filial generation. The first generation of offspring produced from a mating (i.e., the offspring of the parental generation).

facilitated diffusion Passive movement (diffusion) of a substance across a membrane with the assistance of transmembrane carrier proteins or channel proteins.

facilitation In ecological succession, the phenomenon in which early-arriving species make conditions more favorable for later-arriving species. Compare with **inhibition** and **tolerance**.

facultative anaerobe Any organism that can survive and reproduce by performing aerobic respiration when oxygen is available or fermentation when it is not.

FAD/FADH$_2$ Oxidized and reduced forms, respectively, of flavin adenine dinucleotide. A nonprotein electron carrier that functions in the citric acid cycle and electron transport chain.

fallopian tube A narrow tube connecting the uterus to the ovary, through which an egg travels after ovulation. Site of fertilization and cleavage. Also called *oviduct*.

fast muscle fiber A type of skeletal muscle fiber that is white, generates ATP by glycolysis, and contracts rapidly but fatigues easily. Also called *fast glycolytic*, or *Type IIb, fiber*.

fat A class of lipid consisting of three fatty acid molecules joined by ester linkages to a glycerol molecule. Also called *triacylglycerol* or *triglyceride*.

fatty acid A lipid consisting of a hydrocarbon chain bonded at one end to a carboxyl group. Used by many organisms to store chemical energy; a major component of animal and plant fats and phospholipids.

fauna All the animal species characteristic of a particular region, period, or environment.

feather A specialized skin outgrowth, composed of keratin, present in all birds as well as in some non-avian dinosaurs. Used for flight, insulation, display, and other purposes.

feces The waste products of digestion.

fecundity The average number of female offspring produced by a single female in the course of her lifetime.

feedback inhibition A type of control in which high concentrations of the final product of a metabolic pathway inhibit one of the enzymes early in the pathway. A form of negative feedback.

fermentation Any of several metabolic pathways in the cytosol that regenerate oxidizing agents, such as NAD$^+$, by transferring electrons to an electron acceptor in the absence of an electron transport chain. Allows pathways such as glycolysis to continue making ATP.

ferredoxin In photosynthetic organisms, an iron- and sulfur-containing protein that is reduced by electrons from photosystem I. Can transfer electrons to the enzyme NADP$^+$ reductase, which catalyzes formation of NADPH.

fertility The average number of surviving children that each woman has during her lifetime.

fertilization Fusion of the nuclei of two gametes (often haploid) to form a zygote with a nucleus (often diploid). Exceptions to the haploid and diploid rule are seen in polyploid species.

fertilization envelope A physical barrier that forms around a fertilized egg in many animals. Prevents fertilization by more than one sperm (polyspermy).

fetal alcohol syndrome (FAS) A condition marked by hyperactivity, severe learning disabilities, and depression caused by exposure of an individual to high blood alcohol concentrations during embryonic development.

fetus In live-bearing (viviparous) animals, the unborn offspring after the embryonic stage. A fetus is usually developed sufficiently to be recognizable as belonging to a certain species.

fiber In plants, a type of elongated sclerenchyma cell that provides support to vascular tissue. Compare with **sclereid**.

fibroblast A type of cell that makes the fibers and extracellular matrix in loose connective tissue.

Fick's law of diffusion A mathematical relationship that describes the rates of diffusion of gases.

fight-or-flight response Rapid physiological changes that prepare the body for emergencies. Includes increased heart rate, increased blood pressure, and decreased digestion.

filament Any thin, threadlike structure, particularly (1) the threadlike extensions of a fish's gills or (2) part of a stamen: the slender stalk that bears the anthers in a flower.

filter feeder See **suspension feeder**.

filtrate Any fluid produced by filtration, in particular the fluid ("pre-urine") in the Malpighian tubules of insects and the nephrons of vertebrate kidneys.

filtration A process of removing large components from a fluid by forcing it through a filter. Occurs in renal corpuscles of the vertebrate kidney, allowing water and small solutes to pass from the blood into the nephron.

fimbria (plural: fimbriae) A long, needlelike projection from the cell membrane of bacteria that is involved in attachment to nonliving surfaces or other cells.

finite rate of increase (λ) The rate of increase of a population over a given period of time. Calculated as the ending population size divided by the starting population size. Compare with **intrinsic rate of increase** and **per capita rate of increase**.

first law of thermodynamics The principle of physics that energy is conserved in any process. Energy can be transferred and converted into different forms, but it cannot be created or destroyed.

fission (1) A form of asexual reproduction in which a prokaryotic cell divides to produce two genetically similar daughter cells by a process similar to mitosis of eukaryotic cells. Also called *binary fission*. (2) A form of asexual reproduction in which an animal splits into two or more individuals of approximately equal size.

fitness The ability of an individual to produce viable offspring relative to others of the same species.

fitness trade-off See **trade-off**.

fixed action pattern (FAP) Highly stereotyped behavior pattern that occurs in a certain invariant way in a certain species. A form of innate behavior.

flaccid Limp as a result of low internal (turgor) pressure (e.g., a wilted plant leaf). Compare with **turgid**.

flagellum (plural: flagella) A long, cellular projection that undulates (in eukaryotes) or rotates (in prokaryotes) to move the cell through an aqueous environment. See **axoneme**.

flatworms Members of the phylum Platyhelminthes. Distinguished by a broad, flat, unsegmented body that lacks a coelom. Flatworms belong to the lophotrochozoan branch of the protostomes.

flavin adenine dinucleotide See **FAD/FADH₂**.

flexor A muscle that pulls two bones closer together, decreasing the angle of the joint between them, as in the flexion of a limb or the spine. Compare with **extensor**.

floral meristem A group of undifferentiated plant stem cells that can give rise to the four organs making up a flower.

florigen In plants, a protein hormone that is synthesized in leaves and transported to the shoot apical meristem, where it stimulates flowering.

flower In angiosperms, the part of a plant that contains reproductive structures. Typically includes a calyx, a corolla, and one or more stamens and/or carpels. See **perfect** and **imperfect flower**.

fluid connective tissue A type of connective tissue distinguished by having a liquid extracellular matrix; includes blood.

fluid feeder An animal that feeds by sucking or mopping up liquids such as nectar, plant sap, or blood.

fluid-mosaic model The widely accepted hypothesis that cellular membranes consist of proteins embedded in a fluid phospholipid bilayer.

fluorescence The spontaneous emission of light from an excited electron in a pigment falling back to its normal (ground) state.

follicle In a mammalian ovary, a sac of supportive cells containing an egg.

follicle-stimulating hormone (FSH) A peptide hormone produced and secreted by the anterior pituitary; it stimulates (in females) growth of eggs and follicles in the ovaries or (in males) sperm production in the testes.

follicular phase In a menstrual cycle, the phase during which follicles grow and estradiol levels increase; ends with ovulation.

food Any nutrient-containing material that can be consumed and digested by animals.

food chain A relatively simple pathway of energy flow through a few species, each at a different trophic level, in an ecosystem. Might include, for example, a primary producer, a primary consumer, a secondary consumer, and a decomposer. A subset of a **food web**.

food web The complex network of interactions among species in an ecosystem formed by the transfer of energy and nutrients among trophic levels. Consists of many food chains.

foot One of the three main parts of the mollusk body; a muscular appendage, used for movements such as crawling and/or burrowing into sediment.

foraging Searching for food.

forebrain One of the three main regions of the vertebrate brain; includes the cerebrum, thalamus, and hypothalamus. Compare with **hindbrain** and **midbrain**.

fossil Any physical trace of an organism that existed in the past. Includes tracks, burrows, fossilized bones, casts, and so on.

fossil record All of the fossils that have been found anywhere on Earth and that have been formally described in the scientific literature.

founder effect A change in allele frequencies that often occurs when a new population is established from a small group of individuals (founder event) due to sampling error (i.e., the small group is not a representative sample of the source population).

frameshift mutation The addition or deletion of one or a few base pairs in a coding sequence that shifts the reading frame of the mRNA.

free radical A substance containing one or more atoms with at least one unpaired valence electron, which makes it unstable and highly reactive.

frequency The rate at which an event occurs per unit time. As applied to waves, the number of wave crests per second traveling past a stationary point. Determines the pitch of sound and the color of light.

frequency-dependent selection A pattern of selection in which certain alleles are favored only when they are rare; a form of balancing selection.

frontal lobe In the vertebrate brain, one of the four lobes of the cerebrum. Involved in complex decision making in humans.

fruit In flowering plants (angiosperms), a mature, ripened plant ovary (or group of ovaries), along with the seeds it contains and any adjacent fused parts; often functions in seed dispersal. See **aggregate, multiple**, and **simple fruit**.

fruiting body A structure formed in some prokaryotes, fungi, and protists for spore dispersal; usually consists of a base, a stalk, and a mass of spores at the top.

functional genomics The study of how, when, and where specific genes are expressed within the genome and how their products interact to produce a functional organism.

functional group A small group of atoms bonded together in a precise configuration and exhibiting particular chemical properties that it imparts to any organic molecule in which it occurs.

fundamental niche The total theoretical range of environmental conditions that a species can tolerate. Compare with **realized niche**.

fungi A lineage of eukaryotes that typically have a filamentous body (mycelium) and obtain nutrients by absorption.

fungicide Any substance that can kill fungi or slow their growth.

G protein Any of various proteins that are activated by binding to guanosine triphosphate (GTP) and inactivated when GTP is hydrolyzed to GDP. In G-protein-coupled receptors, signal binding by a receptor directly triggers the activation of a G protein, leading to production of a second messenger or initiation of a phosphorylation cascade.

G₁ phase The phase of the cell cycle that constitutes the first part of interphase, before DNA synthesis (S phase).

G₂ phase The phase of the cell cycle between synthesis of DNA (S phase) and mitosis (M phase); the last part of interphase.

gallbladder A small pouch that stores bile from the liver and releases it as needed into the small intestine during digestion of fats.

gametangium (plural: gametangia) (1) The gamete-forming structure found in all land plants except angiosperms. Contains a sperm-producing antheridium and an egg-producing archegonium. (2) The gamete-forming structure of some chytrid fungi.

gamete A haploid reproductive cell that can fuse with another haploid reproductive cell of the opposite sex to form a diploid zygote. Exceptions to the haploid and diploid rule are seen in polyploid species. Most multicellular eukaryotes have two distinct forms of gametes: egg cells (ova) and sperm cells.

gametogenesis The production of gametes (eggs or sperm).

gametophyte In organisms undergoing alternation of generations, the multicellular haploid form that arises from a single haploid spore and produces gametes by mitosis and cell division. Compare with **sporophyte**.

ganglion (plural: ganglia) A mass of neurons in a centralized nervous system.

ganglion cell In the vertebrate retina, a neuron whose axon projects via the optic nerve to the brain.

gap junction A type of cell–cell attachment structure that directly connects the cytosol of adjacent animal cells, allowing passage of water, ions, and small molecules between the cells. Compare with **desmosome** and **tight junction**.

gastrin A hormone produced by cells in the stomach lining in response to the arrival of food or to a neural signal from the brain. Stimulates other stomach cells to release hydrochloric acid.

gastropods A lineage of mollusks distinguished by a large, muscular foot and a unique feeding structure, the radula. Include slugs and snails.

gastrula Stage of embryonic development that follows the blastula during which, in most vertebrate animals, the three distinct germ layers form and the anterior-posterior and dorsal-ventral axes are established. See **endoderm, mesoderm,** and **ectoderm**.

gastrulation The process of coordinated cell shape changes and movements, including the movement of some cells from the outer surface of the embryo to the interior that results in the formation of the three germ layers (endoderm, mesoderm, and ectoderm) and establishes the axes of the embryo.

gated channel A channel protein that opens and closes in response to a specific stimulus, such as the binding of a particular substance or a change in voltage across the membrane.

gene (1) In a molecular context, a section of DNA (or RNA, for some viruses) that contains the regulatory sequences and coding information for the transcription of one or more related functional RNA molecules, some of which encode polypeptides. (2) In Mendelian genetics, the hereditary determinant of a trait, such as flower color or seed shape in pea plants.

gene duplication The formation of an additional copy of a gene, often by misalignment of chromosomes during crossing over. An important evolutionary process in creating new genes.

gene expression The entire set of processes, including transcription and translation, that convert information in DNA into a product of a gene, most commonly a protein.

gene family A set of genes whose DNA sequences are similar because they arose by duplication of an ancestral gene followed by divergence of the sequences due to accumulation of random mutations.

gene flow The movement of alleles between populations; occurs when individuals leave one population, join another, and breed.

gene pool All the alleles of all the genes in a certain population.

gene therapy The treatment of an inherited disease by introducing either a normal form of the gene or a gene that alters expression of the abnormal gene.

general transcription factor Any of a set of proteins that associate with eukaryotic RNA polymerase and the core promoter to assist RNA polymerase in initiating transcription; the same or a similar set of general transcription factors that associate with all core promoters—they are not gene specific. Compare with **regulatory transcription factor**.

generation The average time between a mother's first offspring and her daughter's first offspring.

genetic bottleneck A reduction in the diversity of alleles in a population resulting from a sudden reduction in the size of that population (population bottleneck) due to a random event.

genetic code The set of all codons and their meaning.

genetic correlation A type of evolutionary constraint in which selection on one trait causes a change in another trait as well; may occur when the same gene(s) affect both traits.

genetic diversity The diversity of alleles or genes in a population, species, or group of species.

genetic drift Any change in allele frequencies due to chance. Causes allele frequencies to drift up and down randomly over time, and eventually can lead to the fixation or loss of alleles.

genetic equivalence When all different cell types of a multicellular individual possess the same genome.

genetic homology Similarity in DNA nucleotide sequences, RNA nucleotide sequences, or amino acid sequences due to inheritance from a common ancestor.

genetic map A figure showing the relative positions and distances between genes along a chromosome. Also called a *linkage map*. Compare with **physical map**.

genetic marker A genetic locus that can be identified and traced in populations by laboratory techniques or by a distinctive visible phenotype.

genetic recombination A change in the combination of alleles on a given chromosome or in a given individual. Also called *recombination*.

genetic regulatory cascade A set of regulatory genes that are linked in such a way that one initially activated gene triggers the expression of other regulatory genes, which in turn trigger the expression of yet more regulatory genes. Often used to control development.

genetic screen Any technique that identifies individuals with a particular type of mutation.

genetic variation (1) The number and relative frequency of alleles present in a particular population. (2) The proportion of phenotypic variation in a trait that is due to genetic rather than environmental influences in a certain population in a certain environment.

genetically modified crop (or **GM crop**) Crop produced from cells or individual plants that have had specific changes introduced into their DNA using genetic engineering methods.

genetics The study of the inheritance of traits, the nature of genes, and how genes work.

genital (plural: genitalia) Any external reproductive structure of an animal.

genome All the hereditary material (DNA in cells, DNA or RNA in viruses) in a virus, cell, or organism, including but not confined to genes.

genome annotation The process of analyzing a genome sequence to identify key features such as genes, regulatory sequences, and splice sites.

genome-wide association study (GWAS) A method of locating genes by finding associations between a particular phenotype and a particular polymorphic genetic marker (almost always a SNP) in populations.

genomics The field of study concerned with sequencing, interpreting, and comparing whole genomes from different organisms.

genotype All the alleles of a gene or genes present in a given individual. Compare with **phenotype**.

genus (plural: genera) In Linnaeus' system, a taxonomic category of closely related species. Always italicized and capitalized to indicate that it is a recognized scientific genus.

geologic time scale The sequence of eons, eras, and periods used to describe the geologic history of Earth.

germ layer In animals, one of the three embryonic tissue layers formed during gastrulation; gives rise to all other tissues and organs. See endoderm, mesoderm, and ectoderm.

germ theory of disease The theory that infectious diseases are caused by bacteria, viruses, and other microbes.

germination The process by which a seed becomes a young plant.

gestation In animal species with live birth (viviparous), the period of development inside the mother, from implantation of the embryo to birth.

gibberellins A class of hormones, found in plants and fungi, that stimulate growth. Gibberellic acid (GA) is one of the major gibberellins.

Gibbs free energy The energy of a system that can be converted into work. The amount of this energy that is available may be measured only by how it changes in a reaction (ΔG). See **standard free-energy change**.

gill Any organ in aquatic animals that exchanges gases and other dissolved substances between the blood or hemolymph and the surrounding water. Typically, a filamentous outgrowth of a body surface.

gill arch In aquatic vertebrates, a curved region of tissue between the gills. Gills are suspended from the gill arches.

gill filament In fishes, any of the many long, thin structures that extend from gill arches into the water and that function in gas exchange.

gill lamella (plural: gill lamellae) Any of the hundreds to thousands of sheetlike structures, each containing a capillary bed, that make up a gill filament.

gland An organ whose primary function is to secrete some substance, either into the blood (endocrine gland) or into some other space such as the interior of the gut or the outer surface of the body (exocrine gland).

glia Collective term for several types of cells in nervous tissue that are not neurons and do not conduct electrical signals but perform other functions, such as providing support, nourishment, or electrical insulation. Also called *glial cells*.

global carbon cycle See **carbon cycle, global**.

global climate change The global sum of all the local changes in temperature and precipitation patterns that accompany **global warming** (or in some past events, global cooling).

global gene regulation The regulation of multiple bacterial genes that are not part of one operon.

global nitrogen cycle See **nitrogen cycle, global**.

global phosphorus cycle See **phosphorus cycle, global**.

global warming A sustained increase in Earth's average surface temperature.

global water cycle See **water cycle, global**.

glomerulus (plural: glomeruli) (1) In the vertebrate kidney, a ball-like cluster of capillaries, surrounded by Bowman's capsule, at the beginning of a nephron. (2) In the vertebrate brain, a ball-shaped cluster of neurons in the olfactory bulb.

glucagon A peptide hormone produced by the pancreas in response to low blood glucose levels. Raises blood glucose levels by triggering breakdown of glycogen and stimulating gluconeogenesis. Compare with **insulin**.

glucocorticoid Any of a class of steroid hormones, produced and secreted by the adrenal cortex, that increase blood glucose concentration and mediate the body's long-term stress response. Glucocorticoids include cortisol and corticosterone. Compare with **mineralocorticoid**.

gluconeogenesis Synthesis of glucose, often from non-carbohydrate sources (e.g., proteins and fatty acids). In plants, used to produce glucose from products of the Calvin cycle. In animals, occurs in the liver in response to low insulin levels and high glucagon levels.

glucose A six-carbon monosaccharide that can be oxidized via cellular respiration or fermentation to produce ATP or serve as a source of carbon to synthesize other molecules.

glyceraldehyde-3-phosphate (G3P) The phosphorylated three-carbon carbohydrate formed from the fixation and reduction of CO_2 in the Calvin cycle.

glycerol A three-carbon molecule that forms the "backbone" of phospholipids and most fats.

glycogen A highly branched storage polysaccharide composed of glucose monomers joined by α-1,4- and α-1,6-glycosidic linkages. The major form of stored carbohydrate in animals.

glycolipid Any lipid molecule that is covalently bonded to one or more carbohydrates.

glycolysis A series of 10 chemical reactions in the cytosol that oxidize glucose to produce pyruvate, NADH, and ATP. Used by organisms as part of fermentation and/or cellular respiration.

glycoprotein Any protein with one or more covalently bonded carbohydrates, typically oligosaccharides.

glycosidic linkage The covalent bond formed by a condensation reaction between two sugar monomers; joins the residues of a polysaccharide. Also known as *glycosidic bond*.

glycosylation Addition of a carbohydrate group to a molecule.

glyoxysome Specialized type of peroxisome found in plant cells and packed with enzymes for processing the products of photosynthesis.

gnathostomes Animals with jaws. Most vertebrates are gnathostomes.

Golgi apparatus A eukaryotic organelle, consisting of stacks of flattened membranous sacs (cisternae), that functions in processing and sorting proteins and lipids destined to be secreted or directed to other organelles. Also called *Golgi complex*.

gonad An animal organ (testis or ovary) that produces reproductive cells (gametes).

gonadotropin-releasing hormone (GnRH) A peptide hormone, produced and secreted by the hypothalamus, that stimulates release of follicle-stimulating hormone (FSH) and luteinizing hormone (LH) from the anterior pituitary.

grade In taxonomy, a sequence of lineages that share some, but not all, of the descendants of a common ancestor. Also called a *paraphyletic group*.

Gram stain A dye that distinguishes the two general types of cell walls found in bacteria. Used to routinely classify bacteria as Gram-negative or Gram-positive.

Gram-negative Describing bacteria that look pink when treated with a Gram stain. These bacteria have a cell wall composed of a thin layer of peptidoglycan and an outer phospholipid layer. Compare with **Gram-positive**.

Gram-positive Describing bacteria that look purple when treated with a Gram stain. These bacteria have cell walls composed of a thick layer of peptidoglycan and no outer phospholipid later. Compare with **Gram-negative**.

grana (singular: granum) Stacks of flattened thylakoid discs in chloroplasts where the light reactions of photosynthesis occur.

gravitropism The growth or movement of a plant in a particular direction in response to gravity.

grazing food chain The ecological network of primary producers, herbivores, and the predators and parasites that consume them.

great apes See **hominids**.

green algae A paraphyletic group of photosynthetic organisms that contain chloroplasts similar to those in land plants. Often classified as protists, green algae are the closest living relatives of land plants and form a monophyletic group with them.

greenhouse effect Selective energy absorption by greenhouse gases such as carbon dioxide in the atmosphere, which allows short-wavelength light energy to pass through but absorbs longer wavelength infrared energy and reflects heat back to Earth. Causes a warming effect similar to that in a greenhouse.

greenhouse gas An atmospheric gas that absorbs and reflects infrared radiation, so that heat radiated from Earth is retained in the atmosphere instead of being lost to space. Includes carbon dioxide, methane, water vapor, and nitrous oxides.

gross primary productivity In an ecosystem, the total amount of carbon fixed by photosynthesis (or more rarely, chemosynthesis), including that used for cellular respiration, over a given time period. Compare with **net primary productivity**.

ground meristem An embryonic tissue layer that gives rise to the ground tissue system.

ground tissue An embryonic tissue layer that gives rise to parenchyma, collenchyma, and sclerenchyma—tissues other than the epidermis and vascular tissue. Also called *ground tissue system*.

ground tissue system Most common of the tissue systems; includes the following tissues/cell types: parenchyma, collenchyma, and sclerenchyma—tissues other than the epidermis and vascular tissue.

groundwater Any water below the land surface.

growth factor Any of a large number of signaling molecules that are secreted by certain cells and that stimulate other cells to grow, divide, or differentiate.

growth hormone (GH) A peptide hormone, produced and secreted by the mammalian anterior pituitary, that promotes lengthening of the long bones in children and muscle growth, tissue repair, and lactation in adults. Also called *somatotropin*.

guanosine triphosphate (GTP) A nucleotide consisting of guanine, a ribose sugar, and three phosphate groups. Can be hydrolyzed to release free energy. Commonly used in RNA synthesis and also functions in signal transduction in association with G proteins.

guard cell One of two specialized, crescent-shaped cells forming the border of a plant stoma. Guard cells can change shape to open or close the stoma. See also **stoma**.

gustation The sense of taste.

guttation Excretion of water droplets from plant leaves; visible in the early morning. Caused by root pressure.

gymnosperm A vascular plant that makes seeds but does not produce flowers. The gymnosperms include five lineages of green plants (cycads, ginkgoes, redwoods, pines, and gnetophytes). Compare with **angiosperm**.

gyre A large-scale ocean circulation or cycle that flows in the clockwise direction in the Northern Hemisphere and in the counterclockwise direction in the Southern Hemisphere.

H$^+$-ATPase See **proton pump**.

habitat degradation The human-caused reduction of the quality of a habitat.

habitat destruction Human-caused destruction of a natural habitat, replaced by an urban, suburban, or agricultural landscape.

habitat fragmentation The breakup of a large region of a habitat into many smaller regions, separated from others by a different type of habitat.

Hadley cell An atmospheric cycle of large-scale air movement in which warm equatorial air rises, moves north or south, and then descends at approximately 30° N or 30° S latitude.

hair cell A pressure-detecting sensory cell in vertebrates that has tiny hairlike structures (stereocilia) jutting from its surface. Found in the inner ear, lateral line system, and ampullae of Lorenzini.

hairpin A secondary structure in RNA consisting of a loop of single-stranded RNA at the end of a double helix that is formed by complementary base pairing within the same strand.

Hamilton's rule The proposition that an allele for altruistic behavior will be favored by natural selection only if $Br > C$, where B = the fitness benefit to the recipient, C = the fitness cost to the actor, and r = the coefficient of relatedness between recipient and actor.

haploid (1) Having one set of chromosomes (1*n*, or more commonly, *n* for short). (2) A cell or an individual organism with one set of chromosomes. Compare with **diploid**.

haploid number The number of different types of chromosomes in a cell. Symbolized as *n*.

Hardy–Weinberg equilibrium A state of agreement between observed allele frequencies in a population and allele frequencies predicted by the Hardy–Weinberg principle. See **Hardy–Weinberg principle**.

Hardy–Weinberg principle A principle of population genetics stating that genotype frequencies in a large population do not change from generation to generation in the absence of evolutionary processes (e.g., mutation, gene flow, genetic drift, and selection), and nonrandom mating.

haustorium (plural: haustoria) Highly modified stem or root of a parasitic plant. The haustorium penetrates the tissues of a host and absorbs nutrients and water.

head The anteriormost region of many bilaterian animals, usually containing specialized sensory structures and the brain.

hearing The sensation of the wavelike changes in air pressure called sound.

heart A muscular pump that circulates blood or hemolymph throughout an animal.

heart murmur A distinctive sound caused by backflow of blood through a defective heart valve.

heartwood The older xylem in the center of an older stem or root, containing protective compounds and no longer functioning in water transport.

heat Thermal energy that is transferred from an object at higher temperature to one at lower temperature.

heat of vaporization The energy required to change 1 gram of a liquid into a gas.

heavy chain The larger of the two types of polypeptide chains in an antibody or B-cell receptor; composed of a variable (*V*) region, which contributes to the antigen-binding site, and a constant (*C*) region. Differences in heavy-chain constant regions determine the different classes of immunoglobulins (IgA, IgE, etc.). Compare with **light chain**.

helper T cell A CD4+ effector T cell that secretes cytokines and in other ways promotes the activation of other leukocytes. Activated by interacting with complementary class II MHC–peptide complexes on the surface of antigen-presenting cells such as dendritic cells.

heme A small molecule that binds to each of the four polypeptides in hemoglobin; contains an iron ion that can bind oxygen.

hemimetabolous metamorphosis A type of metamorphosis in which the animal increases in size from one stage to the next, but does not dramatically change its body form. Also called *incomplete metamorphosis*.

hemocoel A body cavity, present in arthropods and some mollusks, containing a pool of circulatory fluid (hemolymph) bathing the internal organs. Unlike a coelom, a hemocoel is not lined in mesoderm.

hemoglobin An oxygen-binding protein consisting of four polypeptide subunits, each containing an oxygen-binding heme group. The major oxygen carrier in mammalian blood.

hemolymph The circulatory fluid of animals with open circulatory systems (e.g., insects) in which the fluid is not confined to blood vessels.

herbaceous Referring to a plant that is not woody.

herbivore (adjective: herbivorous) An animal that eats primarily plants and rarely or never eats meat. Compare with **carnivore** and **omnivore**.

herbivory The practice of eating plant tissues.

heredity The transmission of traits from parents to offspring via genetic information.

heritable Referring to traits that can be transmitted from one generation to the next.

heterokaryotic Describing a fungal mycelium containing haploid nuclei that are genetically distinct.

heterospory (adjective: heterosporous) In seed plants, the production of two distinct types of spores: microspores, which become the male gametophyte, and megaspores, which become the female gametophyte. Compare with **homospory**.

heterotroph Any organism that cannot synthesize reduced organic compounds from inorganic sources and that must obtain them from other organisms. Some bacteria, some archaea, and virtually all fungi and animals are heterotrophs. Also called *consumer*. Compare with **autotroph**.

heterozygote advantage A pattern of natural selection that favors heterozygous individuals compared with homozygotes. Tends to maintain genetic variation in a population and thus is a form of balancing selection.

heterozygous Having two different alleles of a gene.

hexose A monosaccharide (simple sugar) containing six carbon atoms.

hibernation An energy-conserving physiological state, marked by a decrease in metabolic rate, body temperature, and activity, that lasts for a prolonged period (weeks to months). Occurs in some animals in response to winter cold and scarcity of food. Compare with **torpor**.

hindbrain One of the three main regions of the vertebrate brain, responsible for balance and sometimes hearing; includes the cerebellum and medulla oblongata. Compare with **forebrain** and **midbrain**.

hippocampus In the vertebrate brain, a paired structure at the inner edge of the temporal lobes of the cerebrum; involved in formation of new memories and in spatial navigation.

histamine A molecule released from mast cells during an inflammatory response that causes blood vessels to dilate and become more permeable, allowing circulating leukocytes to enter the area.

histone One of several positively charged (basic) proteins associated with DNA in the chromatin of eukaryotic cells.

histone acetyltransferase (HAT) Any of a class of eukaryotic enzymes that loosen chromatin structure by adding acetyl groups to histone proteins.

histone code The hypothesis that specific combinations of chemical modifications of histone proteins contain information that influences chromatin condensation and gene expression.

histone deacetylase (HDAC) Any of a class of eukaryotic enzymes that condense chromatin by removing acetyl groups from histone proteins.

holoenzyme A general term for any multipart enzyme consisting of a core enzyme (containing the active site for catalysis) along with other proteins required for full function.

holometabolous metamorphosis A type of metamorphosis in which the animal completely changes its form; includes a distinct larval stage. Also called *complete metamorphosis*.

homeobox A DNA sequence of about 180 base pairs that codes for a DNA-binding region in the resulting protein. Genes containing a homeobox usually play a role in controlling development of organisms from fruit flies to humans.

homeostasis (adjective: homeostatic) The array of relatively stable chemical and physical conditions in an organism's cells, tissues, and organs. May be achieved by passively matching the conditions of a stable external environment (conformational homeostasis) or by active physiological processes (regulatory homeostasis) triggered by variations in the external or internal environment.

homeotherm An animal that has a constant or relatively constant body temperature. Compare with **poikilotherm**.

homeotic mutation A mutation that causes one body part to be substituted for another.

hominids Members of the family Hominidae; today's representatives are humans, chimpanzees, bonobos, gorillas, and orangutans. Distinguished by large body size, no tail, and an exceptionally large brain. Also called *great apes*.

hominins Any extinct or living species of bipedal ape, such as *Australopithecus africanus*, *Homo erectus*, and *Homo sapiens*.

homologous See **homology**.

homologous chromosome In diploid organisms, a member of a pair of chromosomes that are similar in size, shape, and gene content. Also called *homologous pair*.

homologous pair In diploid organisms, a pair of chromosomes that are the same size and shape and contain the same genes in the same positions along the chromosomes.

homologs The same type of chromosomes (carrying genes for the same traits) in a diploid or polyploid organism.

homology (adjective: homologous) Similarity among organisms of different species due to shared ancestry. Features that exhibit such similarity (e.g., DNA sequences, proteins, body parts) are said to be homologous. Compare with **homoplasy**.

homoplasy Similarity among organisms of different species due to reasons other than common ancestry, such as convergent evolution. Compare with **homology**.

homospory (adjective: homosporous) In seedless vascular plants, the production of just one type of spore. Compare with **heterospory**.

homozygous Having two identical alleles of a gene.

hormone Any of many different signaling molecules that circulate throughout the plant or animal body and can trigger characteristic responses in distant target cells at very low concentrations.

hormone receptor A protein to which a hormone binds in or on a target cell. Located intracellularly for lipid-soluble hormones such as steroids and in the plasma membrane for water-soluble hormones such as polypeptides.

hormone-response element A specific sequence in DNA to which a hormone–receptor complex can bind and affect gene transcription.

host An individual that has been invaded by an organism such as a parasite or a virus, or that provides habitat or resources to a commensal organism.

host cell A cell that can be invaded by a parasitic organism or a virus and provides an environment that is conducive to the growth and reproduction of the organism or the replication of the virus.

Hox **genes** A class of genes found in most animal phyla, including vertebrates, that are expressed in a distinctive pattern along the anterior–posterior axis in early embryos and control formation of specific structures. *Hox* genes code for transcription factors with a DNA-binding sequence called a homeobox.

human Any member of the genus *Homo,* which includes modern humans (*Homo sapiens*) and several extinct species.

human chorionic gonadotropin (hCG) A glycoprotein hormone produced by a human embryo and placenta from about week 3 to week 14 of pregnancy. Maintains the corpus luteum, which secretes hormones that preserve the uterine lining.

Human Genome Project The multinational research project that sequenced the human genome.

human immunodeficiency virus (HIV) A retrovirus that causes acquired immune deficiency syndrome (AIDS) in humans.

humoral (immune) response The type of immune response that is mediated through the production and secretion of antibodies, complement proteins, and other soluble factors that eliminate extracellular pathogens. Compare with **cell-mediated (immune) response**.

humus The decayed organic matter in soils.

hybrid The offspring of parents from two different strains, populations, or species.

hybrid zone A geographic area where interbreeding occurs between two species, sometimes producing fertile hybrid offspring.

hydrocarbon An organic molecule that contains only hydrogen and carbon atoms.

hydrogen bond A weak interaction between two molecules or different parts of the same molecule resulting from the attraction between a hydrogen atom with a partial positive charge and another atom (usually O or N) with a partial negative charge. Compare with **covalent bond** and **ionic bond**.

hydrogen ion (H⁺) A single proton with a positive electric charge of +1; typically, one that is dissolved in solution or that is being transferred from one atom to another in a chemical reaction.

hydrolysis A chemical reaction in which a molecule is split into smaller molecules by reacting with water. In biology, most hydrolysis reactions involve the splitting of polymers into monomers. Compare with **condensation reaction**.

hydrophilic Interacting readily with water. Hydrophilic compounds are typically polar compounds containing partially or fully charged atoms. Compare with **hydrophobic**.

hydrophobic Not readily interacting with water. Hydrophobic compounds are typically nonpolar molecules. Compare with **hydrophilic**.

hydrophobic interactions Very weak interactions between nonpolar molecules, or nonpolar regions of the same molecule, when exposed to an aqueous solvent. The surrounding water molecules support these interactions by interacting with one another and encapsulating the nonpolar molecules.

hydroponic growth Growth of plants in liquid cultures instead of soil.

hydrostatic skeleton A system of body support involving a body wall in tension surrounding a fluid or soft tissue under compression. Compare with **endoskeleton** and **exoskeleton**.

hydroxide ion (OH⁻) An oxygen atom and a hydrogen atom joined by a single covalent bond and carrying a negative electric charge of −1.

hygiene hypothesis The hypothesis that allergies and autoimmune disorders arise in individuals who have had less exposure to pathogens and parasites, especially in early childhood. May explain the increased incidence of allergies and autoimmune disease in countries with high levels of sanitation.

hyperosmotic Referring to a solution that has a greater solute concentration, and therefore a lower water concentration, than another solution. Compare with **hyposmotic** and **isosmotic**.

hyperpolarization A change in membrane potential from its resting negative state to an even more negative state; a normal phase in an action potential. Compare with **depolarization**.

hypersensitive reaction An intense allergic response by cells that have been sensitized by previous exposure to an allergen.

hypersensitive response In plants, the rapid death of a cell that has been infected by a pathogen, thereby reducing the potential for infection to spread throughout a plant. Compare with **systemic acquired resistance**.

hypertension Abnormally high blood pressure.

hypertonic Comparative term designating a solution that, if outside a cell or vesicle, results in the loss of water and shrinkage of the membrane-bound structure. This solution has a greater solute concentration than the solution on the other side of the membrane. Used when the solute is unable to pass through the membrane. Compare with **hypotonic** and **isotonic**.

hypha (plural: hyphae) One of the long, branching strands of a fungal mycelium (the mesh-like body of a fungus). Also found in some protists.

hypocotyl The stem of a very young plant; the region between the cotyledon (embryonic leaf) and the radicle (embryonic root).

hyposmotic Referring to a solution that has a lower solute concentration, and therefore a higher water concentration, than another solution. Compare with **hyperosmotic** and **isosmotic**.

hypothalamic–pituitary axis The functional interaction of the hypothalamus and anterior pituitary gland, which are anatomically distinct but work together to regulate most of the other endocrine glands in the body.

hypothalamus A part of the brain that functions in maintaining the body's internal physiological state by regulating the autonomic nervous system, endocrine system, body temperature, water balance, and appetite.

hypothesis A testable statement that explains a phenomenon or a set of observations.

hypotonic Comparative term designating a solution that, if outside a cell or vesicle, results in the uptake of water and swelling or even bursting of the membrane-bound structure. This solution has a lower solute concentration than the solution on the other side of the membrane. Used when the solute is unable to pass through the membrane. Compare with **hypertonic** and **isotonic**.

immigration The migration of individuals into a particular population from other populations. Compare with **emigration**.

immobile nutrients nutrients that remain in position where they are first deposited, typically tied up in older leaves. Compare with **mobile nutrients**.

immune system The system whose primary function is to defend an organism against pathogens. Includes several types of cells (e.g., leukocytes). In vertebrates, also includes several organs where specialized cells mature or reside (e.g., thymus and lymph nodes).

immunity (adjective: immune) A state of being protected against infection by a pathogen.

immunization The conferring of immunity to a particular disease by artificial means.

immunoglobulin (Ig) An antibody or B-cell receptor.

immunological memory The ability of the immune system to mount a rapid, effective response to an antigen encountered years or decades earlier. In adaptive immunity, it is based on the formation of memory lymphocytes.

impact hypothesis The hypothesis that a collision between Earth and an asteroid caused the mass extinction at the K–Pg boundary, 66 million years ago.

imperfect flower A flower that contains male parts (stamens) *or* female parts (carpels) but not both. Compare with **perfect flower**.

implantation The process by which an embryo becomes embedded in the wall of a uterus or oviduct, leading to the formation of a placenta. Occurs in mammals and some other viviparous vertebrates.

in situ hybridization A technique for detecting specific DNAs and mRNAs in cells and tissues by use of labeled complementary probes. Can be used to determine where and when particular genes are expressed in embryos.

inbreeding Mating between closely related individuals. Increases homozygosity of a population and often leads to a decline in the average fitness via selection (inbreeding depression).

inbreeding depression The decline in average fitness that takes place when homozygosity increases and heterozygosity decreases in a population due to inbreeding; results from the exposure of deleterious recessive alleles to selection.

inclusive fitness The combination of (1) direct production of offspring (direct fitness) and (2) extra production of offspring by relatives in response to help provided by the individual in question (indirect fitness).

incomplete digestive tract A digestive tract that has just one opening.

incomplete dominance An inheritance pattern in which the phenotype of a heterozygote is in between the phenotypes of the homozygotes.

incomplete metamorphosis See **hemimetabolous metamorphosis**.

independent assortment, principle of The concept that each pair of hereditary elements (alleles of the same gene) segregates (separates) independently of alleles of other genes during meiosis. One of Mendel's two principles of genetics. Compare with **principle of segregation**.

indeterminate growth A pattern of growth in which an individual continues to increase its overall body size throughout its life.

induced fit Change in the shape of the active site of an enzyme, as the result of initial weak binding of a substrate, so that it binds substrate more tightly.

induced pluripotent stem cell An undifferentiated cell made by the experimental de-differentiation of a specialized adult cell. Induced pluripotent cells have the potential to form any cell of the body if re-differentiated under appropriate conditions. Also called *iPS cell*.

inducer A small molecule that triggers transcription of a specific gene, often by binding to and inactivating a repressor protein.

inducible defense A defensive trait that is manifested only in response to the presence of a consumer (predator or herbivore) or pathogen. Compare with **constitutive defense**.

induction A mechanism of determining the fate of a cell during development that involves a signal from one cell determining what another cell will become during development.

infection thread An invagination of the plasma membrane of a root hair through which beneficial nitrogen-fixing bacteria enter the roots of their host plants (legumes).

infectious disease Disease caused by viruses, bacteria, fungi, or parasites that can be transmitted from one organism to another or acquired from the environment.

inflammatory response An aspect of the innate immune response, seen in most cases of infection or tissue injury, in which the affected tissue becomes swollen, red, warm, and painful.

ingestion The act of bringing food into the digestive tract.

inhibition In ecological succession, the phenomenon in which early-arriving species make conditions less favorable for the establishment of certain later-arriving species. Compare with **facilitation** and **tolerance**.

inhibitory postsynaptic potential (IPSP) A change in membrane potential, usually hyperpolarization, of a cell that makes the cell less likely to generate an action potential.

initiation (1) In an enzyme-catalyzed reaction, the stage during which enzymes orient reactants precisely as they bind at specific locations within the enzyme's active site. (2) In DNA transcription, the stage during which RNA polymerase and other proteins assemble at the promoter sequence and open the strands of DNA to start transcription. (3) In translation, the stage during which a complex consisting of initiation factor proteins, a ribosome, an mRNA, and an aminoacyl tRNA corresponding to the start codon is formed to begin translation.

initiation factor Any of a class of proteins that assist ribosomes in binding to a messenger RNA molecule to begin translation.

innate behavior Behavior that is inherited genetically, does not have to be learned, and is typical of a species.

innate immunity A set of barriers to infection and generic defenses against broad types of pathogens. Produces an immediate response that involves many different leukocytes, which often activate an inflammatory response. Compare with **adaptive immunity**.

inner cell mass (ICM) A cluster of cells, in the interior of a mammalian blastocyst, that develops into the embryo. Contrast with **trophoblast**.

inner ear The innermost portion of the mammalian ear, consisting of a fluid-filled system of tubes that includes the cochlea (which receives sound vibrations from the middle ear) and the semicircular canals (which function in balance).

insects A mostly terrestrial lineage of arthropods distinguished by three tagmata (head, thorax, abdomen), a single pair of antennae, and unbranched appendages.

insulin A peptide hormone produced by the pancreas in response to high levels of glucose (or amino acids) in the blood. Enables cells to absorb glucose and coordinates synthesis of fats, proteins, and glycogen. Compare with **glucagon**.

integral membrane protein Any membrane protein that spans the entire lipid bilayer. Also called *transmembrane protein*. Compare with **peripheral membrane protein**.

integrated pest management In agriculture or forestry, systems for managing insects or other pests that include carefully controlled applications of toxins, introduction of species that prey on pests, planting schemes that reduce the chance of a severe pest outbreak, and other techniques.

integrator A component of an animal's nervous system that functions as part of a homeostatic system by evaluating sensory information and triggering appropriate responses. See **effector** and **sensor**.

integrin Any of a class of cell-surface proteins that bind to proteins in the extracellular matrix, thus holding cells in place. Some integrins also function in cell–cell adhesions.

intercalated disc A type of specialized connection between adjacent heart muscle cells that contains gap junctions, allowing electrical signals to pass between the cells.

intermediate filament A long fiber, about 10 nm in diameter, composed of one of various proteins (e.g., keratins, lamins); one of the three types of cytoskeletal fibers. Used to form networks that help maintain cell shape and hold the nucleus in place. Compare with **actin filament** and **microtubule**.

intermediate muscle fiber A type of skeletal muscle fiber that is pink, generates ATP by both glycolysis and aerobic respiration, and has contractile properties that are intermediate between those of slow fibers and fast fibers. Also called fast oxidative/glycolytic fiber.

interneuron A neuron that passes signals from one neuron to another. Compare with **motor neuron** and **sensory neuron**.

internode The section of a plant stem between two nodes (sites where leaves attach).

interphase The portion of the cell cycle between one M phase and the next. Includes G_1 phase, S phase, and G_2 phase.

intersexual selection A type of sexual selection in which an individual of one sex choses a particular individual of the other sex for mating (usually occurs through female choice).

interspecific competition Competition between members of different species for the same limited resource. Compare with **intraspecific competition**.

interstitial fluid In animals with a closed circulatory system, extracellular fluid that is not enclosed in blood vessels.

intertidal zone The region between the low-tide and high-tide marks on a seashore.

intrasexual selection A type of sexual selection driven by competition among members of one sex (usually male—male) for an opportunity to mate.

intraspecific competition Competition between members of the same species for the same limited resource. Compare with **interspecific competition**.

intrinsic rate of increase (r_{max}) The rate of increase of a population when conditions are ideal (birth rates per individual are as high as possible and death rates per individual are as low as possible). Compare with **finite rate of increase** and **per capita rate of increase**.

intron A region of a gene that is transcribed into RNA but is later removed. Compare with **exon**.

invasive species An exotic (nonnative) species that, upon introduction to a new area, spreads rapidly and competes successfully with native species.

inversion A mutation in which a DNA sequence or a segment of a chromosome is flipped into the reversed orientation.

invertebrates A paraphyletic group composed of animals without a backbone; includes about 95 percent of all animal species. Compare with **vertebrates**.

involuntary muscle A muscle that contracts without input from the nervous system or in response to stimulation by involuntary (parasympathetic or sympathetic), but not voluntary (somatic), neural stimulation.

ion An atom or a molecule that has lost or gained electrons and thus carries a full electric charge, either positive (cation) or negative (anion), respectively.

ion channel A type of channel protein that allows certain ions to diffuse across a plasma membrane down an electrochemical gradient.

ionic bond A chemical bond that is formed when an electron is completely transferred from one atom to another. Resulting ions remain associated due to their opposite electric charges. Compare with **covalent bond** and **hydrogen bond**.

iPS cell See **induced pluripotent cell**.

iris A ring of pigmented muscle just behind the cornea in the vertebrate eye that contracts or expands to control the amount of light entering the eye through the pupil.

isosmotic Referring to a solution that has the same solute concentration and water concentration as another solution. Compare with **hyperosmotic** and **hyposmotic**.

isotonic Comparative term designating a solution that, if inside a cell or vesicle, results in no net uptake or loss of water and thus no effect on the volume of the membrane-bound structure. This solution has the same solute concentration as the solution on the other side of the membrane. Compare with **hypertonic** and **hypotonic**.

isotope Any of several forms of an element that differ in the number of neutrons contained in their nuclei.

joint A place where two components (bones, cartilages, etc.) of a skeleton meet. May be movable (called an articulation) or immovable (e.g., skull sutures).

juvenile An individual that has adult-like morphology but is not sexually mature.

juvenile hormone An insect hormone that prevents larvae from metamorphosing into adults.

karyogamy Fusion of two haploid nuclei to form a diploid nucleus. Occurs in many fungi, and in animals and plants during fertilization of gametes.

karyotype The distinctive appearance of all the metaphase or prometaphase chromosomes in an individual, including the number of chromosomes, their length, and their banding patterns.

keystone species A species that has an exceptionally great impact on the other species in its ecosystem relative to its abundance.

kidney In terrestrial vertebrates, one of a pair of organs situated at the back, behind the abdominal cavity, that filters the blood, produces urine, and secretes several hormones.

kilocalorie (kcal) A unit of energy often used to measure the energy content of food. A kcal of energy raises 1 kg of water 1°C.

kin selection A form of natural selection that favors traits that increase survival or reproduction of an individual's kin at the expense of the individual.

kinesin A class of motor proteins that uses the chemical energy of ATP to "walk" toward the plus end of a microtubule. Used to transport vesicles, particles, organelles, and chromosomes.

kinetic energy The energy of motion. Compare with **potential energy**.

kinetochore A protein complex that forms on a chromosome during M phase. Forms at the centromere and serves as a site for microtubule attachment. Contains motor proteins and microtubule-binding proteins that are involved in chromosome segregation during M phase.

kinetochore microtubule A microtubule in the spindle apparatus formed during mitosis or meiosis that is attached to the kinetochore on a chromosome.

kinocilium (plural: kinocilia) A single cilium that juts from the surface of many hair cells and functions in the detection of pressure waves.

Koch's postulates Four criteria used to determine whether a suspected infectious agent causes a particular disease.

labium majus (plural: labia majora) One of two outer folds of skin that surround the labia minora, clitoris, and vaginal opening of female mammals.

labium minus (plural: labia minora) One of two folds of skin inside the labia majora and surrounding the opening of the urethra and vagina.

labor The strong muscular contractions of the uterus that expel the fetus during birth.

lac **operon** A set of three genes in *E. coli* that are transcribed into a single mRNA and required for lactose metabolism. Studies of the *lac* operon revealed many insights about gene regulation.

lactation (verb: lactate) Production of milk by the mammary glands of mammals, to feed offspring.

lacteal A small lymphatic vessel extending into the center of a villus in the small intestine. Receives chylomicrons containing fat absorbed from food.

lactic acid fermentation Catabolic pathway in which pyruvate produced by glycolysis is converted to lactic acid in order to oxidize NADH to NAD$^+$.

lagging strand In DNA replication, the new strand of DNA that is synthesized discontinuously (as a series of short pieces that are later joined) in a direction moving away from the replication fork. Also called *discontinuous strand*. Compare with **leading strand**.

laminin An abundant protein in the extracellular matrix (ECM) of animals that binds to other ECM components and to integrins, helping to anchor cells. Predominantly found in the basal lamina. Many tissue-specific subtypes exist.

land plants A monophyletic group of organisms that contain chloroplasts similar to those in green algae. The vast majority of land plants are photosynthetic and live in terrestrial habitats. Includes mosses, hornworts, liverworts, and all vascular plants.

large intestine The posterior portion of the digestive tract, consisting of the cecum, colon, and rectum. Its primary function is to form feces by absorbing water from and compacting the wastes delivered from the small intestine.

larva (plural: larvae) An immature stage of an animal species in which the immature and adult stages have different body forms.

late endosome A membrane-bound vesicle that arises from an early endosome, accepts lysosomal enzymes from the Golgi, and matures into a lysosome.

latency In certain viruses that infect animals, a dormant state of coexistence with the host cell during which no new virions are produced. The viral genetic material is replicated as the host cell replicates. Genetic material may or may not be integrated in the host genome, depending on the virus.

lateral bud A bud that forms at a node and may develop into a lateral (side) branch. Also called *axillary bud*.

lateral gene transfer Transfer of DNA between two different species. Compare with **chromosome-level mutation** and **point mutation**.

lateral line system A pressure-sensitive sensory organ found in many aquatic vertebrates.

lateral root A plant root that extends horizontally from another root.

leaching Loss of nutrients from soil via percolating water.

leading strand In DNA replication, the new strand of DNA that is synthesized in one continuous piece in a direction that follows the replication fork. Also called *continuous strand*. Compare with **lagging strand**.

leaf The main photosynthetic organ of vascular plants.

leak channel An ion channel that allows ions to leak across the membrane of a neuron in its resting state.

learning An enduring change in an individual's behavior that results from a specific experience.

leghemoglobin An iron-containing protein similar to hemoglobin. Found in infected cells of legume root nodules where it binds oxygen, preventing it from poisoning a bacterial enzyme needed for nitrogen fixation.

legumes Members of the pea plant family. Many form symbiotic associations with nitrogen-fixing bacteria in their roots.

lens A transparent structure that focuses incoming light onto a retina or other light-sensing apparatus of an eye.

lenticel Spongy segment in bark that allows gas exchange between cells in a woody stem and the atmosphere.

leukocyte Any of several types of blood cells, including neutrophils, macrophages, and lymphocytes, that reside in tissues and circulate in blood and lymph. Functions in tissue repair and defense against pathogens. Also called *white blood cell*.

lichen A mutualistic association of a fungus, often in the Ascomycota lineage, and a photosynthetic alga or cyanobacterium.

life cycle The sequence of developmental events and phases over the life span of an organism, from fertilization to offspring production.

life history The sequence of events in an individual's life from birth to reproduction to death, including how an individual allocates resources to growth, reproduction, and activities or structures that are related to survival.

life table A data set that summarizes the probability that an individual in a certain population will survive and reproduce in any given year over the course of its lifetime.

ligament A connective tissue that joins bones of an endoskeleton.

ligand Any molecule that binds to a specific site on a receptor molecule.

ligand-gated channel An ion channel that opens in response to binding by a certain molecule. Compare with **voltage-gated channel**.

light chain The smaller of the two types of polypeptide chains in an antibody or B-cell receptor; composed of a variable (*V*) region, which contributes to the antigen-binding site, and a constant (*C*) region. Compare with **heavy chain**.

lignin A complex polymer built from six-carbon rings and found in the secondary cell walls of some plants; it is exceptionally stiff and strong. Most abundant in woody plant parts.

limiting nutrient Any essential nutrient whose scarcity in the environment significantly reduces growth and reproduction of organisms.

limnetic zone Open water (not near shore) that receives enough sunlight to support photosynthesis but is too deep for plants to take root.

LINE (long interspersed nuclear element) Any of the most abundant class of transposable elements in human genomes; can create copies of itself and insert them elsewhere in the genome.

lineage See **monophyletic group**.

lingual lipase An enzyme produced by glands in the tongue that breaks down fats into fatty acids and monoglycerides.

linkage In genetics, a physical association between two genes because they are on the same chromosome; the inheritance patterns showing dependent assortment of alleles that result from this association.

linkage map See **genetic map**.

linkage study A study aimed at establishing linkage between genes or between genes and genetic markers.

lipid Any organic substance that does not dissolve in water, but dissolves well in nonpolar organic solvents. Lipids include fatty acids, fats, oils, waxes, steroids, and phospholipids.

lipid bilayer The basic structural element of all cellular membranes; consists of a two-layer sheet of phospholipid molecules with their hydrophobic tails oriented toward the inside and their hydrophilic heads toward the outside. Also called *phospholipid bilayer*.

liposome An artificial vesicle formed by mixing amphipathic lipids, such as phosopholipids, together in an aqueous solution.

littoral zone Shallow water near shore that receives enough sunlight to support photosynthesis and is shallow enough for plants to take root; often flowering plants are present.

liver A large, complex organ of vertebrates that performs many functions, including storage of glycogen, processing and conversion of food and wastes, and production of bile.

lobe-finned fishes Fishes with fins supported by bony elements that extend the length of the fin.

locomotion Movement of an organism or cell from place to place under its own power.

locus (plural: loci) A gene's physical location on a chromosome.

logistic population growth The density-dependent decrease in growth rate as population size approaches the carrying capacity. Compare with **exponential population growth**.

long interspersed nuclear element See *LINE*.

long noncoding RNA An abundant class of transcribed RNA molecules that are greater than 200 nucleotides in length and do not code for a protein.

long-day plant A plant that blooms in response to short nights (usually in late spring or early summer in the Northern Hemisphere). Compare with **day-neutral** and **short-day plant**.

loop of Henle In the kidneys of mammals and some birds, a long, U-shaped loop in a nephron that extends into the medulla. Functions as a countercurrent exchanger and multiplier in establishing and maintaining an osmotic gradient that allows reabsorption of water from the collecting duct.

loose connective tissue A type of connective tissue consisting of fibrous proteins in a soft matrix. Often functions as padding for organs.

lophophore A specialized feeding structure found in some lophotrochozoans and used in suspension (filter) feeding.

lophotrochozoans A major lineage of protostomes (Lophotrochozoa) that grow by extending their skeletons rather than by molting. Many phyla have a specialized feeding structure (lophophore) and/or ciliated larvae (trochophore). Includes rotifers, flatworms, segmented worms, and mollusks. Compare with **ecdysozoans**.

loss-of-function allele A mutant allele that does not produce a functional product.

LUCA The *last universal common ancestor* of cells. This theoretical entity is proposed to be the product of chemical evolution and provided characteristics of life that are shared by all living organisms on Earth today.

lumen The interior space of any hollow structure (e.g., the rough ER) or organ (e.g., the stomach).

lung Any respiratory organ used for gas exchange between blood or hemolymph and air.

luteal phase In a menstrual cycle, the phase after ovulation, when the progesterone level is high and the body is preparing for a possible pregnancy.

luteinizing hormone (LH) A peptide hormone, produced and secreted by the anterior pituitary, that stimulates estrogen production, ovulation, and formation of the corpus luteum in females and testosterone production in males.

lymph The mixture of fluid and white blood cells that circulates through the ducts and lymph nodes of the lymphatic system in vertebrates.

lymph node Any of many small, oval structures that lymph moves through in the lymphatic system. Filters the lymph and screens it for pathogens and antigens. A major site of lymphocyte activation.

lymphatic system In vertebrates, a body-wide network of thin-walled ducts (or vessels) and lymph nodes that is separate from the circulatory system. Collects excess fluid from body tissues and returns it to the blood; also functions as part of the immune system.

lymphocyte A cell that circulates through the bloodstream and lymphatic system and is responsible for the development of adaptive immunity. Key lymphocytes in the adaptive immune system are B cells and T cells.

lysogeny In certain viruses that infect bacteria (bacteriophages), a dormant state of coexistence with the host cell during which no new virions are produced. The viral genetic material is integrated in the host chromosome and replicated as the host cell replicates. Compare with **lytic cycle**.

lysosome A small, acidified organelle in an animal cell containing enzymes that catalyze hydrolysis reactions and can digest large molecules. Compare with **vacuole**.

lysozyme An enzyme that functions in innate immunity by digesting bacterial cell walls. Occurs in lysosomes of phagocytes and is secreted in saliva, tears, and mucus.

lytic cycle A type of viral replicative growth in which the production and release of virions kills the host cell. Compare with **lysogeny** and **latency**.

M phase The phase of the cell cycle during which cell division occurs. Includes mitosis or meiosis and often cytokinesis.

M-phase-promoting factor (MPF) A complex of a cyclin and cyclin-dependent kinase that, when activated, phosphorylates a number of specific proteins that initiate mitosis or meiosis in eukaryotic cells.

macromolecular machine A group of proteins, and possibly other macromolecules, that assemble to carry out a particular function.

macromolecule Generally, any large organic molecules made up of smaller molecules (monomers) joined together into a polymer. The main biological macromolecules are proteins, nucleic acids, and polysaccharides.

macronutrient Any element (e.g., nitrogen) that is required in large quantities for normal growth, reproduction, and maintenance of a living organism. Compare with **micronutrient**.

macrophage A type of leukocyte in the innate immune system that participates in the inflammatory response by secreting cytokines and phagocytizing invading pathogens and apoptotic cells. Also serves as an antigen-presenting cell in lymphocyte activation.

magnetoreception The detection of magnetic fields.

magnetoreceptor A sensory cell specialized for detecting magnetic fields.

major histocompatibility protein See **class I and class II MHC proteins**.

malaria A human disease caused by five species of the protist *Plasmodium* and passed to humans by mosquitoes.

malignant tumor A tumor that is actively growing and disrupting local tissues or is spreading to other organs. Cancer consists of one or more malignant tumors. Compare with **benign tumor**.

Malpighian tubules A major excretory organ of insects, consisting of blind-ended tubes that extend from the gut into the insect's body cavity. They filter hemolymph and send the filtrate to the hindgut for further processing.

mammals One of the two lineages of amniotes (vertebrates that produce amniotic eggs) distinguished by hair (or fur) and mammary glands. Includes the monotremes (platypus and echidnas), marsupials, and eutherians (placental mammals).

mammary glands Specialized exocrine glands that produce and secrete milk for nursing offspring. A diagnostic feature of mammals.

mandibles Any mouthpart used in chewing. In vertebrates, the lower jaw. In insects, crustaceans, and myriapods, the first pair of mouthparts.

mantle One of the three main parts of the mollusk body; the thick outer tissue that protects the visceral mass and may secrete a calcium carbonate shell.

marsupials A lineage of mammals (Marsupiala) that nourish their young in an abdominal pouch after a very short period of development in the uterus.

mass extinction The extinction of a large number of diverse organisms around the world during a relatively short period of geologic time (about 1 million years). May occur due to sudden and extraordinary environmental changes. Compare with **background extinction**.

mass feeder An animal that ingests chunks of food.

mass number The total number of protons and neutrons in the nucleus of an atom.

mast cell A type of leukocyte that is stationary (embedded in tissue) and secretes factors, including histamine, that help trigger the inflammatory response. Particularly important in allergic responses and defense against parasites.

master regulator A gene or protein that can unleash a series of events that produce a specialized cell type, tissue, or body structure.

maternal chromosome A chromosome inherited from the mother.

mechanoreception The detection of changes in pressure.

mechanoreceptor A sensory cell specialized for detecting distortions caused by touch or pressure. Examples include hair cells in the cochlea and lateral line system of vertebrates.

mediator A large complex of proteins in eukaryotes that creates a physical link between regulatory transcription factors that are bound to DNA, the general transcription factors, and RNA polymerase.

medium A liquid or solid that supports the growth of cells.

medulla The innermost part of an organ (e.g., kidney or adrenal gland).

medulla oblongata In vertebrates, a region of the brain stem that along with the cerebellum forms the hindbrain.

medusa (plural: medusae) The free-floating stage in the life cycle of some cnidarians (e.g., jellyfish). Compare with **polyp**.

megapascal (MPa) A unit of pressure (force per unit area) equivalent to 1 million pascals (Pa).

megasporangium (plural: megasporangia) In heterosporous species of plants, a spore-producing structure that produces megaspores; these develop into female gametophytes.

megaspore In seed plants, a haploid (*n*) spore that is produced in a megasporangium by meiosis of a diploid (2*n*) megasporocyte; develops into a female gametophyte. Compare with **microspore**.

meiosis In sexually reproducing organisms, a special two-stage type of cell division in which one diploid (2*n*) parent cell produces haploid (*n*) cells (gametes); results in halving of the chromosome number. Also called *reduction division*.

meiosis I The first cell division of meiosis, in which synapsis, crossing over, and independent assortment occur. It separates homologous chromosomes from each other, producing daughter cells with half as many chromosomes as the parent cell.

meiosis II The second cell division of meiosis, in which sister chromatids are separated from each other. Similar to **mitosis**.

melatonin A hormone, produced by the pineal gland, that regulates sleep–wake cycles and seasonal reproduction in vertebrates.

membrane potential A difference in electric charge across a cell membrane; a form of potential energy. Also called *membrane voltage*.

memory Retention of learned information.

memory cell A type of lymphocyte responsible for maintaining immunity for years or decades after an infection. Descended from activated B cells or T cells that responded to an infection or vaccination.

meniscus (plural: menisci) The concave boundary layer formed at most air–water interfaces due to adhesion and surface tension.

menstrual cycle A female reproductive cycle seen in Old World monkeys and apes (including humans) in which the uterine lining is shed (menstruation) if no pregnancy occurs. Compare with **estrous cycle**.

menstruation The periodic shedding of the uterine lining through the vagina that occurs in females of Old World monkeys and apes, including humans.

meristem (adjective: meristematic) In plants, a group of undifferentiated cells, including stem cells, that can divide and develop into various adult tissues throughout the life of a plant. See also **apical meristem** and **ground meristem**.

mesoderm The middle of the three basic cell layers (germ layers) in most animal embryos; gives rise to muscles, bones, blood, and some internal organs (kidney, spleen, etc.). Compare with **ectoderm** and **endoderm**.

mesoglea A gelatinous material, containing scattered ectodermal cells, that is located between the ectoderm and endoderm of cnidarians (e.g., jellyfish, corals, and anemones).

mesophyll cell A type of cell, found near the surfaces of plant leaves, that is specialized for the light-capturing reactions of photosynthesis.

Mesozoic era The interval of geologic time, from 252 million to 66 million years ago, during which gymnosperms were the dominant plants and dinosaurs the dominant vertebrates. Ended with extinction of the dinosaurs (except birds).

messenger RNA (mRNA) An RNA molecule transcribed from DNA that carries information (in codons) that specifies the amino acid sequence of a polypeptide.

metabolic pathway A linked series of biochemical reactions that sequentially changes an initial substrate to form a final product; the product of one reaction is the substrate of the next reaction.

metabolic rate The rate of energy use by all the cells of an individual. For aerobic organisms, often measured as the amount of oxygen consumed per hour.

metagenomics The inventory of all the genes in a community or ecosystem created by sequencing, analyzing, and comparing the genomes of the component organisms. Often refers to the study of microbial communities. Also called *environmental sequencing*.

metallothioneins Small plant proteins that bind to and prevent excess metal ions from acting as toxins.

metamorphosis Transition from one developmental stage to another, such as from the larval to the adult form of an animal.

metaphase A stage in mitosis or meiosis during which chromosomes line up across the middle of the spindle.

metaphase plate An imaginary plane (between the spindle poles) along which chromosomes line up during metaphase of mitosis or meiosis.

metapopulation A population made up of many small, physically isolated populations connected by migration.

metastasis The spread of cancerous cells from their site of origin to distant sites in the body, where they may establish additional tumors.

methanogen A prokaryote that produces methane (CH_4) as a by-product of cellular respiration.

methanotroph A prokaryote that uses methane (CH_4) as its primary electron donor and source of carbon.

methyl salicylate (MeSA) A molecule that is hypothesized to function as a signal, transported among tissues, that triggers systematic acquired resistance in plants—a response to pathogen attack.

microbe Any microscopic organism, including bacteria, archaea, and various tiny eukaryotes.

microbiology The field of study concerned with microscopic organisms.

microbiome The ecological community of microbes that share a particular space (e.g., the human gut).

microfibril A bundle of cellulose strands that serves as the fibrous component in plant cell walls.

microfilament See **actin filament**.

micronutrient Any element (e.g., iron, molybdenum, magnesium) that is required in very small quantities for normal growth, reproduction, and maintenance of a living organism. Compare with **macronutrient**.

micropyle The tiny pore in a plant ovule through which the pollen tube reaches the embryo sac.

microRNA (miRNA) A small, single-stranded RNA associated with proteins in an RNA-induced silencing complex (RISC). Processed from a longer miRNA gene transcript. Can bind to complementary sequences in mRNA molecules, allowing the associated proteins of RISC to degrade the bound mRNA or inhibit its translation. See **RNA interference**.

microsatellite See **short tandem repeat (STR)**.

microsporangium (plural: microsporangia) In heterosporous species of plants, a spore-producing structure that produces microspores; these develop into male gametophytes.

microspore In seed plants, a haploid (*n*) spore that is produced in a microsporangium by meiosis of a diploid (2*n*) microsporocyte; develops into a male gametophyte. Compare with **megaspore**.

microtubule A long, tubular fiber, about 25 nm in diameter, formed by polymerization of tubulin protein dimers; one of the three types of cytoskeletal fibers. Involved in cell movement and transport of materials within the cell. Compare with **actin filament** and **intermediate filament**.

microtubule organizing center (MTOC) General term for any structure (e.g., centrosome and basal body) where new microtubules originate in cells.

microvilli (singular: microvillus) Tiny protrusions from the surface of an epithelial cell that increase the surface area for absorption of substances.

midbrain One of the three main regions of the vertebrate brain; includes sensory integrating and relay centers. Compare with **forebrain** and **hindbrain**.

middle ear The air-filled middle portion of the mammalian ear, which contains three small bones that amplify sound and transmit it from the tympanic membrane to the inner ear. Connects to the throat via the eustachian tube.

migration (1) In ecology, a seasonal long-distance movement of large numbers of organisms from one geographic location or habitat to another. (2) In population genetics, movement of individuals from one population to another.

millivolt (mV) A unit of voltage equal to 1/1000 of a volt.

mimicry A phenomenon in which one species has evolved (or learns) to look or sound like another species. See **Batesian mimicry** and **Müllerian mimicry**.

mineral One of various inorganic substances that are important components of enzyme cofactors or of structural materials in an organism.

mineralocorticoid Any of a class of steroid hormones, produced and secreted by the adrenal cortex, that regulate electrolyte levels and the overall volume of body fluids. Aldosterone is the principal mineralocorticoid in humans. Compare with **glucocorticoid**.

minisatellite A noncoding stretch of eukaryotic DNA consisting of a repeating sequence that is from 8 to about 100 base pairs long. Also called *variable number tandem repeat (VNTR)*.

mismatch repair A type of DNA repair used to correct mismatched base pairs in DNA that result from mistakes in DNA synthesis.

missense mutation A point mutation (change in a single base pair) that changes one amino acid for another within the sequence of a protein.

mitochondrial DNA (mtDNA) A small circular (or linear in some species) chromosome that contains some of the genes that encode proteins and functional RNA molecules within mitochondria. There are normally many copies of this DNA within each mitochondrion.

mitochondrial matrix Central compartment of a mitochondrion, which is lined by the inner membrane; contains mitochondrial DNA, ribosomes, and the enzymes for pyruvate processing and the citric acid cycle.

mitochondrion (plural: mitochondria) A eukaryotic organelle that is surrounded by two membranes and is the site of aerobic respiration and ATP synthesis.

mitogen-activated protein kinase (MAPK) Any of a class of enzymes involved in signal transduction pathways that often activate cell division. In a cell, different types of MAPKs are organized in a series, where one activates another via phosphorylation. See also **phosphorylation cascade**.

mitosis In eukaryotic cells, the process of nuclear division that results in two daughter nuclei that are genetically identical to the parent nucleus. Subsequent cytokinesis (division of the cytoplasm) yields two daughter cells.

mobile nutrients Nutrients that can be transported within plants, typically to regions where they are needed most (e.g., from older leaves to younger leaves). Compare with **immobile nutrients**.

mode of transmission The type of inheritance observed as a trait is passed from parent to offspring. Some common types are autosomal recessive, autosomal dominant, and X-linked recessive.

model organism An organism selected for intensive scientific study based on features that make it easy to work with (e.g., body size, life span), in the hope that findings will apply to other species.

molarity The number of moles of a solute present in 1 liter of solution.

mole The amount of a substance that contains 6.022×10^{23} of its elemental entities (e.g., atoms, ions, or molecules). This number of molecules will have a mass equal to its molecular weight expressed in grams.

molecular chaperone A protein that facilitates the folding or refolding of a protein into its correct three-dimensional shape.

molecular formula A notation that indicates only the numbers and types of atoms in a molecule, such as H_2O for the water molecule. Compare with **structural formula**.

molecular weight The sum of the atomic weights of all the atoms in a molecule; roughly, the total number of protons and neutrons in the molecule.

molecule A substance made up of two or more atoms held together by covalent bonds.

molting A method of body growth, used by ecdysozoans, that involves the shedding of an external protective cuticle (exoskeleton in arthropods), expansion of the soft body, and growth of a new external cuticle.

monocot Any flowering plant (angiosperm) that has a single cotyledon (embryonic leaf) upon germination. Monocots form a monophyletic group. Also called a monocotyledonous plant. Compare with **dicot**.

monoecious Describing an angiosperm species that has both male and female reproductive structures on each plant. Compare with **dioecious**.

monohybrid cross A mating between two parents that are both heterozygous for one given gene.

monomer A small molecule that can covalently bind to other similar molecules to form a larger macromolecule. Compare with **polymer**.

monophyletic group An evolutionary unit that includes an ancestral population and all of its descendants but no others. Also called a *clade* or *lineage*. Compare with **paraphyletic group** and **polyphyletic group**.

monosaccharide A molecule that has the molecular formula $(CH_2O)_n$ and cannot be hydrolyzed to form any smaller carbohydrates. Also called *simple sugar*. Compare with **disaccharide, oligosaccharide,** and **polysaccharide**.

monosomy The state of having only one copy of a particular type of chromosome in an otherwise diploid cell.

monotremes A lineage of mammals (Monotremata) that lay eggs and then nourish the young with milk. Includes just five living species: the platypus and four species of echidna, all with leathery beaks or bills.

morphogen A molecule that exists in a concentration gradient and provides spatial information to embryonic cells.

morphology The overall shape and appearance of an organism and its component parts.

morphospecies concept The definition of a species as a population or group of populations that have measurably different anatomical features from other groups. Also called *morphological species concept*. Compare with **biological species concept** and **phylogenetic species concept**.

motor neuron A nerve cell that carries signals from the central nervous system to effector cells in a muscle or gland. Compare with **interneuron** and **sensory neuron**.

motor protein A class of proteins whose major function is to convert the chemical energy of ATP into motion. Includes dynein, kinesin, and myosin.

mRNA See **messenger RNA**.

mucosa-associated lymphoid tissue (MALT) Collective term for lymphocytes and other leukocytes associated with skin cells and mucus-secreting epithelial tissues in the digestive and respiratory tracts. Plays an important role in preventing entry of pathogens into the body.

mucous cell A type of cell found in the epithelial layer of the stomach that secretes mucus into the stomach.

mucus (adjective: mucous) A slimy mixture of glycoproteins (called mucins) and water that is secreted in many animal organs. Functions include providing lubrication and serving as a barrier to protect surfaces from infection.

Müllerian inhibitory substance A peptide hormone, secreted by the embryonic testis, that causes regression (withering away) of the female reproductive ducts.

Müllerian mimicry A type of mimicry in which two (or more) harmful species resemble each other. Compare with **Batesian mimicry**.

multicellularity The state of being composed of many cells that adhere to each other and do not all express the same genes, resulting in some cells having specialized functions.

multiple allelism The existence of more than two common alleles of the same gene.

multiple fruit A fruit (e.g., pineapple) that develops from many separate flowers and thus many carpels. Compare with **aggregate** and **simple fruit**.

multiple sclerosis (MS) A human autoimmune disease in which the immune system attacks the myelin sheaths that insulate axons of neurons.

muscle fiber A muscle cell.

muscle tissue An animal tissue consisting of bundles of long, thin, contractile cells (muscle fibers). Functions primarily in movement.

mutagen Any physical or chemical agent that increases the rate of mutation.

mutant An individual that carries a mutation, particularly a new or rare mutation.

mutation Any permanent change in the hereditary material of an organism (DNA in most organisms, RNA in some viruses). The only source of new alleles in populations.

mutualism (adjective: mutualistic) A species relationship between two organisms (mutualists) that benefits both. Compare with **commensalism, consumption**, and **competition**.

mutualist An organism that is a participant and partner in a mutualistic relationship. See **mutualism**.

mycelium (plural: mycelia) A mass of underground filaments (hyphae) that form the body of a fungus. Also found in some protists and bacteria.

mycorrhiza (plural: mycorrhizae) A mutualistic association between certain fungi and the roots of most vascular plants, sometimes visible as nodules or nets in or around plant roots.

mycorrhizal Describes a fungus that lives symbiotically with the roots of vascular plants.

myelin sheath Multiple layers of myelin, derived from the cell membranes of certain glial cells, wrapped around the axon of a neuron and providing electrical insulation.

myocardial infarction Death of cardiac muscle cells when deprived of oxygen. Also called *heart attack*.

myofibril A long, slender structure composed of contractile proteins organized into repeating units (sarcomeres) in vertebrate cardiac muscle and skeletal muscle.

myosin Any one of a class of motor proteins that use the chemical energy of ATP to move along actin filaments in muscle contraction, cytokinesis, and vesicle transport.

myriapods A lineage of arthropods with long segmented trunks, each segment bearing one or two pairs of legs. Includes millipedes and centipedes.

NAD$^+$/NADH Oxidized and reduced forms, respectively, of nicotinamide adenine dinucleotide. A nonprotein electron carrier that functions in many of the redox reactions of metabolism.

NADP$^+$/NADPH The oxidized and reduced forms, respectively, of nicotinamide adenine dinucleotide phosphate. A nonprotein electron carrier that is reduced during the light-dependent reactions in photosynthesis and extensively used in biosynthetic reactions.

natural experiment A situation in which a natural change in conditions enables comparisons of groups, rather than a manipulation of conditions by researchers.

natural selection The process by which individuals with certain heritable traits tend to produce more surviving offspring than do individuals without those traits, often leading to a change in the genetic makeup of the population. A major mechanism of evolution.

Neanderthal A recently extinct European species of hominin, *Homo neanderthalensis*, closely related to but distinct from modern humans.

nectar The sugary fluid produced by flowers that attracts and rewards pollinating animals.

nectary A nectar-producing structure in a flower.

negative control A type of regulation that works by slowing an ongoing process. In the context of gene transcription, the action of a regulatory protein to shut down transcription by binding to DNA in or near the gene.

negative feedback A self-limiting, corrective response in which a deviation in some variable (e.g., concentration of some compound) triggers responses aimed at returning the variable to a target value. Represents a means of maintaining homeostasis. Compare with **positive feedback**.

negative pressure ventilation Ventilation of the lungs by expanding the rib cage so as to "pull" air into the lungs. Compare with **positive pressure ventilation**.

negative-sense Describing a single strand of RNA that contains sequences complementary to those in the mRNA required to produce viral proteins. Compare with **ambisense** and **positive-sense**.

nematodes See **roundworms**.

nephron One of many tiny tubules inside the kidney that function in the formation of urine.

neritic zone Shallow marine waters beyond the intertidal zone, extending down to about 200 meters, where the continental shelf ends.

nerve A long strand of nervous tissue containing axons wrapped in connective tissue; carries signals between the central nervous system and some other part of the body.

nerve net A nervous system in which neurons are diffuse instead of being clustered into large ganglia or tracts; found in cnidarians and ctenophores.

nervous tissue An animal tissue consisting of nerve cells (neurons) and various supporting cells.

net primary productivity (NPP) In an ecosystem, the total amount of biomass generated by the fixation of carbon through photosynthesis per year minus the amount oxidized during cellular respiration. Compare with **gross primary productivity**.

net reproductive rate (R_0) The growth rate of a population per generation; equivalent to the average number of female offspring that each female produces over her lifetime.

neural tube A folded tube of ectoderm that forms along the dorsal side of an early vertebrate embryo; gives rise to the brain and the spinal cord.

neurogenesis The formation of new neurons from central nervous system stem cells.

neurohormone A hormone produced by a neuron.

neuron An animal cell that is specialized for the transmission of nerve impulses. Typically has dendrites, a cell body, and a long axon that forms synapses with other neurons. Also called *nerve cell*.

neurosecretory cell A nerve cell (neuron) that produces and secretes neurohormones into the bloodstream. In vertebrates, principally found in the hypothalamus. Also called *neuroendocrine cell*.

neurotoxin Any substance that specifically destroys or blocks the normal functioning of neurons.

neurotransmitter A molecule that transmits signals from one neuron to another neuron or to a muscle cell or gland cell. Examples are acetylcholine, dopamine, serotonin, and norepinephrine.

neutral In genetics, referring to any mutation, allele, or trait that has no effect on an individual's fitness. Compare with **deleterious** and **beneficial**.

neutrophil A type of leukocyte that is capable of moving through body tissues to engulf and digest pathogens and other foreign particles; also secretes various compounds that attack bacteria and fungi.

next-generation sequencing A term used to describe a number of different DNA sequencing technologies that are more rapid and cheaper than dideoxy sequencing. Millions of different DNAs can be amplified and sequenced in a single run.

niche The range of resources that a species can use and the range of conditions that it can tolerate. More broadly, the role that a species plays in its ecosystem.

niche differentiation The evolutionary change in resource use by competing species that occurs as the result of character displacement.

nicotinamide adenine dinucleotide See **NAD$^+$/NADH**.

nicotinamide adenine dinucleotide phosphate See **NADP$^+$/NADPH**.

nitrogen cycle, global The movement of nitrogen among terrestrial ecosystems, the oceans, and the atmosphere.

nitrogen fixation The incorporation of atmospheric nitrogen (N_2) into ammonia (NH_3), which can be used to make many organic compounds. Occurs in only a few lineages of prokaryotes.

nociceptor A sensory cell specialized for detecting tissue damage, usually resulting in the sensation of pain.

Nod factors Molecules produced by nitrogen-fixing bacteria that help them recognize and bind to roots of legumes.

node (1) In animals, any small thickening (e.g., a lymph node). (2) In plants, the part of a stem where leaves or leaf buds are attached. (3) In a phylogenetic tree, the point where two branches diverge, representing the point in time when an ancestral group split into two or more descendant groups. Also called *fork*.

node of Ranvier One of the periodic gaps in the myelin sheath of a neuron's axon; serves as a site where an action potential can be regenerated.

nodule Globular structure on roots of legume plants that contain symbiotic nitrogen-fixing bacteria.

noncyclic electron flow Path of electron flow in which electrons originate from oxidizing water in photosystem II and then pass through an electron transport chain to photosystem I, where they ultimately reduce NADP$^+$ during the light-dependent reactions of photosynthesis. See also **Z scheme**.

nondisjunction An error that can occur during meiosis or mitosis; it results in one daughter cell receiving two copies of a particular chromosome while the other daughter cell receives none.

nonpolar covalent bond A covalent bond in which electrons are equally shared between two atoms of the same or similar electronegativity. Compare with **polar covalent bond**.

nonsense mutation A point mutation (change in a single base pair) that converts an amino acid–specifying codon into a stop codon.

non-sister chromatids Any two chromatids that each come from a different member of a homologous chromosome pair. Crossing over occurs between non-sister chromatids. Compare with **sister chromatids**.

non-template strand The strand of DNA that is not transcribed during synthesis of RNA. With the exception of T's instead of U's, its base sequence corresponds to that of the mRNA produced from the other strand. Also called *coding strand*.

nonvascular plants A paraphyletic group of land plants that lack vascular tissue and reproduce using spores. The nonvascular plants include three lineages of green plants (liverworts, mosses, and hornworts).

norepinephrine A catecholamine used as a neurotransmitter in the sympathetic nervous system. Also produced by the adrenal medulla and functions as a hormone that triggers rapid physiological changes relating to the fight-or-flight response.

notochord A supportive, flexible rod that occurs in the back of a chordate embryo, ventral to the developing spinal cord. Replaced by vertebrae in most adult vertebrates. A defining feature of chordates.

nuclear envelope The double-layered membrane enclosing the nucleus of a eukaryotic cell.

nuclear lamina A lattice-like sheet of fibrous nuclear lamins, which are one type of intermediate filament. Lines the inner membrane of the nuclear envelope, stiffening the envelope and helping to organize the chromosomes.

nuclear lamins Intermediate filaments that make up the nuclear lamina layer—a lattice-like layer inside the nuclear envelope that stiffens the structure.

nuclear localization signal (NLS) A short amino acid sequence that marks a protein for delivery to the nucleus.

nuclear pore complex A large complex of about 30 proteins that form an opening in the nuclear envelope connecting the inside of the nucleus with the cytosol and allowing the free diffusion of small molecules and ions; also regulates transport of RNA and proteins.

nuclease Any enzyme that digests RNA or DNA.

nucleic acid A macromolecule composed of nucleotide monomers. Generally used by cells to store or transmit hereditary information. Includes ribonucleic acid and deoxyribonucleic acid.

nucleoid In prokaryotic cells, a dense, centrally located region that contains DNA but is not surrounded by a membrane.

nucleolus In eukaryotic cells, a specialized structure in the nucleus where ribosomal RNA processing occurs and ribosomal subunits are assembled.

nucleosome A bead-like unit of eukaryotic chromatin, consisting of about 200 nucleotides of DNA wrapped twice around eight histone proteins.

nucleotide A molecule consisting of a five-carbon sugar (ribose or deoxyribose), one or more phosphate groups, and one of several nitrogen-containing bases. Equivalent to a nucleoside plus one or more phosphate groups.

nucleotide excision repair A type of DNA repair that removes a damaged region in one strand of DNA and replaces it with the correct sequence using the undamaged strand as a template.

nucleus (1) The center of an atom, containing protons and neutrons. (2) In eukaryotic cells, the large organelle containing the chromosomes and surrounded by a double membrane. (3) A discrete clump of neuron cell bodies in the brain, usually sharing a distinct function.

null allele See **loss-of-function allele**.

null hypothesis A hypothesis that specifies what the results of an experiment will be if the main hypothesis being tested is wrong. Often states that there will be no difference between experimental groups.

nutrient Any substance that an organism requires for normal growth, maintenance, or reproduction.

occipital lobe In the vertebrate brain, one of the four lobes of the cerebrum. Receives and interprets visual information.

oceanic zone The deeper waters of the open ocean beyond the continental shelf.

odorant Any airborne molecule that conveys information about food or the environment.

oil A polyunsaturated fat that is liquid at room temperature.

Okazaki fragment Short segment of DNA produced during replication of the lagging-strand template. The Okazaki fragments are eventually linked together to produce the lagging strand in newly synthesized DNA.

olfaction The sense of smell.

olfactory bulb A bulb-shaped projection of the vertebrate brain just above the nose. Receives and interprets odor information from the nose.

oligodendrocyte A type of glial cell that wraps around axons of some neurons in the vertebrate central nervous system, forming a myelin sheath that provides electrical insulation. Compare with **Schwann cell**.

oligopeptide A chain composed of fewer than 50 amino acid residues linked together by peptide bonds. Often referred to simply as *peptide*.

oligosaccharide A linear or branched carbohydrate chain generally consisting of fewer than 50 monosaccharides joined by glycosidic linkages. Compare with **monosaccharide** and **polysaccharide**.

ommatidium (plural: ommatidia) A light-sensing column in an arthropod's compound eye.

omnivore (adjective: omnivorous) An animal whose diet regularly includes a variety of organisms, including plants, animals, fungi, protists, archaea, and/or bacteria. Compare with **carnivore** and **herbivore**.

oncogene Any gene whose protein product stimulates cell division at all times and thus promotes cancer development. Often is a mutated form of a gene involved in regulating the cell cycle. See **proto-oncogene**.

one-gene, one-enzyme hypothesis The hypothesis that each gene is responsible for making one enzyme. This hypothesis has expanded to include genes that produce proteins other than enzymes or that produce RNAs as final products.

oogenesis The production of egg cells (ova).

oogonium (plural: oogonia) In an ovary, any of the diploid cells that can divide by mitosis to produce primary oocytes (which can undergo meiosis) and more oogonia.

open circulatory system A circulatory system in which the circulating fluid (hemolymph) is not confined to blood vessels. Compare with **closed circulatory system**.

open reading frame (ORF) A sequence of DNA that, if converted into an RNA sequence and translated as a set of non-overlapping codons, would produce a polypeptide of substantial size. Discovery of an open reading frame is an important piece of evidence to identify a protein-coding gene.

operator In bacterial DNA, a binding site for a repressor protein; located near the start of an operon.

operculum The stiff flap of tissue that covers the gills of teleost fishes.

operon A region of bacterial DNA that codes for a series of functionally related genes and is transcribed from a single promoter into one mRNA.

opsin A transmembrane protein that is covalently linked to retinal, the light-detecting pigment in the rods and cones of vertebrate retinas.

optic nerve A bundle of axons that runs from the eye to the brain in vertebrates.

optimal foraging The concept that animals forage in a way that maximizes the amount of usable energy they take in, given the costs of finding and ingesting their food and the risk of being eaten while they're at it.

optogenetics A technique in which specific types of cells are genetically engineered to express light-sensitive proteins. By stimulating or inhibiting the cells with light, researchers can determine the physiological roles of the cells.

orbital The region of space around an atomic nucleus in which an electron is present most of the time. Orbitals are grouped into electron shells.

organ A group of tissues organized into a functional and structural unit.

organ system A group of tissues and organs that work together to perform a function.

organelle Any discrete, membrane-bound structure within a cell (e.g., mitochondrion) that has a characteristic structure and function.

organic compounds A group of molecules that include at least one carbon atom; most have carbon–hydrogen bonds and carbon–carbon bonds. Organic compounds are widely used by living organisms.

organism Any living entity that contains one or more cells.

organogenesis A stage of embryonic development in which organs are formed. In animals, it follows gastrulation.

origin of replication The site on a chromosome at which DNA replication begins.

osmolarity The concentration of dissolved substances in a solution, measured in osmoles per liter.

Osmoregulation The process by which an organism controls the concentration of water and solutes in its body.

osmoregulator An animal that actively regulates the osmolarity of its tissues.

osmosis Diffusion of water across a selectively permeable membrane from a region of low solute concentration (high water concentration) to a region of high solute concentration (low water concentration). For osmosis to occur, the solute would not be able to pass through the membrane.

osteoblast A type of cell in bone that secretes calcium, proteins, and other substances that harden to form new bone tissue.

osteoclast A type of cell in bone that stimulates bone resorption by secreting acid, resulting in the release of calcium and other minerals into the blood.

osteoporosis A disease characterized by reduction in bone mass, leading to fragile bones susceptible to fracture.

ouabain A plant toxin that poisons Na^+/K^+-ATPase of animals.

out-of-Africa hypothesis The hypothesis that modern humans (*Homo sapiens*) evolved in Africa and spread to other continents, replacing other *Homo* species without interbreeding with them.

outcrossing Reproduction by fusion of gametes produced by different individuals. Compare with **self-fertilization**.

outer ear The outermost portion of the mammalian ear, consisting of the pinna (ear flap) and the ear canal. Funnels sound to the tympanic membrane.

outgroup A taxon that is closely related to the taxa being studied, but that diverged earlier; a sister group to the group being studied.

oval window A membrane separating the air-filled middle ear from the fluid-filled cochlea in mammals; sound vibrations pass through it from the middle ear to the inner ear.

ovary The egg-producing organ of a female animal, or the fruit- and seed-producing structure in the female part of a flower.

overexploitation Unsustainable removal of wildlife from the natural environment for use by humans.

oviduct See **fallopian tube**.

oviparous In animals, depositing fertilized eggs outside the body, where they develop and hatch. Compare with **ovoviviparous** and **viviparous**.

ovoviviparous In animals, producing eggs that are retained inside the body (nourished by yolk) until they are ready to hatch. Compare with **oviparous** and **viviparous**.

ovulation The release of an egg from an ovary of a female vertebrate. In humans, an ovarian follicle releases an egg at the end of the follicular phase of the menstrual cycle.

ovule In flowering plants, the structure inside an ovary that contains the female gametophyte and eventually (if fertilized) becomes a seed.

ovum (plural: ova) See **egg**.

oxidation The loss of electrons from an atom or molecule during a redox reaction, either by donation of an electron to another atom or molecule or by the shared electrons in covalent bonds moving farther from the atomic nucleus.

oxidative phosphorylation Production of ATP molecules by ATP synthase using the proton gradient established via redox reactions of an electron transport chain.

oxygen–hemoglobin equilibrium curve The graphed depiction of the percentage of hemoglobin in the blood that is saturated with oxygen at various partial pressures of oxygen.

oxygenic Referring to any process or reaction that produces oxygen. Photosynthesis in plants, algae, and cyanobacteria, which involves photosystem II, is oxygenic because it uses water as an electron source and produces O_2 as a by-product. Compare with **anoxygenic**.

oxytocin A peptide hormone, secreted by the posterior pituitary, that triggers labor and milk production in females and that stimulates pair bonding, parental care, and affiliative behavior in both sexes.

p53 A tumor-suppressor protein (molecular weight of 53 kilodaltons) that responds to DNA damage by stopping the cell cycle, turning on DNA repair machinery, and, if necessary, triggering apoptosis. Encoded by the *p53* gene.

pacemaker cell Any of a group of specialized cardiac muscle cells in the sinoatrial (SA) node of the vertebrate heart that have an inherent rhythm and can generate an electrical impulse that spreads to other heart cells.

paleontologists Scientists who study the fossil record and the history of life.

Paleozoic era The interval of geologic time, from 541 million to 252 million years ago, during which fungi, land plants, and most animal lineages first appeared and diversified. Began with the Cambrian explosion and ended with the extinction of almost all multicellular life-forms at the end of the Permian period.

pancreas A large gland in vertebrates that has both exocrine and endocrine functions. Secretes digestive enzymes into a duct connected to the intestine and secretes several hormones (notably insulin and glucagon) into the bloodstream.

pancreatic amylase An enzyme produced by the pancreas that digests carbohydrates by catalyzing hydrolysis of the glycosidic linkages between glucose residues.

pancreatic lipase An enzyme produced by the pancreas that digests fats, releasing monoglycerides and fatty acids.

pandemic The spread of an infectious disease in a short time over a wide geographic area and often affecting a high proportion of a population. Compare with **epidemic**.

paracrine Relating to a chemical signal that is released by a cell and affects neighboring cells.

paraphyletic group A group that includes an ancestral population and *some* but not all of its descendants. Compare with **monophyletic group**.

parapodia (singular: parapodium) Appendages found in some annelids from which bristle-like structures (chaetae) extend.

parasite An organism that lives on a host species (ectoparasite) or in a host species (endoparasite) and that damages its host.

parasitism (adjective: parasitic) A relationship between two organisms that is beneficial to one organism (the parasite) and detrimental to, but usually not fatal, to the other (the host). Parasites are usually small relative to the host and consume relatively small amounts of tissue or nutrients. Compare with **commensalism** and **mutualism**.

parasitoid An organism that is free-living as an adult, but parasitic as a larva, and often kills the host. Most parasitoids are insects that lay eggs in the bodies of other insects.

parasitoidism A relationship between two organisms where one organism (the parasitoid) lays its eggs in another organism (the host) as a food source for its developing larvae.

parasympathetic nervous system The part of the autonomic nervous system that triggers responses for conserving or restoring energy, such as reduced heart rate and stimulated digestion. Compare with **sympathetic nervous system**.

parenchyma Can refer to tissue or cell type. In plants, a general type of cell with a relatively thin primary cell wall. These cells, found in leaves, the centers of stems and roots, and fruits, are involved in photosynthesis, storage, and transport. Compare with **collenchyma** and **sclerenchyma**.

parental care Any action by which an animal expends energy or assumes risks to benefit its offspring (e.g., building a nest, feeding and defending young).

parental generation The adults used in the first experimental cross of a breeding experiment.

parental strand A strand of preexisting DNA that is used as a template during DNA synthesis.

parietal cell A cell in the stomach lining that secretes hydrochloric acid.

parietal lobe In the vertebrate brain, one of the four lobes of the cerebrum. Involved in integrating sensory and motor functions.

parsimony The logical principle that the most likely explanation of a phenomenon is the most economical or simplest. When applied to comparison of alternative phylogenetic trees, it suggests that the one requiring the fewest character changes is most likely.

parthenogenesis A form of asexual reproduction in which offspring develop from unfertilized eggs.

partial pressure The pressure of one particular gas in a mixture of gases; the contribution of that gas to the overall pressure.

particulate inheritance The concept that inheritance is based on genes that do not blend together in offspring but instead remain separate or particle-like.

pascal (Pa) A unit of pressure (force per unit area).

passive transport Diffusion of a substance across a membrane. When this event occurs with the assistance of membrane proteins, it is called *facilitated diffusion*.

patch clamping A technique for studying the electrical currents that flow through individual ion channels by applying the open tip of a microelectrode to a tiny patch of membrane.

paternal chromosome A chromosome inherited from the father.

pathogen (adjective: pathogenic) Any entity capable of causing disease, such as a microbe, virus, or prion.

pattern formation The series of events that determines the spatial organization of an entire embryo or parts of an embryo by setting the major body axes, for example, or setting up patterns in smaller groups of cells early in development.

pattern-recognition receptor On leukocytes, one of a class of membrane proteins, including Toll-like receptors, that bind to molecules commonly associated with foreign cells and viruses and signal innate immune responses against broad types of pathogens.

pectin A gelatinous polysaccharide found in the primary cell walls of plant cells. Attracts and holds water, forming a gel that resists compression forces and helps keep the cell wall moist.

pedigree A family tree of parents and offspring, showing inheritance of particular traits of interest.

pedipalps A pair of appendages found next to the claw-like chelicerae of certain arthropods called chelicerates (spiders, mites, and relatives); used to manipulate food, transfer sperm, or other functions.

penis The copulatory organ of male mammals, used to insert sperm into a female.

pentose A monosaccharide (simple sugar) containing five carbon atoms.

PEP carboxylase An enzyme that catalyzes addition of CO_2 to phosphoenolpyruvate, a three-carbon compound, forming a four-carbon organic acid. See also **C_4 pathway** and **crassulacean acid metabolism (CAM)**.

pepsin A protein-digesting enzyme secreted in inactive form (as pepsinogen) by chief cells in the stomach lining.

peptide See **oligopeptide**.

peptide bond The covalent bond formed by a condensation reaction between two amino acids.

peptidoglycan A complex structural polysaccharide found in bacterial cell walls.

per capita rate of increase (r) Also called instantaneous rate of increase. The difference between the birth rate per individual and the death rate per individual. Compare with **intrinsic rate of increase** and **finite rate of increase**.

perennial Describing a plant whose life cycle normally lasts for more than one year. Compare with **annual**.

perfect flower A flower that contains both male parts (stamens) and female parts (carpels). Compare with **imperfect flower**.

perforation In plants, a small hole in the primary and secondary cell walls of vessel elements that allows passage of water.

pericarp The part of a fruit, formed from the ovary wall, that surrounds the seeds and protects them. Corresponds to the flesh of most edible fruits and the hard shells of most nuts.

pericycle In plant roots, a layer of cells just inside the endodermis that give rise to lateral roots.

peripheral membrane protein Any membrane protein that does not span the entire lipid bilayer but instead binds to only one side of the bilayer. Compare with **integral membrane protein**.

peripheral nervous system (PNS) All the components of a nervous system that are outside the central nervous system. In vertebrates, includes the somatic nervous system and autonomic nervous system.

peristalsis Rhythmic waves of muscular contraction. In the digestive tract, pushes food along. In animals with hydrostatic skeletons, enables crawling.

permeability The tendency of a structure, such as a membrane, to allow a given substance to diffuse across it.

peroxisome An organelle found in most eukaryotic cells that contains enzymes for oxidizing fatty acids and other compounds, including many toxins, rendering them harmless. See **glyoxysome**.

petal Any of the leaflike organs arranged around the reproductive organs of a flower. Often the color and scent of petals attract pollinators.

petiole The stalk of a leaf.

pH A measure of the concentration of protons in a solution and thus of how acidic or basic the solution is. Defined as the negative of the base 10 logarithm of the proton concentration: $pH = -log[H^+]$.

phagocytosis Uptake by a cell of small particles or cells by invagination and pinching off of the plasma membrane to form small, membrane-bound vesicles; one type of **endocytosis**.

pharyngeal slits or pouches A set of parallel openings from the throat to the outside that function in feeding and/or gas exchange, or in vertebrate embryos, a set of throat pouches that are homologous to slits in other chordates. A diagnostic trait of chordates.

pharyngeal jaw A secondary jaw in the back of the throat; found in some fishes, it aids in food processing. Derived from modified gill arches.

phenology The timing of events during the year, in environments where seasonal changes occur.

phenotype The detectable traits of an individual. Compare with **genotype**.

phenotypic plasticity Within-species variation in phenotype that is due to differences in environmental conditions. Occurs more commonly in plants than animals.

pheophytin The molecule in photosystem II that accepts excited electrons from the reaction center chlorophyll and passes them to an electron transport chain.

pheromone A chemical signal, released by an individual into the external environment, that can trigger changes in the behavior or physiology or both of another member of the same species.

phloem A plant vascular tissue that conducts sugars between roots and shoots; contains sieve-tube elements and companion cells. Primary phloem develops from the procambium of apical meristems; secondary phloem, from the vascular cambium. Compare with **xylem**.

phosphatase An enzyme that removes phosphate groups from proteins or other molecules. Phosphatases often function in the inactivation of signaling pathways that involve the phosphorylation and activation of proteins.

phosphodiester linkage Chemical linkage between adjacent nucleotide residues in DNA and RNA. Forms when the phosphate group of one nucleotide condenses with the hydroxyl group on the sugar of another nucleotide. Also known as *phosphodiester bond*.

phosphofructokinase The enzyme that catalyzes synthesis of fructose-1,6-bisphosphate from fructose-6-phosphate, a key reaction in glycolysis (reaction 3). Also called *6-phosphofructokinase*.

phospholipid A class of lipid having a hydrophilic head (including a phosphate group) and a hydrophobic tail (consisting of two hydrocarbon chains). Major components of the plasma membrane and organelle membranes.

phosphorus cycle, global The movement of phosphorus among terrestrial and aquatic ecosystems.

phosphorylase An enzyme that breaks down glycogen by catalyzing hydrolysis of the α-glycosidic linkages between the glucose residues.

phosphorylation (verb: phosphorylate) The addition of a phosphate group to a molecule.

phosphorylation cascade A series of enzyme-catalyzed phosphorylation reactions commonly used in signal transduction pathways to amplify and convey a signal inward from the plasma membrane.

photic zone In an aquatic habitat, water that is shallow enough to receive some sunlight (whether or not it is enough to support photosynthesis). Compare with **aphotic zone**.

photon A discrete packet of light energy; a particle of light.

photoperiod The amount of time per day (usually in hours) that an organism is exposed to light.

photoperiodism Any response by an organism to the relative lengths of day and night (i.e., photoperiod).

photophosphorylation Production of ATP molecules by ATP synthase using the proton-motive force generated either (1) as light-excited electrons flow through an electron transport chain during photosynthesis, or (2) as rhodopsin-like molecules in some bacteria or archaea absorb light to pump protons across their plasma membranes to create a chemiosmotic gradient.

photoreception The detection of light.

photoreceptor A molecule, a cell, or an organ that is specialized to detect light.

photorespiration A series of light-driven chemical reactions that "undoes" photosynthesis by consuming O_2 and releasing CO_2. Usually occurs when there are high O_2 and low CO_2 concentrations inside plant cells, which occurs in land plants when stomata must be kept closed to prevent dehydration.

photoreversibility A change in conformation that occurs in certain plant pigments when they are exposed to the particular wavelengths of light that they absorb; triggers responses by the plant.

photosynthesis The complex biological process that converts light energy to chemical energy stored in the carbohydrate G3P. Occurs in most plants, algae, and some bacteria.

photosystem One of two types of units, consisting of a central reaction center surrounded by antenna complexes, that is responsible for the light-capturing reactions of photosynthesis.

photosystem I Photosystem that contains antenna complexes and a reaction center with a pair of P700 chlorophyll molecules. Absorbed light energy is used to reduce $NADP^+$ to NADPH in noncyclic electron flow or ATP in cyclic electron flow.

photosystem II Photosystem that contains antenna complexes and a reaction center with a pair of P680 chlorophyll molecules. Absorbed light energy is used to reduce electron carriers in an electron transport chain that produces a proton-motive force for the synthesis of ATP. Oxygen is a by-product when water is split to obtain electrons.

phototroph An organism (most plants, algae, and some bacteria and archaea) that produces ATP through photophosphorylation.

phototropins A class of plant photoreceptors that detect blue light and initiate various responses.

phototropism Growth or movement of an organism in a particular direction in response to light.

phylogenetic species concept The definition of a species as the smallest monophyletic group in a phylogenetic tree. Compare with **biological species concept** and **morphospecies concept**.

phylogenetic tree A branching diagram that depicts the evolutionary relationships among species or other taxa.

phylogeny The evolutionary history of a group of organisms.

phylum (plural: phyla) In Linnaeus' system, a taxonomic category above the class level and below the kingdom level. In plants, sometimes called a *division*.

physical map A map of a chromosome that shows the number of base pairs between various genetic markers and genes. Compare with **genetic map**.

physiology How an organism's body functions.

phytochelatins Enzymatically synthesized peptides that bind to and prevent excess metal ions from acting as toxins.

phytochrome A specialized plant photoreceptor that exists in two shapes depending on the ratio of red to far-red light and is involved in the timing of certain physiological processes, such as flowering, stem elongation, and germination.

picoplankton Plankton cells that are between 0.2 and 2.0 microns in diameter.

pigment Any molecule that absorbs certain wavelengths of visible light and reflects or transmits other wavelengths.

piloting A type of navigation in which animals use familiar landmarks to find their way.

pineal gland An endocrine gland, located in the brain, that secretes the hormone melatonin.

pioneering species Those species that appear first in recently disturbed areas.

pit In plants, a small hole in the secondary cell walls of tracheids and vessel elements that allows passage of water.

pitch The sensation produced by a particular frequency of sound. Low frequencies are perceived as low pitches; high frequencies, as high pitches.

pith In the shoot systems of plants, ground tissue located to the inside of the vascular bundles. Roots of some plants also have a pith.

pituitary gland A small gland located directly under the brain and physically and functionally connected to the hypothalamus. Produces and secretes an array of hormones that affect many other glands and organs.

placenta A structure that forms in the pregnant uterus from maternal and embryonic tissues. Delivers oxygen to the embryo/fetus, exchanges nutrients and wastes between the mother and the embryo/fetus, anchors the embryo/fetus to the uterine wall, and produces some hormones. Occurs in most mammals and in a few other vertebrates.

placental mammals See **eutherians**.

plankton Drifting small or microscopic organisms that serve as a food source in aquatic environments (includes animals, plants, protists, archaea, and bacteria).

plant body An entire plant, generally consisting of the root and shoot systems.

Plantae The monophyletic group that includes red, green, and glaucophyte algae, as well as land plants.

plasma The non-cellular portion of blood.

plasma cell An activated B cell that produces large numbers of antibodies against a specific antigen. Also called *effector B cell*.

plasma membrane A membrane that surrounds a cell, separating it from the external environment and selectively regulating passage of molecules and ions into and out of the cell. Also called *cell membrane*.

plasmid A small, usually circular, supercoiled DNA molecule independent of the cell's main chromosome(s) in prokaryotes and some eukaryotes.

plasmodesmata (singular: plasmodesma) Physical connections between two plant cells, consisting of membrane-lined gaps in the cell walls through which the cells' plasma membranes, cytoplasm, and smooth ER can connect directly. Functionally similar to gap junctions in animal cells.

plasmogamy Fusion of the cytoplasm of two individuals. Occurs in many fungi.

plastocyanin (PC) A small protein that shuttles electrons originating from photosystem II to the reaction center of photosystem I during photosynthesis.

plastoquinone (PQ) A nonprotein electron carrier in the chloroplast electron transport chain. Receives excited electrons from photosystem II (noncyclic) or photosystem I (cyclic) and passes them through an electron transport chain. Also transports protons from the stroma to the thylakoid lumen, generating a proton-motive force.

platelet A small, membrane-bound cell fragment in vertebrate blood that functions in blood clotting. Derived from large cells in the bone marrow.

Platyhelminthes See **flatworms**.

pleiotropy (adjective: pleiotropic) The ability of a single gene to affect more than one trait.

ploidy The number of complete chromosome sets present in a cell. *Haploid* refers to a ploidy of 1; *diploid*, a ploidy of 2; *triploid*, a ploidy of 3; and *tetraploid*, a ploidy of 4.

poikilotherm An animal whose body temperature varies with the environmental temperature. Compare with **homeotherm**.

point mutation A mutation that results in a change in or an insertion or deletion of a single base pair in DNA. Compare with **chromosome-level mutation** and **lateral gene transfer**.

polar (1) Asymmetrical or unidirectional. (2) Carrying a partial positive charge on one side of a molecule and a partial negative charge on the other. Polar molecules are generally hydrophilic.

polar body Any of the tiny, nonfunctional cells that result from the unequal distribution of cytoplasm during meiosis of a primary oocyte.

polar covalent bond A covalent bond in which electrons are shared unequally between atoms differing in electronegativity, resulting in the more electronegative atom having a partial negative charge and the other atom having a partial positive charge. Compare with **nonpolar covalent bond**.

polar microtubules A microtubule that arises from one of the spindle poles in mitosis or meiosis and overlaps in the middle of the spindle apparatus with a similar microtubule from the opposite spindle pole.

polar nuclei In flowering plants, the nuclei in the female gametophyte that fuse with one sperm nucleus to produce the endosperm. Most species have two.

pollen grain In seed plants, a male gametophyte enclosed within a protective coat of sporopollenin.

pollen tube In flowering plants, a structure that grows out of a pollen grain after it reaches the stigma. The tube extends down the style, and two sperm cells travel through it to the ovule.

pollination The process by which pollen reaches the carpel of a flower: (1) in flowering plants, it is transferred from anther to stigma; (2) in gymnosperms, it reaches the ovule directly.

pollination syndrome Suites of flower characters that are associated with certain types of pollinators and that have evolved through natural selection imposed by the interaction between flowers and pollinators.

poly(A) signal In eukaryotes, a short sequence of nucleotides near the 3′ end of pre-mRNAs that signals cleavage of the RNA and addition of the poly(A) tail.

poly(A) tail In eukaryotes, a sequence of about 100–250 adenine nucleotides added to the 3′ end of newly transcribed messenger RNA molecules.

polygenic inheritance Having many genes influence one trait.

polymer Any large molecule composed of small repeating units (monomers) bonded together. The main biological polymers are proteins, nucleic acids, and polysaccharides.

polymerase chain reaction (PCR) A laboratory technique for rapidly generating millions of identical copies of a specific stretch of DNA. Works by multiple rounds of DNA replication, starting from primers designed by an investigator to amplify particular DNA sequences.

polymerization (verb: polymerize) The process by which many identical or similar small molecules (monomers) are covalently bonded to form a large molecule (polymer).

polymorphic species A species that has two or more distinct phenotypes in the same interbreeding population at the same time.

polymorphic trait Having more than one different form of an allele or trait that appears commonly in a population.

polymorphism (adjective: polymorphic) (1) The occurrence of more than one common allele at a genetic locus in a population. (2) The occurrence of more than one common phenotype of a trait in a population.

polyp The immotile (sessile) stage in the life cycle of some cnidarians (e.g., sea anemones). Compare with **medusa**.

polypeptide A chain typically consisting of 50 or more amino acids linked together by peptide bonds. Compare with **oligopeptide** and **protein**.

polyphyletic group An unnatural group based on convergent (homoplastic) characteristics that are not present in a common ancestor. Compare with **monophyletic group**.

polyploidy (adjective: polyploid) The state of having more than two full sets of chromosomes, either from the same species (autopolyploidy) or from different species (allopolyploidy).

polyribosome A messenger RNA molecule that is being translated by two or more attached ribosomes.

polysaccharide A linear or branched carbohydrate chain consisting of many (> 50) monosaccharides joined by glycosidic linkages. Compare with **monosaccharide** and **oligosaccharide**.

polytomy A node in a phylogenetic tree that depicts an ancestral branch dividing into three or more descendant branches; usually indicates that insufficient data were available to resolve which taxa are more closely related.

population A group of individuals of the same species living in the same geographic area at the same time.

population density The number of individuals of a population per unit area.

population dynamics Changes in the size and other characteristics of populations through time and space.

population ecology The study of how and why the number of individuals in a population changes over time and space.

population thinking A way of thinking that emphasizes the importance of variation among individuals in a population; the opposite of typological thinking, which ignores variation or considers it unimportant.

positive control A type of regulation that works by speeding up a process. In the context of gene transcription, the action of a regulatory protein to trigger expression by binding to DNA in or near the gene.

positive feedback A physiological mechanism in which a change in some variable stimulates a response that increases the change. Relatively rare in organisms but important in generation of an action potential. Compare with **negative feedback**.

positive pressure ventilation Ventilation of the lungs by using increased pressure in the mouth to "push" air into the lungs. Compare with **negative pressure ventilation**.

positive-sense Describing a single strand of RNA that contains the same sequences as the mRNA required to produce viral proteins. Compare with **ambisense** and **negative-sense**.

posterior Toward an animal's tail and away from its head. The opposite of anterior.

posterior pituitary The part of the pituitary gland that contains the ends of hypothalamic neurosecretory cells and from which oxytocin and antidiuretic hormone are secreted. Compare with **anterior pituitary**.

postsynaptic cell A cell that receives signals, usually via neurotransmitters, from a neuron at a synapse. Compare with **presynaptic neuron**.

post-translational control Regulation of gene expression by modification of proteins (e.g., addition of a phosphate group or sugar residues) after translation.

postzygotic isolation Reproductive isolation resulting from mechanisms that operate after mating of individuals of two different species occurs. The most common mechanisms are the death of hybrid embryos or reduced fitness of hybrids.

potential energy Energy stored in matter as a result of its position or the position of electrons that form chemical bonds between atoms. Compare with **kinetic energy**.

prebiotic soup model Model of chemical evolution whereby small molecules present in Earth's early atmosphere reacted and condensed into the early oceans, where they combined to form larger organic molecules.

Precambrian The interval between the formation of the Earth, about 4.6 billion years ago, and the appearance of most animal groups about 541 million years ago. Unicellular organisms were dominant for most of this era, and oxygen was virtually absent for the first 2 billion years.

predation The killing and eating of one organism (the prey) by another (the predator).

predator Any organism that kills another organism for food.

prediction A measurable or observable result of an experiment based on a particular hypothesis. A correct prediction provides support for the hypothesis being tested.

pre-mRNA In eukaryotes, the primary transcript of protein-coding genes. Pre-mRNA is processed to form mRNA.

pressure-flow hypothesis The hypothesis that sugar movement through phloem tissue is due to differences in the turgor pressure of phloem sap.

pressure potential (Ψ_P) A component of the potential energy of water caused by physical pressures on a solution. It can be positive or negative. Compare with **solute potential (Ψ_S)**.

presynaptic neuron A neuron that transmits signals, usually by releasing neurotransmitters, to another neuron or to a muscle cell or gland cell at a synapse.

prey An organism that is consumed by another organism.

prezygotic isolation Reproductive isolation resulting from any one of several mechanisms that prevent individuals of two different species from mating.

primary cell wall The outermost layer of a plant cell wall, made of cellulose fibers and gelatinous polysaccharides, that defines the shape of the cell and withstands the turgor pressure of the plasma membrane.

primary consumer An herbivore; an organism that eats plants, algae, or other primary producers. Compare with **secondary consumer**.

primary decomposer A decomposer (detritivore) that consumes detritus from plants.

primary growth In plants, an increase in the length of stems and roots due to the activity of apical meristems. Compare with **secondary growth**.

primary immune response An adaptive immune response to a pathogen that the immune system has not encountered before. Compare with **secondary immune response**.

primary meristem In plants, three types of partially differentiated cells that are produced by apical meristems, including protoderm, ground meristem, and procambium. Compare with **apical meristem** and **cambium**.

primary oocyte Any of the large diploid cells in an ovarian follicle that can initiate meiosis to produce a haploid secondary oocyte and a polar body.

primary plant body All of the cells and tissues derived from apical meristems and primary meristems.

primary producer Any organism that creates its own food by photosynthesis or from reduced inorganic compounds and that is a food source for other species in its ecosystem. Also called *autotroph*.

primary spermatocyte Any of the diploid cells in a testis that can initiate meiosis I to produce two secondary spermatocytes.

primary structure The sequence of amino acid residues in a protein; also the sequence of nucleotides in a nucleic acid. Compare with **secondary, tertiary,** and **quaternary structure**.

primary succession The gradual colonization of a habitat of bare rock or gravel, usually after an environmental disturbance that removes all soil and previous organisms. Compare with **secondary succession**.

primary transcript In eukaryotes, a newly transcribed RNA molecule that has not yet been processed to a mature RNA. Called *pre-mRNA* when the final product is a protein.

primase An enzyme that synthesizes a short stretch of RNA to use as a primer during DNA replication.

primates The lineage of mammals that includes prosimians (lemurs, lorises, etc.), monkeys, and great apes (including humans).

primer A short, single-stranded RNA molecule that base-pairs with a DNA template strand and is used as a starting point for DNA synthesis by DNA polymerase.

prion An infectious particle that consists entirely of protein. Prion proteins adopt two differently folded shapes: a normally folded shape and an infectious, often disease-causing shape. The infectious version can bind normally folded prion proteins and cause them to adopt the infectious shape. Also called *proteinaceous infectious particles*.

procambium A primary meristem tissue that gives rise to the vascular tissue.

product Any of the final materials formed in a chemical reaction.

progesterone A steroid hormone produced and secreted by the corpus luteum in the ovaries after ovulation and by the placenta during gestation; protects the uterine lining.

programmed cell death Regulated cell death that is used in development, tissue maintainance, and destruction of infected cells. Can occur in different ways; apoptosis is the best known.

prokaryote (adjective: prokaryotic) A member of the domain Bacteria or Archaea; a unicellular organism lacking a nucleus and containing relatively few organelles or cytoskeletal components. Compare with **eukaryote**.

prolactin A peptide hormone, produced and secreted by the anterior pituitary, that promotes milk production in female mammals and has a variety of effects on parental behavior and seasonal reproduction in other vertebrates.

prometaphase A stage in mitosis or meiosis during which the nuclear envelope breaks down and microtubules attach to kinetochores.

promoter A short nucleotide sequence in DNA that binds a sigma factor (in bacteria) or basal transcription factors (in eukaryotes) to enable RNA polymerase to begin transcription. In bacteria, several contiguous genes are often transcribed from a single promoter. In eukaryotes, each gene generally has its own promoter.

promoter-proximal element In eukaryotic DNA, a regulatory sequence that is close to a promoter and can bind regulatory transcription factors.

proofreading A mechanism for error correction during DNA synthesis in which a DNA polymerase recognizes and removes a wrong deoxyribonucleotide added during DNA replication and then continues synthesis.

prophase The first stage in mitosis or meiosis, during which chromosomes condense and the spindle apparatus forms. Synapsis and crossing over occur during prophase of meiosis I.

prosimians One of the two major lineages of primates, a paraphyletic group including lemurs, lorises, pottos, and tarsiers. Compare with **anthropoids**.

prostate gland A gland in male mammals that surrounds the base of the urethra and secretes a fluid that is a component of semen.

prosthetic group A non-amino acid atom or molecule that is permanently attached to an enzyme or other protein and is required for its function.

protease An enzyme that can break up proteins by cleaving the peptide bonds between amino acid residues.

proteasome A macromolecular machine that destroys proteins that have been marked by the addition of ubiquitin.

protein A macromolecule consisting of one or more polypeptide chains composed of 50 or more amino acids linked together. Each protein has a unique sequence of amino acids and generally possesses a characteristic three-dimensional shape.

protein kinase An enzyme that catalyzes the addition of a phosphate group to another protein, typically activating or inactivating the substrate protein.

proteinase inhibitors Defense compounds, produced by plants, that induce illness in herbivores by inhibiting digestive enzymes.

proteoglycan A type of highly glycosylated protein found in the extracellular matrix of animal cells; it attracts and holds water, forming a gel that resists compression forces.

proteome The complete set of proteins produced by a particular cell type.

proteomics The systematic study of the full set of proteins (the proteome) in a cell or tissue, including their interactions, localization, functions, regulation, and other features.

protist Any eukaryote that is not a land plant, animal, or fungus. Protists are a diverse paraphyletic group. Most are unicellular, but some are multicellular or form aggregations called colonies.

protocell A hypothetical pre-cell structure consisting of a membrane compartment that encloses replicating macromolecules, such as ribozymes.

protoderm The exterior layer of a young plant embryo that gives rise to the dermal tissue, or epidermis.

proton pump A membrane protein that can hydrolyze ATP to power active transport of protons (H^+ ions) across a membrane against an electrochemical gradient. Also called H^+-ATPase.

proton-motive force The combined effect of a proton gradient and an electric potential gradient across a membrane, which can drive protons across the membrane. Used by prokaryotes, mitochondria, and chloroplasts to power ATP synthesis or other energy-demanding processes via chemiosmosis.

proto-oncogene Any gene that encourages cell division in a regulated manner, typically by triggering specific phases in the cell cycle. Mutation may convert it into an oncogene. See **oncogene**.

protostomes A major lineage of bilaterian animals that share a pattern of embryological development, including formation of the mouth earlier than the anus, and formation of the coelom by splitting of a block of mesoderm. Includes arthropods, mollusks, and annelids. Compare with **deuterostomes**.

proximal tubule In the vertebrate kidney, the convoluted portion of a nephron into which filtrate moves from Bowman's capsule. Involved in the largely unregulated reabsorption of electrolytes, nutrients, and water. Compare with **distal tubule**.

proximate causation In biology, the immediate, mechanistic cause of a phenomenon (how it happens), as opposed to why it evolved. Also called *proximate explanation*. Compare with **ultimate causation**.

pseudocoelomate An animal that has a coelom that is only partially lined with mesoderm. Compare with **acoelomate** and **coelomate**.

pseudogene A DNA sequence that closely resembles a functional gene but is not transcribed. Thought to have arisen by duplication of the functional gene followed by inactivation due to a mutation.

pseudopodium (plural: pseudopodia) A temporary bulge-like extension of certain protist cells used in cell crawling and ingestion of food.

puberty The various physical and emotional changes that an immature human undergoes in reaching reproductive maturity. Also the period when such changes occur.

pulmonary artery A short, thick-walled artery that carries oxygen-poor blood from the heart to the lungs.

pulmonary circuit The part of the circulatory system that carries oxygen-poor blood from the heart to the lungs and returns oxygen-rich blood to the heart. It is separate from the rest of the circulatory system (the systemic circuit) in mammals and birds.

pulmonary vein A short, thin-walled vein that carries oxygen-rich blood from the lungs to the heart. Humans have four such veins.

pulse–chase experiment A type of experiment in which a population of cells or molecules at a particular moment in time is marked by means of a labeled molecule (pulse) and then their fate is followed over time (chase).

pump Any membrane protein that uses energy (e.g., ATP) to change shape and power the active transport of a specific ion or molecule across a membrane in a single direction, often against its gradient. See **proton pump**.

pupa (plural: pupae) In insects undergoing complete (holometabolous) metamorphosis, the life stage during which the juvenile form metamorphoses into the adult form.

pupil The hole in the center of the iris through which light enters a vertebrate or cephalopod eye.

pure line In genetics, a strain that produces offspring identical to the parents when self-fertilized or mated within the strain. Pure lines are homozygous for the gene under study.

purifying selection Selection that lowers the frequency of or even eliminates deleterious alleles.

purine A class of double-ringed nitrogenous bases (guanine, adenine) found in nucleotides. Compare with **pyrimidine**.

pyrimidine A class of single-ringed nitrogenous bases (cytosine, uracil, thymine) found in nucleotides. Compare with **purine**.

pyruvate dehydrogenase A large enzyme complex, located in the mitochondrial matrix of eukaryotes and the cytosol of prokaryotes, that is responsible for converting pyruvate to acetyl CoA during cellular respiration.

quantitative trait A trait that exhibits continuous phenotypic variation (as in human height) rather than the clearly separated phenotypes of a discrete trait.

quaternary structure In proteins, the overall three-dimensional shape formed from the combination of two or more polypeptide chains (subunits); determined by the number, relative positions, and interactions of the subunits. In single-stranded nucleic acids, the hydrogen bonding between two or more distinct strands will form this level of structure through hydrophobic interactions between complementary bases. Compare with **primary, secondary,** and **tertiary structures**.

quorum sensing A type of cell signaling in unicellular organisms in which cells sense population density by detecting signaling molecules secreted by other cells. Cell activity often changes dramatically when the population reaches a threshold size, or quorum.

radial axis An axis extending from the interior of a plant organ to the exterior.

radial symmetry An animal body pattern that has at least two planes of symmetry. Typically, the body is in the form of a cylinder or disk, and the body parts radiate from a central hub. Compare with **bilateral symmetry**.

radiation Transfer of heat between two bodies that are not in direct physical contact. More generally, the emission of electromagnetic energy of any wavelength.

radicle The root of a plant embryo.

radioactive isotope A version of an element that has an unstable nucleus, which will release radiation energy as it decays to a more stable form. Decay often results in the radioisotope losing protons and becoming a different element.

radioimmunoassay A competitive binding assay in which the quantity of hormone in a sample can be estimated. Uses radioactively labeled hormones that compete with the hormone in the sample to bind with an antibody.

radula A rasping feeding appendage in mollusks such as gastropods (snails, slugs).

rain shadow The dry region on the side of a mountain range away from the prevailing wind.

range The geographic distribution of a species.

Ras A small G protein that is often activated by enzyme-linked cell-surface receptors, including receptor tyrosine kinases. Activated Ras then initiates a phosphorylation cascade, culminating in a cell response.

ray In plant shoot systems with secondary growth, a lateral row of parenchyma cells produced by vascular cambium. Transports water and nutrients laterally across the stem.

ray-finned fishes Members of the Actinopterygii, a diverse group of fishes with fins supported by bony rods arranged in a ray pattern.

Rb protein A tumor suppressor protein that helps regulate progression of a cell from G_1 phase to S phase of the cell cycle. Defects in Rb protein are found in many types of cancer.

reactant Any of the starting materials in a chemical reaction.

reaction center Centrally located component of a photosystem containing proteins and a pair of specialized chlorophyll molecules. It is surrounded by antenna complexes that transmit resonance energy to excite the reaction center pigments.

reading frame A series of adjacent non-overlapping, three-base-long sequences (potential codons) in DNA or RNA. The reading frame for a polypeptide is set by the start codon.

realized niche The portion of the fundamental niche that a species actually occupies given limiting factors such as competition with other species. Compare with **fundamental niche**.

receptor-mediated endocytosis Uptake by a cell of certain extracellular macromolecules, bound to specific receptors in the plasma membrane, by pinching off the membrane to form small membrane-bound vesicles.

receptor tyrosine kinase (RTK) Any of a class of enzyme-linked cell-surface receptors that phosphory-late themselves after binding a signaling molecule. The activated, phosphorylated receptor then triggers a signal transduction pathway inside the cell.

recessive Referring to an allele whose phenotypic effect is observed only in homozygous individuals. Compare with **dominant**.

reciprocal altruism Altruistic behavior that is exchanged between a pair of individuals at different times (i.e., sometimes individual A helps individual B, and sometimes B helps A).

reciprocal cross A cross in which the mother's and father's phenotypes are the reverse of those examined in a previous cross.

recombinant Possessing a new combination of alleles. May refer to a single DNA molecule, a chromosome, or an entire organism.

recombinant DNA technology A variety of techniques for isolating specific DNA fragments and linking them to different regions of DNA or adding them to a different host organism.

rectal gland A salt-excreting gland in the digestive system of sharks, skates, and rays.

rectum The most posterior portion of the digestive tract, where feces are held until they are expelled.

red blood cell A hemoglobin-containing cell that circulates in the blood and delivers oxygen from the lungs to the tissues.

redox potential A measure of the ability of a molecule to accept electrons, or become reduced, in a reduction-oxidation reaction. It is measured in volts, and larger values represent greater affinity for electrons. Also called *reduction potential*.

redox reaction Any chemical reaction that involves either the complete transfer of one or more electrons from one reactant to another, or a reciprocal shift in the position of shared electrons within one or more of the covalent bonds of two reactants. Also called *reduction–oxidation reaction*.

reduction The gain of electrons by an atom or molecule during a redox reaction, either by acceptance of an electron from another atom or molecule, or by the shared electrons in covalent bonds moving closer to the atomic nucleus.

reduction–oxidation reaction See **redox reaction**.

reflex An involuntary response to an environmental stimulus.

refractory No longer responding to stimuli that previously elicited a response. An example is the tendency of voltage-gated sodium channels to be less likely to reopen immediately after they have closed.

regulate To actively maintain homeostasis of internal physiological conditions. Compare with **conform**.

regulatory sequence Any segment of DNA or RNA that is involved in controlling the expression of a specific gene by binding a regulatory transcription factor protein or other protein that regulates gene expression.

regulatory transcription factor General term for a protein that binds to DNA regulatory sequences (eukaryotic enhancers, silencers, and promoter-proximal elements), but not to the promoter itself, leading to an increase or decrease in transcription of specific genes. Sometimes simply called a *transcription factor*. Compare with **basal transcription factor**.

regulon A large set of genes distributed in bacterial DNA that are controlled by a single type of regulatory molecule. Regulon genes are transcribed in response to environmental cues and allow cells to respond to changing environments.

reinforcement In evolutionary biology, the natural selection for traits that prevent interbreeding between recently diverged species.

release factor Any of a class of proteins that trigger termination of translation when a ribosome reaches a stop codon.

renal corpuscle In the vertebrate kidney, the ball-like structure at the beginning of a nephron, consisting of a glomerulus and the surrounding Bowman's capsule. Acts as a filtration device.

replacement rate The number of offspring each female must produce over her entire life to "replace" herself and her mate, resulting in zero population growth. The actual number is slightly more than two because some offspring die before reproducing.

replica plating A method of identifying bacterial colonies that have certain mutations by transferring cells from each colony on a master plate to a second (replica) plate and observing their growth when exposed to different conditions.

replication fork The Y-shaped site at which a double-stranded molecule of DNA is separated into two single strands for replication.

replicative growth The process by which cells reproduce or viruses produce new virions.

replisome The macromolecular machine that copies DNA; includes DNA polymerase, helicase, primase, and other enzymes.

repolarization Return to a resting potential after a membrane potential has changed; a normal phase in an action potential.

repressor (1) In bacteria, a protein that binds to an operator sequence in DNA to prevent transcription when an inducer is not present and that comes off DNA to allow transcription when an inducer binds to the repressor protein. (2) In eukaryotes, a protein that binds to a silencer sequence in DNA to prevent or reduce gene transcription.

reproductive development The phase of plant development that involves development of the flower and reproductive cells. Follows vegetative development and

occurs when a shoot apical meristem (SAM) transitions to a flower-producing meristem.

reptiles One of the two lineages of amniotes (vertebrates that produce amniotic eggs) distinguished by adaptations for life and reproduction on land. Living reptiles include turtles, snakes and lizards, crocodiles and alligators, and birds. Except for birds, all are ectotherms.

resilience, community A measure of how quickly a community recovers following a disturbance.

resistance, community A measure of the extent to which a community remains unchanged in the face of a disturbance.

resonance energy transfer Process of transferring energy from an excited donor pigment to an adjacent acceptor pigment, where another electron is excited in response.

respiratory system The collection of cells, tissues, and organs responsible for gas exchange between an animal and its environment.

resting potential The membrane potential of a cell in its resting, or normal, state.

restriction endonuclease Any of a class of bacterial enzymes that cut DNA at a specific base-pair sequence (recognition site). Also called a *restriction enzyme*.

retina A thin layer of light-sensitive cells and neurons at the back of a simple eye, such as that of cephalopods and vertebrates.

retinal A light-absorbing pigment that is linked to an opsin protein in rods and cones of the vertebrate eye.

retrovirus A virus with an RNA genome that reverse-transcribes its RNA into double-stranded DNA, which is then inserted into the host's genome as part of the virus's replicative cycle.

reverse transcriptase An enzyme that can synthesize DNA from an RNA template.

R-group Part of an amino acid's core structure that varies from a single hydrogen atom to large structures containing carbon rings. R-group variability is responsible for the variability in amino acid structure and function. Also called *side chains*.

rhizobia (singular: rhizobium) Members of the bacterial genus *Rhizobium*; nitrogen-fixing bacteria that live in root nodules of members of the pea family (legumes).

rhizoid The hairlike structure that anchors a nonvascular plant to the substrate.

rhizome A modified stem that runs horizontally underground and produces new plants at the nodes (a form of asexual reproduction). Compare with **stolon**.

rhodopsin A transmembrane complex that is instrumental in detection of light by rods of the vertebrate eye. It is composed of the transmembrane protein opsin and covalently linked to retinal, a light-absorbing pigment.

ribonucleic acid (RNA) A usually single-stranded nucleic acid composed of ribonucleotides; functions as catalytic components of ribosomes (rRNA), transporters of amino acids (tRNA), and messages of the DNA code required for protein synthesis (mRNA), among others.

ribonucleotide A nucleotide consisting of a ribose sugar, one or more phosphates, and one of four nitrogen-containing bases: adenine, guanine, cytosine, or uracil.

ribosomal RNA (rRNA) An RNA molecule that forms part of the ribosome.

ribosome A large macromolecular machine that synthesizes proteins by using the genetic information encoded in messenger RNA. Consists of two subunits, each composed of ribosomal RNA and proteins.

ribosome binding site In a bacterial mRNA molecule, the sequence just upstream of the start codon to which a ribosome binds to initiate translation. Also called the *Shine–Dalgarno sequence*.

ribozyme Any RNA molecule that can act as a catalyst to increase the rate of a chemical reaction.

ribulose bisphosphate (RuBP) A five-carbon compound that combines with CO_2 in the first step of the Calvin cycle during photosynthesis or O_2 in the first step of photorespiration.

RNA See **ribonucleic acid**.

RNA interference (RNAi) Degradation of an mRNA molecule or inhibition of its translation following its binding by a short RNA whose sequence is complementary to a portion of the mRNA.

RNA polymerase An enzyme that catalyzes the synthesis of RNA from ribonucleotides using a DNA template.

RNA processing In eukaryotes, the changes that a primary RNA transcript undergoes to become a mature RNA molecule. For pre-mRNA it includes the addition of a 5′ cap and poly(A) tail and splicing to remove introns.

RNA replicase A viral enzyme that can synthesize RNA from an RNA template. Also called an *RNA-dependent RNA polymerase*.

RNA world hypothesis Proposal that at a particular stage in the evolution of life, RNA both stored genetic information and catalyzed its own replication and that RNA emerged before DNA and proteins during chemical evolution.

rod A vertebrate photoreceptor with a rod-shaped outer portion that is particularly sensitive to dim light but does not distinguish colors. Compare with **cone**.

root apical meristem (RAM) A group of undifferentiated cells at the tip of a plant root; these cells divide to produce new cells that differentiate into mature root tissue.

root cap A small group of cells that covers and protects the root apical meristem. Senses gravity and determines the direction of root growth.

root hair A long, thin outgrowth of the epidermal cells of plant roots, providing increased surface area for absorption of water and nutrients.

root pressure Positive pressure of xylem sap in the vascular tissue of roots. Generated during the night as a result of the accumulation of ions from the soil and subsequent osmotic movement of water into the xylem.

root system The belowground part of a plant.

rough endoplasmic reticulum (rough ER) The portion of the endoplasmic reticulum that is dotted with ribosomes. Involved in synthesis of plasma membrane proteins, secreted proteins, and proteins localized to the ER, Golgi apparatus, and lysosomes. Compare with **smooth endoplasmic reticulum**.

roundworms Members of the phylum Nematoda. Distinguished by an unsegmented body with a pseudocoelom and no appendages. Roundworms belong to the ecdysozoan branch of the protostomes. Also called *nematodes*.

rubisco The enzyme that catalyzes the addition of a molecule of CO_2 (Calvin cycle) or O_2 (photorespiration) to ribulose bisphosphate. See also **carbon fixation**.

ruminant Member of a group of mammals (cattle, sheep, goats, deer, antelope, giraffe, and pronghorn) that have a four-chambered stomach specialized for digestion of plant cellulose. Ruminants regurgitate cud, a mixture of partially digested food and cellulose-digesting bacteria and protists, from the largest chamber (the rumen) for further chewing.

S phase The phase of the cell cycle during which DNA is synthesized for the replication of chromosomes.

salinity The proportion of solutes dissolved in water in natural environments, often designated in grams of solute per kilogram of water (cited as parts per thousand).

salivary amylase An enzyme produced by the salivary glands that digests starch and glycogen by catalyzing hydrolysis of the glycosidic linkages between glucose residues.

salivary gland In vertebrates, one of several glands that secrete saliva (a mixture of water, mucus-forming glycoproteins, and the enzyme salivary amylase) into the mouth.

sampling error The selection of a nonrepresentative sample from some larger population, due to chance.

saprophyte An organism that feeds primarily on dead plant material.

sapwood The younger xylem in the outer layer of wood of a stem or root, functioning primarily in water transport.

sarcomere The repeating contractile unit of a skeletal or cardiac muscle cell; the portion of a myofibril located between adjacent Z disks.

sarcoplasmic reticulum Sheets of smooth endoplasmic reticulum in a muscle cell. Stores calcium, which can be released into the cytoplasm to trigger contraction.

saturated Referring to lipids in which all the carbon-carbon bonds are single bonds. Such compounds have relatively high melting points. Compare with **unsaturated**.

scanning electron microscope (SEM) A microscope that produces surface images by reflecting electrons off a specimen coated with a layer of metal atoms. Compare with **transmission electron microscope**.

scarify To scrape, rasp, cut, or otherwise damage the coat of a seed. Necessary in some species to trigger germination.

Schwann cell A type of glial cell that wraps around axons of some neurons in the vertebrate peripheral nervous system, forming a myelin sheath that provides electrical insulation. Compare with **oligodendrocyte**.

scientific name The unique, two-part name given to each species, with a genus name followed by a species name—as in *Homo sapiens*. Scientific names are always italicized. Also known as *Latin names*.

sclereid In plants, a relatively short type of sclerenchyma cell that usually functions in protection, such as in seed coats and nutshells. Compare with **fiber**.

sclerenchyma Can refer to tissue or cell type. In plants, a cell that has a thick secondary cell wall and provides support; typically contains the tough structural polymer lignin and usually is dead at maturity. Includes fibers and sclereids. Compare with **collenchyma** and **parenchyma**.

scrotum A sac of skin that contains the testes and is suspended just outside the abdominal cavity of many male mammals.

second law of thermodynamics The principle of physics that the entropy of the universe or any closed system always increases.

second-male advantage The reproductive advantage, in some species, of the last male to mate with a female after other males have mated with her.

second messenger A nonprotein signaling molecule produced or activated inside a cell in response to stimulation at the cell surface. Commonly used to relay the message of a hormone or other extracellular signaling molecule.

secondary active transport Transport of an ion or molecule in a defined direction (often against its gradient) made possible by the transport of another ion or molecule being moved along its gradient. Also called *cotransport*.

secondary cell wall The thickened inner layer of a cell wall formed by certain plant cells as they mature and after they have stopped growing; contains lignin in water-conducting cells. Provides support or protection.

secondary consumer A carnivore; an organism that eats herbivores. Compare with **primary consumer**.

secondary growth In plants, an increase in the width of stems and roots due to the activity of a cambium. Compare with **primary growth**.

secondary immune response An adaptive immune response to a pathogen that the immune system has encountered before. Normally much faster and more efficient than the primary response, due to immunological memory. Compare with **primary immune response**.

secondary metabolites Molecules that are closely related to compounds in key synthetic pathways and that often function in defense.

secondary oocyte A cell produced by meiosis I of a primary oocyte in an ovary. If fertilized, will complete meiosis II to produce an ootid (which develops into an ovum) and a polar body.

secondary spermatocyte A cell produced by meiosis I of a primary spermatocyte in a testis. Can undergo meiosis II to produce two spermatids.

secondary structure In proteins, localized folding of a polypeptide chain into regular structures (i.e., alpha-helix and beta-pleated sheet) stabilized by hydrogen bonding between atoms of the peptide backbone. In nucleic acids, elements of structure (e.g., helices and hairpins) stabilized by hydrogen bonding and hydrophobic interactions between complementary bases. Compare with **primary, tertiary**, and **quaternary structures**.

secondary succession Gradual colonization of a habitat after an environmental disturbance (e.g., fire, windstorm, logging) that removes some or all previous organisms but leaves the soil intact. Compare with **primary succession**.

secretin A peptide hormone secreted by cells in the small intestine in response to the arrival of food from the stomach. Stimulates secretion of bicarbonate (HCO_3^-) by the pancreas.

sedimentary rock A type of rock formed by gradual accumulation of sediment, particularly sand and mud, as in riverbeds and on the ocean floor. Most fossils are found in sedimentary rocks.

seed A plant reproductive structure consisting of an embryo, associated nutritive tissue (endosperm), and an outer protective layer (seed coat). In angiosperms, develops from the fertilized ovule of a flower.

seed bank A repository where seeds, representing many different varieties of domestic crops or other species, are preserved.

seed coat A protective layer around a seed that encases both the embryo and the endosperm.

segment A well-defined, repeated region of the body along the anterior–posterior body axis.

segmentation Division of the body or a part of it into a series of similar structures; exemplified by the body segments of insects and worms and by the somites of vertebrates.

segregation, principle of The concept that each pair of hereditary elements (consisting of alleles of the same gene) separate from each other during meiosis. One of Mendel's two principles of genetics. Compare with **principle of independent assortment**.

selective adhesion The tendency of cells of one tissue type to specifically adhere to other cells of the same type.

selective permeability The property of a membrane that allows some substances to diffuse across it much more readily than other substances.

self molecule A molecule that is synthesized by an organism and is a normal part of its cells and/or body, in contrast to nonself, or foreign, molecules.

self-fertilization The fusion of two gametes produced by the same individual to form offspring. Also called *selfing*.

self-incompatible Plants that are unable to form viable seed when carpels are pollinated with pollen from the same plant.

semen The combination of sperm and accessory fluids that is released by male mammals and reptiles during ejaculation.

semiconservative replication The way DNA replicates, with each strand of an existing DNA molecule serving as a template to create a new complementary DNA strand.

seminal vesicle In male mammals, one of a pair of reproductive glands that secrete a sugar-containing fluid into semen, which provides energy for sperm movement.

senescence The genetically programmed, active process of aging.

sensor Any cell, organ, or structure with which an organism can sense some aspect of the external or internal environment. Usually functions, along with an integrator and an effector, as part of a homeostatic system.

sensory neuron A nerve cell that carries sensory signals to the central nervous system. Compare with **interneuron** and **motor neuron**.

sepal One of the protective leaflike organs enclosing a flower bud and, after blooming, the outermost portion of the flower.

septum (plural: septa) Any wall-like structure. In fungi, septa divide the filaments (hyphae) of mycelia into cell-like compartments.

serotonin A monoamine neurotransmitter; in vertebrates, involved in many brain functions, including sleep, pleasure, and mood.

serum The liquid that remains when cells and clot material are removed from clotted blood. Contains water, gases, growth factors, nutrients, and other dissolved substances. Compare with **plasma**.

sessile Permanently attached to a substrate; not capable of moving to another location.

set point A normal or target value for a regulated internal variable, such as body temperature or blood pH.

sex chromosome Chromosomes that differ in shape or in number in males and females. For example, the X and Y chromosomes of many animals. Compare with **autosome**.

sex-linked inheritance Inheritance patterns observed in genes carried on sex chromosomes. In this case, females and males have different numbers of alleles of a gene. Often creates situations in which a trait appears more often in one sex. Also called *sex-linkage*.

sexual dimorphism Any trait that differs between males and females.

sexual reproduction Any form of reproduction in which genes from two parents are combined via fusion of gametes, producing offspring that are genetically distinct from both parents. Compare with **asexual reproduction**.

sexual selection A type of natural selection that favors individuals with traits that increase their ability to obtain mates or choose good mates. Compare with **ecological selection**.

shell A hard, protective outer structure.

Shine–Dalgarno sequence See **ribosome binding site**.

shoot apical meristem (SAM) A group of undifferentiated cells at the tip of a plant stem; these cells divide to produce new cells that can differentiate into mature shoot tissues.

shoot system The aboveground part of a plant comprising stems, leaves, and flowers (in angiosperms).

short-day plant A plant that blooms in response to long nights (usually in late summer or fall in the Northern Hemisphere). Compare with **day-neutral** and **long-day plant**.

short tandem repeat (STR) Short (2–6 base pair) DNA sequence that is repeated sequentially along a chromosome. Also called *microsatellite* or *simple sequence repeat (SSR)*.

shotgun sequencing A method of sequencing genomes that is based on breaking the genome into small pieces, sequencing each piece separately, and then figuring out how the pieces are connected.

side chain See **R-group**.

sieve plate In plants, a pore-containing structure at each end of a sieve-tube element in phloem.

sieve-tube element In plants, an elongated sugar-conducting cell in phloem that lacks nuclei and has sieve plates at both ends, allowing sap to flow to adjacent cells.

sigma A bacterial protein that associates with the core RNA polymerase to allow recognition of promoters.

signal In behavioral ecology, any information-containing behavior or characteristic that has been shaped by natural selection.

signal receptor Any cellular protein that binds to a particular signaling molecule (e.g., a hormone or neurotransmitter) and triggers a response by the cell. Receptors for lipid-insoluble signals are transmembrane proteins in the plasma membrane; those for lipid-soluble signals (e.g., steroid hormones) are often located in the cytosol.

signal recognition particle (SRP) An RNA–protein complex that binds to the ER signal sequence in a polypeptide as it emerges from a ribosome and transports the ribosome–polypeptide complex to the ER membrane, where synthesis of the polypeptide is completed.

signal transduction The process by which a stimulus (e.g., a hormone, a neurotransmitter, or sensory information) outside a cell is converted to an intracellular signal required for a cellular response. Usually involves a specific sequence of molecular events called a signal transduction pathway, which may amplify the signal.

signal transduction cascade See **phosphorylation cascade**.

silencer A regulatory sequence in eukaryotic DNA to which repressor proteins can bind, inhibiting gene transcription.

silent mutation A point mutation that changes the sequence of a codon without changing the amino acid that is specified.

simple eye An eye with only one light-collecting apparatus (e.g., one lens), as in vertebrates and cephalopods. Compare with **compound eye**.

simple fruit A fruit (e.g., apricot) that develops from a single flower that has a single carpel or several fused carpels. Compare with **aggregate** and **multiple fruit**.

simple leaf A leaf consisting of a single blade defined by the presence of a single axillary bud where the petiole joins the branch or stem.

simple sequence repeat (SSR) See **short tandem repeat (STR)**.

simple tissue A tissue consisting of a single cell type.

single nucleotide polymorphism (SNP) A site on a chromosome where different versions of the chromosome have different nucleotides. Can be used as a genetic marker to help track the inheritance of nearby genes.

single-strand DNA–binding protein (SSBP) A protein that attaches to separated strands of DNA during replication, preventing them from re-forming a double helix.

sink Any tissue, site, or location where an element or a molecule is consumed or taken out of circulation (e.g., in plants, a tissue where sugar exits the phloem). Compare with **source**.

sinoatrial (SA) node In the right atrium of the vertebrate heart, a cluster of cardiac muscle cells that initiates the heartbeat and determines the heart rate. Compare with **atrioventricular (AV) node**.

siphon A tubelike appendage of many mollusks, often used for feeding or propulsion.

sister chromatids The paired, double-stranded DNA copies of a recently replicated chromosome. They are connected most tightly at the centromere and eventually separate during anaphase of mitosis or meiosis II. Compare with **non-sister chromatids**.

sister groups Two or more lineages that share a recent common ancestor at the node where their branches meet.

skeletal muscle The muscle tissue attached to the bones of the vertebrate skeleton. Consists of long, unbranched muscle fibers with a characteristic striped (striated) appearance; controlled voluntarily. Compare with **cardiac muscle** and **smooth muscle**.

sliding-filament model A model of muscle contraction in which thin (actin) filaments and thick (myosin) filaments slide past each other, thereby shortening the sarcomere. Shortening of all the sarcomeres in a myofibril results in contraction of the entire myofibril.

slow muscle fiber A type of skeletal muscle fiber that is red due to the abundance of myoglobin, generates ATP by oxidative phosphorylation, and contracts slowly but does not fatigue easily. Also called *slow oxidative*, or *Type I, fiber*.

small intestine The portion of the digestive tract between the stomach and the large intestine. The site of the final stages of digestion and of most nutrient absorption.

small nuclear ribonucleoprotein See **snRNP**.

smooth endoplasmic reticulum (smooth ER) The portion of the endoplasmic reticulum that lacks attached ribosomes. Involved in synthesis and secretion of lipids. Compare with **rough endoplasmic reticulum**.

smooth muscle The unstriated muscle tissue that lines the intestine, blood vessels, and some other organs. Consists of tapered, unbranched cells that can sustain long contractions. Not voluntarily controlled. Compare with **cardiac muscle** and **skeletal muscle**.

snRNP (small nuclear ribonucleoprotein) Any of a class of small RNAs associated with proteins and found in the nucleus of eukaryotic cells, where they form the spliceosome and catalyze splicing. Pronounced *snurps*.

sodium–potassium pump A transmembrane protein that uses the energy of ATP to move sodium ions out of the cell and potassium ions into the cell, normally against their electrochemical gradients. Also called Na^+/K^+-*ATPase*.

soil organic matter Organic (carbon-containing) compounds found in soil.

solute Any substance that is dissolved in a liquid.

solute potential (Ψ_S) A component of the potential energy of water caused by a difference in solute concentrations at two locations. Can be zero (pure water) or negative. Compare with **pressure potential (Ψ_P)**.

solution A liquid containing one or more dissolved solids or gases in a homogeneous mixture.

solvent Any liquid in which one or more solids or gases can dissolve.

soma See **cell body**.

somatic cell Any type of cell in a multicellular organism except eggs, sperm, and their precursor cells. Also called *body cell*.

somatic hypermutation Mutation that occurs in the variable regions of immunoglobulin genes when B cells are first activated and in memory cells, resulting in novel variation in the receptors that bind to antigens.

somatic nervous system The part of the vertebrate peripheral nervous system that controls skeletal muscles and is under voluntary control. Compare with **autonomic nervous system**.

somite Blocks of mesoderm that occur in pairs along both sides of the developing neural tube in a vertebrate embryo. Gives rise to muscle, vertebrae, ribs, and the dermis of the skin.

source Any tissue, site, or location where a substance is produced or enters circulation (e.g., in plants, the tissue where sugar enters the phloem). Compare with **sink**.

space-filling model A representation of a molecule where atoms are shown as balls that are color-coded and scaled to indicate the atom's identity and volume. Depicts spatial relationships between atoms more accurately than a ball-and-stick model.

speciation The evolution of two or more distinct species from a single ancestral species.

species An evolutionarily independent population or group of populations. Generally distinct from other species in appearance, behavior, habitat, ecology, genetic characteristics, and so on.

species–area relationship The mathematical relationship between the area of a certain habitat and the number of species that it can support.

species diversity The variety and relative abundance of the species present in a given ecological community.

species richness The number of species present in a given ecological community.

specific heat The amount of energy required to raise the temperature of 1 gram of a substance by 1°C; a measure of the capacity of a substance to absorb energy.

sperm A mature male gamete.

sperm competition Competition between the sperm of different males to fertilize eggs inside the same female.

spermatogenesis The production of sperm. Occurs continuously in a testis.

spermatogonium (plural: spermatogonia) In a testis, any of the diploid cells that can divide by mitosis to produce primary spermatocytes (which can undergo meiosis) and more spermatogonia.

spermatophore A gelatinous package containing sperm that is produced by males of species that have internal fertilization without copulation.

sphincter A muscular valve that can close off a tube, as in a blood vessel or a part of the digestive tract.

spicule Stiff spike of silica or calcium carbonate that provides structural support in the body of many sponges.

spindle apparatus The array of microtubules responsible for moving chromosomes during mitosis and meiosis; includes kinetochore microtubules, polar microtubules, and astral microtubules.

spiracle In insects, a small opening that connects air-filled tracheae to the external environment, allowing for gas exchange.

spleen A dark red organ, found near the stomach of most vertebrates, that filters blood, stores extra red blood cells in case of emergency, and plays a role in immunity.

spliceosome In eukaryotes, a large, complex assembly of snRNPs (small nuclear ribonucleoproteins) and many proteins that catalyzes removal of introns from primary RNA transcripts.

splicing The process by which introns are removed from primary RNA transcripts and the remaining exons are connected together.

sporangium (plural: sporangia) A spore-producing structure found in seed plants, some protists, and some fungi (e.g., chytrids).

spore (1) In bacteria, a dormant form that generally is resistant to extreme conditions. (2) In eukaryotes, a single haploid cell produced by meiosis; it is distinct from a gamete, however, in being able to grow into a multicellular, haploid organism through mitotic divisions directly (no fertilization required).

sporophyte In organisms undergoing alternation of generations, the multicellular diploid form that develops by mitotic divisions after fertilization produces a zygote. Compare with **gametophyte**.

sporopollenin A watertight material that encases spores and pollen of modern land plants.

stabilizing selection A mode of natural selection that favors phenotypes near the middle of the range of phenotypic variation. Reduces overall genetic variation in a population. Compare with **disruptive selection** and **directional selection**.

stamen The male reproductive structure of a flower. Consists of an anther, in which pollen grains are produced, and a filament, which supports the anther. Compare with **carpel**.

standard free-energy change The equation used to measure the change in Gibbs free energy (ΔG) by calculating the changes in enthalpy (ΔH) and entropy (ΔS) that occur in a given chemical reaction. ΔG is less than 0 for spontaneous reactions and greater than 0 for nonspontaneous reactions.

standing defense See **constitutive defense**.

stapes One of three small bones in the middle ear of vertebrates that receive vibrations from the tympanic membrane. The stapes contacts the oval window and passes the vibrations to the cochlea.

starch A mixture of two storage polysaccharides, amylose and amylopectin, both formed from α-glucose monomers. Amylopectin is branched, and amylose is unbranched. The major form of stored carbohydrate in plants.

start codon The AUG triplet in mRNA where protein synthesis begins; codes for the amino acid methionine.

statocyst A sensory organ of many arthropods that detects the animal's orientation in space (e.g., whether the animal is upside down).

statolith A tiny stone or dense particle found in specialized gravity-sensing organs in some animals such as lobsters, and in gravity-sensing tissues of plants.

statolith hypothesis The hypothesis that amyloplasts (dense, starch-storing plant organelles) serve as statoliths in gravity detection by plants.

stem cell Any relatively undifferentiated cell that can divide to produce a daughter cell that remains a stem cell and a daughter cell that can differentiate into specific cell types.

stems Vertical, aboveground structures that make up the shoot system of plants.

stereocilium (plural: stereocilia) One of many stiff projections from the surface of a vertebrate hair cell that are involved in the detection of sound or of water-borne vibrations.

steroid A class of lipid with a characteristic four-ring hydrocarbon structure.

sticky ends The short, single-stranded ends of a DNA molecule cut by a restriction endonuclease; can form hydrogen bonds with complementary sticky ends.

stigma The sticky tip at the end of a flower carpel; pollen grains adhere to it.

stolon A modified stem that runs horizontally over the soil surface and produces new plants at the nodes (a form of asexual reproduction). Compare with **rhizome**.

stoma (plural: stomata) Generally, a pore or opening. In plants, a microscopic pore on the surface of a leaf or stem through which gas exchange occurs; typically surrounded by specialized cells that open the pore. See also **guard cell**.

stomach A tough, muscular pouch in the vertebrate digestive tract between the esophagus and small intestine. Physically breaks up food and begins digestion of proteins.

stop codon Any of three mRNA triplets (UAG, UGA, or UAA) that cause termination of protein synthesis. Also called a *termination codon*.

strain The lowest, most specific level of taxonomy that refers to a population of individuals that are genetically very similar or identical.

striated muscle Muscle tissue containing protein filaments organized into repeating structures that give the cells and tissues a banded appearance.

stroma The fluid matrix of a chloroplast enclosed within a double membrane envelope in which the thylakoids are embedded. Site of the Calvin cycle reactions.

structural formula A two-dimensional notation in which the chemical symbols for the constituent atoms are joined by straight lines representing single (−), double (=), or triple (≡) covalent bonds. Compare with **molecular formula**.

structural homology Similarities in adult organismal structures (e.g., limbs, shells, flowers) that are due to inheritance from a common ancestor.

style The slender stalk of a flower carpel connecting the stigma and the ovary.

suberin Waxy substance found in the cell walls of cork tissue and in the Casparian strip of endodermal cells.

subspecies A population that has distinctive traits and some genetic differences relative to other populations of the same species but that is not distinct enough to be classified as a separate species.

substrate (1) A reactant that interacts with a catalyst, such as an enzyme or ribozyme, in a chemical reaction. (2) A surface on which a cell or organism sits.

substrate-level phosphorylation Production of ATP or GTP by the transfer of a phosphate group from an intermediate substrate directly to ADP or GDP. Occurs in glycolysis and in the citric acid cycle.

succession In ecology, the gradual colonization of a habitat after an environmental disturbance (e.g., fire, flood), usually by a series of species. See **primary** and **secondary succession**.

sucrose A disaccharide formed from glucose and fructose. One of the two main products of photosynthesis.

sugar Synonymous with carbohydrate, though normally used in an informal sense to refer to small carbohydrates (monosaccharides and disaccharides).

summation The additive effect of different postsynaptic potentials on a neuron or muscle cell, enabling several subthreshold postsynaptic potentials to cause an action potential.

supporting connective tissue A type of connective tissue distinguished by having a firm extracellular matrix. Includes bone and cartilage.

surface metabolism model Model of chemical evolution whereby small molecules reacted with one another to form larger organic molecules through catalytic activity associated with a surface, such as the mineral deposits found in deep-sea hydrothermal vents.

surface tension The cohesive force that causes molecules at the surface of a liquid to stick together, thereby resisting deformation of the liquid's surface and minimizing its surface area.

survivorship On average, the proportion of offspring that survive to a particular age.

survivorship curve A graph depicting the percentage of a population that survives to different ages.

suspension feeder An animal that obtains food by filtering small particles or small organisms out of water. Also called *filter feeder*.

suspensor A multicellular structure that extends from the base of an embryo and transfers nutrients from endosperm to the developing embryo.

sustainability The planned use of environmental resources at a rate no faster than the rate at which they are naturally replaced.

sustainable agriculture Agricultural techniques that are designed to maintain long-term soil quality and productivity.

swim bladder A gas-filled organ of many ray-finned fishes; regulates buoyancy.

symbiosis (adjective: symbiotic) Any close and prolonged physical relationship between individuals of two different species. See **commensalism, mutualism**, and **parasitism**.

symmetric competition Ecological competition between two species in which both suffer similar declines in fitness. Compare with **asymmetric competition**.

sympathetic nervous system The part of the autonomic nervous system that stimulates fight or flight responses, such as increased heart rate, increased blood pressure, and slowed digestion. Compare with **parasympathetic nervous system**.

sympatric speciation The divergence of populations living within the same geographic area into different species as the result of their genetic (not physical) isolation. Compare with **allopatric speciation**.

sympatry Condition in which two or more populations live in the same geographic area, or close enough to permit interbreeding. Compare with **allopatry**.

symplast In plants, the space inside the plasma membrane. The symplasts of adjacent cells are often connected through plasmodesmata. Compare with **apoplast**.

symporter A cotransport protein that allows an ion to diffuse down an electrochemical gradient, using the energy of that process to transport a different substance in the same direction *against* its concentration gradient. Compare with **antiporter**.

synapomorphy A shared, derived trait found in two or more taxa that is present in their most recent common ancestor but is missing in more distant ancestors. Useful for inferring evolutionary relationships.

synapse The interface between two neurons or between a neuron and an effector cell.

synapsis The physical pairing of corresponding regions of two homologous chromosomes during prophase I of meiosis. Crossing over occurs during synapsis.

synaptic cleft The space between two communicating nerve cells (or between a neuron and effector cell) at a synapse, across which neurotransmitters diffuse.

synaptic plasticity A change in the responsiveness or structure of a synapse that can occur after particular stimulation patterns. Thought to be the basis of learning and memory.

synaptic vesicle A small neurotransmitter-containing vesicle inside the end of an axon that releases neurotransmitters into the synaptic cleft by exocytosis.

synaptonemal complex A network of proteins that holds non-sister chromatids together during synapsis in meiosis I.

synergid One of two cells flanking the egg in the female gametophyte; releases chemical attractants that direct pollen-tube growth.

system A defined set of interacting chemical components under observation.

systemic acquired resistance (SAR) A slow, widespread response of plants to a localized infection that protects healthy tissue from invasion by pathogens. Compare with **hypersensitive response**.

systemic circuit The part of the circulatory system that carries oxygen-rich blood from the heart to the rest of the body and returns oxygen-poor blood to the heart. It is separate from the pulmonary circuit in mammals and birds.

systemin A peptide hormone, produced by plant cells damaged by herbivores, that initiates a protective response in undamaged cells.

systems biology The study of the structure of networks of genes or proteins and how interactions between individual network components can lead to emergent biological properties.

systole The portion of the cardiac cycle during which the atria or ventricles of the heart are contracting. Compare with **diastole**.

systolic blood pressure The force exerted by blood against artery walls during contraction of the heart's left ventricle. Compare with **diastolic blood pressure**.

T cell A type of lymphocyte that, with B cells, is responsible for adaptive immunity in vertebrates. Originates in the bone marrow and matures in the thymus. Involved in activation of B cells ($CD4^+$ helper T cells) and destruction of infected cells ($CD8^+$ cytotoxic T cells). Also called *T lymphocyte*.

T-cell receptor (TCR) A transmembrane protein in the plasma membrane of a mature T cell that can bind to a specific antigen displayed on the surfaces of other cells. See **antigen presentation**.

T tubule Any of the membranous tubes that extend into the interior of a skeletal muscle cell, propagating action potentials throughout the cell and triggering the release of calcium from the sarcoplasmic reticulum.

tagmata (singular: tagma) Prominent body regions in arthropods, such as the head, thorax, and abdomen in insects.

taproot A large, vertical main root of a plant's root system.

taste bud A sensory structure, found mainly on the mammalian tongue, containing spindle-shaped cells that respond to chemical stimuli.

TATA-binding protein (TBP) A protein that binds to the TATA box in eukaryotic promoters and is a component of the basal transcription complex.

TATA box A short DNA sequence in many eukaryotic promoters that is important for assembling general transcription factors and RNA polymerase at the core promoter; located about 30 base pairs upstream from the transcription start site.

taxon (plural: taxa) Any named group of organisms at any level of a classification system.

taxonomy The branch of biology concerned with the classification and naming of organisms.

tectorial membrane A membrane, located in the vertebrate cochlea, that takes part in the transduction of sound by bending the stereocilia of hair cells in response to sonic vibrations.

telomerase An enzyme that adds DNA to the ends of chromosomes (telomeres) to prevent their shortening by standard DNA synthesis; catalyzes DNA synthesis guided by an RNA template that is part of the enzyme.

telomere The end of a linear chromosome that contains a repeated sequence of DNA.

telophase The final stage in mitosis or meiosis, during which daughter chromosomes (or homologous chromosomes in meiosis I) have moved to opposite poles and new nuclear envelopes begin to form around each set of chromosomes.

temperature A measurement of thermal energy present in an object or substance, reflecting how much the constituent matter is moving.

template strand A strand of RNA or DNA used to make a new, complementary strand via complementary base-pairing.

temporal lobe In the vertebrate brain, one of the four lobes of the cerebrum. Functions in memory, speech (in humans), and interpreting auditory information.

tendon A band of tough, fibrous connective tissue that connects a muscle to a bone.

tentacle A long, thin, muscular appendage typically used for sensing and feeding. Occurs in different forms in diverse animals, such as cephalopod mollusks and sea anemones.

termination (1) In enzyme-catalyzed reactions, the final stage in which the enzyme returns to its original conformation and products are released. (2) In transcription, the dissociation of the RNA and RNA polymerase from DNA. (3) In translation, the release of the polypeptide and dissociation of a ribosome from mRNA when the ribosome reaches a stop codon.

territory An area that is actively defended by an animal and that provides exclusive or semi-exclusive use of its resources by the owner.

tertiary consumers A carnivore; in a food chain or food web, organisms that feed on secondary consumers. Compare with **primary consumer** and **secondary consumer**.

tertiary structure The overall three-dimensional shape of a single polypeptide chain, resulting from multiple interactions among the amino acid side chains and the peptide backbone. In single-stranded nucleic acids, the three-dimensional shape is formed by hydrogen bonding and hydrophobic interactions between complementary bases. Compare with **primary, secondary**, and **quaternary structure**.

testcross The breeding of an individual that expresses a dominant phenotype but has an unknown genotype with an individual having only recessive alleles for the genes of interest. Used in order to infer the unknown genotype from observation of the phenotypes seen in offspring.

testis (plural: testes) The sperm-producing organ of a male animal.

testosterone A steroid hormone, produced and secreted by the testes, that stimulates sperm production and various male traits and reproductive behaviors.

tetrapod Any member of the lineage that includes all vertebrates with two pairs of limbs (amphibians, mammals, and reptiles, including birds).

texture A quality of soil, resulting from the relative abundance of different-sized particles making up the soil.

theory An explanation for a broad class of phenomena that is supported by a wide body of evidence. A theory serves as a framework for the development of new hypotheses.

thermal energy The total kinetic energy of a system that includes the motion of matter and is measured as temperature.

thermocline A steep gradient (cline) in environmental temperature, such as occurs in a thermally stratified lake or ocean.

thermophile A bacterium or archaean that thrives in very hot environments.

thermoreception The detection of heat energy.

thermoreceptor A sensory cell specialized for detecting changes in temperature.

thermoregulation Regulation of body temperature.

thick filament A filament composed of bundles of the motor protein myosin; anchored to the center of the sarcomere. Compare with **thin filament**.

thigmomorphogenesis The response by plants to mechanical stimuli such as wind or touch in which plants alter their growth patterns.

thigmonastic movements Rapid plant movements that occur in response to touch or vibration and that are independent of the direction of the stimulus.

thigmotropism Growth or movement of an organism in response to contact with a solid object.

thin filament A filament composed of two coiled chains of actin and the regulatory proteins tropomyosin and troponin; anchored to the Z disk of the sarcomere. Compare with **thick filament**.

thorax A region of the body; in arthropods, one of the three prominent body regions (tagmata), located between the head and abdomen; in vertebrates, including humans, the chest.

thorn A modified plant stem shaped as a sharp, protective structure. Helps protect a plant against feeding by herbivores.

threshold potential The membrane potential that will trigger an action potential in a neuron or other excitable cell. Also called simply *threshold*.

thylakoid A membrane-bound network of flattened sac-like structures inside a plant chloroplast that functions in converting light energy to chemical energy. Stacks of thylakoid discs make up grana.

thymus An organ, located in the anterior chest or neck of vertebrates, in which immature T cells that originated in the bone marrow undergo maturation.

thyroid gland A gland in the neck that releases thyroid hormone (which increases metabolic rate) and calcitonin (which lowers blood calcium concentration).

thyroid hormone Either of two hormones, triiodothyronine (T_3) or thyroxine (T_4), produced by the thyroid gland. See **triiodothyronine** and **thyroxine**.

thyroid-stimulating hormone (TSH) A peptide hormone, produced and secreted by the anterior pituitary, that stimulates the release of thyroid hormones from the thyroid gland.

thyroxine (T_4) A lipid-soluble hormone, derived from the amino acid tyrosine, containing four iodine atoms and produced and secreted by the thyroid gland. Acts primarily to stimulate cellular metabolism. In mammals, T_4 is converted to the more active hormone triiodothyronine (T_3) in the liver.

tight junction A type of cell–cell attachment structure that links the plasma membranes of adjacent animal cells, forming a barrier that restricts movement of substances in the space between the cells. Most abundant in epithelia (e.g., the intestinal lining). Compare with **desmosome** and **gap junction**.

tissue A group of cells that function as a unit, such as muscle tissue in an animal or xylem tissue in a plant.

tissue system A broad category including tissues and cell types formed by the primary meristems (protoderm, ground meristem, procambium).

tolerance In ecological succession, the phenomenon in which early-arriving species do not affect the probability that subsequent species will become established. Compare with **facilitation** and **inhibition**.

tonoplast The membrane surrounding a plant vacuole.

tool-kit genes A set of key developmental genes that establishes the body plan of animals and plants; present at the origin of the multicellular lineages and elaborated upon over evolutionary time by a process of duplication and divergence. Includes *Hox* genes.

topoisomerase An enzyme that prevents the twisting of DNA ahead of the advancing replication fork by cutting the DNA, allowing it to unwind, and rejoining it.

torpor An energy-conserving physiological state, marked by a decrease in metabolic rate, body temperature, and activity, that lasts for a short period (overnight to a few days or weeks). Occurs in some small mammals when the ambient temperature drops significantly. Compare with **hibernation**.

totipotent Capable of dividing and developing to form a complete, mature organism.

toxin A poison produced by a living organism, such as a plant, animal, or microorganism.

trachea (plural: tracheae) (1) In insects, any of the small, air-filled tubes that extend throughout the body and function in gas exchange. (2) In terrestrial vertebrates, the airway connecting the larynx to the bronchi. Also called *windpipe*.

tracheid In vascular plants, a long, thin, water-conducting cell that has pits where its lignin-containing secondary cell wall is absent, allowing water movement between adjacent cells. Compare with **vessel element**.

trade-off In evolutionary biology, an inescapable compromise between two traits that cannot be optimized simultaneously. Also called *fitness trade-off*.

trait Any observable characteristic at any level of observation of an individual.

transcription The process that uses a DNA template to produce a complementary RNA.

transcription factor General term for a protein that binds to a DNA regulatory sequence to influence transcription. It includes both regulatory and general transcription factors.

transcriptional activator A eukaryotic regulatory transcription factor that binds to regulatory DNA sequences in enhancers or promoter-proximal elements to promote the initiation of transcription. Also called *activator*.

transcriptional control Regulation of gene expression by various mechanisms that change the rate at which genes are transcribed to produce messenger RNA. In negative transcriptional control, binding of a regulatory protein to DNA represses transcription; in positive transcriptional control, binding of a regulatory protein to DNA promotes transcription.

transcriptome The complete set of gene transcripts in a particular cell.

transduction (1) The conversion of information from one mode to another. For example, the process by which a stimulus outside a cell is converted into a response by the cell. (2) The transfer of DNA from one bacterial cell to another by a virus.

transfer RNA (tRNA) An L-shaped RNA molecule that has an anticodon at one end and an amino acid attachment site at the other. Each tRNA carries a specific amino acid and binds to the corresponding codon in messenger RNA during translation.

transformation (1) Incorporation of external DNA into a cell. Occurs naturally in some bacteria; can be induced in the laboratory. (2) Conversion of a normal mammalian cell to one that divides uncontrollably.

transgenic A plant or animal whose genome contains DNA introduced from another individual, often from a different species.

transition state A high-energy intermediate state of the reactants during a chemical reaction that must be achieved for the reaction to proceed. Compare with **activation energy**.

transitional feature A trait that is intermediate between a condition observed in ancestral (older) species and the condition observed in derived (younger) species.

translation The process by which a polypeptide (a string of amino acids joined by peptide bonds) is synthesized from information in codons of messenger RNA.

translational control Regulation of gene expression by various mechanisms that alter the life span of messenger RNA or the efficiency of translation.

translocation (1) In plants, the movement of sugars and other organic nutrients through the phloem by bulk flow. (2) A type of mutation in which a piece of a chromosome moves to a nonhomologous chromosome. (3) The movement of a ribosome down a messenger RNA during translation.

transmembrane protein See **integral membrane protein**.

transpiration Loss of water vapor from aboveground plant parts. Occurs primarily through stomata.

transposable element Any of several kinds of DNA sequences that are capable of moving themselves, or copies of themselves, to other locations in the genome. Include LINEs.

tree of life The phylogenetic tree that includes all organisms.

trichome A hairlike appendage that grows from epidermal cells in the shoot system of some plants. Trichomes exhibit a variety of shapes, sizes, and functions depending on species.

triiodothyronine (T_3) A lipid-soluble hormone, derived from the amino acid tyrosine, containing three iodine atoms and produced and secreted by the thyroid gland. Acts primarily to stimulate cellular metabolism. In mammals, T_3 has a stronger effect than does the related hormone thyroxine (T_4).

triose A monosaccharide (simple sugar) containing three carbon atoms.

triplet code A code in which a "word" of three letters encodes one piece of information. The genetic code is a triplet code because a codon is three nucleotides long and encodes one amino acid.

triploblast (adjective: triploblastic) An animal whose body develops from three basic embryonic cell layers or tissues: ectoderm, mesoderm, and endoderm. Compare with **diploblast**.

trisomy The state of having three copies of any type of chromosome in an otherwise diploid cell.

tRNA See **transfer RNA.**

trochophore A larva with a ring of cilia around its middle that is found in some lophotrochozoans.

trophic cascade A series of changes in the abundance of species in a food web, usually caused by the addition or removal of a key predator.

trophic level A feeding level in an ecosystem.

trophoblast The sheet of cells on the exterior of a blastocyst (the structure that results from cleavage during embryonic development in mammals).

tropomyosin A regulatory protein present in thin (actin) filaments that blocks the myosin-binding sites on these filaments in resting muscles, thereby preventing muscle contraction.

troponin A regulatory protein present in thin (actin) filaments that can move tropomyosin off the myosin-binding sites on these filaments, thereby allowing muscle contraction. Activated by high intracellular calcium concentrations.

true navigation The type of navigation by which an animal can reach a specific point on Earth's surface. Also called *map orientation*.

trypsin A protein-digesting enzyme secreted in inactive form (as trypsinogen) by the pancreas that activates several other protein-digesting enzymes.

tube feet One of the many small, mobile, fluid-filled extensions of the water vascular system of echinoderms; the part extending outside the body is called a podium, while the bulb within the body is the ampulla. Used in locomotion, feeding, and respiration.

tuber A modified plant rhizome that functions in storage of carbohydrates.

tuberculosis A disease of the lungs caused by infection with the bacterium *Mycobacterium tuberculosis*.

tumor A mass of cells formed by uncontrolled cell division. Can be benign or malignant.

tumor suppressor A protein that prevents cell division when conditions are unfavorable, such as when the cell has DNA damage. Defects in the function of tumor suppressors, such as p53 or Rb, are associated with the uncontrolled cell replication in cancer.

turbidity Cloudiness of water caused by sediments and/or microscopic organisms.

turgid Swollen and firm as a result of high internal pressure (e.g., a plant cell containing enough water for the cytoplasm to press against the cell wall). Compare with **flaccid**.

turgor pressure The outward pressure exerted by the fluid contents of a living plant cell against its cell wall.

turnover In lake ecology, the complete mixing of upper and lower layers of water of different temperatures; occurs each spring and fall in temperate-zone lakes.

tympanic membrane (1) The membrane separating the middle ear from the outer ear in terrestrial vertebrates. Also called the *eardrum*. (2) A structure that functions in hearing in insects.

ubiquinone See **coenzyme Q**.

ulcer A hole in an epithelium that exposes the underlying tissues to damage.

ultimate causation In biology, the reason that a trait or phenomenon is thought to have evolved; the adaptive advantage of that trait. Also called *ultimate explanation*. Compare with **proximate causation**.

umami The sensation triggered by glutamate, responsible for the taste of meat and of monosodium glutamate.

umbilical cord The cord that connects a developing mammalian embryo or fetus to the placenta and through which the embryo or fetus receives oxygen and nutrients from the mother.

unequal crossing over An error in crossing over during meiosis I in which the two non-sister chromatids match up at different sites. Results in gene duplication in one chromatid and gene loss in the other.

unsaturated Referring to lipids in which at least one carbon-carbon bond is a double bond. Double bonds produce kinks in hydrocarbon chains and decrease the compound's melting point. Compare with **saturated**.

upstream In genetics, opposite to the direction in which RNA polymerase moves along a DNA strand. Compare with **downstream**.

urea The major nitrogenous waste of mammals, adult amphibians, and cartilaginous fishes. Compare with **ammonia** and **uric acid**.

ureter In vertebrates, a tube that transports urine from one kidney to the bladder.

urethra The tube that drains urine from the bladder to the outside environment. In male vertebrates, also used for passage of semen during ejaculation.

uric acid The major nitrogenous waste of birds, other reptiles, and most terrestrial arthropods. Compare with **ammonia** and **urea**.

urochordates One of the three major chordate lineages (Urochordata), comprising sessile or floating, filter-feeding animals that have a polysaccharide covering (tunic) and two siphons through which water enters and exits; include the ascidians, thaleaceans, and larvaceans. Compare with **cephalochordates** and **vertebrates**.

uterus The organ in which embryos develop in mammals and some other viviparous vertebrates.

vaccination Artificial production of immunological memory against a pathogen. Uses isolated antigens or altered versions of the pathogen to stimulate an adaptive immune response in the absence of disease.

vaccine A preparation designed to stimulate an immune response against a particular pathogen without causing illness. May consist of inactivated pathogens, attenuated (weakened) pathogens, or parts of a pathogen (subunit vaccine).

vacuole A large organelle in plant and fungal cells that ordinarily is used for bulk storage of water, pigments, oils, or other substances. Some vacuoles contain enzymes and have a digestive function similar to lysosomes in animal cells.

vagina The birth canal of female mammals; a muscular tube that extends from the uterus through the pelvis to the exterior.

valence The number of unpaired electrons in the outermost electron shell of an atom; when an atom is involved in covalent bonding, valence often determines how many covalent bonds the atom can form.

valence electron An electron in the outermost electron shell, the valence shell, of an atom. Valence electrons tend to be involved in chemical bonding.

valence shell The outermost electron shell of an atom.

valve In circulatory systems, any of the flaps of tissue that prevent backward flow of blood, particularly in veins and in the heart.

van der Waals interaction A weak electrical attraction between two nonpolar molecules that have been brought together through hydrophobic interactions. Often contributes to tertiary and quaternary structures in proteins.

variable number tandem repeats (VNTR) See **minisatellite**.

variable (*V*) region The amino acid sequence that varies in the polypeptides that comprise antibodies, B-cell receptors, and T-cell receptors. Forms the antigen-binding site. Compare with **constant (*C*) region**.

vas deferens (plural: vasa deferentia) A muscular tube that stores and transports semen from the epididymis to the ejaculatory duct. Also called the *ductus deferens*.

vasa recta In the vertebrate kidney, a network of blood vessels that runs alongside the loop of Henle of a nephron. Functions in reabsorption of water and solutes from the filtrate.

vascular bundle In a plant stem, a cluster of xylem and phloem strands that run the length of the stem.

vascular cambium One of two types of cylindrical meristem, consisting of a ring of undifferentiated plant cells in the stem and root of woody plants; produces secondary xylem (wood) and secondary phloem. Compare with **cork cambium**.

vascular tissue In plants, tissue that transports water, nutrients, and sugars. Made up of the complex tissues xylem and phloem, each of which contains several cell types. Also called *vascular tissue system*.

vascular tissue system In plants, tissues that transport water, nutrients, and sugars. Made up of the complex tissues xylem and phloem, each of which contains several cell types.

vector (1) A biting insect or other organism that transfers pathogens from one species to another. (2) A plasmid or other agent such as a virus used to transfer recombinant genes into cultured host cells. See **cloning vector**.

vegetative development The phase of plant development that involves growth and the production of all plant structures except the flower.

vein Any blood vessel that carries blood (oxygenated or not) under relatively low pressure from the rest of the body toward the heart. Compare with **artery**.

vena cava (plural: venae cavae) Either of two large veins that return oxygen-poor blood to the heart.

ventral Toward an animal's belly and away from its back. The opposite of dorsal.

ventricle (1) A thick-walled chamber of the heart that receives blood from an atrium and pumps it to the body or to the lungs or gills. (2) Any of several small, fluid-filled chambers in the vertebrate brain.

venule A small vessel that collects blood from a capillary bed.

vertebrae (singular: vertebra) The cartilaginous or bony elements that form the backbones of vertebrate animals.

vertebrates One of the three major chordate lineages (Vertebrata), comprising animals with a dorsal column of cartilaginous or bony structures (vertebrae) and a skull enclosing the brain. Includes fishes, amphibians, mammals, and reptiles (including birds). Compare with **cephalochordates** and **urochordates**.

vesicle A membrane enclosed compartment with an aqueous interior that is often used in cells to transport cargo between organelles or to the plasma membrane for secretion.

vessel element In vascular plants, a short, wide, water-conducting cell that has gaps through both the primary and secondary cell walls, allowing unimpeded passage of water between adjacent cells. Compare with **tracheid**.

vestigial trait A reduced or incompletely developed structure that has no function, or reduced function, but is clearly similar to functioning organs or structures in ancestral species or closely related species.

vicariance The physical splitting of a population into smaller, isolated populations by a geographic barrier.

villi (singular: villus) Small, fingerlike projections (1) of the lining of the small intestine or (2) of the fetal portion of the placenta adjacent to maternal arteries. Function to increase the surface area available for absorption of nutrients and gas exchange.

virion The infectious extracellular particle that is produced from a viral infection; used for transmitting the virus between hosts. It consists of a DNA or RNA genome that is often enclosed within a protein shell (capsid) that may be further enveloped in a phospholipid bilayer. Compare with **virus**.

virulence (adjective: virulent) The ability of a pathogen to cause severe disease in a susceptible host.

virus An obligate, intracellular parasite that is acellular but uses host-cell biosynthetic machinery to replicate. Compare with **virion**.

visceral mass One of the three main parts of the mollusk body; contains most of the internal organs and external gill.

visible light The range of wavelengths of electromagnetic radiation that humans can see, from about 400 to 710 nanometers.

vitamin Any of various organic micronutrients that usually function as coenzymes.

vitelline envelope A fibrous sheet of glycoproteins that surrounds mature eggs in many vertebrates. Surrounded by a thick, gelatinous matrix (the jelly layer) in some aquatic species. In mammals, called the *zona pellucida*.

viviparous In animals, producing live young (instead of eggs) that develop within and are nourished by the body of the mother before birth, typically via a placenta. Compare with **oviparous** and **ovoviviparous**.

volt (V) A unit of electrical potential (voltage).

voltage Potential energy created by a separation of electric charges between two points. Also called *electrical potential*.

voltage clamping A technique for imposing a constant membrane potential on a cell. Widely used to investigate ion channels.

voltage-gated channel An ion channel that opens or closes in response to a change in membrane voltage. Compare with **ligand-gated channel**.

voluntary muscle A muscle that contracts in response to stimulation by voluntary (somatic), but not involuntary (parasympathetic or sympathetic), neural stimulation.

vomeronasal organ A sensory organ, located in the nasal cavity of tetrapod vertebrates, containing chemoreceptors that bind odorants and pheromones.

wall pressure The inward pressure exerted by a cell wall against the fluid contents of a living plant cell.

Wallace line A line in the Indonesian region that demarcates two geographic areas, Asian and Australian, each of which is characterized by a distinct set of plant and animal species.

water cycle, global The movement of water among terrestrial ecosystems, aquatic ecosystems, and the atmosphere.

water potential (Ψ) The potential energy of water in a certain environment compared with the potential energy of pure water at room temperature and atmospheric pressure. In living organisms, ψ equals the solute potential (ψ_S) plus the pressure potential (ψ_P).

water-potential gradient A difference in water potential in one region compared with that in another region. Determines the direction that water moves, always from regions of higher water potential to regions of lower water potential.

water table The upper limit of the underground layer of soil that is saturated with water.

water vascular system In echinoderms, a system of fluid-filled tubes and chambers that functions as a hydrostatic skeleton.

watershed The area drained by a single creek or river.

Watson–Crick pairing See **complementary base pairing.**

wavelength The distance between two successive crests or troughs in any regular wave, such as a light wave, sound wave, or wave in water.

wax A class of lipid with extremely long, saturated hydrocarbon tails. Harder and less greasy than fats.

weather The short-term atmospheric conditions of temperature, moisture, sunlight, and wind at a specific place and time.

weathering The gradual wearing down of large rocks by rain, running water, temperature changes, and wind; one of the processes that transform rocks into soil.

weed Any plant that is adapted for growth in disturbed soils.

wild type The most common phenotype(s) seen in a wild population.

wildlife corridor Strips of wildlife habitat connecting populations that otherwise would be isolated by human-made development.

wilt To lose turgor pressure in a plant tissue.

wobble hypothesis The hypothesis that some tRNA molecules can pair with more than one mRNA codon by tolerating particular types of nonstandard base pairing in the third base, so long as the first and second bases are correctly matched.

wood Xylem resulting from secondary growth; forms strong supporting material. Also called *secondary xylem.*

worm An animal with a long, thin, tubelike body lacking limbs.

X-linkage See **X-linked inheritance**.

X-linked inheritance Inheritance patterns for genes located on the X chromosome. Also called *X-linkage.*

X-ray crystallography A technique for determining the three-dimensional structure of large molecules, including proteins and nucleic acids, by analyzing the diffraction patterns produced by X-rays beamed at crystals of the molecule.

xenoestrogen Any foreign chemical that binds to estrogen receptors or otherwise induces estrogen-like effects.

xeroderma pigmentosum (XP) A human disease characterized by extreme sensitivity to ultraviolet light. Caused by an autosomal recessive allele that inactivates the nucleotide excision DNA repair system.

xylem A plant vascular tissue that conducts water and ions; contains tracheids and/or vessel elements. Primary xylem develops from the procambium of apical meristems; secondary xylem, or wood, from the vascular cambium. Compare with **phloem**.

yeast Any fungus growing as a single-celled form. Also, a specific lineage of Ascomycota.

Y-linkage See **Y-linked inheritance**.

Y-linked inheritance Inheritance patterns for genes located on the Y chromosome. Also called *Y-linkage.*

yolk The nutrient-rich cytoplasm inside an egg; used as food for the growing embryo.

Z disk The structure that forms each end of a sarcomere. Contains a protein that binds tightly to actin, thereby anchoring thin filaments.

Z-scheme Model for changes in the potential energy of electrons as they pass from photosystem II to photosystem I and ultimately to NADP$^+$ during the light-capturing reactions of photosynthesis. See also **noncyclic electron flow**.

zero population growth (ZPG) A state of stable population size due to fertility staying at the replacement rate for at least one generation.

zona pellucida The gelatinous layer around a mammalian egg. In other vertebrates, called the *vitelline envelope.*

zone of (cellular) division In plant roots, a group of apical meristematic cells just behind the root cap where cells are actively dividing.

zone of (cellular) elongation In plant roots, a group of young cells, derived from primary meristem tissues and located behind the apical meristem, that are increasing in length.

zone of (cellular) maturation In plant roots, a group of plant cells, located several millimeters behind the root cap, that are differentiating into mature tissues.

zone of (cellular) maturation In plant roots, a group of plant cells, located several millimeters behind the root cap, that are differentiating into mature tissues. Site of most nutrient uptake.

zygosporangium (plural: zygosporangia) The distinctive spore-producing structure in fungi that are members of the Zygomycota.

zygote The cell formed by the union of two gametes; a fertilized egg.

Credits

Photo Credits

Medicine **22.7** Walter J. Gehring **22.9-1** Arco Images GmbH/Alamy **22.9-2** PetStockBoys/Alamy **22.9-3** Juniors Bildarchiv GmbH/Alamy **22.9-4** Reinhard, H/Arco Images/Alamy **22.12** Alison Wright/National Geographic Stock **22.12 inset** AGE Fotostock **22.15T** Campas, O. et al. 2010. Scaling and shar transformations capture beak shape variation in Darwin's finches. *Proceedings of the National Academy of Sciences* 107 (8): 3356–3360. American Association for the Advancement of Science (AAAS) **22.15B** The Royal Society of London **22.T3-3** Tony Garcia/Getty Images **22.T3-1** dibrova/Shutterstock **22.T3-2** Jivko Kazakov/Getty Images **22.16** HO/Reuters/Corbis **Case Study** U.S. Fish and Wildlife Service

Chapter 23 Opener Chaiwat Subprasom/Reuters **23.1** Robert Rattner **23.4** Pearson Education **23.8** Gary Meszaros/Science Source **23.9** Cyril Laubscher/Dorling Kindersley, Ltd. **23.11a** Steve Mackay/Getty Images **23.11b** Phil Savoie/Nature Picture Library **23.13** Andre Karwath/Public Domain **23.16** Mark Conlin/Image Quest Marine **23.18** Alasdair Thomson/Getty Images **Case Study** Westend61/Getty Images

Chapter 24 Opener Jason Rick, Loren H. Rieseberg, Indiana University **24.10B** Cubo Images/Superstock **24.10R** Stephen Lynn Clancy **24.10L** Michael Lustbader/Science Source **24.11** H. Douglas Pratt/National Geographic Image Collection **Case Study** Ryflip/Fotolia

Chapter 25 Opener Indiana9 fossils and L & M Collectibles **25.1** Jun-Yuan Chen **25. T4-1** GEUS **25.T4-2** Ismael Montero Verdu/Getty Images **25.T4-3** Richard Becker/Frank Lane Picture Agency **25.T4-4** Millard H. Sharp/Science Source **25.T4-5** Juan Carlos Cantero/AGE Fotostock **25.7BL** Forest & Kim Starr **25.7R** Forest & Kim Starr **25.7TL** Dr. Gerald D. Carr, PhD **25.8a** Eladio Fernandez **25.8b** Jonathan B. Losos **25.9TL** O. Louis Mazzatenta/ National Geographic/Getty Images **25.9TR** Sinclair Stammers/Science Source **25.9M** O. Louis Mazzatenta/National Geographic/Getty Images **25.9B** Creative Commons Attribution-Share Alike 3.0/Verisimilus **25.10** Jun-Yuan Chen, Nanjing Institute of Geology and Palaeontology **25.T5** Peter Schulte et al. 2010. The Chicxulub Asteroid Impact and Mass Extinction at the Cretaceous-Paleogene Boundary. *Science* 327: 1214–1218, Supporting Online Material, Figure S9. American Association for the Advancement of Science (AAAS) **25.T5-1** National Park Service **25.T5-2** Dr. Glen A. Izett/USGS-NASA **25.T7** NASA **Case Study** Sergey Krasovskiy/Stocktrek Images/Corbis

Chapter 26 Opener Ignacio Palacios/Getty Images **26.1** Doc Searls **26.1 inset** University of Maryland Biotechnology Institute **26.2** Dr. Kari Lounatmaa/Science Source **26.3** Shi Vi Liu et al. 1997. Thermophilic Fe(III)-reducing bacteria from the deep subsurface: The evolutionary implications. *Science* 277: 1106–1109, Figure 2. American Association for the Advancement of Science (AAAS) **26.7aT** Thomas Deerinck, NCMIR/Science Source **26.7aB** Heide Schulz et al. 1999. Dense populations of a giant sulfur bacterium in Namibian shelf sediments. *Science* 284: 493–495, Fig. 1D.American Association for the Advancement of Science (AAAS) **26.7bT** SCIMAT/Science Source **26.7bB** Scimat/Science Source **26.7cT** Dr. Linda M. Stannard, University of Cape Town/Science Source **26.7cB** Dr. Ralf Wagner **26.8** Robert Hubert **26.11** Bruce J. Russell/BioMedia Associates **26.T4-1** S. Amano, S. Miyadoh, and T. Shomura, The Society for Actinomycetes Japan The Society for Actinomycetes Japan **26.T4-2** David M. Phillips/Science Source **26.T4-3** David Dalton **26.T4-4** Andrew Syred/Science Source **26.T4-5** George L. Barron **26.T4-6** James Cavallini/Science Source **26.T5-1** Kenneth M. Stedman, Ph.D. **26.T5-1 inset** Eye of Science/Science Source **26.T5-2** Karl O. Stetter **25.T7-2 inset** Karl O. Stetter **26.T5-3** Martin Könneke

Chapter 27 Opener Martin Kreutz/AGE Fotostock **27.1L** Scenics & Science/Alamy **27.1M** Mark Conlin/Alamy **27.2R** Bob Gibbons/Frank Lane Picture Agency **27.3** Pete Atkinson/PhotoShot **27.3 inset** D. Anderson/Woods Hole Oceanographic Institution **27.5** Biophoto Associates/Science Source **27.11a** Tai-Soon Young **27.11b** David J. Patterson **27.11c** Anna Sagatov **27.12a** Steve Gschmeissner/Science Source **27.12b** Biophoto Associates/Science Source **27.12c** Andrew Syred/Science Source **27.12d** Briand S. Leander **27.13a** Biophoto Associates/Science Source **27.13b** Bruce Coleman/PhotoShot **27.14** Eric V. Grave/Science Source **27.T3-1** Alex Wild **27.T3-2** Gerd Guenther/Science Source **27.T3-3** Sue Daly/Nature Picture Library **27.T3-4** Oxford Scientific/Getty Images **27.T3-5** Inra **27.T3-6** Andrew Syred/Science Source **27.18a** Eye of Science/Science Source **27.18b** David Caron/Science Source **Case Study** L Ray Simons/Science Source **Case Study R** Chris R. Reid et al. 2012. Slime mold uses an externalized spatial "memory" to navigate in complex environments. *Proceedings of the National Academy of Sciences* (PNAS) 109: 17490-17494, Figure 3.

Chapter 28 Opener RF Company/Alamy **28.1** Photo by Lynn Betts, USDA Natural Resources Conservation Service (NRCSIA99129) **28.2** Hugh Iltis and John Doebley **28.3L** Power and Syred/Science Source **28.3M** Linda E. Graham **28.3R** Nick Upton/Nature Picture Library **28.4a** Lee W. Wilcox **28.4b** Michael Sacco/Getty Images **28.4c** Kredo/Shutterstock **28.7** Lee W. Wilcox **28.10L** Jon Monroe **28.10B** BlueRidgeKitties **28.10R** Jon Monroe **28.15a** Lee W. Wilcox **28.15bL** Lee W. Wilcox **28.15bR** Lee W. Wilcox **28.17** Patrick J Lynch/Science Source **28.20a** Larry Deack **28.20b** Quest786/Shutterstock **28.20c** John Severns (Severnjc) **28.22a** Maxim Khytra/Shutterstock **28.22b** Andreas Nilsson/Shutterstock **28.24T-1** Dr Keith Wheeler/Science Source **28.24T-2** Dr Keith Wheeler/Science Source **28.24T-3** iStockphoto **28.24T-4** J. J. Harrison **28.24B-1** Garry DeLong/Science Source **28.24B-2** Dr Keith Wheeler/Science Source **28.24B-3** Atelier Simon/Getty Images **28.24B-4** Shutterstock **28.26a** Peter Bassett/Nature Picture Library **28.26b** Roland Birke/Photolibrary/Getty Images **28.26c** Lee W. Wilcox **28.T2-1** Nick Upton/Nature Picture Library **28.T2-3** Willem Kolvoort/Nature Picture Library **28.T2-2** Linda E. Graham **28.T2-4** M. I. Walker/Science Source **28.T3-1** Adrian Davies/Nature Picture Library **28.T3-2** Joan Edwards **28.T3-3** Lee W. Wilcox **28.T4-1** Andrea and Antonella Ferrari/AGE Fotostock **28.T4-2** Kirk A. Dickson **28.T4-3** Matt Meadows/Stockbyte/Getty Images **28.T4-4** F Hecker/AGE Fotostock **28.T5-1** Brigg/iStockphoto/Getty Images **28.T5-2** Peter H Hallet/Science Source **28.T5-3** Peter Chadwick/Dorling Kindersley, Ltd. **28.T5-4** Lee W. Wilcox **28.T5-5** Geoff Renner/Robert Harding World Imagery **28.T6-1** Scott Zona **28.T6-2** Elburg Botanic Media/AGE Fotostock **28.T6-3** John Beedle/Corbis **28.T6-4** GWI/Botanic Images In/AGE Fotostock **Case Study** Premaphotos/Alamy **Case Study inset** Nigel Cattlin/Alamy

Chapter 29 Opener Chaiwatphotos/Shutterstock **29.1a** Inga Spence/Science Source **29.1b** EGON/Alamy **29.2a** David Read/University of Sheffield **29.2b** Mycorrhizal Applications, Inc **29.3** B. G. Thomson/Science Source **29.4a** Eye of Science/Science Source **29.4b** Hecker/Sauer/AGE Fotostock **29.5a** Susumu Nishinaga/Science Source **29.5bL** George L. Barron **29.5bR** Science Source **29.5c** Patrick Hickey/NIPHT LIMITED **29.6** N. Allen and G. Barron **29.7a** Melvin Fuller **29.7b** Ed Reschke/Photolibrary/Getty Images **29.6c** Biophoto Associates/Science Source **29.7d** Nino Santamaria **29.8L** WebCat/Shutterstock **29.8R** E. Gueho/Science Source **29.12a** Mark Brundrett **29.12b** Mark Brundrett **29.13a** Marko König/imagebroker/AGE Fotostock **29.13b** Ralf Wagner **29.14** Thailand Wildlife/Alamy **29.T1-1** Dr. J. I. Ronny Larsson, Professor of Zoology **29.T1-2** Thomas J. Volk **29.T1-3** Gregory G. Dimijian/Science Source **29.T1-4** Dr. Jim Deacon **29.T1-5** Zoonar/Jürgen Vogt/AGE Fotostock **29.T1-6** Adrian Hepworth/Photoshot License Limited **Case Study** Darlyne A. Murawski/National Geographic/Getty Images, Inc.

Chapter 30 Opener National Geographic Creative **30.4** M. I. Walker/Science Source **30.5a** Steve Gschmeissner/Science Source **30.5b** Susumu Nishinaga/Science Source **30.6** Deepseawaters.com **30.7** J. R. Finnerty et al. Origins of bilateral symmetry: *Hox* and *dpp* expression in a sea anemone. 2004. *Science* 304: 1335–1337, Figure 2I **30.T2-1** Perennou Nuridsany/Science Source **30.T2-2** Barry Mansell/Nature Picture Library **30.T2-3** Pascal Goetgheluck/Science Source **30.T2-4** Joze Maucec/Shutterstock **30.T3-1** Juniors Bildarchiv GmbH/Alamy **30.T3-2** Olga Khoroshunova/Fotolia **30.T3-3** Len Rue, Jr./Science Source **30.T4-1** Sanamyan/Alamy **30.T4-2** Todd Husman **30.T4-3** Heinz-jürgen Landshoe/AGE Fotostock **30.T4-4** Four Oaks/Shutterstock **30.T5-1** Francesco Tomasinelli/Science Source **30.T5-2** Michael Zysman/Shutterstock **30.T5-3** D P Wilson/Frank Lane Picture Agency Limited **30.T5-4** Lawson Wood/Robert Harding World Imagery 30.T5-5 Jeff Rotman/Science Source **30.11LMR** Grace Panganiban et al. The origin and evolution of animal appendages. *Proceedings of the National Academy of Sciences* (PNAS) 94: 5162–5166, Figures 1a, 1c, 1f **30.T6-1** William J Harrigan/Alamy **30.T6-2** David Doubilet/Getty Images **30.T6-3** Horia Bogdan/Shutterstock **30.T7-1** Andrew J. Martinez/Science Source **30.T7-2** Gregory G Dimijian/Science Source **30.T7-3** Alexander Semenov/Science Source **Case Study** Mark Conlin/Alamy

Chapter 31 Opener Jochen Tack/Alamy Stock Photo **31.4a** Carmel McDougall **31.4b** Peter Parks/Image Quest Marine **31.T1-1** Roger Steene/Image Quest Marine **31.T1-2** Franco Banfi/AGE Fotostock **31.T1-3** Cultura Science/Alexander Semenov/Getty Images **31.T1-4** Ethan Daniels/Shutterstock **31.6a** Michael Abbey/Science Source **31.6b** Sinclair Stammers/Science Source **31.6c** J. W. Alker/Imagebroker/Alamy **31.6d** Blickwinkel/Alamy **31.8** Jane Burton/Nature Picture Library **31.9** Adrian Costea/Fotolia **31.9 inset** Josef Ramsauer & Prof. Dr. Robert Patzner **31.T2-1** Martin Almqvist/Alamy **31.T2-2** Iceink/Shutterstock **31.T2-3** WaterFrame/Alamy Stock Photo **31.T2-4** H. Schmidbauer/AGE Fotostock **31.11a** Dave King/Dorling Kindersley, Ltd. **31.11b** Michael Mules/Alamy Stock Photo **31.T3-1** Sinclair Stammers/Science Source **31.T3-2** Steve Gschmeissner/Science Source **31.T3-3** George Grall/National Geographic Image Collection/Alamy Stock Photo **31.T3-4** Chabaphoto/Shutterstock **31.12** Eric Isselée/Shutterstock **31.12b** Holger Mette/Fotolia **31.T4-1** Mark Smith/Science Source **31.T4-2** Juniors Bildarchiv GmbH/Alamy **31.T4-3** Bennyartist/Shutterstock **31.T4-4** AlinaMD/Shutterstock **31.T5-1** Nature Picture Library **31.T5-2** OGphoto/Getty Images **31.T5-3** Getty Images **31.T5-4** Public Domain **31.T5-5** Yxowert/Shutterstock **31.T5-6** Marc Dubus/Fotolia **31.T5-7** Sergey Toronto/Fotolia **31.16a** Nigel Cattlin/Alamy **31.16b** Kim Taylor/Nature Picture Library **31.16b inset** Frank Greenaway/Dorling Kindersley, Ltd. **Case Study** Nipam H. Patel

Chapter 32 Opener Fritz Wilhelm **32.2a** D. P. Wilson/Frank Lane Picture Agency Limited **32.2b** Juri Vinokurov/Fotolia **32.3b** Jeff Rotman/Nature Picture Library **32.4** Richard Wong/Alamy **32.4** Chris Howes/Wild Places Photography/Alamy Stock Photo **32.4a** Mark Conlin/Image Quest Marine **32.T1-1** Hal Beral/Corbis **32.T1-2** Alan James/Nature Picture Library **32.T1-3** Jeffrey L. Rotman/Corbis **32. 32.T1-4** Jeffrey L. Rotman/Science Source **32.T1-5** Reinhard Dirscherl/Reinhard Dirscherl/ullstein bild/Getty Images **32.T2-1** Heather Ange/Alamy **32.T2-2** Borut Furla/AGE Fotostock **32.T2-3** David Fleetham/Alamy **32.T2-4** D P Wilson/Frank Lane Picture Agency Limited **32.T3-1** Mark Conlin/Alamy **32.T3-2** Heather Angel/Natural Visions/Alamy **32.T4-1** Norbert Probst/imageBROKER/Alamy **32.T4-2** Charles Hood/Oceans Image/Photoshot **32.T4-3** Arnaz Mehta **32.T4-4** Rudie Kuiter/Oceanwide Images

Illustration and Text Credits

Chapter 1 1.8a Young, T. P., L. A. Isbell. 1991. *Ethology* 87: 79−89. 1.10 Based on Wittlinger, M., R. Wehner, and H. Wolf. 2006. The ant odometer: Stepping on stilts and stumps. *Science* 312: 1965−1967. **Case Study** Data from Gianoli, E., Carrasco-Urra, F. 2014. *Current Biology* 24: 984−987.

BioSkills B2 CYU Potter, S. L. et al. 2012. *Pediatric Blood Cancer* 58: 362−365. B3 CYU Baldwin, M.W. et al. 2014. *Science* 345: 929−933. B.T18-1 A. Crowe, C. Dicks, and M. P. Wenderoth. 2008. Biology in bloom: Implementing Bloom's Taxonomy to enhance student learning in Biology. *CBE—Life Sciences Education* 7: 368−381, Table 3.

Chapter 2 2.T1 Data from D. R. Lide (editor). 2008. Standard Thermodynamic Properties of Chemical Substances. *CRC Handbook of Physics and Chemistry* 89. Boca Raton, FL: CRC Press. 2.2 Based on Miller, S. L. 1953. A production of amino acids under possible primitive Earth conditions. *Science* 117: 528−529. **Case Study** J. G. Wallis, H. Wang, and D. J. Guerra. 1997. *Plant Molecular Biology* 35: 323−330.

Chapter 3 **Opener** Based on PDB ID: 2DN2. S. Y. Park, T. Yokoyama, N. Shibayama, et al. 2006. 1.25 Å resolution crystal structures of human hemoglobin in the oxy, deoxy and carbonmonoxy forms. *Journal of Molecular Biology* 360: 690−701. 3.8a Based on PDB ID: 1CLG. J. M. Chen, C. D. E. King, S. H. Feairheller, et al. 1991. An energetic evaluation of a "Smith" collagen microfibril model. *Journal of Protein Chemistry* 10: 535−552. 3.8b Based on PDB ID: 1TGH. Z. S. Juo, T. K. Chiu, P. M. Leiberman, et al. 1996. How proteins recognize the TATA box. *Journal of Molecular Biology* 261: 239−254. 3.8c Based on PDB ID: 2X9K. F. Korkmaz-Ozkan, S. Koster, W. Kuhlbrandt, et al. 2010. Correlation between the OmpG secondary structure and its pH-dependent alterations monitored by FTIR. *Journal of Molecular Biology* 401: 56−67. 3.8d Based on PDB ID: 2PTC. M. Marquart, J. Walter, J. Deisenhofer, et al. 1983. The geometry of the reactive site and of the peptide groups in trypsin, trypsinogen and its complexes with inhibitors. *Acta Crystallographica* Section B39: 480−490. 3.11b1 Based on PDB ID: 2MHR. S. Sheriff, W. A. Hendrickson, and J. L. Smith. 1987. Structure of myohemerythrin in the azidomet state at 1.7/1.3 resolution. *Journal of Molecular Biology* 197: 273−296. 3.11b2 Based on PDB ID: 1FTP. N. H. Haunerland, B. L. Jacobson, G. Wesenberg, et al. 1994. Three-dimensional structure of the muscle fatty-acid-binding protein isolated from the desert locust Schistocerca gregaria. *Biochemistry* 33: 12378−12385. 3.11b3 Based on PDB ID: 1IXA. M. Baron, D. G. Norman, T. S. Harvey, et al. 1992. The three-dimensional structure of the first EGF-like module of human factor IX: Comparison with EGF and TGF-alpha. *Protein Science* 1: 81−90. 3.12a Based on PDB ID: 1D1L. P. B. Rupert, A. K. Mollah, M. C. Mossing, et al. 2000. The structural basis for enhanced stability and reduced DNA binding seen in engineered second- generation Cro monomers and dimers. *Journal of Molecular Biology* 296: 1079−1090. 3.12b Based on PDB ID: 2DN2. S.Y. Park, T. Yokoyama, N. Shibayama, et al. 2006. 1.25 Å resolution crystal structures of human hemoglobin in the oxy, deoxy and carbonmonoxy forms. *Journal of Molecular Biology* 360: 690−701. **Case Study** Data from Mitea, C. et al. 2008. *Gut* 57: 25−32.

Chapter 4 4.T1 Based on PDB ID: 1EHZ. H. Shi and P. B. Moore. 2000. The crystal structure of yeast phenylalanine tRNA at 1.93 Å resolution: A classic structure revisited. *RNA* 6: 1091−1105. 4.9 Based on the same PDB file as the 5e figure: 1X8W.

F. Guo, A. R. Gooding, and T. R. Cech. 2004. Structure of the Tetrahymena ribozyme: Base triple sandwich and metal ion at the active site. *Molecular Cell* 16: 351–362. **Case Study** Data from Chargaff, E. 1951. *Federal Proceedings* 10: 654–659.

Chapter 5 **5.7** Based on Florman, H. M., K. B. Bechtol, and P. M. Wassarman. 1984. Enzymatic dissection of the functions of the mouse egg's receptor for sperm. *Developmental Biology* 106: 243–255. Also Florman, H. M., and P. M. Wassarman. 1985. O-linked oligosaccharides of mouse egg ZP3 account for its sperm receptor activity. *Cell* 41: 313–324. **Case Study** Based on R. Agrawal and F. G. Pinilla (2012) "'Metabolic syndrome' in the brain: Deficiency in omega-3 fatty acid exacerbates dsyfunctions in insulin receptor signaling cognition" *Journal of Physiology* 590 (10): 2485–2499. Fig. 1.

Chapter 6 **Opener** Based on CHARMM-GUI Archive—Library of Pure Lipid Bilayer (www.charmm-gui.org/?doc=archive&lib=lipid_pure), POPE Bilayer Library (pope_ n256.pdb). Reference: S. Jo, T. Kim, and W. Im. 2007. Automated builder and database of protein/membrane complexes for molecular dynamics simulations. *PLoS ONE* 2 (9): e880. **6.10** Based on de Gier, J., et al. (1968). Lipid composition and permeability of liposomes. *Biochimica et Biophysica Acta* 150: 666–675. **6.21** Based on Bear, C. A., et al. (1992). Purification and functional reconstitution of the cystic fibrosis transmembrane conductance regulator (CFTR). *Cell* 68: 809–818. **6.22** Based on PDB ID: 2ZZ9. K. Tani, T. Mitsuma, Y. Hiroaki, et al. 2009. Mechanism of aquaporin-4's fast and highly selective water conduction and proton exclusion. *Journal of Molecular Biology* 389: 694–706. **6.23a** Based on PDB ID: 1K4C. Y. Zhou, J. H. Morais-Cabral, A. Kaufman, et al. 2001. Chemistry of ion coordination and hydration revealed by a K+ channel–Fab complex at 2.0 Å resolution. *Nature* 414: 43–48. **6.23b** Based on PDB ID: 3FB7. L. G. Cuello, V. Jogini, D. M. Cortes, et al. Open KcsA potassium channel in the presence of Rb+ ion. (To be published.) **Case Study** Data from Bassett CM, McCullough RS, Edel AL, Maddaford TG, Dibrov E, Blackwood DP, Austria JA, Pierce GN. Trans-fatty acids in the diet stimulate atherosclerosis. 2009. *Metabolism* 58: 1802–1808. doi: 10.1016/j.metabol.2009.06.010.

Chapter 7 **7.2** Data from Jamieson, J. D., and Palade, G. E. 1967. *Journal of Cell Biology* 34: 597–615. **7.5** Republished with permission of Springer Science+Business Media B.V. from David S. Goodsell, *The Machinery of Life*. 2nd ed., 2009. permission conveyed through Copyright Clearance Center, Inc. **7.18** Based on Mills, A. D., R. A. Laskey, P. Black, et al. 1980. An acidic protein which assembles nucleosomes in vitro is the most abundant protein in Xenopus oocyte nuclei. *Journal of Molecular Biology* 139: 561–568; Dingwall, C., S. V. Sharnick, and R. A. Laskey. 1982. A polypeptide domain that specifies migration of nucleoplasmin into the nucleus. *Cell* 30: 449–458. **Case Study** D. Murase et al. 2013. *Journal of Investigative Dermatology* 133: 2416–2424.

Chapter 8 **8.4** A. G. Volkov et al. 2010. *Plant, Cell & Environment* 33: 163–173. **8.8a** Based on PDB ID: 1Q18. V. V. Lunin, Y. Li, J. D. Schrag, et al. 2004. Crystal structures of Escherichia coli ATP-dependent glucokinase and its complex with glucose. *Journal of Bacteriology* 186: 6915–6927. **8.8b** Based on PDB ID: 2Q2R. A. T. Cordeiro, A. J. Caceres, D. Vertommen, et al. 2007. The crystal structure of Trypanosoma cruzi glucokinase reveals features determining oligomerization and anomer specificity of hexose-phosphorylating enzymes. *Journal of Molecular Biology* 372: 1215–1226. **8.15** Data from Nawani, N., B. P. Kapadnis, A. D. Das, et al. 2002. *Journal of Applied Microbiology* 93: 865–975. Also Nawani, N., and B. P. Kapadnis. 2001. *Journal of Applied Microbiology* 90: 803–808.

Chapter 9 **9.7** Based on PDB ID: 4PFK. P. R. Evans and P. J. Hudson. 1981. "Phosphofructokinase: Structure and control" Philosophical Transactions of Royal Society of London, Series B: Biological Sciences 293: 53–62. **9.13** Data from Li, X., R. K. Dash, R. K. Pradhan, et al. 2010. *Journal of Physical Chemistry B* 114: 16068–16082. **9.14** Data from Wilson, D. F., M. Erecinska, and P. L. Dutton. 1974. *Annual Review of Biophysics and Bioengineering* 3: 203–230. Also Sled, V. D., N. I. Rudnitzky, Y. Hatefi, et al. 1994. *Biochemistry* 33: 10069–10075. **9.17** Based on Racker, E., and W. Stoeckenius. 1974. Reconstitution of purple membrane vesicles catalyzing light-driven proton uptake and adenosine triphosphate formation. *Journal of Biological Chemistry* 249: 662–663. **Case Study** C. C. Caldeira da Silva et al. 2008. *Aging Cell* 7: 552–560.

Chapter 10 **10.6** Based on Engelmann, T. W. 1882. Oxygen excretion from plant cells in a microspectrum. *Botanische Zeitung* 40: 419–426. **10.7** Data from Singhal, G. S., et al. 1999. *Concepts in Photobiology: Photosynthesis and Photomorphogenesis*. Fig. 5. Dordrecht: Kluwer Academic; co-published with Narosa Publishing House (New Delhi). **10.11** Based on Govindjee, R., Govindjee, and G. Hoch. 1964. Emerson enhancement effect in chloroplast reactions. *Plant Physiology* 39: 10–14. **10.18** Based on Benson, A. A., J. A. Bassham, M. Calvin, et al. 1950. The path of carbon in photosynthesis. V. Paper chromatography and radioautography of the products. *Journal of the American Chemistry Society* 72: 1710–1718. **10.21** PDB ID: 1RCX. T. C. Taylor and I. Andersson. 1997. The structure of the complex between rubisco and its natural substrate ribulose 1,5-bisphosphate. *Journal of Molecular Biology* 265: 432–444. **Case Study** J. H. Mussgnug et al. 2007. *Plant Biotechnology Journal* 5: 802–814.

Chapter 11 **11.3** Republished with permission of Springer Science+Business Media B.V. from David S. Goodsell, *The Machinery of Life*. 2nd ed., 2009. permission conveyed through Copyright Clearance Center, Inc. **11.8** Republished with permission of Garland Science Books, From B. Alberts, A. Johnson, J. Lewis, et al. 2002. *Molecular*

Biology of the Cell 4: 1069, Fig. 19.5. Permission conveyed through Copyright Clearance Center, Inc. **11.10** Based on Hatta, K., and M. Takeichi. 1986. Expression of N-cadherin adhesion molecules associated with early morphogenetic events in chick development. *Nature* 320: 447–449.; Takeichi, M. 1988. The cadherins: Cell–cell adhesion molecules controlling animal morphogenesis. *Development* 102: 639–655. **Case Study** M. Malleshaiah et al. 2010. *Nature* 456: 101–105.

Chapter 12 **12.9** Based on J. L. Ptacin, S. F. Lee, E. C. Garner, et al. 2010. A spindle-like apparatus guides bacterial chromosome segregation. *Nature Cell Biology* 12: 791–798, Fig. 5. **12.10** Based on Masui, Y., and C. L. Markert. 1971. Cytoplasmic control of nuclear behavior during meiotic maturation of frog oocytes. *Journal of Experimental Zoology* 177: 129–145. **12.6** Based on Gorbsky, G. J., et al. 1987. Chromosomes move poleward during anaphase along stationary microtubules that coordinately disassemble from their kinetochore ends. *Journal of Cellular Biology* 104: 9–18. **12.13** Data from the website of the National Cancer Institute (http://www.cancer.gov), *Common Cancer Statistics*, December 2014. **Case Study** C. Miceli et al. 2013. *Cancer Gene Therapy* 20: 298–307.

Chapter 13 **13.1** Adapted from Calvin Bridges, 1915, 1916, in the public domain. **13.8** Based on the Klustein & Cooper 2014. **13.13** Based on data from www.ndss.org, National Down Syndrome Society (2012). **13.15** Based on Morran, L. T., et al. 2011. Running with the red queen: Host–parasite coevolution selects for biparental sex. *Science* 333: 216–218. **Case Study** Data from Chiang, T., F. E. Duncan, K. Schindler, et al. 2010. *Current Biology* 20: 1522–1528.

Chapter 14 **14.T2** Data from Mendel, G. 1866. *Verhandlungen des naturforschenden Vereines in Brünn* 4: 3–47. **14.3** Based on Mendel, G. 1866. Versuche über Pflanzen-hybriden. *Verhandlungen des naturforschenden Vereines in Brünn* 4: 3–47. English translation available from ESP: Electronic Scholarly Publishing, www.esp.org. **14.12** Based on Morgan, T. H. 1911. An attempt to analyze the constitution of the chromosomes on the basis of sex-limited inheritance in Drosophila. *Journal of Experimental Zoology* 11: 365–414. **14.19** Data from Pan American Health Organization/WHO. 2004. *Epidemiological Bulletin* 25: 9–13, Graph 1.

Chapter 15 **15.2** Based on Hershey, A. D., and M. Chase. 1952. Independent functions of viral protein and nucleic acid in growth of bacteriophage. *Journal of General Physiology* 36: 39–56. **15.5** Based on Meselson, M., and F. W. Stahl. 1958. The replication of DNA in Escherichia coli. *Proceedings of the National Academy of Sciences* 44: 671–682. **15.14** Data from Allsopp, R. C., et al. 1992. *Proceedings of the National Academy of Sciences* 82: 10114–10118. **15.18** Data from Cleaver, J. E. 1972. *Journal of Investigative Dermatology* 58: 124–128, Fig. 1. **Case Study** Data from Fournier, B., et al. 2000. *Antimicrobial Agents and Chemotherapy* 44: 2160–2165.

Chapter 16 **16.2** Based on Srb, A. M., and N. H. Horowitz. 1944. The ornithine cycle in Neurospora and its genetic control. *Journal of Biological Chemistry* 154: 129–139. **Case Study** Data from R. L. Lamason et al. 2005. *Science* 310: 1782–1786.

Chapter 17 **17.2a** Based on PDB ID: 3IYD. B. P. Hudson, J. Quispe, S. Lara-Gonzalez, et al. 2009. Three-dimensional EM structure of an intact activator-dependent transcription initiation complex. *Proceedings of the National Academy of Sciences* 106: 19830–19835. **17.10** Based on Hoagland, M. B., M. L. Stephenson, J. F. Scott, et al. 1958. A soluble ribonucleic acid intermediate in protein synthesis. *Journal of Biological Chemistry* 231: 241–257. **17.12** Based on PDB ID: 1ZJW: I. Gruic-Sovulj, N. Uter, T. Bullock, et al. 2005. tRNA-dependent aminoacyl-adenylate hydrolysis by a nonediting class I aminoacyl-tRNA synthetase. *Journal of Biological Chemistry* 280: 23978–23986. **17.13b** Based on PDB IDs: 3FIK, 3FIH. E. Villa, J. Sengupta, L. G. Trabuco, et al. 2009. Ribosome-induced changes in elongation factor Tu conformation control GTP hydrolysis. *Proceedings of the National Academy of Sciences* 106: 1063–1068. **Case Study** Lindell, T.J., F. Weinberg, P.W. Morris, R.G. Roeder, and W.J. Rutter (1970). Specific inhibition of nuclear RNA polymerase II by alpha-amanitin. *Science* 170: 447–449, Fig. 2.

Chapter 18 **18.3** Based on Pardee, A. B., F. Jacob, and J. Monod. 1959. The genetic control and cytoplasmic expression of "inducibility" in the synthesis of ß-galactosidase by E. coli. *Journal of Molecular Biology* 1: 165–178.

Chapter 19 **Opener** Based on PDB ID: 1ZBB. T. Schalch, S. Duda, D. F. Sargent, et al. 2005. X-ray structure of a tetranucleosome and its implications for the chromatin fibre. *Nature* 436: 138–141. **19.3** Bolzer A, Kreth G, Solovei I, Koehler D, Saracoglu K, et al. (2005) Three-Dimensional Maps of All Chromosomes in Human Male Fibroblast Nuclei and Prometaphase Rosettes. *PLoS Biol* 3 (5): e157. doi: 10.1371/journal.pbio.0030157. http://127.0.0.1:8081/plosbiology/article?id=info:doi/10.1371/journal.pbio.0030157. **19.6** Based on Sandovici, I., N. H. Smith, and M. D. Nitert. 2011. Maternal diet and aging alter the epigenetic control of a promoter–enhancer interaction at the Hnf4a gene in rat pancreatic islets. *Proceedings of the National Academy of Sciences* 108: 5449–5454. **19.8b** PDB ID: 1MDY. P. C. Ma, M. A. Rould, H. Weintraub, et al. 1994. Crystal structure of MyoD bHLH domain–DNA complex: Perspectives on DNA recognition and implications for transcriptional activation. *Cell* 77: 451–459. **Case Study** C.A. Guenther et al. 2014. *Nature Genetics* 46: 748–752.

Chapter 20 **Opener** Data from V. Pancaldi et al. 2012. Predicting the Fission Yeast Protein Interaction Network. *G3: Genes, Genomes, Genetics* 2: 453–467. **20.5a** Data from Hou, Y., and S. Lin. 2009. PLoS ONE 4(9): e6978, Supplemental Table S1.

20.5b Data from KEGG: Kyoto Encyclopedia of Genes and Genomes, KEGG Organisms: Complete Genomes. www.genome.jp/kegg/. **20.10** Data from Gregory, T. R. 2005. *Nature Reviews Genetics* 6: 699–708.

Chapter 21 **21.12** Reprinted by permission from Macmillan Publishers Ltd after J. C. Pearson, D. Lemons, and W. McGinnis. 2005. Modulating Hox gene functions during animal body patterning. *Nature Reviews Genetics* 6: 893–904, Fig. 1. **21.13** Based on Weintraub, H., S. J. Tapscott, R. L. Davis, et al. 1989. Activation of muscle-specific genes in pigment, nerve, fat, liver, and fibroblast cell lines by forced expression of MyoD. *Proceedings of the National Academy of Sciences* 86: 5434–5438.

Chapter 22 **22.4** Based on E. B. Daeschler et al. 2006. A Devonian tetrapod-like fish and the evolution of the tetrapod body plan. *Nature* 440: 757–763, Fig. 6; P. E. Ahlberg and J. A. Clack. 2006. A firm step from water to land. *Nature* 440: 747–749, Fig. 1; N. H. Shubin et al. 2006. The pectoral fin of Tiktaalik roseae and the origin of the tetrapod limb. *Nature* 440: 764–771, Fig. 4; M. Hildebrand and G. Goslow. 2001. *Analysis of Vertebrate Structures* 5. **22.8b** Republished with permission of AAAS after P. D. Gingerich, M. ul Haq, I. S. Zalmout, et al. 2001. Origin of whales from early Artiodactyls: Hands and feet of Eocene Protocetidae from Pakistan. *Science* 293: 2239–2242, (http://www.sciencemag.org/content/293/5538/2239.abstract); permission conveyed through Copyright Clearance Center, Inc. **22.8c** Republished with permission of AAAS after P. D. Gingerich, M. ul Haq, I. S. Zalmout, et al. 2001. Origin of whales from early Artiodactyls: Hands and feet of Eocene Protocetidae from Pakistan. *Science* 293: 2239–2242, Fig. 3. (http://www.sciencemag.org/content/293/5538/2239. abstract); permission conveyed through Copyright Clearance Center, Inc. **22.8e** Delphinapterus reproduced by permission of Skulls Unlimited International, Inc. (www.SkullsUnlimited.com). **22.11** Based on data from Centers for Disease Control, 2004. **22.13** Based on Boag, P. T., and P. R. Grant. 1981. Intense natural selection in a population of Darwin's finches (Geospizinae) in the Galápagos. *Science* 214: 82–85. **22.14** Based on data from Grant, P. R., and B. R. Grant. 2002. *Science* 296: 707–711; Grant, P. R., and B. R. Grant. 2006. *Science* 313: 224–226. **22.15** Based on Fig. 3 in Campas, O. et al. 2010. Scaling and shar transformations capture beak shape variation in Darwin's finches. *Proceedings of the National Academy of Sciences* 107 (8): 3356–3360. **22.8a** Reprinted by permission from Macmillan Publishers Ltd: J. G. M. Thewissen, L. N. Cooper, M. T. Clementz, et al. Whales originated from aquatic artiodactyls in the Eocene epoch of India, *Nature* 450: 1190–1194, Copyright 2007. **Case Study** Based on Vignieri, S. N., J. G. Larson, and H. E. Hoekstra. 2010. *Evolution* 64: 2153–2158.

Chapter 23 **23.T1** Data from W. C. Boyd. 1950. Boston: Little, Brown and Company. **23.T2** Markow, T., P. H. Hedrick, K. Zuerlein, et al. 1993. *American Journal of Human Genetics* 53: 943–952, Table 3. **23.4** Johnson, W. E., E. P. Onorato, M. E. Roelke, et al. 2010. *Science* 329: 1641–1645. **23.5** Brown, C. R., and M. B. Brown. 1998. *Evolution* 52: 1461–1475. **23.6** Karn, M. N., H. Lang-Brown, J. J. MacKenzie, et al. 1951. *Annals of Eugenics* 15: 306–322. **23.7** Smith, T. B. 1987. *Nature* 329: 717–719. **23.9b** Blount, J. D., N. B. Metcalf, T. R. Birkhead, et al. 2003. *Science* 300: 125–127. **23.10bc** Le Boeuf, B. J., and R. S. Peterson. 1969. *Science* 163: 91–93. **23.12** Reproduced by permission of Pearson Education, Inc., from S. Freeman and J. Herron. 2004. *Evolutionary Analysis* 3. Figs. 6.15a, 6.15c. ©2004. **23.13** Based on Kerr, W. E., and S. Wright. 1954. Experimental studies of the distribution of gene frequencies in very small populations of Drosophila melanogaster: I. Forked. *Evolution* 8: 172–177. **23.13b** Araki, H., B. Cooper, and M. S. Blouin. 2009. *Biology Letters* 5 (5): 621–624. **23.17** Data from Lenski, R. E. and M. Travisano. 1994. *Proceedings of the National Academy of Sciences* 91: 6808–6814. **23.18b** Based on N. Moran and T. Jarvik. 2010. Lateral transfer of genes from fungi underlies carotenoid production in aphids. *Science* 328: 624–627. **Case Study** Data from Galetti, M, R. Guevara, and M. C. Côrtes, et al. 2013. *Science* 340: 1086–1090.

Chapter 24 **24.1** Republished with permission of Royal Society, from Ribas C. et al. 2011. A paleobiogeographic model for biotic diversification within Amazonia over the past three million years, *Proceedings of the Royal Society B* 279: 681–689; permission conveyed through Copyright Clearance Center, Inc. **24.2** Roca, A. L., et al. 2001. *Science* 293: 1473–1477. **24.3** Based on Avise, J. C., and W. S. Nelson. 1989. *Science* 243: 646–648. **24.5** Based on Ribas, C., et al. 2012. *Proceedings of the Royal Society B* 279: 681–689. **24.8** Dambroski, H. R., C. Linn Jr., S. H. Berlocher, et al. 2005. *Evolution* 59: 1953–1964. **24.11** Rohwer, S., E. Bermingham, and C. Wood. 2001. *Evolution* 55: 405–422. **24.12** Based on Rieseberg, L. H., B. Sinervo, C. R. Linder, et al. 1996. Role of gene interactions in hybrid speciation: Evidence from ancient and experimental hybrids. *Science* 272: 741–745. **Case Study** Based on Prüfer, K., et al. 2014. *Nature* 505: 43–49.

Chapter 25 **25.T1** E. Cline. 2012. *Food Research International* 45: 388–393. **25.4c** Data for (c): Nikaido, M., A. P. Rooney, and N. Okada. 1999. *Proceedings of the National Academy of Sciences* 96: 10261–10266. **25.5** International Stratigraphic Chart, 2009. International Commission on Stratigraphy (www.stratigraphy.org/column.php?id=Chart/TimeScale). The data on this site are modified from F. M. Gradstein and J. C. Ogg (eds.). 2004. *A Geologic Time Scale 2004*. Cambridge, UK: Cambridge University Press; and J. G. Ogg, G. Ogg, and F. M. Gradstein. 2008. The Concise Geologic Time Scale. Cambridge, UK: Cambridge University Press. **25.6**

International Commission on Stratigraphy, February 2014. http://www.stratigraphy.org/ICSchart/ChronostratChart2014-02.pdf. **25.7** B. G. Baldwin, D. W. Kyhos, and J. Dvorak. 1990. Chloroplast DNA evolution and adaptive radiation in the Hawaiian Silversword Alliance (Asteraceae—Madiinae). *Annals of the Missouri Botanical Garden* 77 (1): 96–109, Fig. 2. **25.8c** Based on J. B Losos, K. I. Warheit, and T. W. Schoener. 1997. Adaptive differentiation following experimental island colonization in Anolis lizards. *Nature* 387: 70–73. **25.11** J. W. Valentine, D. H. Erwin, and D. Jablonski. 1996. Developmental evolution of metazoan body plans: The fossil evidence. *Developmental Biology* 173: 373–381, Fig. 3. Also R. de Rosa et al. 1999. Hox genes in brachiopods and priapulids and protostome evolution. *Nature* 399: 772–776; D. Chourrout, F. Delsuc, P. Chourrout, et al. 2006. Minimal ProtoHox cluster inferred from bilaterian and cnidarian Hox complements. *Nature* 442: 684–687. **25.12** Benton, M. J., 1995. *Science* 268: 52–58. **TYPSS** Figure 2 in Liu. W. et al. 2010. Origin of human malaria parasite Plasmodium falciparum in gorillas. *Nature* 467: 420–427 **Case Study** Data from Godefroit, P., A. Cau, H. Dong-Yu, F. Escuillie, W. Wenhao, and G. Dyke. 2013. A Jurassic avialan dinosaur from China resolves the early phylogenetic history of birds. *Nature* 498: 359–362.

Chapter 26 **26.3** Based on Liu, S. V., J. Zhou, C. Zhang, et al. 1997. Thermophilic Fe(III)-reducing bacteria from the deep subsurface: the evolutionary implications. *Science* 277: 1106–1109. **26.12** Wilson, D. F., M. Erecinska, and P. L. Dutton. 1974. *Annual Review of Biophysics and Bioengineering* 3: 203–230; Tables 1 and 3.

Chapter 27 **27.6** S. M. Adl, A. G. Simpson, M. A. Farmer, et al. 2005. The new higher level classification of eukaryotes with emphasis on the taxonomy of protists. *Journal of Eukaryotic Microbiology* 52: 399–451. Also N. Arisue, M. Hasegawa, and T. Hashimoto. 2005. Root of the eukaryota tree as inferred from combined maximum likelihood analyses of multiple molecular sequence data. *Society for Molecular Biology and Evolution* 22: 409–420; V. Hampl, L. Hug, J. W. Leigh, et al. 2009. Phylogenomic analyses support the monophyly of Excavata and resolve relationships among eukaryotic "supergroups." *Proceedings of the National Academy of Sciences* 106 (10): 3859–3864, Figs. 1, 2, 3; J. D. Hackett, H. S. Yoon, S. Li, et al. 2007. Phylogenomic analysis supports the monophyly of cryptophytes and haptophytes and the association of Rhizaria with chromalveolates. *Molecular Biology and Evolution* 24: 1702–1713, Fig. 1; P. Schaap, T. Winckler, M. Nelson, et al. 2006. Molecular phylogeny and evolution of morphology in the social amoebas. *Science* 314: 661–663. **Case Study L** Adamatzky, Andrew. Slime Mold Solves Maze in One Pass, Assisted by Gradient of Chemo-Attractants. *IEEE Transactions on Nanobioscience* 11 (2): 131, Fig. 1d. **Case Study R** Reid, C. R., et al. 2012. Slime mold uses an externalized spatial "memory" to navigate in complex environments. *Proceedings of the National Academy of Science* 109: 17490–17494.

Chapter 28 **28.6** Based on Y.-L. Qiu, L. Li, B. Wang, et al. 2006. The deepest divergences in land plants inferred from phylogenomic evidence. *Proceedings of the National Academy of Sciences* 103 (42): 15511–15516, Fig. 1. **28.9** Based on K. S. Renzaglia, S. Schuette, R. J. Duff, et al. 2007. Bryophyte phylogeny: Advancing the molecular and morphological frontiers. American Bryological and Lichenological Society, *The Bryologist* 110 (2): 179–213. **28.21** Based on Hoballah, M. E., T. Gübitz, J. Stuurman, et al. 2007. Single gene-mediated shift in pollinator attraction in Petunia. *The Plant Cell* 19: 779–790. **28.23** Based on J.F. Pombert, C. Otis, C. Lemieux, et al. 2005. The chloroplast genome sequence of the green alga Pseudendoclonium akinetum (Ulvophyceae) reveals unusual structural features and new insights into the branching order of chlorophyte lineages. *Molecular Biology and Evolution* 22: 1903–1918. **28.25** Based on P. S. Soltis and D. E. Soltis. 2004. The origin and diversification of angiosperms. *American Journal of Botany* 91 (10): 1614–1626, Figs. 1, 2, 3. **Case Study** Cronberg, N., Natcheva, R., and Hedlund, K. 2006. *Science* 313: 1255.

Chapter 29 **29.9** Based on S. M. Adl, A. G. Simpson, M. A. Farmer, et al. 2005. The new higher level classification of eukaryotes with emphasis on the taxonomy of protists. *Journal of Eukaryotic Microbiology* 52: 399–451. **29.10** Based on T. Y. James, F. Kauff, C. L. Schoch, et. al. 2006. Reconstructing the early evolution of fungi using a six-gene phylogeny. *Nature* 443: 818–822, Fig. 1. **29.11** Based on Finlay, R. D., and B. Söderström. 1992. Mycorrhiza and carbon flow to the soil. In Mycorrhizal Functioning. An Integrative Plant-Fungal Process. Ed. M. J. Allen. 134–160. New York: Chapman. Bücking, H., and W. Heyser. 2001. Microau-toradiographic localization of phosphate and carbohydrates in mycorrhizal roots of Populus tremula × Populus alba and the implications for transfer processes in ectomy-corrhizal associations. *Tree Physiology* 21: 101–107. **Case Study** Yafetto, L., et al. 2008. *PLoS ONE*, 3 (9): e3237.

Chapter 30 **30.2** Based on A. M. A. Aguinaldo, J. M. Turbeville, L. S. Linford, et al. 1997. Evidence for a clade of nematodes, arthropods, and other moulting animals. *Nature* 387: 489–493, Figs. 1, 2, 3. **30.7** Based on Finnerty, J. R., K. Pang, P. Burton, et al. 2004. Origins of bilateral symmetry: Hox and dpp expression in a sea anemone. *Science* 304: 1335–1337. **30.11** Panganiban, G., S. M. Irvine, C. Lower, et al. 1997. *Proceedings of the National Academy of Sciences* 94: 5162–5166. **Case Study** Sperling, E. A., C. A. Frieder, A. V. Raman, et al. 2013. *Proceedings of the National Academy of Sciences* 110: 13446–13451.

Chapter 31 **31.1** The IUCN Red List of Threatened Species. Version 2014.3. **31.2** Based on A. M. A. Aguinaldo, J. M. Turbeville, L. S. Linford, et al. 1997. Evidence for a clade of nematodes, arthropods, and other moulting animals. *Nature* 387: 489–493, Figs. 1, 2, 3. Also C. W. Dunn, A. Hejnol, D. Q. Matus, et al. 2008. Broad phylogenomic sampling improves resolution of the animal tree of life. *Nature* 452: 745–750, Figs. 1, 2. **31.15** Based on data in J. Regier, J. W. Schultz, A. Zwick, et al. 2010. Arthropod relationships revealed by phylogenomic analysis of nuclear protein-coding sequences. *Nature* 463: 1079–1083. **Case Study** Averof, M., and N. H. Patel. 1997. *Nature* 388: 682–686.

Chapter 32 **32.1** C. W. Dunn, A. Hejnol. D. Q. Matus, et al. 2008. Broad phylogenomic sampling improves resolution of the animal tree of life. *Nature* 452: 745–750, Figs. 1, 2. **32.2** Based on J. Z. Li, D. M. Absher, H. Tang, et al. 2008. Worldwide human relationships inferred from genome-wide patterns of variation. *Science* 319: 1100–1104, Fig. 1. **32.4** Paine, R. T. 1966. *American Naturalist* 100: 65–75. **32.6** American Museum of Natural History; birdlife.org; fishbase.org; IUCN red list 2010; Reptile-database.org. **32.7** Based on J. E. Blair and S. B. Hedges. 2005. Molecular phylogeny and divergence times of deuterostome animals. *Molecular Biology and Evolution* 22: 2275–2284, Figs. 1, 3, 4. **32.T8** Robson, S. L., and B. Wood. 2008. *Journal of Anatomy* 212: 394–425; Berger, L. R. et al. 2015. eLife 4e09560. **32.9** Based on E. B. Daeschler, N. H. Shubin, F. A. Jenkins, et al. 2006. A Devonian tetrapod-like fish and the evolution of the tetrapod body plan. *Nature* 440: 757–763, Fig. 6. **32.12** Color plate by Michael DiGiorgio. From Q. Li, K.-Q. Gao, J. Vinther, et al. 2010. Plumage color patterns of an extinct dinosaur. *Science* 327: 1371, Fig. 4. Reprinted by permission of the artist, Michael DiGiorgio. **32.16** A. B. Prasad, M. W. Allard, E. D. Green, et al. 2008. Confirming the phylogeny of mammals by use of large comparative sequence data sets. *Molecular Biology and Evolution* 25 (9): 1795–1808, Figs. 1, 2, 3. Oxford University Press. **32.17** Stringer, C. 2014. *Nature* 514: 427–429. **32.21** After L. L. Cavalli-Sforza and M. W. Feldman. 2003. The application of molecular genetic approaches to the study of human evolution. *Nature Genetics Supplement* 33: 266–275, Fig. 3; Data: Genographic Project at National Geographic: https://genographic.nationalgeographic.com/genographic/lan/en/atlas.html; dates from August 2009 summary map: http://ngm.nationalgeographic.com/big-idea/02/queens-genes; M. Rasmussen, X. Guo, Y. Wang, et al. 2011. An Aboriginal Australian genome reveals separate human dispersals into Asia. *Science* 334: 94–98. **Case Study** Luo, X-X. 2011. *Annual Review of Evolution, Ecology, and Systematics* 42: 355–350.

Chapter 33 **33.2** Arias, E. 2010. United States life tables, 2006. *National Vital Statistics Reports* 58 (21): 1–40, Table 10. Hyattsville, MD: National Center for Health Statistics. **33.3** Pantaleo, G., and Fauci, A. S. 1996. *Annual Review of Microbiology* 50: 825–854. **33.7** Courtesy of the Undergraduate Biotechnology Laboratory, California Polytechnic State University, San Luis Obispo. **33.8** Based on Dalgleish, A. G., P. C. Beverley, P. R. Clapham, et al. 1984. The CD4 (T4) antigen is an essential component of the receptor for the AIDS retrovirus. *Nature* 312: 763–767. Also Klatzmann, D., E. Champagne, S. Chamaret, et al. 1984. T-lymphocyte T4 molecule behaves as the receptor for human retrovirus LAV. *Nature* 312: 767–768. **33.16** Based on F. Gao, E. Bailes, D. L. Robertson, et al. 1999. Origin of HIV-1 in the chimpanzee Pan troglodytes troglodytes. *Nature* 397: 436–441, Fig. 2. **Case Study** E. Miller et al. 2012. *EMBO Journal* 31: 1947–1960.

Chapter 34 **34.4** Based on Clausen, J., D. D. Keck, and W. M. Hiesey. 1940. Experimental studies on the nature of species. I. Effect of varied environments on western North American plants. Publication 520. Washington, DC: Carnegie Institution. **Case Study** Based on Fan, H. B. and Y. H. Wang. 2000. *Forest Ecology and Management* 126: 321–329.

Chapter 35 **35.3** Cline, R. G., and W. S. Campbell. 1976. *Ecology* 57: 367–373. **35.12** Based on Wei, C., M. T. Tyree, and E. Steudle. 1999. Direct measurement of xylem pressure in leaves of intact maize plants. A test of the cohesion-tension theory taking hydraulic architecture into consideration. *Plant Physiology* 121: 1191–1205. **35.21** Data from Gottwald, J. R., P. J. Krysan, J. C. Young, et al. 2000. *Proceedings of the National Academy of Sciences* 97: 13979–13984. **Case Study T** Data from Emmy I. Lammertsma, Hugo Jan de Boer, Stefan C. Dekker, David L. Dilcher, André F. Lotter, and Friederike Wagner-Cremer. Global CO2 rise leads to reduced maximum stomatal conductance in Florida vegetation. *Proceedings of the National Academy of Sciences* 2011; published ahead of print February 17, 2011, doi:10.1073/pnas.1100371108. **Case Study B** Data from E. I. Lammertsma et al. 2011. *Proceedings of the National Academy of Sciences* 108: 4035–4040.

Chapter 36 **36.3** Based on D. I. Arnon and P. R. Stout. 1939. The essentiality of certain elements in minute quantity for plants with special reference to copper. *Plant Physiology* 14: 371–375. **Case Study** Data from Bazile, V. et al. 2012. *PLoS ONE* 7: e36179.

Chapter 37 **37.T1** H. A. Borthwick, S. B. Hendricks, M. W. Parker, et al. 1952. A reversible photoreaction controlling seed germination. *Proceedings of the National Academy of Sciences* 38: 662–666, Table 1. **37.5** Based on Darwin, C., and F. Darwin. 1897. *The Power of Movement in Plants*. New York: D. Appleton & Co. **37.11** Based on Lang, A., M. K. Chailakhyan, and I. A. Frolova. 1977. Promotion and inhibition of flower formation in a day-neutral plant in grafts with a short-day plant and a long-day plant. *Proceedings of the National Academy of Sciences* 74: 2412–2416. **37.21** Based on Blackman, P. G., and W. J. Davies. 1985. Root to shoot communication in maize plants of the effects of soil drying. *Journal of Experimental Botany* 36: 39–48. **Case Study** A. G. Volkov et al. 2010. *Plant, Cell & Environment* 33: 163–173.

Chapter 38 **38.9** Based on Y.-L. Qiu, L. Li, B. Wang, et al. 2006. The deepest divergences in land plants inferred from phylogenomic evidence. *Proceedings of the National Academy of Sciences* 103 (42): 15511–15516, Fig. 1. **38.14** Based on Tewksbury, J. J., and G. P. Nabhan. 2001. Directed deterrence by capsaicin in chilies. *Nature* 382: 403–404. **Case Study** Chautá-Mellizo, A., S. Campbell, M. Argenis Bonilla et al. 2012. *Basic and Applied Ecology* 13: 524–532.

Chapter 39. **39.2** Based on Kerr, A. M., S. N. Gershman, and S. K. Sakaluk. 2010. Experimentally induced spermatophore production and immune responses reveal a trade-off in crickets. *Behavioral Ecology* 21: 647–654. **39.10** K. Schmidt-Nielsen. 1984. *Scaling: Why Is Animal Size So Important?* Cambridge, UK: Cambridge University Press **39.11** Based on Wells, P. R., and A. W. Pinder. 1996. The respiratory development of Atlantic salmon. *Journal of Experimental Biology* 1996: 2737–2744. **Case Study** Based on Jaffe, A. L., G. J. Slater, and M. E. Alfaro. 2011. *Biology Letters* 7: 558–561.

Chapter 40 **40.11** K. J. Ullrich, K. Kramer, and J.W. Boyer. 1961. *Progress in Cardiovascular Diseases* 3: 395–431. **40.16** Davis, J. R., and D. F. DeNardo. 2007. *The Journal of Experimental Biology* 210: 1472–1480. **Case Study** Data from Camargo, M. M. P., M. N. Fernandes, and C. B. R. Martinez. 2009. *Aquatic Toxicology* 94: 40–46.

Chapter 41 **41.14** Based on Wright, E. M. 1993. The intestinal Na+/glucose cotransporter. *Annual Review of Physiology* 55: 575–589. **41.17** N. T. Nguyen, et al. 2011. *Obesity Surgery* 21: 351–355. **Case Study** D. P. German et al. 2010. *Physiological and Biochemical Zoology* 83: 1–18.

Chapter 42 **42.8** Based on Komai, Y. 1998. *The Journal of Experimental Biology* 201: 2359–2366. **42.10** Berner, R. A. 1999. *Proceedings of the National Academy of Sciences* 96: 10955–10957. **42.13** Based on W. Bretz and K. Schmidt Nielsen. 1971. Bird respiration: Flow patterns in the duck lung. *Journal of Experimental Biology* 54: 103–118. **42.22** E. H. Starling. 1896. On the absorption of fluids from the connective tissue spaces. *Journal of Physiology* 19: 312–326. **42.24** Based on J. E. Blair and S. B. Hedges. 2005. Molecular phylogeny and divergence times of deuterostome animals. *Molecular Biology and Evolution* 22: 2275–2284, Figs. 1, 3, 4. **Case Study** Data from Shapiro, L. M. 1984. *British Heart Journal* 52: 130–135.

Chapter 43 **43.9** Based on Loewi, O. 1921. Über humorale Übertragbarkeit der Herznervenwirkung. *Pflügers Archiv European Journal of Physiology* 189: 239–242. **43.19** Quiroga, R. Q., L. Reddy, G. Kreiman, et al. 2005. *Nature* 435: 1102–1107. **43.22bc** Martin, K. C., A. Casadio, H. Zhu, et al. 1997. Synapse-specific, long-term facilitation of Aplysia sensory to motor synapses, a function for local protein synthesis in memory storage. *Cell* 91: 927–938. **Case Study** Data from Narahashi, T., E. X. Albuquerque, and D. Deguchi. 1971. Effects of batrachotoxin on membrane potential and conductance of squid giant axons. *The Journal of General Physiology* 58: 54–70.

Chapter 44 **44.2** J. E. Rose, J. E. Hind, D. J. Anderson, et al. 1971. Some effects of stimulus intensity on response of auditory nerve fibers in the squirrel monkey. *Journal of Neurophysiology* 34: 685–699. **44.9** Based on Pohlmann, K., J. Atema, and T. Breithaupt. 2004. The importance of the lateral line in nocturnal predation of piscivorous catfish. *The Journal of Experimental Biology* 207: 2971–2978. **44.15** Based on D. M. Hunt, K. S. Dulai, J. K. Bowmaker, et al. 1995. The chemistry of John Dalton's color blindness. *Science* 267: 984–988, Fig. 3. **TYPSS** McClintock, M. K. 1971. Menstrual synchrony and suppression. *Nature* 229: 244–245, Figure 1. **Case Study** Data from Hoover, S. E. R., Keeling, C. I., Winston, M. L., and Slessor, K. N. (2003). The effect of queen pheromones on worker honey bee ovary development. *Naturwissenschaften* 90: 477–480.

Chapter 45 **45.3** Based on PDB ID: 1KWO. D. M. Himmel, S. Gourinath, L. Reshetnikova, et al. 2002. Crystallographic findings on the internally uncoupled and near-rigor states of myosin: Further insights into the mechanics of the motor. *Proceedings of the National Academy of Sciences* 99: 12645–12650. **45.7** Based on After Exercise Information—Interactive Muscle Map (www.askthetrainer.com/exercise-information/). **45.14** Reprinted with permission of Nature Publishing, after, Anterolateral view reproduced by permission from Macmillan Publishers Ltd after S. E. Pierce, J. A. Clack, and J. R. Hutchinson. 2012. Three-dimensional limb joint mobility in the early tetrapod Ichthyostega. *Nature* 486: 523, Fig. 1. Permission conveyed through Copyright Clearance Center, Inc. **45.17** Based on Hoyt, D. F., and C. R. Taylor. 1981. Gait and the energetics of locomotion in horses. *Nature* 292: 239–240. **45.18** Reprinted with permission from AAAS from K. Schmidt-Nielsen. 1972. Locomotion: Energy cost of swimming, flying, and running. *Science* 177: 222–228. (http://www.sciencemag.org/content/177/4045/222.extract). Permission conveyed through Copyright Clearance Center, Inc. **45.19** Schmidt-Nielsen, K. 1972. Locomotion: Energy cost of swimming, flying, and running. *Science* 177: 222–228. **Case Study** Fink, W. J., D. L. Costill, and M. L. Pollock. 1977. *Annals of the New York Academy of Sciences* 301: 323–327.

Chapter 46 **46.3** Berthold, A. A. 1849. Transplantation der Hoden. *Arch. Anat. Physiol. Wiss. Med.* 16: 42–49. **46.5** Toft, D., and J. Gorski. 1966. *Proceedings of the National Academy of Sciences* 55: 1574–1581. **46.7** Rall, T. W., E. W. Sutherland, and J. Berthet. 1957. *Journal of Biological Chemistry* 224: 463–475. **46.11** Illnerova H., K. Hoffmann, and J. Vanecek. 1984. *Neuroendocrinology* 38: 226–231. **46.13** Based on King, B. D., L.

Sokoloff, and R. L. Wechsler. 1952. The effects of l-epinephrine and l-nor-epinephrine upon cerebral circulation and metabolism in man. *Journal of Clinical Investigation* 31: 273–279.; Mueller, P. S., and D. Horwitz. 1962. Plasma free fatty acid and blood glucose responses to analogues of norepinephrine in man. *Journal of Lipid Research* 3: 251–255. **TYPSS** Hayes, T. B., A. Collins, M. Lee, et al. 2002. *Proceedings of the National Academy of Sciences* 99: 5476–5480. **Case Study** Walker, B. G., P. D. Boersma, J. C. Wingfield. 2006. *Conservation Biology* 20: 146–154.

Chapter 47 **47.11** Based on Price, C. S. C., K. A. Dyer, and J. A. Coyne. 1999. Sperm competition between Drosophila males involves both displacement and incapacitation. *Nature* 400: 449–452. **47.12b** C. Hotzy and G. Arnqvist. 2009. Sperm competition favors harmful males in seed beetles. *Current Biology* 19: 404–407, Fig. 2. **47.15** R. Shine and M. S. Y. Lee. 1999. A reanalysis of the evolution of viviparity and egg-guarding in squamate reptiles. The Herpetologists' League, Inc., *Herpetologica* 55 (4): 538–549, Figs. 1, 2, 3. **47.3a** Data for (a) from R. G. Stross and J. C. Hill. 1965. Diapause induction in Daphnia requires two stimuli. *Science* 150: 1462–1464, Fig. 3. **47.3b** Data for (b) from O. T. Kleiven, P. Larsson, and A. Hobæk. 1992. Sexual reproduction in Daphnia magna requires three stimuli. *Oikos* 65: 197–206, Table 4. **TYPSS** Anderson, S. E., G. E. Dallal, and A. Must. 2003. Relative weight and race influence average age at menarche: results from two nationally representative surveys of US girls studied 25 years apart. *Pediatrics* 111: 844–850. **Case Study** Data from Gaspard, U. J., M. A. Romus, D. Gillain, et al. 1983. Plasma hormone levels in women receiving new oral contraceptives containing ethinyl estradiol plus levonorgestrel or desogestrel. *Contraception* 27: 577–590.

Chapter 48 **48.2** Lemaitre, B., et al. 1996. *Cell* 86: 973–983. **48.5a** Based on PDB ID: 1IGT. L. J. Harris, S. B. Larson, K. W. Hasel, et al. 1997. Refined structure of an intact IgG2a monoclonal antibody. *Biochemistry* 36: 1581–1597. **48.5b** Based on PDB ID: 1TCR. K. C. Garcia, M. Degano, R. L. Stanfield, et al. 1996. An αβ T cell receptor structure at 2.5 Å and its orientation in the TCR–MHC complex. *Science* 274: 209–219. **48.6** Based on PDB ID: 1HMG. M. Knossow, R. S. Daniels, A. R. Douglas, et al. 1984. Three-dimensional structure of an antigenic mutant of the influenza virus haemagglutinin. *Nature* 311 (5987): 678–680. **48.10** Based on PDB ID: 1DLH. L. J. Stern, J. H. Brown, T. S. Jardetzky, et al. 1994. Crystal structure of the human class II MHC protein HLA–DR1 complexed with an influenza virus peptide. *Nature* 368: 215–221. **48.17** Based on B. Alberts, A. Johnson, J. Lewis, et al. 2002. *Molecular Biology of the Cell* 4. New York: Garland Science, Taylor & Francis Group. Modified from Fig. 24-10. **Case Study** Mishra, P. K., et al. 2013. *Mucosal Immunology* 6: 297–308.

Chapter 49 **49.2** Food and Agriculture Organization of the United Nations. **49.5** Based on Menke, S. B., et al. 2007. Biotic and abiotic controls of Argentine ant invasion success at local and landscape scales. *Ecology* 88 (12): 3164–3173. **49.11** Olson, D. M., E. Dinerstein, E. D. Wikramanayake, et al. 2001. Terrestrial ecoregions of the world: A new map of life on earth. *BioScience* 51: 933–938. **49.12** Ellis, E. C., K. Klein Goldewijk, S. Siebert, et al. 2010. Anthropogenic transformation of the biomes, 1700 to 2000. *Global Ecology and Biogeography* 19: 589–606. **49.14a** Saffo, M. B. 1987. New light on seaweeds. *BioScience* 37: 654–664. **Case Study** Data from Green, S. J., et al. 2014. Linking targets to the ecological effects on invaders: A predictive model and field test. *Ecological Applications* 24: 1311–1322.

Chapter 50 **50.3** After M. Sokolowski. 2001. Drosophila: Genetics meets behavior. *Nature Reviews Genetics* 2: 879–890, Fig. 2. **50.4** Based on Abramsky, Z., M. L. Rosenzweig, and A. Subach. 2002. The costs of apprehensive foraging. *Ecology* 85: 1330–1340. **50.5b** Crews, D. 1975. Psychobiology of reptilian reproduction. *Science* 189: 1059–1065. **50.7** Data from T. Driessens, B. Vanhooydonck, and R. Van Damme. 2014. Deterring predators, daunting opponents or drawing partners? Signaling rates across diverse contexts in the lizard Anolis sagrei. *Behavioral Ecology and Sociobiology* 68: 173–184. Figs. 1A and B. **50.9** Based on Lohmann, K. J., C. M. F. Lohmann, L. M. Ehrhart, et al. 2004. Geomagnetic map used in sea-turtle navigation. *Nature* 428: 909–910. **50.10** C. Egevang, et al. 2010. Tracking of Arctic terns Sterna paradisaea reveals longest animal migration. *Proceedings of the National Academy of Sciences* 107 (5): 2078–2081, Fig. 1B. ©2010 National Academy of Sciences, USA. Reprinted with permission. **50.16** Based on Hoogland, J. L. 1983. Nepotism and alarm calling in the black-tailed prairie dog (Cynomys ludovicianus). *Animal Behaviour* 31: 472–479. **Case Study** Data from Goldbogen, J.A., Southall, B.L., DeRuiter, S.L., Calambokidis, J., Friedlaender, A.S., Hazen, E.L., Falcone, E.A., Schorr, G.S., Douglas, A., Moretti, D.J., Kyburg, C., McKenna, M.F., Tyack, P.L. Tyack, P. L. 2013. Blue whales respond to simulated mid-frequency military sonar. *Proceedings of the Royal Society B* 280 (1765), 20130657. doi:10.1098/rspb.2013.0657.

Chapter 51 **51.T1** Based on H. Strijbosch and R. C. M. Creemers, 1988. Comparative demography of sympatric populations of Lacerta vivipara and Lacerta agilis. *Oecologia* 76: 20–26. With kind permission of Springer Science and Business Media. **51.5** Fenchel, T. 1974. *Oecologia* 14: 317–326. **51.6** Gause, G. F. 1934. *The Struggle for Existence*. New York: Hafner Press. **51.7** MacLulich, D. A. 1937. University of Toronto Studies Biological Series 43. **51.8** Based on Krebs, C. J., S. Boutin, R. Boonstra, et al. 1995. Impact of food and predation on the snowshoe hare cycle. *Science* 269: 1112–1115. **51.10** United Nations, World Population Prospects: The 2012 Revision. **51.11** Vince, G. 2011. *Science* 334: 32–37. **51.12** United Nations, World Population Prospects: The 2012 Revision. **Case Study** Dorcas, M. E., J. D. Willson, R. N. Reed, et al. 2012. *Proceedings of the National Academy of Sciences* 109: 2418–2422.

Chapter 52 **52.2** G. F. Gause. 1934. *The Struggle for Existence*. Baltimore, MD: Williams & Wilkins. **52.3** Gause, G. F. 1934. *The Struggle for Existence*. New York: Hafner Press. **52.5** Based on Connell, J. H. 1961. The influence of interspecific competition and other factors on the distribution of the barnacle Chthamalus stellatus. *Ecology* 42: 710–723. **52.7** Grant, P. 1999. Ecology and Evolution of Darwin's Finches. Princeton, NJ: Princeton University Press. **52.10** Based on Leonard, G. H., M. D. Bertness, and P. O. Yund. 1999. Crab predation, waterborne clues, and inducible defenses in the blue mussel, Mytilus edulis. *Ecology* 80: 1–14. **52.13** Based on Cushman, J. H., and T. G. Whitham. 1989. Conditional mutualism in a membracid–ant association: temporal, age-specific, and density-dependent effects. *Ecology* 70: 1040–1047. **52.15** Based on Jenkins, D. G., and A. L. Buikema. 1998. Do similar communities develop in similar sites? A test with zooplankton structure and function. *Ecological Monographs* 68: 421–443. **52.17** Swetnam, T. W. 1993. *Science* 262: 885–889. **52.21a** Adapted by permission of Wiley-Blackwell from R. H. MacArthur and E. O. Wilson. 1963. An equilibrium theory of insular zoogeography. *Evolution* 17 (4): 373–387, Fig. 4. **52.21bc** R. H. MacArthur and E. O. Wilson. 1963. An equilibrium theory of insular zoogeography. *Evolution* 17 (4): 373–387, Fig. 5. **52.22** Reid, W. V., and K. R. Miller. 1989. *Keeping Options Alive: The Scientific Basis for Conserving Biodiversity*. Washington, DC: World Resources Institute. **Case Study** Keesing, F., J. Brunner, S. Duerr, et al. 2009. *Proceedings of the Royal Society B* 276: 3911–3919.

Chapter 53 **53.1** These data are from the Hubbard Brook Experimental Forest. **53.2** Emission Database for Global Atmospheric Research, Ver. 4.2, 2014. **53.7** http://earthobservatory.nasa.gov. **53.8** Leith, H., and R. H. Whittaker (eds.). 1975. Primary Productivity in the Biosphere. *Ecological Studies and Synthesis* 14. New York: Springer-Verlag. **53.11** Data from Likens, G. E., F. H. Bormann, N. M. Johnson, et al. 1970. Effects of forest cutting and herbicide treatment on nutrient budgets in the Hubbard Brook watershed-ecosystem. *Ecological Monographs* 40: 23–47. **53.12** Oki, T., and S. Kanae. 2006. *Science* 313: 1068–1072. **53.13** U.S. Geological Survey. **53.14** Fowler, D., et al. 2013. *Philosophical Transactions of the Royal Society B* 368 (1621): 20130165. **53.16** Hönisch, B., A. Ridgwell, D. N. Schmidt, et al. 2012. *Science* 335: 1058–1063. **53.17** Carbon Dioxide Information Analysis Center. **53.19** NOAA; Karl, T. R., J. M. Melillo, T. C. Peterson, and S. J. Hassol (eds.). 2009. Global Climate Change Impacts in the United States. Cambridge University Press; National Climatic Data Center (http://www.ncdc.noaa.gov). **53.21** Moritz, C., and R. Agudo. 2013. *Science* 341: 504–508; IPCC. 2014. Climate Change 2014: Synthesis Report. Core Writing Team, R. K. Pachauri and L. A. Meyer (eds.). Intergovernmental Panel on Climate Change, Geneva, Switzerland, 151. **53.22** Dai, A. 2013. *Nature Climate Change* 3: 52–58. **53.23** Zhao, M., and S. W. Running. 2010. *Science* 329: 940–943. **Case Study** Brando, P. M., et al. 2014. *Proceedings of the National Academy of Sciences* 111: 6347–6352.

Chapter 54 **54.10** Diamond, J. M. 1975. *Biological Conservation* 7: 129–146. **54.11** Sinervo, B., F. Mendez-de-la-Cruz, D. B. Miles, et al. 2010. *Science* 328: 894–899. **54.2** F.R. Liu, M. M. Miyamoto, N. P. Freire, et al. 2001. Molecular and morphological supertrees for eutherian (placental) mammals. *Science* 291: 1786–1789, Fig. 1. **54.4** Orme, C. D. L., R. G. Davies, M. Burgess, et al. 2005. *Nature* 436: 1016–1019. **54.5** © WWF **54.6** IUCN 2015. The IUCN Red List of Threatened Species. Ver. 2015.2. **54.7** Ventner, O., et al. 2006. *BioScience* 56: 903–910. **54.9** Based on Laurance, W. F., S. G. Laurance, L. V. Ferreira, et al. 1997. Biomass collapse in Amazonian forest fragments. *Science* 278: 1117–1118. **54.12** Based on Tilman, D., J. Knops, D. Wedin, et al. 1997. The influence of functional diversity and composition on ecosystem processes. *Science* 277: 1300–1302. **54.15** Eshel, G., A. Shepon, T. Makov, et al. 2014. *Proceedings of the National Academy of Sciences* 111: 11996–12001. **TYPSS T** A. P. Dobson. 1996. *Conservation and Biodiversity*. Scientific American Library. New York: Freeman. Original source of England maps: Reproduced by permission of the author from D. S. Wilcove, C. H. McLellan, and A. P. Dobson. 1986. Habitat fragmentation in the temperate zone. *Conservation Biology: The Science of Scarcity and Diversity*: 237–256, Fig. 1. Edited by M. E. Soule. Sunderland, MA: Sinauer Associates. **TYPSS B** A. P. Dobson. 1996. Conservation and Biodiversity. Scientific American Library. New York: Freeman. Original source of U.S. Maps: W. B. Greeley, Chief, U.S. Forest Service. 1925. Relation of geography to timber supply. *Economic Geography* 1: 1–11. **Case Study T** Karp, D. S., et al. 2013. *Ecology Letters* 16: 1339–1347. **Case Study B** Karp, D. S., et al. 2013. *Ecology Letters* 16: 1339–1347.

Index

Boldface page numbers indicate a glossary entry; page numbers followed by an *f* indicate a figure; those followed by *t* indicate a table.

Cofactors with enzymes, **182**
Cognitive skills, Bloom's taxonomy of, 53, 53f, 54t
Cohen, Stephen, 648
Cohesins, 254, 278f, 279
Cohesion, **63**, 63f, **734**
Cohesion-tension theory, 732, **734**–737, 735f, 736f, 737f
Cohorts, **1074**
Cold virus, 699
Coleochaetes, 583t
Coleochaetophyceae (coleochaetes), 565f
Coleoptera, 650t
Coleoptiles, **768**, 770–771
Collagen, 83, 84f, 235–236, 236f
Collagen fibers, 822, 822t
Collecting duct, 845, 845f, **850**–851, 850f, 851t
Collenchyma cells, **715**, 715f, 718t
Colon, **868**
Colonies, **617**, 617f, 650t
Colonization, habitat, 1078
Color, flower, 578, 578f, 579f, 769–797, 797f
Color blindness, 311, 312f, 473, 932–933, 933f
Color variations, mutations and, 475–476, 476f
Color vision, 932–934, 933f
Coloration, cryptic, 1098t
Colorimetric signals, 31
Comb jellies, 615t, 630t, 631
Commensal relationships, **599**
Commensalism, **1093**, 1093f, 1103t
Commercial applications, extremophiles and, 520
Commitment, embryonic cell fate and, **430**
Common ancestry, 4–5, 8, 437, 440, 443
Communication, animal, **1061**
    deceitful, 1063–1064, 1063f
    proximate causation of, 1061–1062, 1061f, 1062f
    ultimate causation of, 1062
Communication, plant, 789
Communities, **1031**, **1092**
    biodiversity and stability of, 1153–1154, 1153f
    community ecology and, 1030t, 1031, 1092
    disturbance regimes in, 1107–1108, 1107f
    effects of global climate change on, 1149
    genetic diversity of, 1140
    key attributes of, 1103
    keystone species in, 1104–1105, 1105f
    post-disturbance succession in, 1108–1111, 1108f, 1110f
    predictability of, 1105–1107, 1106f
    structure of, 1103–1107, 1105f, 1106f
Community ecology
    communities in, 1030t, 1031, 1092
    community dynamics in, 1107–1111, 1107f, 1108f, 1110f
    community structure in, 1103–1107, 1105f, 1106f
    global patterns of species richness in, 1113, 1113f
    species interactions in, 1093, 1103t
Companion cells, **717**, 717f, **740**
Comparative genomics, 615, 617
Comparative morphology, 615
Compartmentalization, in eukaryotic cells, 146
Compass orientation, migration and, **1058**–1059, 1059f
Competition, **1093**

in ant behavior, 1052–1053, 1052f
as biotic factor in geographic distribution and abundance of organisms, 1033
competitive exclusion principle of, 1095, 1095f
experimental studies of, 1095–1096, 1096f
fitness and impacts of, 1103t
fitness trade-offs in, 1095
giraffe necks and food vs. sexual, 9–11
intraspecific and interspecific, 1094
male–male, 467–468, 468f
niche differentiation and mechanisms of coexistence vs., 1097, 1097f
niches and, 1094–1097, 1094f, 1095f, 1096f, 1097f
as threat to biodiversity, 1146
Competitive exclusion principle, **1095**, 1095f
Competitive inhibition, 114–115, 115f, **183**, 183f
    of citric acid cycle, 197, 198f
Complement system proteins, 1022f, **1023**
Complementary base pairing, **98**, **319**, 319f
    in DNA synthesis, 100, 100f
    in double helix DNA structure, 98, 98f
    in mistakes in DNA synthesis, 330, 330f
    in RNA secondary structure, 101, 101f
    in RNA synthesis, 103, 103f
    transcription factors and, 386, 386f
    in tRNAs (wobble hypothesis), 358–359
Complementary DNA (cDNA), **401**, **691**
    creating library of, 36, 36f
    deep sequencing for, 414
    in genome annotation, 405
    in long interspersed nuclear element spread, 409f
    searching for, in library, 36–37, 37f
Complementary strand, **100**, 100f
Complete digestive tracts, **860**, 860f
Complete metamorphosis, **652**, 652f
Complexes I-IV, 201, 201f, 202t
Complexity, evolution and, 451t, 452
Compound eyes, **648**–649, **929**–930, 930f
Compound leaves, 710–711, 711f
Compound light microscopes, 33
Compounds, **58**
Compression fossil, 503t
Compression-resisting elements, 235, 235f
Computer programs
    asteroid impact models, 512
    genetic drift simulations, 470, 470f
    in parsimony analysis, 500
Concentration
    hormone, 966–967
    of reactants, 173–175, 174f
Concentration gradient, **127**
    diffusion across, 127
    loop of Henle creation of, 847–850, 848f, 849f
    morphogen, 424–425, 425f
    osmoregulation and, 837
    in proximal tubule, 847, 847f
    tips on modeling, 135
Concept maps, 46–47, 47f
Concurrent exchange, 878, 879f
Condensation, chromosome, 276–277f, 278f, 279
Condensation reactions, **81**, 81f
    monosaccharide polymerization with, 110
Condensed replicated chromosomes, 254, 254f, 257
Condoms, 1002t

Conducting cells, plant, 732
Conduction, heat exchange using, **831**, 831f
Cones
    eye, **930**–934, 931f, 933f
    gymnosperm, 576, 586t
Confocal microscopy, 35, 35f
Conformation, in homeostasis, **829**
Conjugation, **525**
    prokaryote genetic variation with, 525–526, 526f
Connective tissue, **822**–823, 822t
Connell, Joseph, 1095, 1096f
Conservation, soil, 751–752, 752f
Conservation biology, **1031**, **1140**
    addressing ultimate causes of biodiversity losses in, 1156, 1156f
    bioremediation in, 522
    conservation of ecosystem function in, 1159
    conservation of genetic diversity, populations, and species in, 1157–1159, 1158t
    ecology and, 1031
    estimating biodiversity using surveys in, 1142, 1143f
    genetic drift in, 470
    mapping of biodiversity in, 1142–1144, 1143f, 1145f
    phylogenetic species concept and, 484–485, 484f
    population ecology role in, 1087–1089, 1087f, 1088f, 1089f
    population growth equations in, 1078
    predicting extinctions in, 1149–1151, 1150f, 1151f
    preservation of phylogenetically distinct species by, 1141, 1141f
Conservation International, 1144
Conservative replication, DNA, **320**, 321f
Constant (C) regions, 1016, 1016f
Constitutive defenses, **1098**–1099, 1098t, 1099f
Constitutive mutants, **371**
Constitutive transcription, **368**
Constraints, natural selection, 453
Consumers, **1118**
    animals as, 614, 625–626
    as biocontrol agents, 1101
    biomagnification in, 1120–1121, 1120f
    in trophic structure, 1118–1119, 1118f, 1119f
Consumption, **1093**
    adaptation and arms races in, 1101
    constitutive defenses against, 1098
    consumers as biocontrol agents and, 1101
    fitness and impacts of, 1103t
    human, of resources, 1130–1131, 1131f, 1156
    inducible defenses against, 1099–1100, 1100f
    parasite manipulation of hosts in, 1100–1101, 1100f
    types of, 1098
Continental drift, in time line of life, 1033f
Continental shelf, **1044**
Continuous data, graphing, 21–23, 22f, 23f
Continuous population growth, 1078
Continuous strands, **324**
Contraception, human, **1002**, 1002t, 1007
Contractile proteins, 90
Contraction, muscle. See Muscle contraction
Control groups, 13, 24–25

Convection, heat exchange using, **831**, 831f
Convention on Biological Diversity (CBD), 1156
Convergent evolution, **500**–501, 500f, 501f, 620–621, 620f, 956
Conversions, metric units to English units, 19t
Cooking, saturated fats and, 139
Cooperation, 1064–1067, 1065f, 1066f, 1067f
Cooperative binding, **884**–**885**, 885f
    importance of, 886, 886f
Copepods, 541–542, 541f, 648, 649t, 1134
Copper, as plant nutrient, 750–751, 750t, 751f
    metallothioneins exclusion of, 757
Coprophagy, **869**
Copulation, **989**
Copulatory plugs, 987
Copying, DNA, 320, 321f. See also DNA synthesis
Coral polyps, 628
Coral reefs, **1044**
    communities of, 1092
    impacts of global climate change on, 1135, 1149
    in ocean biomes, 1044
    red algae and, 557t
Corals, 630t, 631–632, 631f, 1135
Core enzymes, **350**
Core promoter, **384**
    enhancers and, 385–386, 385f
    promoter-proximal elements near, 385
    TATA box as, 384–385
Co-receptors, viral, **689**
Cork cambium, **722**, 722f, 722t, 724, 724f
Cork cells, **724**
Corms, **794**, 794f
Corn, 563, 563f, 798f
    double-stranded RNA viruses in, 698
    genetic engineering of, 401
    genome sequencing of, 404
    transposable elements in, 407
Cornea, **930**, 931f
Corolla, flower, **796**
Corona, 639t
Corpus callosum, **914**, 914f
Corpus luteum, **1000**, 1000f
Correlation analysis, 25
Corridors, wildlife, 1089, 1157, 1158t
Cortex, kidney, 845, 845f
Cortex, plant root, **732**, 732f, 733f
Cortex, plant shoot, **721**, 721f
Cortical granules, 992, 993f
Corticotropin-releasing hormone (CRH), 964f, **976**–977, 976f
Cortisol, 964f, **967**, 974–976, 976f
Cost, of animal locomotion, 956–958, 957f, 958f
Costa Rica, ecotourism in, 1159
Costanza, Robert, 1154
Cost–benefit analysis, **1053**
    in behavior, 1053–1054
    in foraging, 1054–1056, 1055f
Cotransport. See also Secondary active transport
    in osmoregulation, 839–842, 841f
    in salt excretion, 840–841, 841f
Cotransporters, **742**
    in animal glucose transport and absorption, 866f, 867
    glucose transport with, 137
    in plant nutrient uptake, 755, 755f
    resting potential and, 902–903

E

E2F protein, 268, 268f
E. coli. See Escherichia coli
E site, ribosome, 359, 359f
Ear, evolution of, 453
Eardrums, 925–926, 926f
Early earth
  monosaccharide synthesis in, 109
  nucleotide production in, 95
  polymerization in, 81–82, 81f
  polysaccharide synthesis in, 113
  RNA world hypothesis of, 93, 104
Early endosome, **161**, 162f
Early prophase I, 276f, 277
Ears, mammalian, 925–928, 926f, 927f, 928f
Earthworms, 635, 637, 889, 951, 951f
Ebola virus (EBOV), 694–695, 699, 701
EBOV. *See* Ebola virus
Ecdysone, 645, **972**, 972f
Ecdysozoans, 615t, **623**
  characteristics of, 644–645, 645f
  key lineages of, 645–653, 646t
  phylogeny of, 636, 636f
Echidnas, 670t
Echinoderms, 615t, 619, 656–658, 657f, 658f, 659t
  abundance of, 635, 635f
Echolocation, **927**–928, 928f
ECM. *See* Extracellular matrix
Ecological opportunity, 507–508, 508f
Ecological selection, **468**
Ecology. *See also* Community ecology; Conservation biology; Ecosystem ecology; Global ecology; Population ecology
  aquatic biomes in, 1043–1048, 1044f, 1045f, 1046f, 1047t, 1048f
  biodiversity scenarios in, 1149–1151, 1150f, 1151f
  climate patterns in, 1036–1039, 1036f, 1037f, 1038f, 1039f
  geographic distribution and abundance of organisms in, 1031–1035, 1032f, 1033f, 1034f, 1035f
  levels of study in, 1030–1031, 1030t
  organismal, 1030–1031, 1030t
  terrestrial biomes in, 1039–1043, 1040f, 1041t, 1042t, 1043f
Economic benefits
  of biodiversity, 1154–1155, 1154t
  of fungi, 591–592
Ecosystem diversity, **1141**–1142
Ecosystem ecology, 1030t, 1031
Ecosystem function, 1141, **1142**
  in biodiversity, 1142
  conservation of, 1159
Ecosystem services, **562**, **1154**
  benefits of, 1154–1155, 1154t
  of green plants, 562, 562f
  protostome, 635
  quantifying, 1158t, 1159
Ecosystems, **562**, **1031**, **1116**
  animal color vision and, 934
  animal locomotion in, 956
  animal sensory organs and, 624–625, 624t
  animals in, 625–626
  background extinctions *vs.* mass extinctions and, 511, 511f
  balancing selection and, 465
  changes of, in time line of life, 505
  cues from, in mating, 1056–1057, 1056f
  ecology and, 1029–1030
  ecosystem ecology and, 1030t, 1031
  effects of, on phenotypes, 307, 310t

  energy flow through, 1117–1123, 1117f, 1118f, 1119f, 1120f, 1121f, 1122f
eukaryotic differential gene expression and internal, 380
  fungi in, 591–592, 591f
  gene expression and, 368
  in global ecology, 1116–1117
  human impacts on, 1117
  impacts of global climate change on, 1135
  most productive, 1121–1123, 1121f, 1122f
  natural selection and changes in, 448–450, 449f, 450f
  nutrient cycling in, 1123–1128, 1123f, 1124f, 1125f, 1126f, 1127f, 1128f, 1129f
  plant adaptations to dry and salty, 727–728, 730–731, 730f, 731f, 737–738, 738f
  plant development in response to, 807
  plant sensory systems and, 765–766
  plant shoot systems and, 709
  prokaryotes in, 531–534, 531f, 532f, 533f
  prokaryotic impacts on, 531–534, 531f, 532f, 533f
  protists in, 542–543, 543f
  protostomes in, 635
  restoration of, 1158t, 1159
  seed germination and conditions in, 806
  in triggering switch between reproductive modes, 983, 983f
Ecotourism, 979, **1159**
Ecstasy, 910t
Ectocarpus siliculosus, 554, 555f
Ectoderm, **618**, 619f, 996–998, 996f, 997f
Ectomycorrhizal fungi (EMF), **599**, 601f, 609t, 610
Ectoparasites, **625**, 641, **1098**
Ectotherms, 670, **832**–833, 1120
Edge effects, habitat fragmentation and, 1147
Ediacaran fauna fossils, 509, 509f
Education, human population growth and, 1086
Effector B cells, 1021, 1021f
Effector cells, hormone, 963–964, 963f
Effector genes, 426, 427f
Effector T cells, 1020–1021, 1021f
Effectors, **830**–831, 830f
Efferent division, PNS, **912**, 912f
Eggs, **271**, **795**, **982**
  amniotic, **668**–669, 669f
  bird, 987, 987f
  cell-cycle regulation and frog, 263–264, 264f
  fertilization of, 5, 989–993, 989f, 990f, 991f, 993f
  gametogenesis of, 275, 984–986, 984f, 985f
  glycoproteins and, 114–115, 115f
  human, 271f
  insect, 637
  land plant, 572, 572f
  mammalian, 988
  meiosis and, 253, 271–272
  oogenesis of, 284
  plant, 795, 795f, 797, 810
  reptile and bird, 670
  in sexual reproduction, 982–983
  sexual selection and, 466, 466f
  structure and function of, 985–986, 985f
  variations in development of, 992–993, 993f

Either-or rule, probability, 26–27
Ejaculation, 987
Ejaculatory duct, 986f, **987**
EKG. *See* Electrocardiogram
Elastase, 868t
Electric currents, 901–**902**
  in action potential production, 904–905, 905f
Electric eels, 938
Electrical activation, heart, 894–895, 894f
Electrical fields
  electroreception of, 624, 624t
  in gel electrophoresis, 28–29, 28f, 29f
  generation of, by fishes, 938, 938f
  sensation of, 938, 938f
Electrical gradients, 901–902
Electrical potential, **901**, 901–902
Electrical signaling, animal, 899
  action potentials in, 903–907, 903f, 905f, 906f, 907f
  anatomy of neurons and, 901, 901f
  electrical activation of hearts, 894–895, 894f
  hormones and, 963–964, 963f
  membrane potentials in, 901–903, 902f
  nervous tissue and, 823, 823f
  resting potentials in, 902–903, 902f
  synapses in, 908–912, 908f, 909f, 910t, 911f
  types of neurons and, 900, 900f
Electrical signaling, plant, 778
Electrical stimulation, of brain, 915–916, 915f, 916f
Electrocardiogram (EKG), 894, 894f
Electrochemical gradient, **132**, **755**, **902**
  ion channels and, 132, 132f
  Na+/K+-ATPase established, 136
  in photosystems, 220
  pumps and, 135
  root nutrient uptake with, 755, 755f
  secondary active transport with, 136–137
Electrodes, membrane potential measurement with, 903
Electrogenic fishes, **938**, 938f
Electrolyte balance, 836–837
  in freshwater fishes, 841–842, 842f
  hormones involved in, 975
  in marine fishes, 840–841, 841f
  in nonmammalian vertebrates, 851–852, 851f, 852f
  osmoregulation and excretion in, 837–840, 837f, 838f, 839t
  in terrestrial insects, 842–844, 843f
  in terrestrial vertebrates, 844–852, 845f, 846f, 847f, 848f, 849f, 850f, 851f, 851t, 852f
  water pollution and, 854
Electrolytes, **836**–837
  as animal nutrients, 857, 857t
Electromagnetic radiation, 213, 213f
Electromagnetic spectrum, **213**, 213f
Electron acceptors, **176**, 201
  diversity of, 205–206, 205f
Electron carriers, **176**
Electron donors, **176**
Electron microscopy
  of bacterial translation, 355f
  in cell research, 154–155
  of DNA replication, 323f
  of DNA synthesis, 316f
  freeze-fracture, 130–131, 131f
  of introns and exons, 353, 353f
  of karyotypes, 335f, 346f
  of prokaryotic cell, 143, 143f
  of protist cells, 544, 544f

  scanning. *See* Scanning electron microscopy
  of smooth endoplasmic reticulum, 149, 149f
  in study of muscle contraction, 944–945
  transmission. *See* Transmission electron microscopy
  types of, 34–35, 34f
Electron shells, **57**–58
Electron tomography, 35
Electron transfer, during photosynthesis, 211, 211f
Electron transport, in cellular respiration, 191, 191f
Electron transport chain (ETC)
  aging and, 209
  ATP synthase discovery, 203, 203f
  in cellular respiration, 191, 191f, 201
  chemiosmosis hypothesis, 203–204, 204f
  organization of, 201, 201f, 202t
  in photosystem II, 219–220, 219f
  process of, 202f
  prokaryotic cellular respiration and, 529–530, 529f, 530t
  role of, 202f, 203
Electronegativity, 50, 50f, **58**–60, 58f, 62, 68–69, 68f
Electrons
  in atomic structure, 56–58, 56f, 57f
  covalent bonds of, 58, 58f, 59f
  in energy transformations, 172, 173f
  excitation of, in photosynthetic pigments, 216–217
  ionic bonds and, 59, 59f
  in photosynthesis, 115–116, 116f
  in photosystems, 219–223, 219f, 221f, 222f, 223f
  potential energy and, 68, 68f
  prokaryotic donors and acceptors of, 528–531, 529f, 529t, 530t
  in redox reactions, 175–176, 176f
Electroreception, **938**, 938f
Electroreceptors, **923**
Elements, 49, **56**, 57f
Elephant seals, 467–468, 468f
Elephantiasis, 891
Elephants, 818–819, 827, 827f, 832, 927, 957f, 958
  genome sequencing of, 404
  phylogenetic species of, 483, 483f
Elevational gradients
  shoot systems and, 709
  tree ranges and, 1106–1107
Elimination, animal nutrition and, 856, 856f, 861, 868–869
ELISA (enzyme-linked immunosorbent assay), 31
Ellis, Erle, 1042, 1042f
Ellis, Hillary, 421–422
Elongation, stem, 771–774
Elongation factors, **362**
Elongation phase, transcription, **351**
Elongation phase, translation, 360–361f, 361–362
Embryo sac, **798**
Embryogenesis, plant, 807–808, 807f
Embryonic development
  animal modes of, 628–629, 628t
  apoptosis in, 421–422, 421f
  cleavage in, 994, 995f
  deuterostome, 655
  developmental biology and, 418–419
  embryonic tissue layers in, 618–619, 619f
  gastrulation in, 622–623, 995–996, 995f, 996f

GLUT-1 membrane carrier protein, 135, 135*f*
Glutamate, 80*f*, 910*t*, 935
 in sickle-cell disease, 84, 84*f*
Glutamine, 80*f*, 358–359, 412
Gluten, 92
Glyceraldehyde-3-phosphate (G3P), **225**, 229
Glyceraldehyde-3-phosphate dehydrogenase, 195*t*
Glycerol, **122**, 192, 192*f*
Glycine, 80*f*
Glycogen, **111**
 animal storage polysaccharide, 111
 fungi and, 597
 glycosidic linkages of, 112*t*, 113
 hydrolysis of, 116
Glycolipid, **114**, 114*f*
 in bacterial cell walls, 145
Glycolysis
 in cellular respiration, 190, 191*f*
 enzymes in, 193
 glucose oxidation to pyruvate in, 193
 in muscle contraction, 949*t*, 950
 nucleotide synthesis from intermediates of, 192, 193*f*
 reaction sequence of, 193–194, 194–195*f*, 195*t*
 regulation of, 194–196, 196*f*
Glycoprotein, **114**, 114*f*, **160**
 in Ebola virus, 701
Glycosidic linkage, **110**
 α- and β-, 110–111, 111*f*
 of cellulose, 112*t*, 113
 of chitin, 112*t*, 113
 enzyme cleavage of, 114
 enzyme hydrolysis of, 116
 of glycogen, 112*t*, 113
 of peptidoglycan, 112*t*, 113
 of starch, 111, 112*t*
 in sucrose, 118
Glycosylation, **160**
Glyoxysomes, **151**
GM crop. *See* Genetically modified crop
Gnathostomes, 615*t*, **662**, 665–667
Gnetophytes, 586*t*
GnRH. *See* Gonadotropin-releasing hormone
Goal-oriented thinking, as misconception, 53*t*
Goatsbeard, 480
Goldman, Steven, 918
Golgi, Camillo, 901
Golgi apparatus, **149**
 activity inside, 160
 in cytokinesis, 262
 in endomembrane system, 150
 endoplasmic reticulum transport to, 160
 extracellular matrix components and, 236–237
 post-translational protein modifications in, 363
 in pulse–chase experiment, 158–159, 158*f*
 structure and function of, 149–150, 149*f*, 153*t*
Gonadal hormones, 999
Gonadotropin-releasing hormone (GnRH), **999**–1001, 999*f*, 1001*f*
Gonads, **972**, **984**
 gametogenesis in mammalian, 984–986, 984*f*, 985*f*
Google Scholar (online database), 52
Gorillas, 674, 674*f*
GPP. *See* Gross primary productivity

G-protein-coupled receptors
 in pheromone signaling, 252
 quorum sensing via, 250, 250*f*
 signal transduction via, 245–248
Gracile australopithecines, 675–676, 676*t*, 677*f*
Graded postsynaptic potentials, 911
Grades (paraphyletic lineages), **665**
Grafting, plant, 774
Gram stain technique, **527**, 527*f*
Gram-negative cells, **528**, 528*f*
Gram-positive cells, **528**, 528*f*
Grana (singular: granum), **152**, 152*f*, **212**, 213*f*
Grant, Peter and Rosemary, 448–450, 485–486, 1097
Graphic concept maps, 46–47, 47*f*
Graphs, 21–23, 22*f*, 23*f*
Grasses, 1040
Grasslands, temperate, 1041*t*
Gravitational forces, animal locomotion and, 956
Gravitropism, plant, **775**, 790*t*
Gravity
 animal sensing of, 624, 624*t*
 hearts and, 892
Gray whales, 833–834, 833*f*
Grazers, in trophic structure, 1118–1119, 1118*f*, 1119*f*
Grazing food chains, **1118**–1119, 1119*f*
Great apes, **674**, 674*f*
Great chain of being, 436
Great tits, 1134
Greek and Latin word roots, 51*t*
Green algae, **561**, 581. *See also* Algae
 key lineages of, 556, 557*t*, 581–582, 582*f*, 583*t*
 land plants and, as green plants, 561–562
 in lichens, 582, 582*f*, 602, 602*f*, 609*t*, 610
 as model organism, 44
 photosystems and, 218
 rRNA sequences for, 7
 similarities between land plants and, 564, 565*f*
Green fluorescent protein (GFP), 35, 35*f*
Green iguanas, 472, 472*f*
Green plants
 analysis of morphological traits of, 564–565, 565*f*
 biological importance of studying, 562–563, 564*t*
 biological methods for studying, 564–568, 565*f*, 566*f*, 567*f*
 ecosystem services of, 562, 562*f*
 in fossil record, 565–566, 566*f*
 green algae and land plants as, 561–562
 green algae lineages, 581–582, 582*f*, 583*t*
 importance of, to humans, 563, 563*f*, 564*t*
 key lineages of, 581–583, 584*t*, 585*t*, 586*t*, 587*t*
 molecular phylogenies of, 566–568, 567*f*
 non-vascular plant lineages, 582, 584*t*
 seed plant lineages, 582–583, 586*t*, 587*t*
 seedless vascular plant lineages, 582, 585*t*
Green sea turtles, 1059–1060, 1060*f*
Greenhouse effect, **1130**, 1130*f*
Greenhouse gases, **1130**–1131, 1130*f*, 1131*f*, 1151
Greider, Carol, 328–329

Griffin, Donald, 927
Grooves, chemical structure, 50, 50*f*
Gross primary productivity (GPP), **1117**
 in ecosystem energy flow, 1117–1118, 1117*f*
Groudine, Mark, 382
Ground finches, 485–486
Ground force, animal locomotion, 956
Ground meristem, **718**, 718*t*
Ground substance, 235, 235*f*
Ground tissue, 808*f*, **809**
Ground tissue system, plant, **714**–716, 718*t*
 embryogenesis and, **809**
 in primary plant body, 718, 719*f*
Groundwater, **1126**
Groups, control, 13, 24–25
Growing seasons, plant translocation and, 738, 739*f*
Growth
 cancer as out-of-control, 266–268, 267*f*, 268*f*
 in energy flow, 1117
 lophotrochozoan vs. ecdysozoan, 644
 mammalian, 972
 mitosis and, 254
 plant, 569, 777, 808*f*, 809
Growth factors, **267**–268, 268*f*
Growth hormone (GH), 964*f*, **966**–967, 972, 977*f*, 978
Growth regulators, plant, 778
Growth rings, tree, 724*f*, 725, 1107–1108, 1107*f*
GTP. *See* Guanosine triphosphate
Guanine, 94, 94*f*, 97, 319, 319*f*
Guanosine diphosphate (GDP), 245–246, 246*f*, 248
Guanosine triphosphate (GTP), **245**
 acetyl CoA oxidation and production of, 197, 198*f*
 in cell–cell signal deactivation, 248
 in cell–cell signal processing, 245–246, 246*f*
 in translation, 356
Guard cells, **227**, 227*f*, **568**, 569*f*, **714**, 714*f*, **781**–782, 783*f*
Gurdon, John, 422
Gustation (taste), 624, 624*t*, **934**–935, 934*f*
Guttation, **734**
GWAS. *See* Genome-wide association study
Gymnophiona, 668*t*
Gymnosperms, **565**
 diversification of, 566
 lineages of, 582–583, 586*t*
 in Mesozoic era, 505
 molecular phylogeny of, 567, 567*f*
 seed evolution in, 576

H

H1 histones, 381, 381*f*
H_2O_2. *See* Hydrogen peroxide
H_2S. *See* Hydrogen sulfide
Haberl, Helmut, 1122
Habitat, colonization of, 1078
Habitat degradation, **1146**–1148, 1147*f*, 1148*t*
Habitat destruction, 1145–**1146**, 1146*f*, 1148*t*
 human population size and, 1086
Habitat fragmentation, **1146**–1148, 1147*f*, 1148*t*
Habitats
 animal communication modes and, 1062
 carrying capacity of, 1079–1080, 1079*f*, 1080*t*

fossil record bias for, 504
 metapopulation, 1088–1089, 1089*f*
 model organism, 42
 nitrogenous wastes and, 839–840
 prezygotic isolation and, 482*t*
 prokaryotic diversity in, 519
 species richness and area of, 1150–1151, 1150*f*
 sympatric speciation and, 487–488, 488*f*
Hadean eon, 505, 505*f*
Hadley, George, 1036
Hadley cell, **1036**, 1037*f*
Haeckel, Ernst, 1029–1030
Haemophilus influenzae, genome sequencing of, 404
Hagfish, 661, 664*t*
Hagfish hypothesis, 664–665, 664*t*
Hair
 color of, 395
 proteins in structure of, 90, 164
Hair cells, **924**–928, 925*f*, 927*f*, 928*f*, 929*f*
Hairpin RNA secondary structure, 101*f*, **102**
 in RNA interference, 390, 390*f*
 in transcription termination, 351, 351*f*
Haldane, J. B. S., 70
Hamadryas baboons, 981
Hamilton, William D., 1064
Hamilton's rule, **1064**–1066, 1066*f*
Hamstring muscles, 953, 953*f*
Hands, primate, 674
Hanski, Ilkka, 1083–1084
Hanson, Jean, 944
Haploid cells, life cycles dominated by, 553, 554*f*
Haploid number, **273**, 274*t*
Haploid organisms, **273**, 274*t*
Hardy, G. H., 457–458
Hardy–Weinberg equilibrium, 458
Hardy–Weinberg principle, **457**
 application of, 459–461, 459*t*, 460*t*
 assumptions of, 458–459
 derivation of, 458, 458*f*
 gene pool concept, 457–458, 457*f*
 nonrandom mating and, 461–462, 461*f*, 462*f*
Hares, 1081–1083, 1081*f*, 1082*f*
Hartwell, Leland, 265
Hatch, Hal, 228
HATs. *See* Histone acetyltransferases
Haustoria (singular: haustorium), 760, 762*f*
Havasupai tribe, 460–461, 460*t*
Hawaiian bobtail Squid, 378
Hawaiian silverswords, 507, 507*f*, 709
Hawkmoths, 879–880, 879*f*
Hawthorn maggot flies, 487–488, 488*f*
Hay fever, 1026
hCG. *See* Human chorionic gonadotropin
HCl. *See* Hydrochloric acid
HDACs. *See* Histone deacetylases
Head, **647**
 arthropod, 647, 647*f*
 cephalization and, 621
 insect, 648
Head-to-tail axes, 426, 427*f*
Hearing, 453, 624, 624*t*, **925**–928, 926*f*, 927*f*, 928*f*
Heart attacks, 896
Heart disease
 genome-wide association study for, 412
 iPS cells in treatment of, 431
 lipid structure and, 139
Heart murmurs, **893**

Impact hypothesis, **512**–513, 512*t*
Imperfect flowers, **797**, 797*f*
Implantation, **1003**
Import, nutrient, 1124
In situ conservation, 1157
In situ hybridization, **425**, 425*f*, 449, 449*f*, 812, 812*f*
In vitro protein-synthesis systems, 356–357, 357*f*
In vitro study, of metabolic pathways, 193
In vitro translation systems, 355
Inactivated virus vaccines, 1025
Inbreeding, **461**–462, 461*f*, 462*f*
Inbreeding depression, **462**, 462*f*, 1147
Inclusive fitness, 1064–**1065**
Incomplete digestive tracts, **859**, 860*f*
Incomplete dominance, **306**, 307*f*, 309, 310*t*
Incomplete metamorphosis, **652**, 652*f*
Independent assortment, principle of, **281**–282, 296–**298**, 297*f*
  linked genes and, 303, 303*f*
  meiosis as explanation for, 300, 300*f*
  testcross and predictions with, 298–299, 299*f*
Independent variables, graphing, 21–23, 22*f*, 23*f*
Indeterminate growth, **704**–705
Induced fit, **179**
Induced pluripotent (iPS) cells, **431**, 434
Inducer exclusion, 374, 374*f*
Inducers, **370**, 374
Inducible defenses, **786**, **1099**–1100, 1100*f*
Induction, 420*f*, **421**
Industrial pollutants, 1149
Inertia, population growth, 1085
Infant diarrhea, 698
Infection threads, nitrogen-fixing bacteria, 759–**760**, 759*f*, 760*f*
Infectious diseases, **521**. *See also* Diseases and disorders, human
Inflammatory response, **1011**–1012, 1011*f*, 1012*t*
Influenza viruses, 683, 684*f*, 695, 695*f*, 699, 1010, 1016, 1016*f*, 1025
Infolding hypothesis, 549, 549*f*
Information
  gene regulation and, 368–370, 369*f*, 370*f*
  genetic, **2**, 289–290
  hormones as carriers of, 243–244
  nucleus storage and transmittance of, 148, 148*f*
  plant processing of, 766–768
  RNA world hypothesis and, 104
Infrasound hearing, 927
Ingestion, 551, 551*f*, 614, **856**, 856*f*
Inhalation, 882, 883*f*
Inheritance
  of acquired characters, 437, 451
  autosomal, 302
  epigenetic, 383–384, 384*f*
  human, 310–312, 311*f*, 312*f*
  hypotheses on, 290
  particulate, 294–296, 295*f*, 296*t*
  polygenic, 308–309, 308*f*, 309*f*, 310*t*
  sex-linked, 301–302, 301*f*, 302*f*, 310*t*
  of transposable elements, 409
Inheritance of acquired characters hypothesis, 290
Inhibition
  competitive, 114–115, 115*f*, **183**, 183*f*
  feedback, **185**, 185*f*, **963**
  successional, **1109**

Inhibitory postsynaptic potentials (IPSPs), **910**–911, 911*f*
Initiation, of enzyme catalysis, 181, 181*f*
Initiation factors, **361**
Initiation phase, **349**
  eukaryotic transcription, 384–388, 385*f*, 386*f*, 387*f*
  of transcription, 349–351, 350*f*, 351*f*
  of translation, 360*f*, 361
Innate behavior, **1053**
Innate immune response, 1010–1013, 1010*f*, 1011*f*, 1012*t*
Innate immunity, **1009**, 1009*t*
  barriers to entry in, 1009–1010, 1009*f*
  characteristics of, 1009
  dysfunction of, 1025–1027
  immune response in, 1010–1013, 1010*f*, 1011*f*, 1012*t*
Inner cell mass (ICM), **994**, 995*f*
Inner ear, **925**–926, 926*f*
Inner membrane, of chloroplasts, 212, 213*f*
Inner membrane, of mitochondria, 196, 196*f*
  electron transport chain in, 201
  proton transport across, 201
Inorganic molecules, 73
Inorganic soil elements, **751**, 751*f*, 752*f*
Inositol triphosphate (IP₃), 246*t*
Insecticides, 541, 1120–1121, 1120*f*
Insects, **648**
  altruism in, 1066
  behavior of, 1052–1053, 1052*f*, 1061–1062, 1061*f*, 1062*f*
  carnivorous plants and, 762, 762*f*
  characteristics and orders of, 649*t*, 650*t*
  circulatory systems of, 889
  exoskeletons of, 953–954, 954*f*
  eyes of, 929–930, 930*f*, 934
  fertilization of eggs of, 989–991, 990*f*, 991*f*
  fungal infections of, 608–609
  fungal mutualisms with, 602, 602*f*
  gas exchange in, 843, 843*f*, 879–881, 879*f*, 880*f*, 881*f*
  metamorphosis in, 652–653, 652*f*
  metamorphosis of, 961, 972, 972*f*
  mimicry in, 1098
  mutualisms of, 1101
  osmoregulation in, 842–844, 843*f*
  pheromones of, 936, 941
  plant defense responses to, 787, 789
  pollination by, 578, 578*f*, 579*f*
  as protostomes, 634–635, 635*f*
  terrestrial adaptations of, 637
Instantaneous rate of increase, 1077–1078
Insulin, **870**, **962**
  cortisol effects on, 974
  discovery of, 869
  in homeostasis, 870, 870*f*, 975
Intact fossil, 503*t*
Integral membrane proteins, **131**, 131*f*, 138
Integrase, in long interspersed nuclear element spread, 409*f*
Integrated pest management, **1101**
Integrators, **830**–831, 830*f*
Integrins, **236**, 237*f*
  long interspersed nuclear element coding of, 409*f*
Interbreeding, 491–493, 491*f*, 492*f*, 493*t*
Intercalated discs, **894**
Intercellular connections
  cell–cell attachments, 238–241, 238*f*, 239*f*, 240*f*, 241*f*
  cell–cell gaps, 241–243, 242*f*
Interferon, 1011

Intergovernmental Panel on Climate Change (IPCC), 1131–1132
Interleukin 2, 962
Intermediate filaments, 163*t*, **164**
Intermediate muscle fibers, 949*t*, **950**
Intermediate phenotypes, 307*f*
Intermediates, in metabolic pathways, 185
Intermembrane space, of mitochondria, 196, 196*f*
  proton transport into, 201
Internal consistency, evolution and, 443–444, 443*t*, 444*f*
Internal environments, eukaryotic differential gene expression and, 380
Internal fertilization, animal, 628, 628*t*, 989–991, 990*f*, 991*f*
Internal membrane complexes, of photosynthetic prokaryotic cells, 144, 144*f*
International System of Units, 19, 19*t*
International Union for the Conservation of Nature (IUCN), 1145, 1145*f*
Interneurons, **900**, 900*f*
Internodes, stem, **708**
Interphase, **255**, 257*f*, 258*f*, 276*f*
Intersexual selection, **466**, **1057**, 1057*f*
Interspecific competition, **1094**
Interspecific interactions, 1080–1081
Interstitial fluid, **840**
  blood plasma exchange with, 890–891, 891*f*
  in proximal tubule, 847, 847*f*
Intertidal zone, **1044**, 1045*f*
Intracellular environment, plasma membranes and, 137–138, 137*f*, 143
Intracellular pathogens, elimination of, 1023, 1023*f*
Intracellular receptors, hormone, 967–968, 967*f*, 968*f*
Intrasexual selection, **466**, 1057*f*, **1058**
Intraspecific competition, **1094**
Intraspecific interactions, 1080–1081
Intrauterine device (IUD), 1002*t*
Intrinsic rate of increase, population, **1077**
Introduction, primary literature, 51*t*
Introns, **353**, 354*f*, 380, 385, 388–389, 389*f*
  in human genome, 410, 410*f*
Invasive species, **1034**, 1035*f*, 1052–1053, 1052*f*, 1148–**1149**, 1148*t*, 1157
Inversions, chromosome, **345**
Invertebrates, **623**, **656**
  segmentation in, 623
Involuntary muscles, **947**
Iodine, as animal nutrient, 857*t*
Ion balance. *See* Electrolyte balance
Ion channels, **132**, **902**
  in action potential depolarization, 904–905, 905*f*
  cystic fibrosis and, 132–133, 133*f*
  diffusion with, 132, 132*f*, 137*f*
  in gustation, 934–935
  in mechanoreception, 925, 925*f*
  as neurotransmitter receptors, 910
  in neurotransmitter release, 909, 909*f*
  in photoreception, 932, 932*f*
  regulation of, 134, 134*f*
Ion currents, in action potential production, 904
Ionic bonds, 59, 59*f*
  in protein tertiary structures, 86*f*, 87
Ions, 59, **752**
  as animal nutrients, 857, 857*t*
  as cofactors, 182
  diffusion of, across membranes, 127–128, 127*f*
  electrolytes as, 836

ionic bonds and, 59, 59*f*
plant exclusion mechanism for, 756–758, 757*f*, 758*f*
plant nutrients in soil as, 753, 753*f*
plant uptake mechanisms for, 755–756, 755*f*
vacuole storage of, 150
IP₃. *See* Inositol triphosphate
IPCC. *See* Intergovernmental Panel on Climate Change
Ipecac, 564*t*
iPS cells. *See* Induced pluripotent stem cells
IPSPs. *See* Inhibitory postsynaptic potentials
Iridium, 512, 512*t*
Iris, **930**, 931*f*
Irish potato famine, 540, 557*t*, 558, 787
Iron, 543
  as animal nutrient, 857*t*
  in heme, 884
  as plant nutrient, 750*t*
Iron-containing heme groups, 201
Iron–sulfur complexes, 201
Irrigation, 1126–1127, 1126*f*, 1127*f*
Island biogeography theory, 1112–1113, 1112*f*
Island gigantism, 835
Islets of Langerhans, 962, 964*f*, 965
Isocitrate, in citric acid cycle, 197, 198*f*
Isocitrate dehydrogenase, 199*t*
Isoleucine, 80*f*
Isopods, 649*t*
Isoprene, 526
  structure of, 120, 120*f*
Isoprenoids
  in archaea, 145
  in cholesterol, 121, 121*f*
  structure of, 120, 120*f*
Isosmotic solution, **837**
Isotonic solutions, **128**, 129*f*, **729**
Isotopes, 31, **56**, 599
Isthmus of Panama, 1034
IUCN. *See* International Union for the Conservation of Nature
IUD. *See* Intrauterine device

J

Jacob, François, 2, 338–339, 369–370, 370*f*, 372–374
Japanese honeybees, 832, 832*f*
Jasmonic acid, 788
Jawless vertebrates, 664, 664*t*
Jaws
  food capture and, 858–859, 858*f*, 859*f*
  vertebrate, 665–666
Jellyfish, 613*f*, 630*t*, 631–632, 631*f*
Jenkins, David, 1105–1106, 1106*f*
Jenner, Edward, 1024–1025
Jet propulsion, mollusk, 643*t*, 644, 644*f*
JH. *See* Juvenile hormone
Joint angles, 952
Jointed appendages, 647, 647*f*
Jointed limbs, 627*t*
Joints, **952**–953, 952*f*
Joly, John, 735
Juçara palms, 479
Junk DNA, 407
Jürgens, Gerd, 809
Juvenile hormone (JH), **972**, 972*f*
Juveniles, **629**, 629*f*

K

Kakapo, 862
Kandel, Eric, 917–918
Kangaroo rats, 1053, 1053*f*

Mosses, 565, 565f, 584t, 589, 761, 761f
Moths, 879–880, 879f, 922–923, 936
Motor neurons, **900**, 900f, 946, 947f
Motor proteins, 90, **163**
  in cytokinesis, 262
  dynein as, 167
  myosin as, 163
  in vesicle transport, 165–166, 166f
Mottle viruses, 699
Mountain pine beetles, 1134, 1134t
Mountain ranges, climate and, 1038, 1038f
Mouse, 43f, 45
Mouths
  digestion in, 860–861, 861f
  food capture adaptations of, 858–859, 858f, 859f
  human, 860f
  lophotrochozoan, 637
  protostome *vs.* deuterostome, 622, 635
  taste as chemoreception by, 934–935, 934f
Movement. *See also* Animal movement
  prokaryotic, 527, 527f
  protein function in, 90
  protist, 552, 552f
  wind/touch responses and plant, 778
MPa. *See* Megapascal
MPF. *See* M phase-promoting factor; Mitosis-promoting factor
mRNA. *See* Messenger RNA
MS. *See* Multiple sclerosis
MSG. *See* Monosodium glutamate
mtDNA. *See* Mitochondrial DNA
MTOC. *See* Microtubule-organizing center
Mucosa-associated lymphoid tissue (MALT), **1014**
Mucous cells, **863**, 863f
Mucus, **861**, 863, 863f, **1009**–1010, 1009f
Müller, Fritz, 1099
Müllerian inhibitory substance, **972**
Müllerian mimicry, 1099, 1099f
Multicellularity, **238**, **550**
  of animals, 614
  cell–cell interactions of, 235
  cell–cell signaling and, 243–249, 244f, 245f, 246f, 246t, 247f, 249f
  cellular structure and function in, 154–155, 154f
  in eukaryotes, 8, 539, 550–551
  gene regulation and, 379–380
  intercellular connections and, 238–241, 238f, 239f, 240f, 241f
  origin of, in animal evolution, 616–618, 617f
  in Paleozoic era, 505
  protist, 550–551
Multichambered hearts, 891–892, 892f
Multidrug resistance, 448
Multinucleate muscle cells, 947
Multiple allelism, **306**, 306f, 310t
Multiple fruits, **804**, 804f
Multiple sclerosis (MS), **907**, 1026
Multiplication rule, probability, 26
Mumps virus, 699
Münch, Ernst, 740
Mus musculus, 43f, 45
  genome sequencing of, 404
Muscle cells, 614
  differentiation of, 430, 431f
  evolution of neurons and, 900
  glycoproteins of, 114
  micrograph of, 234f
  precursors to, 998, 998f
  structure and function of, 154, 154f
Muscle contraction, 614

actin–myosin interactions in, 944–946, 945f, 946f
  animal locomotion and, 943, 954–958, 955f, 956f, 957f, 958f
  in atria and ventricles, 894–895, 894f
  early experiments on, 943
  in evolution of animal movement, 942–943
  neuron initiation of, 946, 947f
  of skeletal muscles, 949–950, 949t, 950f
  skeletal systems and, 950, 953–954, 953f, 954f
  sliding-filament model of, 943–944, 943f, 944f
Muscle fibers, **943**–944, 943f, 960
  skeletal, 948–950, 949t, 950f
Muscle tissues, **823**, 823f, 947–950, 948t, 949f, 949t, 950f
  origin of, 619
Muscular dystrophy, dystrophin deficiency in, 234f
Muscular hydrostats, 951
Musculoskeletal structure, 955, 955f
Mushrooms, 365, 592, 595, 605, 606–607f, 609t, 610
Mussels, 642, 643t, 1099–1100, 1100f
Mustard plant. *See also Arabidopsis thaliana*
  in population ecology, 1076
Mutagens, **370**
Mutants, **300**
  creating experimental, 336, 370
  homeotic, 427–428, 427f, 428f
  in study of flower development, 811–813, 811f, 812f
  in study of plant embryogenesis, 809–810, 809f, 810f
  in testing of chromosome theory of inheritance, 301–302, 302f
  types of, in lactose metabolism, 370–371, 371t
Mutations, **300**, **343**, **457**, **475**
  animal pollination and plant, 801
  antibiotic resistance in bacterial, 446–448, 447f, 448f
  bicoid gene and, 424–425, 425f
  cancer and, 392–393, 393f
  chromosome mutations, 345, 346t
  DNA synthesis mistakes and, 329–331, 330f, 331f
  in duplicated genes, 409
  effects on genetic diversity of types of, 475
  as evolutionary process, 451t, 452, 457, 475–477, 476f
  experimental studies of, 475–476, 476f
  genetic diversity and, 1142
  and genetic variation in plants, 811–812, 811f, 812f
  Hardy–Weinberg principle and, 459
  homeotic, 427–428, 427f, 428f
  of model organisms, 44–45
  in natural populations, 476–477, 477f
  point mutations, 344–345, 344f, 345t
  RNA interference and, 390
  in sympatric speciation by polyploidy, 489–490, 489f, 490f
  types of, 344–345, 346f
  in xeroderma pigmentosum (XP), 331–332, 332f
  of zebra fish, 347
Mutualisms, **800**, **1093**
  cooperation and, 1067
  diversity of, 1101–1102, 1101f
  diving ants and fanged pitcher plant, 764

dynamism of, 1102–1103, 1102f
  endophytes and, 599–601, 600f, 601f
  fitness and impacts of, 1103t
  fungal, 599–602, 600f, 601f
  mycorrhizae as, 599, 756
  natural selection and, 1102
  in pollination, 578, 578f, 579f, 800, 800f, 801f
Mutualistic relationships, **599**, **756**
Mutualists, **591**
Muybridge, Eadweard, 955, 955f
mV. *See* Millivolt
Mycelia, 535t, **594**, 594f
Mycobacterium, 446–448, 447f, 448f
Mycorrhizae, **756**
Mycorrhizal fungi, **592**–593, 592f, 599–602, 600f, 601f, 1101
Myelin sheath, **907**, 907f
Myelination, 906–907, 907f
Myelomas, B-cell, 1016
Myers, Norman, 1144
Myocardial infarctions, **896**
MyoD gene, 430
Myofibrils, **943**–944, 943f
Myoglobin, 949–950, 949t
Myosin, **944**
  actin interactions with, 163–164, 164f, 944–946, 945f, 946f
  in cytokinesis, 262, 262f
  movement and, 90
Myriapods, **648**, 649t
Myxinoidea, 664t

N

Nabhan, Gary, 805, 805f
N-acetylglucosamine (NAG), 112t, 113
N-acetylmuramic acid (NAM), 112t, 113
Na$^+$/Cl$^-$/K$^+$ cotransporter, in osmoregulation, 842, 842f
NAD$^+$. *See* Nicotinamide adenine dinucleotide
NADH, **176**, 177f
  acetyl CoA oxidation and production of, 197, 198f
  fate of, in cellular respiration, 199–200, 199f, 200f
  fermentation and, 206, 207f
  in glycolysis, 190, 191f, 194, 195f
  oxidation of, 201
  in photosystem I, 220–221, 221f
  in pyruvate processing, 196, 197f
NADH dehydrogenase, 202t
NADP$^+$. *See* Nicotinamide adenine dinucleotide phosphate
NADPH, **212**
  photosynthesis production of, 212, 212f
  in photosystem I, 220–221, 221f
Naegleria fowleri, 542t
NAG. *See* N-acetylglucosamine
Na$^+$/K$^+$-ATPase. *See* Sodium–potassium pump
Naked mole rats, 832
Naked viruses, 686
Nalidixic acid, 334
Naloxone, 910f
NAM. *See* N-acetylmuramic acid
Names, scientific, 8–9
Nanobiology, 685
Nanotechnology, DNA in, 106
National Center for Biotechnology Information (NCBI), 404
Native Americans, viral epidemics and, 683
Natural catastrophes, genetic bottlenecks and, 472–473, 472f

Natural experiments, **448**, **1153**–1154, 1153f
Natural logarithms, 27
Natural populations
  genetic drift in, 472–473, 472f
  mutation studies in, 476–477, 476f
Natural selection, **4**, **445**, **456**
  in allopatric speciation, 486
  of animal mouthparts, 858–859, 858f, 859f
  artificial selection *vs.*, 5–6, 445
  balancing selection as, 465
  common misconceptions about evolution, adaptation, and, 451–453, 451t
  constraints on, 453
  deceitful communication and, 1063–1064, 1063f
  directional selection as, 463–464, 463f
  disruptive selection as, 464–465, 465f
  effects of, on individuals and on populations, 451–452, 452f
  effects of modes of, on genetic variation, 462–463
  in evolution of antibiotic resistance, 446–448, 447f, 448f
  as evolutionary process, 456, 477t
  fitness and adaptations in, 6, 446
  four postulates of Charles Darwin on, 445–446
  in Galápagos finches, 448–450, 449f, 450f
  Hardy–Weinberg principle and, 459
  mice and, 455
  modes of, 465t
  mutualisms and, 1102
  as not goal oriented, 451t, 452
  as process component of theory of evolution by, 5–6, 435–436
  as process of theory of evolution by, 445–446, 445f
  research on, 446–450
  sexual selection and, 466–469
  species interactions and, 1093
  stabilizing selection as, 464, 464f
  types of, 463–465, 465t
  viruses and, 693
Nature, cultural services of, 1155
Nautilus, 643t
Navigation, migration and, 1058–1060, 1059f, 1060f
NCBI. *See* National Center for Biotechnology Information
Neanderthals, 402–403, 495, 676–**678**, 677f
Nectar, **578**, **796**
Nectary, **796**
Needlelike leaves, 710, 711f
Negative control, **372**–375, 372f, 373f, 374f, 376f, 383
Negative feedback, **265**, **831**, **963**
  in global climate change, 1133
  by glucocorticoids, 976, 976f
  in homeostatic systems, 830f, 831
  in hormone signaling pathways, 963–964, 963f
  by sex hormones, 999–1001
Negative pressure ventilation, **881**–882, 883f
Negative-sense single-stranded RNA ([·] ssRNA) viruses, **687**, 698, 698t, 699
Neher, Erwin, 904–905
Nematodes, 615t, **645**, 646t
Neogene period, 505, 506f
Nepenthes bicalcarata, 764

Uterus, **988**, 988*f*
UTRs. *See* Untranslated regions
UV radiation. *See* Ultraviolet radiation

V

V regions. *See* Variable regions
Vaccination, 1024–**1025**
Vaccines, 685, **1025**
Vacquier, Victor, 992
Vacuoles, **150**, **713**
  in eukaryotic cells, 150–151, 150*f*, 153*t*
  plant active exclusion via,
    757–758, 758*f*
  plant cell, 713
Vagina, **988**, 988*f*
Vagus nerve, 908, 908*f*
Vale, Ronald, 165
Valence, **57**
Valence electrons, **57–58**
Valence shells, **57–58**
Valine, 80*f*
  in sickle-cell disease, 84, 84*f*
Valves, heart, 891, 893, 893*f*
Valves, vein, **890**
Vampire bats, 1067
van Damme, Raoul, 1058, 1058*f*
van der Waals interactions, **86**
  in double-stranded DNA, 99
  membrane permeability and, 125, 125*f*
  in protein tertiary structures,
    86–87, 86*f*
  in RNA secondary structures, 102
van Helmont, Jean-Baptiste, 748
van Leeuwenhoek, Anton, 2, 3*f*, 544
van Niel, Cornelius, 211
Vapor, water, 731
Variable number tandem repeats (VNTRs),
  402
Variable (V) regions, 1016, 1016*f*
Variables, experimental, 13
Vas deferens, 986*f*, **987**
Vasa recta, **849–850**, 849*f*
Vascular bundles, **721**, 721*f*
Vascular cambium
  auxin and, 779
  production by, 723
  secondary growth functions of, **722**,
    722*f*, 722*t*
Vascular tissue, plant, **732**, **809**
  formation of, 808*f*, 809
  translocation (sugar transport) and,
    738–744
  water transport and, 732–737
Vascular tissue system, plant, **564**, **716**,
  718*t*
  elaboration of, into tracheids and vessel
    elements, 570, 570*f*
  embryogenesis and, **809**
  in land plants, 564–565, 565*f*
  origin of, 569–570, 570*f*
  phloem structure in, 717, 717*f*
  in primary plant body, 718, 719*f*
  root and shoot systems and, 705, 705*f*
  xylem structure in, 716–717, 716*f*
Vectors, cloning, **399**
Vegetation, emergent, 1047*t*
Vegetative development, **807**
  flexibility of cell determination in,
    810–811
  genetic control of leaf shape in, 810,
    810*f*
  meristems in lifelong growth and, 808*f*,
    809
  reproductive development *vs.*, 807
Veins, **889–893**, 890*f*, 893*f*

blood pressure homeostasis and, 896
  of kidneys, 844, 845*f*
Veliger, 643*t*
Velvet worms, 646*t*
Venae cavae, **892**, 893*f*
Ventilation
  of fish gills, 878
  in gas exchange, 875, 875*f*
  homeostatic control of, 883–884
  of insect tracheae, 880–881, 880*f*, 881*f*
  of vertebrate lungs, 881–882, 882*f*, 883*f*
Ventral body axis, **424**, 424*f*
Ventricles, **891–893**, 892*f*, 893*f*
  contraction of, 894–895, 894*f*
Venules, **889**
Venus flytraps, 762, 778
Vertebrae, **661**, 664
Vertebral column, 661
Vertebrates, 623, **656**, 662–673
  amniotes, 668–669, 669*f*
  amphibians, 668, 668*t*
  body plan of, 660*t*, 661, 661*f*
  closed circulatory systems of, 889
  deuterostome chordates as, 656
  endoskeletons of, 952–953, 952*f*, 953*f*
  evolution of, 662–664, 663*f*
  eyes of, 930–934, 931*f*, 932*f*, 933*f*
  fishes, 664, 665*t*
  in fossil record, 664
  gill-arch hypothesis, 666, 666*f*
  gnathostomes, 665–667
  hagfish hypothesis, 664–665, 664*t*
  hormones in sexual development and
    activity of, 972–973, 973*f*
  jaw origin, 665–667, 665*t*, 666*f*
  lungs of, 881–882, 882*f*, 883*f*, 888
  mammals, 669–670, 670*t*
  nervous systems of, 912–919, 912*f*,
    913*f*, 914*f*, 915*f*, 916*f*, 917*f*, 918*f*,
    919*f*
  osmoregulation by terrestrial, 844–852,
    845*f*, 846*f*, 847*f*, 848*f*, 849*f*, 850*f*,
    851*f*, 851*t*, 852*f*
  phylogenetic tree of, 663*f*
  reptiles, 670–672, 671*t*, 672*f*
  segmentation in, 623
  species abundance of, 662*f*
  tetrapods, 667, 667*f*
  vertebrae, cranium, and brain structure
    of, 661–662
Vervet monkeys, 1067, 1067*f*
Vesicles, **124**
  artificial membrane-bound, 124, 124*f*
  in cytokinesis, 262, 262*f*
  endocytic, 161
  fatty acid formation of, 129
  microtubules and transport of, 165–166,
    165*f*, 166*f*
  osmosis and volume of membrane-
    bound, 128, 129*f*
  protein sorting and transport in, 160,
    161*f*
  in pulse–chase experiment, 158–159,
    158*f*
  synaptic, **908–909**, 909*f*
Vessel elements, **570**, **716**, 716*f*
Vessels, angiosperm, 580
Vestigial hip, 444, 444*f*
Vestigial tail, 440, 440*f*
Vestigial traits, 440, 440*f*
  of cetaceans, 444
  as evidence for evolutionary change,
    440, 440*f*
  as nonadaptive, 453
Vibrations, sound, cell response to,
  924–928, 925*f*, 926*f*, 927*f*, 928*f*, 929*f*

Vibrio cholera, 376, 376*f*
Vibrio fischeri, 249–250, 378
Vicariance, **485–487**, 485*f*, 486*f*
Video microscopy
  in biological imaging, 35
Villi, **828**, 829*f*, **864–865**, 865*f*
Vinblastine, 564*t*
Vincristine, 564*t*
Viral replicative growth, **687**, 687*f*
Virchow, Rudolf, 3, 253
Virions, **683**
  assembly of, 691–692
  exiting host cell, 692, 692*f*
  transmission of, 693
Virulent infections, 521, **683**
Virus vaccines, 1025
Viruses, **682**
  abundance and diversity of, 683
  analyzing coexistence of, with host cells,
    693, 693*f*
  analyzing genetic material of, 686–687
  analyzing morphological traits of, 686
  analyzing phases of replicative growth
    of lytic cycle of, 687, 687*f*, 688*f*
  Baltimore classification system for,
    696–697, 697*f*, 697*t*, 698*t*, 699*t*
  biological methods of studying, 685–693
  biological reasons for studying, 683
  cell entry of, 687–690, 688*f*, 689*f*
  characteristics of living organisms *vs.*
    characteristics of, 682–683, 683*t*
  diversification themes of, 694–696, 695*f*
  emerging diseases and emerging,
    694–695, 695*f*
  in gene therapy, 413, 413*f*
  Hershey–Chase experiment on DNA in
    genes of, 317–318, 317*f*, 318*f*
  human epidemics and pandemics from,
    683, 684*f*
  identification of emerging, 695–696,
    695*f*
  infection of host cells by, 682–683
  key lineages of, 696–699, 697*f*, 697*t*,
    698*t*, 699*t*
  lateral gene transfer with, 407
  living organisms *vs.*, 682–683, 683*t*
  nanobiology in isolation of, 685
  origins of, 694
  outbreak of, response to, 696
  photomicrograph of, 682*f*
  phylogenies as defense against, 90
  proteins as defense against, 90
  RNA in, 340–341
  in splitting eukaryotic genes, 353, 353*f*
Visceral mass, **641–642**, 642*f*
Viscosity, animal locomotion and fluid,
  958
Visible light, **213**, 213*f*
Vision, 929–934, 930*f*, 931*f*, 932*f*, 933*f*
Visual communication, 1062
Visual cues, mating and, 1057
Visual models, 45–46, 46*t*
Visualization, molecular, 31, 31*f*
Vitamin B₁, 857*t*
Vitamin B₆, 336
Vitamin B₁₂, 857*t*
Vitamin C, 857*t*
Vitamin D, 857*t*
Vitamin D-resistant rickets (hypophospha-
  temia), 311–312, 312*f*
Vitamin K, 869
Vitamins, **856**
  as animal nutrients, 856, 857*t*
  coenzyme production from, 182
Vitelline envelope, **985–986**, 985*f*,
  991–992, 991*f*, 993*f*

Viviparous species, **628**, 628*t*, 669, **987**,
  992–993, 993*f*
Vivipary, 805
VNO. *See* Vomeronasal organ
VNTRs. *See* Variable number tandem
  repeats
Volcanic gases, 61, 67, 71
Volt, **901**
Voltage, **755**, **901**
Voltage clamping, 904
Voltage-gated channels, 134, 134*f*,
  904–905, 905*f*, 909, 909*f*
Volume
  in chemical reactions, 173
  of membrane-bound vesicle, osmosis
    and, 128, 129*f*
  metric units and conversions for, 19*t*
Volume/surface area relationships
  animal body, 826–828, 826*f*, 827*f*, 828*f*
  plant, 705, 705*f*
Voluntary muscles, **947**, 949
Vomeronasal organ (VNO), **936**
Von Békésy, Georg, 926
Von Frisch, Karl, 1053, 1061–1062

W

Waggle dance, honeybee, 1061–1062,
  1061*f*, 1062*f*
Waldeyer, Wilhelm, 254
Walking, 954–958, 958*f*
Wall pressure, **729**
Wallace, Alfred Russel, 4–5, 435, 437,
  445, 1034
Wallace line, **1034**, 1034*f*
Warblers, 1032–1033
Wasps, 476, 650*t*, 790
Wassarman, Paul, 114–115, 115*f*
Wastes, of animal digestion, 861, 868–869
Wasting disease, 698
Water
  in acid-base reactions, 65–67
  angiosperm vessels for conducting, 580
  animal heat exchange by evaporation of,
    831, 831*f*
  animal locomotion in, 954–958, 958*f*
  aquaporin movement of, 133–134, 134*f*
  cohesion, adhesion, and surface tension
    of, 63, 63*f*
  in condensation reaction, 81, 81*f*
  covalent bonds of, 58, 58*f*, 59*f*
  in decomposition rates, 1124
  density of, as liquid and as solid, 64, 64*f*
  depth and flow of in aquatic biomes,
    1044–1045, 1044*f*, 1045*f*
  energy absorbing capacity of, 64–65,
    64*t*, 65*t*
  formation of in cellular respiration,
    199–200, 199*f*, 200*f*
  green plant holding of, and moderation
    of climate, 562
  in hydrolysis, 81, 81*f*
  insects reabsorption of, 844
  intestinal absorption of, 861, 868–869
  kidney reabsorption of, 846–847, 847*f*
  land plant adaptations to prevent loss of,
    568, 569*f*
  lipid insolubility in, 120, 120*f*
  membrane lipids interaction with,
    122–123
  molecular structure of, 49–50, 49*f*
  in net primary production of terrestrial
    biomes, 1121–1122
  nitrate pollution of, 532–533, 533*f*
  noncyclic electron flow between, and
    NADP in Z-scheme model, 222, 222*f*